# Calculus and Analytic Geometry

# A SERIES OF BOOKS IN MATHEMATICS

R. A. Rosenbaum, Editor

Introduction to Matrices and Linear Transformations (Second Edition)
*Daniel T. Finkbeiner, II*

Introduction to Probability and Statistics (Third Edition)
*Henry L. Alder and Edward B. Roessler*

The USSR Olympiad Problem Book: Selected Problems and Theorems
of Elementary Mathematics
*D. O. Shklarsky, N. N. Chentzov, and I. M. Yaglom*

Mathematics: The Man-made Universe
*Sherman K. Stein*

Set Theory and Logic
*Robert R. Stoll*

Problems in Differential Equations
*J. L. Brenner*

Foundations of Linear Algebra
*A. I. Mal'cev*

Computational Methods of Linear Algebra
*D. K. Faddeev and V. N. Faddeeva*

Geometry and Analysis of Projective Spaces
*C. E. Springer*

University Mathematics, I and II
*Jack R. Britton, R. Ben Kriegh, and Leon W. Rutland*

Problems in Higher Algebra
*D. K. Faddeev and I. S. Sominskii*

Calculus and Analytic Geometry
*Jack R. Britton, R. Ben Kriegh, and Leon W. Rutland*


Golden Gate Editions

A Concrete Approach to Abstract Algebra
*W. W. Sawyer*

A Modern View of Geometry
*Leonard M. Blumenthal*

Sets, Logic, and Axiomatic Theories
*Robert R. Stoll*

The Solution of Equations in Integers
*A. O. Gelfond*

An Elementary Introduction to the Theory of Probability
*B. V. Gnedenko and A. Ya. Khinchin*

The Real Number System in an Algebraic Setting
*J. B. Roberts*

Elements of Astromechanics
*Peter van de Kamp*

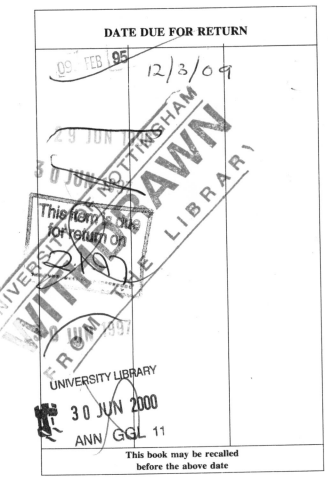

# Calculus and Analytic Geometry

JACK R. BRITTON  *University of Colorado*

R. BEN KRIEGH  *University of Colorado*

LEON W. RUTLAND  *Virginia Polytechnic Institute*

 W. H. FREEMAN AND COMPANY

*San Francisco and London*

# Preface

This book is a condensation and a rearrangement of the authors' two-volume work, *University Mathematics* I, II. Most of the review material from high school algebra and trigonometry has been omitted and the order of some topics has been changed to enable the student to reach the calculus within the first few weeks of the course.

As in *University Mathematics*, this volume is intended to provide college and university students with a sensible continuation of the modern approach to mathematics that is being introduced in most elementary and secondary schools, with more emphasis than in the past placed on an understanding of fundamental concepts. It is assumed here that the student has a good background in algebra and trigonometry. On this basis, calculus and analytic geometry are unified into a sequential exposition that eliminates much unnecessary duplication and is conducive to an efficient development and use of ideas and techniques. Fundamental concepts are discussed in a reasonably rigorous fashion, with adequate emphasis on important skills and without an excess of sophistication. Many applications of mathematics have been included, and they have frequently been made the motivation for the introduction of mathematical concepts. An intuitive discussion often precedes the formal treatment of a new idea.

Although the book was written with students in engineering and the sciences in mind, it is also well suited for a good liberal arts course in mathematics. The exposition has, in the main, been kept at a level that has proved to be reasonable for the average student. However, a number of optional sections, problems, and proofs, each of which is marked by a star and may be omitted without loss of continuity, have been included as a challenge to the better students.

Important definitions, axioms, and theorems are clearly labeled, and a conscientious effort has been made to utilize each new idea and notation as frequently as possible in order to promote its intelligent use by the student. New materials and new points of view are not introduced merely for the sake of novelty, but are brought in only if they make a genuine contribution to the understanding that can be imparted to the reader.

There are several features of particular interest that we have found helpful in providing the student with a deeper understanding of elementary mathematical analysis, as well as a better background for mathematics beyond the sophomore level. First, there is the development and consistent use of the neighborhood concept in the treatment of limits. This approach gives the student a better intuitive feeling for the meaning of a limit than the more usual formal $\epsilon$-$\delta$ attack. The second significant feature is the introduction and use of matrices for the solution of systems of linear equations and for the discussion of linear transformations in reducing a quadratic polynomial to a canonical form, as well as the application of these ideas to the solution of simple systems of differential equations. A third important feature is the use of vector algebra for the discussion of geometric ideas relating to the line and the plane in three-dimensional space, and the use of vector calculus for the development of a number of basic notions relating to curves and surfaces as well as to velocity and acceleration. The introduction and application of some elementary ideas in the calculus of complex-valued functions motivates and simplifies the use of the exponential function with an imaginary exponent.

The first three chapters are concerned with basic ideas and the development of a consistent language and terminology for the remainder of the book. Such topics as polynomials, inequalities, relations and functions, and graphs—as well as the preliminary ideas of analytic geometry—are covered in these chapters. Not more than two or three weeks are needed for these topics, so that the class is then able to begin the serious work on limits and continuity in Chapter 4.

A good modern course in calculus and analytic geometry can be based on Chapters 4 to 23. Chapters 24 and 25 contain adequate material for a short course in differential equations.

We wish to thank Professors R. A. Rosenbaum and Morris Kline for their editorial suggestions, which contributed in a notable fashion to the clarity of the exposition. Many other valuable suggestions came from our colleagues in the Department of Applied Mathematics at the University of Colorado and from the long-suffering students who have seen the book through the many pains of its birth. To these students and colleagues we owe a debt that can be repaid only by the gratitude of a newer generation of students for whom the exposition has been made simpler and clearer. We are particularly appreciative of the intelligent effort put in by Mrs. Dorothy Vaughn in typing the manuscript in its many revisions. Finally, we wish to express our gratitude to our families for putting up with us during the trials and tribulations of this project.

*August 1966*                                                    JACK R. BRITTON
                                                                  R. BEN KRIEGH
                                                                  LEON W. RUTLAND

# Contents

# Chapter 9. Exponential and Logarithmic Functions 321

# Chapter 10. The Calculus of Trigonometric and Hyperbolic Functions 345

# Chapter 11. Vectors and Complex-Valued Functions 391

# Chapter 25. Linear Differential Equations                930

# Appendix A. List of Symbols                               978

# Appendix B. Formulas from Algebra and Trigonometry   980

# Appendix C. Table of Integrals                           982

# Appendix D. Numerical Tables                             991

# Answers, Hints, and Solutions to Odd-numbered Problems   1000

# Index                                                    1059

# Chapter 1  Fundamental Ideas

## 1.1 INTRODUCTION

Most basic mathematical concepts have their roots in the physical situations that men face in their daily lives. For instance, one of the most primitive and basic of all concepts is that of counting, which is the root of the more abstract concepts of number and arithmetic. Thus, statements of the form

> Two spears and three spears are five spears

or

> Two stones and three stones are five stones

have led to the more general kind of statement that

> Two things and three things are five things,

or, in the most abstract and concise form,

$$2 + 3 = 5.$$

Man's ability to formulate concepts related to physical experience in short, concise "abstract" statements of this type has been the basis for his development of a civilization founded on an understanding of his environment. Much of mathematics consists of the formulation and development of abstract concepts from specific situations that arise in connection with the development of a social structure and a civilization. For example, the ancient Arab merchants developed a convenient and systematic notation as an aid to keeping track of their money. The ancient Egyptians developed many of the fundamental ideas of trigonometry so that they could relocate property lines after a flood along the Nile river bottom. In more recent times, Sir Isaac Newton was led to consider the fundamental concepts of the mathematical subject now called the calculus in order to describe the behavior of moving objects. In each case, these fundamental concepts have arisen as a result of necessity and as a supplement to our ordinary language.

Almost all mathematical developments are characterized by the use of special symbols, in terms of which it is possible to attain the necessary clarity and conciseness of language. Consequently, any practical understanding of mathematics requires a clear and thorough comprehension of the characteristic language of mathematics. We shall therefore exercise particular care to set forth new ideas by means of clearly stated definitions.

For example, misunderstandings have occasionally arisen in connection with the symbol for equality, $=$. These difficulties are the result of the use of the symbol in at least two (and sometimes three) different senses. To clarify this point we shall use the equals sign as indicated in the following definitions:

**Definition 1.1a.** The statement

$$a = b$$

means that $a$ is another name for the object whose name is $b$.

**Definition 1.1b.** The statement

$$a \neq b$$

means that $a$ and $b$ are names of different objects.

**Definition 1.1c.** The statement

$$a .=. b$$

means that $a$ is *defined* to be another name for the object whose name is $b$.

The symbol $.=.$ may be read "is equal, by definition, to," or "is defined to be the same as."

At first sight there may appear to be no significant difference between the two notations $.=.$ and $=$, and it is true that the difference is essentially conceptual. However, this alone is sufficient reason for us to make such a distinction. An illustration based on the next definition will help to clarify this point.

**Definition 1.1d.** The symbol

$$[\![x]\!] .=. n,$$

where $n$ is the largest integer less than or equal to $x$.

The sentence of Definition 1.1d gives the bracket symbol $[\![x]\!]$ meaning. Once this meaning has been given, we may use the symbol in connection with ordinary equality. For example, we have $[\![2.34]\!] = 2$. Here the symbol $.=.$ is not used because $[\![2.34]\!]$ is not being defined as 2, but instead, $[\![2.34]\!] = 2$ by virtue of Definition 1.1d. Another example will illustrate this idea further.

---

*Example 1.1a.* Let $a_1 .=. 1$, and let $a_{n+1} .=. \frac{1}{2} a_n$, $n = 1, 2, 3, \ldots$. (The ellipsis customarily means "and so forth.") These statements define a sequence of numbers, denoted by $a_1, a_2, a_3, \ldots$. Which of the following statements is correct?

$$\text{(a) } a_5 .=. \tfrac{1}{16}.$$
$$\text{(b) } a_5 = \tfrac{1}{16}.$$

The formula $a_{n+1} = \frac{1}{2} a_n$ is called a **recurrence formula** because it can be used to determine $a_{n+1}$ when $a_n$ is known. For example,

$$a_2 = \frac{1}{2} a_1 = \frac{1}{2} \cdot 1 = \frac{1}{2},$$

$$a_3 = \frac{1}{2} a_2 = \frac{1}{2} \cdot \frac{1}{2} = \frac{1}{2^2},$$

$$a_4 = \frac{1}{2} a_3 = \frac{1}{2} \cdot \frac{1}{2^2} = \frac{1}{2^3},$$

and

$$a_5 = \frac{1}{2} a_4 = \frac{1}{2} \cdot \frac{1}{2^3} = \frac{1}{2^4} = \frac{1}{16}.$$

In each case, the expression obtained for $a_n$ is a **consequence** of the given definition so that it is *not* correct to say that

$$a_5 . = . \frac{1}{16},$$

but it is correct to say that

$$a_5 = \frac{1}{16}.$$

## 1.2 LOGIC

While it is not our purpose to make a detailed study of logic, there are certain of its principles that we need in order to develop the succeeding mathematics.

**Definition 1.2a.** A **proposition** is a complete declarative sentence with a definite meaning.

For example, the following sentences are all propositions:

$$2 + 3 = 5,$$
$$2 + 3 = 8,$$

Gold is a precious metal,

If it rains tonight, then tomorrow it will be fair.

Logic is concerned with the rules according to which propositions may be combined in order to give valid conclusions. The most fundamental rule of logic is

**Law 1.2a.** *The Law of the Excluded Middle.* Every proposition in the language must be either true or false, but it cannot be both, nor can it be neither.

Thus, $2 + 3 = 8$ is a false proposition, whereas $2 + 3 = 5$ is a true proposition.

An immediate consequence of Law 1.2a is that if a given proposition is true, then its denial is false, and, conversely, if a proposition is false then its denial is true. For example, since $2 + 3 = 8$ is false, it follows that $2 + 3 \neq 8$ is true. It is upon these facts that the technique of proof by contradiction is based. This technique is discussed in detail in Section 1.4.

In the development of a science, we are frequently interested in establishing a chain of valid reasoning from a given proposition, called the **hypothesis,** to another proposition, called the **conclusion.** For example, if we are told that it is raining, then we conclude at once that the sky must be cloudy. In other words, the statement "It is raining" suggests that certain other conditions must also be true. In this example, the conclusion that it is cloudy is suggested by the meaning of the statement "It is raining" and our own physical experience that rain must be associated with clouds. In mathematics, it is not always so easy to obtain conclusions from given hypotheses, since we must rely only upon the previously established rules or theorems and definitions, rather than on actual physical experience.

The assertion that a given hypothesis leads to a certain conclusion is called an **implication**. For example, if $x$ is a number such that $x + 3 = 5$, then according to the rules of ordinary arithmetic, it follows that $x = 2$. In mathematics it is important to indicate clearly what propositions are used as hypotheses and what propositions follow as conclusions from these hypotheses. Since an implication is usually stated in the form

$$\text{if } p, \text{ then } q \quad \text{or} \quad p \text{ implies } q,$$

where $p$ denotes the hypothesis and $q$ denotes the conclusion, it is convenient to use a special symbol to denote an implication.

**Definition 1.2.b** The symbol

$$p \Rightarrow q$$

means that the hypothesis, $p$, implies the conclusion, $q$, according to some rule. The sign $\Rightarrow$ is usually read "implies."

The sentences

$$x + 3 = 5 \quad \Rightarrow \quad x = 2$$

and

$$\text{It is raining} \Rightarrow \text{there are clouds in the sky}$$

illustrate correct uses of the implication symbol.

It sometimes happens that each of two propositions implies the other. In that case we write

$$p \Leftrightarrow q$$

to mean that an implication exists both ways. For example,

$$\text{A triangle has three equal sides} \Leftrightarrow \text{the triangle has three equal angles.}$$

This proposition is often written as "A triangle has three equal sides *if and only if* it has three equal angles" or "For a triangle to have three equal sides, it is *necessary and sufficient* that it have three equal angles." The symbol $\Leftrightarrow$ will be used in place of the phrase "if and only if" or "necessary and sufficient," since these phrases are often a source of confusion for the student. However, $\Leftrightarrow$ may be read "if and only if" or "implies and is implied by." The statement $p \Leftrightarrow q$ is a combination of the two statements

$$p \Rightarrow q, \quad q \Rightarrow p.$$

**Definition 1.2c.** The statement $q \Rightarrow p$ is called the **converse** of the statement $p \Rightarrow q$.

It is necessary for the reader to realize that $p \Rightarrow q$ does not guarantee that $q \Rightarrow p$. The statement,

It is raining $\Rightarrow$ there are clouds in the sky

is valid, but it does not follow that the converse

There are clouds in the sky $\Rightarrow$ it is raining

is valid. Again,

$$a = 2 \quad \text{and} \quad b = 3 \quad \Rightarrow \quad ab = 6,$$

is valid, but the converse

$$ab = 6 \quad \Rightarrow \quad a = 2, \quad b = 3,$$

is not valid.

Even though a proposition may imply a second proposition in the sense of Definition 1.2b, there is no guarantee that the second proposition is true. It is still necessary to specify the conditions under which the conclusion of an implication will be true. This is done by

**Law 1.2b.** *The Law of Inference.* Suppose that

> (1) a proposition, $p$, is true, and that
> (2) $p \Rightarrow q$ is a valid implication.

Then $q$ is also true.

To make clear the significance of this law, consider the following example.

---

*Example 1.2a.* Does the proposition "two sides of a triangle are equal" imply the proposition "the angles opposite these sides are equal?"

By drawing a line from the vertex of the third angle to the midpoint of the third side, we divide the triangle into two triangles with the sides of one equal, respectively, to the sides of the other. Thus, the two triangles are congruent and the corresponding angles are equal.

This is the essential chain of reasoning used in high school geometry to arrive at the fact that the implication proposed in this example is correct. If $p$ is the proposition, "two sides of a triangle are equal," and $q$ the proposition, "the angles opposite these sides are equal," then we have shown that

$$p \Rightarrow q.$$

Consequently, for any triangle for which $p$ is true, the Law of Inference guarantees that $q$ is also true.

---

In order to emphasize another important point, we consider one of the popular fallacies.

Let $x$ and $y$ represent two nonzero numbers for which

$$x = y.$$

Assuming that the usual rules of arithmetic are valid, we may write

$$x^2 = xy$$

(by multiplying both members by $x$) and

$$x^2 - y^2 = xy - y^2$$

(by subtracting $y^2$ from both sides). From the rules of factoring, we may write

$$(x - y)(x + y) = (x - y)y.$$

By division, we have

$$(x + y) = y$$

or, since $y = x$,

$$x + y = x, \quad 2x = x, \quad \text{or} \quad 2 = 1.$$

Here we have reached a contradiction with an accepted fact. The initial statement, $x = y$, may be considered true without causing difficulty. What, then, is wrong with the reasoning process? Is

$$x = y \Rightarrow 2 = 1$$

a valid statement? If not, we evidently do not have a valid implication, which is to say that some basic rule of algebra must have been violated. Indeed the violation occurred when the factor $(x - y)$ was "divided" from both sides of the equation. Since $x = y$, this factor is 0 and therefore may not be divided into the members of the equation.

This fallacy is intended to illustrate the need for obeying the rules of the "game," and to show that the validity of the process of obtaining conclusions depends upon following these rules.

## Exercises 1.2

1. Let $1! .=. 1$ and $n! .=. n(n - 1)!$ for $n = 2, 3, 4, \ldots$.
   (a) Is it true that $4! = 1 \cdot 2 \cdot 3 \cdot 4$? Why or why not?
   (b) Does $n! .=. n(n - 1)! \Rightarrow 0! = 1$ if $n = 1$? Why or why not?
   (c) Which of the following statements, if any, is (are) correct?

$$\frac{10!}{8!} .=. 10 \cdot 9, \quad \frac{10!}{8!} = \frac{10}{8}, \quad \frac{10!}{8!} \neq \frac{10}{8}, \quad \frac{10!}{8!} \text{ is undefined.}$$

   Give reasons for your answers.
2. Let $a_1 .=. 2$ and $a_n .=. 2a_{n-1}$. Which of the following expressions is (are) correct?

$$a_n = 2n, \quad a_n .=. 2^n, \quad a_n = 2^n, \quad a_n \neq 2^n, \quad a_n .=. 2n.$$

3. Are the following implications valid or not?
   (a) Two lines in three-dimensional space are both perpendicular to the same line $\Rightarrow$ the two lines are perpendicular to each other.
   (b) One side of a triangle is shorter than a second side $\Rightarrow$ the angle opposite the first side is smaller than that opposite the second side.
   (c) The diagonals of a parallelogram bisect each other $\Rightarrow$ the parallelogram is a rhombus.
4. Are the following implications valid or not? Explain why. (Assume that $x$ and $y$ represent integers.)

(a) $x = 3 \Rightarrow x^2 = 9$.

(d) $\dfrac{x^2 - y^2}{x - y} = 0 \Rightarrow x = y$.

(b) $x^2 = 9 \Rightarrow x = 3$.

(e) $2 = 1 \Rightarrow 2 = 2$.

(c) $x^2 = 4 \Rightarrow x^2 - 2x + 2 \neq 5$.

(f) $xy + y = 0 \Rightarrow y = 0$.

5. State the converse of each of the following implications. Is the converse valid? Why?
   (a) $a = 3$ and $b = 4 \Rightarrow ab = 12$.
   (b) Two straight lines in a plane are parallel $\Rightarrow$ the two lines do not intersect.
   (c) Two triangles are congruent $\Rightarrow$ the corresponding angles are equal.
   (d) $a = 2$ and $b = 3 \Rightarrow a + b = 5$.
   (e) $x = 3 \Rightarrow x^2 = 9$.
   (f) $3 = 5 \Rightarrow 4 = 6$.
   (g) Two angles of a triangle are equal, respectively, to two angles of a second triangle $\Rightarrow$ the third angles of the two triangles are equal.

## 1.3 AXIOMS

Just as not every word can be defined in terms of other words, not every proposition can be proved true or false by using other propositions. A circular type of reasoning is no better than a circular type of definition. Hence it is necessary to assume that some propositions are true to start with, and from these propositions to deduce the truth or falsity of other propositions.

A proposition that is assumed to be true is called an **axiom**. However, an axiom can not be considered to be a "self-evident truth," even though this definition can be found in many dictionaries. An axiom may be true in the sense that it is consistent with experience, but in mathematics it is immaterial if axioms are true in this sense. The mathematician is interested only in the consequences of the *supposed* truth of the axiom. Of course, the branches of mathematics that are of most value to us in a practical sense are those that can best be used to describe our experiences. Thus we ordinarily use axioms that seem to be consistent with experience, so that many axioms *appear* to be "self-evident truths." The important point is that axioms are propositions which are *assumed* to be true.

One of the most notable examples of a supposed "self-evident truth" is the famous euclidean axiom that *one and only one line parallel to a given line can be drawn through a point not on the given line.* This axiom was considered a "self-evident truth" for nearly twenty centuries until a brilliant Russian mathematician, Nikolai Lobachevsky, who lived from 1793 to 1856, questioned its truth. He discovered several other kinds of geometry by means of modifications of this axiom.

There are two axioms fundamental to all of mathematics. These may be stated as

**Axiom 1.3a.** *Axiom of Identity.* For any object $a$, $a = a$.

**Axiom 1.3b.** *Axiom of Substitution.* If $a = b$, then $a$ may be used to replace $b$

in any part of a proposition containing $b$ without altering the validity of the proposition.

We have discussed briefly the use of definitions, axioms, and certain rules of logic in mathematics. Using these primitive concepts, we can establish the validity of certain implications. Those valid implications that are regarded as basic to the development of mathematics are called **theorems.**

These remarks are illustrated very simply by two theorems that follow immediately from Axioms 1.3a and 1.3b.

**Theorem 1.3a.** *The symmetry property of* $=$ :

$$a = b \implies b = a.$$

PROOF: A proof of this theorem is given by the following observations:

$b = b$ by the Identity Axiom,
$b = a$ by the Substitution Axiom and the given proposition, $a = b$.

**Theorem 1.3b.** *The transitive property of* $=$ :

$$a = b \quad \text{and} \quad b = c \implies a = c.$$

PROOF: $a = b$ (by hypothesis) and
$b = c$ (by hypothesis),

so that by substituting from the second equality into the first, we may write

$$a = c \quad \text{(by Axiom 1.3b).}$$

## 1.4 METHODS OF PROOF

The preceding laws of logic, definitions, axioms, and theorems form the basis on which the mathematics of this book rests. It would be possible for us to build, detail by detail, upon this basis to obtain the structure with which we shall work. Such a procedure would, however, become quite tedious. Consequently, we shall prove most of the key theorems, but we shall not hesitate to introduce some ideas in an intuitive fashion.

There are, of course, various ways of proving theorems. It may be possible to prove a proposition *directly* by starting with something known (a definition, an axiom, or a previously proved theorem) and proceeding step by step, using the laws of logic and other known results to arrive at the desired result. This process has been illustrated in the simple proofs of Theorems 1.3a and 1.3b. It may also be possible to prove a theorem *indirectly* by demonstrating that the denial of the theorem cannot be true. This procedure is based on the Law of the Excluded Middle (Law 1.2a).

An indirect proof, in which the denial of a proposition is proved false, is called a **proof by contradiction.** The procedure of constructing a proof by contradiction may be expressed symbolically in terms of implication. Suppose we are given a true proposition, $p$, and are required to demonstrate the truth of a proposition, $q$, by the use of the Law of Inference. Now it may not be clear how to establish the implication

$$p \Rightarrow q,$$

by starting with $p$ and proceeding to $q$. In that case it may be possible to prove the implication *indirectly* by establishing another implication that is equivalent to $p \Rightarrow q$. For this purpose we introduce the notation $-p$ to denote the negation or denial of the proposition $p$. If $p$ represents the statement "It is raining," then $-p$ represents "It is not raining." Again, if $p$ is "$x = 2$," then $-p$ is "$x \neq 2$."

The technique of proof by contradiction is based on the equivalence of the two statements

$$p \Rightarrow q \quad \text{and} \quad -q \Rightarrow -p.$$

The latter implication is called the **contrapositive** of the former. To see why these statements are logically equivalent, let us first consider some examples of contrapositive statements. The contrapositive of

$$\text{It is raining} \Rightarrow \text{it is cloudy}$$

is

$$\text{It is not cloudy} \Rightarrow \text{it is not raining.}$$

Similarly, the contrapositive of

$$x = 2 \quad \Rightarrow \quad x^2 = 4$$

is

$$x^2 \neq 4 \quad \Rightarrow \quad x \neq 2.$$

The reader is cautioned to observe the difference between the *converse* of an implication and the *contrapositive* of the same implication. In particular, if the implication is $p \Rightarrow q$, then the converse is

$$q \Rightarrow p$$

and the contrapositive is

$$-q \Rightarrow -p.$$

In general, these two statements are distinct. Thus, if $p \Rightarrow q$ is

$$\text{It is raining} \Rightarrow \text{it is cloudy}$$

the converse is

$$\text{It is cloudy} \Rightarrow \text{it is raining,}$$

which is certainly not a valid implication.

To show that the statements $p \Rightarrow q$ and $-q \Rightarrow -p$ are equivalent, let us refer again to Law 1.2b of logic. In order to prove that a statement $q$ is true whenever another statement $p$ is true, we must establish that $p \Rightarrow q$. In case this cannot be done directly, we may be able to establish the connection indirectly by using the fact that if $q$ is false, then $-q$ is true. Now, suppose we can show that $-q \Rightarrow -p$, so that $-p$ is true by Law 1.2b. Then $p$ is false, contrary to the originally given statement that $p$ is true. Evidently the contradiction arises from the assumption that $q$ is false. Thus, in order to avoid the contradiction, we must conclude that $q$ is true and that $p \Rightarrow q$ is therefore also true, since a true statement can never imply a false one. In other words, we have established that

$$(-q \Rightarrow -p) \Rightarrow (p \Rightarrow q).$$

In a similar way, we may establish that

$$(p \Rightarrow q) \Rightarrow (-q \Rightarrow -p)$$

so that the statements $p \Rightarrow q$ and $-q \Rightarrow -p$ are logically equivalent. That is, one of the statements is true if, and only if, the other is true. The following example is an excellent illustration of a proof by contradiction.

---

*Example 1.4a.* Prove that the square of the ratio of two integers cannot be exactly 2.

In this example the proposition states that if $a$ and $b$ are integers, then $(a/b)^2 \neq 2$. We may, without loss of generality, assume that $a$ and $b$ are relatively prime integers (integers with no common factor except 1), since if they were not relatively prime, we could divide out the factor common to $a$ and $b$ in the ratio $a/b$. The proposition to be proved may thus be stated in the form $p \Rightarrow q$, where $p$ is the statement "$a$ and $b$ are relatively prime integers," and $q$ is the statement "$(a/b)^2 \neq 2$."

Since it appears difficult to establish the direct implication, let us consider its contrapositive, that is $-q \Rightarrow -p$, or

$$\left(\frac{a}{b}\right)^2 = 2 \Rightarrow a \text{ and } b \text{ are not relatively prime.}$$

If $(a/b)^2 = 2$, then

$$a^2 = 2b^2.$$

The right member of this equation is divisible by 2, so the left member must also be divisible by 2. However, $a$ is an integer; hence, if $a^2$ is divisible by 2, then it must be divisible by 4. This follows easily from the fact that $p$ is an even integer $\Leftrightarrow p = 2n$, where $n$ is an integer, so that $a^2 = 4c^2$ and

$$4c^2 = 2b^2 \quad \text{or} \quad 2c^2 = b^2.$$

Application of the same argument again shows that $b^2$ must be divisible by 2 and hence by 4. Thus $b = 2d$, where $d$ is some integer. But $a = 2c$ and $b = 2d$ imply that $a$ and $b$ are not relatively prime. We have therefore established the contrapositive of the required proposition and hence have proved that if $a$ and $b$ are integers, then $(a/b)^2 \neq 2$.

## Exercises 1.4

1. Write (i) the converse and (ii) the contrapositive for each of the following statements, and determine which are valid.
   (a) Two triangles are congruent $\Rightarrow$ the triangles have corresponding angles equal.
   (b) A polygon has 4 equal sides $\Rightarrow$ the polygon is a parallelogram.
   (c) $x = 2 \Rightarrow x^2 = 4$.
   (d) A triangle is isosceles $\Rightarrow$ the triangle has two equal sides.
   (e) $x$ is a factor of $a$ and $x$ is a factor of $b \Rightarrow x$ is a factor of $a + b$.

2. Is it true or false that the number of sides of a polygon is always equal to the number of its vertices?

3. Try to obtain a formula that will give the number of regions into which a plane is partitioned by $n$ straight lines, no two of which are parallel and no three of which are concurrent. *Note*: Prove, by mathematical induction, that the formula is correct.

4. In a plane there are $n$ straight lines, no two of them being parallel and no three of them concurrent. Determine how many points of intersection there are.

5. Let $d(n)$ be the number of distinct divisors of the positive integer $n$. For example, $d(1) = 1$, $d(2) = 2$, $d(3) = 2$, $d(4) = 3$, $d(5) = 2$, $d(9) = 3$, etc. Is the statement "$d(n)$ is odd $\Leftrightarrow n$ is a perfect square" a reasonable conjecture? If you think so, try to prove it.

6. Let $F$ denote the number of faces of a polyhedron, $V$ the number of its vertices, and $E$ the number of its edges. Is the statement

$$F + V = E + 2$$

a reasonable conjecture? (In connection with this problem, you might like to read pages 236–240, of Courant and Robbins, *What Is Mathematics?*)

7. Show that the square of the ratio of two integers cannot be exactly 3.

8. Are there any two integers whose ratio is exactly $\sqrt{2} + \sqrt{3}$? Prove that your answer is correct.

9. It can be shown that there is no greatest prime by assuming the contrary and showing that this assumption leads to a contradiction. Thus, suppose that there is a greatest prime, say $p_n$. Form the number

$$m .=. (2)(3)(5) \cdots (p_{n-1})(p_n) + 1,$$

where the first term is the product of all the primes from 2 to $p_n$, inclusive. Is $m$ divisible by 2? by 3? by 5? $\cdots$ by $p_{n-1}$? by $p_n$? What conclusion may be drawn? This proof is essentially that of Euclid (Greek, about 300 B.C.).

## 1.5 THE CONCEPT OF SET

The concept of set is the most primitive and fundamental concept underlying any mathematical structure. It arises as a generalization of a concept familiar in daily life. For example, a collection of atoms forms a larger unit called a *molecule*. The furniture in a bedroom is sometimes called a *set* or *suite*. The collection of books owned by a particular individual is his *library*. In each case the word—molecule, suite, or library—is a name used to designate a collection of objects. The collection itself is considered as an individual object.

A gathering of distinct objects into a whole need not be confined to physical objects. A collection may equally well consist of several abstract ideas. For example, the *Ten Commandments* is the name of a collection of moral laws.

It is generally accepted in mathematics that the word *set* is an undefined term. Rather than adopt this point of view here, we shall consider the word to be definable in terms of other words in a basic vocabulary. Thus, we have

**Definition 1.5a.** A **set** is a collection of well-defined objects regarded as a single unit. The objects belonging to a set are called **elements** of the set.

As an example, let us consider the objects $a, e, i, o, u$ as a unit. If we choose a name, say $\mathcal{V}$, for this unit, then we write

$$\mathcal{V} .=. \{a, e, i, o, u\}.$$

This collection of symbols is read, "$\mathcal{V}$ is defined to be the set of elements $a, e, i, o, u$." The braces will consistently be used to designate a set, and the symbols written within the braces indicate the elements that constitute the set. Script capital letters will be used for names of sets.

The set $\mathcal{V}$ can be defined in another way. We may say that it is the set of vowels of the English alphabet. Indeed, this example illustrates a second way in which a set may be defined. In the first method, the elements in the set are explicitly listed. In the second method the set is defined by means of a property possessed by the elements and only by the elements that are to be in the set. By this method, we write

$$\mathcal{V} .=. \{*: * \text{ is a vowel of the English alphabet}\},$$

which is read "$\mathcal{V}$ is defined to be the set of objects $*$ such that $*$ is a vowel of the English alphabet." If $*$ is replaced by the name of some object, and if the resulting statement is true, then that object is considered to be an element of the set $\mathcal{V}$; if the resulting statement is false, or if it is meaningless, then the object is not an element of the set. Thus, in the definition of $\mathcal{V}$, if we replace $*$ by 3, we obtain the false statement, "3 is a vowel of the English alphabet." Hence 3 is not an element of $\mathcal{V}$.

Similarly, we may write

$$\mathcal{N} .=. \{x: x \text{ is a positive integer}\}.$$

That is, $\mathcal{N}$ is the collection of objects $x$ such that $x$ is a positive integer. This set cannot be defined by listing all its elements, so that the method of defining a set by means of a property is an essential one. The statement giving the property for the elements in the set being defined is called a **defining relation.**

Some other examples of sets are

(a) $\mathcal{A} .=. \{x: x = a, x = b, \text{ or } x = c\}$ or, more concisely,
   $\mathcal{A} .=. \{a, b, c\}$ ;
(b) $\mathcal{P} .=. \{x: x \text{ is a prime number}\}$ ;
(c) $\mathcal{B} .=. \{x: x \text{ is an animal}\}$ ;
(d) $\mathcal{S} .=. \{x: x \text{ is a planet of Sol}\}.$

Some of the elements of $\mathcal{P}$ are 2, 3, 5, 641. Some objects that are not in $\mathcal{P}$ are 12, *dog*, *Venus*, *pencil*, and *a*.

The following notations are convenient for indicating that an object does or does not belong to a set.

**Definition 1.5b.** The notation $a \in \mathcal{S}$ means that the object $a$ is an element of the set $\mathcal{S}$.

**Definition 1.5c.** The notation $a \notin \mathcal{S}$ means that $a$ is not an element of $\mathcal{S}$.

Referring to the preceding examples of sets, we may write $2 \in \mathcal{P}$, Venus $\in \mathcal{S}$, dog $\notin \mathcal{A}$, $a \notin \mathcal{B}$, cat $\in \mathcal{B}$, etc.

In Definition 1.5a, a set was described as a collection of well-defined objects. The adjective *well-defined* has been inserted in order to indicate that not every "defining relation" may be adequate to define a set. A careless use of defining relations may lead to paradoxical situations. For example, may

$$\mathcal{A} .=. \{x: x \text{ is } a \text{ or } b \text{ or } \mathcal{A}\}$$

be properly considered to define a set? This is clearly a case of trying to define a set in terms of itself. Such a definition cannot be considered valid, and we shall not regard it as defining any set at all. It is necessary that a defining relation clearly determine the elements that belong to the set.

It is also necessary to distinguish between an *element* of a set and the *set* to which the element belongs. There is little danger of confusion when there are several elements in the set, but if a set contains only one element the situation may become delicate. For example, let

$$\mathcal{S} .=. \{a\}.$$

The name of the set consisting of the one object, $a$, is $\mathcal{S}$. It is desirable to maintain a distinction between the two entities—the element and the set consisting of that element.

Sometimes sets having other sets as elements are important. For example, let

$$\mathcal{A} .=. \{a, b\},$$
$$\mathcal{B} .=. \{b, d, e\}.$$
$$\mathcal{C} .=. \{2, 3, 4, 5\}.$$

Then we may wish to consider a set

$$\mathcal{J} .=. \{\mathcal{A}, \mathcal{B}, \mathcal{C}\}.$$

The elements of $\mathcal{J}$ are $\mathcal{A}$, $\mathcal{B}$, and $\mathcal{C}$. However, the elements of $\mathcal{A}$, $\mathcal{B}$, and $\mathcal{C}$ are *not* elements of $\mathcal{J}$.

In working with sets, we might encounter a defining relation such as "$x$ is a prime number less than 2." Since 1 is not considered a prime, we find that there are no objects for which the defining relation is true. Rather than prohibit the use of such a definition, we regard it as a defining relation for a set having no elements

**Definition 1.5d.** A defining relation that is satisfied by no element is said to define a set called the **empty set,** denoted by $\varnothing$.

It is generally agreed that there can be only one empty set, since there is no way of distinguishing between two such sets. Accordingly, we speak of *the* empty set rather than *an* empty set.

As a further illustration of the difference between a set and the elements of a set, consider the set

$$\mathcal{A} .=. \{\varnothing\}.$$

This set consists of the single element $\emptyset$, itself a set that contains no elements.

Suppose we consider a set consisting of elements that belong to another set. The fact that such a relationship exists between the two sets is indicated by saying the first set is a **subset** of the given set. To indicate this relationship between two sets $\mathcal{A}$ and $\mathcal{B}$, we introduce a special notation.

**Definition 1.5e.** $\mathcal{A} \subset \mathcal{B}$ (read "$\mathcal{A}$ is a subset of $\mathcal{B}$") means that every element of $\mathcal{A}$ is also an element of $\mathcal{B}$.

**Definition 1.5f.** If there is at least one element in $\mathcal{B}$ that is not also in $\mathcal{A}$, then $\mathcal{A}$ is called a **proper** subset of $\mathcal{B}$.

**Definition 1.5g.** $\mathcal{A} \not\subset \mathcal{B}$ means that $\mathcal{A}$ is *not* a subset of $\mathcal{B}$, which means that there is at least one element of $\mathcal{A}$ that is not in $\mathcal{B}$.

For example, if

$$\mathcal{A} .=. \{a, b, c, d\},$$
$$\mathcal{B} .=. \{c, d\},$$
$$\mathcal{C} .=. \{d, b, a, c\},$$

then $\mathcal{B}$ is a proper subset of $\mathcal{A}$ and $\mathcal{C}$, and $\mathcal{C}$ is a subset but not a proper subset of $\mathcal{A}$. In fact, $\mathcal{A}$ and $\mathcal{C}$ both consist of the same elements, so that

$$\mathcal{A} \subset \mathcal{C} \quad \text{and} \quad \mathcal{C} \subset \mathcal{A}.$$

Also, we have $\mathcal{A} \not\subset \mathcal{B}$ because there are elements in $\mathcal{A}$ that are not in $\mathcal{B}$.

A simple consequence of the definition of subset is

**Theorem 1.5a.** The empty set is a subset of every set.

PROOF: If the empty set is not a subset of an arbitrary set $\mathcal{A}$, then there must be an element in $\emptyset$ that is not in $\mathcal{A}$. But since $\emptyset$ contains no elements, this relationship is impossible. Hence $\emptyset$ must be considered a subset of $\mathcal{A}$.

To illustrate the difference in meaning between the symbols $\in$ and $\subset$, observe that $\subset$ may stand only between sets, and $\in$ may stand only between an object in a set and a set. Thus, all of the subsets of $\mathcal{A} .=. \{a, b, c\}$ are $\emptyset$, $\{a\}$, $\{b\}$, $\{c\}$, $\{a, b\}$, $\{b, c\}$, $\{a, c\}$, and $\mathcal{A}$ itself. Hence, we may write

$$\{a\} \subset \mathcal{A} \quad \text{or} \quad \{b\} \subset \mathcal{A} \quad \text{or} \quad \{a, b\} \subset \mathcal{A}$$

and

$$a \in \mathcal{A} \quad \text{or} \quad b \in \mathcal{A}$$

but *not*

$$a \subset \mathcal{A} \quad \text{or} \quad \{a\} \in \mathcal{A}.$$

The reader should notice the difference in the treatment of the object $a$ and the set $\{a\}$, whose only element is $a$.

---

*Example 1.5a.* If $\mathcal{A} .=. \{2, 4, 7, 9\}$ and $\mathcal{B} .=. \{2, 3, 4\}$, show that neither set is a subset of the other.

We have

$$7 \in \mathcal{A} \quad \text{and} \quad 7 \notin \mathcal{B} \Rightarrow \mathcal{A} \not\subset \mathcal{B}.$$

Similarly,

$$3 \in \mathcal{B} \quad \text{and} \quad 3 \notin \mathcal{A} \Rightarrow \mathcal{B} \not\subset \mathcal{A}.$$

Thus, neither set is a subset of the other.

---

The last example shows that a subset relationship need not exist between two arbitrary sets. It is clear already that a set may be defined in many ways. Hence, an important question that must sometimes be answered is whether or not two sets defined in different ways are really the same set. In fact, although we may have an intuitive idea of what is meant by saying that two sets $\mathcal{A}$ and $\mathcal{B}$ are the same, it is necessary to state formally the circumstances under which two sets shall be considered identical.

**Definition 1.5h.** Two sets $\mathcal{A}$ and $\mathcal{B}$ are the same if, and only if, they contain the same elements. In this case, we write $\mathcal{A} = \mathcal{B}$.

This definition is almost equivalent to

**Theorem 1.5b.** If $\mathcal{A}$ and $\mathcal{B}$ are sets,

$$\mathcal{A} = \mathcal{B} \Leftrightarrow \mathcal{A} \subset \mathcal{B} \quad \text{and} \quad \mathcal{B} \subset \mathcal{A}.$$

The next example illustrates these ideas in an elementary way.

---

*Example 1.5b.* Let $\mathcal{P}$ and $\mathcal{Q}$ be two sets such that

$\mathcal{P} .=. \{x : x \text{ is the square of a positive integer}\}$,

and

$\mathcal{Q} .=. \{y : y \text{ is a positive integer having an odd number of distinct divisors}\}$.

Are the sets $\mathcal{P}$ and $\mathcal{Q}$ the same?

In other words, while we may think that we have defined two *different* sets by using different defining relations, it may happen that we have not. In fact, in view of Exercises 1.4, Number 5, we know that if $x = n = p^2$, then $d(n)$ is an odd number, so that $\mathcal{P} \subset \mathcal{Q}$. Also, if $n$ has an odd number of divisors, then $n$ is a perfect square, so that $\mathcal{Q} \subset \mathcal{P}$. Hence $\mathcal{P} = \mathcal{Q}$.

---

*Example 1.5c.* Let $\mathcal{P}$ and $\mathcal{Q}$ be two sets such that

$\mathcal{P} .=. \{y : y \text{ is the sum of consecutive odd positive integers}\}$,
$\mathcal{Q} .=. \{x : x \text{ is the square of a positive integer}\}$.

Are the sets $\mathcal{P}$ and $\mathcal{Q}$ the same, or is one a subset of the other?

In order to demonstrate a method of argument that is applicable to more difficult problems, we shall make a slightly more detailed analysis than is necessary. Let $x$ be an element of $\mathcal{Q}$. Then $x = n^2$, where $n$ is a positive integer. It can be shown by mathematical induction (see Appendix B) that, for each positive integer $n$,

$$n^2 = 1 + 3 + 5 + \cdots + (2n - 1).$$

Hence $x$ is the sum of consecutive odd integers and is therefore an element of $\mathcal{P}$. This shows that $\mathcal{Q} \subset \mathcal{P}$.

Next, let $y \in \mathcal{P}$, so that

$$y = (2k + 1) + (2k + 3) + \cdots + (2m + 1), \qquad k < m.$$

Now $y$ may be written in the form

$$y = (m + 1)^2 - k^2.$$

(Why?) This expression is not always the square of an integer. (Prove this.) Hence, $\mathcal{P} \not\subset \mathcal{Q}$, and $\mathcal{Q}$ is a proper subset of $\mathcal{P}$.

## Exercises 1.5

1. For each of the following descriptions, write out specifically the elements of the set $\mathcal{Q}$.

   (a) $\mathcal{Q} .=. \{x: x \text{ is a positive even integer not exceeding } 10\}$.
   (b) $\mathcal{Q} .=. \{x: x^2 - 1 = 0\}$.
   (c) $\mathcal{Q} .=. \{x: x \text{ is a prime number between 30 and 40}\}$.

2. Determine the common property possessed by the elements of each set $\mathcal{Q}$ if

   (a) $\mathcal{Q} .=. \{1, 3, 5, 7, 9\}$ ;
   (b) $\mathcal{Q} .=. \{4, 8, 12, 16, 20\}$ ;
   (c) $\mathcal{Q} .=. \{[\![2.1]\!], [\![2.67]\!], [\![2.78]\!], [\![2.95]\!]\}$ ;
   (d) $\mathcal{Q} .=. \{\frac{1}{2}, \frac{3}{2}, \frac{5}{2}, \frac{7}{2}, \frac{9}{2}, \frac{11}{2}\}$.

3. Determine for each of the following if (i) $\mathcal{Q}$ is a subset of $\mathcal{B}$; (ii) $\mathcal{B}$ is a subset of $\mathcal{Q}$; (iii) $\mathcal{Q}$ is a proper subset of $\mathcal{B}$; (iv) $\mathcal{B}$ is a proper subset of $\mathcal{Q}$.

   (a) $\mathcal{Q} .=. \{1, 3, 5, 6, 8\}$, $\mathcal{B} .=. \{1, 5, 7\}$.
   (b) $\mathcal{Q} .=. \{1, 3, 7\}$, $\mathcal{B} .=. \{x: x \text{ is an odd integer}\}$.
   (c) $\mathcal{Q} .=. \{a, b, c, d\}$, $\mathcal{B} .=. \{d, c, a, b\}$.
   (d) $\mathcal{Q} .=. \{2, 4, 5\}$, $\mathcal{B} .=. \{x: x \text{ is an even integer}\}$.

4. If

$$\mathcal{Q} .=. \{a, b\} \quad \text{and} \quad \mathcal{B} .=. \{a, c, \mathcal{Q}\},$$

which of the following statements is (are) correct?

   (a) $a \in \mathcal{Q}$.  (f) $b \in \mathcal{B}$.
   (b) $a \subset \mathcal{Q}$.  (g) $b \notin \mathcal{B}$.
   (c) $\mathcal{Q} \in \mathcal{Q}$.  (h) $b \subset \mathcal{B}$.
   (d) $\mathcal{Q} \notin \mathcal{Q}$.  (i) $\mathcal{Q} \notin \mathcal{B}$.
   (e) $\mathcal{Q} \subset \mathcal{Q}$.  (j) $\mathcal{Q} \subset \mathcal{B}$.

5. Let $\mathcal{Q}$, $\mathcal{B}$, $\mathcal{C}$ be sets. Which of the following is (are) valid?

   (a) $\mathcal{Q} \neq \mathcal{B}$ and $\mathcal{B} \neq \mathcal{C} \Rightarrow \mathcal{Q} \neq \mathcal{C}$.
   (b) $\mathcal{Q} \not\subset \mathcal{B}$ and $\mathcal{B} \not\subset \mathcal{C} \Rightarrow \mathcal{Q} \not\subset \mathcal{C}$.

6. A set $\mathcal{Q}$ contains $n$ elements. How many subsets of $\mathcal{Q}$ are there?

7. The fact that there can be only one empty set—that is, that the empty set is unique—can be proved by means of Theorem 1.5b. Assume that $\varnothing'$ is another empty set, and prove that $\varnothing = \varnothing'$.

# 1.6 OPERATIONS ON SETS

It is frequently convenient to consider new sets constructed in some prescribed manner from given sets. There are two particularly important ways in which such a construction can be accomplished.

Let $\alpha$ and $\mathcal{B}$ be sets. Then the **union** of the two sets, written $\alpha \cup \mathcal{B}$, is described in

**Definition 1.6a.**     $\alpha \cup \mathcal{B} .=. \{x: x \in \alpha$ and/or $x \in \mathcal{B}\}$.

Thus, $\alpha \cup \mathcal{B}$ represents the set obtained by putting the elements of $\alpha$ and $\mathcal{B}$ together into one set. To illustrate, let

$$\alpha .=. \{a, b\} \quad \text{and} \quad \mathcal{B} .=. \{a, c, d\}.$$

Then

$$\alpha \cup \mathcal{B} = \{a, b, c, d\}.$$

Notice that the element common to both sets is *not* counted twice in the union of $\alpha$ and $\mathcal{B}$.

The second important set construction consists of the elements that are common to $\alpha$ and $\mathcal{B}$ and is called the **intersection** of the sets $\alpha$ and $\mathcal{B}$. The intersection of $\alpha$ and $\mathcal{B}$ is denoted by $\alpha \cap \mathcal{B}$ and is described by

**Definition 1.6b.**     $\alpha \cap \mathcal{B} .=. \{x: x \in \alpha$ and $x \in \mathcal{B}\}$.

In the preceding illustration,

$$\alpha \cap \mathcal{B} = \{a\}.$$

---

*Example 1.6a.* Let

$$\mathcal{I}_e .=. \{x: x \text{ is an even integer}\},$$
$$\mathcal{I}_o .=. \{x: x \text{ is an odd integer}\}.$$

Describe the sets $\mathcal{I}_e \cup \mathcal{I}_o$ and $\mathcal{I}_e \cap \mathcal{I}_o$.

Since $\mathcal{I}_e \cup \mathcal{I}_o$ is the set $\mathcal{I}$ of all the integers, we have

$$\mathcal{I}_e \cup \mathcal{I}_o = \mathcal{I}.$$

Furthermore, no integer can be both odd and even, so

$$\mathcal{I}_e \cap \mathcal{I}_o = \varnothing.$$

---

In addition to the operations of union and intersection, it is useful to have an operation on sets that picks out the elements in one set that are not in another. Such an operation is given by

**Definition 1.6c.**     $\alpha - \mathcal{B} .=. \{x: x \in \alpha$ and $x \notin \mathcal{B}\}$.

This operation is called the **set difference**. It removes from $\alpha$ those elements that are in $\alpha \cap \mathcal{B}$. In certain special cases the operation yields what at first sight may appear to be rather surprising results. For example, let

$$\alpha .=. \{a, b, c\} \quad \text{and} \quad \mathcal{B} .=. \{a, d\}.$$

Then

$$\alpha - \mathcal{B} = \{b, c\},$$

and

$$\mathcal{B} - \alpha = \{d\}.$$

Moreover, if

$$\mathcal{C} .= . \{d, e\} \quad \text{and} \quad \mathcal{D} .= . \{d, e, f\},$$

then

$$\mathcal{D} - \mathcal{C} = \{f\},$$

and

$$\mathcal{C} - \mathcal{D} = \varnothing.$$

Sets formed by unions or intersections may be represented pictorially by means of diagrams (called Venn diagrams) as shown in Figure 1.6a.

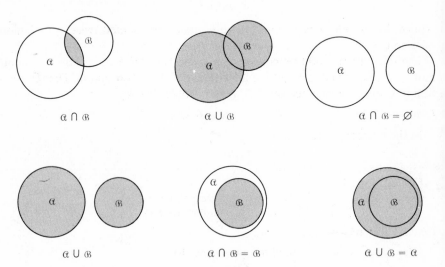

The sets $\alpha$ and $\mathcal{B}$ are represented by the regions interior to the closed curves. The shaded region is the region indicated below each diagram. Note that $\alpha \cap \mathcal{B} \subset \alpha \cup \mathcal{B}$.

**FIGURE 1.6a**

We shall usually be interested only in sets that are contained in a fixed given set, called a **universal set** or a **universe**. For example, we may wish to carry out an extended discussion using only sets whose elements are letters of the English alphabet. In this case, we call the alphabet the universal set, since every set in the discussion is a subset of it. Two particular subsets are

$$\mathcal{V} .= . \{a, e, i, o, u\}$$

and

$$\mathcal{C} .= . \{b, c, d, f, g, h, j, k, l, m, n, p, q, r, s, t, v, w, x, y, z\},$$

that is, the set of vowels and the set of consonants. These two sets have the property that their union is the universal set and their intersection is the empty set. When two sets are so related, we say that one set is the **complement** of the other with respect to the universe. Hence, if $\mathcal{U}$ denotes a universe (the alphabet in the above illustration) and $\mathcal{C}'$ the complement of a given set $\mathcal{C}$, we have

**Definition 1.6d.**         $\mathcal{C}' .=. \mathcal{U} - \mathcal{C}.$

This is read "the complement of $\mathcal{C}$ is defined to be the set of elements in the universe that are not in $\mathcal{C}$." Hence, in the previous illustration, $\mathcal{C}' = \mathcal{V}$ and $\mathcal{V}' = \mathcal{C}$, with respect to $\mathcal{U}$. It is important that a statement of complementation be qualified unless it is clearly understood what is the universe.

For example, if we wish to form the complement of a set $\mathcal{A}$ with respect to a set $\mathcal{U}$ on one occasion and with respect to a set $\mathcal{V}$ on another occasion, we must so indicate. A notation such as $\mathcal{A}'_{\mathcal{U}}$ or $\mathcal{A}'_{\mathcal{V}}$ may be used for this purpose.

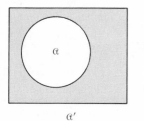
$\mathcal{A}'$

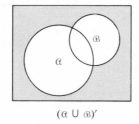
$(\mathcal{A} \cup \mathcal{B})'$

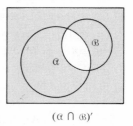
$(\mathcal{A} \cap \mathcal{B})'$

The shaded region is the region indicated below each diagram.
**FIGURE 1.6b**

The complement can also be illustrated by means of Venn diagrams. Let the universe be the region enclosed within a rectangle. The complements of various sets are shown in Figure 1.6b.

## Exercises 1.6

1. Given the sets $\mathcal{A} .=. \{a, b, c, d\}$, $\mathcal{B} .=. \{a, b, e, f, g\}$, $\mathcal{C} .=. \{b, c, e, h\}$, and the universe $\mathcal{U} .=. \{a, b, c, d, e, f, g, h\}$, express each of the following sets in terms of its elements.

(a) $\mathcal{A} \cap \mathcal{C}$.

(b) $\mathcal{A} \cup \mathcal{C}$.

(c) $\mathcal{A} - \mathcal{B}$.

(d) $\mathcal{A}'$.

(e) $\mathcal{A}' \cup \mathcal{B}'$.

(f) $\mathcal{B}' \cap \mathcal{C}$.

(g) $(\mathcal{A} \cap \mathcal{B}) - \mathcal{B}$.

(h) $(\mathcal{B} \cap \mathcal{C}')'$.

(i) $\mathcal{B}' - \mathcal{A}'$.

(j) $(\mathcal{C} - \mathcal{B}) - \mathcal{A}$.

(k) $\mathcal{C} - (\mathcal{B} - \mathcal{A})$.

If $\mathcal{A} .=. \{0, 1, 2\}$, $\mathcal{B} .=. \{0, 2, 4\}$, and $\mathcal{C} .=. \{1, 2, 3\}$, find the following.

(a) All possible sets obtained from $\mathcal{A}$, $\mathcal{B}$, and $\mathcal{C}$ by using only the operations $\cup$ and $\cap$.

(b) All possible sets obtained from $\mathcal{A}$, $\mathcal{B}$, and $\mathcal{C}$ by using only the operation $-$.

3. Let $\mathfrak{U}$ denote a universal set. Study the following list, in which some of the relations are incorrect. Determine which are incorrect and correct them.

(a) $\mathfrak{A} \cup \varnothing = \mathfrak{A}$.

(b) $\mathfrak{A} \cap \mathfrak{U} = \mathfrak{A}$.

(c) $\mathfrak{A} \cup \mathfrak{A}' = \mathfrak{U}$.

(d) $\mathfrak{A} \cap \mathfrak{A}' = \mathfrak{A}$.

(e) $\mathfrak{A} \cup \mathfrak{A} = \mathfrak{A}$.

(f) $\mathfrak{A} \cap \mathfrak{A} = \varnothing$.

(g) $\mathfrak{A} \cup \mathfrak{U} = \mathfrak{U}$.

(h) $\mathfrak{A} \cap \varnothing = \varnothing$.

(i) $(\mathfrak{A}')' = \mathfrak{U}$.

(j) If $\mathfrak{A} = \mathfrak{B}'$ then $\mathfrak{B} = \mathfrak{A}'$.

(k) $(\mathfrak{A} - \mathfrak{B}) \cup \mathfrak{B} = \mathfrak{A} - \mathfrak{B}$.

(l) $(\mathfrak{A} \cup \mathfrak{B}) - \mathfrak{B} = \mathfrak{A} - \mathfrak{B}$.

(m) $\mathfrak{A} \cap (\mathfrak{A} - \mathfrak{B}) = \mathfrak{A} \cup \mathfrak{B}$.

(n) $(\mathfrak{A} - \mathfrak{B})' = \mathfrak{A}' - \mathfrak{B}'$.

4. Find three sets, $\mathfrak{A}$, $\mathfrak{B}$, and $\mathfrak{C}$, such that any two of them have nonempty intersections but all three have an empty intersection.

5. If $\mathfrak{A}$, $\mathfrak{B}$, $\mathfrak{C}$, and $\mathfrak{D}$ are sets, show that

(a) if $\mathfrak{A} \subset \mathfrak{C}$ and $\mathfrak{B} \subset \mathfrak{D}$, then $\mathfrak{A} \cup \mathfrak{B} \subset \mathfrak{C} \cup \mathfrak{D}$;

(b) if $\mathfrak{A} \subset \mathfrak{C}$ and $\mathfrak{B} \subset \mathfrak{D}$, then $\mathfrak{A} \cap \mathfrak{B} \subset \mathfrak{C} \cap \mathfrak{D}$.

6. Let $\mathfrak{A}$ and $\mathfrak{B}$ be sets such that

(i) $\mathfrak{A} \cup \mathfrak{B} = \{a, b, c, d\}$;

(ii) $\mathfrak{A} \cap \mathfrak{B} = \{a, c\}$;

(iii) $\mathfrak{A} - \mathfrak{B} = \{b\}$.

Find $\mathfrak{A}$ and $\mathfrak{B}$.

## 1.7 THE REAL NUMBERS

The numbers with which much of mathematics deals constitute the set of real numbers, which we shall denote by the symbol $\mathfrak{R}$. It is assumed that the reader has a general familiarity with the real numbers and in particular that he knows how to carry out the common operations of arithmetic with these numbers. In order to facilitate further discussion of the real numbers, it is convenient here to describe briefly some of the more important subsets of $\mathfrak{R}$.

The set of numbers with which all of us first become familiar is the set of "counting" numbers, the so-called natural numbers. The symbol $\mathfrak{N}$ will be used to denote this set, so that

$$\mathfrak{N} .=. \{1, 2, 3, 4, \ldots\}.$$

Perhaps the next simplest set of numbers is the set of integers consisting of all the natural numbers and their negatives and the number zero. The symbol $\mathfrak{g}$ is used to denote this set, so that

$$\mathfrak{g} .=. \{\ldots, -3, -2, -1, 0, 1, 2, 3, \ldots\}.$$

A number that can be expressed as the ratio of two integers is called a rational number. We shall use the symbol $\mathfrak{F}$ to denote the set of rational numbers; that is,

$$\mathfrak{F} .=. \left\{\frac{a}{b} : a, b \in \mathfrak{g}, b \neq 0\right\}.$$

Any number that cannot be expressed as the ratio of two integers is called an irrational number. Examples of irrational numbers are $\sqrt{2}$, $\sqrt[3]{5}$, $\sqrt[5]{16}$, and $\pi$. We shall have more to say about irrational numbers in our discussion of decimals. The totality of all rational numbers and all irrational numbers constitutes the set $\mathcal{R}$.

Note that

$$\mathcal{N} \subset \mathcal{I} \subset \mathcal{F} \subset \mathcal{R}.$$

The reader, in his previous mathematics, has undoubtedly made much use of the following basic laws, which are here taken as axioms. Let $a$, $b$, and $c$ be real numbers in the following axioms.

**Axiom 1.7a.** *The Closure Law of Addition:* The sum $a + b$ of any two real numbers is a unique real number $c$.

We say that the set $\mathcal{R}$ of real numbers is *closed* under the operation of addition.

**Axiom 1.7b.** *The Commutative Law of Addition:*

$$a + b = b + a.$$

This axiom states that *the sum of any two real numbers does not depend on the order in which the numbers are added.*

**Axiom 1.7c.** *The Associative Law of Addition:*

$$(a + b) + c = a + (b + c).$$

This law states that *the sum of three (or more) real numbers is independent of the way in which the numbers are grouped.* Since both groupings yield the same result, the notation $a + b + c$ is unambiguous. However, the reader should note that this statement does *not* concern itself with a rearrangement of the order of the numbers; such a rearrangement was dealt with by Axiom 1.7b.

**Axiom 1.7d.** *The Closure Law of Multiplication.* The product $ab$ of any two real numbers is a unique real number $c$.

**Axiom 1.7e.** *The Commutative Law of Multiplication:*

$$ab = ba.$$

**Axiom 1.7f.** *The Associative Law of Multiplication:*

$$(ab)c = a(bc).$$

The reader should state both the preceding laws in his own words in order to be certain he understands them.

**Axiom 1.7g.** *The Distributive Law:*

$$a(b + c) = ab + ac.$$

This law is the basic principle on which is based the operation of factoring in algebra.

The operations of addition and multiplication are examples of an operation that combines two elements of a set to produce a third element of the set. We say that the set is closed with respect to the operation. For example, the set of natural numbers is not closed with respect to the operation of subtraction, but the set of integers is closed with respect to this operation.

A set having one or more closed operations which satisfy certain axioms is called an **algebraic structure.** Certain types of algebraic structures are important in many mathematical studies. One of these is given in the following definition. The symbol $*$ may represent any closed operation on the given set.

**Definition 1.7a.** A **group** is an algebraic structure on a set $\mathcal{Q}$ having a closed operation $*$ for which the following axioms are satisfied.

$G_1$. The operation $*$ is associative; that is, for any three elements $a$, $b$, $c \in \mathcal{Q}$, $a * (b * c) = (a * b) * c$.

$G_2$. The set contains an identity element, $e$, for which $x * e = e * x = x$ for every $x \in \mathcal{Q}$.

$G_3$. For each element $x \in \mathcal{Q}$, there exists an inverse element $y$ in $\mathcal{Q}$ such that $x * y = y * x = e$.

For example, the set $\mathcal{J}$ of integers is a group with respect to the operation of addition because (i) the set is closed with respect to addition, (ii) addition is an associative operation on $\mathcal{J}$, (iii) the identity element is 0, and (iv) each element $x$ in $\mathcal{J}$ has an additive inverse $(-x)$ in $\mathcal{J}$. (An *additive inverse* is an inverse with respect to addition.) The set $\mathcal{N}$ is *not* a group with respect to addition because it does not contain 0 and it does not have additive inverses.

The set $\{0, \pm 2, \pm 4, \ldots, \pm 2n, \ldots\}$, with $n \in \mathcal{N}$, is another example of a group with respect to addition, as the reader may verify. A set that is a group with respect to the operation of addition is called an **additive group.** A simple example of a set that is a group with respect to multiplication is $\{1, -1\}$. It is clear that the set $\mathcal{J}$ is *not* a **multiplicative group;** that is, it is not a group with respect to multiplication, because it does not contain multiplicative inverses for all its elements. However, we shall see that the set $\mathcal{F}$ of rational numbers is an algebraic structure of greater breadth and versatility. First we observe that $\mathcal{F}$ is a group with respect to addition. Since addition is also a commutative operation on the set $\mathcal{F}$, that is, since $a + b = b + a$, we say that $\mathcal{F}$ is a **commutative group** with respect to addition. Next, we see that in $\mathcal{F}$ each nonzero element has an inverse with respect to multiplication. For example, if $(a/b) \in \mathcal{F}$, and if $a \neq 0$, then its multiplicative inverse is $b/a$, which is also in $\mathcal{F}$.

Since the element 0 has no multiplicative inverse, it is not possible for the set $\mathcal{F}$ to be a multiplicative group. However, the set $\mathcal{F} - \{0\}$ is a commutative multiplicative group. We therefore have a new and more complex type of mathematical structure which satisfies the following definition.

**Definition 1.7b.** Any set $\mathcal{Q}$ on which two closed operations (usually denoted by $+$ and $\cdot$) are defined is called a **field,** provided that

**F₁.** the set $\mathcal{C}$ is a commutative group with respect to $+$;

**F₂.** the set $\mathcal{C} - \{0\}$, where 0 is the additive identity, is a commutative group with respect to $\cdot$;

**F₃.** the operation $\cdot$ is distributive with respect to $+$.

Thus, the set $\mathfrak{F}$ of rational numbers is a field.

Another property possessed by the rational numbers, but clearly not by the integers, is that between any two given rational numbers there is always at least one other rational number. For, if $a$ and $b$ are rational, then $\frac{1}{2}(a + b)$ is a rational number that is greater than the lesser and less than the greater of $a$ and $b$. It follows easily that infinitely many rational numbers exist between $a$ and $b$. Because of this property, the set of rational numbers is said to be **dense**.

By ordinary long division, a rational number $a/b$ can be expressed in decimal form. If the denominator contains no prime factors other than 2 or 5, the decimal terminates. Otherwise, the decimal is periodic; that is, eventually a sequence of digits will repeat endlessly. For example, consider the division of $a$ by $b$. Once the remainder is less than $b$, only the $b - 1$ natural numbers less than $b$ are possible remainders. After at most $b - 1$ divisions, a remainder must occur for the second time. Thereafter, all remainders will repeat indefinitely in the same order. Thus, every rational number can be represented in repeating or else in terminating decimal form.

As a specific illustration, we may divide 4 by 7 to show that

$$\frac{4}{7} = 0.571428 + \frac{0.000004}{7},$$

and the remainders from this point on repeat in the same order in which they have already occurred. This means that the rational number 4/7 may be expressed in the form of an endless repeating decimal, $0.571428\ldots$, where the six digits following the decimal point are repeated again and again without end.

It is also possible to show that every repeating decimal represents a rational number. In order to illustrate the argument, consider

$$2.1353535\ldots,$$

and let

$$x = 2.1\overline{35},$$

where the line above the digits 3 and 5 indicates the repeating part. Then,

$$100x = 213.5\overline{35}$$

and

$$100x - x = 213.5\overline{35} - 2.1\overline{35}$$

or

$$99x = 211.4.$$

Hence,

$$x = \frac{2114}{990} = \frac{1057}{495}.$$

Since $2.1\overline{35}$ is not a terminating decimal, the preceding manipulations require justification, which we shall give at a later point. However, since every repeating decimal may be dealt with in the same manner, it follows that every such decimal represents a rational number.

It is not difficult to show by the same method that the terminating decimal 0.2 and the repeating decimal 0.1999 . . . represent the same number, $2/10$ or $1/5$. If we agree always to diminish the last digit of a terminating decimal by unity and annex an endless sequence of nines, as in

$$0.348 = 0.347999\ldots,$$

then we may state that *every rational number is a repeating decimal*, and conversely, *every repeating decimal is a rational number*.

On the other hand, not every *infinite* (endless) *decimal* corresponds to a rational number. For example,

$$0.202002000200002\ldots,$$

in which the $n$th 2 is followed by $n$ zeros, does not correspond to a rational number since it is not a repeating decimal. Evidently, the rational number system is full of "gaps"; it contains no representatives of the nonrepeating infinite decimals.

**Definition 1.7c.** An **irrational number** is a number corresponding to a nonrepeating infinite decimal.

In view of this definition, we say that 0.2020020002 . . . represents a certain irrational number. Furthermore, irrational numbers occur in many ways. The most common way is perhaps in the process of finding roots such as $\sqrt[3]{4}$, $\sqrt{5}$, $\sqrt[10]{15}$, and so on. Other well-known irrational numbers are $\pi$, the ratio of the circumference of a circle to its diameter, and the number called $e$, which is used as the base of the system of "natural logarithms." From an elementary point of view, we regard all of these numbers as being represented by infinite decimals. The set of all numbers represented by repeating or by nonrepeating decimals, that is, the set of all rational and irrational numbers is the set $\Re$ of all real numbers.

The real numbers can be ordered by means of the following definition.

**Definition 1.7d.** If $a$, $b \in \Re$, then $a < b$ means that $b - a$ is a positive number $p$, and we say that $a$ is less than $b$.

A similar definition can be given for $a > b$ (read "$a$ is greater than $b$" or "$b$ is less than $a$"). With Definition 1.7d it can be shown that the real numbers form an **ordered field** just as the rational numbers do.

In order to understand an important difference between the two fields, we need two additional concepts.

**Definition 1.7e.** Let $\mathcal{S}$ be a subset of $\Re$. A number $p$ is said to be an upper bound of $\mathcal{S}$ if

$$x \in S \Rightarrow x \leq p.$$

For example, if $S .=. \{x: 0 \leq x < 2\}$, then 5, $\pi$, 2.34, and 2 are upper bounds of $S$. If $S .=. \{x: x = \pi/n, n \in \mathfrak{N}\}$, then 4, 3.1416, $2\pi$, and 1001 are upper bounds of $S$. It is clear that if a subset $S$ of $\mathfrak{R}$ has one upper bound $p$, then it has infinitely many since every number greater than $p$ is also an upper bound of $S$. It is also possible to select a subset $S$ of $\mathfrak{R}$ that has no upper bound. Such a set is $\{x: x = n\pi, n \in \mathfrak{N}\}$.

Among the upper bounds of a set $S$, there may be a smallest one.

**Definition 1.7f.** If $M$ is an upper bound for a set $S$ and if every other upper bound $p$ of $S$ is such that $M \leq p$, then $M$ is called the **least upper bound** of $S$.

For example, if $S .=. \{x: 0 \leq x < 2\}$, then 2 is the least upper bound of $S$. If $S .=. \{x: x = \pi/n, n \in \mathfrak{N}\}$, then $\pi$ is the least upper bound of $S$.

Now, suppose we consider the subset $S$ of $\mathfrak{F}$, where

$$S .=. \left\{ x: x = 1 - \frac{1}{2^n}, n \in \mathfrak{N} \right\}.$$

Then the least upper bound of $S$ is 1, which is an element of $\mathfrak{F}$. Similarly, if $S .=. \{x: x = b_n$, where $b_n$ is the $n$th decimal approximation to the number $1/3\}$, then $S \subset \mathfrak{F}$ and the least upper bound of $S$ is $1/3$. (That is, $S$ contains the elements 3/10, 33/100, 333/1000, etc., and this set of elements has $1/3$ as a least upper bound.) Again, the least upper bound is in $\mathfrak{F}$.

Now consider the set $S .=. \{x: x = b_n$, where $b_n$ is the $n$th decimal approximation to $\sqrt{2}\}$. Then $S$ contains the rational numbers 14/10, 141/100, 1414/1000, 14142/10000, and so on, and $S \subset \mathfrak{F}$. In this case, the least upper bound of $S$ is $\sqrt{2}$, which is *not* a rational number. This illustration shows that even if a subset $S$ of $\mathfrak{F}$ has a least upper bound, then that least upper bound is *not* necessarily in $\mathfrak{F}$.

However, as the preceding discussion has shown, it is reasonable to assume that if $S$ is any subset of $\mathfrak{R}$ that has a least upper bound, then the least upper bound is a number in $\mathfrak{R}$. Hence, $\mathfrak{R}$ has a kind of *completeness* that $\mathfrak{F}$ does not possess. Accordingly, $\mathfrak{R}$ is called a **complete ordered field**, whereas $\mathfrak{F}$ is *not* a complete ordered field.

## Exercises 1.7

1. Is the set of numbers $\{x: x = 3k, k \in \mathcal{J}\}$ a group with respect to addition? Explain.
2. Is the set $\{x: x = 2k + 1, k \in \mathcal{J}\}$ a group with respect to addition? multiplication? Explain.
3. Let $S .=. \{x: x = a + b\sqrt{2}, a, b \in \mathfrak{F}\}$. Is $S$ a group with respect to ordinary addition? Is the set $S - \{0\}$ a group with respect to multiplication? Explain.
4. Is the set $S$ in Number 3 a field? Explain.
5. Is the set of all numbers of the form $a + b\sqrt{2} + c\sqrt{3}$, $a, b, c \in \mathfrak{F}$, a field? Explain.

In Numbers 6 to 11, find the simple fraction equivalent to the given repeating decimal.

6. $2.200200\overline{200}$.

7. $0.\overline{285714}$.

8. $0.1\overline{30}$.

9. $0.9\overline{8}$.

10. $0.\overline{1101}$.

11. $0.1\overline{3}$.

In Numbers 12 to 18, find the repeating decimal representation of the given fraction.

12. $4/7$.

13. $3/5$.

14. $11/17$.

15. $22/7$. (Compare this with the best value of $\pi$ that you are able to find.)

16. $100/101$.

17. $1/9$.

18. $2/3$.

19. Verify that
$$0.2020\overline{20} + 0.0303\overline{03} = 0.2323\overline{23}$$
by calculating the corresponding simple fractions.

In numbers 20 to 24, find the least upper bound of the given set $S$. State whether $S \subset \mathfrak{F}$ or $S \not\subset \mathfrak{F}$, and indicate whether or not the least upper bound is an element of $\mathfrak{F}$.

20. $S = \left\{ x : x = \dfrac{n}{2n + 1},\, n \in \mathfrak{N} \right\}$.

21. $S = \left\{ x : x = (-1)^n + \dfrac{1}{n},\, n \in \mathfrak{N} \right\}$.

22. $S = \{ x : x = b_n, \text{ where } b_n \text{ is the } n\text{th decimal approximation to the infinite deci-}$
    mal $2.\overline{13} \}$.

23. $S = \{ x : x \in \mathfrak{F},\, x \geq 0,\, x^2 < 5 \}$.

24. $S = \{ x : x \in \mathfrak{F},\, x \geq 0,\, x^2 < 0.25 \}$.

25. Is the sum of two irrational numbers always irrational? What about the product?

26. If $a$ and $b$ are rational numbers and $c$ is irrational, prove that
$$a + bc = 0 \implies a = b = 0.$$

(*Hint*: Suppose $b \neq 0$; then solve for $c$.)

## 1.8 THE FIELD OF COMPLEX NUMBERS

It follows from the discussion in the preceding section that within the field of real numbers, we can always find numbers $x$ such that $x^2 = a$, if $a$ is nonnegative. But what about the equation $x^2 = -a$, if $a$ itself is positive? There is no real number that will satisfy this equation since the square of any real number is positive or zero. Hence, in order to be able to solve the equation, we must make a further extension of the number system.

First, let us suppose that we have defined a new "number," $\theta$, such that $\theta^2 = -1$. Then we may investigate the set of "numbers" of the form $a + b\theta$, where $a$ and $b$ are chosen from the set of real numbers. Since we should like to preserve as much of our familiar algebra as possible, let us consider what would be likely properties of such "numbers."

If we should have $a + b\theta = 0$, then we might use the rules of our ordinary algebra to write

$$a = -b\theta,$$

and, by squaring both members,

$$a^2 = b^2\theta^2.$$

Now, $\theta^2 = -1$, so that

$$a^2 = -b^2,$$

an equation that is not possible for real $a$ and $b$ unless $a = b = 0$. Thus, it seems desirable to say that

$$a + b\theta = 0 \text{ if, and only if, } a = b = 0.$$

Again, if we have

$$a + b\theta = c + d\theta,$$

then

$$(a - c) + (b - d)\theta = 0$$

follows with just a little manipulation, assuming that we may operate with the "number" $\theta$ using the ordinary rules of algebra. However, the last equation, by the preceding agreement, can be valid only if $a = c$ and $b = d$.

Addition would present no problem, since it would seem reasonable to ask that

$$(a + b\theta) + (c + d\theta) = (a + c) + (b + d)\theta.$$

For multiplication, we have

$$(a + b\theta)(c + d\theta) = ac + ad\theta + bc\theta + bd\theta^2$$
$$= (ac - bd) + (ad + bc)\theta,$$

where we have again used $\theta^2 = -1$, as well as the ordinary algebraic manipulations.

Since $a, b, c, d$ are all real, it appears that the results of adding or multiplying "numbers" of the form $a + b\theta$ and $c + d\theta$ are again "numbers" of the same form. This looks so promising that we make our extension of the number system on the basis of these results.

Quantities of the form $a + b\theta$ are actually pairs of real numbers, where the symbol $\theta$ serves only to keep the two numbers separate. Another way of specifying a pair of numbers so that each is distinguished from the other is by the notation $(a, b)$ where $a$ denotes the first element and $b$ the second element of the pair. That is, $(a, b)$ is called an **ordered pair** of real numbers. Because of the order concept associated with the numbers, we may not say that $(a, b)$ and $(b, a)$ are the same. They are *different* pairs if $a \neq b$.

**Definition 1.8a.** A **complex number** is an ordered pair of real numbers, $(a, b)$, that obeys the following rules.

(1) Equality:       $(a, b) = (c, d) \Leftrightarrow a = c$ and $b = d$.
(2) Addition:       $(a, b) + (c, d) .=. (a + c, b + d)$.
(3) Multiplication:       $(a, b)(c, d) .=. (ac - bd, ad + bc)$.

Notice that we have used exactly the number pairs that seemed desirable from our preliminary investigations. It is now easy to see that a number pair of the form $(a, 0)$ corresponds to the real number $a$. To illustrate, observe that

$$(a, 0) + (b, 0) = (a + b, 0)$$

and that

$$(a, 0)(b, 0) = (ab, 0).$$

It follows that the element $(a, 0)$ behaves exactly like the real number $a$ in relation to other elements of the form $(b, 0)$. For example, $(1, 0)$ is the multiplicative identity for the elements $(a, 0)$, and $(a^{-1}, 0)$ is the multiplicative inverse for $(a, 0)$. Therefore, let us agree to write $a$ for $(a, 0)$. Under this condition we may, for any complex number, write

$$\begin{aligned} (a, b) &= (a, 0) + (0, b) \\ &= (a, 0)(1, 0) + (b, 0)(0, 1) \\ &= a \cdot 1 + b(0, 1) \\ &= a + b(0, 1). \end{aligned}$$

Since $(0, 1)(0, 1) = (-1, 0) = -1$, it appears that the $\theta$, which was introduced earlier, represents the number pair $(0, 1)$. Since $\theta^2 = -1$, it is natural to call $\theta$ a square root of $-1$.

Let us now examine the problem of finding $(a, b)$ so that

$$[(a, b)]^2 = -1 = (-1, 0).$$

Since $[(a, b)]^2 = (a, b)(a, b) = (a^2 - b^2, 2ab)$, we must have, by the preceding definition of equality,

$$a^2 - b^2 = -1 \quad \text{and} \quad 2ab = 0.$$

From the second equation it follows that

$$a = 0 \quad \text{or} \quad b = 0.$$

But, keeping in mind that $a$ and $b$ are real, we see that $b \neq 0$. (If it were zero, the first equation would reduce to $a^2 = -1$, an impossibility for any real number $a$.) Thus, we must have $a = 0$, so that $b^2 = 1$, and $b = 1$ or $-1$. Consequently, we have two candidates for square roots of $-1$; they are $(0, 1)$ and $(0, -1)$. The student should verify that $[(0, -1)]^2$ is the same as $(-1, 0)$, or $-1$.

In order to have a handier symbol, it is customary to designate the number pair $(0, 1)$ by the symbol $i$, and the pair $(0, -1)$ by $-i$. The result of the last discussion may then be written in usual algebraic fashion:

$$i^2 = -1 \quad \text{and} \quad (-i)^2 = -1.$$

The square roots of $-1$ are accordingly $i$ and $-i$. The number $i$ has unfortunately been called the **imaginary unit,** a name that must not be interpreted literally since it should be evident that the number pairs $(a, b)$ that we have called complex numbers are no more "imaginary" than the pairs $a/b$ that we called rational numbers earlier.

With the preceding agreements, we may replace the number pair $(a, b)$ by the symbol $a + bi$. Our preliminary discussion has shown that we may operate with these symbols in a formal algebraic manner, replacing $i^2$ by $-1$, and that the results will be consistent with the definitions that we have set down for the complex numbers.

For any complex number, $a + bi$, the real number $a$ is known as the *real part*, and the real number $b$ as the *coefficient of the imaginary part* of the complex number. If $a = 0$ and $b \neq 0$, the complex number is called a **pure imaginary number**. If $b = 0$, the complex number is identified with the real number $a$.

We shall use the symbol $\mathcal{C}$ for the set of all complex numbers so that the set $\mathcal{R}$ of real numbers is a proper subset of the complex numbers; that is, $\mathcal{R} \subset \mathcal{C}$. Any complex number with a nonzero imaginary part is called **imaginary**. Thus, $2 - 3i$, $2.48 + 0.93i$, and $-i\sqrt{3}$ are all examples of imaginary numbers. The set $\mathcal{C}$ includes all such numbers as well as all the real numbers.

The definition of equality means that two complex numbers are equal if, and only if, their real parts are equal and the coefficients of their imaginary parts are equal.

The definition of addition indicates that we add the real parts of the two complex numbers to get the real part of the sum, and we add the coefficients of the imaginary parts to get the coefficient of the imaginary part of the sum.

The subtraction of complex numbers is defined as the inverse of addition. Hence, if $z$ represents a complex number,

$$z_1 - z_2 = z_3 \text{ means } z_1 = z_2 + z_3.$$

We can thus develop a formula for subtraction. Let

$$(a, b) - (c, d) = (e, f);$$

then

$$(a, b) = (c, d) + (e, f)$$
$$= (c + e, d + f).$$

This means that $a = c + e$ and $b = d + f$, or $e = a - c$ and $f = b - d$. Consequently, we have the formula

$$(a, b) - (c, d) = (a - c, b - d)$$

or

$$(a + bi) - (c + di) = (a - c) + (b - d)i.$$

The division of complex numbers is defined as the inverse of multiplication, so

$$\frac{z_1}{z_2} = z_3 \text{ means } z_1 = z_2 z_3.$$

Let us find an expression for the quotient of the complex numbers $(a, b)$ and $(c, d)$.

$$\frac{(a, b)}{(c, d)} = (e, f) \text{ means}$$

$$(a, b) = (c, d)(e, f)$$
$$= (ce - df, de + cf).$$

Thus, $a = ce - df$, and $b = de + cf$. Solving for $e$ and $f$, we have

$$e = \frac{ac + bd}{c^2 + d^2},$$

$$f = \frac{bc - ad}{c^2 + d^2},$$

or

$$\frac{(a, b)}{(c, d)} = \left(\frac{ac + bd}{c^2 + d^2}, \frac{bc - ad}{c^2 + d^2}\right).$$

If we think of the complex numbers in the form $a + bi$ and $c + di$, we may get the same result by multiplying numerator and denominator of the fraction by $c - di$, which is called the **conjugate** of $c + di$. Thus,

$$\frac{a + bi}{c + di} = \frac{(a + bi)(c - di)}{(c + di)(c - di)}$$

$$= \frac{ac + bd}{c^2 + d^2} + i\frac{bc - ad}{c^2 + d^2}.$$

The set of complex numbers is closed under the four fundamental operations of addition, subtraction, multiplication, and division (except for division by zero), and the associative, commutative, and distributive laws are satisfied. Hence, the complex numbers form a field.

It is reasonable to ask if it is possible to continue making extensions of the number system to obtain an even more comprehensive kind of number system, and it is rather surprising to learn that it can be shown that any further extension of the complex number system entails the loss of at least one of the properties possessed by the field of complex numbers. As the reader will discover in his progress through this book, the complex number system embodies many surprising and important relationships that make the system most useful in dealing with problems in engineering and physics.

The following chart illustrates the relationship between the various number systems that we have discussed:

natural numbers ⎫
zero ⎬ integers ⎫
negative integers ⎭ ⎬ rational numbers ⎫
     ratios of ⎭ ⎬ real numbers ⎫
     integers ⎫ ⎬ complex
     irrational numbers ⎭ imaginary ⎭ numbers
     numbers ⎫

That is,

$$\mathfrak{N} \subset \mathfrak{I} \subset \mathfrak{F} \subset \mathfrak{R} \subset \mathfrak{C}.$$

## Exercises 1.8

1. Verify the Commutative Law of Multiplication for complex numbers.
2. Verify the Associative Law of Addition for complex numbers.

3. Verify the Distributive Law for complex numbers.
4. Verify the Associative Law of Multiplication for complex numbers.
5. Show that the set of complex numbers forms a field.

In Numbers 6 to 22, inclusive, perform the indicated operation, and write the answer in the form $a + bi$.

6. $(4 + i) + (3 - 5i)$.
7. $(2 + 7i) - (3 - 2i)$.
8. $(5 + 7i)(3 + i)$.
9. $(1 + 2i)(3 - 4i)$.
10. $(3 - i)(4 + 2i)$.
11. $(x + iy)(x - iy)$.
12. $(8 - i\sqrt{3})(8 + i\sqrt{3})$.
13. $(1 - i)(1 - i)(1 + i)$.

14. $\dfrac{3 - 2i}{4 + 5i}$.

15. $\dfrac{5 + 4i}{3 - 4i}$.

16. $\dfrac{1}{2 - 3i}$.

17. $\dfrac{3 + 4i}{3 - 4i}$.

18. $\dfrac{5 + i}{1 - 3i}$.

19. $\dfrac{2 + 10i}{5 - i}$.

20. $i^5 + i^8$.

21. $\dfrac{6 - i}{5 + 2i} - \dfrac{3 + 4i}{2 - 5i}$.

22. $\dfrac{7 + 2i}{3 - 4i} + \dfrac{2 + 5i}{4 + 5i}$.

In Numbers 23 to 25, show that the given set of complex numbers is a multiplicative group.

23. $\{1, -1, i, -i\}$.

24. $\{1, \omega, \omega^2\}$, where $\omega = \dfrac{-1 + i\sqrt{3}}{2}$.

25. $\left\{1, -1, \dfrac{1 + i\sqrt{3}}{2}, \dfrac{-1 + i\sqrt{3}}{2}, \dfrac{-1 - i\sqrt{3}}{2}, \dfrac{1 - i\sqrt{3}}{2}\right\}$.

26. In Definition 1.8a, suppose (1) and (2) are retained as they are, but that (3) is replaced by

$$(a, b)(c, d) . = . (ac + bd, ad - bc).$$

   (a) Is there a subset of the set $\{(a, b)\}$ that corresponds to the real numbers?
   (b) Is there a pair that can serve as a square root of $-1$?
   (c) Which pairs would serve as square roots of 1?

## 1.9 POLYNOMIALS

Certain types of algebraic expressions having coefficients belonging to a field are important enough to have a special designation.

**Definition 1.9a.** An algebraic expression of the form

$$a_0x^n + a_1x^{n-1} + \cdots + a_{n-1}x + a_n,$$

where $n$ is a nonnegative integer and the numbers $a_i$ are numbers in a specified field (say $\mathcal{F}$ or $\mathcal{R}$ or $\mathcal{C}$), is called a *polynomial of degree n in x on this field*.

Since polynomials occur frequently in the following discussions, it is worthwhile to give them special attention. We shall use notations such as $p(x)$, $q(x)$, $r(x)$, and $s(x)$ to represent polynomials in $x$. Thus,

$$p(x) \overset{.}{=} . \; 4x^3 - 7x^2 + \sqrt{2}x - 1$$

is a polynomial of degree three on the field $\mathfrak{R}$.

In a similar fashion, a *polynomial in x and y* on a given field is a sum of terms of the type $a_i x^m y^n$, where the $a_i$ are numbers in the field and the $m$ and $n$ are nonnegative integers. We may denote such polynomials by $p(x, y)$, $q(x, y)$, and so on. For example,

$$x^3 + \sqrt{3}\,xy^2 + y^4 - \pi y + 2$$

is a polynomial in $x$ and $y$ on the field $\mathfrak{R}$.

Evidently, the sum of two polynomials is another polynomial, and if 0 is considered to be a polynomial in which all the coefficients are 0, then the set of all polynomials in $x$, $\{p(x)\}$, over the field $\mathfrak{F}$, $\mathfrak{R}$, or $\mathfrak{C}$ has an additive identity. Also, if $p(x)$ is a polynomial, $-p(x)$ is also a polynomial such that $p(x) + (-p(x)) = 0$. Finally, addition of polynomials is an associative operation so that the set $\{p(x)\}$ of polynomials on a given field forms an additive group.

The set $\{p(x)\}$ is closed and has the associative property with respect to ordinary multiplication. Furthermore, 1 is the multiplicative identity, but the multiplicative inverse of a polynomial is generally not a polynomial. Consequently, the set $\{p(x)\} - \{0\}$ is not a multiplicative group. For example, the multiplicative inverse of $1 - x$, is not a polynomial, although we may write

$$\frac{1}{1-x} = 1 + x + x^2 + \cdots + x^{n-1} + \frac{x^n}{1-x}.$$

It follows from this discussion that the set $\{p(x)\}$ of polynomials is not a field. However, the set possesses many of the properties possessed by the set of integers. The set $\{p(x)\}$ is an additive group; it is closed with respect to multiplication, possesses a multiplicative identity element, and its elements obey the Associative Law of Multiplication and the Distributive Law.

The concepts of prime and composite numbers in the set of natural numbers have analogies in the set of polynomials over a field.

**Definition 1.9b.** A polynomial $p(x)$ is said to be **factorable** in a given field if the polynomial can be written as a product of polynomials of degree greater than 0 with coefficients in that field. The polynomials in the product are called **factors** of $p(x)$.

---

*Example 1.9a.* Factor the polynomial $x^2 - 1$ in $\mathfrak{F}$.

In this case, we may write

$$x^2 - 1 = (x - 1)(x + 1)$$

by inspection and trial. The expressions $x - 1$ and $x + 1$ are the factors of $x^2 - 1$.

---

The expression $2x + 4$ may be written as $2(x + 2)$. However, since the factor 2 is a polynomial of degree 0, the factorization is considered to be a trivial one. Hence, we are led to

**Definition 1.9c.** If a polynomial *cannot* be expressed as a product of *other polynomials* of degree greater than 0 over a given field, then the polynomial is said to be **irreducible** in that field.

Thus, $2x + 4$ is irreducible in the fields $\mathfrak{F}$, $\mathfrak{R}$, and $\mathfrak{C}$.

---

*Example 1.9b.* Show that $x^2 - 2$ is irreducible in the field $\mathfrak{F}$ of rational numbers, but is reducible in the field $\mathfrak{R}$ of real numbers.

Suppose that $x^2 - 2$ is reducible. Then it must be the product of two first degree factors $x - a$ and $x - b$. But it is easy to see by trial that if $b \neq -a$, then $(x - a)(x - b)$ will have a term $-(a + b)x$. Consequently, $b = -a$ and the factors are $x - a$ and $x + a$, so that

$$(x - a)(x + a) = x^2 - a^2 = x^2 - 2.$$

This means that $a^2 = 2$, which we have shown impossible for rational $a$. Therefore, $x^2 - 2$ is irreducible in $\mathfrak{F}$.

If $a$ does not have to be rational, we may write $a = \sqrt{2}$, and

$$x^2 - 2 = (x - \sqrt{2})(x + \sqrt{2}),$$

which displays the fact that $x^2 - 2$ is reducible in $\mathfrak{R}$.

---

It was shown that the set of polynomials over a given field forms an additive group, but that the set is *not* closed with respect to division. Nevertheless, it is possible to develop a number of interesting and important properties of polynomials associated with the operation of division. The following basic theorem is essentially a statement of the·result of dividing a polynomial $p(x)$ by a polynomial $q(x)$.

**Theorem 1.9a.** For any two polynomials $p(x)$ and $q(x)$ in a given field, where the degree of $q(x)$ is less than or equal to the degree of $p(x)$, there exist polynomials $r(x)$ and $s(x)$ in the field such that

$$p(x) = q(x)s(x) + r(x),$$

where the degree of $r(x)$ is less than the degree of $q(x)$, and the sum of the degrees of $q(x)$ and $s(x)$ is equal to the degree of $p(x)$.

The formal proof, which is in essence a description of the division process, is omitted. The equation

$$p(x) = q(x)s(x) + r(x)$$

is a direct consequence of the equation resulting from the division—namely,

$$\frac{p(x)}{q(x)} = s(x) + \frac{r(x)}{q(x)}.$$

---

*Example 1.9c.* Find the polynomials $r(x)$ and $s(x)$ required by Theorem 1.9a, if

$$p(x) .=. x^4 + 1 \quad \text{and} \quad q(x) .=. x + 1.$$

We may write, by division,

$$\frac{x^4 + 1}{x + 1} = x^3 - x^2 + x - 1 + \frac{2}{x + 1}.$$

Hence,

$$r(x) = 2, \quad s(x) = x^3 - x^2 + x - 1.$$

---

An important special case of Theorem 1.9a occurs when the polynomial $q(x)$ is simply $x - c$.

**Theorem 1.9b.** *The Remainder Theorem.* Under the conditions of Theorem 1.9a, if $q(x) = x - c$, so that

$$p(x) = (x - c)s(x) + r(x),$$

then $r(x)$ is a constant equal to the value of $p(x)$ when $x$ is replaced by $c$. The symbol $p(c)$ is used to indicate this value.

PROOF: This theorem follows immediately from Theorem 1.9a by replacing $x$ by $c$ in the equation

$$p(x) = (x - c)s(x) + r(x),$$

a procedure that gives $p(c) = r(c)$. Furthermore, since the degree of $r(x)$ is less than that of $x - c$, its degree must be zero; that is, $r(x)$ is a constant and has the value $p(c)$.

It follows from Theorem 1.9b that the division of $p(x)$ by $x - c$ yields a constant remainder, $p(c)$, the value of $p(x)$ when $x$ is replaced by the number $c$.

---

*Example 1.9d.* What is the value of

$$p(x) .=. x^4 + 3x^3 - 2x^2 - 6x - 7,$$

when $x$ is replaced by $-3$?

In Theorem 1.9b, we put $c = -3$ so that $x - c$ is $x + 3$. Division of the polynomial $p(x)$ by $x + 3$ yields a remainder of $-7$, which shows that $p(-3) = -7$.

---

In the special case when $p(c) = 0$ in Theorem 1.9b, it follows that $x - c$ is a factor of $p(x)$, since then

$$p(x) = (x - c)s(x).$$

**Definition 1.9d.** A number $c$ for which the value of a polynomial $p(x)$ is 0 is called a **zero** of the polynomial.

For example, if

$$p(x) .=. x^3 - 2x^2 + 4x - 8,$$

then $p(2) = 0$ and 2 is a zero of the polynomial $p(x)$. Note that a zero of a polynomial $p(x)$ is a *root* of the equation $p(x) = 0$.

The next theorem is an important one concerning the zeros of a polynomial over the field $\mathfrak{C}$ of complex numbers.

**Theorem 1.9c.** *The Fundamental Theorem of Algebra.* Every polynomial of degree greater than 0 in the field $\mathfrak{C}$ has at least one zero in $\mathfrak{C}$.

The proof of this theorem is too elaborate to be included here. However, a proof may be found in Schreier and Sperner, *Introduction to Modern Algebra and Matrix Theory* (Chelsea, 1952).

It is a direct consequence of the preceding theorem that every polynomial of degree greater than 0 in $\mathfrak{C}$ has at least one factor of the form $x - r$, or $\alpha x + \beta$, where $r$ (or $\alpha$ and $\beta$) $\in \mathfrak{C}$. Factors of this form are called **linear factors**. This result follows from Theorem 1.9b, where the remainder is 0.

The preceding remarks and Theorem 1.9c lead to a result of considerable importance in practical and theoretical work involving polynomials.

**Theorem 1.9d.** A polynomial $p(x)$ of degree $n$ in $\mathfrak{C}$ is reducible to a product of exactly $n$ linear factors in $\mathfrak{C}$.

PROOF: The proof can be made by mathematical induction. Let $p(x)$ be a polynomial of degree 1. Then it is of the form

$$p(x) = a_0 x + a_1, \qquad a_0 \neq 0,$$

or

$$p(x) = a_0(x - r_1),$$

where

$$r_1 = -a_1/a_0,$$

as required by the theorem.

Now suppose that every polynomial of degree $n - 1$ in $\mathfrak{C}$ is reducible to a product of $n - 1$ linear factors in $\mathfrak{C}$, in the form

$$s(x) = a_0(x - r_1)(x - r_2) \cdots (x - r_{n-1}).$$

Let $p(x)$ be a polynomial of degree $n$. Then, by Theorem 1.9c, we know that

$$p(x) .=. a_0 x^n + a_1 x^{n-1} + \cdots + a_n$$

has at least one zero in $\mathfrak{C}$. If this zero is $r_n$, then, by Theorem 1.9b,

$$p(x) = (x - r_n)s(x),$$

where the remainder is 0, since $r_n$ is a zero of $p(x)$, and the degree of $s(x)$ is $n - 1$. By the inductive assumption, $s(x)$ is reducible to a product of $n - 1$ linear factors, so that

$$p(x) = a_0(x - r_1)(x - r_2) \cdots (x - r_{n-1})(x - r_n).$$

This completes the proof.

It is clear that each of the numbers $r_i$ in the preceding proof is a zero of $p(x)$. However, it is possible that some of the $r_i$'s are equal. In that case, we make the following

**Definition 1.9e.** If exactly $k$ of the factors $(x - r_i)$ in the expression

$$p(x) = a_0(x - r_1)(x - r_2) \cdots (x - r_n)$$

are identical, then the zero $r_i$ is said to have **multiplicity** $k$.

For example, the polynomial

$$p(x) = x^5 - 4x^4 + x^3 + 10x^2 - 4x - 8$$

may be written as

$$p(x) = (x - 2)(x - 2)(x - 2)(x + 1)(x + 1).$$

The zero 2 has a multiplicity 3 and the zero $-1$ has a multiplicity 2.

Theorem 1.9d is equivalent to the statement that a polynomial in $\mathcal{C}$ of degree $n$ has exactly $n$ zeros in $\mathcal{C}$, provided that the multiplicity of each zero is counted according to Definition 1.9e. Thus, the preceding polynomial is of the fifth degree and has five zeros, $-1$ counted twice and 2 counted three times.

As a further illustration of Theorem 1.9d, the polynomial

$$p(x) = x^3 + 2x^2 + 2x + 4$$

must have 3 zeros in $\mathcal{C}$. Since

$$p(x) = (x^2 + 2)(x + 2)$$
$$= (x + i\sqrt{2})(x - i\sqrt{2})(x + 2),$$

it is apparent that the zeros of $p(x)$ are $i\sqrt{2}$, $-i\sqrt{2}$, and $-2$.

The preceding theorems lead to a useful result that specifies a condition for two polynomials to be identical.

**Theorem 1.9e.** If the value of a polynomial $p(x)$ of degree $n$ is equal to the value of a polynomial $q(x)$ of degree $m$, where $m \leq n$, for at least $n + 1$ values of $x$, then the polynomials are identical and have equal values for all values of $x$.

PROOF: Suppose that $p(x) = q(x)$ for the values

$$x_1, x_2, \ldots, x_{n+1},$$

and consider the polynomial

$$s(x) = p(x) - q(x).$$

Then, $s(x)$ is of degree $n$ or less and each $x_i$ is a zero of $s(x)$. If

$$p(x) = a_0 x^n + a_1 x^{n-1} + \cdots + a_n$$

and

$$q(x) = b_0 x^n + b_1 x^{n-1} + \cdots + b_n,$$

where $b_0$, $b_1$, and so on, may be 0 if $m < n$, then

$$s(x) = (a_0 - b_0)x^n + (a_1 - b_1)x^{n-1} + \cdots + (a_n - b_n).$$

If $a_0 \neq b_0$, then $s(x)$ is actually of degree $n$. However, by hypothesis, $s(x)$ has at least $n + 1$ zeros, which contradicts Theorem 1.9d. Therefore, $a_0 = b_0$.

If $a_1 \neq b_1$, then $s(x)$ is of degree $n - 1$ and the same contradiction results. Thus, $a_1 = b_1$, and it follows similarly that $a_i = b_i$, $i = 2, 3, \ldots, n - 1$. Finally, $s(x_1) = 0$ implies $a_n - b_n = 0$, which implies that $a_n = b_n$.

Accordingly, all the coefficients of $s(x)$ are zero, the polynomials $p(x)$ and $q(x)$ are identical and, of course, have equal values for all values of $x$.

---

*Example 1.9e.* For what values of $A$, $B$, and $C$ will

$$(x^2 + 3x + 4) = A(x + 1)^2 + B(x + 1) + C$$

for all $x$?

Since the two polynomials are to be identical, we may equate coefficients of corresponding powers of $x$ by the proof of Theorem 1.9e. Thus,

$$1 = A,$$
$$3 = 2A + B,$$
$$4 = A + B + C.$$

The last two equations yield $B = 1$, $C = 2$, so that we have

$$x^2 + 3x + 4 = (x + 1)^2 + (x + 1) + 2.$$

---

There are a number of theorems pertaining to the zeros of a polynomial over the field $\mathcal{R}$, and of these the following one is fundamental.

**Theorem 1.9f.** If $p(x)$ is a polynomial in the field $\mathcal{R}$, then

$$p(a + ib) = 0 \Rightarrow p(a - ib) = 0, \qquad b \neq 0.$$

That is, if $a + ib$ is a zero of a polynomial with real coefficients, then $a - ib$ is also a zero of the polynomial.

PROOF: The product $(x - a - ib)(x - a + ib) = (x - a)^2 + b^2$ is a polynomial in $\mathcal{R}$. By Theorem 1.9a,

$$p(x) = q(x)[(x - a)^2 + b^2] + r(x),$$

where the degree of $r(x)$ is *less* than 2. Hence, it must be that

$$r(x) = cx + d.$$

Since $p(a + ib) = 0$ and $(x - a)^2 + b^2 = 0$ for $x = a + ib$, it follows that

$$0 = c(a + ib) + d$$

or that

$$(ca + d) + bci = 0.$$

Thus, $bc = 0$ so that $c = 0$ because $b \neq 0$ by hypothesis. Consequently, $d = 0$ also, and thus $r(x) = 0$, which shows that

$$p(x) = q(x)[(x - a)^2 + b^2].$$

If $x = a - ib$, then, since $(x - a)^2 + b^2 = 0$ for $x = a - ib$,

$$p(a - ib) = 0.$$

Hence, $a - ib$ is a zero of $p(x)$, as was to be shown.

In Theorem 1.9d, allowance was made for the fact that some of the linear factors of a polynomial might have imaginary coefficients. As a consequence of Theorems 1.9d and 1.9f, it follows that every polynomial with *real* coefficients may be factored into an essentially unique product of *real linear* and/or *quadratic* factors. For instance, as an illustration of Theorem 1.9d, we had

$$x^3 + 2x^2 + 2x + 4 = (x^2 + 2)(x + 2),$$

where the factor $x^2 + 2$ is irreducible in the field $\mathcal{R}$.

## Exercises 1.9

1. For each of the following find the polynomials $r(x)$ and $s(x)$ required by Theorem 1.9a.
   (a) $p(x) .=. 2x^4 - x^3 + 5x^2 - x + 3, q(x) .=. x^2 + 1$.
   (b) $p(x) .=. 3x^3 + 2x^2 - 2x - 1, q(x) .=. 2x^2 - 2$.

   In each of Numbers 2 to 9, use division and the remainder theorem to find the indicated values of the given polynomial.

2. $p(x) .=. 2x^4 - 3x^3 + 2x^2 + x - 7; p(-2), p(3)$.
3. $g(x) .=. x^5 - 4x^3 + 2x - 5; g(2), g(-2)$.
4. $r(x) .=. 3x^4 + 2x^2 - 7x; r(3), r(-2)$.
5. $s(x) .=. 3x^4 + 2x^3 - 5x^2 - 3x - 1; s(-3), s(2)$.
6. $p(x) .=. 5x^4 - 6x^2 + 2x + 3; p(-2), p(4)$.
7. $r(y) .=. y^5 + 4y^4 + 16y^3 + 96; r(-2), r(2)$.
8. $s(w) .=. 9w^4 - 2w^2 + w; s(3), s(-3)$.
9. $g(x) .=. 3x^3 - 7x^2 + 5x - 2; g(-4), g(2)$.

10. Show that the set of polynomials on the field of complex numbers forms an additive group.

    In each of Numbers 11 to 14, show by division that the given value is or is not a zero of the given polynomial.

11. $p(x) .=. 6x^3 - 4x^2 + 5x - 42; x = 2$.
12. $p(s) .=. s^4 + s^2 + 27s - 9; s = -3$.
13. $q(t) .=. t^4 - 3t^3 + t + 4; t = 2$.
14. $q(x) .=. x^5 - 6x^4 - x^3 + 2x; x = 3$.

    In each of Numbers 15 to 17, find the values of the constants $A, B, C, D$ so that the given polynomials will be equal for all values of $x$.

15. $2x^2 - 3x - 1 = A(x - 1)^2 + B(x - 1) + C$.
16. $x^3 - 3x^2 + 2x - 7 = A(x - 1)^3 + B(x - 2)^2 + C(x + 1) + D$.
17. $16x^3 + 1 = A(2x + 1)^3 + B(x - 1)^2 + C(x + 1) + D$.

18. Prove that if $a + b\sqrt{c}$, where $c$ is not a perfect square, is a zero of a polynomial $p(x)$ with rational coefficients, then $a - b\sqrt{c}$ is also a zero of $p(x)$. *Hint:* See the proof of Theorem 1.9f.

    Use the given zero to obtain the other zeros of the polynomials in Numbers 19 to 30.

19. $x^3 + 6x^2 + 11x + 6$; one zero is $-3$.
20. $x^3 - 2x^2 - 9x + 18$; one zero is 2.

21. $3x^3 - 2x^2 - 11x + 10$; one zero is $5/3$.
22. $5x^3 + 28x^2 + 45x + 18$; one zero is $-3/5$.
23. $x^4 - x^3 + 2x^2 - 4x - 8$; one zero is $2i$.
24. $x^4 - 2x^3 + 10x^2 - 18x + 9$; one zero is $-3i$.
25. $x^4 - 3x^3 - x^2 + 13x - 10$; one zero is $2 + i$.
26. $x^3 + (3 - 2i)x^2 + (2 - 6i)x - 4i$; one zero is $2i$.
27. $x^3 + (4 + i)x^2 + 4x(1 + i) + 4i$; one zero is $-i$.
28. $x^4 + x^3 - 4x^2 - 2x + 4$; one zero is $\sqrt{2}$. *Hint*: See Number 18.
29. $x^4 - x^3 - 9x^2 - 5x + 2$; one zero is $2 + \sqrt{3}$.
30. $x^3 - x^2(1 + \sqrt{3}) + x(-2 + \sqrt{3}) + 2\sqrt{3}$; one zero is $\sqrt{3}$.

31. Suppose an equation $a_0x^n + a_1x^{n-1} + \cdots + a_n = 0$, where the $a$'s are all integers, has a rational root $c/d$. Show that $d$ must be a divisor of $a_0$ and $c$ must be a divisor of $a_n$.

## 1.10 INEQUALITIES

We have seen that the set $\mathcal{R}$ of real numbers has an order property, customarily denoted by the symbol $<$. For any two elements $a$, $b \in \mathcal{R}$, one and only one of the following is valid:

$$a < b, \quad a = b, \quad a > b.$$

This statement is called the **trichotomy law** of numbers.

An expression of the form

$$a < b, \quad b > a,$$

where $a$, $b \in \mathcal{R}$, is called an **inequality**. Inequalities are perhaps as important in the applications of mathematics as are equations. In fact, insofar as our knowledge of the physical world is obtained by measurement (not mere counting), that knowledge is described by inequalities rather than by equations. For instance, if we say that the diameter $d$ of the planet Venus is 7,700 miles, we mean that

$$7650 < d < 7750.$$

A moment's reflection shows that an absolutely exact measurement of any physical quantity such as distance, weight, velocity, and so on, is completely impossible; the accuracy depends on the measuring instruments, and such instruments can be made to measure only within certain specified tolerances— never exactly. We shall also see later that inequalities are essential in clarifying such fundamental concepts as that of a limit, on which the entire calculus is built. It is for these reasons that a good basic understanding of inequalities is necessary, and we shall next develop a number of fundamental laws concerning them.

**Theorem 1.10a.** *The Transitive Property of Inequalities:*

$$a > b \text{ and } b > c \Rightarrow a > c, \qquad a, b, c \in \mathcal{R}.$$

PROOF: $a > b \Rightarrow a - b = p$, where $p$ is a positive number. Similarly,

$$b > c \Rightarrow b - c = q,$$

where $q > 0$. Then, by adding the two equations $a - b = p$ and $b - c = q$, we obtain

$$a - c = p + q,$$

where $p + q$ is a positive number. Hence,

$$a > c.$$

That we may add (subtract) the same real number to (from) both members of an inequality and retain the direction or the "sense" of the inequality is contained in the following theorem.

**Theorem 1.10b.** $\quad a > b \Rightarrow a + c > b + c, \quad\quad a, b, c \in \mathcal{R}.$

PROOF: $a > b \Rightarrow a - b = p$, a positive number. Furthermore,

$$a - b = (a + c) - (b + c),$$

so that

$$(a + c) - (b + c) = p,$$

a positive number. Therefore

$$a + c > b + c.$$

Subtraction of the same real number from both sides of an equality is also taken care of since in Theorem 1.10b, $c$ may be either positive or negative.

Another important result is that both members of an inequality may be multiplied by the same *positive* number without changing the sense of the inequality.

**Theorem 1.10c.** $a > b$ and $c > 0 \Rightarrow ac > bc, \quad\quad a, b, c \in \mathcal{R}.$

PROOF: Since $a - b = p$, a positive number, and $c$ is also positive, then

$$(a - b)c = pc,$$

a positive number. Thus,

$$ac - bc = pc,$$

and

$$ac > bc.$$

Division is also taken care of, since $c$ is any positive number and could be of the form $1/d$.

**Theorem 1.10d.** $a > b$ and $c < 0 \Rightarrow ac < bc, \quad\quad a, b, c \in \mathcal{R}.$

The proof is left for the exercises.

Still another important theorem is that if all the members of two inequalities of the same sense are positive, and the corresponding members are multiplied together, an inequality of the same sense is obtained.

**Theorem 1.10e.** $a > b > 0$ and $c > d > 0 \Rightarrow ac > bd, \quad\quad a, b, c \in \mathcal{R}.$

PROOF: We have $a - b = p$, $c - d = q$, with $p$ and $q$ positive. Thus

$$a = b + p, \, c = d + q,$$

and

$$ac = (b + p)(d + q),$$

or

$$ac = bd + bq + pd + pq.$$

Accordingly,

$$ac - bd = bq + pd + pq,$$

which is a positive number. Therefore,

$$ac > bd.$$

(Why?)

A number of useful results concerning rational exponents and inequalities can be obtained from Theorem 1.10e. If both members of an inequality are positive, the same positive integral powers of both members are unequal in the same sense.

**Theorem 1.10f.** $a > b > 0$ and $p \in \mathfrak{N} \Rightarrow a^p > b^p$, $a, b \in \mathfrak{R}$.

PROOF: The proof is a simple exercise in mathematical induction using Theorem 1.10e, and is left for the reader.

Sometimes inequality signs are combined with equals signs to give symbols such as $\geq$ (read "greater than or equal to") and $\leq$ (read "less than or equal to"). For example, if $m$ is any real number whatsoever, we have $m^2 \geq 0$. (Why?)

Theorem 1.10f can be extended to include rational values for $p$.

**Theorem 1.10g.** $a > b > 0$, $p > 0$, and $p \in \mathfrak{F} \Rightarrow a^p > b^p$, $a, b \in \mathfrak{R}$.

PROOF: The proof is by contradiction. Let $p = m/n$, where $m$ and $n$ are positive integers, and assume that

$$a^{m/n} \leq b^{m/n}.$$

Then

$$(a^{m/n})^n \leq (b^{m/n})^n$$

or

$$a^m \leq b^m.$$

But since $a > b$, $a^m > b^m$, which is a contradiction of the preceding result. Evidently, $a^{m/n} > b^{m/n}$.

The preceding theorems of this section are useful in establishing many important relationships of inequality. The following examples illustrate the use of these theorems.

---

*Example 1.10a.* Show that the arithmetic mean of two positive numbers is never less than their positive geometric mean; that is,

$$a > 0 \text{ and } b > 0 \Rightarrow \tfrac{1}{2}(a + b) \geq \sqrt{ab}$$

We shall illustrate two possible procedures for proving this result. The first goes directly back to the meaning of the symbol $>$. Thus, we write

$$\tfrac{1}{2}(a + b) - \sqrt{ab} = \tfrac{1}{2}(a - 2\sqrt{ab} + b)$$
$$= \tfrac{1}{2}(\sqrt{a} - \sqrt{b})^2,$$

which cannot be a negative number. Hence

$$\tfrac{1}{2}(a + b) \geq \sqrt{ab}.$$

The second procedure consists of an analysis in which the required proposition is assumed true. Then we attempt to derive a known result. A reversal of these steps can then be used as the needed proof.

1. We assume that $\tfrac{1}{2}(a + b) \geq \sqrt{ab}$ is true.
2. $a + b \geq 2\sqrt{ab}$.     Why?
3. $a + b - 2\sqrt{ab} \geq 0$.     Why?
4. $(\sqrt{a} - \sqrt{b})^2 \geq 0$.     Why?

This last result is known to be valid since the square of any real number is non-negative. Therefore, we may construct the *proof*:

1. $(\sqrt{a} - \sqrt{b})^2 \geq 0$.     $m^2 \geq 0$ for any real number $m$.
2. $a + b - 2\sqrt{ab} \geq 0$.     Why?
3. $a + b \geq 2\sqrt{ab}$.     Why?
4. $\tfrac{1}{2}(a + b) \geq \sqrt{ab}$.     Why?

---

*Example 1.10b.* If $a$, $b$, $c$ are positive numbers, and $d/a < e/b < f/c$, show that

$$\frac{d}{a} < \frac{d + e + f}{a + b + c} < \frac{f}{c}.$$

Let $f/c = r$. Then we have $e/b < r$, and $d/a < r$.
Since $a$ and $b$ are positive, we have $d < ar$, and $e < br$. Also, $f = cr$. Consequently,

$$d + e + f < ar + br + cr$$
$$d + e + f < (a + b + c)r$$

(why?) or

and

$$\frac{d + e + f}{a + b + c} < r$$

(why?); that is,

$$\frac{d + e + f}{a + b + c} < \frac{f}{c}.$$

The left portion of the inequality may be proved in a similar manner.

---

*Example 1.10c.* Without using decimal approximations, determine the proper order relationship $>$, $=$, or $<$ between the numbers $\sqrt{15} - \sqrt{14}$ and $\sqrt{32} - \sqrt{31}$.

Let $\theta$ denote the proper one of the three symbols. Then,

$$\sqrt{15} - \sqrt{14} \,\theta\, \sqrt{32} - \sqrt{31} \Leftrightarrow \sqrt{15} + \sqrt{31} \,\theta\, \sqrt{32} + \sqrt{14}$$
$$\Leftrightarrow (\sqrt{15} + \sqrt{31})^2 \,\theta\, (\sqrt{32} + \sqrt{14})^2$$
$$\Leftrightarrow 46 + 2\sqrt{465} \,\theta\, 46 + 2\sqrt{448}$$
$$\Leftrightarrow \sqrt{465} \,\theta\, \sqrt{448}.$$

Clearly, the proper symbol is $>$, and the preceding analysis can be made into a proof by proceeding through the steps in reverse order, that is, by starting with the true inequality $\sqrt{465} > \sqrt{448}$, and deriving the desired result $\sqrt{15} - \sqrt{14} > \sqrt{32} - \sqrt{31}$.

## Exercises 1.10

In Numbers 1 to 5, show the validity of the inequalities.

1. $\dfrac{d}{3c} > 1 - \dfrac{3c}{4d}$, where $c > 0$, $d > 0$, $2d \neq 3c$.

2. $x^2 + \dfrac{9}{x^2} \geqq 6$, where $x \neq 0$.

3. $\dfrac{\sqrt{x}}{\sqrt{y}} + \dfrac{\sqrt{y}}{\sqrt{x}} > 2$, if $x > 0$, $y > 0$, $x \neq y$.

4. $\dfrac{3a}{5b} + \dfrac{5b}{3a} > 2$, if $a > 0$, $b > 0$, $3a \neq 5b$.

5. $a^2 + b^2 + c^2 > ab + ac + bc$, unless $a = b = c$.

In each of Numbers 6 to 9, without using decimal expansions, determine which of the symbols, $>$, $=$, $<$ should be substituted for $\theta$.

6. $\sqrt{6} - \sqrt{8} \,\theta\, \sqrt{3} - 2$.

7. $\sqrt{15} - \sqrt{5} \,\theta\, 3 - \sqrt{2}$.

8. $\sqrt{22} - \sqrt{17} \,\theta\, \sqrt{37} - \sqrt{31}$.

9. $\sqrt{19} - \sqrt{14} \,\theta\, \sqrt{29} - \sqrt{22}$.

10. Prove Theorem 1.10d.
11. Prove Theorem 1.10f.
12. Prove that $0 < a < b \Rightarrow 1/a > 1/b$.
13. Prove that if $a < b$, then $-a > -b$.
14. Prove that for any real numbers $a$, $b$, $c$, $d$,

$$(ab + cd)^2 \leqq (a^2 + c^2)(b^2 + d^2) \qquad \text{(Cauchy's Inequality)}.$$

15. Is the statement

$$a, b, c, d > 0 \Rightarrow (ab + cd)(ac + bd) \leqq 4abcd$$

true or false?

16. For what positive numbers, if any, is the sum of the number and its reciprocal less than 2?

17. Prove that if $a > b > 0$, then $p \in \mathfrak{N} \Rightarrow a^{1/p} > b^{1/p}$.
18. Prove that if $0 < a < 1$, then $p \in \mathfrak{N} \Rightarrow a \leqq a^{1/p} < 1$.
19. Prove that if $1 < a$, then $p \in \mathfrak{N} \Rightarrow 1 < a^{1/p} \leqq a$.
20. Show that if $a$, $b$, $c > 0$, then

$$3abc \leqq a^3 + b^3 + c^3.$$

*Hint:* One factor of $a^3 + b^3 + c^3 - 3abc$ is $a + b + c$.

21. For $a$, $b$, $c$ real, show that $ax^2 + bx + c$ is positive for all real $x$ if and only if $a > 0$, $b^2 - 4ac < 0$. *Hint*: Try to convert most of the expression into a perfect square involving $x$.

22. Prove by mathematical induction that

$$\left(\frac{1}{2}\right)\left(\frac{3}{4}\right)\left(\frac{5}{6}\right) \cdots \left(\frac{2n-1}{2n}\right) \leqq \frac{1}{\sqrt{3n+1}}.$$

---

# Summary of Chapter 1

---

The essential concepts that are used throughout the book include

  (1) the meaning and correct usage of the symbols $.=.$ and $[\![\ ]\!]$ (Section 1.1);

  (2) the correct usage and meaning of the implication symbol (Section 1.2);

  (3) the fundamental laws of logic (Section 1.2);

  (4) the converse of an implication (Section 1.2);

  (5) the meaning and significance of the term "axiom" (Section 1.3);

  (6) the methods of proving mathematical statements (Section 1.4);

  (7) the contrapositive of an implication (Section 1.4);

  (8) sets and the meaning of the symbols $\in$, $\notin$, $\subset$, and $\not\subset$ (Section 1.5);

  (9) the meaning of union, intersection, and complement of a set (Section 1.6);

  (10) the fundamental sets of numbers and the notation used for each (Section 1.7);

  (11) the definitions of group and field, with examples of each (Section 1.7);

  (12) the complex number system (Section 1.8);

  (13) polynomials and related theorems (Section 1.9);

  (14) the fundamental properties of inequalities (Section 1.10).

# Chapter 2  Functions and Graphs

## 2.1 A GEOMETRIC INTERPRETATION OF THE REAL NUMBERS

The reader is undoubtedly familiar with the idea of interpreting real numbers geometrically on a straight line, as is done on a ruler, for example. We can make this idea more precise by defining what is meant by the "distance" between two elements of $\mathcal{R}$.

**Definition 2.1a.** Let $a$ and $b$ be two real numbers. The quantity

$$d(a, b) .= .\sqrt{(a - b)^2}$$

is called the **distance** between the two numbers $a$ and $b$.

According to this definition, distance is a nonnegative numerical quantity that is defined on the set $\mathcal{R}$ of real numbers. Let us attempt to associate these numbers with points on a straight line $m$ in such a way that "distance" will have a consistent geometric interpretation. On the line $m$, an arbitrary point, called the origin, is chosen to be associated with the number 0. For the present, this point will be denoted by (0). Another arbitrary point distinct from (0), and usually located to the right of (0), is chosen to be associated with the number 1, and is denoted by (1) (see Figure 2.1a).

$$(-1) \qquad (0) \qquad (1) \quad (a) \quad (2) \quad m$$

**FIGURE 2.1a**

Since $d(0, 1) = 1$, the line segment on $m$ between (0) and (1) is a geometrical representation of a distance of one unit, and is called a **unit length.** Furthermore, once we have established the correspondence between points on $m$ and the real numbers, we may define the **length** of a line segment on $m$ as the distance between the numbers associated with the points that determine the line segment. However, it is desirable to establish the correspondence so that the following axiom is satisfied.

**Axiom 2.1a.** Two line segments that are geometrically congruent have the same length.

This requirement forces us to locate the point (2) in such a way that the line segment from (1) to (2) is geometrically congruent to the segment from (0) to (1). Consequently, the two points (0) and (1), with the concept of distance in Definition 2.1a, and Axiom 2.1a, determine the point on *m* to be associated with the real number *a*. On occasion, where it is necessary to distinguish between the number *a* and the point associated with this number, we shall use the notation (*a*) for the point. However, this notation is often clumsy, and when there is no danger of confusion we shall use *a* to denote both the real number *a* and the point associated with the number.

The following example illustrates some of the preceding ideas.

---

*Example 2.1a.* Find the length of the line segment determined by the following pairs of points: (a) $(-2)$ and $(3)$; (b) $(\sqrt{2})$ and $(\sqrt{5})$.

Using the expression in Definition 2.1a, we get

(a) $$d(-2, 3) = \sqrt{(-2-3)^2} = 5,$$

and

(b) $$d(\sqrt{2}, \sqrt{5}) = \sqrt{(\sqrt{2}-\sqrt{5})^2} = \sqrt{5} - \sqrt{2}.$$

---

In (b) of Example 2.1a, why is

$$d(\sqrt{2}, \sqrt{5}) = \sqrt{2} - \sqrt{5}$$

an incorrect statement?

For convenience in specifying the location of a point *P* with respect to a point *Q*, we need to introduce the concept of a **directed line segment.** Since points associated with positive numbers are located to the right of (0), the direction of a line *m* from (0) to any point (*a*), where $a > 0$, is called the *positive direction* of *m*. The opposite direction is the *negative direction* of *m*. If the direction from a point *P* on *m* to a point *Q* on *m* is in the positive direction of *m*, then the line segment *PQ* is called a *positively directed* line segment. Otherwise it is called a *negatively directed* line segment. Hence, the segment from (0) to (1) is positively directed, and the segment from (1) to (0) is negatively directed.

The straight line *m* is usually called the **real number axis,** or the *x-axis*, and the set of points on *m* is said to constitute a **one-dimensional space.** The real number *a* that corresponds to a point $A = (a)$ on the axis is called the coordinate of the point. Thus, the point $(-1/2)$ has the coordinate $-1/2$. Accordingly, the real number *a*, by means of its sign and magnitude, determines the distance and the direction of the point (*a*) from the origin.

The next definition is useful in relating distance to a directed line segment.

**Definition 2.1b.** The **directed distance** from a point $P_1$ to a point $P_2$ on the real axis is a number whose magnitude is the number of units in the length of the segment joining the two points and whose sign is plus or minus, according as the direction is the same as or is opposite from the positive direction of the axis.

The directed distance will be designated by $P_1P_2$. Note that $P_2P_1$ is in the opposite direction from $P_1P_2$ so that we have $P_2P_1 = -P_1P_2$.

It follows at once from Definition 2.1b that the directed distance $OP$ from the origin to any point $P$ on the axis is given by the coordinate of $P$. Thus if $P$ has the coordinate $x$, then $OP = x$. Another important consequence of Definition 2.1b is given in

**Theorem 2.1a.** On the real axis, the directed distance $P_1P_2$ is always given by

$$P_1P_2 = OP_2 - OP_1.$$

PROOF: The proof of this theorem consists of direct verification from the few possible different placements of the points $P_1$ and $P_2$ relative to the origin. Figure 2.1b shows three of the possibilities. For example, in the middle line

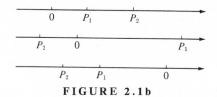

FIGURE 2.1b

of the figure we see that $OP_1$ is positive, $OP_2$ is negative, and $P_1P_2$ is negative. Clearly, $OP_2 - OP_1$ will be negative and will have the correct magnitude so that $P_1P_2 = OP_2 - OP_1$. The reader should make a careful analysis for all other possible placements of $P_1$ and $P_2$. Note that, if $P_1$ and $P_2$ coincide, the theorem correctly gives zero for the directed distance.

**Theorem 2.1b.** If the coordinates of $P_1$ and $P_2$ are $x_1$ and $x_2$, respectively, then

$$P_1P_2 = x_2 - x_1.$$

In view of our recognition that $OP_1 = x_1$ and $OP_2 = x_2$, this theorem is essentially a restatement of Theorem 2.1a.

We have, for instance,

(a) $x_1 = \phantom{-}5, \quad x_2 = -3 \Rightarrow P_1P_2 = -3 - 5 = -8;$
(b) $x_1 = -4, \quad x_2 = \phantom{-}2 \Rightarrow P_1P_2 = \phantom{-}2 + 4 = \phantom{-}6.$

An order relation is established among the points on the real number axis corresponding to the order relation among the real numbers. The point $(a)$ is said to *precede* the point $(b)$ if and only if the real number $a$ is *less* than the real number $b$. Thus we have a geometric picture that corresponds to the statement $a < b$.

A set of points on the real number axis is defined by stating a certain property which the elements of the set possess, but which other points of the $x$-axis do not possess. A set such as $\{(x): a \leq x \leq b\}$, where $a < b$, is called a **closed**

**interval.** It is important to notice that the end points (a) and (b) must be elements of the set if the interval is closed. If neither end point is included, the set is said to be an **open** interval; if only one end point is included, the set is said to be a **half-open** interval.

We frequently need to refer to sets of points such as

$$\{(x): x > a\} \quad \text{or} \quad \{(x): x \leqq b\},$$

where $a$ and $b$ are fixed real numbers. These sets correspond, respectively, to the entire real axis to the right of the point $(a)$ and the entire real axis to the left of and including the point $(b)$. Such intervals are termed **semi-infinite,** since they correspond to half-lines which are endless in one direction. We shall not employ the adjectives open or closed with semi-infinite intervals.

*Example 2.1b.* Describe the interval $\{(x): 1 \leqq x < 2\}$.

This set consists of all the points on the segment of the $x$-axis between the points (1) and (2) and including the point (1). The interval is half open, since only one end point is included. In sketching a point set consisting of a segment of the axis, we indicate the end points by small circles. If the end point is included, the interior of the circle is black, and if the end point is not included, the interior of the circle is white (see Figure 2.1c).

$$\{(x): 1 \leqq x < 2\}$$

**FIGURE 2.1c**

If $(x_0)$ is a given point on the real number axis and $h$ is a given positive number, then the interval

$$\{(x): x_0 - h < x < x_0 + h\}$$

consists of all points of the segment between $(x_0 - h)$ and $(x_0 + h)$ (see Figure 2.1d). This important type of open interval is called a **neighborhood** of the

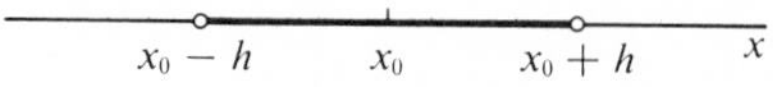

$$x_0 - h \qquad x_0 \qquad x_0 + h \qquad x$$

$$\{(x): x_0 - h < x < x_0 + h\}$$

**FIGURE 2.1d**

point $(x_0)$, and the positive number $h$ is often called the **radius** of the neighborhood. For instance, the neighborhood of radius 0.5 of the point $(-2)$ is the open interval $\{(x): -2.5 < x < -1.5\}$. The idea of a neighborhood will play an important role in some of our later discussions.

## Exercises 2.1

1. Find the distance between the following points on the real number axis. What is the directed distance from the first to the second of the given points in each case?

(a) $(-3), (-7)$.

(b) $(\sqrt{3}), (\sqrt{6})$.

(c) $(2 - \sqrt{2}), (5 - \sqrt{2})$.

(d) $(2 - \sqrt{2}), (\sqrt{2} - 5)$.

(e) $(3), (-10)$.

(f) $(\sqrt{3}), (-\sqrt{6})$.

2. Which of the following point sets constitutes an open interval? a closed interval? a half-open interval? a semi-infinite interval?

(a) $\{(x): -4 < x \leq -2\}$.

(b) $\{(x): x$ is an integer and $0 \leq x \leq 100\}$.

(c) $\{(x): 0 \leq x \leq 1\}$.

(d) $\{(x): x \geq 4\}$.

(e) $\{(x): 2 < x < 3\}$.

(f) $\{(x): x < -10\}$.

3. Represent each of the following sets graphically.

(a) $\mathcal{A} .=. \{(x): 2 < x \leq 5\}$.

(b) $\mathcal{B} .=. \{(x): -2 \leq x \leq 3\}$.

(c) $\mathcal{C} .=. \{(x): -1 < x < 4\}$.

(d) $\mathcal{D} .=. \{(x): -3 \leq x < 1\}$.

4. If $\mathcal{A}, \mathcal{B}, \mathcal{C}, \mathcal{D}$ are the sets in Number 3, describe each of the following sets and represent it graphically. For example, we would describe $\mathcal{A} \cup \mathcal{C}$ by writing

$$\mathcal{A} \cup \mathcal{C} = \{(x): -1 < x \leq 5\}.$$

(a) $\mathcal{A} \cap \mathcal{B}$.

(b) $\mathcal{A} \cup \mathcal{B}$.

(c) $(\mathcal{A} \cup \mathcal{B}) \cap \mathcal{C}$.

(d) $(\mathcal{A} \cup \mathcal{B}) \cap (\mathcal{C} \cup \mathcal{D})$.

5. If complementation is with respect to the set $\mathcal{R}$ of all real numbers and we refer to the sets in Number 3, then $\mathcal{A}'$, for example, would be the set

$$\{(x): x \leq 2 \text{ or } x > 5\}.$$

Describe each of the following sets.

(a) $\mathcal{A}' \cap \mathcal{B}'$.

(b) $(\mathcal{A}' \cup \mathcal{C}') \cap \mathcal{D}'$.

(c) $(\mathcal{A}' \cup \mathcal{C}') \cap (\mathcal{A}' \cup \mathcal{D}')$.

(d) $(\mathcal{A} \cup \mathcal{C}') \cap (\mathcal{B} \cup \mathcal{D}')$.

## 2.2 TWO-DIMENSIONAL EUCLIDEAN SPACE

We may construct a reference system for two-dimensional euclidean geometry by choosing two perpendicular lines in a plane and using the same number scale on each line with the zero points coincident. The common zero point of the two lines is called the **origin,** $O$. One of the lines is designated the $x$-axis and the other the $y$-axis. Usually the $x$-axis is taken as the horizontal axis, with the positive direction to the right, and the $y$-axis as the vertical axis, with the positive direction upward (see Figure 2.2a).

In order to locate a point $P$ of the plane, we construct a line $L_1$ through $P$ perpendicular to the $x$-axis and a line $L_2$ through $P$ perpendicular to the $y$-axis, as shown in Figure 2.2a. If the point where $L_1$ meets the $x$-axis is $P_1$, and the point where $L_2$ meets the $y$-axis is $P_2$, then the directed distance $a$ from the origin to $P_1$ is called the **x-coordinate** or the **abscissa** of the point $P$, and the directed distance $b$ from the origin to $P_2$ is called the **y-coordinate** or the **ordinate** of the point $P$. Thus, a point in the plane is located relative to $O$ by means of

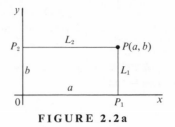

**FIGURE 2.2a**

the numbers, $a$ and $b$. We regard the point as being represented by the ordered pair of numbers $(a, b)$, the $x$-coordinate being given first. It is a basic assumption that there is a one-to-one correspondence between the ordered pairs of real numbers $(x, y)$ and the points of the plane.

The points $(3, 4)$, $(-2, 6)$, $(-7, -3)$, and $(5, -2)$ are plotted as indicated in Figure 2.2b. Notice that the $x$- and $y$-axes divide the plane into four parts.

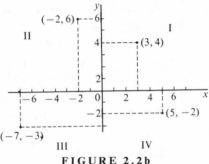

**FIGURE 2.2b**

These parts are called **quadrants,** and are numbered counterclockwise, the quadrant where both of the coordinates are positive being quadrant I (see Figure 2.2b).

The distance between the points $(x_1, a)$ and $(x_2, a)$ is $\sqrt{(x_2 - x_1)^2}$, as can be shown by drawing the rectangle with the line from $(x_1, a)$ to $(x_2, a)$ as one side and with the opposite side on the $x$-axis (see Figure 2.2c). Similarly, the distance between the points $(b, y_1)$ and $(b, y_2)$ is $\sqrt{(y_2 - y_1)^2}$.

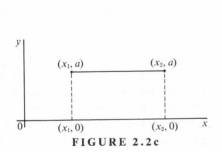

**FIGURE 2.2c**

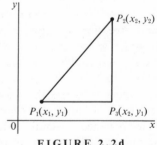

**FIGURE 2.2d**

Using the preceding results, it is easy to obtain a formula for the distance $P_1P_2$ between any two points $P_1$ and $P_2$ in the plane. We first apply the Theorem of Pythagoras to the right triangle $P_1P_2P_3$ in Figure 2.2d to obtain

$$(P_1P_2)^2 = (P_2P_3)^2 + (P_1P_3)^2.$$

If the distances $P_1P_3$ and $P_2P_3$ are now replaced by their values in terms of the coordinates, the result is

$$(P_1P_2)^2 = (x_2 - x_1)^2 + (y_2 - y_1)^2.$$

Thus, by taking the positive square root on both sides of this equation, we have the proof of

**Theorem 2.2a.** The distance $d$ between the point $P_1$ with coordinates $(x_1, y_1)$ and the point $P_2$ with coordinates $(x_2, y_2)$ is given by

$$d(P_1, P_2) = \sqrt{(x_2 - x_1)^2 + (y_2 - y_1)^2}.$$

The following example illustrates how some geometric questions can be answered by the use of the concept of distance in conjunction with the representation of points in a plane by means of ordered number pairs.

---

*Example 2.2a.* Do the points $A(1, 3)$, $B(5, 6)$, $C(8, 2)$ determine an equilateral triangle?

To answer the question we need only to find the distance between each pair of points. Thus,

$$d(A, B) = [(5 - 1)^2 + (6 - 3)^2]^{1/2} = 5,$$
$$d(B, C) = [(8 - 5)^2 + (2 - 6)^2]^{1/2} = 5,$$
$$d(C, A) = [(8 - 1)^2 + (2 - 3)^2]^{1/2} = \sqrt{50} = 5\sqrt{2}.$$

Since $d(C, A) \neq d(B, C)$, the triangle is not equilateral. However, it is an isosceles right triangle. (Why?)

---

Another illustration of the use of coordinates in geometry is given next.

---

*Example 2.2b.* Determine the point $P_0(x_0, y_0)$ on the line segment from $P_1(2, 3)$ to $P_2(5, 7)$ that is two-thirds of the distance from $P_1$ to $P_2$.

The problem is illustrated in Figure 2.2e, where lines parallel to the $y$-axis have been constructed through $P_0$, $P_1$, and $P_2$, and intersecting the $x$-axis at points $Q$, $A(2, 0)$, and $B(5, 0)$, respectively. In addition, a line parallel to the $x$-axis has been constructed through $P_1$. The triangles $P_1P_0R$ and $P_1P_2S$ are similar, so that corresponding sides are proportional. Thus

$$\frac{P_1P_0}{P_1P_2} = \frac{P_1R}{P_1S} = \frac{AQ}{AB}.$$

In terms of the coordinates of the points, these ratios are

$$\frac{x_0 - 2}{5 - 2} = \frac{4 - 2}{5 - 2} = \frac{2}{3}.$$

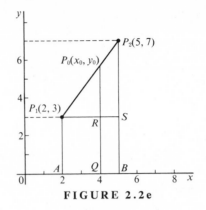

**FIGURE 2.2e**

Hence

$$x_0 = 2 + \left(\frac{2}{3}\right)(3) = 4.$$

In the same way,

$$\frac{P_1P_0}{P_1P_2} = \frac{P_0R}{P_2S} \quad \text{or} \quad \frac{2}{3} = \frac{y_0 - 3}{7 - 3}.$$

This gives

$$y_0 = 5\tfrac{2}{3},$$

so that $P_0$ is the point $(4, 17/3)$.

---

Example 2.2b illustrates a method that can be used to locate a point on a line segment which divides that line segment in a specified manner. Perhaps the most important special instance of such a problem is that of locating the midpoint of a given line segment. If the line segment joins $P_1(x_1, y_1)$ to $P_2(x_2, y_2)$, then the reader may easily show that the coordinates of the midpoint, say $P_0(x_0, y_0)$, are given by

$$x_0 = x_1 + \tfrac{1}{2}(x_2 - x_1) = \tfrac{1}{2}(x_1 + x_2),$$
$$y_0 = y_1 + \tfrac{1}{2}(y_2 - y_1) = \tfrac{1}{2}(y_1 + y_2).$$

Notice that *the coordinates of the midpoint are the simple arithmetic averages of the corresponding coordinates of the end points of the segment.*

The use of coordinates and algebra frequently makes it possible to write down quite simple proofs for certain theorems in geometry. The next problem is an illustration of this procedure.

---

*Example 2.2c.* Show that the line segment joining the midpoints of the nonparallel sides of a trapezoid is equal in length to one-half the sum of the parallel sides.

Place the axes so that one end of the base of the trapezoid is at the origin and the *x*-axis runs along this base as in Figure 2.2f. Then the other end of the base will have coordinates $(a, 0)$ and the remaining vertices will be labeled $(b, c)$ and $(d, c)$. The *y*-coordinates of the last two points are the same, since the bases of the trapezoid are parallel.

If $P$ and $Q$ are the midpoints of the nonparallel sides as shown in the figure, then the coordinates of $P$ are $(\frac{1}{2}d, \frac{1}{2}c)$ and those of $Q$ are $[\frac{1}{2}(a+b), \frac{1}{2}c]$. Consequently,

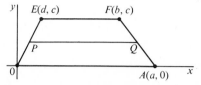

**FIGURE 2.2f**

$$PQ = \frac{a+b}{2} - \frac{d}{2} = \frac{a+b-d}{2}.$$

The sum of the lengths of the two bases is

$$OA + EF = a + (b-d) = a+b-d,$$

so that

$$PQ = \tfrac{1}{2}(OA + EF),$$

as was to be shown.

---

The reader should notice the convenient placement of the coordinate axes in the preceding problem. Such a wise choice frequently is the key to a simple proof. The study of geometry using coordinates and algebra is called **coordinate geometry** or **analytic geometry.** The preceding proof is an example of a proof by the methods of analytic geometry.

## Exercises 2.2

1. In each of (a) and (b), use the distance formula to determine if the given three points lie in a straight line.

    (a) $(-3, -2)$, $(6, 1)$, $(0, -1)$.
    (b) $(-2, 3)$, $(7, -1)$, $(1, 2)$.

2. In each of (a) and (b), use the distance formula to determine if the quadrilateral whose vertices are at the given points is a parallelogram.

    (a) $(0, 0)$, $(5, 1)$, $(8, -4)$, $(3, -5)$.
    (b) $(-1, 8)$, $(1, 2)$, $(-3, -2)$, $(-5, 4)$.

3. Work Number 2 by another method.

4. Determine which of the triangles whose vertices are at the given points is an equilateral triangle or an isosceles triangle.

    (a) $(0, 5)$, $(-3, 4)$, $(-1, 2)$.
    (b) $(-1, 4)$, $(-4, -1)$, $(-1, -2)$.
    (c) $(-3, 2)$, $(1, -1)$, $(-2, -5)$.

5. Is the triangle with vertices at $(-2, 1)$, $(-1, -1)$, and $(-5, -3)$ a right triangle? Explain.

6. The diagonals of a square lie along the coordinate axes. If the length of the side of the square is four units, find the coordinates of the vertices.

7. The points (1, 3), (1, 6), and (4, 2) are three vertices of a parallelogram. At what points could the fourth vertex be?

8. Is it possible to draw a circle that has its center at the point (2, 1) and that passes through the points $(-1, 3)$, $(5, -1)$, and $(0, -2)$?

9. Find the point equidistant from the points $(-3, 1)$, $(2, -4)$, and $(1, 1)$.

10. Find the center and radius of the circle passing through the points (0, 6), (7, 5), and $(6, -2)$.

11. Let $P_0(x_0, y_0)$ be a point on the line through the points $P_1(-3, 4)$ and $P_2(5, -7)$. If $P_1P_0/P_1P_2 = k$, find the coordinates of $P_0$ for each of the following values of $k$.

    (a) $k = \frac{2}{5}$.
    (b) $k = \frac{3}{4}$.
    (c) $k = \frac{4}{3}$. (Remember that $P_1P_0$ and $P_1P_2$ are directed distances.)
    (d) $k = -\frac{1}{2}$.
    (e) $k = -\frac{3}{2}$.

12. A triangle has one vertex at the origin and another at the point (2, 3). If the midpoint of the side opposite the origin is at (0, 5), what are the coordinates of the third vertex?

13. Find the vertices of a triangle having the midpoints of its sides at (3, 2), $(5, -1)$, (6, 4).

Use the methods of analytic geometry to prove the following theorems.

14. The diagonals of a rectangle are equal.

15. If the diagonals of a parallelogram are equal, the figure is a rectangle.

16. The sum of the squares of the medians of a triangle is equal to three-fourths the sum of the squares of the sides.

17. If two medians of a triangle are equal, the triangle is isosceles.

18. If the midpoints of the opposite sides of a quadrilateral are joined by line segments, these segments bisect each other.

## 2.3 RELATIONS AND FUNCTIONS

Most applications of mathematics in practical problems make use of sets of ordered pairs of numbers. For example, suppose we are interested in the temperature of a cold storage room at any time as its temperature is lowered to 0°F from an initial temperature of 50°F. We know that at any time $t$ (minutes) when we look at a thermometer in the room, we can read the temperature $u$. Thus, when $t = 1$, we might read 48.5°; at $t = 5$, we might read 36.3°; and so on. It is clear that we are making use of ordered pairs of real numbers $(t, u)$, with $t \geq 0$, where the first number gives the time and the second gives the temperature at that time.

A study of an object moving in a straight line also requires the use of ordered pairs of numbers in specifying the location of the object as $x$ units from an origin 0 at a given time $t$. In fact, in physics, the well-known law for the distance traversed by a falling object is expressed in approximate form by the equation $x = \frac{1}{2}gt^2$, where $x$ is the number of feet the object falls in $t$ seconds and $g$ is the gravitational acceleration. If the value $g = 32$ is used, then the equation is $x = 16t^2$, giving $x = 16$ for $t = 1$, $x = 64$ for $t = 2$, and so on. Thus, again we are concerned with a set of ordered pairs of real numbers,

$$\{(t, x): x = 16t^2, t \geq 0\}.$$

Since sets of ordered pairs of numbers are encountered in so many important ways, it is essential that we consider such sets in greater detail. These sets are, of course, subsets of the set $\{(x, y): x, y \in \mathcal{R}\}$. Illustrations of this type of set are

(a) $S_1 .=. \{(0, 3), (0, 4), (6, 1)\}$,
(b) $S_2 .=. \{(x, y): y = x^2\}$,
(c) $S_3 .=. \{(x, y): x^2 + y^2 = 25\}$,
(d) $S_4 .=. \{(x, y): x > y\}$.

Thus, in (b) the pairs $(1, 1)$, $(3, 9)$, $(-2, 4)$ are all in $S_2$, whereas pairs such as $(0, 4)$, $(2, 2)$, and $(5, 3)$ are not in $S_2$. In illustration (c) it is understood that $x$ and $y$ are to be real numbers so that a value of $x$ leading to an imaginary value for $y$ is not allowed. Hence, pairs such as $(3, 4)$, $(-3, 4)$, $(-3, -4)$, $(5, 0)$, and $(-2, \sqrt{21})$ are all in $S_3$, whereas pairs with $x > 5$ or $x < -5$ are not in $S_3$. Notice that the sets $S_2$, $S_3$, and $S_4$ are defined by means of a characteristic property of their elements but that $S_1$ is defined by simply stating what its elements are.

Sets of the type just described are important in many mathematical problems and they are given a special name.

**Definition 2.3a.** A set of ordered pairs of real numbers is called a **binary relation** in $\mathcal{R}$.

**Definition 2.3b.** The set of first elements of a binary relation is called the **domain** of the relation, and the set of second elements is called the **range** of the relation.

For a given set $\{(x, y)\}$, we frequently call $x$ and $y$ **variables.** The variable $x$ which takes on values in the domain is usually called the **independent** variable, and $y$, which takes on values in the range, is called the **dependent** variable. When the number of variables is clear from the context, we often drop the adjective "binary" and speak simply of a *relation*.

---

*Example 2.3a.* Describe the domain and range of the relation

$$Q .=. \{(0, 5), (0, 6), (1, 4), (2, 5), (3, 6), (4, 4)\}.$$

The domain of $Q$ is the set $\{0, 1, 2, 3, 4\}$ and the range of $Q$ is the set $\{4, 5, 6\}$. It is, of course, possible to construct many other relations with the same domain and range as those in this example. For instance, the relation

$$T .=. \{(0, 4), (1, 5), (2, 6), (3, 4), (4, 5)\}$$

has the same domain and range as $Q$.

---

*Example 2.3b.* Describe the relation

$$Q .=. \{(x, y): x > y, x \in \mathcal{I}, y \in \mathcal{I}\}.$$

Since $Q$ is the set of pairs $(x, y)$ of integers such that $x > y$, some elements of the relation are the pairs $(7, 3)$, $(7, 4)$, $(7, 5)$, $(-4, -5)$, $(-2, -5)$, and $(3, -5)$. The domain of $Q$ is the set of all integers and the range of the relation is also the set of all integers. Notice that this is not the same relation as in illustration (d). Why?

---

*Example 2.3c.* Let a relation $Q$ be defined as the set of ordered pairs $(x, y)$ of real numbers such that $y = x^2$; that is,

$$Q .=. \{(x, y): y = x^2, x \in \mathcal{R}\}.$$

Some of the elements of the relation are the pairs $(0, 0)$, $(2, 4)$, $(-2, 4)$, $(\sqrt{3}, 3)$, and $(-\sqrt{3}, 3)$. What is the domain and what is the range of $Q$?

The domain of $Q$ is the set $\mathcal{R}$ and the range is the set of all nonnegative numbers. Why can no negative number belong to the range?

---

*Example 2.3d.* Describe the relation

$$T .=. \{(x, y): y = x^2, 0 \leq x \leq 1\}.$$

The set of first elements in the pairs—that is, the domain of the relation $T$—is the set $\{x: 0 \leq x \leq 1\}$. The rule used for determining the elements of the range is the same as that used in the preceding example, except that the domain has been restricted.

---

It is often necessary to restrict the domain of a relation in setting up mathematical equations to describe physical problems. In fact, different rules may be used to determine the second element of a pair corresponding to different parts of the domain.

---

*Example 2.3e.* Determine the domain and range of

$$T .=. \{(x, y): y = x^2 \text{ if } 0 \leq x \leq 1, y = 2 - x \text{ if } 1 < x < 2, \text{ and } y = 2 \text{ if } x = 2\}.$$

The domain of $T$ is the set $\{x: 0 \leq x \leq 2\}$, and the range is $\{y: 0 \leq y \leq 1, y = 2\}$. This example illustrates the importance of not confusing a relation with the rule used to determine the pairs belonging to the relation.

---

It is to be emphasized that in many examples of relations a rule is given that determines the range and the domain of the relation, provided it is understood that we are concerned with pairs of *real* numbers. Hence, if no additional information is given, it is to be understood that the permissible values in the domain and range are those *real* numbers for which the given rule is satisfied.

---

*Example 2.3f.* Describe the domain and range of

$$T .=. \{(x, y): x^2 + y^2 = 1\}.$$

Since it is not specified that the values of $x$ and $y$ are to be taken from some particular set, we may use any pair of real numbers $(x, y)$ for which $x^2 + y^2 = 1$. Several such pairs are

$$(1, 0), \left(\frac{1}{2}, \frac{\sqrt{3}}{2}\right), \left(\frac{3}{5}, \frac{4}{5}\right), \left(-\frac{1}{2}, \frac{\sqrt{3}}{2}\right), \left(-\frac{1}{2}, -\frac{\sqrt{3}}{2}\right), \left(\frac{1}{2}, -\frac{\sqrt{3}}{2}\right).$$

Note that there can be no pair where $x < -1$ or where $x > 1$, since there is no corresponding real value for $y$. Hence we conclude that the domain is $\{x: -1 \leq x \leq 1\}$ and the range is $\{y: -1 \leq y \leq 1\}$.

---

A very important type of relation is one in which a multiplicity of values corresponding to a given element of the domain is not allowed. Relations of this kind are given a special name.

**Definition 2.3c.** A **function** $f$ is a relation such that to each element of the domain, $\mathfrak{D}_f$, there corresponds *one and only one* element of the range, $\mathfrak{R}_f$.

According to this definition, it is apparent that every function is a relation, but not every relation is a function. Thus, of the preceding illustrations, only Examples 2.3c, 2.3d, and 2.3e give relations that are functions.

There is an important special notation for functions that is used to indicate the element of the range corresponding to an element of the domain. If $f$ denotes a function $\{(x, y)\}$, then the number $y$ associated with a given $x$ is denoted by $f(x)$, read "$f$ of $x$." With this notation, the sets of pairs defining $f$ may then be written as $\{(x, f(x))\}$.

Using the functional notation just described, we may write for the function defined in Example 2.3c, the set of pairs

$$\{(x, f(x)): f(x) = x^2, x \in \mathfrak{R}\}.$$

Thus, corresponding to $x = 3$, we should have $f(3) = 3^2 = 9$, and the pair is $(3, 9)$. Similarly, $f(-2) = (-2)^2 = 4$ means that $(-2, 4)$ is one of the set of pairs that belong to the given function. More generally, we have $f(a) = a^2$. It is important to notice that, in each case, $x$ in the defining rule has been replaced by the number in the parentheses in $f(\ )$.

In the preceding illustrations, we have specifically indicated a restriction to real numbers. In most of our work, this is a natural restriction and from now on is to be understood, unless the contrary is stated. It is to be further understood that, unless otherwise stated, the domain of a given function $\{(x, f(x))\}$ is that subset of the set of real numbers for which $f(x)$ is a real number.

For example, the domain of the function $\{(x, \sqrt{x})\}$ is the set $\{x: x \geq 0\}$, since $\sqrt{x}$ is a real number if and only if $x$ is a nonnegative number. However, the domain of the function $\{(x, \sqrt{x}): 1 \leq x \leq 4\}$ is the interval $\{x: 1 \leq x \leq 4\}$, as specifically stated in the description of the function.

Suppose a function is given by $\{(x, g(x)): g(x) = x + 1/x\}$. The domain of this function is the set of all real numbers with the exception of zero. Why? Notice that the letter $g$ has been used here in place of the symbol $f$. Other letters, as $F$, $G$, $\varphi$, $\Gamma$, and so on, are frequently used in the same manner, and indicate a name for the function. The formula $g(x) = x + 1/x$ tells us how to form the second member of the pair whose first member is $x$. Such a formula is said to define the function, although the function itself is *not the formula* but is the set of number-pairs $\{(x, g(x))\}$.

*Example 2.3g.* For the function $g$, defined by $g(x) = x + (1/x)$, find the formula that corresponds to

$$\text{(a) } g\left(\frac{1}{x}\right), \quad \text{(b) } g\left(x - \frac{1}{x}\right), \quad \text{(c) } xg(x) - g(1).$$

(a) The symbol $g(1/x)$ means that, in the formula for $g(x)$, the $x$ is to be replaced by $1/x$. Thus,

$$g\left(\frac{1}{x}\right) = \frac{1}{x} + \frac{1}{\dfrac{1}{x}} = \frac{1}{x} + x.$$

Notice that for this special case we have $g(x) = g(1/x)$.

(b) Similarly,

$$g\left(x - \frac{1}{x}\right) = x - \frac{1}{x} + \frac{1}{x - \dfrac{1}{x}}$$

$$= x - \frac{1}{x} + \frac{x}{x^2 - 1}$$

$$= \frac{x^4 - x^2 + 1}{x(x^2 - 1)}.$$

(c) Finally,

$$xg(x) - g(1) = x\left(x + \frac{1}{x}\right) - \left(1 + \frac{1}{1}\right)$$

$$= x^2 + 1 - 2$$
$$= x^2 - 1.$$

## Exercises 2.3

In each of Numbers 1 to 16, state the domain and range of the given relation. In each case, indicate whether the relation is a function and why.

1. $Q .=. \{(1, 3), (3, 2), (2, 2), (3, 1), (4, 3), (3, 3)\}$.
2. $S .=. \{(1, 5), (2, 5), (3, 5), (4, 5), (5, 5)\}$.
3. $T .=. \{(x, y): y = x^2 \text{ and } x \leq 10, x \in \mathfrak{N}\}$.
4. $S .=. \{(x, y): y = \sqrt{x} \text{ and } y \leq 10, y \in \mathfrak{N}\}$.
5. $S .=. \{(x, y): y^2 = x \text{ and } |y| \leq 10, y \in \mathcal{J}\}$.
6. $S .=. \{(x, y): y^2 = x, y \in \mathcal{J}\}$.
7. $Q .=. \{(x, y): x < y\}$.
8. $Q .=. \{(x, y): x \geq y\}$.
9. $T .=. \{(x, y): y = 2x + 3 \text{ for } 0 \leq x \leq 1 \text{ and } y = -5x + 10 \text{ for } 1 < x \leq 2\}$.
10. $T .=. \{(x, y): y = 2 \text{ if } 0 < x < 1 \text{ and } y = 3 \text{ if } 1 < x < 2\}$.
11. $Q .=. \{(x, y): y = x \text{ if } 0 \leq x < 1 \text{ and } y = x^2 \text{ if } 1 \leq x \leq 2\}$.
12. $T .=. \{(x, y): y = 1/x, y \in \mathfrak{N}\}$.
13. $P .=. \{(x, y): y = 1/x \text{ if } 0 < x < 2\} \cup \{(x, y): y = x^2 \text{ if } 1 \leq x \leq 3\}$.
14. $P .=. \{(x, y): y = 2 \text{ if } -2 \leq x \leq 0\} \cap \{(x, y): y = 2 \text{ if } 0 \leq x < 2\}$.
15. $P .=. \{(x, y): x^2 + y^2 = 1\} \cap \{(x, y): y = 3/5\}$.
16. $P .=. \{(x, y): y = x, 0 \leq x \leq 1\} \cup \{(x, y): y = x + 1, -1 \leq x \leq 0\}$.

17. Given the sets $\mathcal{Q} . = . \{2, 4, 6\}$ and $\mathcal{B} . = . \{3, 5\}$.
    (a) Define a relation on $\mathcal{Q}$ and $\mathcal{B}$ which is not a function by indicating a correspondence between the elements of $\mathcal{Q}$ and the elements of $\mathcal{B}$. Use $\mathcal{Q}$ as the domain and $\mathcal{B}$ as the range of the relation.
    (b) How many different *functions* can be defined on these two sets if $\mathcal{Q}$ is the domain of the function, and the range is a subset of $\mathcal{B}$?

In each of Numbers 18 to 31, if the set $\{(x, y)\}$ of pairs of real numbers formed according to the given rule is a function, give the domain and range of the function. If the set is not a function, tell why it is not.

18. $y = x^2 + 3$.
19. $y = 2x + 3$.
20. $y = \pm\sqrt{4 - x^2}$.
21. $y = -\sqrt{4 - x^2}$.
22. $y = \sqrt{4 - x^2}$.
23. $y = 1/x$.
24. $y = 1/(x^2 - 4)$.

25. $y = (x^2 - 4)/(x - 2)$.
26. $y = \sqrt{x^2 - 9}$.
27. $y^2 = x$.
28. $x + y = 1$.
29. $x^2 + y = 1$.
30. $x^2 + y^2 = 1$.
31. $y = \pm\sqrt{6 - x - x^2}$.

32. If $f(x) = x^2 - 2x$, find $f(2)$; $f(1/2)$; $f(a)$; $f(1/h)$.
33. If $g(x) = 1/(x - 4)$, find $g(3)$; $g(4)$; $g(1/h)$; $g(1/x)$.
34. If $h(x) = x/(x - 1)$, find $h(0)$; $h(1/2)$; $h(1/x)$; $h(x + k)$.
35. If $f(x) = 2x + 3$, find $f(x + h)$; $f(1/x)$.
36. If $f(x) = 1/x$, find $2f(4) - f(2)$; $f(a) + f(b)$; $af(a)$; $1/f(a)$.
37. If $g(x) = 2x - x^2$, find $g(3) - g(2)$; $g(1) \cdot g(3)$; $g(1/2)/g(1/3)$.
38. If $f(x) = x^3$, find $f(a + h) - f(a)$; $f(a) + 1/f(a)$; $[f(a)]^2$.

## 2.4 GRAPHS OF RELATIONS AND FUNCTIONS

In Section 2.2, a two-dimensional rectangular coordinate system was established by choosing two perpendicular lines in the plane and setting up a number scale on each axis. In the definition of a relation, each ordered pair, or element of the relation, may be considered to be the $x$ and $y$ coordinates of a point in two-dimensional space. Consequently, a pictorial representation, or **graph,** of a relation may be obtained by plotting the number-pairs belonging to the relation.

Graphs play an important role in mathematics by providing a geometric visualization for many problems. It is frequently helpful to graph a function in order to arrive at the proper procedure for setting up a problem. Graphs are nearly always employed in experimental work where an attempt is made to discover a natural law or a pattern for the data obtained. When such a pattern is found, it is sometimes possible to describe the natural phenomenon by a mathematical formula. Consequently, it is important to examine in some detail the process of making graphs.

*Example 2.4a.* Graph the relation

$$\{(0, 2), (0, 1), (1, 3), (2, -1), (3, 2), (4, 0)\}.$$

The graph is shown in Figure 2.4a. In this case, the graph consists of just the six isolated points.

---

*Example 2.4b.* Graph the function consisting of the set of ordered pairs $(x, y)$ such that $y = 4$.

The fact that every number-pair in this set has 4 for its second element means that all the points are at a distance of 4 units above the $x$-axis. Hence, the set of points constitutes a straight line parallel to the $x$-axis and 4 units above it (see Figure 2.4b).

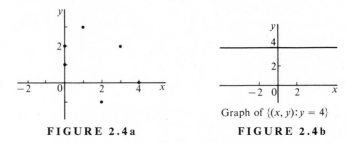

Graph of $\{(x, y): y = 4\}$

**FIGURE 2.4a**          **FIGURE 2.4b**

---

*Example 2.4c.* Graph the relation defined by the set of ordered pairs $(x, y)$ of real numbers such that $x > y$.

The graph of the relation $\{(x, y): y = x\}$ is the bisector of the angles formed by the two axes in the first and third quadrants. Accordingly, the desired graph consists of all points below this bisector, as indicated by the shaded region in Figure 2.4c.

---

*Example 2.4d.* Graph the relation $\{(x, y): y^2 = x\}$.

We first plot a few points of the graph such as $(0, 0)$, $(1, 1)$, $(1, -1)$, $(4, 2)$, $(4, -2)$, $(9, 3)$, and $(9, -3)$. As we plot more and more points whose coordinates satisfy the equation $y^2 = x$, these points suggest the curve that is shown in Figure 2.4d. We call

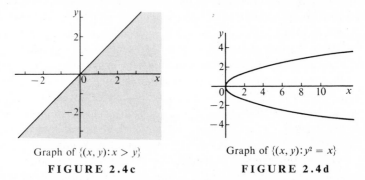

Graph of $\{(x, y): x > y\}$          Graph of $\{(x, y): y^2 = x\}$

**FIGURE 2.4c**          **FIGURE 2.4d**

this curve the graph of the given relation. We shall later discuss certain concepts of calculus that will justify the smooth curve drawn here.

---

If the coordinates of every point on a graph satisfy an equation (as in the preceding example), and no other points satisfy the same equation, then the equation is called *an equation of the graph* and the graph is called *the graph of the equation*. In accordance with standard custom, we shall use this terminology so that we may speak of the graph in Figure 2.4d as the graph of the equation $y^2 = x$. Also, $y^2 = x$ is an equation of this graph.

The graph in Figure 2.4d displays a certain symmetry that will be of interest in the succeeding work. If the figure were folded along the *x*-axis, the part of the curve below the axis would coincide exactly with the part above the axis. We call the *x*-axis a **line of symmetry** of the curve.

In general, a line $L$ is said to be a line of symmetry of a graph if to each point $P$ on the graph there corresponds another point $P_1$ on the graph such that $L$ is the perpendicular bisector of the segment $PP_1$ (see Figure 2.4e).

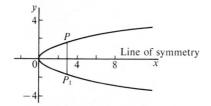

**FIGURE 2.4e**

If a graph is symmetric with respect to the *x*-axis, then, by the definition of symmetry, for each point $(x, y)$ on the graph, the point $(x, -y)$ must also be on the graph. Conversely, if both $(x, y)$ and $(x, -y)$ are on the graph, then the graph is symmetric with respect to the *x*-axis. This means that the coordinates $(x, -y)$ must satisfy an equation of the graph, so that the replacement of $y$ by $-y$ in this equation should yield the original equation. Thus, in Example 2.4d, if we replace $y$ by $-y$ we get $(-y)^2 = x$ or $y^2 = x$, which is the original equation.

---

*Example 2.4e.* Graph the function $f . = . \{(x, x^2)\}$. Note that this will be the graph of the equation $y = x^2$.

Following the procedure of the preceding example, we obtain the graph shown in Figure 2.4f. Notice that this curve can be obtained from that in Figure 2.4d by the rotation of the curve in that figure through 90°.

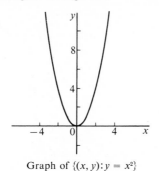

Graph of $\{(x, y): y = x^2\}$

**FIGURE 2.4f**

The graph of $y = x^2$ is symmetric with respect to the $y$-axis, since replacement of $x$ by $-x$ does not change the equation. That is, if $(x, y)$ is a point on the graph, then $(-x, y)$ must also be a point on the graph.

A point $O$ is said to be a **point of symmetry** with respect to a given graph if and only if for every point $P$ on the graph, there is another point $P_1$ on the graph such that $O$ is the midpoint of the line segment $PP_1$ (see Figure 2.4g). For

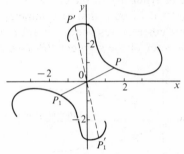

**FIGURE 2.4g**

each point $(x, y)$ on a graph that is symmetric with respect to the origin, the point $(-x, -y)$ must also lie on the graph. This is illustrated in the following example.

*Example 2.4f.* Graph the function $f .=. \{(x, x^3)\}$. An equation that connects the elements of the ordered pairs is $y = x^3$.

The graph of this function is not symmetric to the $x$-axis or to the $y$-axis, but if we replace $x$ by $-x$ and $y$ by $-y$ in the equation $y = x^3$, we get $-y = (-x)^3$ or $y = x^3$. Hence, the graph is symmetric with respect to the origin. The curve is shown in Figure 2.4h.

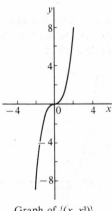

Graph of $\{(x, x^3)\}$

**FIGURE 2.4h**

*Example 2.4g.* Graph the function $f$ consisting of the set of ordered pairs $\{(x, y)\}$, where

$$
\begin{array}{lll}
y = 1 & \text{if} & x \le 0, \\
y = x^2 + 1 & \text{if} & 0 < x \le 1, \\
y = 2 & \text{if} & 1 < x.
\end{array}
$$

The graph of $f$ is shown in Figure 2.4i. Notice that the pieces join to form a continuous graph.

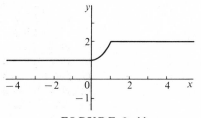

**FIGURE 2.4i**

---

*Example 2.4h.* Graph the relation $S .=. \{(x, y): x^2 + y^2 = 1\}$.

The graph is symmetric with respect to the $x$-axis, the $y$-axis, and the origin. If several points are plotted, they appear to lie on a circle of radius 1 with its center at the origin (see Figure 2.4j). Since a circle is defined as a set of points all equidistant from a given point, this conjecture can be verified by determining the condition on the coordinates $(x, y)$ of a point $P$ so that $P$ is at a distance of one unit from the origin. In that case, we have

$$(x - 0)^2 + (y - 0)^2 = 1,$$

or

$$x^2 + y^2 = 1.$$

This result shows that every point $(x, y)$ in $S$ is on the circle and that every point on the circle must be in $S$. Hence, the graph of $S$ is the circle shown in Figure 2.4j.

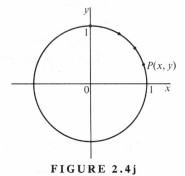

**FIGURE 2.4j**

---

It is easy to see from the special case in the preceding example that a relation described by the equation $x^2 + y^2 = a^2$ must have a graph that is a circle of radius $a$ with its center at the origin. Verify this.

## Exercises 2.4

In each of the following, a relation consists of a set of ordered pairs $(x, y)$, determined by the indicated rule. State whether the relation is also a function; give the domain and range; discuss the symmetry of the graph of the relation, and sketch the graph.

1. $\{(0, 0), (3, 0), (1, 2), (-2, 1), (-1, 2), (-3, 0), (0, 3), (2, 1)\}$.
2. $\{(0, 0), (0, -3), (0, 1), (0, 3), (0, -1)\}$.
3. $y = -x$.
4. $y = -3$.
5. $x = -4$.
6. $x = 2y$.
7. $y^2 = -4x$.
8. $y = 2x^2$.
9. $y = 4 - x^2$.
10. $x = 9 - y^2$.
11. $y = \begin{cases} x \text{ if } x \geq 0, \\ -x \text{ if } x < 0. \end{cases}$
12. $y = \begin{cases} 1 \text{ if } 0 \leq x \leq 1, \\ 2 \text{ if } x = 3. \end{cases}$
13. $y = \begin{cases} 1 - x \text{ if } x \leq 1, \\ 1 + x \text{ if } x > 1. \end{cases}$

14. $y = \begin{cases} 2 \text{ if } x \leq 2, \\ 3 \text{ if } 2 < x \leq 3, \\ 4 \text{ if } 3 < x \leq 4. \end{cases}$
15. $x^2 + y^2 = 16$.
16. $x^2 + 2y^2 = 4$.
17. $2x^2 + y^2 + 4 = 0$.
18. $x^2 - 2y^2 = 4$.
19. $2y^2 - x^2 = 4$.
20. $x^2 + y = 1$.
21. $y > x$.
22. $0 \leq x \leq 1, 0 \leq y \leq 1$.
23. $x^2 + (y - 1)^2 = 0$.
24. $x^2 - y^2 = 0$.
25. $xy - x - y + 1 = 0$.

## 2.5 GRAPHS OF CERTAIN SPECIAL FUNCTIONS

If the equation $y^2 = x$, with $x > 0$, is solved for $y$, then $y = \sqrt{x}$ or $y = -\sqrt{x}$. Thus there are two values of $y$ which satisfy the equation for a given positive value of $x$; the two $y$ values are negatives of each other. Recall that for $x > 0$, $\sqrt{x}$ designates the positive square root of $x$. If both roots are intended, then the symbol $\pm\sqrt{x}$ must be employed.

*Example 2.5a.* Graph

$$f .=. \{(x, \sqrt{x})\}, \quad g .=. \{(x, -\sqrt{x})\}, \quad \text{and} \quad Q .=. \{(x, \pm\sqrt{x})\}.$$

The graphs are shown in Figure 2.5a. Notice that $f$ and $g$ are functions but that $Q$ is not. Why?

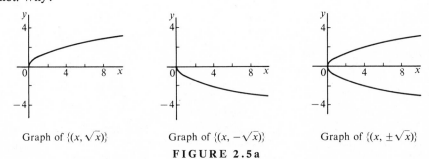

Graph of $\{(x, \sqrt{x})\}$      Graph of $\{(x, -\sqrt{x})\}$      Graph of $\{(x, \pm\sqrt{x})\}$

**FIGURE 2.5a**

Furthermore, it is important for the reader to understand that

$$\sqrt{x^2} = \begin{cases} x & \text{for } x \geq 0, \\ -x & \text{for } x < 0. \end{cases}$$

Thus, we have $\sqrt{2^2} = 2$ and $\sqrt{(-2)^2} = \sqrt{4} = 2$. It is imperative to realize that $-2$ is an *incorrect* result for $\sqrt{4}$.

Another symbol, that is equivalent to $\sqrt{x^2}$ for real values of $x$ is $|x|$, the **absolute value** of $x$.

**Definition 2.5a.**
$$|x| .=. \begin{cases} x & \text{for } x \geq 0, \\ -x & \text{for } x < 0. \end{cases}$$

Thus, $|-2| = -(-2) = 2$. Similarly, by virtue of Definition 2.5a,

$$|x - a| = \begin{cases} x - a & \text{if } x - a \geq 0 \text{ or if } x \geq a, \\ a - x & \text{if } x - a < 0 \text{ or if } x < a. \end{cases}$$

---

*Example 2.5b.* Graph the function $\{(x, f(x)): f(x) = |x - 2|\}$.

The statement $f(x) = |x - 2|$ means that

$$f(x) = \begin{cases} x - 2 \text{ for } x - 2 \geq 0, \text{ or } x \geq 2, \\ -(x - 2) \text{ for } x - 2 < 0, \text{ or } x < 2. \end{cases}$$

The graph is shown in Figure 2.5b.

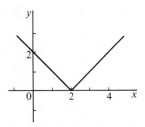

Graph of $\{(x, y): y = |x - 2|\}$

**FIGURE 2.5b**

---

*Example 2.5c.* In Section 1.1 we introduced the "greatest integer" symbol, $[\![x]\!]$, where $[\![x]\!]$ stands for the greatest integer that is less than or equal to $x$. Sketch the graph of the function $\{(x, [\![x]\!])\}$.

From the definition of $[\![x]\!]$, we see that

$$\begin{aligned} \text{for } -2 \leq x < -1, \quad [\![x]\!] &= -2, \\ \text{for } -1 \leq x < \phantom{-}0, \quad [\![x]\!] &= -1, \\ \text{for } \phantom{-}0 \leq x < \phantom{-}1, \quad [\![x]\!] &= \phantom{-}0, \\ \text{for } \phantom{-}1 \leq x < \phantom{-}2, \quad [\![x]\!] &= \phantom{-}1, \text{ and so on.} \end{aligned}$$

Thus, we are led to the graph shown in Figure 2.5c.

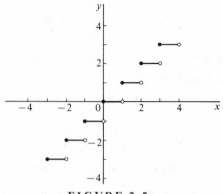

**FIGURE 2.5c**

---

*Example 2.5d.* Graph the function $f .=. \{(x, x - [\![x]\!])\}$.

Since $f(x) = x - [\![x]\!]$, then for $0 \leq x < 1$, the greatest integer in $x$ is 0, and $f(x) = x$. For $1 \leq x < 2$, the greatest integer in $x$ is 1, and $f(x) = x - 1$. For $-1 \leq x < 0$, $[\![x]\!] = -1$, and $f(x) = x + 1$. The reader should check the values of $x - [\![x]\!]$ for additional portions of the domain. The graph is shown in Figure 2.5d.

---

It appears from Figure 2.5d that the graph of the function $\{(x, x - [\![x]\!])\}$ can be easily constructed once we have the graph of this function for the interval $0 \leq x < 1$. The remainder of the graph is obtained by moving this portion

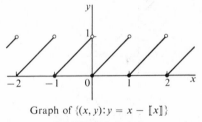

Graph of $\{(x, y): y = x - [\![x]\!]\}$

**FIGURE 2.5d**

to the right or left exactly one unit, then to the right or left exactly two units, then three units, four units, and so on. A function whose graph has the repetitive character of this one is called **periodic.** Using the notation $\{(x, y): y = f(x)\}$, we may define a periodic function as one for which there exists a fixed real number $k$ such that

$$f(x + k) = f(x)$$

for all $x$ for which $f(x)$ is defined. The smallest such positive number $k$ is called the **period** of the function. For the function in Example 2.5d, we have $f(x + 1) = f(x)$, and, since no positive number smaller than 1 will serve here, the function has a period of 1. Periodicity is an important characteristic of many of the functions that occur in the applications of mathematics. For example, the reader may recall that each of the trigonometric functions is periodic.

Another function that is quite useful in various applications is given in

**Definition 2.5b.** Let

$$U(x) .=. \begin{cases} 0 & \text{for } x < 0, \\ 1 & \text{for } x \geq 0. \end{cases}$$

The function $U .=. \{(x, y): y = U(x)\}$ is called the **unit step function.** The graph of the function $U(x)$ is shown in Figure 2.5e.

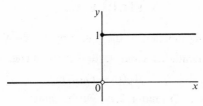

Graph of the Unit Step Function

**FIGURE 2.5e**

Many of the functions that are important in scientific and engineering practice may be constructed in a rather simple fashion by the use of the unit step function. The next two examples illustrate the procedure.

*Example 2.5e.* Graph the function described by

$$y = U(x - a),$$

where $U$ is the unit step function.

Upon comparing $y = U(x - a)$ with the definition of $U$, it is apparent that

$$U(x - a) = \begin{cases} 0 & \text{for } x - a < 0, \\ 1 & \text{for } x - a \geq 0, \end{cases}$$

or

$$U(x - a) = \begin{cases} 0 & \text{for } x < a, \\ 1 & \text{for } x \geq a. \end{cases}$$

Hence, the "step" occurs at $x = a$, and the graph is shown in Figure 2.5f.

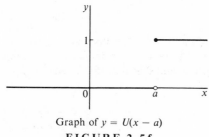

Graph of $y = U(x - a)$

**FIGURE 2.5f**

*Example 2.5f.* It is common practice to check the behavior of an electric circuit under the influence of a "pulse" of voltage such as that supplied by a battery that can be switched in and out of the circuit. Figure 2.5g shows a graph of such a pulse. Rep-

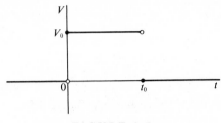

**FIGURE 2.5g**

resent the corresponding function of the time $t$ by means of the unit step function.

A step voltage of magnitude $V_0$ and starting at $t = 0$ is given by

$$V_1(t) = V_0 U(t).$$

This follows directly from Definition 2.5a. Furthermore,

$$V_2(t) = V_0 U(t - t_0)$$

would correspond to a step voltage of the same magnitude but starting at $t = t_0$. Consequently, the desired representation is

$$V(t) = V_0[U(t) - U(t - t_0)].$$

---

It should be noted that the "pulse" type function may also represent a constant force acting for a finite time interval. A pulse of this kind is sometimes used as an idealized representation of the force exerted on a pile by a pile driver. Such representations are frequently used in order to make an analysis of the effect of forces of this type.

A large part of scientific research consists of gathering data about a given phenomenon, and then trying to find a mathematical function that can be used to describe these data. Once such a function is found, it can serve as a basis for the prediction of future events or it may be employed to indicate ways in which changes in the environment may affect the phenomenon.

## Exercises 2.5

Let a function consist of the set of ordered pairs $(x, y)$, where $y$ is related to $x$ as indicated in each of Numbers 1 to 19. Give the domain and the range, discuss the symmetry of the graph of the function, and sketch it. If a function is periodic, specify the period.

1. $y = [\![x + 1]\!]$.
2. $y = -\sqrt{4 - x^2}$.
3. $y = \sqrt{x^2 - 4}$.
4. $y = |x + 1|$.

5. $y = |x| + x$.
6. $y = x|x|$.
7. $y = [\![x]\!] - x$.
8. $x = \sqrt{y + 1}$.

9. $y = [[x]]$ for $-1 \leq x < 1$, and the function is periodic with a period of 2.
10. $y = |x|$ for $-2 \leq x < 0$, and the function is periodic with a period of 2.
11. $y = x - |[[x]]|$.
12. $y = x - [[|x|]]$.

13. $y = \begin{cases} \dfrac{|x|}{x} & \text{for } x \neq 0, \\ 0 & \text{for } x = 0. \end{cases}$

14. $y = \dfrac{1 + (-1)^n}{2}$, where $n = [[x]]$.

15. $y = x^2 - [[x^2]]$.
16. $y = U(x) - 2U(x - 1) + U(x - 2)$, where $U$ is the unit step function.
17. $y = xU(x) - (x - 1)U(x - 1)$.
18. $y = xU(x) - 2(x - 1)U(x - 1) + (x - 2)U(x - 2)$.
19. $y = U(x) - U(x - 2)$ for $0 < x \leq 4$, and the function is periodic of period 4.
20. For the function defined in Example 2.5d, show that for $n \leq x < n + 1$, where $n \in \mathcal{I}$, $f(x) = x - n$. Use this result to show that $f$ is periodic with period 1.
21. The load on a beam of length $2c$ is 1000 pounds per foot on the portion of the beam from one end to the middle and 3000 pounds per foot on the remainder of the beam. Represent the loading function by means of the unit step function $U$.
22. A battery of voltage $E$ is connected to a circuit in such a manner that a switch can reverse the connections so that the polarity of the voltage is reversed. Suppose that the impressed voltage is $E$ for 2 seconds and $-E$ for the next 2 seconds, and zero thereafter. (The battery is shunted out after 4 seconds.) Describe the impressed voltage by means of the unit step function.

## 2.6 INVERSE FUNCTIONS

Suppose that $\$P$ is invested at an interest rate $r$ compounded annually for $n$ years. It is quite easy to show by mathematical induction that the total amount $A$ (original principal $P$ plus all interest) is given by

$$A = P(1 + r)^n.$$

In order to simplify matters, let $P = 100$ and $n = 10$. Then we have

$$A = 100(1 + r)^{10},$$

which defines a function $f = \{(r, A): A = 100(1 + r)^{10}\}$. This is a natural form to consider if we wish to study the way in which $A$ changes with $r$, since the formula for $A$ shows exactly how $A$ depends on $r$.

However, suppose we are interested in the way in which $r$ depends on $A$, having in mind perhaps such questions as what interest rate will double our money in ten years. This suggests that we solve the equation $A = 100(1 + r)^{10}$ for $r$ to get

$$(1 + r)^{10} = 0.01A,$$
$$1 + r = \sqrt[10]{0.01A},$$
$$r = \sqrt[10]{0.01A} - 1.$$

The last equation may be regarded as defining a function

$$g = \{(A, r): r = \sqrt[10]{0.01A} - 1\},$$

a study of which will answer many of our questions concerning the dependence of $r$ on $A$. For instance, if $A = 200$, then $r = \sqrt[10]{2} - 1 = 0.072$ (approximately).

There are many applications which lead to considerations similar to those in the preceding discussion. These are problems in which it is desirable to interchange the roles of the two variables in a given function and to study the resulting relation. These ideas are made more precise in the following paragraphs.

Consider a function $f$ that consists of the set $\{(0, 1), (1, 3), (2, 4), (3, 2)\}$ and let the elements of each pair in this set be interchanged so that there is obtained a new relation $\{(1, 0), (3, 1), (4, 2), (2, 3)\}$, whose domain is the range of $f$ and whose range is the domain of $f$. For this particular $f$, the new relation is also a function, since one and only one element of the range corresponds to each element of the domain.

The domain and range of any relation may be interchanged in like manner to form a new relation. Each pair in the new relation is obtained by interchanging the elements of a corresponding pair in the original relation. Two such sets of pairs are called **inverse relations**; each relation is said to be the inverse of the other.

In the special case where both relations are functions, they are called **inverse functions**. The inverse of a function $f$ is denoted by the symbol $f^{-1}$. It is essential to realize that the superscript $-1$ in this notation is *not* an exponent; it signifies only that $f^{-1}$ is the inverse of $f$. For example, in the preceding illustration, it would be proper to use the notation $f^{-1}$ for the second set of pairs, since it is the inverse of the first set $f$. These important ideas are summarized in

**Definition 2.6a.** If a function $f$ is such that to each element of its range there corresponds one and only one element of its domain, then the set obtained by interchanging the elements in each of the pairs of the function $f$ is called the *inverse function* of $f$ and is denoted by $f^{-1}$.

---

*Example 2.6a.* Let $g .=. \{(x, y): y = 2x - 1\}$. For each value of $x$, there is just one value of $y$, and conversely. Determine the inverse function $g^{-1}$, and graph both functions on the same set of axes.

A representative element of $g$ may be indicated by $(x, 2x - 1)$, so that the corresponding element of $g^{-1}$ is $(2x - 1, x)$. For most purposes, this way of giving the pair is awkward; we prefer to specify directly the manner in which the second element of the pair may be formed from the first one. Thus, if we write $s = 2x - 1$, then we find $x = \frac{1}{2}(s + 1)$, so that the same pair may be indicated by $(s, \frac{1}{2}(s + 1))$. Consequently, we have

$$g^{-1} = \{(s, t): t = \tfrac{1}{2}(s + 1)\}.$$

Since the particular letters used to indicate numbers of the domain and the range are immaterial, we may also write, as is customary,

$$g^{-1} = \{(x, y): y = \tfrac{1}{2}(x + 1)\}.$$

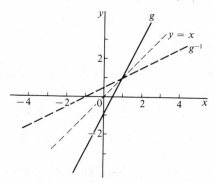

**FIGURE 2.6a**

The graphs of the two functions $g$ and $g^{-1}$ are shown in Figure 2.6a. Notice that the two graphs are symmetric with respect to the line $y = x$. Explain why this should be so.

---

*Example 2.6b.* Find the inverse of the function $F . =. \{(x, y)\}$, where $x = \sqrt{y}$.

Observe that the specification $x = \sqrt{y}$ means that the domain of $F$ is $x \geq 0$. Also $y = x^2$, so that an equivalent definition of $F$ is $\{(x, x^2): x \geq 0\}$.

From this last result, it follows that the inverse function is $F^{-1} = \{(x^2, x): x \geq 0\}$. Thus, if we write $x^2 = t$, with $x \geq 0$, then $x = \sqrt{t}$ and $F^{-1} = \{(t, \sqrt{t})\}$, or, in terms of the letters $x$ and $y$,

$$F^{-1} = \{(x, \sqrt{x})\} = \{(x, y): y = \sqrt{x}\}.$$

The graphs of the two functions are shown in Figure 2.6b. Notice again the symmetry with respect to the line $y = x$.

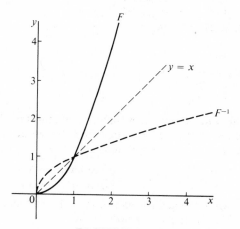

**FIGURE 2.6b**

A functional form obtained by the substitution of one form into another is described in

**Definition 2.6b.** If $y .=. f(x)$ and $u .=. g(y)$, and if

$$u = g[f(x)] .=. h(x),$$

then $h$ is called the $g$ **composite** of $f$.

---

*Example 2.6c.* If $f(x) .=. x^2 - x - 1$ and $g(x) .=. x - 1$, find $f[g(x)]$ and $g[f(x)]$.

We have, by direct substitution,

$$f[g(x)] = (x - 1)^2 - (x - 1) - 1 = x^2 - 3x + 1,$$

and

$$g[f(x)] = (x^2 - x - 1) - 1 = x^2 - x - 2.$$

---

This example illustrates that, in general, $f[g(x)] \neq g[f(x)]$.

The notion of a composite function is often useful in describing functions in terms of other functions that may be simpler in some desirable respect. To illustrate, consider

$$h(x) .=. \sqrt{1 - x^2}.$$

If $f(x) .=. 1 - x^2$ and $g(y) .=. \sqrt{y}$, then $h(x)$ is the $g$ composite of $f$. In order that $h(x) \in \mathcal{R}$, we must restrict the domain of $f$ to the interval $-1 \leq x \leq 1$ so that the range of $f$ will be a subset of the domain of $g$.

## Exercises 2.6

1. In each of the following, does the function have a corresponding inverse function? If so, find the inverse function and sketch its graph.

    (a) $f .=. \{(1, 10), (2, 20), (3, 30)\}$.
    (b) $g .=. \{(1, 5), (2, 4), (3, 3), (4, 2), (5, 1)\}$.
    (c) $h .=. \{(2, 1), (4, 3), (6, 5), (8, 1), (10, 2)\}$.
    (d) $F .=. \{(1, 2), (2, 3), (3, 2), (4, 1)\}$.
    (e) $H .=. \{(x, x)\}$.
    (f) $G .=. \{(u, -u^2)\}, u \geq 0$.
    (g) $f .=. \{(x, y): y = -x\}$.
    (h) $F .=. \{(x, y): y = 2 - 2x\}$.
    (i) $G .=. \{(t - 1, t + 1)\}$.

2. In each of the following, the inverse relation is not a function. Make an alteration in the domain of the given function so that the new relation is a function with an inverse, and sketch the graphs of both functions.

    (a) $\{(x, y): y = x^2 + 1\}$.           (c) $\{(u, v): v = \sqrt{1 - u^2}\}$.
    (b) $\{(x, y): y = 1 - x^2\}$.           (d) $\{(s, t): t = |s|\}$.

3. Attention was called to the fact that in $f^{-1}$, the $-1$ is not an exponent. However, we can justify writing $(f^{-1})^{-1} = f$. How?

4. Find $f[g(x)]$ and $g[f(x)]$ and state any necessary restrictions on the domain of $g$ or of $f$, if

(a) $f(x) = \dfrac{1}{x-1}$, $g(x) = \dfrac{x^2}{x^2-1}$;

(b) $f(x) = \dfrac{x}{1-x}$, $g(x) = \dfrac{x}{x-1}$;

(c) $f(x) = g(x) = \dfrac{x-1}{x+1}$;

(d) $f(x) = \sqrt{x-1}$, $g(x) = \dfrac{1}{x+1}$.

5. Express each of the following as a composite of two "simpler" functions, and state any necessary restrictions on the domains.

(a) $h(x) = \dfrac{x-1}{\sqrt{x}}$.

(b) $h(x) = \sqrt{\dfrac{x}{x-1}}$.

6. (a) Show that $f[f^{-1}(x)] = x$ if

$$f(x) = \frac{x-1}{x+1}, \quad x \neq 1.$$

(b) Is it true in general that $f[f^{-1}(x)] = f^{-1}[f(x)] = x$?

7. If $f(x+2) = x^2 + 1$, then $f(x)$ can be found as follows. Let $x + 2 = t$ so that $x = t - 2$. Then

$$f(t) = (t-2)^2 + 1 = t^2 - 4t + 5 \Rightarrow f(x) = x^2 - 4x + 5.$$

This method may always be applied in case we have given $f[g(x)]$, where $g^{-1}$ is a function. Use this procedure in each of the following.

(a) $f(\tfrac{1}{2}x + 1) = \tfrac{1}{2}x - 1$; $f(x) = $ ?   (c) $F(\sqrt{x} - 1) = x^3$; $F(x) = $ ?

(b) $g(x-1) = \dfrac{x+1}{x-1}$; $g(x) = $ ?   (d) $G\left(\dfrac{1}{x}\right) = \dfrac{x-1}{x+1}$; $G(x) = $ ?

8. Suppose a function $f$ has an inverse function $f^{-1}$, and that $f$ obeys a "functional equation" such as

$$f(x) + f(y) = f(xy).$$

What is the corresponding property of the function $f^{-1}$?

The given equation may be solved for $xy$ by "taking inverses" of both sides to get

$$f^{-1}[f(x) + f(y)] = f^{-1}[f(xy)] = xy.$$

Now, let $u = f(x)$ and $v = f(y)$ so that

$$x = f^{-1}(u) \quad \text{and} \quad y = f^{-1}(v).$$

Then substitution yields

$$f^{-1}(u + v) = f^{-1}(u)f^{-1}(v),$$

which is the desired result.

(a) Use the same procedure to obtain the result

$$f^{-1}(x^n) = nf^{-1}(x)$$

from the equation

$$[f(x)]^n = f(nx).$$

(b) If $f(ax + by) = af(x) + bf(y)$, $a$ and $b$ being specified numbers, show that $f^{-1}$ obeys this same equation; that is,

$$f^{-1}(ax + by) = af^{-1}(x) + bf^{-1}(y).$$

9. If $g(x) = x^2 + 1$, find $g[g(x)]$.

10. What formula defines $f(g)$ if $f(x) = \sqrt{x - 1}$ and $g(x) = x^2 - 3$? Give the domain and range of each of $f$, $g$, and $f(g)$.

11. What formula defines $G(H)$ if $G(x) = \sqrt{4 - x}$ and $H(x) = 1/x$? Give the domain and range of each of $G$, $H$, and $G(H)$.

12. Suppose $f(xy) = f(x) + f(y)$ and that $f^{-1}$ is a function.

(a) Show that $f(1) = 0$.

(b) If $f(2) = 1$, show that $f(4) = 2$ and $f^{-1}(3) = 8$.

---

# Summary of Chapter 2

---

The following ideas are fundamental to much of the work to come later:

(1) one-dimensional euclidean space and distance between two points in the space (Section 2.1);

(2) length of a line segment and directed distance (Section 2.1);

(3) open, closed, half-open intervals, and neighborhoods (Section 2.1);

(4) two-dimensional euclidean space and distance between two points in the space (Section 2.2);

(5) relation, domain, range, function, and dependent and independent variables (Section 2.3);

(6) graphs, and lines and points of symmetry of a graph (Section 2.4);

(7) the difference between a function, the equation (or equations) defining the function, and the graph of the function (Section 2.4);

(8) the absolute value notation, periodic functions, and the unit step function (Section 2.5);

(9) inverse functions and composite functions (Section 2.6).

# Chapter 3     Linear and Quadratic Functions

## 3.1 DIRECTION NUMBERS

Consider the line determined by the points (2, 1) and (5, 5) in Figure 3.1a. How can we determine other points on this line? Since the straight line is characterized by the fact that its "direction" is fixed, we should be able to use this property in answering the question. If we let $(x, y)$ be a point on the line and construct lines parallel to the coordinate axes, as shown in Figure 3.1a, it is

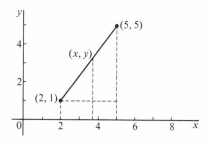

**FIGURE 3.1a**

apparent that the two triangles formed are similar. Hence, the corresponding sides are proportional and we may write

$$\frac{y - 1}{4} = \frac{x - 2}{3}.$$

If we denote this common ratio by $k$, then we have

$$x - 2 = 3k \quad \text{and} \quad y - 1 = 4k.$$

The numbers 3 and 4 in the right members of these equations characterize the line to the extent that its direction is determined by these numbers. For example, if $k = 1$, then there is a 4-unit increase in the $y$-direction for a 3-unit increase in the $x$-direction in reaching the point (5, 5) from the point (2, 1). Furthermore, starting at any point on the line, a 4-unit increase in $y$ and a 3-unit increase in $x$ will yield a second point on the line. Similarly, if $k = \frac{1}{2}$, then a second point on the line is reached by moving $\frac{3}{2}$ units to the right and 2 units up from any starting point on the line. In fact, $k$ may have any nonzero value and statements similar to the preceding ones may be made. These facts constitute the basis for

**Definition 3.1a.** Any ordered pair of numbers, $p$ and $q$, that completely characterize the direction of a straight line are called **direction numbers** of the line. A number-pair used in this fashion is denoted by $[p, q]$.

For the line given by the two equations

$$x - 2 = 3k, \quad y - 1 = 4k,$$

a set of direction numbers is $[3, 4]$, $[3/2, 2]$, $[-6, -8]$, or any other pair obtained by the choice of some nonzero value of $k$. It follows that if $(x_1, y_1)$ and $(x_2, y_2)$ are two distinct points on a line, then a set of direction numbers of the line is

$$[x_2 - x_1, y_2 - y_1].$$

The direction numbers of a nonvertical line determine another number described in the next definition and often used to characterize the direction of a line.

**Definition 3.1b.** If the direction numbers of a line are $[p, q]$, where $p \neq 0$, then the ratio $m = q/p$ is called the **slope** of the line.

In the preceding illustration, the slope of the line is $4/3$.

If the slope of a line is positive, then $y$ increases as $x$ increases, so that the line rises as one proceeds to the right. If the slope is negative, then $y$ decreases as $x$ increases, and the line falls as one proceeds to the right. Thus, if the slope is $-4/3$, then $y$ decreases by 4 units for each 3 unit increase in $x$. For a horizontal line, the direction numbers are $[k, 0]$, with $k \neq 0$, and the slope is $0/k = 0$. For a vertical line, the direction numbers are $[0, k]$, with $k \neq 0$, but the slope does *not* exist, since the ratio $k/0$ is not defined.

As will be seen in the following theorems, direction numbers are helpful in describing geometric relationships between two or more lines.

**Theorem 3.1a.** Two lines are parallel $\Leftrightarrow$ the direction numbers of the lines are proportional.

PROOF: In Figure 3.1b, suppose that $L_1$ and $L_2$ are two parallel lines, with $P_1$

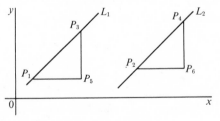

**FIGURE 3.1b**

and $P_3$ two points on $L_1$ and $P_2$ and $P_4$ two points on $L_2$. Then the right triangles $P_1P_5P_3$ and $P_2P_6P_4$, which have their legs parallel to the respective axes, are similar, and their corresponding sides are proportional. The converse of this result also follows from the same considerations. Hence, the theorem is proved.

---

*Example 3.1a.* Is the line through the points $P_1(-1, 3)$ and $P_2(2, 9)$ parallel to the line through the points $P_3(1, 2)$ and $P_4(5, 10)$?

We find that a set of direction numbers for the first line is $[3, 6]$ and a set of direction numbers for the second line is $[4, 8]$. Since $\frac{3}{4} = \frac{6}{8}$, the direction numbers are proportional and so the lines are parallel.

---

Notice in the preceding example that the slope of $P_1P_2$ is $6/3 = 2$ and that the slope of $P_3P_4$ is $8/4 = 2$. This suggests the following theorem, whose proof is left to the reader.

**Theorem 3.1b.** Two nonvertical lines are parallel if, and only if, their slopes are equal.

The next theorem gives an important criterion for determining by means of direction numbers whether or not two lines are perpendicular.

**Theorem 3.1c.** A line $L_1$ with direction numbers $[m, n]$ is perpendicular to a line $L_2$ with direction numbers $[p, q] \Leftrightarrow mp + nq = 0$.

PROOF: Figure 3.1c will aid in visualizing the basis for this proof. Let the

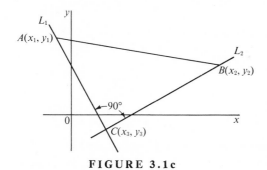

**FIGURE 3.1c**

point of intersection of $L_1$ and $L_2$ be denoted by $C(x_3, y_3)$ and let $A(x_1, y_1)$ and $B(x_2, y_2)$, respectively, be second points on $L_1$ and $L_2$. Then, since $[m, n]$ and $[p, q]$ are direction numbers of the respective lines,

$$x_3 - x_1 = k_1m, \quad y_3 - y_1 = k_1n, \quad k_1 \neq 0,$$

and

$$x_3 - x_2 = k_2p, \quad y_3 - y_2 = k_2q, \quad k_2 \neq 0.$$

Then, $L_1$ is perpendicular to $L_2 \Leftrightarrow$ triangle $ABC$ is a right triangle with $AB$ as its hypotenuse

$$\Leftrightarrow (AB)^2 = (AC)^2 + (BC)^2$$
$$\Leftrightarrow (x_2 - x_1)^2 + (y_2 - y_1)^2 = (x_3 - x_1)^2 + (y_3 - y_1)^2 + (x_3 - x_2)^2 + (y_3 - y_2)^2$$
$$\Leftrightarrow (x_3^2 - x_1 x_3 - x_2 x_3 + x_1 x_2 + y_3^2 - y_1 y_3 - y_2 y_3 + y_1 y_2 = 0$$
$$\Leftrightarrow (x_3 - x_1)(x_3 - x_2) + (y_3 - y_1)(y_3 - y_2) = 0$$
$$\Leftrightarrow k_1 k_2 mp + k_1 k_2 nq = 0$$
$$\Leftrightarrow mp + nq = 0.$$

*Example 3.1b.* Find direction numbers of a line perpendicular to the line through the two points $P_1(1, -2)$ and $P_2(-3, 4)$.

A set of direction numbers of the line $P_1 P_2$ is

$$[-3 - 1, 4 - (-2)] = [-4, 6].$$

It then follows, from Theorem 3.1c, if $[m, n]$ is a set of direction numbers of a line perpendicular to $P_1 P_2$, that

$$-4m + 6n = 0.$$

Any values of $m$ and $n$, not both zero, that satisfy this equation may be chosen as the desired direction numbers. Thus a suitable set is $[6, 4]$ or any other numbers proportional to these, such as $[3, 2]$.

---

The next theorem is a direct consequence of Theorem 3.1c and its proof is left to the reader.

**Theorem 3.1d.** Let $m_1$ and $m_2$ be the slopes of two lines $L_1$ and $L_2$, respectively. Then

$$L_1 \text{ is perpendicular to } L_2 \Leftrightarrow m_1 m_2 = -1.$$

---

*Example 3.1c.* Show by means of slopes that the line through $P_1(-1, 3)$ and $P_2(2, 9)$ is perpendicular to the line through $P_3(1, 2)$ and $P_4(5, 0)$.

The slope of the first line is

$$m_1 = \frac{9 - 3}{2 - (-1)} = 2,$$

and the slope of the second line is

$$m_2 = \frac{0 - 2}{5 - 1} = -\frac{1}{2}.$$

Since these two slopes are negative reciprocals of each other, the lines are perpendicular, as was to be shown.

## Exercises 3.1

1. Plot the points $A(-3, -4)$, $B(5, -2)$, $C(4, 2)$, and $D(0, 1)$, and then answer the following questions about the quadrilateral $ABCD$.

   (a) Is the figure a trapezoid, a parallelogram, or neither?
   (b) Does the figure include any right angles?

2. Show that the midpoints of the sides of the quadrilateral in Number 1 are the vertices of a parallelogram.

3. Describe at least two ways in which you can determine whether or not three points lie in a straight line.

4. Show by two different methods that the points $(1, -1)$, $(-7, 1)$, and $(5, -2)$ lie in a straight line.

5. Prove in two ways that the points $(3, 0)$, $(4, 5)$, and $(6, 2)$ are vertices of a right triangle.

6. If the three points in Number 5 are three of the vertices of a rectangle, what are the coordinates of the fourth vertex?

7. If a right-angled wedge *DEF* is placed on an inclined plane, as shown in Figure 3.1d, find direction numbers of faces *DE* and *DF*.

8. Find the direction numbers of the shortest line segment that can be drawn from the point $(-4, 2)$ to the line through the points $(0, 2)$ and $(1, -1)$.

9. Find the direction numbers of the altitudes and medians of the triangle with vertices at $(-2, 3)$, $(-1, -2)$, $(-3, -4)$.

10. If a line through the points $(1, 2)$ and $(-1, -1)$ is perpendicular to a line through $(-4, 1)$ and $(a, -3)$, find $a$.

11. If a line through the points $(1, 2)$ and $(-1, -1)$ is parallel to a line through $(-4, 1)$ and $(a, -3)$, find $a$.

12. Prove Theorem 3.1b.

13. Which of the points $(-3, 0)$, $(6, 3)$, $(1, 1)$ lie on the line through the points $(-6, -1)$ and $(3, 2)$?

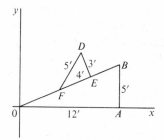

**FIGURE 3.1d**

Use the methods of analytic geometry to prove the following theorems.

14. The diagonals of a square are mutually perpendicular.

15. If the midpoints of the successive sides of a rectangle are joined by line segments, the resulting figure is a rhombus.

16. If the midpoints of the successive sides of a quadrilateral are joined by line segments, the resulting figure is a parallelogram.

17. In a parallelogram the sum of the squares of the diagonals is equal to the sum of the squares of the sides.

## 3.2 LINEAR EQUATIONS

An equation of the form

1)
$$Ax + By + C = 0$$

is called a **linear equation** because of its close connection with the straight line in plane geometry. Assuming $B \neq 0$, we may solve Equation (1) for $y$ to obtain a result of the form

$$(2) \qquad\qquad y = mx + b,$$

where $m = -A/B$ and $b = -C/B$. Equation (2) clearly determines a unique value of $y$ for each real value of $x$, so that we may associate with it the solution set

$$\{(x, y): y = mx + b\}.$$

The function defined by this set is called a **linear function.**

The equations

$$Ax + C = 0 \qquad A \neq 0,$$

and

$$By + C = 0, \qquad B \neq 0,$$

are special cases of Equation (1). The graph of the first equation is a straight line parallel to the $y$-axis, as can be seen from the fact that the equation is equivalent to $x = d$, where $d = -C/A$ is a constant. Thus this equation is satisfied by the set of points $\{(d, y)\}$, where $y$ is any real number. Similarly, the second equation has for its graph a straight line parallel to the $x$-axis. Figure 2.4b shows the graph for the special case $-C/B = 4$.

Before proceeding to a discussion of the relationship between the general linear equation and the straight line, it should be made clear that a straight line is regarded as being completely determined by any given point on the line and the direction of the line. Thus, a line is considered to be specified by a pair of coordinates $(x_1, y_1)$ and a set of direction numbers $[m, n]$.

**Theorem 3.2a.** Every straight line has an equation of the form

$$Ax + By + C = 0.$$

PROOF: Let the line be specified by the coordinates $(x_1, y_1)$ of a point $P_1$ on the line and the direction numbers $[m, n]$ of the line. Let $P(x, y)$ be any second point on the line. Then $[x - x_1, y - y_1]$ must also be direction numbers of the line, so that

$$x - x_1 = km, \quad y - y_1 = kn.$$

If $k$ is eliminated by multiplying both members of the first of these equations by $n$ and of the second equation by $m$ and subtracting, the result is

$$n(x - x_1) - m(y - y_1) = 0,$$

or

$$nx - my + my_1 - nx_1 = 0.$$

With $A = n$, $B = -m$, and $C = my_1 - nx_1$, the equation is of the form $Ax + By + C = 0$, which was to be shown.

The next theorem is essentially the converse of Theorem 3.2a, and completes the description of the connection between the straight line and the general linear equation (1).

**Theorem 3.2b.** The equation $Ax + By + C = 0$, where at least one of $A$, $B$ is different from zero, has a straight line for its graph.

PROOF: In order to prove this theorem, we must show two things: (i) that the solution set of the equation consists of points all on a straight line, and (ii) that every point on this line is in the solution set of the equation.

(i) Let $P_1(x_1, y_1)$ and $P_2(x_2, y_2)$ be two points whose coordinates satisfy the given equation. This means that

$$Ax_1 + By_1 + C = 0$$

and

$$Ax_2 + By_2 + C = 0.$$

By subtraction, we get

$$A(x_2 - x_1) + B(y_2 - y_1) = 0.$$

It is not difficult to see that this equation is equivalent to the pair of equations

(3) $$x_2 - x_1 = kB, \quad y_2 - y_1 = -kA,$$

where $k$ is a constant. (The reader may check this statement in case $A \neq 0$, by setting $y_2 - y_1 = -kA$ and solving for $x_2 - x_1$. If $B \neq 0$, he may set $x_2 - x_1 = kB$ and solve for $y_2 - y_1$.) It follows from the discussion in Section 3.1 that the direction from any point $P_1(x_1, y_1)$ to any other point $P_2(x_2, y_2)$ has the direction numbers $[B, -A]$. Thus, all points in the solution set lie on the line specified by the point $P_1(x_1, y_1)$ and the set of direction numbers $[B, -A]$.

(ii) Now suppose that $P_3(x_3, y_3)$ is any other point on the line specified by $P_1(x_1, y_1)$ and the direction numbers $[B, -A]$. Then

$$x_3 - x_1 = pB, \quad y_3 - y_1 = -pA.$$

If these two equations are solved for $x_3$ and $y_3$, respectively, and the results substituted into the left member of Equation (1), we find

$$Ax_3 + By_3 + C = A(x_1 + pB) + B(y_1 - pA) + C$$
$$= Ax_1 + By_1 + C = 0,$$

since $(x_1, y_1)$ was assumed to be in the solution set of Equation (1). We have thus shown that every point on the line is in the solution set of the equation. Hence the proof of the theorem is complete.

The following examples illustrate the application of the preceding theorems and of some of the ideas that occurred in their proofs. It is important to note that Equations (3) show that $[B, -A]$ may be taken as a set of direction numbers for the line $Ax + By + C = 0$.

---

*Example 3.2a.* Find an equation for the straight line passing through the points $P_1(2, -1)$ and $P_2(4, 5)$.

It follows from the work in Section 3.1 that these two points determine the direction characterized by the direction numbers $[2, 6]$. Suppose $P(x, y)$ is any point on the line determined by $P_1$ and $P_2$ (Figure 3.2a). Then direction numbers that characterize the

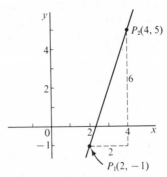

**FIGURE 3.2a**

line through $P$ and $P_1$ are $[x - 2, y + 1]$. Since the two sets of direction numbers must be proportional, we may write

$$x - 2 = 2t, \quad y + 1 = 6t,$$

where $t$, the proportionality factor, may be any real number. For each value of $t$, the two equations determine a point on the line. For instance, if $t = 0$, we get $x = 2$, $y = -1$, that is, the point $(2, -1)$; if $t = 1$, then the point is $(4, 5)$; if $t = -3$, the point is $(-4, -18)$, and so on.

In this example, since neither direction number is zero, we may solve for $t$ in both equations to obtain

$$t = \frac{x - 2}{2} \quad \text{and} \quad t = \frac{y + 1}{6},$$

so that

$$\frac{x - 2}{2} = \frac{y + 1}{6} \quad \text{or} \quad 3x - y - 7 = 0.$$

Thus, every point $P$ that lies on the straight line determined by $P_1$ and $P_2$ must have coordinates that satisfy the equation $3x - y - 7 = 0$. As a check, notice that direction numbers of this line are indicated to be $[-1, -3]$ which are proportional to $[2, 6]$.

---

In the solution of Example 3.2a, there occurred the equations $x - 2 = 2t$ and $y + 1 = 6t$. Equations of this form constitute a useful way of describing a straight line. It is clear from the proofs of the preceding theorems that a pair of equations

$$(4) \qquad\qquad x - x_1 = mt, \quad y - y_1 = nt$$

always describes the straight line specified by the point $(x_1, y_1)$ and the direction numbers $[m, n]$. Equations (4) are called **parametric equations** of the line and the auxiliary variable $t$ is called a **parameter**.

---

*Example 3.2b.* A straight line is described by the equations $x = 2 + t$, $y = 3 - 3t$. Write an equation for this line in the general linear form.

This problem can be solved by eliminating the parameter $t$. This can be done by adding $3x$ and $y$ to get

$$3x + y = 6 + 3t + 3 - 3t$$

or

$$3x + y - 9 = 0.$$

(See Figure 3.2b.)

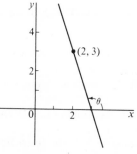

FIGURE 3.2b

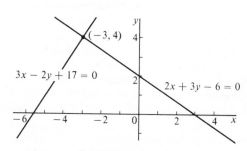

FIGURE 3.2c

---

*Example 3.2c.* Find an equation of the straight line that is perpendicular to the line $2x + 3y - 6 = 0$ and that passes through the point $(-3, 4)$ (Figure 3.2c).

Direction numbers of the given line are $[B, -A] = [3, -2]$. If $[m, n]$ is a set of direction numbers of a line perpendicular to the given line, then, by Theorem 3.1c,

$$3m - 2n = 0.$$

A set of numbers satisfying this condition is $[2, 3]$. Hence the desired equation is of the form

$$3x - 2y + C = 0.$$

(Why?) The value of $C$ may be determined from the fact that the point $(-3, 4)$ must be on this line. Thus, by substituting the coordinates of this point into the equation, we get

$$3(-3) - 2(4) + C = 0 \quad \text{or} \quad C = 17.$$

Therefore the desired equation is $3x - 2y + 17 = 0$.

# Exercises 3.2

1. Find an equation of the line passing through the two given points.

   (a) $(-2, 3)$ and $(4, -1)$.      (d) $(-1, -2)$ and $(2, -2)$.
   (b) $(-2, -3)$ and $(-2, 1)$.      (e) $(3, 0)$ and $(0, -4)$.
   (c) $(-2, -3)$ and $(3, 2)$.      (f) $(0, -2)$ and $(-5, 0)$.

2. Write an equation for the straight line that passes through the point $(2, -2)$ and is parallel to the line $3x - 5y = 8$. (After determining the direction numbers of the desired line, use the method of Example 3.2c.)

3. A line $L$ passes through the point $(2, \frac{3}{2})$ and is perpendicular to the line $3x + 4y = 12$. At what point does $L$ cut the $x$-axis?

4. (a) Find the area of the triangle enclosed by the coordinate axes and the line $5x - 4y = 20$.
   (b) Use the result of (a) to find the length of the altitude to the hypotenuse of the triangle.
   Can you find another method to work (b)?

5. Write an equation for a line that passes through the points $(x_1, y_1)$, $(x_2, y_2)$, with $x_1 \neq x_2$.

6. (a) Express by an algebraic equation the statement that the point $(x, y)$ is equidistant from $(-5, -2)$ and $(3, 0)$.
   (b) Determine the algebraic equation of (a) by another method.

7. For the triangle with vertices at $(2, 6)$, $(5, 3)$, and $(3, 1)$, find the coordinates of the point where the altitude from the vertex $(5, 3)$ intersects the base.

8. For the triangle of Number 7, find an equation of the line passing through the vertex $(5, 3)$ and the midpoint of the opposite side.

9. Find an equation of the set of points equidistant from the points $(3, -1)$ and $(-3, 3)$.

10. Write parametric equations for the same line as in Number 5. Is the restriction $x_1 \neq x_2$ needed in these equations? Why?

11. Write an equation for a line having direction numbers $[k, 1]$ and passing through $(x_0, y_0)$. What would have to be the value of $k$ if the line also passes through the origin?

12. Find parametric equations for the line that passes through $(2, 3)$ and is parallel to the line $4x - y = 6$.

13. Find parametric equations for the line that passes through $(2, 3)$ and is perpendicular to the line $4x - y = 6$.

14. Where does the line $x = 2 - 3t$, $y = 1 + 4t$ cut the coordinate axes?

15. Does the line $x = 5 - 3t$, $y = -3 + 2t$ pass through the point $(14, 2)$? Explain.

16. A line passes through the point $(0, 2)$ and has direction numbers $[1, -4]$. Does the point $(100, -392)$ lie on this line? Explain.

17. Find the point on the line $3x - 2y - 15 = 0$ that is equidistant from the points $(-3, -1)$ and $(5, 3)$.

18. Find the point on the line $x + y + 7 = 0$ that is equidistant from the points $(-4, 1)$ and $(2, -3)$.

19. Find the center of the circle that passes through the points $(1, -3)$, $(-3, -7)$ and $(-1, -1)$.

20. Prove that the lines $ax + by = c_1$ and $ax + by = c_2$ are parallel.

21. Prove that the lines $ax + by = c_1$ and $bx - ay = c_2$ are perpendicular.

## 3.3 SPECIAL FORMS OF THE LINEAR EQUATION

The direction of any nonvertical line may be characterized by its slope, which was defined in Section 3.1 to be the ratio $m = k_2/k_1$ of its direction number $[k_1, k_2]$. An equation for a line having the slope $m$ and passing through a given point $(a, b)$ may easily be obtained by equating slopes. Thus, if $(x, y)$ is any point other than $(a, b)$ on the line, then

$$\frac{y - b}{x - a} = m \quad \text{or} \quad y - b = m(x - a).$$

The last equation is called the **point-slope form** of the equation of a straight line.

A special case of the point-slope form of the equation occurred in Equation (2) of Section 3.2. There, the point is $(0, b)$, which is where the line cuts the $y$-axis. The number $b$ is called the **y-intercept** of the line and the equation

$$y = mx + b$$

is the **slope-intercept form** of the equation of a straight line.

---

*Example 3.3a.* Find an equation of the line that passes through the point $(2, 3)$ with a slope of $-3$ (see Figure 3.2b).

If $(x, y)$ is a point on the line, then the slope determined by $(x, y)$ and $(2, 3)$ is $(y - 3)/(x - 2)$, which must equal $-3$. Hence an equation of the line is $y + 3x = 9$.

---

Sometimes the points where the line cuts the two axes are of special interest. Suppose these points are denoted by $(a, 0)$ and $(0, b)$ so that $a$ and $b$, respectively, are the $x$- and $y$-intercepts of the line (see Figure 3.3a). Then, if $(x, y)$ is any

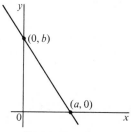

**FIGURE 3.3a**

other point on the line, an equation of the line can be found by equating two expressions for the slope. Thus

$$\frac{y - 0}{x - a} = \frac{0 - b}{a - 0} \quad \text{or} \quad bx + ay = ab.$$

By division by $ab$, the usual **intercept form** is obtained:

$$\frac{x}{a} + \frac{y}{b} = 1.$$

---

*Example 3.3b.* The $y$-intercept of a line exceeds the $x$-intercept by 1 and the line passes through the point $(10, -6)$ (see Figure 3.3b). Find an equation of the line.

If the $x$-intercept is $a$, then the $y$-intercept must be $a + 1$. Hence, the equation may be written in the form

$$\frac{x}{a} + \frac{y}{a + 1} = 1.$$

Since the line is to pass through $(10, -6)$, it follows that

$$\frac{10}{a} - \frac{6}{a+1} = 1,$$

or

$$a^2 - 3a - 10 = 0,$$

or

$$(a - 5)(a + 2) = 0.$$

Thus,

$$a = 5 \quad \text{and} \quad a + 1 = 6$$

or

$$a = -2 \quad \text{and} \quad a + 1 = -1.$$

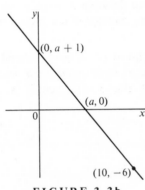

FIGURE 3.3b

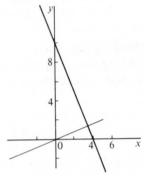

FIGURE 3.3c

Consequently, there are two lines that satisfy the given conditions, and their equations are

$$\frac{x}{5} + \frac{y}{6} = 1 \quad \text{or} \quad 6x + 5y - 30 = 0$$

and

$$\frac{x}{-2} + \frac{y}{-1} = 1 \quad \text{or} \quad x + 2y + 2 = 0.$$

*Example 3.3c.* A line has an $x$-intercept of 4 and a $y$-intercept of 10. Find the perpendicular distance from the origin to this line (see Figure 3.3c).

The equation of the line may be written

$$\frac{x}{4} + \frac{y}{10} = 1$$

or

$$y = -\frac{5}{2}x + 10.$$

This equation shows that the slope of the line is $-5/2$, so that the slope of a line perpendicular to it is $2/5$. Hence, the line through the origin and perpendicular to the given line has an equation

$$y = \frac{2}{5}x.$$

In order to solve the equations of the two lines for their point of intersection, the values of $y$ may be equated to get

$$\frac{2}{5}x = -\frac{5}{2}x + 10$$

or

$$29x = 100 \quad \text{and} \quad x = \frac{100}{29}.$$

Since $y = \frac{2}{5}x$, the corresponding value of $y$ is $\frac{40}{29}$.

Accordingly, the distance from the origin to the line is

$$d = \sqrt{\left(\frac{100}{29}\right)^2 + \left(\frac{40}{29}\right)^2} = \frac{20}{\sqrt{29}}.$$

## Exercises 3.3

1. Find the slope and the $y$-intercept of each of the following lines.
   (a) $2x - 3y + 7 = 0$.
   (b) $3x - 5y = 0$.
   (c) $1.2x + 0.04y = 2.4$.
   (d) $x = 1 + 2t, y = 3 - 4t$.
   (e) $x = -2 + 5t, y = 4t$.
   (f) $x/2 + y/3 = 4$.

2. Find the equation of a line having the sum of its intercepts equal to 5 and passing through the point $(2, -4)$.

3. Determine the slope and intercepts of the line passing through the two given points.
   (a) $(-2, 5), (3, -2)$.
   (b) $(-4, -1), (2, -3)$.
   (c) $(3, 4), (-2, -1)$.
   (d) $(a, b), (c, d)$.

4. What is the $x$-intercept of the line that has a slope $-3$ and a $y$-intercept 4?

5. A line has a slope $-4$ and a $y$-intercept 2. Does the point $(100, -392)$ lie on this line? Explain.

6. What is the $y$-intercept of the line that has a slope $-2$ and an $x$-intercept $-3$?

7. Find the distance from the origin to the line having an $x$-intercept of 4 and a $y$-intercept of $-2$.

8. A certain line has its $y$-intercept twice its $x$-intercept and passes through the point $(1, 4)$. Find an equation for this line.

9. Find the point of intersection of the altitudes of the triangle with vertices at $(1, 5), (3, -2), (-1, 1)$.

10. Find the equations of the perpendicular bisectors of the sides of the triangle in Number 9. Do all three bisectors intersect in a single point?

11. Find the point of intersection of the medians of the triangle in Number 9.

12. Are the three points found in Numbers 9, 10, and 11 collinear?

13. Do the lines $2x + 3y = 7$, $6x = 4y + 5$, $3x - 2y - 4 = 0$, and $6y = 9 - 4x$ form a rectangle?

14. Under standard atmospheric pressure, the freezing point of water is $32°$ on the Fahrenheit scale ($F$) and the boiling point is $212°$. On the centigrade scale ($C$), the freezing point is $0°$ and the boiling point is $100°$. Assuming that $C$ is a linear function of $F$ such that $C = mF + b$, find the centigrade temperature corresponding to $0°$ Fahrenheit.

15. Will the centers of all circles tangent to the line $2x - 3y = 6$ at the point $(6, 2)$ lie on a line? If so, find the equation of the line.
16. According to Hooke's law, if a spring is stretched or compressed, its change in length $(x)$ is proportional to the force $(F)$ exerted upon it, and when the force is removed, the spring will return to its original position. If a force of 10 pounds stretches a spring $\frac{1}{4}$ inch, write an equation showing the relation between $F$ and $x$ and draw the graph.

## 3.4 SOLUTION SETS OF EQUATIONS

Much of the power of mathematics as a practical tool in science and engineering lies in its applicability to physical problems. A physical problem is frequently represented by a mathematical model in the form of an expression called an *equation*. A solution to the physical problem is then obtained when a solution to the mathematical problem is found. Since a mathematical equation arising in connection with a physical problem is usually in the form of an open statement, the problem of finding a solution to the mathematical problem is simply that of finding elements of a given set for which the open statement is true.

**Definition 3.4a.** The set $S$ of elements for which a given equation, $p(x) = q(x)$, is true is called the **solution set** of the equation, and is denoted by $S[p(x) = q(x)]$.

For example,

$$S[2x - 3 = 5] = \{4\},$$
$$S[x^2 = x^2 + 1] = \varnothing,$$

and

$$S[x(x - 1) = x^2 - x] = \mathcal{C}.$$

In discussing an equation such as $2x - 3 = 0$, we may associate with it the function $\{(x, y): y = 2x - 3\}$, whose graph is shown in Figure 3.4a. The point $(\frac{3}{2}, 0)$ is a point on this graph, and the $x$-coordinate of this point satisfies the equation $2x - 3 = 0$. This fact is interpreted geometrically by saying that the solution of the equation $2x - 3 = 0$ is the $x$-coordinate of the point where the line $y = 2x - 3$ crosses the $x$-axis. This idea will be of great value in discussing the solution sets of other types of equations.

---

*Example 3.4a.* Compare the solution set of $x + 2|x - 2| = 5$ with the graph of an appropriate function.

The function that is associated with the given equation is

$$\{(x, y): y = x + 2|x - 2| - 5\}.$$

In order to obtain the graph of this function easily, we shall rewrite

$$y = x + 2|x - 2| - 5$$

as

$$y = 3x - 9 \quad \text{if } 2 \leq x \quad \text{and} \quad y = -x - 1 \quad \text{if } x < 2.$$

The graph is shown in Figure 3.4b. Among the points corresponding to the function are the points for which $y = 0$, namely, $(3, 0)$ and $(-1, 0)$. In this case these points may be obtained easily from the defining equations of the function. The solution set

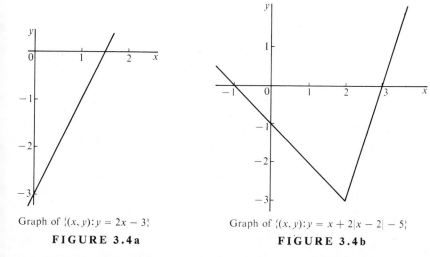

Graph of $\{(x, y): y = 2x - 3\}$

**FIGURE 3.4a**

Graph of $\{(x, y): y = x + 2|x - 2| - 5\}$

**FIGURE 3.4b**

of the original equation is $S = \{-1, 3\}$. The elements in the solution set of an equation in one unknown are called **roots** of the equation. Thus, the roots of the given equation are $-1$ and $3$.

Just as we were able to associate a function with a linear equation $ax + b = 0$, so we may associate a function $\{(x, y): y = ax^2 + bx + c\}$ with a quadratic equation $ax^2 + bx + c = 0$. For example, to the equation $x^2 - 4x + 3 = 0$, we may associate the function $\{(x, y): y = x^2 - 4x + 3\}$, whose graph is shown in Figure 3.4c. This curve, which is characteristic of the quadratic function, is called a **parabola**. As we might expect, the solution set of the equation $x^2 - 4x + 3 = 0$ consists of the $x$-coordinates of the points at which the graph of the related function crosses the $x$-axis.

A study of the graph in Figure 3.4c suggests that we investigate certain properties that the parabola seems to possess. In particular, we might consider the possibility of determining the lowest point or vertex of the curve and whether or not there is a line of symmetry. Such information would be useful in obtaining the graphs of other functions that are similar to this one.

It is easy to see that the line $x = 2$ is a line of symmetry by completing the square in $x$:

$$y = x^2 - 4x + 3$$
$$= (x^2 - 4x + 4) - 1$$
$$= (x - 2)^2 - 1$$

or

$$y + 1 = (x - 2)^2.$$

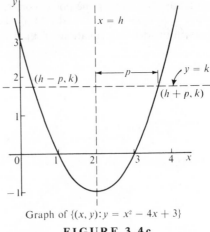

Graph of $\{(x, y): y = x^2 - 4x + 3\}$

**FIGURE 3.4c**

This equation implies that $x - 2 = \pm\sqrt{y + 1}$, so that for each value of $y > -1$ there are two values of $x$ equidistant from the value 2. For $y = -1$, the equation gives $0 = (x - 2)^2$ so that $x = 2$ is the only corresponding value.

The line of symmetry of a parabola is called the **axis** of the parabola. The point where the axis intersects the curve is called the **vertex** of the parabola. A perpendicular to the line of symmetry must intersect the parabola at two symmetrically located points, at just one point, or at no points at all. If a perpendicular to the line of symmetry intersects the parabola at only one point, then that point is the vertex of the parabola. From the equation $y = x^2 - 4x + 3$, we found that $y = -1 \Rightarrow x = 2$, so that the vertex of this parabola is the point $(2, -1)$. The axis and the vertex of a parabola $y = Ax^2 + Bx + C$ can always be found by completing the square in $x$ as in the preceding discussion. Thus, if the final equation is of the form $(x - h)^2 = m(y - k)$, then the vertex is at the point $(h, k)$ and the axis is the line $x = h$.

We recall from algebra that the quantity $B^2 - 4AC$ is called the **discriminant** of the quadratic expression

$$Ax^2 + Bx + C.$$

From the foregoing discussion it follows that if the discriminant of the equation

$$y = Ax^2 + Bx + C$$

is positive, then the parabola crosses the x-axis at two distinct points, since the quadratic equation

$$Ax^2 + Bx + C = 0$$

will then have two real distinct roots. If the discriminant is equal to zero, then the parabola intersects the x-axis at only one point, since in that case $Ax^2 + Bx + C = 0$ has equal real roots. If the discriminant is negative, the graph of the equation $y = Ax^2 + Bx + C$ cannot cross the x-axis. (Why?)

In a more general case, we may not be able to find the exact roots of an equation of the form $f(x) = 0$, and we may be obliged to use an approximation to a root. Such an approximation can be obtained geometrically by drawing the graph of the associated function $\{(x, y): y = f(x)\}$, and then determining the points where this graph crosses the $x$-axis. The accuracy of the approximation so obtained depends on the accuracy with which the graph can be drawn and the accuracy with which the coordinates of a point can be read.

## Exercises 3.4

Find the solution set in the field $\Re$ for each of Numbers 1 to 16.

1. $x^2 - 7x + 12 = 0$.
2. $x^2 - x - 2 = 0$.
3. $x^3 + 3x^2 + 2x = 0$.
4. $y^3 + 5y^2 - 14y = 0$.
5. $x^3 - 4x^2 + x + 6 = 0$.
6. $x^3 + 2x^2 - 9x - 18 = 0$.
7. $\sqrt{u+2} = \sqrt{u-3} + 1$.
8. $\sqrt{x+4} - \sqrt{2} = \sqrt{x-6}$.

9. $|x| + 3 = 0$.
10. $|s| = 2$.
11. $2w - |w| = 3$.
12. $[\![x - 1]\!] = 3$.
13. $2[\![t]\!] = 3$.
14. $2|x - 1| - 3|x| = 4$.
15. $|s + 1| - 2|s| + 3|s - 2| = 6$.
16. $w - [\![w]\!] = \frac{1}{2}$.

In each of Numbers 17 to 26, find the solution set in the field $\mathcal{C}$ for the given equation.

17. $x^2 + 2x + 2 = 0$.
18. $-3x^2 + 4x - 3 = 0$.
19. $4x^2 - 3x - 2 = 0$.
20. $x^2 + x + 1 = 0$.
21. $x^2 + 2px + q = 0$.

22. $x^2 + \sqrt{2}x - 4 = 0$.
23. $x^2 + 2\sqrt{3}x + 3 = 0$.
24. $x^2 - 0.1x + 0.05 = 0$.
25. $1000x^2 + 5x - 2 = 0$.
26. $x^2 - 3ix - 2 = 0$.

27. Find the sum of the roots of the equation $ax^2 + bx + c = 0$.
28. Find the product of the roots of the equation $ax^2 + bx + c = 0$.
29. Show that the roots of the equation $ax^2 + bx + a = 0$ are reciprocals of each other.
30. One root of the equation $ax^2 - bx + 2a = 0$ is 4. What is the other root?
31. Find the roots of $2x^2 + 9x + c = 0$ if it is known that the product of the roots is 2.
32. Is it always possible to put an equation of the form $x^4 + ax^3 + bx^2 + cx + d = 0$ into the form $(x^2 + mx)^2 + p(x^2 + mx) + d = 0$?
33. Put the equation $x^4 + 4x^3 + 5x^2 + 2x - 2 = 0$ into the form suggested in Number 32 and then find the solution set.
34. Use the method of Number 33 to solve the equation
$$x^4 + 6x^3 + 8x^2 - 3x - 6 = 0.$$

In each of Numbers 35 to 38, solve the given equation.

35. $x + 1 - 2x^{-1} = 0$.
36. $x^2 + 5 - 6x^{-2} = 0$.

37. $x^{1/2} - 1 = 12x^{-1/2}$.
38. $27x^{3/2} - 217x^{3/4} + 8 = 0$.

39. Show that the axis of symmetry of the graph of $y = Ax^2 - 2Bx + C$ is given by $x = B/A$.

40. Sketch each of the following parabolas. Find the equation of the axis and the coordinates of the vertex.

(a) $y = 4x^2 + 6x + 3$.
(b) $y = 2x^2 + 4x$.

(c) $y = -3x^2 + 6x + 2$.
(d) $2x^2 + 8x + 1 + y = 0$.

41. Find the value of $b$ so that the graph of the equation $y = 8x^2 + bx + 8$ will have its vertex on the line $y = 4$.

42. Find the equation of a parabola with vertex at the origin, axis along the $y$-axis, and passing through the point $(3, -1)$.

43. Find the equation of a parabola with vertex at the point $(-3, 2)$, axis the line $x = -3$, and passing through the point $(0, 5)$.

44. Find the number that exceeds its square by the greatest amount.

45. Find a number such that the sum of it and its reciprocal is 1.

46. A rectangular piece of cardboard is to have a square 4 inches on a side cut from each corner. The remaining piece is to be folded up to form an open box. It is required that the box be 4 inches longer than it is wide and that it have a volume of 48 cubic inches. What must be the dimensions of the original rectangle?

## 3.5 SOLUTION SETS OF INEQUALITIES

We now propose to obtain results for inequalities similar to those obtained for equations in Section 3.4. For example, corresponding to the idea of the solution set of an equation, we have the following definition for inequalities.

**Definition 3.5a.** The set of values for which a given inequality is true is called the **solution set** of the inequality.

The following theorems indicate what operations may be performed on an inequality in order to arrive at the solution set. By the use of Theorem 1.10b, the reader should be able to prove

**Theorem 3.5a.** The solution set of an inequality

$$f(x) > g(x)$$

is not altered by adding to both sides a term $p(x)$, where $p$ is any function such that $\mathcal{D}_p = \mathcal{D}_f \cap \mathcal{D}_g$. That is,

$$\mathcal{S}[f(x) > g(x)] = \mathcal{S}[f(x) + p(x) > g(x) + p(x)].$$

Similarly, Theorem 1.10c suffices to prove

**Theorem 3.5b.** The solution set of an inequality

$$f(x) > g(x)$$

is not altered by multiplying both members by a factor $p(x)$ that is *positive* for all $x \in \mathcal{R}$; that is,

$$p(x) > 0 \text{ for } x \in \mathcal{R} \Rightarrow \mathcal{S}[f(x) > g(x)] = \mathcal{S}[p(x)f(x) > p(x)g(x)].$$

In order to find the solution set of a given inequality, we apply the preceding theorems to obtain simpler inequalities until the solution set is apparent. This will be illustrated in the next examples.

*Example 3.5a.* Solve the inequality $5x + 7 > 3x + 15$.

We apply Theorem 3.5a by adding $-3x - 7$ to both members to obtain

$$2x > 8.$$

Then dividing both members by 2, we find the solution set to be $\{x: x > 4\}$.

---

*Example 3.5b.* Solve the inequality $x^2 - 5x + 6 > 0$.

We note that $x^2 - 5x + 6 = (x - 2)(x - 3)$. But a product of two factors is positive ($> 0$) only if both factors are positive or if both are negative. The set of numbers for which both factors are positive may be expressed as the intersection of two sets:

$$\mathbb{S}[x - 2 > 0] \cap \mathbb{S}[x - 3 > 0].$$

This is the same as $\{x: x > 3\}$. Why?

Similarly, the set of numbers for which both factors are negative may be written

$$\mathbb{S}[x - 3 < 0] \cap \mathbb{S}[x - 2 < 0],$$

and this is the set $\{x: x < 2\}$.

Since any number in either of the sets $\{x: x < 2\}$ and $\{x: x > 3\}$ is an element of $\mathbb{S}[x^2 - 5x + 6 > 0]$, the desired solution set is

$$\{x: x < 2\} \cup \{x: x > 3\}.$$

---

*Example 3.5c.* Solve the inequality $1/(x - 1) > 1$.

By subtracting 1 from both members, we get

$$\frac{1}{x - 1} > 1 \Leftrightarrow \frac{1}{x - 1} - 1 > 0$$

or

$$\frac{2 - x}{x - 1} > 0.$$

The last inequality is satisfied if, and only if, both $2 - x$ and $x - 1$ are positive or both are negative. We find

$$\mathbb{S}[2 - x > 0] \cap \mathbb{S}[x - 1 > 0] = \{x: x < 2\} \cap \{x: x > 1\}$$
$$= \{x: 1 < x < 2\}.$$

Also,

$$\mathbb{S}[2 - x < 0] \cap \mathbb{S}[x - 1 < 0] = \{x: x > 2\} \cap \{x: x < 1\}$$
$$= \varnothing.$$

Accordingly, the required solution set is

$$\{x: 1 < x < 2\}.$$

---

The solution set for an inequality can be related to the graph of a function by exploiting more fully than in the preceding discussion the relationship between the graph and the order properties of the real numbers. The following examples will illustrate this idea.

---

*Example 3.5d.* Obtain the solution set of the inequality $3x < 2$ by means of the graph of an appropriate function.

The inequality may be rewritten as $3x - 2 < 0$. A function associated with this form is $\{(x, y): y = 3x - 2\}$, whose graph is shown in Figure 3.5a. We are interested in

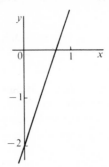

Graph of $\{(x, y): y = 3x - 2\}$

**FIGURE 3.5a**

the values of $y$ that are less than zero. These correspond to points on the line that are below the $x$-axis. Since the line is below the $x$-axis whenever $x < 2/3$, the solution set of the inequality is graphically found to be $S = \{x: x < 2/3\}$.

---

*Example 3.5e.* Find the solution set of the inequality

$$2|x| + |x - 1| < 4.$$

Since

$$|x| = \begin{cases} -x & \text{for } x < 0, \\ x & \text{for } x \geq 0, \end{cases}$$

it follows that

$$|x - 1| = \begin{cases} -x + 1 & \text{for } x < 1, \\ x - 1 & \text{for } x \geq 1. \end{cases}$$

Thus it is natural to divide the domain of definition of the left side of the inequality into three parts: $x < 0$, $0 \leq x < 1$, and $x \geq 1$.

For $x < 0$, the given inequality is the same as

$$-2x - (x - 1) < 4 \quad \text{or} \quad -3x - 3 < 0.$$

Similarly, for $0 \leq x < 1$, we must have

$$2x - (x - 1) < 4 \quad \text{or} \quad x - 3 < 0.$$

And, for $x \geq 1$,

$$2x + (x - 1) < 4 \quad \text{or} \quad 3x - 5 < 0.$$

The function defined by

$$y = \begin{cases} -3x - 3 & \text{for } x < 0, \\ x - 3 & \text{for } 0 \leq x < 1, \\ 3x - 5 & \text{for } 1 \leq x, \end{cases}$$

has the graph that is shown in Figure 3.5b. From this graph it appears that the solution set of the original inequality is $\{x: -1 < x < 5/3\}$.

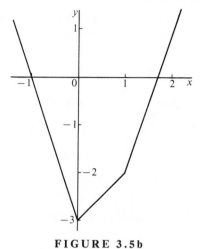

**FIGURE 3.5b**

*Example 3.5f.* Determine the solution set of the inequality

$$x^2 - x < 6.$$

First Method: We first complete the square on the left by adding $1/4$ to both sides of the given inequality which becomes

$$x^2 - x + \frac{1}{4} < \frac{25}{4}$$

or

$$\left(x - \frac{1}{2}\right)^2 < \left(\frac{5}{2}\right)^2.$$

Since, for $a > 0$, it is true that $Y^2 < a^2 \Leftrightarrow -a < Y < a$, we have

$$-\frac{5}{2} < x - \frac{1}{2} < \frac{5}{2},$$

which can be simplified to yield

$$-2 < x < 3.$$

Thus

$$S[x^2 - x < 6] = \{x: -2 < x < 3\}.$$

Second Method: This time we use the function

$$\{(x, y): y = x^2 - x - 6\},$$

where the defining equation is obtained from the left side of the inequality

$$x^2 - x - 6 < 0$$

that results by subtracting 6 from both sides of the given one. The graph of the function is shown in Figure 3.5c. This graph is easily sketched by first noting that

$$x^2 - x - 6 = (x - 3)(x + 2),$$

so that $y = 0$ for $x = -2$ and for $x = 3$. Since the equation is that of a parabola, the reader should be able to make the sketch on the basis of the preceding information.

Now the solution set required is that set of values of $x$ for which $y < 0$, that is, for which the graph lies below the $x$-axis. From the graph it is easy to see that

$$y < 0 \quad \text{for} \quad -2 < x < 3,$$

which gives the same solution set as before.

---

*Example 3.5g.* Find the solution set of the inequality

$$\left| \frac{x-1}{x+1} \right| \le 2.$$

From the definition of absolute value, it follows that the given inequality is equivalent to

$$-2 \le \frac{x-1}{x+1} \le 2.$$

The required solution set must accordingly be the intersection of the solution sets of the two inequalities

(i) $-2 \le \dfrac{x-1}{x+1}$,  (ii) $\dfrac{x-1}{x+1} \le 2$.

We shall solve (ii) in detail.

An equivalent inequality that involves a linear or quadratic polynomial rather than a fractional expression can be obtained from the given inequality by means of the theorems governing inequalities. We have

$$\frac{x-1}{x+1} \le 2 \Leftrightarrow \frac{x-1}{x+1} - 2 \le 0$$

$$\Leftrightarrow \frac{-x-3}{x+1} \le 0$$

$$\Leftrightarrow \frac{x+3}{x+1} \ge 0.$$

For $x \ne -1$, the last inequality is equivalent to

$$\frac{(x+3)(x+1)}{(x+1)^2} \ge 0,$$

and since $(x+1)^2 > 0$, we have

$$(x+3)(x+1) \ge 0, \qquad x \ne -1.$$

A graph (Figure 3.5d) of the equation

$$y = (x+3)(x+1)$$

shows that $y \ge 0$ for $x \ge -1$, and for $x \le -3$. Since $x \ne -1$, the solution set of (ii) is

$$S = \{x : x \le -3\} \cup \{x : x > -1\}.$$

By a procedure precisely identical with the preceding one, the reader may show that the solution set of (i) is

$$\mathfrak{I} = \{x : x \le -1\} \cup \{x : x \ge -\tfrac{1}{3}\}.$$

The solution set of the given inequality is therefore

$$S \cap \mathfrak{I} = \{x : x \le -3\} \cup \{x : x \ge -\tfrac{1}{3}\}.$$

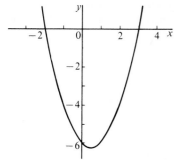

Graph of $\{(x, y): y = x^2 - x - 6\}$

**FIGURE 3.5c**

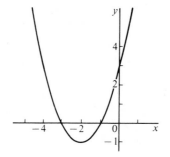

Graph of $\{(x, y): y = x^2 + 4x + 3\}$

**FIGURE 3.5d**

## Exercises 3.5

Determine the solution set for the given inequality in each of Numbers 1 to 22.

1. $\dfrac{1}{3x - 5} > 0$.

2. $\dfrac{4}{2x + 9} < 0$.

3. $6x + 27 < 2x + 9$.
4. $\frac{2}{3}x - 15 > 6 - \frac{1}{2}x$.
5. $3|x - 1| + |x| < 1$.
6. $|x - 1| + |x + 1| < 4$.

7. $x + \dfrac{4}{x} > 4$.

8. $4a + \dfrac{25}{a} > 20$.

9. $x^2 - 2x - 3 > 0$.
10. $x^2 - x - 12 \leq 0$.
11. $2w^2 - 3w - 2 \leq 0$.
12. $2x^2 + 5x + 1 > 0$.

13. $\dfrac{1}{x - 2} < 2$.

14. $\left|\dfrac{1}{x - 2}\right| < 2$.

15. $\dfrac{1}{x + 3} > 1$.

16. $\left|\dfrac{1}{x + 3}\right| > 1$.

17. $x - \dfrac{2}{x} > 1$.

18. $\sqrt{2x + 3} > x$.

19. $\left|\dfrac{x - 2}{x + 3}\right| \geq 2$.

20. $\left|\dfrac{1}{(x + 1)(x - 2)}\right| \leq 1$.

21. $\dfrac{1}{x^2 - 2x + 2} > 4$.

22. $\dfrac{x - 2}{x + 2} < \dfrac{x + 1}{x - 1}$.

23. Express the inequalities $-1 < x < 5$ by a single inequality, making use of absolute values.

24. A person found what he thought to be the solution set of the inequality $x + 1 < 4x + 4$ as follows:
$$x + 1 < 4x + 4 \Rightarrow x + 1 < 4(x + 1)$$
$$\Rightarrow 1 < 4$$
$$\Rightarrow \text{the given inequality is true for all } x \in \mathcal{R}.$$
Criticize his solution.

25. Prove Theorem 3.5a.
26. Prove Theorem 3.5b.

27. A student makes grades of 60, 70, and 80 on three tests. How well must he do on two more tests in order to average 80 or better on all five?
28. The specific gravity $s$ of a body is given by the formula $s = A/(A - W)$, where $A$ is the weight in air and $W$ the weight in water. Show, for bodies with specific gravity greater than 3, that $A > W > \frac{2}{3}A$.
29. For bodies having specific gravities between 1.25 and 1.50, show that $\frac{1}{5}A < W < \frac{1}{3}A$. (See the preceding problem.)
30. If air friction is neglected, the height $h$ (feet) above the ground of an "upper atmosphere" rocket $t$ seconds after lift-off is given approximately by $h = 6800t - 16t^2$. Find the interval of time during which the rocket is above 160,000 feet.
31. A wire 14 inches long is to be bent into a rectangle. What condition must the shorter side satisfy if the diagonal of the rectangle is to be less than 5 inches long?
32. The sum of two unequal numbers is to be 25. What condition must the smaller number satisfy if the sum of the positive square roots of the numbers is to exceed 7?
33. For what set of values of $x$ will $\sqrt{(x + 1)(x - 3)}$ be real?
34. A square 2 inches on a side is cut from each corner of a rectangular piece of tin and the remaining piece is folded up to form an open box. It is required that the box be 4 inches longer than it is wide and that its volume be between 40 and 50 cubic inches. What condition must the width of the box satisfy?
35. A uniform wire coil having an electrical resistance of 10 ohms is to be cut in two and the two pieces are to be connected in parallel. Let the resistance of one of the pieces be $R_1$. What range of values may $R_1$ have if the resistance equivalent to the two coils in parallel is not to exceed 1.6 ohms? *Note*: The resistance $R$ equivalent to two resistances $R_1$ and $R_2$ in parallel is given by
$$1/R = 1/R_1 + 1/R_2.$$

## 3.6 OTHER QUADRATIC POLYNOMIAL EQUATIONS

In Section 3.4, it was stated that the graph of an equation of the form
$$y = ax^2 + bx + c, \qquad a \neq 0,$$
is a parabola, and this curve was discussed there. The axis and the vertex of the parabola can easily be found by completing the square in $x$.

The preceding equation is a special case of a more general type of polynomial equation of the second degree which will be considered in this section.

**Definition 3.6a.** A polynomial expression of the form
$$q(x, y) .=. Ax^2 + Bxy + Cy^2 + Dx + Ey + F,$$
where the coefficients $A$, $B$, $C$, $D$, $E$, $F$ are constants, is called a **quadratic polynomial in two variables.**

Our attention here will be confined to polynomials with real coefficients. The expression
$$5x^2 - 2\sqrt{2}xy + 6y^2 - 1.2x + 15y - \pi$$
is such a polynomial with
$$A = 5, \quad B = -2\sqrt{2}, \quad C = 6, \quad D = -1.2, \quad E = 15, \quad F = -\pi.$$
Certain simple special cases of the general quadratic equation $q(x, y) = 0$, are

of considerable interest in mathematics as well as of great importance in many applications of mathematics. In the particular cases to be considered now, the coefficient $B$ will be zero so that the $xy$ term will be absent from the equation. If, in addition, $A = 0$ or $C = 0$, then the equation is of the form

$$Cy^2 + Dx + Ey + F = 0,$$

or

$$Ax^2 + Dx + Ey + F = 0.$$

If $E \neq 0$ in the second of these equations, then it can be solved for $y$ to obtain the form $y = ax^2 + bx + c$, which describes a parabola. Similarly, if $D \neq 0$ in the first of the equations, it can be solved for $x$ to give the form $x = ay^2 + by + c$. The following definition is thus consistent with the discussion in Section 3.4.

**Definition 3.6b.** The graph of an equation of the form

$$y = ax^2 + bx + c, \qquad a \neq 0,$$

or of the form

$$x = ay^2 + by + c, \qquad a \neq 0,$$

is called a **parabola**.

In the discussion of the parabola in Section 3.4, the roles of $x$ and $y$ may be interchanged in order to determine the salient features of the parabola corresponding to an equation of the form $x = ay^2 + by + c$. Evidently, in this case, the curve will have a horizontal axis rather than a vertical one, but the axis and the vertex can easily be found by completing the square in $y$.

---

*Example 3.6a.* Locate the axis and the vertex of the parabola described by $x = 2y^2 - 4y$, and sketch the curve.

By completing the square in $y$, we may write the equation in the form

$$x + 2 = 2(y^2 - 2y + 1)$$

or

$$x + 2 = 2(y - 1)^2.$$

This shows that the vertex is at the point $(-2, 1)$ and the axis is the line of symmetry $y = 1$. The graph appears in Figure 3.6a.

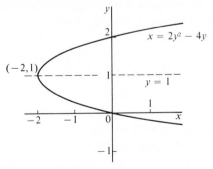

**FIGURE 3.6a**

Some additional special cases of the equation $q(x, y) = 0$ will be considered next. In these cases, $B = D = E = 0$, so that the equation is of the form

$$Ax^2 + Cy^2 + F = 0.$$

If $F = 0$ and $AC > 0$, then this equation has only $(0, 0)$ for a real solution and has a graph consisting only of the origin. If $F = 0$ and $AC < 0$, then the equation may be written as

$$\alpha^2 x^2 - \beta^2 y^2 = 0.$$

It follows that $(\alpha x - \beta y)(\alpha x + \beta y) = 0$ and this equation is satisfied if either $\alpha x - \beta y = 0$ or $\alpha x + \beta y = 0$. The graph of each of these equations is a straight line through the origin, so that the graph of the original equation consists of two intersecting straight lines. As an illustration of these remarks, consider the equation

$$4x^2 - 3y^2 = 0,$$

which may be written

$$(2x - \sqrt{3}y)(2x + \sqrt{3}y) = 0.$$

The graph consists of the two intersecting lines having the respective equations $2x - \sqrt{3}y = 0$ and $2x + \sqrt{3}y = 0$. If $ACF \neq 0$ and $A$, $C$, $F$ are all of the same sign, then the equation has no real solutions at all.

The more interesting graphs occur for $ACF \neq 0$ and $A$, $C$, $F$ not all of the same sign. Under these circumstances, the equation may be written in one of the following three forms, in which the numbers $\alpha$, $\beta$, $\gamma$, are *all positive*:

(i) $\alpha x^2 + \beta y^2 = \gamma$, (ii) $\alpha x^2 - \beta y^2 = \gamma$, (iii) $\alpha y^2 - \beta x^2 = \gamma$.

Since these three equations involve only the squares of $x$ and $y$, their graphs must be symmetric with respect to both axes and the origin.

**Definition 3.6c.** The graph of an equation of the form

$$\alpha x^2 + \beta y^2 = \gamma, \qquad \alpha, \beta, \gamma \text{ all positive},$$

is called an **ellipse**.

Note that if $\alpha = \beta$, the graph will be a circle with an equation of the form $x^2 + y^2 = a^2$, which has already been discussed. The circle is thus regarded as a special form of an ellipse.

---

*Example 3.6b.* Sketch the ellipse given by the equation

$$x^2 + 4y^2 = 16.$$

The intercepts on the axes are easily found by setting $y = 0$ to get $x = \pm 4$, and setting $x = 0$ to get $y = \pm 2$. Additional points can be obtained by solving for $y$ with the result $y = \pm \frac{1}{2}\sqrt{16 - x^2}$. Notice that the domain of the relation defined by this equation is the set $\{x: -4 \leq x \leq 4\}$. The values $x = \pm 2$ each yields $y = \pm \sqrt{3}$, so that four points are found: $(-2, -\sqrt{3})$, $(-2, \sqrt{3})$, $(2, -\sqrt{3})$, and $(2, \sqrt{3})$. Other points can be calculated in a similar fashion. The graph in Figure 3.6b shows the ellipse described by the given equation.

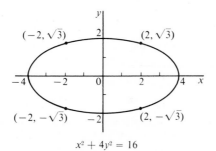

$$x^2 + 4y^2 = 16$$

FIGURE 3.6b

---

**Definition 3.6d.** The graph of an equation of the form

$$\alpha x^2 - \beta y^2 = \gamma \quad \text{or} \quad \alpha y^2 - \beta x^2 = \gamma, \qquad \alpha, \beta, \gamma \text{ all positive,}$$

is called a **hyperbola.**

---

*Example 3.6c.* Sketch the hyperbola given by the equation

$$x^2 - 4y^2 = 16.$$

The solution of this equation for $y$ is $y = \pm\frac{1}{2}\sqrt{x^2 - 16}$, which shows that $y$ is real only if $|x| \geq 4$. Hence, the interval $-4 < x < 4$ is not part of the domain of the relation defined by the given equation. The graph cuts the $x$-axis at $(\pm 4, 0)$, and other points can be found by setting $x$ equal to additional values in the domain. For instance, $x = 5$ (or $-5$) yields $y = \pm 3/2$ so that the four points $(-5, -3/2)$, $(-5, 3/2)$, $(5, -3/2)$, $(5, 3/2)$ are all on the curve (see Figure 3.6c).

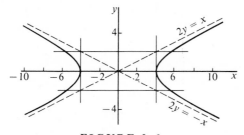

FIGURE 3.6c

There are two straight lines that are closely approached by the hyperbola for points that are distant from the origin. Let us write the equation in the form

$$1 - \frac{4y^2}{x^2} = \frac{16}{x^2}.$$

It is then clear that for very large values of $x$ the term $16/x^2$ is small in comparison with the other two terms. Hence, for such values of $x$, the points that satisfy the equation

$$1 - \frac{4y^2}{x^2} = 0$$

are quite near the points that satisfy the equation of the hyperbola. For $x \neq 0$, the preceding equation describes the same points as the equation

$$x^2 - 4y^2 = 0,$$

which is an equation of the two straight lines

$$x - 2y = 0 \quad \text{and} \quad x + 2y = 0.$$

These two lines are called the **asymptotes** of the hyperbola and are quite helpful in making the sketch (see Figure 3.6c).

---

The asymptotes in the preceding example can be obtained from the equation of the hyperbola by replacing the constant 16 by zero and factoring the result. It can, moreover, be shown that the hyperbola given by either of the equations in Definition 3.6d has as asymptotes the lines obtained by replacing $\gamma$ by zero and factoring the resulting equation. A more thorough discussion of asymptotes will be given in Sections 4.2 and 12.9.

Another special case of the equation $q(x, y) = 0$ that is important in various applications is the equation

$$xy = \gamma.$$

It will be shown later that the graph is again a hyperbola. The asymptotes of the curve are the coordinate axes. The equation $PV = k$, which relates the volume $V$ and the pressure $P$ of a gas according to Boyle's Law, is an important instance of this last type of equation.

## Exercises 3.6

In Numbers 1 to 16, identify and sketch the curves defined by the given equations.

1. $y + 2x^2 = 0$.
2. $x + 4y^2 = 0$.
3. $4x^2 + 4y^2 = 9$.
4. $4x^2 - y^2 = 4$.
5. $4x^2 - 8y^2 = 0$.
6. $y^2 - x^2 - 9 = 0$.
7. $y = 3x^2 - 6x + 5$.
8. $y^2 - 4x + 6y + 9 = 0$.

9. $4y^2 + x - 16y + 19 = 0$.
10. $4x^2 + 9y^2 = 36$.
11. $9x^2 + 4y^2 = 36$.
12. $xy = 5$.
13. $xy + 4 = 0$.
14. $xy = 0$.
15. $y^2 + 2x^2 + 1 = 0$.
16. $4x^2 + 8y^2 = 0$.

17. Find the equation of a circle with center at the origin and passing through the point $(-1, -4)$.
18. Does the condition that the curve pass through the point $(3, 4)$ determine a unique ellipse of the type described in Definition 3.6c? Explain.
19. How many parabolas, with equations of the type given in Definition 3.6b, can be drawn with vertices at $(-1, -4)$ and passing through the origin? Find their equations and sketch them.

20. Find $A$ if the longer axis of the ellipse $Ax^2 + 4y^2 = 9$ is to be 4.
21. Figure 3.6d shows the dimensions of a parabolic arch. What is the height $h$ of the arch at a distance of 3 feet from the axis of symmetry?

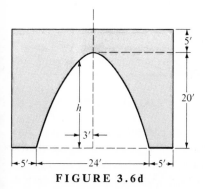

**FIGURE 3.6d**

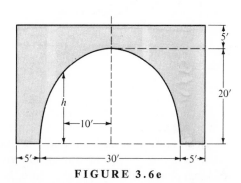

**FIGURE 3.6e**

22. Figure 3.6e shows the dimensions of a semielliptic arch. What is the height $h$ of the arch at a distance of 10 feet from the center?
23. Sketch the line $2y + x = 4$ and the parabola $y^2 = -4x$ on the same set of axes. Do you think the line is tangent to the parabola? Defend your answer.

## 3.7 FAMILIES OF CURVES

In many of the applications of mathematics, it is necessary to work with an equation in which certain coefficients may assume various values corresponding to the physical constants that describe the particular problem. For example, Boyle's Law states that if the temperature of a given mass of an ideal gas is constant, then the product of the pressure $P$ and the volume $V$ of the gas is a constant $k$. This statement may be expressed in mathematical form by the equation

$$PV = k.$$

The coefficient $k$, however, is different for each different temperature. Thus, for each value of $k$, the equation describes the branch of a hyperbola that lies in the first quadrant, since $P$ and $V$ must both be positive. Some of these curves are shown in Figure 3.7a.

As another illustration, consider a physical problem associated with a ball starting from rest and rolling down an inclined plane of length $s_p$. It is known by experiment that the distance $s$ of the ball from its starting point at time $t$ is given quite accurately by the equation

$$s = \tfrac{1}{2}at^2, \qquad 0 \leqq s \leqq s_p,$$

where $a$ is a constant that depends on the force of gravity and the inclination of the plane. To each value of $a$, there corresponds a piece of a parabola, as illustrated in Figure 3.7b.

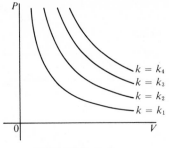

FIGURE 3.7a

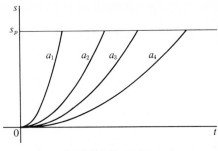

FIGURE 3.7b

The reader should be warned that neither of the preceding figures is a picture of the *physical* phenomenon under consideration. The graphs, being geometric representations of the equations that give a more or less accurate description of some phases of the physical picture, are essentially only mathematical devices for studying the phenomenon.

In the preceding examples, $k$ is a constant for each particular curve, but varies from curve to curve in Figure 3.7a, and a similar statement applies to $a$ in Figure 3.7b. A letter used in this manner is called a **parameter**. [Although this is a slightly different usage of the word parameter from that in Section 3.2, the context will always make clear which usage is intended. Students have suggested (not without reason) the name "variable constant" for the usage of the present section.]

**Definition 3.7a.** An equation in two variables in which there occurs a single parameter is said to represent a **one-parameter family of curves**.

In general, a family of curves is characterized by the fact that all members of the family have some property in common. For example, the family of hyperbolas in Figure 3.7a all have the coordinate axes as asymptotes, and the family of parabolas in Figure 3.7b all have their vertices at the origin, with the $s$-axis as their common axis.

We shall be concerned here with two types of problems: (i) to write an equation for a set of curves with a given geometric property in common; (ii) to find the common property of a family of curves described by a given equation.

*Example 3.7a.* Find the equation of the family of straight lines all passing through the point (2, 3).

In this problem, as in similar ones, we must choose some parameter representing a geometric condition which varies from member to member of the family, but is fixed for any one of the curves. This is relatively easy here since the slope, say $m$, varies from line to line but is fixed for any one line. Thus, if $m$ is the slope of any line in the family, then an equation of the line is

$$y - 3 = m(x - 2) \quad \text{or} \quad y = mx + 3 - 2m.$$

This equation represents all the nonvertical lines through the point (2, 3). See Figure 3.7c.

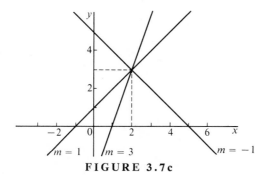

**FIGURE 3.7c**

---

*Note*: In the preceding example, if it is desired to represent all lines without exception through the point (2, 3), then it is preferable to use direction numbers, say $[a, b]$, rather than slope. In this case, the equation is of the form

$$a(y - 3) = b(x - 2) \quad \text{or} \quad bx - ay = 2b - 3a.$$

---

*Example 3.7b.* Find the equation of the family of lines all having slope 2.

In this case, it is convenient to choose as a parameter the $y$-intercept, $b$. Then the slope-intercept form of the equation yields

$$y = 2x + b.$$

(Of course, it is possible to choose some other quantity as a parameter, but the choice of $b$ leads to the simplest form for an equation of the family.)

---

*Example 3.7c.* What common property is possessed by each member of the family of lines described by $kx + py = 0$?

At first sight it appears that there are two parameters in the equation. However, if $k \neq 0$, we may write $x + (p/k)y = 0$, and then consider the ratio $p/k$ as the parameter. It is easy to see that, regardless of the values assigned to $k$ and $p$, the point (0, 0) will lie on the graph of the resulting equation. Hence, the given equation represents a family of lines passing through the origin.

---

If $p \neq 0$, the preceding family can be characterized by the equation $y = mx$, where $m$ is the parameter that represents the slope. In many cases, where it is difficult to recognize the family property, it may be necessary to put the given equation into various equivalent forms, one of which may reveal the desired property.

*Example 3.7d.* Find an equation of the family of parabolas, each of which has its axis parallel to the *x*-axis and passes through the origin and the point (0, 2). See Figure 3.7d.

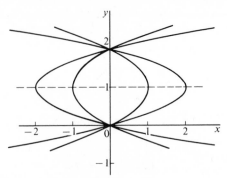

**FIGURE 3.7d**

We know from the discussion in Section 3.6 that the desired equation must be of the form

$$x = ay^2 + by + c.$$

Furthermore, the equation must be satisfied by (0, 0) and by (0, 2). Hence

$$0 = 0 + 0 + c$$

and

$$0 = 4a + 2b + c.$$

Therefore $c = 0$ and $b = -2a$, so that the desired equation is

$$x = ay^2 - 2ay.$$

The reader should check to see that this one-parameter family does satisfy the given conditions.

---

*Example 3.7e.* Describe the one-parameter family of curves represented by the equation

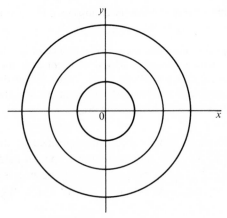

**FIGURE 3.7e**

$$x^2 + y^2 = a^2,$$

where $a$ is the parameter.

For any given value of $a$, the equation represents a circle of radius $a$ having its center at the origin. Hence, the family of curves described by the equation is the family of concentric circles whose centers are at the origin (see Figure 3.7e).

## Exercises 3.7

In Numbers 1 to 5, determine an equation for the family of straight lines satisfying the given condition.

1. The lines all pass through the point $(3, -1)$.
2. The lines are all parallel to the line $3x - y - 6 = 0$.
3. The lines are all perpendicular to the line $-2x + 3y - 6 = 0$.
4. Each line has the same constant, $k$, for the sum of its intercepts.
5. Each line has a slope equal numerically to its $y$-intercept.

In Numbers 6 to 10, determine the property common to all members of the family of lines whose equation is given.

6. $3x - ky = 4$.
7. $mx + 2y = 6$.
8. $2x - y = k$.

9. $mx + (m - 1)y = 6$.
10. $3x + my = m + 4$.

11. Let $L(x, y)$ stand for the linear expression $Ax + By + C$. We shall understand that $L(x_1, y_1)$ means $Ax_1 + By_1 + C$. Accordingly, we see that $(x_1, y_1)$ is a point on the line
$$Ax + By + C = 0 \Leftrightarrow L(x_1, y_1) = 0.$$
Now suppose that
$$L_1(x, y) .=. A_1x + B_1y + C_1$$
and
$$L_2(x, y) .=. A_2x + B_2y + C_2.$$
If the two lines $L_1(x, y) = 0$ and $L_2(x, y) = 0$ intersect in the point $(x_1, y_1)$, then for any real constants $a$ and $b$ (not both zero),
$$aL_1(x, y) + bL_2(x, y) = 0$$
is an equation of a line through $(x_1, y_1)$. Prove this last statement. Note that we may regard the last equation as that of a family of lines all passing through the intersection of the given two lines.
12. Use the idea of Number 11 to find an equation of the line that passes through the intersection of the lines $2x + 3y - 5 = 0$ and $4x - 7y + 11 = 0$, and
    (a) has a slope of 1;
    (b) passes through the point $(1, -1)$;
    (c) has a $y$-intercept of 3.
13. What property is possessed by the family of ellipses $ax^2 + 4y^2 = 4a$, where $a > 0$?
14. (a) Find the equation of the family of parabolas with vertices at $(-2, 3)$ and axes parallel to the $y$-axis.
    (b) Sketch several members of the family in (a).
    (c) Find the member of the family in (a) that passes through the origin.

15. What property is common to each of the following families of parabolas? Sketch several members of each family.

(a) $x^2 = ay$.

(b) $y^2 = ax$.

(c) $(x - a)^2 = 2y$.

(d) $(y + b)^2 + x = 0$.

(e) $y^2 + 2y + ax = 0$.

16. What property is possessed by the family of curves $ax^2 + (1 - a)y^2 = 1$? Identify and sketch members of the family such that

(a) $a > 1$;

(b) $a = 1$;

(c) $0 < a < 1$ (note especially $a = \frac{1}{2}$);

(d) $a = 0$;

(e) $a < 0$.

---

# Summary of Chapter 3

---

The following ideas in this chapter are of fundamental importance to much of the succeeding material:

(1) direction numbers, slope of a line, conditions for two lines to be perpendicular (Section 3.1);

(2) the meaning of the terms "linear equation" and "linear function" (Section 3.2);

(3) parametric equations of a straight line (Section 3.2);

(4) standard forms for the equation of a straight line (Section 3.3);

(5) the use of graphs in determining solution sets of equations and inequalities (Sections 3.4 and 3.5);

(6) characteristic properties of the parabola (Section 3.5);

(7) the characteristic forms for the equations of the parabola, ellipse, hyperbola, and circle (Section 3.6);

(8) families of curves (Section 3.7).

# Chapter 4    Limits and Continuity

The ideas and concepts which are introduced in this chapter are the basic notions necessary for any genuine understanding of the calculus, which we shall begin in Chapter 5. The reader is urged to devote the greatest effort to make certain that he attains as full a comprehension of these ideas as possible. Without this comprehension it is impossible to understand exactly the technical meaning of such things as velocity, acceleration, area enclosed by a curved line, the work done by the exploding gasoline-air mixture in an automobile motor, and many other everyday notions in the highly technological civilization of the present and of the foreseeable future.

## 4.1 CLUSTER POINTS

In Section 2.1, a neighborhood of a point $a$ was defined to be the set $\{x: a - h < x < a + h\}$. Recall that this set is an open interval of length $2h$ with the point $a$ as its midpoint. We shall denote such an interval by $\mathfrak{N}(a, h)$, or simply by $\mathfrak{N}(a)$ if we wish to speak of a neighborhood in general without specifying its radius. Since the neighborhood concept is frequently used to advantage in discussing some of the properties of functions and their graphs, we need to examine the consequences of the definition in some detail.

It is sometimes necessary to consider intervals for which a given point $a$ is one of the end points. That is, the interval may extend only to the right or only to the left of the given point. The neighborhood concept is specialized to handle these situations by the following definitions.

**Definition 4.1a.** A **right neighborhood** of a point $a$ is the set

$$\mathfrak{N}(a^+, h) .=. \{x: a \leq x < a + h\},$$

and a **left neighborhood** of $a$ is the set

$$\mathfrak{N}(a^-, h) .=. \{x: a - h < x \leq a\}.$$

We may denote a general right or left neighborhood by $\mathfrak{N}(a^+)$ or $\mathfrak{N}(a^-)$, respectively, if the specific size of the neighborhood is not important for the discussion.

---

*Example 4.1a.* If $\mathcal{S} .=. \{x: x = 0 \text{ or } 1 \leq x < 2\}$, what points of $\mathcal{S}$ have at least one neighborhood contained entirely within $\mathcal{S}$?

We see that any point *a*, where $1 < a < 2$, has a neighborhood that is contained entirely in S (see Figure 4.1a). Thus if $a = 1.99$, then a neighborhood of *a* that is contained entirely in S is the set $\mathfrak{N}(1.99, 0.005) = \{x: 1.985 < x < 1.995\}$. Of course there are many other possible neighborhoods, since we may choose for *h* any value such that $0 < h < 0.01$. The reader should describe for himself neighborhoods of 1.9999 and 1.0005 that are contained in S. As Figure 4.1a illustrates, the point 0 has

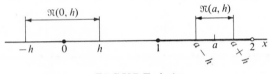

**FIGURE 4.1a**

no neighborhood *contained entirely in* S, even though 0 does have neighborhoods. Furthermore, the points 1 and 2 do not have neighborhoods contained entirely in S, although 1 does have right neighborhoods and 2 has left neighborhoods that are subsets of S.

---

Another useful concept is that of the **deleted neighborhood** of a point—that is, a neighborhood with the point itself excluded from the set. For such a set, we shall use the notation $\mathfrak{N}^*(a)$ given by the following definition.

**Definition 4.1b.** $\qquad\qquad \mathfrak{N}^*(a) .=. \mathfrak{N}(a) - \{a\}$.

Note that $\mathfrak{N}^*(a) = \mathfrak{N}^*(a^+) \cup \mathfrak{N}^*(a^-)$. (It is usually desirable to read the symbol $\mathfrak{N}(a)$ as "neighborhood"; for example, read the symbol $\mathfrak{N}(a, h)$ as "neighborhood of *a* of radius *h*." Similarly, the symbol $\mathfrak{N}^*(a, h)$ is to be read "deleted neighborhood of *a* of radius *h*." We shall write "a $\mathfrak{N}(a, h)$" with the expectation that it will be read "a neighborhood.")

In Example 4.1a, every $\mathfrak{N}(0, h)$, where $0 < h < 1$, contains only one point of S, namely 0, and no $\mathfrak{N}^*(0, h)$, where $0 < h < 1$, contains any points of S. Also, the point 1 has a deleted right neighborhood contained entirely in S, and the point 2 has a deleted left neighborhood contained entirely in S, even though 2 does not belong to S.

Consider next the set $\mathfrak{I} .=. \{x: x = 1/10^n, n \in \mathfrak{N}\}$. This set consists of the numbers with decimal representations 0.1, 0.01, 0.001, and so on. None of the points of this set has a deleted neighborhood contained entirely in the set. For instance, for $h \leq 0.0009$, the $\mathfrak{N}^*(0.001, h)$ contains no points of $\mathfrak{I}$. On the other hand, if $h > 0.0009$, then the $\mathfrak{N}^*(0.001, h)$ contains both points that do and points that do not belong to $\mathfrak{I}$. There is one point of particular interest relative to the set $\mathfrak{I}$. This is the point 0, which has the property that every $\mathfrak{N}^*(0)$ contains points that are in $\mathfrak{I}$. In this respect, the point 0 relative to the set $\mathfrak{I}$ is like every point in the closed interval $\{x: 1 \leq x \leq 2\}$ relative to the set S of Example 4.1a. That is, every $\mathfrak{N}^*(a)$, where $1 \leq a \leq 2$, contains points that are in S. Points with this property relative to the domain of a given function are important in describing the behavior of the function, as we shall soon see. This is the reason for making the next definition.

**Definition 4.1c.** A point $a$ is called a **cluster point** of a set $S$ if *every* $\mathfrak{N}^*(a, h)$ contains at least one point of $S$.

Thus, it follows from the preceding discussion that for the set $S$ in Example 4.1a, every point $x$ where $1 \leq x \leq 2$ is a cluster point of $S$. However, 0 is not a cluster point of $S$ since not every deleted neighborhood of 0 contains points of $S$. For instance, the $\mathfrak{N}^*(0, \frac{1}{2})$ contains no points of $S$. Notice that 2 is a cluster point of $S$ even though $2 \notin S$. Furthermore, for the set $\mathfrak{J} .=. \{x: x = 1/10^n, n \in \mathfrak{N}\}$, 0 is a cluster point although $0 \notin \mathfrak{J}$. Does $\mathfrak{J}$ have any other cluster points?

---

*Example 4.1b.* Determine the cluster points of $S$ if

$$S .=. \{x: x = 1/n, n \in \mathfrak{N}\}.$$

The only possible cluster point is 0, since for $x = 1/n$ we need only take a $\mathfrak{N}^*(1/n, h)$, where $h < 1/n - 1/(n + 1)$, to have a deleted neighborhood containing no points of $S$. That 0 is a cluster point follows from the fact that for every value of $h$ there will always be a value of $n$ large enough so that $1/n < h$ and therefore $1/n \in \mathfrak{N}^*(0, h)$.

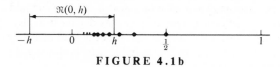

**FIGURE 4.1b**

Thus, if $h = 1/10^6$, then the point $1/(10^6 + 1)$ is in the $\mathfrak{N}^*(0, 1/10^6)$ (see Figure 4.1b).

---

*Example 4.1c.* Determine the cluster points, if there are any, of the set

$$S .=. \{(x): x = n, n \in \mathfrak{N}\}.$$

There are no cluster points for $S$ because, for any $n$, a $\mathfrak{N}^*(n, \frac{1}{2})$ contains no points of $S$.

---

The following example illustrates how the concept of cluster point is of value to us in describing the behavior of functions in the neighborhood of certain special points.

---

*Example 4.1d.* Discuss the behavior of the function

$$f .=. \left\{(x, y): y = \frac{x^3 - 1}{x - 1}\right\}$$

in the neighborhood of the point 1.

Although $f$ is not defined at $x = 1$, it is defined in every $\mathfrak{N}^*(1, h)$, so that 1 is a cluster point of the domain $S$ of $f$. For values of $x \in \mathfrak{N}^*(1, h)$, the function may be described by

$$y = \frac{(x - 1)(x^2 + x + 1)}{(x - 1)} = x^2 + x + 1.$$

From this equation, it is apparent that for values of $x$ very near to 1, the values of $y$ are very near to 3, as the following table of values illustrates:

| $x$ | 0.9 | 1.1 | 0.99 | 1.01 | 0.999 | 1.001 |
|---|---|---|---|---|---|---|
| $y$ | 2.71 | 3.31 | 2.9701 | 3.0301 | 2.997001 | 3.003001 |

Hence, it appears intuitively that the point 3 is a cluster point of the range of $f$ corresponding to the cluster point 1 of the domain of $f$. This situation is described by saying that "as $x$ approaches 1, $y$ approaches 3."

This idea is illustrated again in the next example.

*Example 4.1e.* If $f .=. \{(x, y): y = x^3, x \in \mathfrak{R}\}$, what cluster point of the range of $f$ corresponds to the cluster point 2 of the domain?

On an intuitive basis it seems clear that as $x$ approaches 2, $y$ approaches 8. That is, if we choose any value of $x$ very near 2, the corresponding value of $y$ is very near 8. For example, if

$$x = 2.001, \quad y = 8.012006001.$$

Conversely, if we choose any value of $y$ very near 8, then we can find a corresponding value of $x$ very near 2. Of course, although we may demonstrate that these statements are true in particular cases, it is desirable that we be able to make a general statement that will hold for *all* values of $x$ or $y$ in suitable neighborhoods. It is for this reason that the neighborhood concept becomes important.

We may convert the statement "as $x$ approaches 2, $y$ approaches 8" into a more precise mathematical statement by saying that for any $\mathfrak{R}(8, k)$ in the range of $f$, a corresponding $\mathfrak{R}^*(2, h)$ can be found in the domain of $f$ such that

$$x \in \mathfrak{R}^*(2, h) \Rightarrow y \in \mathfrak{R}(8, k).$$

The details of actually finding the $\mathfrak{R}^*(2, h)$ for a given $\mathfrak{R}(8, k)$ are somewhat involved and will be postponed until Section 4.4. For the present, we shall rely entirely on the intuitive point of view that is suggested by the results of direct calculation, as in Examples 4.1d and 4.1e.

The terminology introduced in the preceding discussion is so useful that it is convenient to have a symbolic way of writing it.

**Definition 4.1d.** If $a$ is a cluster point of the domain of a function $f .=. \{(x, y)\}$ and if,

(i) $b$ is a cluster point of the range such that for each prescribed $\mathfrak{R}(b, k)$, there is a $\mathfrak{R}^*(a, h)$ for which

$$x \in \mathfrak{R}^*(a, h) \Rightarrow y \in \mathfrak{R}(b, k),$$

or if

(ii) $y$ has a constant value $b$ for all values of $x$ in some $\mathfrak{R}^*(a)$, then we write

$$\text{as } x \to a, \quad y \to b.$$

which is read "as $x$ approaches $a$, $y$ approaches $b$."

It is sometimes necessary to consider the behavior of a function on a one-sided neighborhood of a cluster point of its domain. In that case, a modification of the notation in Definition 4.1d may be used. For instance,

$$\text{as } x \to 2^-, \quad y \to 8^-$$

means that 2 and 8 are *corresponding* cluster points of the domain and range, respectively, of a function $f$ such that whenever $x \in \mathfrak{N}^*(2^-, h)$, then $y \in \mathfrak{N}(8^-, k)$, where $\mathfrak{N}^*(2^-, h)$ is a one-sided neighborhood in the domain of $f$ that is determined by the corresponding one-sided neighborhood $\mathfrak{N}(8^-, k)$ in the range of $f$. The notation

$$\text{as } x \to 2^-, \quad y \to 8^-$$

may be read "as $x$ approaches 2 from below (or from the left), $y$ approaches 8 from below." Similarly,

$$\text{as } x \to 2^+, \quad y \to 8^-$$

is read "as $x$ approaches 2 from above, $y$ approaches 8 from below." (How would the notation "as $x \to 2^+$, $y \to 2^+$" be read?)

In any case, the statement that $x \to a^+$ means that the values of the independent variable $x$ are restricted to a deleted right neighborhood of $a$, and $x \to a^-$ means that the values of $x$ are restricted to a deleted left neighborhood of $a$. For example, if $y = -\sqrt{x - 1}$, then

$$\text{as } x \to 1^+, \quad y \to 0^-.$$

This statement means that 0 is the cluster point of the range corresponding to the cluster point 1 of the domain. In this case, $y$ is real only if $x \geq 1$, and for such values of $x$, $y \leq 0$.

**Definition 4.1e.** The domain $\mathcal{S}$ of a function is said to be **unbounded above** if there exists no number $M_1$ such that for all $x \in \mathcal{S}$, $x < M_1$. The domain is said to be **unbounded below** if there exists no number $M_2$ such that for all $x \in \mathcal{S}$, $x > M_2$.

If the domain $\mathcal{S}$ of a function $f .=. \{(x, y)\}$ is unbounded above, then it is frequently desirable to know the behavior of $y$ for "all very large values of $x \in \mathcal{S}$," that is, for all values of $x > M$, where $M$ is any given positive number no matter how large. In this connection, the following notation, to be read "$x$ increases without bound," is used:

$$x \to \infty.$$

For instance, a correct statement using this notation is

$$\text{as } x \to \infty, \quad 1/x \to 0^+.$$

This may be read "as $x$ increases without bound, $1/x$ approaches zero through positive values."

In a similar fashion, the notation

$$x \to -\infty,$$

to be read "$x$ decreases without bound," is employed if the domain is unbounded below. Thus, it is correct to write

$$\text{as } x \to -\infty, \quad 1 - \frac{1}{x} \to 1^+,$$

or

$$\text{as } x \to -\infty, \quad x^2 \to \infty.$$

The reader should translate these statements into meaningful English for himself.

## Exercises 4.1

1. Determine which points of each of the following sets have neighborhoods contained entirely within the set.
   (a) $\mathcal{S} .=. \{x: x = 1/n, n \in \mathfrak{N}\}$.
   (b) $\mathcal{S} .=. \{x: 0 \leq x \leq 1\}$.
   (c) $\mathcal{S} .=. \{x: 0 < x < 1\} \cup \{x: 1 < x < 2\}$.
   (d) $\mathcal{S} .=. \{x: 0 \leq x \leq 1 \text{ and } x \in \mathfrak{F}\}$.

2. What is the set of cluster points for each of the following sets?
   (a) $\{x: x = 1 - (1/n), n \in \mathfrak{N}\}$.
   (b) $\{x: 0 < x < 1\}$.
   (c) $\{t: t = (1/n) + (-1)^n, n \in \mathfrak{N}\}$.
   (d) $\{x: 0 < x < 1\} \cup \{x: 1 < x < 2\}$.
   (e) $\{x: 0 < x < 1 \text{ and } x \in \mathfrak{F}\}$.
   (f) $\{x: 0 < x < 1 \text{ and } x \in \mathfrak{R} - \mathfrak{F}\}$.

3. Use the neighborhood concept or the discussion that follows Definition 4.1e to explain what is meant by each of the following statements.
   (a) If $y = x^2 + 2x$, then as $x \to 1$, $y \to 3$.

   (b) If $y = \dfrac{x^2 - 4}{x - 2}$, then as $x \to 2$, $y \to 4$.

   (c) If $y = [\![x]\!]$, then as $x \to 2^-$, $y \to 1$,
   and as $x \to 2^+$, $y \to 2$.

   (d) If $y = \dfrac{1}{x}$, then as $x \to \infty$, $y \to 0^+$,

   and as $x \to -\infty$, $y \to 0^-$.

   (e) If $y = \dfrac{x^2}{x^2 - 1}$, then as $x \to 1^-$, $y \to -\infty$,

   and as $x \to 1^+$, $y \to \infty$.

(f) If $y = x - [\![x]\!]$, then as $x \to 2^-$, $y \to 1^-$,
and as $x \to 2^+$, $y \to 0^+$.

4. Discuss the behavior of $y$

(a) as $x \to 0$ if $y = |x|$;
(b) as $x \to 1$ if $y = x^2 - x + 1$;
(c) as $x \to 0$ if $y = 1/|x|$;

(d) as $x \to 0^+$ if $y = \dfrac{1}{x + |x|}$;

(e) as $x \to \infty$ if $y = 1/|x|$;

(f) as $x \to 0^+$ if $y = \dfrac{x}{x + |x|}$;

(g) as $x \to \infty$ if $y = \dfrac{x}{x + |x|}$.

In many problems in applied mathematics, part of the solution consists of finding the values of arbitrary constants so that a function will satisfy certain conditions called boundary conditions (such as one end of a rod being held at constant temperature, or the ends of a vibrating string held stationary). In Numbers 5 to 9, find those values of the constants $A$ and $B$ for which the given function satisfies the stated conditions.

5. $x(t, = t^2 + 2Bt + 4A$; as $t \to 0$, $x(t) \to 5$, and as $t \to 3$, $x(t) \to 2$.

6. $u(x) = \dfrac{Ax}{B + |x|}$; as $x \to -1$, $u(x) \to \dfrac{1}{3}$, and as $x \to \infty$, $u(x) \to -1$.

7. $s(x) = \dfrac{Ax}{Bx + |x|}$; as $x \to 1$, $s(x) \to 2$, and as $x \to -\infty$, $s(x) \to 3$.

8. $u(x) = \dfrac{Ax^2}{1 - Bx^2}$; as $x \to \infty$, $u(x) \to -\dfrac{4}{3}$, and as $x \to -2$, $u(x) \to -\dfrac{32}{23}$.

9. $u(t) = -2t + \sqrt{At - Bt^2}$; as $t \to 1$, $u(t) \to 0$, and as $t \to -1$, $u(t) \to 2$.

## 4.2 SIMPLE ALGEBRAIC FUNCTIONS

It is frequently advantageous to be able to visualize the graph of a function from the properties of the function. Certain of such properties—the domain and range of the function, symmetry, and periodicity—have already been discussed. With the aid of these and additional properties to be discussed in this section, the student should be able to sketch the graphs of many functions with a minimum of point plotting.

In many of the examples that we have previously considered, we were concerned with simple expressions, called algebraic expressions, that did not involve fractional forms. (In general, an expression formed by using the operations of addition, subtraction, multiplication, division, and the extraction of roots collectively a finite number of times to combine a finite number of letters, representing elements of a number system, is called an algebraic expression.) In this section we shall concentrate on expressions involving fractions.

*Example 4.2a.* Graph the function

$$\left\{(x, y): y = \frac{1}{x}\right\}.$$

The domain of this function is the set of all real numbers with the exception of zero; the range is the same set of numbers. It should be clear that zero is not a permissible value for $x$ because of the prohibition on division by zero.

Since the equation $y = 1/x$ or $xy = 1$ is unchanged when $x$ and $y$ are simultaneously replaced by $-x$ and $-y$, respectively, its graph must be symmetric with respect to the origin. Furthermore, the product $xy$ is to be positive, so that $x$ and $y$ must have the same sign. Consequently, the graph appears in the first and third quadrants only.

It is to be particularly noticed that this graph does not intersect either axis. However, as smaller and smaller positive values are chosen for $x$, the corresponding values of $y$ are larger and larger. In fact, by taking $x$ sufficiently small, we may force the $y$ values to be arbitrarily large—the smaller the $x$ value, the larger the $y$. This is an appropriate place to employ the notation of the preceding section, since the sense of the last two sentences is given precisely by the statement

$$\text{as } x \to 0^+, \text{ then } y \to \infty.$$

Also, the graph becomes straighter and more nearly vertical and gets closer and closer to the positive $y$-axis as $x \to 0^+$. This kind of geometric behavior is described by saying that the $y$-axis is an **asymptote** to the curve, or that the graph approaches the $y$-axis asymptotically.

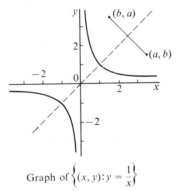

Graph of $\left\{(x, y): y = \dfrac{1}{x}\right\}$

**FIGURE 4.2a**

In a similar fashion, $y \to -\infty$ as $x \to 0^-$, and the graph approaches the negative $y$-axis. Furthermore, as $x \to \infty$, $y \to 0^+$, and as $x \to -\infty$, $y \to 0^-$, so that we may also say that the $x$-axis is an asymptote to the curve, or that the graph approaches the $x$-axis asymptotically. The curve is shown in Figure 4.2a.

The concepts of asymptote introduced in the preceding example are summarized in the next definition.

**Definition 4.2a.** If $y = f(x)$, where $f(x)$ is an algebraic expression, and if $a$ is a cluster point of the domain of $f$ such that $|y| \to \infty$ as $x \to a^+$ or $x \to a^-$, then the line $x = a$ is called a **vertical asymptote** to the curve. If $b$ is a cluster point of the range of $f$ such that $y \to b^+$ or $y \to b^-$ as $|x| \to \infty$, then the line $y = b$ is called a **horizontal asymptote** to the curve.

As Figure 4.2a shows, the graph of $y = 1/x$ is symmetric to the line $y = x$. In general, as the reader may easily verify, the point $(b, a)$ is symmetric to the point $(a, b)$ with respect to the line $y = x$. Consequently, a test for such symmetry in the graph of an equation is as follows. In the given equation, interchange the two variables. If the equation is unchanged, then its graph is symmetric with respect to the line $y = x$. For example, $x^2 + y^2 - 3xy = 0$ and $y^2 + x^2 - 3yx = 0$ express the same relationship between $x$ and $y$. Hence the graph of this equation is symmetric with respect to the line $y = x$.

---

*Example 4.2b.* Graph the equation

$$y = \frac{4}{x^2 + 4}.$$

The domain for this equation is $\mathfrak{R}$. From the form of the fraction, it follows that as $x \to 0$, $y \to 1^-$ and that $y = 1$ is the largest possible value for $y$. Furthermore, $y$ cannot be zero or negative for any value of $x \in \mathfrak{R}$, so that the range of $y$ is $0 < y \leq 1$. Also, as $x \to \infty$, $y \to 0^+$ and as $x \to -\infty$, $y \to 0^+$. Thus the $x$-axis is an asymptote to the curve.

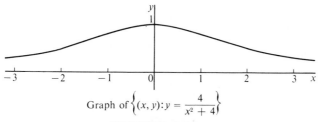

Graph of $\left\{ (x, y) : y = \dfrac{4}{x^2 + 4} \right\}$

**FIGURE 4.2b**

If $f(x) \doteq 4/(x^2 + 4)$, then $f(-x) = f(x)$ so that the curve must be symmetric with respect to the $y$-axis. The graph is shown in Figure 4.2b.

---

*Example 4.2c.* Graph the function $\{(x, y)\}$ described by

$$y = \frac{x^2}{x^2 - 1}.$$

The domain of the function consists of all real numbers except 1 and $-1$. Solving for $x^2$, we get $x^2 = y/(y - 1)$, from which it follows that the range is $\{y : y \leq 0$ or $y > 1\}$. (For any value of $y$ in the interval $0 < y < 1$, $x^2$ is negative, and for $y = 1$, $x^2$ is undefined.)

The curve passes through the origin but intersects the axes at no other point. Since $x$ may be replaced by $-x$ without changing the equation, the curve is symmetric to the $y$-axis.

As $x \to 1^-$, $y \to -\infty$. For example, $x = 0.9 \Rightarrow y = -4.26$, $x = 0.99 \Rightarrow y = -49.8$, and so on. Thus the curve is asymptotic on the left to the lower portion of the line $x = 1$. Similarly, as $x \to 1^+$, $y \to \infty$, so that the curve is asymptotic on the right to the upper portion of the line $x = 1$ (see Figure 4.2c). It follows by the symmetry previously noted that the line $x = -1$ is also an asymptote to the curve.

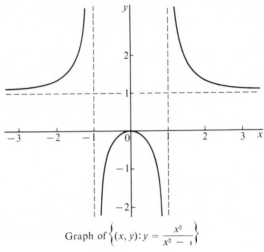

Graph of $\left\{ (x, y) : y = \dfrac{x^2}{x^2 - 1} \right\}$

**FIGURE 4.2c**

Moreover, as $x \to \infty$ or as $x \to -\infty$, $y \to 1^+$, since for $x$ large in absolute value, the corresponding value of $y$ is close to 1 but a little greater than 1. This conclusion follows from the fact that $x^2/(x^2 - 1) = 1 + 1/(x^2 - 1)$. Hence, $y = 1$ is a horizontal asymptote to the curve.

---

The work on asymptotes which has been presented in connection with the preceding examples will now be summarized in order to help clarify the concept. This discussion is restricted to equations of the form $y = f(x)$, where $f(x)$ is a **rational fraction**—that is, a fraction whose numerator and denominator are each polynomials in $x$. This means that

$$f(x) = \frac{a_0 x^m + a_1 x^{m-1} + \cdots + a_m}{b_0 x^n + b_1 x^{n-1} + \cdots + b_n}.$$

It is assumed that numerator and denominator have no common factors.

Upon setting the denominator equal to zero and solving the resulting equation for $x$, we obtain the real values of $x$ (if any) that describe the *vertical asymptotes*. This follows from the fact that in a sufficiently small deleted neighborhood of such a value of $x$, the fraction becomes arbitrarily large in absolute value.

There are three separate cases to discuss in connection with *horizontal asymptotes*.

(a) If the degree of the numerator is less than the degree of the denominator, then, as in Example 4.2a and Example 4.2b, $y \to 0$ as $x \to \infty$ or as $x \to -\infty$, and the $x$-axis is a horizontal asymptote.

(b) If the degree of the numerator is equal to the degree of the denominator, then, as in Example 4.2c, $y \to a_0/b_0$ as $x \to \pm\infty$, and the line $y = a_0/b_0$ is a horizontal asymptote.

(c) If the degree of the numerator is greater than the degree of the denominator, then $|y| \to \infty$ as $|x| \to \infty$, and there is no horizontal asymptote.

To illustrate Case (b), let $y = (2x^2 + 3x + 4)/(3x^2 + 7x + 8)$. Then, as $x \to \pm\infty$, $y \to \frac{2}{3}$. This is apparent if the numerator and denominator are divided by $x^2$, so that, for $x \neq 0$,

$$\frac{2x^2 + 3x + 4}{3x^2 + 7x + 8} = \frac{2 + \dfrac{3}{x} + \dfrac{4}{x^2}}{3 + \dfrac{7}{x} + \dfrac{8}{x^2}}.$$

As $x$ increases, all the terms of both numerator and denominator, except the coefficients of $x^2$ in the original fraction, approach zero.

Notice that a curve may intersect an asymptote at one or more points (see Exercises 4.2, Number 5, for example).

## Exercises 4.2

In Numbers 1 to 24, discuss and sketch the graph of the given equation.

1. $xy = -1.$

2. $x^2y = -1.$

3. $y = \dfrac{3}{x - 1}.$

4. $y = \dfrac{4}{x^2 + 1}.$

5. $y = \dfrac{x}{x^2 + 1}.$

6. $y = \dfrac{x^2}{(x - 1)(x - 4)}.$

7. $y = \dfrac{-x^2}{x^2 - 4x + 3}.$

8. $y = \dfrac{x^2}{1 - x^2}.$

9. $y = \dfrac{2}{4 - x^2}.$

10. $y = \dfrac{x + 4}{x - 4}.$

11. $y = \dfrac{x}{x^2 - 1}.$

12. $y = \dfrac{x}{x - 4}.$

13. $y = \dfrac{x}{(x - 3)^2}.$

14. $y = \dfrac{2x}{(x + 4)^2}.$

15. $y = \dfrac{x^2 - 9}{x^2 + 9}.$

16. $y = \dfrac{4x^2}{x^2 - 9}.$

17. $y = \dfrac{4 - x^2}{x^2 - 9}.$

18. $y = \dfrac{1}{\sqrt{x^2 - 1}}.$

19. $y = \dfrac{x - 2}{x^2 - 4}.$

20. $y^2 = \dfrac{x}{x+1}.$

23. $y^2 = \dfrac{4}{9+x^2}.$

21. $y = \sqrt{\dfrac{x}{x+1}}.$

24. $y^2 = \dfrac{x^2}{x^2-1}.$

22. $y^2 = \dfrac{x^2-4x}{x-2}.$

25. Since

$$\frac{2x^2+3}{6x} = \frac{x}{3} + \frac{1}{2x},$$

sketch the graph of

$$y = \frac{2x^2+3}{6x}$$

by sketching the graphs of $y = x/3$ and $y = 1/(2x)$ and adding the ordinates. Does this curve have an oblique asymptote?

26. Since

$$\frac{x^2-8}{x-3} = x + 3 + \frac{1}{x-3},$$

sketch the graph of

$$y = \frac{x^2-8}{x-3}$$

by sketching the graphs of $y = x + 3$ and $y = 1/(x-3)$ and adding the ordinates. Does this curve have an oblique asymptote?

27. The lateral area of a right circular cone is equal to one-half the perimeter of the base times the slant height, and the total surface area is the lateral area plus the area of the base. If the total surface area of a right circular cone is $4\pi$ square units, find its altitude as a function of the radius and sketch the graph of this function.

28. A right circular cone of height $h$ is circumscribed about a sphere of radius 4 inches. Express the volume of the cone as a function of its height and sketch the graph of this function.

## 4.3 THE INTUITIVE NOTION OF LIMIT

The definition of function as given in Chapter 2 is quite broad and includes many relations that are too general to be of use in most applications of mathematics to physical problems. For example, we are often interested in functions whose graphs exhibit certain properties of "connectedness" and "smoothness." In fact, in the graphing of functions, we have often assumed a great deal concerning the behavior of the function.

*Example 4.3a.* Graph the function $f$ described by

$$y = (x-1)(2-x).$$

First, the points $(1, 0)$, $(2, 0)$, $(3/2, 1/4)$, $(3, -2)$, $(0, -2)$ are plotted, as in Figure 4.3a. These points are then connected by a curve as shown in the figure. But what right do we have to assume that the plotted points should be connected in this manner?

The procedure seems intuitively sound; we have simply assumed that if we choose a particular point, say 2, then as $x \to 2$, $y \to 0$, as discussed in Section 4.1. That is, we have assumed that for values of $x$ in a small neighborhood of 2, $\mathfrak{N}(2, h)$, the cor-

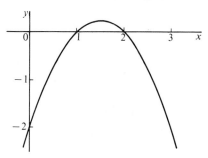

**FIGURE 4.3a**

responding values of $y$ are in a small neighborhood of 0, $\mathfrak{N}(0, \epsilon)$. However, we have not actually proved this to be the case.

Our intuitive feeling about the matter can be strengthened by numerical calculations such as those given in the following table:

| $x$ | $y$ |
|---|---|
| 2.4 | $-0.56$ |
| 2.2 | $-0.24$ |
| 2.1 | $-0.11$ |
| 2.01 | $-0.0101$ |
| 2.001 | $-0.001001$ |
| 2.0001 | $-0.00010001$ |

The table seems to show that the nearer $x$ is to 2, the nearer $y$ is to 0. But this process of numerical verification is tedious and not very practical since it doesn't really prove anything. Therefore, it is desirable to find a reasonably simple and general way of showing precisely what seems to be suggested intuitively.

Rather than making calculations for different values of $x$ near 2, such as 2.01, 2.001, and so on, let us simply investigate what happens to $y$ when $x$ is in a general neighborhood of 2, say $\mathfrak{N}(2, h)$. In this way we may be able to determine the behavior of the function for *all* values of $x$ in $\mathfrak{N}(2, h)$ rather than for just particular values of $x$. Consequently, in order to insure that only values of $x$ near 2 will be considered, we shall require that $h < 1$ for any neighborhood $\mathfrak{N}(2, h)$ under consideration.

Since it appears that $y \to 0$ as $x \to 2$, let us consider the difference between the apparent value approached by $y$ and other values of $y$ corresponding to values of $x$ in $\mathfrak{N}(2, h)$. That is, we shall consider

$$|y - 0|,$$

which is

$$|y| = |x - 1||x - 2|$$

when $y$ is written in terms of $x$. From the fact that $x \in \mathfrak{N}(2, h)$, it follows that

$$2 - h < x < 2 + h.$$

Hence

$$-h < x - 2 < h,$$

which is equivalent to

$$|x - 2| < h.$$

Also, since $h < 1$, the first inequality implies that

$$1 < x < 3$$

or

$$0 < x - 1 < 2,$$

so that surely

$$|x - 1| < 2.$$

Thus, by the use of this inequality and the fact that $|x - 2| < h$, we get

$$|y| = |x - 1||x - 2| < 2h,$$

or

$$-2h < y < 2h,$$

which is equivalent to the statement that $y \in \mathfrak{N}(0, 2h)$.

It has therefore been established that as long as $h < 1$,

$$x \in \mathfrak{N}(2, h) \Rightarrow y \in \mathfrak{N}(0, 2h).$$

In other words, for any small neighborhood of 0 in the range of the function, there is a corresponding neighborhood of 2 in the domain such that if $x$ is in this neighborhood

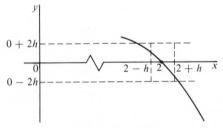

**FIGURE 4.3b**

of 2, then $y$ is in the specified small neighborhood of 0. See Figure 4.3b. Accordingly, we may write

$$\text{as } x \to 2, \quad y \to 0.$$

Another example will help to illustrate the idea further.

*Example 4.3b.* Show that if $y = x^2 - 3$, then as $x \to 2$, $y \to 1$.

Since we are interested in values of $y$ near 1, it is natural to consider the difference between 1 and values of $y$ corresponding to values of $x$ near 2. Thus,

$$|y - 1| = |x^2 - 4| = |x - 2||x + 2|.$$

For values of $x \in \mathfrak{N}(2, h)$, we have

$$2 - h < x < 2 + h$$

or
$$|x - 2| < h.$$
Again, we may restrict $x$ to be near 2 by requiring $h < 1$ so that
$$1 < x < 3.$$
By adding 2 to each member of this inequality, we get
$$3 < x + 2 < 5,$$
so that surely
$$|x + 2| < 5.$$
The last result and the inequality $|x - 2| < h$ together imply that
$$|y - 1| = |x - 2||x + 2| < 5h,$$

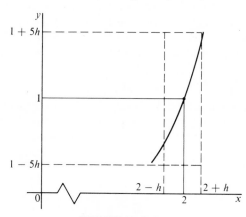

**FIGURE 4.3c**

which means that $y \in \mathfrak{N}(1, 5h)$. That is, $x \in \mathfrak{N}(2, h) \Rightarrow y \in \mathfrak{N}(1, 5h)$ (see Figure 4.3c), no matter how small $h$ may be, and we may write
$$\text{as } x \to 2, \quad y \to 1.$$

In each of the two preceding examples, the radius of the neighborhood in the range of the function was found to be related to the radius of the neighborhood in the domain. In fact, the smaller the first neighborhood, the smaller must be the second, so that the two neighborhoods may be thought of as shrinking to a point together as $h \to 0$. The relationship between the radii of the two neighborhoods is the essentially important result obtained in the preceding examples.

The result illustrated in the last example may be stated in another way. If $\mathfrak{N}(1, \epsilon)$ is a given arbitrarily small neighborhood of 1 in the range of $f$, and if there is a corresponding neighborhood $\mathfrak{N}(2, \delta)$ in the domain such that
$$x \in \mathfrak{N}(2, \delta) \Rightarrow y \in \mathfrak{N}(1, \epsilon),$$
then we say that as $x \to 2$, $y \to 1$. In this form, for a given $\mathfrak{N}(1, \epsilon)$, the existence

of $\mathfrak{N}(2, \delta)$ must be demonstrated by finding an appropriate $\delta$. This can be done in the preceding example by letting $5h = \epsilon$, from which it follows that the required $\delta = h = \epsilon/5$.

The next example illustrates a somewhat different case, in which we consider the behavior of a function in a neighborhood of a point at which the function is undefined.

---

*Example 4.3c.* Discuss the behavior as $x \to \frac{1}{2}$ of the function described by

$$y = \frac{4x^2 - 1}{2x - 1}.$$

In this case, the functional value is not defined at $x = \frac{1}{2}$. However, the behavior of the function still may be considered for values of $x$ in a *deleted* neighborhood of $\frac{1}{2}$. In other words, we may still consider what happens to the function for values of $x$ near $\frac{1}{2}$, but not equal to $\frac{1}{2}$. Hence, let $x \in \mathfrak{N}^*(\frac{1}{2}, h)$. (Recall that $\mathfrak{N}^*(\frac{1}{2}, h)$ denotes the neighborhood with $x = \frac{1}{2}$ deleted.) For all such values of $x$,

$$y = \frac{(2x - 1)(2x + 1)}{2x - 1} = 2x + 1,$$

and it appears that $y$ is near 2 when $x$ is near $\frac{1}{2}$. Accordingly, let us consider

$$|y - 2| = |2x + 1 - 2| = |2x - 1|.$$

If $x \in \mathfrak{N}^*(\frac{1}{2}, h)$, then

$$\tfrac{1}{2} - h < x < \tfrac{1}{2} + h, \quad \text{or} \quad |2x - 1| < 2h,$$

so that

$$|y - 2| < 2h.$$

That is,

$$x \in \mathfrak{N}^*(\tfrac{1}{2}, h) \Rightarrow y \in \mathfrak{N}(2, 2h).$$

Even though $y$ is not defined at $x = \frac{1}{2}$, we still may write

$$y \to 2 \quad \text{as} \quad x \to \tfrac{1}{2}.$$

---

The examples thus far have dealt with fairly simple situations. There are other examples in which the behavior of a function near a point must be analyzed on either side of the point by means of right or left neighborhoods.

---

*Example 4.3d.* Discuss the behavior of

$$y = \frac{x}{|x| + x^2} \quad \text{as} \quad x \to 0.$$

Again, the given expression is undefined at the point of interest. Since $y > 0$ if $x > 0$, and $y < 0$ if $x < 0$, it appears that a separate investigation of the behavior of $y$ must be made (i) for $x > 0$ and (ii) $x < 0$.

(i) If $x > 0$, then $|x| = x$ and $y = 1/(1 + x)$. Let $x \in \mathfrak{N}^*(0^+, h)$ so that $0 < x < h$. Then,

$$1 < 1 + x < 1 + h$$

and

$$1 > \frac{1}{1 + x} > \frac{1}{1 + h} = 1 - \frac{h}{1 + h}.$$

In other words,

$$x \in \mathfrak{N}^*(0^+, h) \Longrightarrow y \in \mathfrak{N}(1, \epsilon),$$

where $\epsilon = h/(1 + h)$. Again, we have been able to establish a connection between the radii of the neighborhoods in the domain and range of the function. Accordingly, we say that as $x \to 0^+$, $y \to 1$.

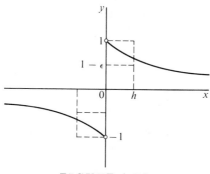

**FIGURE 4.3d**

(ii) Similarly, if $x \in \mathfrak{N}^*(0^-, h)$ so that $-h < x < 0$, it follows that $y \in \mathfrak{N}(-1, \epsilon)$, where $\epsilon = h/(1 + h)$. This shows that as $x \to 0^-$, $y \to -1$. (The reader should supply the details.) A graph of

$$y = \frac{x}{|x| + x^2}$$

in the vicinity of $x = 0$ is shown in Figure 4.3d.

## Exercises 4.3

1. If $g(x) .=. x^2 + 2$, find values of $h$ such that

   (a) $g(x) \in \mathfrak{N}(6, \frac{1}{10})$ for all $x \in \mathfrak{N}^*(2, h)$;
   (b) $g(x) \in \mathfrak{N}(6, \frac{1}{100})$ for all $x \in \mathfrak{N}^*(2, h)$;
   (c) $g(x) \in \mathfrak{N}(6, \epsilon)$ for all $x \in \mathfrak{N}^*(2, h)$.
   Note: In (c) the $h$ will be given in terms of $\epsilon$.

2. If $f(x) .=. 2x^2 - 2x - 1$, find values of $h$ such that

   (a) $f(x) \in \mathfrak{N}(3, \frac{1}{10})$ for all $x \in \mathfrak{N}^*(2, h)$;
   (b) $f(x) \in \mathfrak{N}(3, \frac{1}{100})$ for all $x \in \mathfrak{N}^*(2, h)$;
   (c) $f(x) \in \mathfrak{N}(3, \epsilon)$ for all $x \in \mathfrak{N}^*(2, h)$.

3. If $g(x) .=. \dfrac{x - 2}{x + 3}$, find values of $h$ such that

   (a) $g(x) \in \mathfrak{N}(\frac{1}{6}, \frac{1}{10})$ for all $x \in \mathfrak{N}^*(3, h)$;
   (b) $g(x) \in \mathfrak{N}(\frac{1}{6}, \frac{1}{100})$ for all $x \in \mathfrak{N}^*(3, h)$;
   (c) $g(x) \in \mathfrak{N}(\frac{1}{6}, \epsilon)$ for all $x \in \mathfrak{N}^*(3, h)$.

4. If $f(x) .=. \dfrac{x + 2}{x - 1}$, find values of $h$ such that

(a) $f(x) \in \mathfrak{N}(4, 10^{-2})$ for all $x \in \mathfrak{N}^*(2, h)$;

(b) $f(x) \in \mathfrak{N}(4, 10^{-4})$ for all $x \in \mathfrak{N}^*(2, h)$;

(c) $f(x) \in \mathfrak{N}(4, \epsilon)$ for all $x \in \mathfrak{N}^*(2, h)$.

5. Let

$$f(x) .=. \begin{cases} x^3 & \text{if } x < 0, \\ x^2 + 1 & \text{if } x \geq 0. \end{cases}$$

Explain why you *cannot* find a value for $h$ so that $f(x) \in \mathfrak{N}(1, \frac{1}{10})$ for all $x \in \mathfrak{N}^*(0, h)$.

6. If

$$g(x) .=. \begin{cases} \dfrac{x^2}{x^2 + 1} & \text{if } x \leq 4, \\ \dfrac{4}{x} & \text{if } x > 4, \end{cases}$$

is it possible to find an $h$ for each $\mathfrak{N}(1, \epsilon)$ so that $g(x) \in \mathfrak{N}(1, \epsilon)$ for all $x \in \mathfrak{N}^*(4, h)$? Explain why or why not.

7. If $y .=. \sqrt{x}$, find the values of $h$ for which

(a) $x \in \mathfrak{N}^*(0^+, h) \Rightarrow y \in \mathfrak{N}(0^+, 0.1)$;

(b) $x \in \mathfrak{N}^*(0^+, h) \Rightarrow y \in \mathfrak{N}(0^+, 0.001)$;

(c) $x \in \mathfrak{N}^*(0^+, h) \Rightarrow y \in \mathfrak{N}(0^+, \epsilon)$.

8. If

$$g(x) .=. \frac{x^2 + 8x + 15}{x + 3},$$

find a value of $h$ such that

$$x \in \mathfrak{N}^*(-3, h) \Rightarrow g(x) \in \mathfrak{N}(2, \epsilon).$$

9. Let

$$y .=. \begin{cases} |1 - x| & \text{for } x > 0, \\ \frac{1}{2} & \text{for } x = 0, \\ |x| & \text{for } x < 0. \end{cases}$$

Is it possible to find an $h$ corresponding to each arbitrary $\epsilon$ such that the following statements are true? Explain.

(a) $x \in \mathfrak{N}^*(0, h) \Rightarrow y \in \mathfrak{N}(\frac{1}{2}, \epsilon)$.

(b) $x \in \mathfrak{N}^*(1, h) \Rightarrow y \in (0, \epsilon)$.

10. Suppose $n \in \mathfrak{N}$, and let

$$g(x) .=. \begin{cases} 0 & \text{for } x \neq 1/n, \\ 1 & \text{for } x = 1/n. \end{cases}$$

Is there any value of $h$ such that the following statement is true?

$$x \in \mathfrak{N}^*(0^+, h) \Rightarrow g(x) \in \mathfrak{N}(0^+, \epsilon).$$

Explain.

## 4.4 LIMITS

In the preceding section, we discussed in an intuitive fashion the set of values of a function when the independent variable is restricted to a small neighborhood of a given point. The ideas presented there form the basis for a major portion of the ensuing work in mathematical analysis and motivate the following precise statement.

**Definition 4.4a.** A number $A$ is said to be the limit of $f(x)$ as $x \to a$ if for each given $\mathfrak{N}(A, \epsilon)$ there is a corresponding $\mathfrak{N}^*(a, h)$ in the domain of $f$ such that

$$x \in \mathfrak{N}^*(a, h) \Rightarrow y \in \mathfrak{N}(A, \epsilon).$$

The limit is denoted by writing

$$\lim_{x \to a} f(x) = A.$$

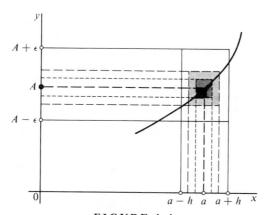

**FIGURE 4.4a**

This concept is illustrated geometrically in Figure 4.4a. For every $\mathfrak{N}(A, \epsilon)$, no matter how small, there must be a deleted neighborhood $\mathfrak{N}^*(a, h)$ such that the points of $f$ are in the rectangle as shown, for all values of $x \in \mathfrak{N}^*(a, h)$.

---

*Example 4.4a.* Prove that

$$\lim_{x \to 2} x^3 = 8.$$

We shall follow the procedure illustrated by the examples of the preceding section. For simplicity, we restrict $h$ so that $h < 1$, and then consider the difference

$$x^3 - 8 = (x - 2)(x^2 + 2x + 4).$$

For values of $x \in \mathfrak{N}^*(2, h)$, we have

$$2 - h < x < 2 + h$$

or

$$|x - 2| < h.$$

Also for $h < 1$, it is true that $1 < x < 3$, so that for these values of $x$, $x^2 < 9$ and $|2x| < 6$. Therefore

$$|x^2 + 2x + 4| < 19,$$

and

$$|x^3 - 8| = |x - 2||x^2 + 2x + 4| < 19h.$$

Accordingly,

$$x \in \mathfrak{N}^*(2, h) \Rightarrow x^3 \in \mathfrak{N}(8, 19h).$$

If it is required that $x^3 \in \mathfrak{N}(8, \epsilon)$ for some given $\epsilon$, then we may choose $h = \epsilon/19$, as long as $\epsilon < 19$, in order to be sure that

$$x \in \mathfrak{N}^*(2, h) \Rightarrow x^3 \in \mathfrak{N}(8, \epsilon).$$

Although a neighborhood of radius greater than 19 about the value 8 would ordinarily not be of interest, it may be stated, for those who insist on knowing what to do if $\epsilon \geq 19$, that in this case the choice should be $h = 1$. As a general conclusion, the choice $h = \min(1, \epsilon/19)$, that is, the minimum of 1 and $\epsilon/19$, makes the preceding implication true for each $\epsilon$. This completes the required proof.

---

*Example 4.4b.* Show that for $a > 0$,

$$\lim_{x \to a} \sqrt{x} = \sqrt{a}.$$

Again, for simplicity, restrict $h$ so that $h < \frac{1}{2}a$. This restriction on $h$ is made so that if $a$ is very near 0, the neighborhood $\mathfrak{N}(a, h)$ will not extend so far as to include negative values of $x$. Now consider the difference

$$\sqrt{x} - \sqrt{a} = \frac{(\sqrt{x} - \sqrt{a})(\sqrt{x} + \sqrt{a})}{\sqrt{x} + \sqrt{a}} = \frac{x - a}{\sqrt{x} + \sqrt{a}},$$

where the numerator has been rationalized in order to bring in the difference $x - a$. For values of $x \in \mathfrak{N}^*(a, h)$, we have

$$|x - a| < h,$$

and for $h < \frac{1}{2}a$,

$$\tfrac{1}{2}a < x < \tfrac{3}{2}a.$$

Therefore,

$$\sqrt{x} > \sqrt{\tfrac{1}{2}a}$$

and

$$\sqrt{x} + \sqrt{a} > \sqrt{\tfrac{1}{2}a} + \sqrt{a} = \left(1 + \frac{1}{\sqrt{2}}\right)\sqrt{a}.$$

Since $\dfrac{1}{\sqrt{2}} > 0.5$, we may replace the last inequality by

$$\sqrt{x} + \sqrt{a} > 1.5\sqrt{a}.$$

We now have

$$|\sqrt{x} - \sqrt{a}| = \left|\frac{x - a}{\sqrt{x} + \sqrt{a}}\right| < \frac{h}{1.5\sqrt{a}},$$

so that

$$x \in \mathfrak{N}^*(a, h) \Rightarrow \sqrt{x} \in \mathfrak{N}\left(\sqrt{a}, \frac{h}{1.5\sqrt{a}}\right).$$

It is certain then that

$$\sqrt{x} \in \mathfrak{N}(\sqrt{a}, \epsilon) \quad \text{if } x \in \mathfrak{N}^*(a, h),$$

where $h = \min(a/2, 1.5\epsilon\sqrt{a})$—that is, the minimum of $a/2$ and $1.5\epsilon\sqrt{a}$. This proves that $\lim_{x \to a} \sqrt{x} = \sqrt{a}$ for $a > 0$.

If we wish to discuss the behavior of $f(x)$ as $x \to a^+$, we modify Definition 4.4a by considering $\mathfrak{N}^*(a^+, h)$ and, if the limit exists, by writing

$$\lim_{x \to a^+} f(x) = A.$$

A similar procedure can be followed for $x \to a^-$ and $\lim_{x \to a^-} f(x) = A$. These limits are called one-sided limits, or limits from the right or left, respectively.

---

*Example 4.4c.* Examine $\lim_{x \to 0} (1/x)$.

Suppose $x \in \mathfrak{N}^*(0, h)$. Then $|x| < h$, and

$$\left| \frac{1}{x} \right| > \frac{1}{h}.$$

This shows that the smaller the value of $h$, the larger is the absolute value of $1/x$. Hence, there can be no limit as $x \to 0$. For, let any fixed number, say $A$, be proposed as the limit; then, for $x > 0$, we have

$$\frac{1}{x} > \frac{1}{h},$$

and

$$\frac{1}{x} - A > \frac{1}{h} - A.$$

For all sufficiently small values of $h$, $(1/h) - A$ is arbitrarily large. Thus, for all values of $h$ so small that $(1/h) - A > \epsilon$, that is $h < 1/(A + \epsilon)$, we have

$$x \in \mathfrak{N}^*(0^+, h) \Rightarrow \frac{1}{x} \notin \mathfrak{N}(A, \epsilon).$$

This proves the statement that $\lim_{x \to 0} (1/x)$ does not exist. The student should compare this discussion with that in Example 4.4a.

---

A further general result is given in

**Theorem 4.4a.** $\lim_{x \to a} f(x) = A \Leftrightarrow \lim_{x \to a^-} f(x) = \lim_{x \to a^+} f(x) = A.$

PROOF:

(a) If $\lim_{x \to a} f(x) = A$, then for a given $\mathfrak{N}(A, \epsilon)$ there is a $\mathfrak{N}^*(a, h)$ such that $x \in \mathfrak{N}^*(a, h) \Rightarrow y \in \mathfrak{N}(A, \epsilon)$. Hence, if $x \in \mathfrak{N}^*(a^-, h)$, then it is still true that $y \in \mathfrak{N}(A, \epsilon)$. Similarly, if $x \in \mathfrak{N}^*(a^+, h)$ then $y \in \mathfrak{N}(A, \epsilon)$. Accordingly,

$$\lim_{x \to a^-} f(x) = A \quad \text{and} \quad \lim_{x \to a^+} f(x) = A.$$

(b) The proof of the converse part of the theorem is left for the reader.

It is important to observe that the definition of limit as $x \to a$ does not require the function under consideration to be defined at $x = a$. The limit of a function is concerned with the behavior of the function in the *deleted neighborhood* of the point $x = a$, but *not* with the value of the function at the point. The preceding definition of limit unfortunately requires some knowledge of the limit number $A$ in order to be used in a practical way. Since such knowledge is not always available, other methods of discussing limits are needed. Some of these methods will be discussed in a later chapter.

The next example illustrates a slightly more complex situation.

*Example 4.4d.* Find $\lim_{x \to 0} \sin (1/x)$ if it exists.

Since we have no hint as to a possible limit number or value of $A$, we must examine the behavior of $\sin (1/x)$ in a different way. Because

$$\sin \frac{(2n - 1)\pi}{2} = (-1)^{n+1},$$

it follows that

$$\sin \frac{1}{x} = (-1)^{n+1} \quad \text{if } x = \frac{2}{(2n - 1)\pi}, \qquad n \in \mathfrak{N}.$$

Hence, $\sin (1/x)$ oscillates infinitely often between $+1$ and $-1$ as $x \to 0$. Consequently, for a given $\mathfrak{N}(A, \epsilon)$, there exists no $\mathfrak{N}(0, h)$ such that

$$x \in \mathfrak{N}^*(0, h) \Rightarrow y \in \mathfrak{N}(A, \epsilon)$$

for any number $A$. That is, no matter how small a neighborhood about $x = 0$ we consider, there is no number $A$ such that the value of the function is always between

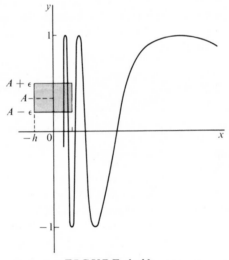

**FIGURE 4.4b**

$A - \epsilon$ and $A + \epsilon$ (see Figure 4.4b). The functional value oscillates between $+1$ and $-1$ more and more "rapidly" as $x \to 0$. Evidently, a limit does not exist.

To sum up the preceding discussion, we may conclude that a function will fail to possess a limit at a point if the functional value "oscillates violently" without settling down, or increases without bound in absolute value, or if the limits from the right and from the left are different as $x \to a$.

## Exercises 4.4

In each of Numbers 1 to 9, show that the given statement is correct.

1. $\lim\limits_{x \to 2} (x^2 - x + 1) = 3$.

2. $\lim\limits_{x \to 1} (x^2 + 3x + 1) = 5$.

3. $\lim\limits_{x \to 2} (x^3 - 2x^2 + x) = 2$.

4. $\lim\limits_{x \to -1} \dfrac{x + 3}{x + 2} = 2$.

5. $\lim\limits_{x \to 2} |x - 2| = 0$.

6. $\lim\limits_{x \to -3} |x + 3| = 0$.

7. $\lim\limits_{x \to 3} \dfrac{x^2 - 9}{x - 3} = 6$.

8. $\lim\limits_{x \to -1} \dfrac{x^2 - 1}{x + 1} = -2$.

9. $\lim\limits_{x \to 2} \dfrac{x - 2}{x^2 + 2x - 8} = \dfrac{1}{6}$.

10. Prove the second part of Theorem 4.4a.

11. Examine $\lim\limits_{x \to 0} \dfrac{x}{|x|}$.

12. Examine $\lim\limits_{x \to 0} \dfrac{x^2}{|x|}$.

13. Examine $\lim\limits_{x \to 0} \dfrac{|x|}{x^2}$.

14. Examine $\lim\limits_{x \to 0} \cos \dfrac{1}{x}$.

15. Does $\lim\limits_{x \to 0} x \sin \dfrac{1}{x}$ exist?

16. Prove that $\lim\limits_{x \to 2} \dfrac{1}{x^2 - 4}$ does not exist.

17. Does $\lim\limits_{x \to 2^+} \dfrac{1}{\sqrt{x - 2}}$ exist?

18. Examine $\lim\limits_{x \to 2^+} \dfrac{\sqrt{x^2 - 4}}{x - 2}$.

## 4.5 THEOREMS ON LIMITS

The apparently complicated procedure of evaluating limits directly from the definition can frequently be replaced by a simpler procedure based on certain important theorems on limits. These theorems are concerned with limits of sums, differences, products, and quotients of functions and justify the intuitive arguments used in the next illustration.

*Example 4.5a.* Evaluate

$$\lim_{x \to 0} \frac{2x^2 - 3x + 1}{3x^2 - x + 2}.$$

On a moment's reflection, it seems natural to say that

$$\text{as } x \to 0, \quad \frac{2x^2 - 3x + 1}{3x^2 - x + 2} \to \frac{1}{2}.$$

However, in order to arrive at this conclusion, we mentally argue perhaps as follows:

$$\lim_{x \to 0} \frac{2x^2 - 3x + 1}{3x^2 - x + 2} = \frac{\lim\limits_{x \to 0} (2x^2 - 3x + 1)}{\lim\limits_{x \to 0} (3x^2 - x + 2)}$$

$$= \frac{\lim\limits_{x \to 0} (2x^2) + \lim\limits_{x \to 0} (-3x) + 1}{\lim\limits_{x \to 0} (3x^2) + \lim\limits_{x \to 0} (-x) + 2}$$

$$= \frac{0 + 0 + 1}{0 + 0 + 2} = \frac{1}{2}.$$

The seeming reasonableness of these steps is, of course, no justification for the argument; it is not difficult to produce an example for which the procedure does not work.

---

*Example 4.5b.* Evaluate

$$\lim_{x \to -2} \frac{x^3 + 8}{|x| - 2}.$$

If we attempt to use the same steps here as in Example 4.5a, we get

$$\frac{\lim\limits_{x \to -2} (x^3 + 8)}{\lim\limits_{x \to -2} (|x| - 2)} = \frac{0}{0},$$

a *meaningless* symbol. This "dead-end" result must by no means be regarded as showing that the original limit does not exist. Instead, it illustrates the necessity for knowing the conditions under which the limits may be handled as in Example 4.5a.

By the definition of $|x|$, it is clear that for $x \in \mathfrak{N}(-2, h)$ and $h < 1$, $|x| = -x$. Hence, we have

$$\lim_{x \to -2} \frac{x^3 + 8}{|x| - 2} = \lim_{x \to -2} \frac{x^3 + 8}{-x - 2}$$

$$= \lim_{x \to -2} \frac{(x + 2)(x^2 - 2x + 4)}{-(x + 2)}$$

$$= \lim_{x \to -2} [-(x^2 - 2x + 4)]$$

$$= -12.$$

---

The last step in the preceding example is justified by the following two theorems. The first theorem is quite simple, and its proof is left as an exercise for the reader, after he has studied the proof of the second theorem.

**Theorem 4.5a.** $\lim\limits_{x \to a} f(x) = A$ and $c \in \mathfrak{R}$

$$\Rightarrow \lim_{x \to a} cf(x) = c \lim_{x \to a} f(x) = cA.$$

**Theorem 4.5b.** $\lim\limits_{x \to a} f(x) = A$ and $\lim\limits_{x \to a} g(x) = B$

$$\Rightarrow \lim_{x \to a} [f(x) + g(x)] = \lim_{x \to a} f(x) + \lim_{x \to a} g(x) = A + B.$$

In words, Theorem 4.5b states that the limit of a sum is equal to the sum of the limits *provided the limits exist!*

PROOF: In order to prove the theorem, we must show that for each given $\mathfrak{N}(A + B, \epsilon)$ there is a $\mathfrak{N}^*(a, h)$ such that

$$x \in \mathfrak{N}^*(a, h) \Rightarrow [f(x) + g(x)] \in \mathfrak{N}(A + B, \epsilon).$$

The statements that $\lim_{x \to a} f(x) = A$ and $\lim_{x \to a} g(x) = B$ may be rewritten as

$$x \in \mathfrak{N}_1^*(a, h_1) \Rightarrow f(x) \in \mathfrak{N}(A, \epsilon_1)$$

and

$$x \in \mathfrak{N}_2^*(a, h_2) \Rightarrow g(x) \in \mathfrak{N}(B, \epsilon_2).$$

These are equivalent to saying that

for $x \in \mathfrak{N}_1^*(a, h_1)$,

$$A - \epsilon_1 < f(x) < A + \epsilon_1,$$

and for $x \in \mathfrak{N}_2^*(a, h_2)$,

$$B - \epsilon_2 < g(x) < B + \epsilon_2.$$

Since $\epsilon_1$ and $\epsilon_2$ are arbitrary, let each be taken equal to $\epsilon/2$. Then, by adding corresponding parts of the last inequalities, we get

$$A + B - \epsilon < f(x) + g(x) < A + B + \epsilon$$

for $x \in \mathfrak{N}_1^* \cap \mathfrak{N}_2^*$. (Why?) That is, given any $\epsilon$, there is a $\mathfrak{N}^*(a, h)$ such that $x \in \mathfrak{N}^*(a, h) \Rightarrow [f(x) + g(x)] \in \mathfrak{N}(A + B, \epsilon)$.

There is a similar theorem on the limit of a product of two functions

**Theorem 4.5c.** $\lim\limits_{x \to a} f(x) = A$ and $\lim\limits_{x \to a} g(x) = B$

$$\Rightarrow \lim\limits_{x \to a} [f(x) \cdot g(x)] = \lim\limits_{x \to a} f(x) \cdot \lim\limits_{x \to a} g(x) = AB.$$

PROOF: This time we must show that for each $\mathfrak{N}(AB, \epsilon)$, there is a $\mathfrak{N}^*(a, h)$ such that

$$x \in \mathfrak{N}^*(a, h) \Rightarrow f(x) \cdot g(x) \in \mathfrak{N}(AB, \epsilon),$$

or that for $x \in \mathfrak{N}^*(a, h)$,

$$|f(x)g(x) - AB| < \epsilon.$$

The statements that $\lim_{x \to a} f(x) = A$ and $\lim_{x \to a} g(x) = B$ mean that $|f(x) - A|$ and $|g(x) - B|$ can both be made arbitrarily small by restricting $x$ to a sufficiently small neighborhood of $a$. This suggests that we introduce these two differences into the inequality by subtracting and adding the product $f(x)B$. Thus, we write

$$\begin{aligned}|f(x)g(x) - AB| &= |f(x)g(x) - f(x)B + f(x)B - AB| \\ &= |f(x)[g(x) - B] + [f(x) - A]B| \\ &\leqq |f(x)||g(x) - B| + |f(x) - A||B|.\end{aligned}$$

But

$$|g(x) - B| < \epsilon_1 \quad \text{when } x \in \mathfrak{N}_1^*(a, h_1)$$

and

$$|f(x) - A| < \epsilon_2 \quad \text{when } x \in \mathfrak{N}_2^*(a, h_2),$$

so that

$$|f(x)g(x) - AB| \leqq |f(x)|\epsilon_1 + |B|\epsilon_2$$

when $x \in \mathfrak{N}_1^* \cap \mathfrak{N}_2^*$. Also, the statement that

$$|f(x) - A| < \epsilon_2$$

shows that $|f(x)|$ is bounded. (Why?) Hence, we know that $|f(x)| < M$, where $M$ is a positive constant. Since $\epsilon_1$ and $\epsilon_2$ are arbitrary, $\epsilon_1$ may be chosen equal to $\epsilon/(2M)$ and $\epsilon_2$ equal to $\epsilon/(2|B|)$. It follows that

$$x \in \mathfrak{N}_1^* \cap \mathfrak{N}_2^* \Rightarrow |f(x)g(x) - AB| < \epsilon,$$

and the proof is complete.

The next theorem frequently makes it possible to consider the limit of a quotient $f(x)/g(x)$ as a special case of the limit of a product.

**Theorem 4.5d.** If $\lim\limits_{x \to a} f(x) = A$ and $A \neq 0$, then

$$\lim_{x \to a} \frac{1}{f(x)} = \frac{1}{A}.$$

PROOF: We shall prove this theorem under the assumption that $A$ is positive. (The argument for $A < 0$ is similar and is left for the reader.) It is necessary to show that there exists an $h$ corresponding to a given $\epsilon > 0$ such that

$$x \in \mathfrak{N}^*(a, h) \Rightarrow \left| \frac{1}{f(x)} - \frac{1}{A} \right| < \epsilon.$$

First, we establish an auxiliary result—namely, that there exists an $h_1$ such that

$$x \in \mathfrak{N}^*(a, h_1) \Rightarrow f(x) > \tfrac{1}{2}A.$$

The truth of this follows at once from the definition of limit. Thus $\lim_{x \to a} f(x) = A$ means that there exists an $h_1$ such that

$$x \in \mathfrak{N}^*(a, h_1) \Rightarrow f(x) \in \mathfrak{N}(A, A/2),$$

so that

$$\tfrac{1}{2}A < f(x) < \tfrac{3}{2}A.$$

Now let us write

$$\left| \frac{1}{f(x)} - \frac{1}{A} \right| = \frac{|A - f(x)|}{|Af(x)|}.$$

As a further consequence of $\lim_{x \to a} f(x) = A$, there is an $h_2$ such that

$$x \in \mathfrak{N}^*(a, h_2) \Rightarrow f(x) \in \mathfrak{N}(A, \epsilon_2),$$

and thus

$$|f(x) - A| < \epsilon_2.$$

Accordingly, for $h = \min{(h_1, h_2)}$,

$$x \in \mathfrak{N}^*(a, h) \Rightarrow \frac{|A - f(x)|}{|Af(x)|} < \frac{\epsilon_2}{A^2/2}.$$

If $\epsilon_2$ is chosen equal to $\tfrac{1}{2}A^2\epsilon$, then it has been shown that there is an $h$ such that

$$x \in \mathfrak{N}^*(a, h) \Rightarrow \frac{1}{f(x)} \in \mathfrak{N}\left( \frac{1}{A}, \epsilon \right),$$

and the proof of the theorem is complete.

Using Theorem 4.5c, the reader should be able to prove the next result quite easily.

**Theorem 4.5e.** $\lim_{x \to a} f(x) = A$, $\lim_{x \to a} g(x) = B$, and $B \neq 0$

$$\Rightarrow \lim_{x \to a} \frac{f(x)}{g(x)} = \frac{A}{B}.$$

The preceding theorems show at once that

$$\lim_{x \to a} x^2 = (\lim_{x \to a} x)(\lim_{x \to a} x) = a^2.$$

It follows by induction that

$$\lim_{x \to a} x^n = a^n, \qquad n \in \mathfrak{N}$$

We also have $\lim_{x \to a} cx^n = ca^n$, with $c$ a constant. Thus, by a simple extension of the theorem on the limit of a sum, it follows that for a polynomial $P(x)$

$$\lim_{x \to a} P(x) = P(a).$$

That is,

$$\lim_{x \to a} (p_0 x^n + p_1 x^{n-1} + \cdots + p_n) = p_0 a^n + p_1 a^{n-1} + \cdots + p_n.$$

The following examples illustrate further the use of the fundamental limit theorems.

---

*Example 4.5c.* Find

$$\lim_{x \to 1} \frac{2x^2 - x + 1}{x^2 - 2}.$$

Since $\lim_{x \to 1}(2x^2 - x + 1) = 2$ and $\lim_{x \to 1}(x^2 - 2) = -1$, we get, by Theorem 4.5e,

$$\lim_{x \to 1} \frac{2x^2 - x + 1}{x^2 - 2} = \frac{2}{-1} = -2.$$

---

*Example 4.5d.* Evaluate

$$\lim_{x \to 4} \frac{x^{5/2} - 16 x^{1/2}}{x - 4}.$$

First, the given fraction may be written in the form

$$\left( \frac{x^2 - 16}{x - 4} \right) x^{1/2}.$$

It follows from Example 4.5b that

$$\lim_{x \to 4} x^{1/2} = 2.$$

Also,

$$\lim_{x \to 4} \frac{x^2 - 16}{x - 4} = \lim_{x \to 4} \frac{(x - 4)(x + 4)}{x - 4}$$

$$= \lim_{x \to 4} (x + 4) \qquad \text{(Why?)}$$

$$= 8.$$

Therefore,

$$\lim_{x \to 4} \left( \frac{x^2 - 16}{x - 4} \cdot x^{1/2} \right) = (8)(2) = 16.$$

The theorems on limits have all been stated for the case $x \to a$, where $a$ is a real number. The theorems can also be shown to be valid for $x \to \infty$, provided, of course, that the other conditions of the theorems are satisfied.

*Example 4.5e.* Find

$$\lim_{x \to \infty} \frac{x^2 - 2x + 4}{3x^2 + x - 1},$$

if it exists.

As the problem stands, the limits of the numerator and denominator do not exist. However, if the fraction is rewritten as

$$\frac{1 - \dfrac{2}{x} + \dfrac{4}{x^2}}{3 + \dfrac{1}{x} - \dfrac{1}{x^2}},$$

then, as $x \to \infty$, the limits of the new numerator and denominator do exist, since $1/x \to 0$ as $x \to \infty$. Hence

$$\lim_{x \to \infty} \frac{x^2 - 2x + 4}{3x^2 + x - 1} = \lim_{x \to \infty} \frac{1 - \dfrac{2}{x} + \dfrac{4}{x^2}}{3 + \dfrac{1}{x} - \dfrac{1}{x^2}} = \frac{1}{3}.$$

*Example 4.5f.* Find

$$\lim_{x \to 0} x \sin \frac{1}{x},$$

if it exists.

Since $\lim_{x \to 0} \sin(1/x)$ does not exist, the theorems on limits cannot be used. However, we know $|\sin(1/x)| \leq 1$ so that

$$\left| x \sin \frac{1}{x} \right| \leq |x|,$$

and since $x \to 0$, $|x \sin(1/x)| \to 0$. Therefore,

$$\lim_{x \to 0} x \sin \frac{1}{x} = 0.$$

The preceding result suggests the following general theorem on limits.

**Theorem 4.5f.** $\qquad \lim_{x \to a} f_1(x) = A, \quad \lim_{x \to a} f_2(x) = A,$

and

$$f_1(x) \leq g(x) \leq f_2(x) \text{ for all } x \in \mathfrak{N}^*(a, h) \Rightarrow \lim_{x \to a} g(x) = A.$$

PROOF: The proof is left for the reader.

In using the basic theorems, one must be certain that the proper conditions are fulfilled. Thus, Example 4.5f shows that

$$\lim_{x \to 0} x \sin \frac{1}{x} = 0.$$

Nevertheless, it does *not* follow that $\lim_{x \to 0} \sin (1/x)$ exists!

Occasionally it is necessary to use the theorems on limits when the limits are of the one-sided variety.

---

*Example 4.5g.* Let

$$f(x) .=. \begin{cases} x^2 + 2x, & x \le 1, \\ 2x, & x > 1, \end{cases}$$

and let

$$g(x) .=. \begin{cases} 2x^3, & x \le 1, \\ 3, & x > 1. \end{cases}$$

Find $\lim_{x \to 1} [f(x) \cdot g(x)]$ if it exists.

Neither $f(x)$ nor $g(x)$ have limits as $x \to 1$, but one-sided limits exist for both functions. Thus

$$\lim_{x \to 1^-} f(x) = 3, \quad \lim_{x \to 1^+} f(x) = 2,$$
$$\lim_{x \to 1^-} g(x) = 2, \quad \lim_{x \to 1^+} g(x) = 3.$$

Therefore, $\lim_{x \to 1^-} [f(x) \cdot g(x)] = 6$ and $\lim_{x \to 1^+} [f(x) \cdot g(x)] = 6$. Consequently, $\lim_{x \to 1} [f(x) \cdot g(x)] = 6$.

---

This example shows that even though two functions do not individually have limits at a particular point, the product function may have a limit.

The reader should be warned that although the preceding theorems on limits are useful in many problems, they cannot always be used, and other techniques must be employed. We shall return to this question at a later time.

# Exercises 4.5

In Numbers 1 to 18, find the specified limit, provided it exists.

1. $\lim_{x \to 2} \dfrac{8 - x^3}{x^2 - 2x}$.

2. $\lim_{x \to 3} \dfrac{x^3 - 27}{x^2 - 9}$.

3. $\lim_{x \to -1} \dfrac{3x^2 + 2x - 1}{2x^2 + 5x + 3}$.

4. $\lim_{x \to \infty} \dfrac{x^2 + x - 1}{2x^2 + 2x - 3}$.

5. $\lim_{x \to \infty} \dfrac{5x^3 - 7x + 3}{25x^2 + 10x + 1}$.

6. $\lim_{x \to \infty} \dfrac{2x^2 - x}{x^3 + 2x^2}$.

7. $\lim_{x \to \infty} \dfrac{3x^2 - 2x + 3}{2x^2 + x - 4}$.

8. $\lim_{h \to 0} \dfrac{(3 + h)^3 - 3^3}{h}$.

9. $\lim_{x \to 1} \dfrac{x^3 - 1}{|x - 1|}$.

10. $\lim_{x \to \frac{1}{2}} \dfrac{x^{-2} - x^{-1} - 2}{2x - 1}$.

11. $\lim\limits_{x\to\infty} \dfrac{\cos 2x}{x}$.

12. $\lim\limits_{x\to\infty} \dfrac{\tan x}{x}$.

13. $\lim\limits_{x\to 0} \dfrac{1}{1 - (1/x)}$.

14. $\lim\limits_{x\to 0} x^2 \sin\dfrac{1}{x}$.

15. $\lim\limits_{x\to\infty} (\sqrt{x^2 + 1} - x)$.

16. $\lim\limits_{h\to 0} \dfrac{\sqrt{2} - \sqrt{2 + h}}{h}$.

17. $\lim\limits_{x\to -1} \dfrac{|x| - 1}{x + 1}$.

18. $\lim\limits_{h\to 0} \dfrac{1}{h}\left[\dfrac{1}{\sqrt{2 + h}} - \dfrac{1}{\sqrt{2}}\right]$.

19. Prove Theorem 4.5a.
20. Prove Theorem 4.5e.
21. Define what is meant by $\lim_{x\to\infty} f(x) = A$.
22. Prove Theorem 4.5b for the case $x \to \infty$.
23. Prove Theorem 4.5f.

## 4.6 CONTINUOUS AND DISCONTINUOUS FUNCTIONS

The graph of a function frequently indicates a lack of connectedness or smoothness that the reader might be inclined to regard as peculiar and worthy of closer investigation. Figures 4.6a, 4.6b, and 4.6c illustrate three simple instances of such behavior which will be of interest to us in the following discussion. For the first function, the limit as $x \to a$ of $f(x)$ exists, but $f(a)$ is not the same as the limit. For the second, the functional value simply increases without bound as $x \to a$. For the third, the functional value has different limits from the right and from the left.

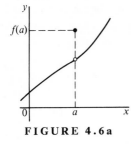

FIGURE 4.6a

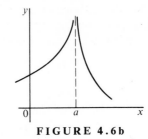

FIGURE 4.6b

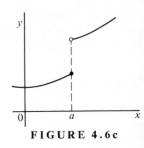

FIGURE 4.6c

A study of the peculiarities of various functions is of considerable interest both in advanced mathematics and in its applications. However, from an elementary point of view, we rather expect functions that describe simple physical phenomena to be fairly "well-behaved." Well-behaved functions have a number of intuitively characteristic properties, which we shall now consider.

**Definition 4.6a.** A function $f$ for which $\lim_{x\to a} f(x) = f(a)$ is called a **continuous** function at $x = a$. A function that is continuous at every point in an interval $b \leq x \leq c$ is said to be *continuous on that interval*.

Notice carefully that the statement, $\lim_{x \to a} f(x) = f(a)$, implies that

(i) $f(a)$ is defined;

(ii) $\lim_{x \to a} f(x)$ exists; and

(iii) $\lim_{x \to a} f(x) = f(a)$.

In fact, it is worthwhile to compare this definition with that for limit. If $\lim_{x \to a} f(x) = A$, then there is an $h$ for each given $\epsilon$ such that

$$x \in \mathfrak{N}^*(a, h) \Rightarrow f(x) \in \mathfrak{N}(A, \epsilon),$$

where $\mathfrak{N}^*(a, h)$ is contained in the domain of $f$. If $f$ is *continuous*, then we may replace $A$ by $f(a)$ and $\mathfrak{N}^*(a, h)$ by $\mathfrak{N}(a, h)$, since we are now concerned with what happens at $x = a$ as well as what happens *near* $x = a$. Hence, if $f$ is continuous at $x = a$, we have

$$x \in \mathfrak{N}(a, h) \Rightarrow f(x) \in \mathfrak{N}(f(a), \epsilon)$$

when $\mathfrak{N}(a, h)$ is in the domain of $f$.

If either $f(a)$ is undefined or $\lim_{x \to a} f(x)$ does not exist, the statement that $\lim_{x \to a} f(x) = f(a)$ becomes meaningless. Thus, in examining a function for continuity, it is helpful to determine the values in $\mathfrak{R}$ for which the function is undefined. If a function is not defined at a point, it cannot be continuous there; nevertheless it is often necessary to consider the behavior of the function in a neighborhood of such a point.

In general, a function $f$ is said to be **discontinuous** at $x = a$ if (1) the domain of $f$ includes some deleted neighborhood of $a$, and (2) $f$ is not continuous at $x = a$. We shall usually not be concerned with questions of continuity at a point that possesses no deleted neighborhood contained in the domain of the function. This applies in particular to points that possess neighborhoods lying entirely outside this domain.

Figures 4.6a, 4.6b, and 4.6c illustrate three kinds of discontinuities. For further illustration, consider a function $f$ having a graph as shown in Figure 4.6d. At $x = a$, the function is undefined and there is a $\mathfrak{N}^*(a, h)$ contained in the domain of $f$, so that $f$ is discontinuous at $x = a$. For values of $x$ for which

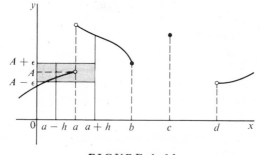

**FIGURE 4.6d**

$b < x < d$ and $x \neq c$, $f(x)$ is undefined. At $x = c$, the function is defined at an *isolated point* of the domain of $f$. Nothing more need be said about $f$ on this interval.

For values of $x$ in the interior of an interval contained entirely in the domain of a function, the theorems on limits can be used to demonstrate continuity in many cases where the function is described by a "simple" formula.

For example, in the preceding section it was shown that

$$\lim_{x \to a} x^n = a^n \quad \text{for } n \in \mathfrak{N}.$$

This result shows that $f(x) = x^n$ describes a continuous function for all values of $x$ since $a^n = f(a)$. It can be extended, as in the following theorem, to include every $n \in \mathcal{I}$.

**Theorem 4.6a.** The function $f$ described by $f(x) .=. x^n$, for $n \in \mathcal{I}$, is continuous for all values of $x$ when $n > 0$, and is continuous for all values of $x \neq 0$ when $n \leq 0$.

PROOF: Left for the reader.

Furthermore, it was shown for a polynomial $P(x)$ that,

$$\lim_{x \to a} P(x) = P(a),$$

which proves the following theorem.

**Theorem 4.6b.** A function $f$ for which $f(x) .=. P(x)$, a polynomial in $x$, is continuous for all $x \in \mathfrak{R}$.

The next theorem also follows easily.

**Theorem 4.6c.** Every function for which $y = P(x)/Q(x)$, where $P(x)$ and $Q(x)$ are polynomials, is continuous at every value of $x$ for which $Q(x) \neq 0$.

PROOF: Left for the reader.

---

*Example 4.6a.* At what values of $x$ is the function

$$f .=. \left\{ (x, y): y = \frac{x^2 + 2x - 3}{x^2 - 1} \right\}$$

continuous?

Since the function is undefined at $x = \pm 1$, and since both $\mathfrak{N}^*(-1, h)$ and $\mathfrak{N}^*(1, h)$ are in the domain of $f$, then $f$ is discontinuous at these points. For other values of $x$, by Theorem 4.6c, $f$ is continuous since, if $a \neq \pm 1$,

$$\lim_{x \to a} \frac{x^2 + 2x - 3}{x^2 - 1} = \frac{a^2 + 2a - 3}{a^2 - 1} = \frac{a + 3}{a + 1} = f(a).$$

---

The concept of continuity can be extended to include continuity at an end point of an interval.

**Definition 4.6b.** If $f(x)$ is defined on the interval $a \leq x \leq b$, where $a < b$, then $f$ is said to be continuous from the right at the point $a$ if

$$\lim_{x \to a^+} f(x) = f(a)$$

and continuous from the left at the point $b$ if

$$\lim_{x \to b^-} f(x) = f(b).$$

---

*Example 4.6b.* Let $f.=. \{(x, y): y = [\![x]\!], 0 \le x \le 2\}$. At what points is $f$ continuous?

At any point for which $0 < a < 1$, $[\![a]\!] = 0$, so that

$$\lim_{x \to a} [\![x]\!] = 0 = f(a)$$

and $f$ is continuous there. Since $f$ is defined at $x = 0$ but is not defined for $x < 0$, we must consider the limit from the right. Then,

$$\lim_{x \to 0^+} f(x) = 0 = f(0)$$

so that $f$ is continuous from the right at $x = 0$ (see Figure 4.6e). At $x = 1$, however, $[\![1]\!] = 1$, but

$$\lim_{x \to 1^-} f(x) = 0,$$

so that $f$ is not continuous from the left and hence not continuous at this point.

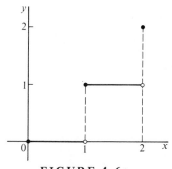

**FIGURE 4.6e**

In the same way, $f$ is continuous at every point $a$ for which $1 < a < 2$. At $x = 1$, $f$ is continuous from the right, since $f(1) = 1$ and $\lim_{x \to 1^+} f(x) = 1$. At $x = 2$, the function is discontinuous, since $f(2) = 2$ and $\lim_{x \to 2^-} f(x) = 1$.

---

Although it is fairly easy to determine the points at which a "simple" function is continuous or discontinuous, the techniques developed so far are not adequate to handle most functions. Even though we may intuitively feel that functions described by formulas such as

$$y = \sin x \quad \text{or} \quad y = \sqrt{1 - x^2}$$

are continuous at certain points, we do not yet have the means for *proving* such a conjecture. This lack of tools will be remedied to a large extent in the succeeding work.

One very important result enables us to evaluate a limit of a composite function in a simple manner.

**Theorem 4.6d.** Let $y = f(x)$ and $u = g(y)$. If $\lim_{x \to a} f(x) = A$ and $g$ is continuous at $y = A$, then

$$\lim_{x \to a} g[f(x)] = g[\lim_{x \to a} f(x)] = g(A).$$

PROOF: Since $g$ is continuous at $y = A$, we know that there is a $\delta$ such that

$$y \in \mathfrak{N}(A, \delta) \Rightarrow g(y) \in \mathfrak{N}[g(A), \epsilon]$$

for each given $\epsilon$. Also, since $f(x) \to A$ as $x \to a$, there is an $h$ for which

$$x \in \mathfrak{N}^*(a, h) \Rightarrow f(x) \in \mathfrak{N}(A, \delta).$$

Hence, since $y = f(x)$,

$$x \in \mathfrak{N}^*(a, h) \Rightarrow y \in \mathfrak{N}(A, \delta) \Rightarrow g(y) \in \mathfrak{N}[g(A), \epsilon],$$

which is to say that

$$\lim_{x \to a} g[f(x)] = g[\lim_{x \to a} f(x)].$$

This result often allows us to interchange the taking of a limit with the formation of a functional value, as in the next illustration.

---

*Example 4.6c.* Show that the function $F$, where

$$F(x) .=. \sqrt{1 - x^2},$$

is continuous on its entire domain.

Since we may regard the given function as a composite of the two functions described by

$$g(y) .=. \sqrt{y} \quad \text{and} \quad y = f(x) .=. 1 - x^2,$$

we try to apply Theorem 4.6d.

It has been shown in Example 4.4b that

$$\lim_{x \to a} \sqrt{x} = \sqrt{a} \quad \text{for } a > 0,$$

which means that the square root function is continuous for $x > 0$. It is almost trivial, and it is left to the reader to show that

$$\lim_{x \to 0^+} \sqrt{x} = 0,$$

which completes the demonstration that the square root function is continuous on its entire domain.

Since $y = 1 - x^2$ defines a polynomial function that is continuous for all real values of $x$ and is nonnegative for $|x| \leq 1$, then, by Theorem 4.6d, the function $F$, given by

$$F(x) = \sqrt{1 - x^2} = g[f(x)],$$

is continuous for $-1 \leq x \leq 1$.

---

Occasionally it is possible to "improve" discontinuous functions at points where the function is undefined. In Example 4.6a the function described by $f(x) = (x^2 + 2x - 3)/(x^2 - 1)$ was discussed, and was found to be discontinuous at $x = 1$ and at $x = -1$, because it is undefined there. However, $\lim_{x \to 1} [(x^2 + 2x - 3)/(x^2 - 1)] = 2$. Is it possible to define a function $g$, which is identical to $f$ everywhere that $f$ is defined, and which will also be defined and continuous at $x = 1$? If such a function $g$ exists, it must be defined at $x = 1$ so that

$$\lim_{x \to 1} g(x) = g(1).$$

If $g(x) = f(x)$ everywhere else, then we must have $g(1) .=. 2$. Hence,

$$g(x) .=. \begin{cases} \dfrac{x^2 + 2x - 3}{x^2 - 1}, & x \neq 1, -1, \\ 2, & x = 1. \end{cases}$$

The discontinuity of $f$ at $x = 1$ is said to be **removable**. We may ask if the discontinuity at $x = -1$ is also removable. The reader can soon convince himself that it is not. As this discussion suggests, a discontinuity at a point $x = a$ is removable only if $\lim_{x \to a} f(x)$ exists.

The simpler types of discontinuities are classified as *removable* (Figure 4.6a); *finite* (Figure 4.6c); and *infinite* (Figure 4.6b). The discontinuity at $x = a$, illustrated in Figure 4.6a, is regarded as removable even though $f(a)$ is defined, because a new function $g$ can be defined that is identical to $f(x)$ everywhere except at $x = a$, where $g(a) .=. \lim_{x \to a} f(x)$.

Another more complicated type of discontinuity is shown in Figure 4.4b, which illustrates the failure of $\lim_{x \to 0} \sin(1/x)$ to exist because of the badly oscillatory character of the function.

An additional example will further illustrate some of these ideas.

---

*Example 4.6d.* Discuss the continuity of the function described by

$$f(x) = \frac{x - 1}{x\sqrt{x^2 - 1}}.$$

We see that $f(x)$ is undefined for $|x| \leq 1$. As $x \to -1^-$, $f(x) \to \infty$, so that $f$ has an infinite discontinuity at $-1$. As $x \to 1^+$, $f(x) \to 0^+$ (why?), so that $f$ has a removable discontinuity at $x = 1$ if only the one-sided limit is considered.

# Exercises 4.6

In each of Numbers 1 to 17, for the function described by the given equation, determine the points of continuity and discontinuity, and describe the discontinuities. If a discontinuity is removable, explain how it can be removed.

1. $y = \dfrac{x}{x^2 - 1}.$

2. $y = \dfrac{x}{x^2 + 1}.$

3. $y = |x + 1|.$

4. $y = \dfrac{x + 4}{x^2 - 16}.$

5. $f(x) .=. \begin{cases} x, & x \leq 2, \\ x - 2, & x > 2. \end{cases}$

6. $g(x) .=. \begin{cases} x, & x \leq 0, \\ \dfrac{1}{x}, & x > 0. \end{cases}$

7. $y = \dfrac{x - 2}{x^2 + x - 6}.$

8. $y = \sqrt{1 - x^2}.$

9. $y = \dfrac{x - 1}{\sqrt{1 - x}}.$

10. $y = \dfrac{x + 3}{x^2 + 7x + 12}.$

11. $s = \dfrac{a - t}{\sqrt{|a^2 - t^2|}}.$

12. $f(x) .=. \begin{cases} |x|, & |x| < 1, \\ x^2 - 1, & |x| > 1. \end{cases}$

13. $g(t) .=. \begin{cases} \dfrac{t^2}{2} - 2, & 0 < t < 2, \\ 2 - \dfrac{8}{t^2}, & 2 < t. \end{cases}$

14. $h(x) .=. \dfrac{[\![\frac{1}{2} + x]\!] - [\![\frac{1}{2}]\!]}{x}, \quad 0 \leq x \leq 3.$

15. $f(x) .=. \dfrac{|1 + x| - |x| - 1}{x}, \quad -2 \leq x < 2.$

16. $f(s) .=. \begin{cases} s^2, & s \leq 1, \\ s^2 - 8s^{-1}(s - 1)^3, & s > 1. \end{cases}$

17. $g(t) .=. [\![t [\![1/t]\!]]\!], \quad t > 0.$

18. Prove Theorem 4.6a.
19. Prove Theorem 4.6c.
20. Prove that if $P(x)$ is a polynomial, then $\sqrt{|P(x)|}$ is continuous for all values of $x$.
21. Prove that $y = x^{1/3}$ describes a continuous function for all values of $x$. *Hint:* Compare Example 4.4b and consider $x \in \mathfrak{N}^*(a, \frac{7}{8}a), a > 0$.
22. In Example 4.6d, prove that $\lim_{x \to 1^+} f(x) = 0$.
23. Suppose $g$ is a continuous function for $a \leq x \leq b$ and $h$ is a continuous function for $b < x \leq c$. Is the function $f$, where

$$f(x) .=. \begin{cases} g(x), & a \leq x \leq b, \\ h(x), & b < x \leq c, \end{cases}$$

necessarily continuous on the interval $a \leq x \leq c$? Why or why not?
24. Let $f$ and $g$ be functions that are discontinuous at $x = a$. Is it possible for the function described by the following equations to be continuous at $x = a$?

(a) $y = f(x) + g(x).$      (b) $y = f(x) \cdot g(x).$      (c) $y = f(x)/g(x).$

## 4.7 PROPERTIES OF CONTINUOUS FUNCTIONS

As we indicated in the preceding section, continuous functions have a number of interesting and important properties, some of which are simple consequences of the theorems on limits. In the following discussion, if $f$ is given as continuous over a closed interval $a \leq x \leq b$, then it is understood to have one-sided continuity at $a$ and $b$.

**Theorem 4.7a.** Let $f$ and $g$ be continuous functions defined on the interval $a \leq x \leq b$. Then

$$\text{(i) } f(x) + g(x), \text{ and}$$
$$\text{(ii) } f(x) \cdot g(x)$$

define continuous functions on $a \leq x \leq b$, and

$$\text{(iii) } \frac{f(x)}{g(x)}$$

defines a continuous function at points where $g(x) \neq 0$.

PROOF: The proof of (i) will be given, the remaining proofs being left to the reader.

Let $F$ be defined by $F(x) = f(x) + g(x)$. The hypothesis that $f$ and $g$ are continuous implies that for each $c$, such that $a \leq c \leq b$,

$$\lim_{x \to c} f(x) = f(c) \quad \text{and} \quad \lim_{x \to c} g(x) = g(c).$$

Accordingly, by the basic theorem on the limit of a sum,

$$\lim_{x \to c} [f(x) + g(x)] = f(c) + g(c),$$

or

$$\lim_{x \to c} F(x) = F(c).$$

This means that $F$ is continuous at $c$. Since $c$ is any point in the interval, the proof of the statement that $F$ is continuous on the interval $a \leq x \leq b$ is complete. Note that a restriction to the proper one-sided neighborhood is necessary if $c = a$ or $c = b$.

It has been shown in Theorem 4.6d that if $g(u)$ defines a continuous function at $u = A$, and if $f(x) \to A$ as $x \to a$, then for the composite function $g(f)$, we have

$$g[f(x)] \to g(A) \quad \text{as } x \to a.$$

This result can be extended by

**Theorem 4.7b.** If $u = f(x)$ defines a continuous function $f$ on the domain $a \leq x \leq b$, and if $g(u)$ defines a continuous function on the range of $f$, then $g(f)$ is continuous on $a \leq x \leq b$.

PROOF: By Theorem 4.6d, if $x_0$ is any point in $a \leq x \leq b$,

$$\lim_{x \to x_0} g[f(x)] = g[\lim_{x \to x_0} f(x)] = g[f(x_0)].$$

Briefly, Theorem 4.7b states that *a continuous function of a continuous function is continuous.* The theorem allows us to conclude that certain functions are continuous without direct appeal to the definition of continuity. For example, the function defined by

$$y = \sqrt{x + 1}$$

is continuous for $x \geq -1$.

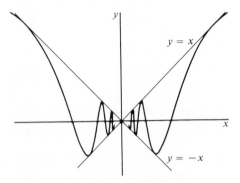

**FIGURE 4.7a**

A number of the properties of continuous functions seem to be intuitively obvious. However, an examination of the function $f$ defined by

$$f(x) = \begin{cases} x \sin \dfrac{1}{x}, & x \neq 0, \\ 0, & x = 0, \end{cases}$$

in the neighborhood of $x = 0$ shows that it is easy to be misled by a preconceived notion of what the word *continuous* means. The function $f$ is continuous at $x = 0$ and yet its graph (see Figure 4.7a) is so "crinkly" in every small neighborhood of the origin that we can only with difficulty imagine its appearance there and cannot draw it at all.

The following simple theorem is frequently used in advanced analysis.

**Theorem 4.7c.** Let $f$ be defined on an interval $a \leq x \leq b$, and let $f$ be continuous at an interior point $c$ of this interval. If $f(c) > 0$, then there is a $\mathfrak{N}(c, h)$ such that $f(x) > 0$ for all $x \in \mathfrak{N}(c, h)$.

PROOF: Since $f$ is continuous at $x = c$, then for any given $\epsilon$ there is a $\mathfrak{N}(c, h)$ such that

$$x \in \mathfrak{N}(c, h) \Rightarrow f(x) \in \mathfrak{N}[f(c), \epsilon]$$

or

$$f(c) - \epsilon < f(x) < f(c) + \epsilon.$$

Since this statement is true for every $\epsilon$, it is true when $\epsilon = f(c)/2$, so that

$$\frac{f(c)}{2} < f(x) < \frac{3f(c)}{2}$$

when $x \in \mathfrak{N}(c, h)$. But $f(c) > 0$, so that $f(x) > 0$ for all $x \in \mathfrak{N}(c, h)$.

The proof of the corresponding theorem where $f(c) < 0$ can be carried out in a similar way, and is left for the reader. Figure 4.7b illustrates the fact that if $f$ is discontinuous at a point, $c_2$, the theorem does not necessarily hold, as it does at $c_1$, where $f$ is continuous.

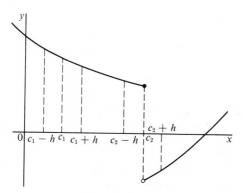

**FIGURE 4.7b**

Another important property of continuous functions is related to the concept of a bounded function.

**Definition 4.7a.** A function $f$ is said to be **bounded** if there is a positive number $M$ such that $|f(x)| \le M$ for all values of $x$ in the domain of $f$.

This definition can be modified to describe boundedness over an interval by saying that if $f$ is defined and if $|f(x)| \le M$ on $a \le x \le b$, then $f$ is bounded on the interval. As an illustration, the function defined by $y = 1/(x - 1)$ is unbounded on any interval containing 1, but it is bounded on any interval

$$a \le x \le b$$

such that $a < b < 1$ or $1 < a < b$.

The next theorem expresses an important property that is intuitively evident. An actual proof, however, is beyond the scope of this book.

**Theorem 4.7d.** If $f$ is a continuous function on a closed interval $a \le x \le b$, then $f$ is bounded on the interval.

To illustrate this result, consider the function defined by $y = 1/x$. On any closed interval $\delta \le x \le b$, where $\delta > 0$, the function is continuous and bounded. However, on the half-open interval $0 < x \le b$, $f$ is continuous and unbounded.

The next theorem expresses an important property that has a simple geometric interpretation. Suppose $f$ is a function defined by $y = f(x)$ on an interval $a \le x \le b$, where $f(a) < f(b)$. Let $f(a) < k < f(b)$. Does there exist a point $x_0$ in the interval such that $f(x_0) = k$? This question is equivalent to asking if the graphs of $y = f(x)$ and $y = k$ intersect. As Figure 4.7c indicates, it is possible for there to be no intersection if $f$ is a discontinuous function. However,

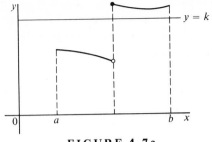

**FIGURE 4.7c**

if $f$ is continuous, then it seems "intuitively obvious" that there must be a point of intersection. As with the preceding theorem, the proof must be omitted.

**Theorem 4.7e.** *The Intermediate Value Theorem.* Let $f$ be a continuous function on $a \leq x \leq b$. If $k$ is a number between $f(a)$ and $f(b)$, then there is at least one point $c$ in the interval at which $f(c) = k$.

This theorem plays a central role in many widely used methods for the approximate solution of equations. These methods depend on the following idea. Suppose we wish to solve an equation of the form $f(x) = 0$. If there are found two numbers $x_1$ and $x_2$ such that $f(x_1)$ and $f(x_2)$ are opposite in sign and if $f$ is continuous on the interval $x_1 \leq x \leq x_2$, then there must be at least one root of $f(x) = 0$ between $x_1$ and $x_2$. This is an immediate consequence of the Intermediate Value Theorem. Why?

The concept of boundedness of a function which was introduced earlier in this section has an important refinement.

**Definition 4.7b.** A number $M$ is called an *upper bound* for a function $f$ on an interval $a \leq x \leq b$ if $f(x) \leq M$ for every $x$ in the interval. A *lower bound* is defined in a similar manner.

Evidently, a function may have many upper or lower bounds (see Figures 4.7d and 4.7e).

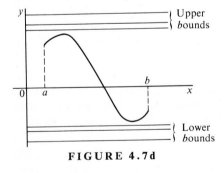

**FIGURE 4.7d**

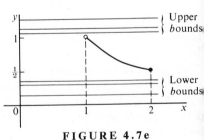

**FIGURE 4.7e**

**Definition 4.7c.** If an upper bound $U$ of a function $f$ on an interval $a \leq x \leq b$ has the property that for every other upper bound $M$ of $f$ on the interval $U \leq M$, then $U$ is called the *least upper bound* of $f$. A *greatest lower bound* can be defined in a similar fashion.

The reader should notice that these last two definitions can be modified for a function defined over any domain $\mathcal{D}$ rather than over an interval.

An example will help to illustrate these ideas.

---

*Example 4.7a.* Find the least upper bound and the greatest lower bound of $f$ if $f(x) = 1/x$, $1 < x \leq 2$ (see Figure 4.7e).

Any number greater than 1 is an upper bound and 1 is the least upper bound. The greatest lower bound is $\frac{1}{2}$. The function does not actually take on the value of its least upper bound, but it does take on the value of its greatest lower bound.

---

*Example 4.7b.* Discuss the function $f$ defined by

$$f(x) = \sec x, \qquad 0 \leq x < \pi/3,$$

with respect to upper and lower bounds.

Since $\sec x = 1/\cos x$, and $\cos x$ decreases from the value 1 to the value $\frac{1}{2}$ as $x$ increases from 0 to $\pi/3$, $\sec x$ increases from the value 1 to the value 2 for the same variation in the value of $x$. Thus 1 is a lower bound and is the greatest lower bound of $f$. In the same way, 2 is an upper bound and is the least upper bound of $f$. The fact that the domain of $f$ is $0 \leq x < \pi/3$ means in this case that $f$ takes on the value of its greatest lower bound ($\sec 0 = 1$) but does not take on the value of its least upper bound.

---

In the last examples it was assumed that a greatest lower bound and a least upper bound exist for the given functions. This assumption is justified by the next theorem, which is stated without proof.

**Theorem 4.7f.** If $f$ is defined and bounded on $a \leq x \leq b$, then $f(x)$ has a least upper bound and a greatest lower bound.

It is sometimes easy to discover a least upper bound or a greatest lower bound from the graph of a simple function, but not every function can be graphed. However, it is possible to show that, under certain conditions, points exist where the function takes on a least upper bound or a greatest lower bound.

**Theorem 4.7g.** If $M$ is the least upper bound of a continuous function $f$ over an interval $a \leq x \leq b$, then there is a point $x_0$ in the interval such that $f(x_0) = M$.

PROOF: Suppose, on the contrary, that there is no point $x_0$ such that $f(x_0) = M$. Then let $g(x) = 1/(M - f(x))$, so that $g(x) > 0$ for all $x$ in the interval. But

$g(x)$ is a continuous function, and so must be bounded. (Why?) Let $P$ be an upper bound on $g(x)$; that is,

$$\frac{1}{M - f(x)} < P.$$

Then

$$\frac{1}{P} < M - f(x)$$

and

$$f(x) < M - \frac{1}{P}$$

for all $x$ in the interval. This shows that $f$ has an upper bound $M - (1/P)$ that is less than $M$, which contradicts the supposition that $M$ is the least upper bound. Hence, the theorem is proved.

The number $M$ in Theorem 4.7g is the greatest or *maximum* value of $f$ on the closed interval. The reader may prove a similar result for the greatest lower bound, say $m$, which is the least or *minimum* value of $f$ on the closed interval.

We shall close this section with a basic theorem on inverse functions. Suppose a continuous function $f$, defined on the interval $a \leq x \leq b$, has a graph that rises as $x$ increases, so that for all pairs of values $x_1$, $x_2$ in the interval such that $x_1 < x_2$, it is true that $f(x_1) < f(x_2)$. The graph will then have the appearance shown in Figure 4.7f. It looks extremely plausible, judging from the graph, that the inverse function $f^{-1}$ exists and is of the same general character as the given function $f$. We shall prove that such is the case, but first we need a preliminary definition.

**Definition 4.7d.** A function $f$ defined on an interval $a \leq x \leq b$ is said to be *strictly increasing* if, for any $x_1$, $x_2$ in the interval, $x_1 < x_2 \Rightarrow f(x_1) < f(x_2)$. The function is said to be *strictly decreasing* if $x_1 < x_2 \Rightarrow f(x_1) > f(x_2)$.

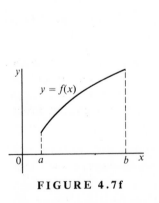

**FIGURE 4.7f**

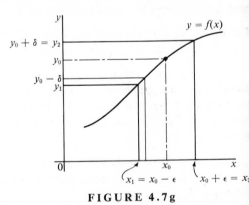

**FIGURE 4.7g**

The graph shown in Figure 4.7f is that of a strictly increasing function. If the graph falls steadily as $x$ increases, then the function is strictly decreasing.

**Theorem 4.7h.** If a function $f$ is continuous and strictly increasing on an interval $a \leq x \leq b$, then the inverse function $f^{-1}$ exists on the interval $f(a) \leq y \leq f(b)$ and is also continuous and strictly increasing.

PROOF: Let us write $y = f(x)$ so that $f = \{(x, y)\}$. Consider the inverse relation $\{(y, x)\}$, and let us suppose that $f$ is strictly increasing. Then there is one value of $y$ for each value of $x$, and conversely. Hence, the inverse relation is a function. Moreover, if $x_1$ and $x_2$ are in the given interval and if $y_1 = f(x_1)$ and $y_2 = f(x_2)$, then, by hypothesis

$$x_1 < x_2 \Rightarrow y_1 < y_2.$$

Therefore,

$$y_1 < y_2 \Rightarrow x_1 < x_2;$$

otherwise, the strictly increasing character of $f$ is contradicted. Accordingly, $f = \{(x, y)\}$ is strictly increasing $\Leftrightarrow f^{-1} = \{(y, x)\}$ is strictly increasing.

With $c .=. f(a)$ and $d .=. f(b)$, the range of $f$ is $f(a) \leq y \leq f(b)$. For each $y_0$ such that $f(a) < y_0 < f(b)$, there is a unique $x_0$ such that $a < x_0 < b$ and $y_0 = f(x_0)$.

Now let $\mathfrak{N}(x_0, \epsilon)$ be an arbitrary neighborhood (see Figure 4.7g) in the domain of $f$, and let $x_1 = x_0 - \epsilon$ and $x_2 = x_0 + \epsilon$, so that

$$y_1 = f(x_1) < y_0 < y_2 = f(x_2).$$

Since $f$ and $f^{-1}$ are strictly increasing, and since $f$ is continuous, we have

$$x \in \mathfrak{N}(x_0, \epsilon) \Leftrightarrow y_1 < y < y_2.$$

Consequently, if $\delta = \min(y_0 - y_1, y_2 - y_0)$, then

$$y \in \mathfrak{N}(y_0, \delta) \Rightarrow x \in \mathfrak{N}(x_0, \epsilon),$$

which shows that $f^{-1} .=. \{(y, x)\}$ is continuous at $y_0$.

Since this argument holds for each point $y_0$ such that $f(a) < y_0 < f(b)$, then $f^{-1}$ is a continuous function of $y$ in this interval. A similar argument shows that $f^{-1}$ has one-sided continuity at $f(a)$ and at $f(b)$, so that $f^{-1}$ is continuous for all $y$ in $f(a) \leq y \leq f(b)$.

The reader may show that a corresponding result applies if $f$ is a strictly decreasing function. A simple illustration of the preceding theorem is given by

$$f(x) = x^2, 0 \leq x \leq p, \quad \text{and} \quad f^{-1}(y) = \sqrt{y}, 0 \leq y \leq p^2.$$

# Exercises 4.7

1. If $f(x) .=. x^2 + 2x + 1$ and $g(x) .=. \sqrt{x}$, where is $g[f(x)]$ continuous?
2. If $r(x) .=. x^2 - 4$ and $s(x) .=. \sqrt{x}$, where is $s[r(x)]$ continuous?

In Numbers 3 to 6, discuss the continuity of the function defined by the given equation. Indicate what theorems justify your conclusions.

3. $f(x) .=. x^5(x^2 - 7)^4.$

4. $r(x) .=. \left[\dfrac{(x^2 - 1)}{(x^2 + 2x - 3)}\right]^{1/3}.$

5. $g(x) .=. x^3[x^{-1} - (x^2 + 1)^{-1/2}]^3.$

6. $s(x) .=. \left[\dfrac{x^3}{(x^3 - 8)^2} - \dfrac{1}{x}\right]^{2/3}.$

7. Let $f(x) .=. \dfrac{x^2 - 4}{x - 2}$, $-4 \leq x \leq 4$ and $x \neq 2$, and let $f(2) .=. 4$. Does Theorem 4.7c apply to $f$ on the interval $-4 \leq x \leq 4$? Explain.

In Numbers 8 to 13, find a number $M$ (if one exists) such that $|f(x)| < M$ for the function defined by the given equation. (Be sure that you can demonstrate the validity of the inequality for the $M$ you use.)

8. $f(x) .=. x^3 - 2x^2 + 3x - 4$, $-2 \leq x \leq 2$.

9. $f(x) .=. \dfrac{x^3 - 2x^2 - 1}{1 + x^4}$, $-1 \leq x \leq 4$.

10. $f(x) .=. \dfrac{2x^2 + x - 3}{x^2 + 2}$, $-3 \leq x \leq 4$.

11. $f(x) .=. x - [\![x]\!]$, $0 \leq x \leq 3$.
12. $f(x) .=. x[\![1/x]\!]$, $0 < x$.

13. $f(x) .=. \dfrac{4}{x + 1} \sin \dfrac{1}{x}$, $0 < x$.

14. Let $f(x) .=. x/(x^2 + 1)$, $0 < x < 2$. What is the greatest lower bound and the least upper bound of $f(x)$ over its domain? At what points, if any, does $f(x)$ take on its least upper bound and its greatest lower bound?

15. For each of the following, find the greatest lower bound and the least upper bound for $f(x)$, and determine if the function actually takes on these values.

(a) $f(x) .=. x - [\![x]\!]$, $0 \leq x \leq 3$.
(b) $f(x) .=. x[\![1/x]\!]$, $0 < x$.
(c) $f(x) .=. x^2 + 4x + 5$, $-3 < x < 0$.

16. Let $P$ be a point inside a circle $C$, and let $s$ be the distance from $P$ to a point on $C$ nearest $P$, and let $d$ be the distance from $P$ to a point on $C$ farthest from $P$. Can you prove that there is a point on $C$ whose distance from $P$ is $\frac{1}{2}(s + d)$?

17. Must a function be continuous in order to be bounded on an interval? Explain.
18. Is the function defined by $g(x) = 1/(1 + |x|)$ bounded? Explain.
19. Prove Theorem 4.7a (ii).
20. Prove Theorem 4.7a (iii).
21. State and prove the theorem corresponding to Theorem 4.7c for the case $f(c) < 0$.
22. Consider the function $f$, where

$$f(x) .=. \begin{cases} |x|, & -1 < x < 0, \\ x + 1, & 0 \leq x < 1. \end{cases}$$

This function is discontinuous at $x = 0$. But $f(0) > 0$, and $f(x) > 0$ on every $\mathfrak{N}(0, h)$. Does this result contradict Theorem 4.7c? Explain.

23. Consider the function $f$, where

$$f(x) .=. \begin{cases} 3, & -1 \leq x < 0, \\ 2 - x^2, & 0 \leq x \leq 4. \end{cases}$$

Here, $f(-1) = 3$ and $f(4) = -14$. Does the Intermediate Value Theorem guar antee that there is a point $x_0$ in $-1 \leq x \leq 4$ such that $f(x_0) = 0$? Is there actually such a point? Does this contradict the theorem? Why?

24. If $p(x) .=. x^3 - x^2 - 1$, show that there must be a value, say $x_1$, such that $p(x_1) = 0$. Use tables of squares and cubes to find an approximate value for $x_1$.

25. State whether the following propositions are true or false. Discuss.

    (a) If $f$ is defined on $a \leq x \leq b$, then $f(x)$ must have a least upper bound and a greatest lower bound.

    (b) If $f$ has a least upper bound $M$ over an interval $a \leq x \leq b$, then there must exist a point $x_0$ in the interval such that $f(x_0) = M$.

    (c) If $f$ is a continuous function on an open interval, then $f$ may or may not be bounded on the interval.

    (d) If $f$ is defined on $a \leq x \leq b$ and $k$ is a number between $f(a)$ and $f(b)$, then there must exist a point $c$ in the interval at which $f(c) = k$.

    (e) If $f$ is a continuous function on a closed interval $a \leq x \leq b$, then $f$ has a least upper bound $M$ and there is a point $x_0$ in the interval such that $f(x_0) = M$.

26. Explain why $f .=. \{(x, x^3)\}$ has a strictly increasing, continuous inverse on its entire domain $\Re$.

27. Show by means of a graph that the inverse of a function that is not strictly increasing (decreasing) is a relation but not a function.

28. You can't find an explicit formula for the inverse of the function defined by $y = x^5 + x$. Is the inverse a function? What are some of the properties of the inverse?

29. Explain why Theorem 4.7h does not apply to the function defined by $y = x^2 - x$. Can you restrict the domain of the function so that the theorem does apply?

---

# Summary of Chapter 4

---

A number of important terms and intuitive ideas have been introduced in this chapter. The reader should have a clear understanding of each of the following items:

    (1) right and left neighborhoods of a point, deleted neighborhoods (Section 4.1);

    (2) cluster points of a set of points (Section 4.1);

    (3) the meaning of symbols such as "as $x \to a$, $y \to b$," "$x \to \infty$," etc., and their use in describing the behavior of functions (Sections 4.1, 4.2);

    (4) the meaning of boundedness and unboundedness of a function (Section 4.1);

    (5) asymptotes of a graph (Section 4.2);

    (6) The fundamental notion of calculus is the concept of limit. Calculus in the classical sense is concerned with "limiting processes," and it is therefore particularly important that the reader understand the *limit concept* on an intuitive basis, as well as on an analytical basis. That is, the meaning of "as $x \to a$, $y \to b$" must be clear, and the process for determining the relationship between $h$ and $\epsilon$ in "$x \in \Re^*(a, h) \Rightarrow y \in \Re(b, \epsilon)$" is essential (Section 4.3) so that the definition of *limit* is clear (Section 4.4);

In addition, the following ideas are important:

(7) theorems on limits (Section 4.5);

(8) elementary techniques for finding limits (Section 4.5);

(9) continuity of a function at a point and on an interval (Section 4.6);

(10) the difference between the limit concept and continuity (Sections 4.3, 4.6);

(11) types of discontinuities (Section 4.6);

(12) properties of continuous functions and the Intermediate Value Theorem (Section 4.7);

(13) the concepts of least upper bound and greatest lower bound (Section 4.7).

# Chapter 5

# The Derivative and the Inverse Derivative

## 5.1 THE TANGENT PROBLEM

Many of the important problems of mathematical analysis can be translated into or made to depend on one basic problem that has been of interest to mathematicians since the Greeks (about 300–200 B.C.). This is the problem of constructing a tangent line to a given curve at a specified point on the curve.

This problem was solved by special methods in a number of isolated instances even in the early history of mathematics. For example, it is quite easy to solve the problem if the curve is a circle, and every student studies this solution in his high school geometry. However, it was not until the time of Isaac Newton (1642–1727) and Gottfried Wilhelm Leibniz (1646–1716) that a systematic general method for obtaining the solution was given. It is on this account that these two men are credited with the invention of the calculus.

Although the tangent problem may appear to be of only minor interest to nonmathematicians, the fact is that the techniques developed for the solution of this problem are the very backbone of much of the science and technology of today. For example, the direction of motion of an object along a curve at each instant is defined in terms of the direction of the tangent line to the path of motion. The paths of the planets around the sun and of artificial satellites around the earth are studied essentially by starting out with information about the tangent line to the path of the motion. A different type of problem is that of studying the decay of a radioactive substance such as radium when we know that the rate of decay at each instant is proportional to the amount of radium present. The key to this problem, as well as to the problem of motion, lies in an analysis of what we mean by the word *rate*. As we shall soon see, this concept is so closely related to the slope of the tangent line to a curve that the abstract mathematical formulation of a rate problem is indistinguishable from the formulation of the tangent problem.

We begin with the tangent problem, not only because of its historical and its practical significance, but also because the reader's geometric intuition will lend concreteness to an otherwise rather abstract notion. Figure 5.1a illustrates an intuitively plausible procedure for drawing a tangent line to a continuous curve, C, at a point, P. If a straight line is rotated about the point P, it generally will cross the curve at P and possibly at another point. A line that crosses the curve at P and at another point (such as Q) is called a **secant line** to the curve. As the point Q approaches the point P along the curve, the secant line rotates about P and appears to reach a limiting position, which is that of a line PT coincident in direction with the curve at P. In this sense, we regard the line PT as the limit of the secant line PQ. This apparently simple-minded idea motivates the next definition and is the origin of much of the important analysis that ensues.

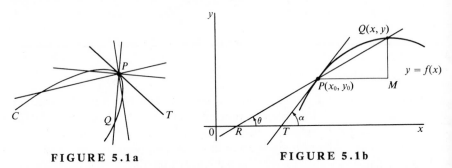

FIGURE 5.1a                    FIGURE 5.1b

**Definition 5.1a.** Let PQ be a secant line through two points P and Q on a continuous curve C. The limit (if it exists) of the secant line as Q approaches P along the curve is called the **tangent line** to the curve at P.

Suppose that an equation of a curve is given in the form $y = f(x)$, where $f$ is a specified continuous function and x and y are the usual rectangular coordinates. Let it be required to construct the tangent line at a point $P(x_0, y_0)$ on the curve (see Figure 5.1b). We wish to use Definition 5.1a and therefore we consider another point $Q(x, y)$ on the curve. The points P and Q determine a secant line whose slope is

$$\tan \theta = \frac{y - y_0}{x - x_0}.$$

Assuming that the curve has a tangent line PT, we find that as Q approaches P along the curve, the inclination $\theta$ of the secant line approaches the inclination $\alpha$ of the tangent line, that is,

$$\lim_{Q \to P} \theta = \alpha.$$

Furthermore, the slope of the secant line approaches the slope of the tangent line, so that

$$\lim_{Q \to P} \tan \theta = \tan \alpha.$$

Since for each point $(x, y)$ on the curve, we have $y = f(x)$, the coordinates of P may be written $(x_0, f(x_0))$ and those of Q, $(x, f(x))$. Consequently,

$$Q \to P \Leftrightarrow x \to x_0$$

and

$$\lim_{Q \to P} \tan \theta = \lim_{x \to x_0} \frac{f(x) - f(x_0)}{x - x_0}.$$

**Definition 5.1b.** The slope $m(x_0)$ of the tangent to the curve with equation $y = f(x)$ at the point $(x_0, y_0)$ is

$$m(x_0) .=. \lim_{x \to x_0} \frac{f(x) - f(x_0)}{x - x_0},$$

provided this limit exists.

*Note*: For the sake of brevity, we frequently call $m(x_0)$ the slope of the *curve* at $x_0$ rather than the slope of the line tangent to the curve at $x_0$.

---

*Example 5.1a.* Find an equation of the line tangent to the curve $y = x^3 + 2$ at the point $(2, 10)$ (see Figure 5.1c).

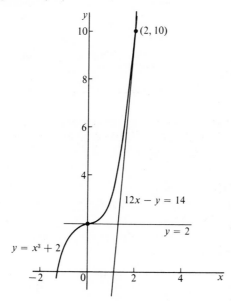

**FIGURE 5.1c**

Using Definition 5.1b, we first find the slope of the tangent line as follows:

$$m(2) = \lim_{x \to 2} \frac{f(x) - f(2)}{x - 2}$$

$$= \lim_{x \to 2} \frac{(x^3 + 2) - 10}{x - 2}$$

$$= \lim_{x \to 2} \frac{x^3 - 8}{x - 2}$$

$$= \lim_{x \to 2} \frac{(x - 2)(x^2 + 2x + 4)}{x - 2}$$

$$= \lim_{x \to 2} (x^2 + 2x + 4) = 12.$$

An equation of the tangent line may now be found by using the point-slope form of the straight line equation. This gives

$$y - 10 = 12(x - 2) \quad \text{or} \quad 12x - y = 14.$$

---

*Example 5.1b.* Find the points (if there are any) where the curve $y = x^3 + 2$ has its tangent line parallel to the $x$-axis.

Since this is equivalent to finding the points where the slope of the curve is zero, we must first find a general formula for the slope. Thus

$$m(x_0) = \lim_{x \to x_0} \frac{f(x) - f(x_0)}{x - x_0}$$

$$= \lim_{x \to x_0} \frac{(x^3 + 2) - (x_0^3 + 2)}{x - x_0}$$

$$= \lim_{x \to x_0} \frac{x^3 - x_0^3}{x - x_0}$$

$$= \lim_{x \to x_0} \frac{(x - x_0)(x^2 + xx_0 + x_0^2)}{x - x_0}$$

$$= \lim_{x \to x_0} (x^2 + xx_0 + x_0^2) = 3x_0^2.$$

It is now evident that the slope will be zero for $3x_0^2 = 0$ or $x_0 = 0$. Also if $x_0 = 0$, then $y_0 = f(x_0) = 2$. Thus the point $(0, 2)$ is a point on the curve where the tangent line is parallel to the $x$-axis (see Figure 5.1c).

---

A **normal** to a curve at a given point is a line perpendicular to the tangent line at that point. For instance, in Examples 5.1a and b, the $y$-axis, or the line $x = 0$, is a normal to the curve $y = x^3 + 2$ at the point $(0, 2)$. The normal to this curve at the point $(2, 10)$ has a slope $-1/12$. (Why?)

---

*Example 5.1c.* At what point (if any) on the curve $y = \sqrt{x}$ is the normal parallel to the line $4x + y = 4$?

We shall first find a general expression for the slope of the tangent line to this curve. Thus,

$$m(x_0) = \lim_{x \to x_0} \frac{f(x) - f(x_0)}{x - x_0}$$

$$= \lim_{x \to x_0} \frac{\sqrt{x} - \sqrt{x_0}}{x - x_0}$$

$$= \lim_{x \to x_0} \frac{\sqrt{x} - \sqrt{x_0}}{(\sqrt{x} - \sqrt{x_0})(\sqrt{x} + \sqrt{x_0})}$$

$$= \lim_{x \to x_0} \frac{1}{\sqrt{x} + \sqrt{x_0}} = \frac{1}{2\sqrt{x_0}}.$$

The slope of the normal at $x = x_0$ is $-2\sqrt{x_0}$ (why?), and the slope of the given line is $-4$. Hence, at the required point,

$$-2\sqrt{x} = -4$$

or

$$\sqrt{x} = 2 \quad \text{and} \quad x = 4.$$

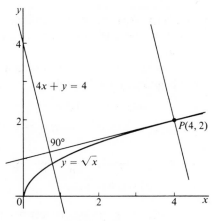

**FIGURE 5.1d**

Since $y = \sqrt{x}$, we have $y = 2$, and the required point is $(4, 2)$. See Figure 5.1d.

## Exercises 5.1

In each of Numbers 1 to 10, find the equation of the tangent and the normal to the given curve at the indicated point.

1. $y = 2x^2 - 5$; $(1, -3)$.
2. $y = x^3 + 2x$; $(0, 0)$.
3. $y = x - 2x^3$; $(1, -1)$.
4. $y = 4/x$; $(2, 2)$.
5. $y = \sqrt{2x}$; $(8, 4)$.

6. $y = 2x^{3/2}$; $(4, 16)$.
7. $y = 1/(2 + x)$; $(-1, 1)$.
8. $y = 3/(2 + x^2)$; $(1, 1)$.
9. $y = 4/\sqrt{x}$; $(4, 2)$.

10. $y = x^{1/3}$; $(8, 2)$. *Hint:* $a - b = (a^{1/3} - b^{1/3})(a^{2/3} + a^{1/3}b^{1/3} + b^{2/3})$.

11. Find the equation of the line that is tangent to the parabola $y = x^2$ and is parallel to the line $y = 4x$.

12. A normal is drawn to the curve $y = x - x^2$ at the point $(1, 0)$. Where does this normal intersect the curve a second time?

13. At what points on the curve $y = x^3 + 2x - 1$ does the normal have a slope $-\frac{1}{5}$?

14. Find the equations of the lines drawn from the origin normal to the parabola $4y = 8x^2 - 9$.

15. Show that the $x$-intercept of the line tangent to the curve $cy = \sqrt{x}$ is always the negative of the $x$-coordinate of the point of tangency. Note that $c$ is a constant.

16. A right triangle with its base on the $x$-axis is formed by the $x$-axis, a normal to the curve $y = 2\sqrt{x}$, and the ordinate through the point where the normal cuts the curve. Show that the length of the base of the triangle is a constant (independent of the point chosen on the curve).

## 5.2 THE VELOCITY PROBLEM

A second important problem involving limits is concerned with describing the velocity of a particle moving in a straight line. This is a problem that was of special interest to Isaac Newton.

Suppose a particle moves along a straight line in such a manner that its distance from a fixed point $O$ is given by the formula

$$s(t) = t^2 + 1,$$

where $s$ is measured in feet and $t$ in seconds. When $t = 6$, the particle is 37 feet

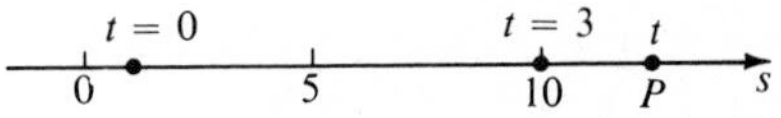

FIGURE 5.2a

from $O$, and when $t = 3$ seconds, the particle is 10 feet from $O$ (see Figure 5.2a). The average velocity in the interval from $t = 3$ to $t = 6$ is

$$v_{av} = \frac{37 - 10}{6 - 3} = 9 \text{ feet per second.}$$

We have used the fact that the average velocity for a given time interval is the ratio of the net distance traversed to the length of the time interval; that is, it is the average rate of change of distance with respect to time. In general, the average velocity for the preceding motion from time $t = 3$ to any other time $t$ is given by

$$v_{av} = \frac{s(t) - s(3)}{t - 3} = \frac{s(t) - 10}{t - 3}.$$

Let it now be required to find the "velocity at the end of three seconds." The phrase in quotation marks is, of course, meaningless until we define it. It is clearly not possible to put $t = 3$ in the formula for the average velocity, since this would result in a zero denominator. However, we have an intuitive feeling that it is possible to come as close as we please to the "velocity at the end of three seconds" by choosing $t$ sufficiently close to 3. Consequently, meaning can be given to the problem by the following definition.

**Definition 5.2a.** If a particle moves in a straight line in such a way that its (directed) distance $s$ from a fixed point on the line is given in terms of the time $t$ by a formula $s = s(t)$, the **velocity** *at any instant* $t_1$ is

$$v(t_1) .=. \lim_{t \to t_1} \frac{s(t) - s(t_1)}{t - t_1}$$

provided this limit exists. (The velocity $v(t_1)$ is frequently called the **instantaneous** velocity at $t_1$ and $|v(t_1)|$ is called the speed at $t_1$.)

We are now in a position to complete the original problem. Using the preceding definition, we have

$$v(3) = \lim_{t \to 3} \frac{s(t) - s(3)}{t - 3}$$

$$= \lim_{t \to 3} \frac{(t^2 + 1) - 10}{t - 3} = \lim_{t \to 3} \frac{t^2 - 9}{t - 3}$$

$$= \lim_{t \to 3} \frac{(t - 3)(t + 3)}{t - 3} = \lim_{t \to 3} (t + 3)$$

$$= 6.$$

Thus the instantaneous velocity at $t = 3$ is 6 feet per second in the positive direction.

---

*Example 5.2a.* A particle moves along the $x$-axis so that its distance from the origin is given by $x = 1/t$. Find a formula for the instantaneous velocity at time $t_0$.

We have

$$v(t_0) = \lim_{t \to t_0} \frac{s(t) - s(t_0)}{t - t_0}$$

$$= \lim_{t \to t_0} \frac{\dfrac{1}{t} - \dfrac{1}{t_0}}{t - t_0}$$

$$= \lim_{t \to t_0} \frac{t_0 - t}{t t_0 (t - t_0)}$$

$$= \lim_{t \to t_0} \frac{-1}{t t_0}$$

$$= -\frac{1}{t_0^2}.$$

What is the significance of the minus sign?

---

*Example 5.2b.* A particle moves in a straight line so that its distance $s$ (feet) from the origin at time $t$ (seconds) is given by $s = t^3 - 4t^2$, $t \geq 0$. At what instants is its speed (absolute value of its velocity) 3 feet per second?

We must first find a general expression for the velocity, as follows:

$$v(t_0) = \lim_{t \to t_0} \frac{s(t) - s(t_0)}{t - t_0}$$

$$= \lim_{t \to t_0} \frac{(t^3 - 4t^2) - (t_0^3 - 4t_0^2)}{t - t_0}$$

$$= \lim_{t \to t_0} (t^2 + t t_0 + t_0^2 - 4t - 4t_0)$$

$$= 3t_0^2 - 8t_0.$$

It is now necessary to find the solution set of the equation

$$|3t_0^2 - 8t_0| = 3, \qquad t_0 > 0.$$

This is done by solving the two equations

$$3t_0^2 - 8t_0 = 3 \quad \text{and} \quad 3t_0^2 - 8t_0 = -3.$$

The first of these gives $t_0 = 3$ and the second gives $t_0 = \frac{1}{3}(4 \pm \sqrt{7})$. The student should check to see that the speed is actually 3 feet per second at each of these three times.

## Exercises 5.2

In Numbers 1 to 8, the given equation describes the motion of a particle in a straight line. The distance $s$ from the origin is in feet and $t$ is in seconds. Find the velocity at the given instant.

1. $s = 6 + 9t$; $t = 2$.
2. $s = t^2 + 2t$; $t = 3$.
3. $s = 8 - 4t^2$; $t = 3$.
4. $s = t^3 + 2t^2 - 4$; $t = 2$.

5. $s = 5 + 3t - t^3$; $t = 2$.
6. $s = 1/(4t + t^2)$; $t = 2$.
7. $s = \sqrt{2t}$; $t = 8$.
8. $s = 3/t^2$; $t = 2$.

9. A body thrown in a vertical direction near the surface of the earth moves so that its distance from the starting point is given by

$$s = -\tfrac{1}{2}gt^2 + v_0t,$$

where $g$ is the gravitational acceleration (approximately 32 feet per second per second) and $v_0$ is the initial velocity. (The upward direction has been taken positive here.) Find a formula for the velocity at time $t_1$.

10. In Number 9, suppose the body is thrown upward with a speed of 96 feet per second. Take $g = 32$ feet per second per second and find at what instants the speed of the body will be 48 feet per second.

11. A particle $P$ moves in a straight line in accordance with the equation $s = 15t - 3t^2$, where $s$ (feet) is the distance from the starting point at time $t$ (seconds). Find the distance of $P$ from the starting point when the velocity is zero.

12. For the particle $P$ of Number 11, what is the velocity of $P$ at the instant it returns to the starting point?

13. A particle $P$ moves in a straight line in accordance with the equation $s = t^3 - 9t^2 + 24t$, where $s$ (feet) is the distance from the origin at time $t$ (seconds). During what periods of time is $P$ moving in a positive direction and during what periods of time is $P$ moving in a negative direction?

14. Two particles $P_1$ and $P_2$ start from the same position on a line and move along that line in accordance with the equations

$$s_1 = t^2 - 4t \quad \text{and} \quad s_2 = 3t - t^2,$$

where $s_1$ and $s_2$ are in feet and $t$ is in seconds. At what times will the two particles have the same speed?

15. Find the velocities of the particles in Number 14 at the times when they are at the same position on the line.

## 5.3 THE DERIVATIVE

The reader will certainly have noticed that the limit defining the slope of the curve $y = f(x)$ at $x_0$,

$$m(x_0) = \lim_{x \to x_0} \frac{f(x) - f(x_0)}{x - x_0},$$

and the limit defining the velocity at $t_0$ of a point moving on a straight line according to the formula $s = s(t)$,

$$f(t_0) = \lim_{t \to t_0} \frac{s(t) - s(t_0)}{t - t_0},$$

have exactly the same form. Furthermore, since many other problems involve this same type of limit, it is worthwhile to investigate such limits in more detail. In order to avoid any connection with a particular problem, these limits are given a name devoid of such a connotation.

**Definition 5.3a.** If

$$\lim_{x \to x_0} \frac{f(x) - f(x_0)}{x - x_0}$$

exists, it is called the **derivative** of $f$ at $x_0$, and is denoted by $f'(x_0)$.

It is frequently somewhat simpler to write $x = x_0 + h$ so that $x \to x_0$ as $h \to 0$. Then the derivative at $x_0$ is given in the form

$$f'(x_0) = \lim_{h \to 0} \frac{f(x_0 + h) - f(x_0)}{h}.$$

The fraction on the right side of this definition is called a **difference quotient.** Since the limit of the difference quotient is unique for each value $x_0$ for which it exists, it may be used to define a new function,

$$f' = \{(x, f'(x))\},$$

called the derivative of $f$. The formula for $f'(x)$ is, of course, the formula for $f'(x_0)$ with the $x_0$ replaced by $x$.

It is instructive to repeat the definitions of the slope of a curve and the velocity in a rectilinear motion in terms of the derivative.

(a) *The slope of the tangent to a curve $y = f(x)$ at the point $x_0$ is the derivative $f'(x_0)$.*

(b) *The velocity at time $t = t_0$ in a straight line motion where the distance from the origin is $s = f(t)$ is the derivative $f'(t_0)$.*

Velocity may be interpreted as a *rate of change* of distance with respect to time, and if $s = f(t)$ describes a straight line motion, this rate of change at any instant $t_0$ is represented by $f'(t_0)$. In a similar way we are often interested in a rate of change of one quantity with respect to some other quantity. Examples are the rate of change of the area of a circle with respect to its diameter, the rate of change of the length of a metal rod with respect to its temperature, and the rate of solution of a chemical in a solvent with respect to the time.

Such problems can frequently be analyzed in a manner exactly like that used for the tangent and the velocity problems. Thus, if $u$ is given in terms of $v$ by a formula

$$u = f(v)$$

we can discuss the rate of change of $u$ with respect to $v$.

The average rate of change of $u$ with respect to $v$ from $v = v_1$ to $v = v_1 + h$ is

$$\frac{f(v_1 + h) - f(v_1)}{h}.$$

If this difference quotient has a limit as $h \to 0$, this limit meets our intuitive conception of an instantaneous rate of change of $u$ with respect to $v$. Accordingly we make the following

**Definition 5.3b.** The *instantaneous rate of change* of $f(x)$ with respect to $x$ at $x_1$ is the derivative $f'(x_1)$, whenever this derivative exists.

---

*Example 5.3a.* Find a formula for the instantaneous rate of change of the area of a circle with respect to its radius.

The formula

$$A = f(r) = \pi r^2$$

gives the area of a circle as a function of its radius. This example requires us to find $f'(r)$. Thus,

$$f'(r) = \lim_{h \to 0} \frac{f(r + h) - f(r)}{h}$$

$$= \lim_{h \to 0} \frac{\pi[(r + h)^2 - r^2]}{h}$$

$$= \lim_{h \to 0} \pi(2r + h) = 2\pi r.$$

Notice that the answer is exactly the formula for the circumference of the circle. In this connection, consider the very plausible fact that the increase in the area of a circle of radius $r$ caused by increasing the radius by a small amount $h$ is approximately $2\pi r h$.

---

In physics, the acceleration of a particle moving in a straight line is defined to be the instantaneous time rate of change of the velocity. This means that if the velocity is given by

$$v = v(t),$$

then the *acceleration at time* $t = t_1$ is $v'(t_1)$.

---

*Example 5.3b.* In Example 5.2b, we found the velocity in a certain straight line motion to be given by

$$v(t) = 3t^2 - 8t.$$

What is the acceleration at the end of 3 seconds?

We first calculate $v'(t)$ as follows:

$$v'(t) = \lim_{h \to 0} \frac{v(t+h) - v(t)}{h}$$

$$= \lim_{h \to 0} \frac{3(t+h)^2 - 8(t+h) - 3t^2 + 8t}{h}$$

$$= \lim_{h \to 0} (6t + 3h - 8) = 6t - 8.$$

Therefore, $v'(3) = 18 - 8 = 10$ feet per second per second.

## Exercises 5.3

1. Find the rate of change of the area of a square with respect to a side when the side is 5 inches long.

2. A metal disk expands when heated. Determine the rate of change of the area of a face of the disk with respect to the diameter when the diameter is 6 inches.

3. A right circular cylinder has a fixed height of 8 inches. Find the rate of change of the volume with respect to the radius when the radius is 4 inches.

4. Determine the rate of change of the volume of a spherical balloon with respect to the radius when the radius is 5 inches.

5. A cone has a fixed radius of 3 inches. Find the rate of change of the volume with respect to the height when the height is 4 inches and when the height is 8 inches.

6. The horsepower that can be transmitted by a shaft is proportional to the cube of the diameter of the shaft if the speed is constant. Find the rate of change of the horsepower with respect to the diameter when the diameter is 7 inches.

7. An engineering student discovered that the radius of a melting snowball was $(4 - 0.04t)$ inches, where $t$ is the time in minutes. Find the rate of change of the volume with respect to time at the end of 60 minutes.

8. The formula $Q = a + bT + cT^2$, where $a$, $b$, and $c$ are constants, determines the amount of heat $Q$ in calories needed to raise the temperature of 1 gram of water from $0°$ to $T°$C. If the specific heat at any temperature is the rate of change of $Q$ with respect to $T$ at that temperature, find a formula for the specific heat at $20°$C.

9. If the equation of motion of a point along a straight line is $s = t^3 - 3t^2 + 7$ ($s$ feet, $t$ seconds), find the acceleration at the points where the speed is zero.

10. The pressure and volume of a gas at constant temperature are connected by the relation $pv = c$, where $p$ is the pressure, $v$ the volume, and $c$ a constant. Determine the rate of change of $p$ with respect to $v$ when $v = v_1$.

11. Find the point (or points) on the parabola $y = x^2 + 2x$ where the rate of change with respect to $x$ of the slope of the normal is 2 per linear unit.

12. If the equation of motion of a particle along a straight line is $s = 3t^2 - t^3$ ($s$ feet, $t$ seconds), find the speed at the point where the acceleration is zero. For what interval of time is $v$ increasing?

13. If the radius and altitude of a cone are always equal, find the rate of change of the volume with respect to the radius.

14. A particle moving on a straight line is at distance $s = t^3 + 4t^2 - 1$ from the origin, where $s$ is in feet and $t$ in seconds. Find the speed when the acceleration is 14 feet per second per second.

## 5.4 THE DERIVATIVE OF A POLYNOMIAL

In order to facilitate the use of the derivative, we must develop formulas for the derivatives of the commonly occurring functions. In this section we shall show how this can be done for a power function and for a polynomial.

It will also be convenient to introduce another widely used notation for the derivative, namely,

$$D_x f(x) .=. f'(x).$$

Since a polynomial $P(x)$ is a sum of the type

$$a_0 x^n + a_1 x^{n-1} + \cdots + a_n,$$

the derivative will be built up by first considering derivatives of the separate terms and showing that $P'(x)$ is exactly the sum of these derivatives. This procedure results in the following basic theorems, in which it is assumed that all the functions involved actually possess derivatives. A function that possesses a derivative at a point is said to be **differentiable** at that point.

**Theorem 5.4a.** The derivative of a constant function is zero:

$$D_x c = 0.$$

PROOF: If $f(x) = c$, then $f(x + h) = c$ and

$$\lim_{h \to 0} \frac{f(x + h) - f(x)}{h} = \lim_{h \to 0} 0 = 0.$$

Notice that this agrees with the fact that a line $y = c$ has zero slope.

**Theorem 5.4b.** The derivative of a variable with respect to itself is unity:

$$D_x x = 1.$$

PROOF: If $f(x) = x$, then $f(x + h) = x + h$ and

$$\lim_{h \to 0} \frac{f(x + h) - f(x)}{h} = \lim_{h \to 0} \frac{h}{h} = 1.$$

Notice again the agreement with the graphical representation of the equation $y = x$, which is a line of slope 1.

**Theorem 5.4c.** The derivative of a constant times a differentiable function is the constant times the derivative of the function:

$$D_x[cf(x)] = c \, D_x f(x).$$

PROOF:
$$D_x[cf(x)] = \lim_{h \to 0} \frac{cf(x + h) - cf(x)}{h}$$

$$= c \lim_{h \to 0} \frac{f(x + h) - f(x)}{h}$$

$$= c \, D_x f(x).$$

**Theorem 5.4d.** The derivative of $F(x) .=. xf(x)$, where $f$ is continuous and differentiable, is given by

$$D_x[xf(x)] = x \, D_x f(x) + f(x).$$

PROOF: $\lim\limits_{h \to 0} \dfrac{F(x + h) - F(x)}{h} = \lim\limits_{h \to 0} \dfrac{(x + h)f(x + h) - xf(x)}{h}$

$$= \lim_{h \to 0} \left\{ x \left[ \frac{f(x + h) - f(x)}{h} \right] + f(x + h) \right\}$$

$$= xf'(x) + f(x).$$

By applying Theorem 5.4d with $f(x) = x$, we get

$$D_x x^2 = D_x(x \cdot x) = x \cdot 1 + x = 2x,$$

and again, by Theorem 5.4d,

$$D_x x^3 = D_x(x \cdot x^2) = x \cdot D_x x^2 + x^2 = x \cdot 2x + x^2 = 3x^2.$$

In each of these derivatives, the final coefficient is the original exponent, and the final exponent is obtainable by subtracting 1 from the original exponent. This pattern for the coefficient and exponent suggests the general result in

**Theorem 5.4e.** $\qquad D_x x^n = nx^{n-1}, \qquad n \in \mathfrak{N}.$

PROOF: It is easy to prove this result by mathematical induction. The formula is certainly correct for $n = 1$ since it gives

$$D_x x = 1x^0 = 1,$$

in agreement with Theorem 5.4b. Now suppose that the theorem is true for $n = k$; that is,

$$D_x x^k = kx^{k-1}.$$

Then

$$D_x x^{k+1} = D_x[x \cdot x^k],$$

which, upon application of Theorem 5.4d, becomes

$$x \cdot kx^{k-1} + x^k = kx^k + x^k$$
$$= (k + 1)x^k.$$

This completes the proof by induction and the formula has been shown correct for all $n \in \mathfrak{N}$.

As illustrations of the preceding theorem, we may write

$$D_x x^{10} = 10x^9, \quad D_x x^{81} = 81x^{80}, \quad \text{and so on.}$$

Furthermore, by the use of Theorem 5.4c, we have

$$D_x(5x^{10}) = 50x^9, \quad D_x(-20x^{81}) = -1620x^{80}, \quad \text{and so on.}$$

These examples show that we can write by inspection the derivatives of the separate terms of a polynomial. The next theorem shows how to combine these separate derivatives.

**Theorem 5.4f.** If $f$ and $g$ are two differentiable functions, then the derivative of their sum is the sum of their derivatives; that is,

$$D_x[f(x) + g(x)] = D_x f(x) + D_x g(x).$$

PROOF: Write $F(x) = f(x) + g(x)$. Then

$$F'(x) = \lim_{h \to 0} \frac{F(x + h) - F(x)}{h}$$

$$= \lim_{h \to 0} \frac{f(x + h) + g(x + h) - f(x) - g(x)}{h}$$

$$= \lim_{h \to 0} \frac{f(x + h) - f(x)}{h} + \lim_{h \to 0} \frac{g(x + h) - g(x)}{h}$$

$$= f'(x) + g'(x).$$

Theorem 5.4f is easily extended to the sum of any finite number of different functions. This result, along with the other theorems so far obtained, allows the derivative of a polynomial to be written down essentially by inspection. Thus,

$$
\begin{aligned}
D_x P(x) &= D_x(a_0 x^n + a_1 x^{n-1} + \cdots + a_{n-1} x + a_n) \\
&= D_x(a_0 x^n) + D_x(a_1 x^{n-1}) + \cdots + D_x(a_{n-1} x) + D_x a_n \\
&= a_0 D_x x^n + a_1 D_x x^{n-1} + \cdots + a_{n-1} D_x x + D_x a_n \\
&= a_0 n x^{n-1} + a_1(n - 1)x^{n-2} + \cdots + a_{n-1} + 0 \\
&= n a_0 x^{n-1} + (n - 1)a_1 x^{n-2} + \cdots + a_{n-1}.
\end{aligned}
$$

---

*Example 5.4a.* Find $D_x(5x^3 - 6x^2 + 10x - 7)$.

Using the preceding result, we have

$$D_x(5x^3 - 6x^2 + 10x - 7) = 15x^2 - 12x + 10.$$

---

In Theorem 5.4e the formula for the derivative of a power was established for positive integral powers only. The formula itself holds, however, for all real exponents, a fact which will be demonstrated after a consideration of the logarithm function later in our work. For the present, we shall accept the following theorem without proof.

**Theorem 5.4g.** $\qquad D_x x^k = k x^{k-1}, \qquad k \in \mathcal{R}.$

---

*Example 5.4b.* Find $D_t \left( \sqrt{t} + \frac{1}{t} \right)$.

We write

$$D_t \left( \sqrt{t} + \frac{1}{t} \right) = D_t t^{1/2} + D_t t^{-1}$$

$$= \tfrac{1}{2} t^{-1/2} + (-1)t^{-2}$$

$$= \frac{1}{2\sqrt{t}} - \frac{1}{t^2}.$$

As a verification, the student should compare this result with those in Examples 5.1c and 5.2a.

## Exercises 5.4

In Numbers 1 to 16, find the derivative by inspection.

1. $f(x) = 5x^2 - 7x^3$.
2. $f(t) = b_0 + b_1t + b_2t^2 + b_3t^3$.
3. $f(x) = 2x^2 + 3x + 4$.
4. $G(u) = (u + 1)^2$.
5. $f(y) = y^3 + 2y^2 - 1$.
6. $g(\theta) = 3 - 5\theta^3 + \theta^4$.
7. $f(t) = (t - 1)^3$.
8. $F(y) = (y + 1)/\sqrt{y}$.
9. $F(x) = 1/(2x^2)$.
10. $U(z) = z^2 + 2z^{-4}$.

11. $g(x) = 1/\sqrt{3x}$.
12. $f(x) = 2x^{3/2} + 5x^{-3/5}$.
13. $W(t) = \dfrac{1}{t} - \dfrac{3}{t^2} + \dfrac{1}{3t^3}$.
14. $Y(x) = \sqrt[5]{5x} + \dfrac{5}{\sqrt[5]{5x}}$.
15. $H(u) = u^{-3/2} + a^{-3/2}$.
16. $G(x) = 2x^{-\pi} + x^{\sqrt{2}} + b^{-1/2}$.

In Numbers 17 to 20, find (a) the slope of the tangent line and (b) the rate of change of the slope with respect to $x$ for the given value of $x$.

17. $y = x^2 + 2x$; $x = 0$.
18. $y = 5x^3 - 3x^5$; $x = 1$.
19. $y = 1/\sqrt{x} - 4/(x\sqrt{x})$; $x = 4$.
20. $y = \dfrac{1 + x}{x^2}$; $x = -1$.

In Numbers 21 to 24, $s$ is distance in feet from the origin and $t$ is time in seconds. The equations are for straight line motion. Find the distance, velocity, and acceleration at the indicated times.

21. $s = 16t - 16t^2$; $t = 0$ and $t = \frac{1}{2}$.
22. $s = t^4 - 4t^3 + 6t^2 - 4t$; $t = 1$.
23. $s = 2\sqrt{t}$; $t = 1$ and $t = 4$.
24. $s = 9 - 9/\sqrt{3t}$; $t = 3$.

25. Find the equations of the tangents to the curve $y = x^3 - 9x$ that are parallel to the $x$-axis.
26. Find the point on the curve $y = x^2 + 4x + 7$ where the angle of inclination of the normal is $\pi/6$.
27. Find the equations of the tangents to the curve $y = x^2 + 4x$ that pass through the point $(-1, -4)$.
28. Show that the tangent to the curve $xy = 1$ forms with the coordinate axes a triangle of constant area; that is, the area does not depend on the point of tangency.
29. Find the rate of change of the volume of a spherical balloon with respect to the surface area.
30. Obtain a formula for $D_x(ax + b)^n$, where $a$ and $b$ are constants and $n \in \mathfrak{N}$. *Hint:* You can do this easily for $n = 1, 2, 3$. Then make a conjecture and prove it by mathematical induction.
31. It was found experimentally that the quantity of heat $Q$ (calories) required to raise the temperature of 1 gram of water from $0°C$ to $t°C$ in the range $0°C$ to $100°C$ is given by

$$Q = t + 2 \cdot 10^{-5}t^2 + 3 \cdot 10^{-7}t^3.$$

The specific heat at any temperature is the rate of increase of the quantity of heat per degree rise in temperature. Find the specific heat of water at $50°C$.
32. The kinetic energy $E$ of a moving mass is given by the formula $E = \frac{1}{2}mv^2$, where $m$

is the mass ($m = W/g$) and $v$ is the velocity. A weight $W = 10$ pounds moves in a straight line according to the formula $s = 32t - 16t^2$, where $s$ is in feet and $t$ in seconds. Find the time rate of change of the kinetic energy when $t = 2$. Use $g = 32$ feet per second per second and give the units of your answer.

33. By repeated application of Theorem 5.4d, show that

$$D_x[x^n f(x)] = x^n f'(x) + n x^{n-1} f(x), \qquad n \in \mathfrak{N}.$$

## 5.5 THE INVERSE DERIVATIVE

It is frequently necessary to solve problems such as the tangent problem or the velocity problem in reverse. That is, a formula for the slope may be known and it is required to find a formula for the functional values, or a formula for the velocity may be known and it is required to find the distance. The simplest problems of this kind are essentially equivalent to the following: given $f(x)$, find a function $F$ such that $F'(x) = f(x)$.

**Definition 5.5a.** An **inverse derivative** of a function $f$ is a function $F$ such that $F' = f$. The value of $F$ at $x$ is designated by $D_x^{-1} f(x)$.

Having seen, for instance, that $D_x x^2 = 2x$, we know that one inverse derivative of $2x$ is $x^2$. However, $D_x(x^2 + 3) = D_x(x^2 - 10) = D_x(x^2 + C) = 2x$, so that it would be correct to say

$$D_x^{-1}(2x) = x^2 + C,$$

where $C$ is any constant. A proof that there is no other continuous function having the derivative formula $2x$ will appear in a later chapter when we show that two functions with the same derivative on an interval can differ only by a constant on that interval. For the present, the truth of the theorem is to be assumed. We shall confine our attention here to the inverse derivative of a power and of a polynomial.

Since $D_x(x^{n+1}) = (n + 1)x^n$, it follows that

$$D_x\left(\frac{x^{n+1}}{n + 1}\right) = x^n, \qquad n \neq -1,$$

or that

$$D_x^{-1}(x^n) = \frac{x^{n+1}}{n + 1} + C, \qquad n \in \mathfrak{R}, n \neq -1.$$

(The exceptional case, $n = -1$, of the last formula is quite important, but must be postponed for consideration until we have studied some additional functions.)

As illustrations of the use of the formula, we have

$$D_x^{-1} x^5 = \frac{x^6}{6} + C,$$

$$D_x^{-1} x^{-3/2} = -2x^{-1/2} + C,$$

and

$$D_x^{-1}\left(\frac{1}{x^2}\right) = D_x^{-1} x^{-2} = -x^{-1} + C.$$

The reader should check any proposed inverse derivative by finding its derivative which must, of course, agree with the given expression.

---

*Example 5.5a.* Find $D_x^{-1}(x^3 + 5x^2 + 7x + 8)$.

We have

$$D_x^{-1}(x^3 + 5x^2 + 7x + 8) = \frac{x^4}{4} + \frac{5x^3}{3} + \frac{7x^2}{2} + 8x + C,$$

as may easily be verified by differentiation of the result.

---

Since the general form for the inverse derivative of a function involves an arbitrary constant $C$, the inverse derivative may be interpreted as a one-parameter family of functions. The graphs of these functions are called **integral curves.** If information is given that can be used to determine a particular value of $C$, then a particular member of the family is determined. A given condition of this type is called an "initial" condition. A problem in which a derivative and an initial condition are given is called an **initial value problem.** The following examples illustrate this type of problem.

---

*Example 5.5b.* The slope, $m$, of a curve at any point is given by the formula $m(x) = 2x - 2$. Find the equation of the curve if it passes through the point $(3, 2)$.

If the equation of the curve is $y = f(x)$, then

$$f'(x) = 2x - 2$$

and

$$f(x) = D_x^{-1}(2x - 2) = x^2 - 2x + c.$$

The curve must pass through the point $(3, 2)$ so the coordinates of this point must satisfy the equation. Thus,

$$2 = 3^2 - 2(3) + c$$

or

$$-1 = c.$$

Therefore, the equation of the curve is

$$y = x^2 - 2x - 1.$$

---

*Example 5.5c.* A body is thrown upward from the ground with an initial velocity of $v_0$ feet per second. If the acceleration due to gravity (considered constant) is $g$ feet per second per second, find a formula for the distance, $s$, from the starting point at the end of $t$ seconds.

Since velocity and acceleration are vectors, we must consider direction as well as magnitude. If upward directed distances are considered positive, then the initial velocity is positive and the gravitational acceleration is negative. Thus,

$$D_t v = -g$$

and

$$v = -D_t^{-1} g = -gt + c_1.$$

Furthermore,

$$v = D_t s,$$

so that

$$s = D_t^{-1} v = -\tfrac{1}{2}gt^2 + c_1 t + c_2.$$

Values for $c_1$ and $c_2$ may be determined from the initial conditions that $v = v_0$ and $s = 0$ when $t = 0$. Hence, we have

$$v_0 = 0 + c_1,$$

and

$$0 = 0 + 0 + c_2.$$

Thus, $c_1 = v_0$ and $c_2 = 0$, so that

$$s = -\tfrac{1}{2}gt^2 + v_0 t.$$

---

The preceding problems are typical of many initial value problems in which the value of the function and/or the derivative at certain points are known.

*Note*: An alternative notation which is quite commonly used for the inverse derivative is defined by

$$\int f(x)\, dx = D_x^{-1} f(x).$$

## Exercises 5.5

In Numbers 1 to 15, find the indicated inverse derivative.

1. $D_x^{-1}(2x^3 - 3x^2 - 2x + 7)$.
2. $D_s^{-1}(5 + 4s^2 - 5s^3)$.

3. $D_x^{-1}\left(\dfrac{1}{2x^3} + \dfrac{3}{x^2} + 4\right)$.

4. $D_r^{-1}\left(5 - \dfrac{7}{2r^2} - \dfrac{1}{3r^3}\right)$.

5. $D_s^{-1}\left(\sqrt{2s} + \dfrac{1}{\sqrt{2s}}\right)$.

6. $D_x^{-1}\left(\sqrt[3]{x^2} - \dfrac{1}{\sqrt[3]{4x^2}}\right)$.

7. $D_x^{-1}(3 + 2x^2)^2$.
8. $D_t^{-1}(3t^3 + 2)^3$.

9. $D_x^{-1}\left(\dfrac{x^4 + 3x^3 + 4x^2 + 1}{x^2}\right)$.

10. $D_s^{-1}\left(\dfrac{s^4 + 3s^3 + 1}{\sqrt{s}}\right)$.

11. $D_t^{-1}\left(\dfrac{1 - 8t^3}{\sqrt[3]{t}}\right)$.

12. $D_x^{-1}[(2x^2 - 3)(x^3 + 1)]$.
13. $D_s^{-1}[s^2(2s^3 - 1)^3]$.

14. $D_t^{-1}\left[\dfrac{(1 - 2t^2)^2}{\sqrt{t}}\right]$.

15. $D_x^{-1}[\sqrt{x}(1 - 2x^2)^3]$.

In Numbers 16 to 21, find the equation of the curve that has the given slope and passes through the indicated point.

16. $D_x y = 3x - 2$; $(2, 2)$.
17. $D_x y = 6x^2 + 4x + 3$; $(-1, 1)$.
18. $D_x y = x - x^2$; $(2, -1)$.
19. $D_x y = x^3 - 4x + 1$; $(-2, 3)$.

20. $D_x y = 1 + \dfrac{1}{x^2}$; $(2, 3)$.

21. $D_x y = \sqrt{2x}$; $(2, 4)$.

22. A particle starts from rest at a point 15 feet from the origin. If it moves in a straight

line away from the origin with a speed of $4t^3$ feet per second, at what time will the particle be 96 feet from the origin?

23. A particle starts from the origin with an initial velocity of 10 feet per second. If the particle moves away in a straight line with an acceleration of $2t^2 + 3t + 4$ feet per second per second, develop a formula for its distance from the origin at the end of $t$ seconds.

24. Find the equation $y = f(x)$ of a curve that is tangent to the line $x + y = 4$ if $f'(x) = 2x + 3$.

25. If a ball is thrown vertically upward with an initial velocity of 64 feet per second from the top of a tower 100 feet high, find
    (a) the greatest height reached, and
    (b) the velocity with which the ball strikes the ground.
    Use the value $g = 32$ feet per second per second.

26. If a ball is thrown vertically upward with a velocity of $v_0$ feet per second from the top of a tower $h$ feet high, develop a formula for the distance between the ball and the ground at time $t$.

27. The slope of a curve at each point is proportional to the square of the abscissa of the point. Find the equation of the curve if it passes through the point (2, 2) with a slope of 1.

28. The rate of change of the slope of a curve at each point is proportional to $1/x^3$. Find the equation of the curve if it passes through the points (1, 0) and $(-1, 0)$ with a slope of 1 at $(-1, 0)$.

---

# Summary of Chapter 5

---

(1) The tangent problem and the velocity problem are important primitive illustrations of the fundamental ideas leading to the concept of the derivative of a function. A good understanding of the ideas illustrated by these two problems is essential to the succeeding material (Sections 5.1, 5.2).

(2) An understanding of the definition of the derivative of a function at a point in terms of the difference quotient and the interpretation of the derivative as an instantaneous rate of change are essential to an understanding of differential calculus (Section 5.3).

The reader must also have a thorough understanding of

(3) the meaning of "differentiability at a point" (Section 5.4);

(4) the theorems on derivatives (Section 5.4);

(5) the development of the derivative of a polynomial and the formula for the derivative of a power (Section 5.4);

(6) the inverse derivative (Section 5.5);

(7) the concept of an integral curve (Section 5.5);

(8) the meaning of "initial value problem" (Section 5.5).

# Chapter 6  Theorems on Derivatives

## 6.1 CONTINUITY AND DIFFERENTIABILITY

In Chapter 5 it was shown how the derivative of a power function or a polynomial function can be found more efficiently by the use of special formulas than by the direct application of the definition of the derivative. In this chapter, we shall develop additional theorems and formulas in order to increase the efficiency with which the derivatives of more complicated functions can be found. There will also be introduced some new concepts that contribute toward a better understanding of the derivative and its role in mathematical analysis.

The reader should recall that a function is said to be differentiable at $x_0$ if its derivative exists at $x_0$. If the derivative exists at all points of an open interval, then $f$ is said to be *differentiable on the interval*, and the value of the derivative at a point $x$ in the interval is denoted by $f'(x)$. As the reader may have observed earlier, a function $f$ may fail to have a derivative at some points of its domain. Consequently, the domain of $f'$ is always a subset of the domain of $f$.

The assertion that a function is continuous over an interval means that the function has certain properties that are illustrated graphically by a kind of "connectedness." As we shall see later, the assertion that a function $f$ is differentiable over an interval is related to certain properties of "smoothness" of the graph of $f$. Therefore, it is appropriate to ask if there is some connection between the continuity and differentiability of $f$ at a point $x_0$. An answer to this question is contained in

**Theorem 6.1a.** If a function $f$ is differentiable at a point $x_0$, then $f$ is continuous at $x_0$.

PROOF: In order to show that $f$ is continuous at $x_0$, it is sufficient to show that $\lim_{x \to x_0} [f(x) - f(x_0)] = 0$. We have

$$\lim_{x \to x_0} [f(x) - f(x_0)] = \lim_{x \to x_0} \left[ \frac{f(x) - f(x_0)}{x - x_0} (x - x_0) \right].$$

Since $f$ has a derivative at $x_0$, the limit defining $f'(x_0)$ exists; in fact,

$$\lim_{x \to x_0} \frac{f(x) - f(x_0)}{x - x_0} = f'(x_0).$$

Thus,

$$\lim_{x \to x_0} [f(x) - f(x_0)] = f'(x_0) \cdot 0 = 0,$$

which was to be shown.

We shall soon see that the converse of the preceding theorem is *not* true. That is, a function may be continuous at a point $x_0$ without being differentiable there. In this connection it is useful to have the notion of a *one-sided derivative*, which is obtained by considering a one-sided limit of the difference quotient, as in

**Definition 6.1a.** For a continuous function $f$ defined at $x = a$, the *derivative from the right* is denoted by $f'_+(a)$ and

$$f'_+(a) .=. \lim_{x \to a^+} \frac{f(x) - f(a)}{x - a}.$$

Similarly, the *derivative from the left* is denoted by $f'_-(a)$ and

$$f'_-(a) .=. \lim_{x \to a^-} \frac{f(x) - f(a)}{x - a}.$$

**Theorem 6.1b.** If the function $f$ is continuous at $x = a$, then

$$f'(a) \text{ exists} \Leftrightarrow f'_-(a) = f'_+(a).$$

PROOF: This follows immediately from the definitions, and details are left to the student.

---

*Example 6.1a.* Investigate the differentiability at $x = 0$ of the function

$$\{(x, y) : y = x^{3/2}, 0 \leq x\}.$$

Since only the derivative from the right needs to be investigated, we have

$$f'_+(0) = \lim_{x \to 0^+} \frac{f(x) - f(0)}{x - 0}$$

$$= \lim_{x \to 0^+} \frac{x^{3/2} - 0}{x - 0}$$

$$= \lim_{x \to 0^+} x^{1/2} = 0.$$

Thus the function has a derivative from the right at $x = 0$, the value of this derivative being zero. What does this mean for the graph of $f$?

---

It should now be clear that if a function $f$ is differentiable on a closed interval $a \leq x \leq b$, then $f'$ exists on the open interval $a < x < b$ and $f'_+(a)$ and $f'_-(b)$ also exist. For example, the function defined by

$$f(x) = x^2, \qquad 0 \leq x \leq 2,$$

is differentiable on its entire domain. In fact, the reader may easily obtain

$$f'(x) = 2x, \qquad 0 \leq x \leq 2.$$

It is now possible to show by means of a simple example that the converse of Theorem 6.1a is not true—that is, to show that continuity of a function is not sufficient to guarantee differentiability.

---

*Example 6.1b.* Investigate the differentiability at $x = 0$ of the function defined by $f(x) = |x|$.

It is a direct consequence of the definition of $|x|$ that $f$ is continuous for all real $x$. Since

$$|x| .=. \begin{cases} -x & \text{for } x < 0, \\ x & \text{for } x \geq 0, \end{cases}$$

a good procedure is to consider the one-sided derivatives at $x = 0$. Thus,

$$f'_-(0) = \lim_{x \to 0^-} \frac{f(x) - f(0)}{x - 0}$$

$$= \lim_{x \to 0^-} \frac{-x - 0}{x - 0} = -1,$$

and

$$f'_+(0) = \lim_{x \to 0^+} \frac{f(x) - f(0)}{x - 0}$$

$$= \lim_{x \to 0^+} \frac{x - 0}{x - 0} = 1.$$

Therefore, by Theorem 6.1b, $f'(0)$ does not exist. The reader should sketch the graph of $y = |x|$ to see that the result of this problem is geometrically obvious. (Why?)

## Exercises 6.1

In each of Numbers 1 to 6, state the domain of $f$ and the domain of $f'$, where $f .=. \{(x, y)\}$.

1. $y = x^2 - 5x$.
2. $y = x^{-1}$.
3. $y = \sqrt{x}$.
4. $y = \sqrt{-x}$.
5. $y = |x|/x$.
6. $y = x - [[x]]$.

In each of Numbers 7 to 13, find the points where $f'_-(x) \neq f'_+(x)$. Sketch a graph of $f$ showing the behavior at each of these points.

7. $f(x) = |x - 1|$.

8. $f(x) = \begin{cases} 0, & x < 0. \\ x^2, & x \geq 0. \end{cases}$

9. $f(x) = \begin{cases} -x, & x < 0, \\ x^3, & x \geq 0. \end{cases}$

10. $f(x) = \begin{cases} x^2, & x < 1, \\ x^3, & x \geq 1. \end{cases}$

11. $f(x) = 2 + |x + 3|$.

12. $f(x) = \begin{cases} x^2, & x > 0, \\ -x^2, & x \leq 0. \end{cases}$

13. $f(x) = \begin{cases} x^2, & x > 0, \\ \sqrt{-x}, & x \leq 0. \end{cases}$

14. Prove Theorem 6.1b.

★15. Consider a set of functions with domain $0 \leq x \leq 1$, whose graphs are shown in Figure 6.1a. The graph of each of $f_2, f_3, \ldots$ is obtained from the preceding one

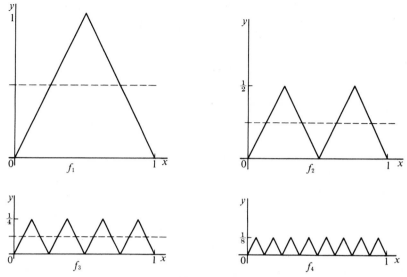

**FIGURE 6.1a**

by "folding" the figure about a line through the midpoints of the sides of the triangles. (This is the dashed line shown in the graphs of $f_1$, $f_2$, and $f_3$.)

(a) Is $f_1$ differentiable everywhere? If not, where is it differentiable?

(b) At what points does $f_n$ fail to be differentiable? Is $f_n$ continuous everywhere?

(c) Imagine letting $n \to \infty$, so that $f_n \to F$. Is $F$ continuous? differentiable?

## 6.2 FURTHER GENERAL THEOREMS ON DERIVATIVES

In this section we shall derive general formulas for the derivatives of products and quotients of functions, and we shall introduce a somewhat more convenient notation for difference quotients.

The standard difference notation for the number $x_2 - x_1$ is $\Delta x_1$, read "delta $x_1$." Thus,

$$\Delta x_1 \,.=.\, x_2 - x_1,$$

so that $\Delta x_1$ must be regarded as a single symbol; the $\Delta$ is *not* a multiplier of $x_1$. It is helpful to think of $\Delta x_1$ as the change in $x$ from $x_1$ to $x_2$. In a similar manner, the change in $y$ from $y_1$ to $y_2$ is given by

$$\Delta y_1 = y_2 - y_1.$$

If $y = f(x)$, then

$$\Delta y_1 = \Delta f(x_1) = f(x_2) - f(x_1) = f(x_1 + \Delta x_1) - f(x_1).$$

In terms of the difference notation, we may rewrite the definition of the derivative at $x_1$ as

$$f'(x_1) = \lim_{\Delta x_1 \to 0} \frac{\Delta f(x_1)}{\Delta x_1} = \lim_{\Delta x_1 \to 0} \frac{f(x_1 + \Delta x_1) - f(x_1)}{\Delta x_1}.$$

Since $x_1$ denotes any point in the domain of $f$, the subscripts may be dropped, so that the general formula for the derivative reads

$$f'(x) = \lim_{\Delta x \to 0} \frac{\Delta f(x)}{\Delta x} = \lim_{\Delta x \to 0} \frac{f(x + \Delta x) - f(x)}{\Delta x}.$$

Furthermore, if $y = f(x)$, so that $\Delta y = f(x + \Delta x) - f(x)$, then

$$D_x y = \lim_{\Delta x \to 0} \frac{\Delta y}{\Delta x}.$$

It must, of course, be understood that $\Delta y$ is the $y$ difference, or the change in the $y$ value, corresponding to the $x$ difference, $\Delta x$. The convenience of the difference notation will appear in the next theorems.

**Theorem 6.2a.** Let $f$ and $g$ be differentiable functions. Then, in the domain common to $f'$ and $g'$,

$$D_x[f(x)g(x)] = f(x)\, D_x g(x) + g(x)\, D_x f(x).$$

PROOF: Write $\qquad u = f(x), \quad v = g(x), \quad y = uv.$

Then

$$\Delta u = f(x + \Delta x) - f(x)$$

and

$$\Delta v = g(x + \Delta x) - g(x).$$

We also have

$$\Delta y = (u + \Delta u)(v + \Delta v) - uv$$
$$= u\, \Delta v + v\, \Delta u + \Delta u\, \Delta v$$

and

$$\frac{\Delta y}{\Delta x} = u \frac{\Delta v}{\Delta x} + v \frac{\Delta u}{\Delta x} + \frac{\Delta u}{\Delta x} \Delta v,$$

so that

$$D_x y = \lim_{\Delta x \to 0} \left( u \frac{\Delta v}{\Delta x} + v \frac{\Delta u}{\Delta x} + \frac{\Delta u}{\Delta x} \Delta v \right).$$

Since $f$ and $g$ were assumed to be differentiable,

$$\lim_{\Delta x \to 0} \frac{\Delta u}{\Delta x} = D_x u, \quad \lim_{\Delta x \to 0} \frac{\Delta v}{\Delta x} = D_x v,$$

and

$$\lim_{\Delta x \to 0} \Delta v = \lim_{\Delta x \to 0} [g(x + \Delta x) - g(x)] = 0.$$

Hence,

$$D_x y = u \lim_{\Delta x \to 0} \frac{\Delta v}{\Delta x} + v \lim_{\Delta x \to 0} \frac{\Delta u}{\Delta x} + \left( \lim_{\Delta x \to 0} \frac{\Delta u}{\Delta x} \right) \left( \lim_{\Delta x \to 0} \Delta v \right)$$
$$= u\, D_x v + v\, D_x u,$$

which is the required formula.

As an aid to the reader in remembering the content of Theorem 6.2a, we restate it as

*The Product Rule for Differentiation.* The derivative of the product of two functions is the first function times the derivative of the second, plus the second function times the derivative of the first. Symbolically,

$$(fg)' = f'g + fg'.$$

---

*Example 6.2a.* Find $D_x y$ if

$$y = (x^2 + 5)(x^3 - 9x + 2).$$

We use Theorem 6.2a to obtain

$$
\begin{aligned}
D_x y &= (x^2 + 5) D_x(x^3 - 9x + 2) + (x^3 - 9x + 2) D_x(x^2 + 5) \\
&= (x^2 + 5)(3x^2 - 9) + (x^3 - 9x + 2)(2x) \\
&= 5x^4 - 12x^2 + 4x - 45.
\end{aligned}
$$

The reader should check this by first multiplying out the expression for $y$ and then finding the derivative of the resulting polynomial.

---

*Example 6.2b.* Find $D_t s$ if $s = (t^2 + 2t)\sqrt{t}$.

Writing $s = (t^2 + 2t)t^{1/2}$, we have

$$
\begin{aligned}
D_t s &= (t^2 + 2t)D_t t^{1/2} + t^{1/2}D_t(t^2 + 2t) \\
&= (t^2 + 2t)\tfrac{1}{2}t^{-1/2} + t^{1/2}(2t + 2) \\
&= \tfrac{5}{2}t^{3/2} + 3t^{1/2}.
\end{aligned}
$$

Again, this result can be checked by first multiplying out the factors of $s$ and then finding $D_t s$.

---

**Theorem 6.2b.** Let $f$ and $g$ be differentiable functions. Then, in the domain common to $f'$, $g'$, and $f/g$,

$$D_x \left[ \frac{f(x)}{g(x)} \right] = \frac{g(x) D_x f(x) - f(x) D_x g(x)}{[g(x)]^2}.$$

PROOF: Write $u = f(x)$, $v = g(x)$, and $y = u/v$.
Then,

$$
\begin{aligned}
\Delta y &= \frac{u + \Delta u}{v + \Delta v} - \frac{u}{v} \\[2mm]
&= \frac{v\Delta u - u\Delta v}{v(v + \Delta v)},
\end{aligned}
$$

$$\frac{\Delta y}{\Delta x} = \frac{v\dfrac{\Delta u}{\Delta x} - u\dfrac{\Delta v}{\Delta x}}{v(v + \Delta v)}.$$

As in the proof of Theorem 6.2a, the differentiability of $f$ and $g$ implies that

$$\lim_{\Delta x \to 0} \frac{\Delta u}{\Delta x} = D_x u, \quad \lim_{\Delta x \to 0} \frac{\Delta v}{\Delta x} = D_x v,$$

and

$$\lim_{\Delta x \to 0} \Delta v = \lim_{\Delta x \to 0} [g(x + \Delta x) - g(x)] = 0.$$

Therefore,

$$D_xy = \frac{v\, D_xu - u\, D_xv}{v^2},$$

the required formula.

The formula of Theorem 6.2b may be described as

*The Quotient Rule for Differentiation*. The derivative of the quotient of two functions is the denominator times the derivative of the numerator, minus the numerator times the derivative of the denominator, all divided by the square of the denominator. Symbolically,

$$\left(\frac{f}{g}\right)' = \frac{f'g - fg'}{g^2}.$$

---

*Example 6.2c.* Find

$$D_z\left(\frac{z^2 - 1}{z^2 + 1}\right).$$

Theorem 6.2b gives

$$
\begin{aligned}
D_z\left(\frac{z^2 - 1}{z^2 + 1}\right) &= \frac{(z^2 + 1)D_z(z^2 - 1) - (z^2 - 1)D_z(z^2 + 1)}{(z^2 + 1)^2} \\
&= \frac{(z^2 + 1)(2z) - (z^2 - 1)(2z)}{(z^2 + 1)^2} \\
&= \frac{4z}{(z^2 + 1)^2}.
\end{aligned}
$$

---

*Example 6.2d.* Find

$$D_m\left(\frac{m^2}{1 + m^{1/2}}\right).$$

Again, the formula of Theorem 6.2b gives

$$
\begin{aligned}
D_m\left(\frac{m^2}{1 + m^{1/2}}\right) &= \frac{(1 + m^{1/2})D_m m^2 - m^2 D_m(1 + m^{1/2})}{(1 + m^{1/2})^2} \\
&= \frac{(1 + m^{1/2})(2m) - m^2(\tfrac{1}{2}m^{-1/2})}{(1 + m^{1/2})^2} \cdot \\
&= \frac{4m + 3m^{3/2}}{2(1 + m^{1/2})^2}.
\end{aligned}
$$

---

It should be noted that the product rule can be extended in an obvious way if there are more than two factors.

---

*Example 6.2e.* If $y = (x + 1)(x^2 + 2)(x - 9)$, find $D_xy$.

$$
\begin{aligned}
D_xy &= (x - 9)D_x[(x + 1)(x^2 + 2)] + (x + 1)(x^2 + 2)D_x(x - 9) \\
&= (x - 9)[(x^2 + 2)D_x(x + 1) + (x + 1)D_x(x^2 + 2)] \\
&\qquad\qquad\qquad\qquad\qquad + (x + 1)(x^2 + 2)D_x(x - 9
\end{aligned}
$$

$$= (x - 9)(x^2 + 2)D_x(x + 1) + (x + 1)(x - 9)D_x(x^2 + 2)$$
$$+ (x + 1)(x^2 + 2)D_x(x - 9)$$
$$= (x - 9)(x^2 + 2)(1) + (x + 1)(x - 9)(2x) + (x + 1)(x^2 + 2)(1)$$
$$= 4x^3 - 24x^2 - 14x - 16.$$

## Exercises 6.2

In each of Numbers 1 to 10, find $D_{x}y$.

1. $y = (x - 1)(x + 1)$.

2. $y = (x + 10)(x^2 - 9)^2$.

3. $y = x(x + 1)(x + 2)(x + 3)$.

4. $y = (3x - 9)(x^2 + 18)$.

5. $y = \dfrac{x + 1}{x - 1}$.

6. $y = \dfrac{1}{x^2 + 2}$.

7. $y = \dfrac{x}{x + 1}$.

8. $y = \dfrac{x^2}{x^2 - 1}$.

9. $y = \dfrac{x}{\sqrt{x} + 1}$.

10. $y = \dfrac{\sqrt{x} + 1}{\sqrt{x} - 1}$.

In each of Numbers 11 to 14, $s$ is the distance in feet and $t$ the time in seconds in a straight line motion. Find the time when the velocity is zero.

11. $s = \dfrac{2t}{t^2 + 4}$, $t \geq 0$.

12. $s = \dfrac{t^2 - 1}{t^2 + 1}$, $t \geq 0$.

13. $s = \dfrac{\sqrt{t}}{t + 1}$, $t > 0$.

14. $s = \dfrac{t^2}{\sqrt{t} - 1}$, $t > 0$.

In each of Numbers 15 to 18, find an equation of the tangent line at the indicated point for the curve whose equation is given.

15. $y = \dfrac{1}{x^2 + 4}$; $(1, \frac{1}{5})$.

16. $y = \dfrac{x}{x - 1}$; $(2, 2)$.

17. $y = \dfrac{x}{x^2 - 1}$; $(0, 0)$.

18. $y = \dfrac{x^4 - 1}{x^2 + 4}$; $(1, 0)$.

19. Suppose a function $F$ is the product of $n$ differentiable functions $f_1, f_2, \ldots, f_n$, so that
$$F(x) = f_1(x)f_2(x) \cdots f_n(x).$$
Prove that $F'(x)$ is the sum of all the terms that can be formed by differentiating $f_1, f_2, \cdots, f_n$ one at a time, each time multiplying by all the remaining functions.

20. Using the result of Number 19, find a formula for $F'(x)$, where $F(x) = [f(x)]^n$, with $n \in \mathfrak{N}$.

21. Write $u/v = uv^{-1}$ and use Theorem 6.2a to obtain the formula of Theorem 6.2b.

22. Is the set of all differentiable functions on an open interval $a < x < b$ a group under addition? under multiplication? Explain.

## 6.3 COMPOSITE FUNCTIONS

It is frequently desirable to break down the consideration of a complicated function into steps involving simpler functions. For this purpose, it is convenient to use the notation of a composite function as given by Definition 2.6b. It should be noted that many authors call a composite function a *function of a function*. Clearly, there is no unique way of expressing a given function as a composite of other functions. For instance, for the function defined by $y = \sqrt{1 - x^2}$, we may write $y = f[g(x)]$, where $f(u) = \sqrt{u}$, and $g(x) = 1 - x^2$, with $|x| \leq 1$, or we may write

$$y = f\{h[w(x)]\},$$

where

$$f(u) = u^{1/2},$$
$$h(v) = 1 - v, \qquad v \leq 1,$$

and

$$w(x) = x^2, \qquad |x| \leq 1.$$

In this last illustration, the domain of $f$ is $u \geq 0$, so that the domain of $h$ must be $v \leq 1$ in order that $h(v) \geq 0$. Similarly, the domain of $w$ must be $|x| \leq 1$, so that the range of $w$ falls into the domain of $h$.

Before obtaining a formula for the derivative of a composite function, we return to the definition of the derivative in the form

$$D_x y = \lim_{\Delta x \to 0} \frac{\Delta y}{\Delta x}$$

and rewrite it as

$$\frac{\Delta y}{\Delta x} = D_x y + \eta, \quad \text{where } \lim_{\Delta x \to 0} \eta = 0.$$

A moment's reflection shows that these two forms of the definition are completely equivalent. For, whenever the derivative exists, it is true that

$$\lim_{\Delta x \to 0} \left( \frac{\Delta y}{\Delta x} - D_x y \right) = 0,$$

and we have merely designated the difference between $\Delta y / \Delta x$ and $D_x y$ by $\eta$. The second form of the definition leads to the following result:

$$\Delta y = (D_x y)\, \Delta x + \eta\, \Delta x, \quad \text{where } \lim_{\Delta x \to 0} \eta = 0.$$

This is a useful formula that expresses the change $\Delta y$ in the functional value in terms of the derivative and the change $\Delta x$, and it indicates that for sufficiently small values of $\Delta x$, the change $\Delta y$ is given as closely as desired by the product $(D_x y)\, \Delta x$. This fact is, of course, clear from the definition of the derivative.

We are now ready to consider the problem of finding the derivative of a composite function. Let $f$ and $g$ be differentiable functions and write

$$y = f(u), \quad u = g(x).$$

Then $f$ may be regarded as a composite function $F$ of the argument $x$; that is,

$$y = f[g(x)] = F(x).$$

Furthermore, $\Delta y$ may be expressed in terms of $\Delta u$, and $\Delta u$ in terms of $\Delta x$ as follows:

$$\Delta y = (D_u y)\,\Delta u + \epsilon_1\,\Delta u, \quad \text{where } \lim_{\Delta u \to 0} \epsilon_1 = 0,$$

and

$$\Delta u = (D_x u)\,\Delta x + \epsilon_2\,\Delta x, \quad \text{where } \lim_{\Delta x \to 0} \epsilon_2 = 0.$$

Upon substituting for $\Delta u$ from the second equation into the first term of the first equation, there results

$$\Delta y = (D_u y)(D_x u)\,\Delta x + (D_u y)\,\epsilon_2\,\Delta x + \epsilon_1\,\Delta u,$$

which, after division by $\Delta x$, becomes

$$\frac{\Delta y}{\Delta x} = (D_u y)(D_x u) + (D_u y)\,\epsilon_2 + \epsilon_1\,\frac{\Delta u}{\Delta x}.$$

Since $f$ and $g$ were both assumed differentiable, it follows that $\lim_{\Delta x \to 0} (\Delta u/\Delta x)$ exists. Furthermore, $\Delta u \to 0$ as $\Delta x \to 0$, so that

$$\lim_{\Delta x \to 0} \epsilon_1 = \lim_{\Delta u \to 0} \epsilon_1 = 0.$$

We also had $\lim_{\Delta x \to 0} \epsilon_2 = 0$, so that the limit as $\Delta x \to 0$ of each of the last two terms in the formula for $\Delta y/\Delta x$ is zero, and we obtain

$$D_x y = (D_u y)(D_x u).$$

This formula for the derivative of a function of a function is frequently called the **chain rule**. By deriving it we have proved the following theorem.

**Theorem 6.3a.** If $f$ and $g$ are differentiable functions so that $f'(u_0)$ exists, where $u_0 = g(x_0)$ and $g'(x_0)$ exists, then the derivative of the composite function $F = f(g)$ exists at $x_0$ and is given by the formula

$$F'(x_0) = f'(u_0)g'(x_0).$$

*Note:* The derivation of the chain rule assumes that there is a neighborhood about $\Delta x = 0$ for which $\Delta u \neq 0$ since $\epsilon_1$ is undefined if $\Delta u = 0$. In order to avoid this assumption, we may define $\epsilon_1 = 0$ for $\Delta u = 0$ so that, for each value of $u$, $\epsilon_1$ is a continuous function of $\Delta u$. With this additional definition, the derivation of the formula is satisfactory even if there are zero values of $\Delta u$ in every neighborhood of $\Delta x = 0$.

As an example of the use of Theorem 6.3a, let us return to our first illustration of a composite function.

---

*Example 6.3a.* Find $D_x \sqrt{1 - x^2}$.

We write $y = u^{1/2}$ and $u = 1 - x^2$. Then

$$\begin{aligned}
D_x y &= (D_u y)(D_x u) \\
&= (\tfrac{1}{2}u^{-1/2})(-2x) \\
&= \tfrac{1}{2}(1 - x^2)^{-1/2}(-2x) \\
&= -x(1 - x^2)^{-1/2}.
\end{aligned}$$

---

The next theorem follows immediately as an application of the chain rule The details are left to the student.

**Theorem 6.3b.** Let $u = f(x)$ define a differentiable function. Then, in the domain common to $f'$ and the $(n-1)$th power of $f$,

$$D_x u^n = n u^{n-1} D_x u.$$

---

*Example 6.3b.* Find $D_x(2x^2 + 3x)^{10}$.

We use Theorem 6.3b to get

$$\begin{aligned} D_x(2x^2 + 3x)^{10} &= 10(2x^2 + 3x)^9 D_x(2x^2 + 3x) \\ &= 10(2x^2 + 3x)^9(4x + 3). \end{aligned}$$

---

*Example 6.3c.* Find $D_x y$ if

$$y = \sqrt{\frac{x^2 + 1}{x^2 - 1}}.$$

Let us write

$$y = \left(\frac{x^2 + 1}{x^2 - 1}\right)^{1/2}.$$

Then we have

$$\begin{aligned} D_x y &= \frac{1}{2}\left(\frac{x^2 + 1}{x^2 - 1}\right)^{-1/2} D_x\left(\frac{x^2 + 1}{x^2 - 1}\right) \\ &= \frac{1}{2}\left(\frac{x^2 - 1}{x^2 + 1}\right)^{1/2} \frac{(x^2 - 1)(2x) - (x^2 + 1)(2x)}{(x^2 - 1)^2} \\ &= \frac{-2x}{(x^2 + 1)^{1/2}(x^2 - 1)^{3/2}}. \end{aligned}$$

Notice that the quotient rule as well as the power rule is used in this example.

---

The chain rule is easily extended to longer chains of functions than tha considered in Theorem 6.3a. For example, in the case of three functions, w have

$$D_x y = (D_u y)(D_v u)(D_x v).$$

The reader may derive this result by making two applications of the chain rule

---

*Example 6.3d.* Find $D_x y$ if

$$y = \sqrt{1 - \frac{1}{x^2 + 1}}.$$

Consider the following chain of functions:

$$\{(u, y): y = u^{1/2}\},$$

$$\left\{(v, u): u = 1 - \frac{1}{v}\right\},$$

$$\{(x, v): v = x^2 + 1\}.$$

Then, $D_x y = (D_u y)(D_v u)(D_x v)$, where $D_u y = \frac{1}{2} u^{-1/2}$, $D_v u = v^{-2}$, and $D_x v = 2x$. Hence,

$$D_x y = \frac{1}{2} u^{-1/2} \frac{1}{v^2} (2x) = \frac{x}{(x^2 + 1)^2} \left(1 - \frac{1}{x^2 + 1}\right)^{-1/2}$$

$$= \frac{x}{(x^2 + 1)^2} \frac{\sqrt{x^2 + 1}}{|x|}.$$

Notice that $D_x y$ is discontinuous at $x = 0$. Is the function defined by the given formula discontinuous at $x = 0$? Explain.

## Exercises 6.3

In Numbers 1 to 10, write out a chain of functions and find the indicated derivative.

1. $y = \sqrt{x + 2}$; $D_x y$.
2. $y = \sqrt[3]{1 + 2x^2}$; $D_x y$.
3. $s = \dfrac{1}{\sqrt{2 - t}}$; $D_t s$.
4. $y = |x|$; $D_x y$.
   Hint: $|x| = \sqrt{x^2}$.
5. $u = \left(\dfrac{2s - 1}{2s + 1}\right)^{1/2}$; $D_s u$.
6. $y = \sqrt[3]{\dfrac{x^2 + 4}{x^2 - 4}}$; $D_x y$.

7. $v = \sqrt{1 + \dfrac{4}{4 + u^3}}$; $D_u v$.
8. $y = [1 + \sqrt{x}]^{3/2}$; $D_x y$.
9. $s = \dfrac{1}{1 - \dfrac{1}{1 - t}}$; $D_t s$.
10. $y = \dfrac{t}{\sqrt{1 - t^2}}$; $D_t y$.

11. Find $f'(x)$ for $f(x) = |x^2 - 9|$. *Hint*: See Number 4.
12. Derive a general formula for finding $D_x y$ if $y = |f(x)|$. *Hint*: See Number 4.

In Numbers 13 to 18, find the indicated derivative.

13. $f(x) = x\sqrt{x^2 - 1}$; $f'(x)$.
14. $y = \left(\dfrac{x}{x^2 - 1}\right)^{3/2}$; $D_x y$.
15. $w = \dfrac{z^2}{\sqrt{z^2 + 1}}$; $D_z w$.

16. $z = \left(1 + \dfrac{2a}{w}\right)^{3/2}$; $D_w z$.
17. $y = (a^{1/2} - x^{1/2})^2$; $D_x y$.
18. $y = (a^{2/3} - x^{2/3})^{3/2}$; $D_x y$.

19. Find the point (or points) on the graph of $y = 1/(x + \sqrt{x^2 + 1})$ where the tangent line has a slope of $-1$.
20. Find the points on the circle $x^2 + y^2 = 25$ where the tangent line is inclined $30°$. (When solving for $y$ be sure to get both halves of the circle.)
21. Examine $y = \sqrt{|x|}$ to find values of $x$ for which the graph has a vertical tangent. *Hint*: If the tangent is vertical at $x = a$, then $|f'(x)| \to \infty$ as $x \to a$.
22. Find the points (if there are any) where $y = \sqrt{x^2 + 4x + 3}$ has a horizontal tangent. (Caution!)
23. Prove Theorem 6.3b.
24. Derive the formula $D_x y = (D_u y)(D_v u)(D_x v)$ for a chain of three differentiable functions.

25. Show that if $y = f(x)$ has a horizontal tangent at any point, then $y = [f(x)]^n$, $n \in \mathfrak{N}$, has a horizontal tangent for the same value of $x$. Is the converse necessarily true?

26. Write equations for the tangent lines to the graph of the equation $y = 1/(\sqrt{x^2 - 9})$ at the points for which $|x| = 5$.

In Numbers 27 and 28, $s$ is measured in feet and $t$ in seconds.

27. A certain motion of a point in a straight line is descfibed by

$$s = \sqrt{t^2 + 1} - 1.$$

Find the times when the velocity is zero. Are there any times when the velocity is 1 foot per second?

28. The motion of a point in a straight line is given by

$$s = t\sqrt{1 - t^2}, \quad 0 < t < 1.$$

At what time is the velocity zero?

29. Is the set of all differentiable functions on an open interval $a < x < b$ closed with respect to composition—that is, does $g[f(x)]$ always define a differentiable function on $a < x < b$ if $f$ and $g$ are differentiable there?

## 6.4 HIGHER ORDER DERIVATIVES

We have seen that we may look upon the function

$$f' .=. \{(x, y'): y' = f'(x) = D_x y\}$$

as a new function derived from the function

$$f .=. \{(x, y): y = f(x)\}.$$

It is natural to consider the possibility of differentiating the derived function to obtain a second derived function and perhaps even to continue this sequence of differentiations.

The derivative (if it exists) of the function $f'$ is called the **second derivative** of $f$ and is denoted by $f''$. Also, the value of $f''$ at $x$ may be written in one of the following equivalent ways:

$$f''(x) .=. D_x(D_x y) .=. D_x^2 y .=. y''.$$

Thus, we have

$$f'' = \{(x, y''): y'' = D_x^2 y\}.$$

The *third, fourth,* ..., *n*th, ..., *derivatives* are all defined in a similar manner and are denoted by $f''', f^{(4)}, \ldots, f^{(n)}, \ldots$, respectively. The corresponding func tional values at $x$ are written

$$f'''(x) = D_x^3 y, \quad f^{(4)}(x) = D_x^4 y, \ldots,$$

the upper index on the $f$ or the $D$ indicating the order of the derivative.

If we wish to distinguish $f'$ from the higher order derivatives, we call it the *first derivative*.

*Example 6.4a.* Find $D_x^2(1 + x^2)^{3/2}$.

We first find

$$D_x(1 + x^2)^{3/2} = \tfrac{3}{2}(1 + x^2)^{1/2}(2x) = 3x(1 + x^2)^{1/2}.$$

Then,

$$D_x^2(1 + x^2)^{3/2} = 3[(1 + x^2)^{1/2} + (x)(\tfrac{1}{2})(1 + x^2)^{-1/2}(2x)]$$
$$= 3(1 + x^2)^{-1/2}(1 + 2x^2).$$

---

*Example 6.4b.* If $z = (1 - x)^n$, find $D_x^k z$, where $n$ and $k$ are positive integers and $k < n$.

First, we find

$$D_x z = n(1 - x)^{n-1}(-1) = -n(1 - x)^{n-1}.$$

Next,

$$D_x^2 z = -n(n - 1)(1 - x)^{n-2}(-1) = n(n - 1)(1 - x)^{n-2}.$$

Continuing in the same manner, we see that

$$D_x^k z = (-1)^k n(n - 1) \cdots (n - k + 1)(1 - x)^{n-k}.$$

---

If $s$ is the distance from the origin and $t$ is the time in a straight line motion with $s = f(t)$, we know that the derivative of $s$ with respect to $t$ is the velocity at time $t$; also, the derivative of the velocity with respect to $t$ is the acceleration at time $t$. Thus,

$$v = D_t s \quad \text{and} \quad a = D_t v,$$

so that

$$a = D_t^2 s.$$

That is, *the acceleration is the second derivative of the distance with respect to the time.*

If $x$ and $y$ are interpreted as the rectangular coordinates of a point on a curve $y = f(x)$, then $D_x y$ gives the slope of the curve at the point $(x, y)$, and $D_x^2 y$ is the *rate of change of the slope* with respect to $x$. We shall discuss some important geometrical implications of this interpretation in Chapter 7.

Derivatives of order higher than the second are not susceptible of any such simple physical or geometrical interpretations. However, as we shall see at a later time, these derivatives are of considerable importance in both theoretical and practical investigations.

## Exercises 6.4

Find the indicated derivative in each of Numbers 1 to 8.

1. $y = \dfrac{x + 1}{x - 1}$; $D_x^2 y$.

2. $y = \sqrt{x^2 + 2x + 3}$; $y''$.

3. $f(x) = \dfrac{x}{\sqrt{x + 1}}$; $f''(x)$.

4. $g(s) = s(s^2 + 1)$; $g'''(s)$.

5. $h(t) = (1 + 3t)^{1/3}$; $h'''(t)$.

6. $x = v^{4/5}$; $D_v^3 x$.

7. $y = x^{1/2}$; $D_x^n y$.

8. $w = \dfrac{1}{1 + 2u}$; $D_u^n w$.

In Numbers 9 to 14, $s$ (feet) is the distance at time $t$ (seconds) of a particle from the origin in a straight line motion. Find the time, the distance, and the velocity at each instant when the acceleration is zero.

9. $s = t^2 - \dfrac{1}{t}$, $t > 0$.

10. $s = 6t^{1/2} + t^{3/2}$, $t > 0$.

11. $s = t^4 - 24t^2 + 12t - 12$, $t \geq 0$.

12. $s = t^3 - 3t^2 + 2t - 1$, $t \geq 0$.

13. $s = \dfrac{32}{t^2 + 12}$, $t \geq 0$.

14. $s = t^2 + \sqrt{t - 1}$, $t > 1$.

15. Find the slope at each point on the following curve where the rate of change of the slope is zero:

$$y = 3x^5 - 40x^3 + x.$$

16. Compare the behavior of $f''$ at $x = 0$ for the three functions defined by

$$\text{(a) } f(x) = \frac{x^2}{|x|}, \quad \text{(b) } f(x) = \frac{x^3}{|x|}, \quad \text{(c) } f(x) = \frac{x^4}{|x|},$$

if $f(0) .=. 0$ in all three cases.

17. Find the rate of change of the slope at $(3, 27)$ for the curve $y = (2x - 3)^3$.

18. If $u$ and $v$ are functions of $x$, and $y = uv$, derive the formula

$$y'' = uv'' + 2u'v' + u''v.$$

Develop a similar formula for $y'''$.

19. If $f(x) = x|x|$, find the values of $x$ for which $f'(x)$ and $f''(x)$ exist. Sketch the graphs of $f$, $f'$, $f''$.

20. Show that if $y = x^2 - 3x$, then $x^2y'' - 2xy' + 2y = 0$.

21. If $f(x)$ and $g(x)$ are differentiable functions of $x$, determine which of the following statements are true.

(a) If $f'(x) = g'(x)$ for all $x$, then $f(x) = g(x)$ for all $x$.

(b) If $f(x) = g(x)$ for all $x$, then $f'(x) = g'(x)$ for all $x$.

(c) The domain of $f'' \subset$ the domain of $f'$.

(d) $(f^{(3)})^{(4)} = f^{(12)}$.

(e) $(f^{(4)})^{(3)} = f^{(7)}$.

## 6.5 EXPLICIT AND IMPLICIT FUNCTIONS

Most of the functions that we have met up to this point have been described by a statement of the form

$$f .=. \{(x, y): y = f(x)\},$$

where the equation $y = f(x)$ represents a formula or rule telling how to compute the value of the dependent variable $y$ directly in terms of the value of the independent variable $x$. Such a function is generally called an **explicit function**.

Let us represent an expression involving both $x$ and $y$ by the symbol $F(x, y)$ so that an equation involving both $x$ and $y$ but not solved for $y$ may be put into the form

$$F(x, y) = 0.$$

For example, the equation

$$x^2 + xy = 3 - y^2$$

may be written in the form $F(x, y) = 0$, where

$$F(x, y) .=. x^2 + xy + y^2 - 3.$$

In this last example, we may think of the equation

$$x^2 + xy + y^2 - 3 = 0$$

as a quadratic equation in $y$,

$$y^2 + xy + (x^2 - 3) = 0,$$

with the solutions for $y$,

$$y = \tfrac{1}{2}(-x \pm \sqrt{12 - 3x^2}).$$

Since there are two values of $y$ for each value of $x$ such that $|x| < 2$, the set of pairs $\{(x, y)\}$ is a relation but not a function. However, if we specify which sign to use before the radical, then the relation implies the existence of a function, either

$$f_1 = \{(x, y): y = \tfrac{1}{2}(-x + \sqrt{12 - 3x^2})\}$$

or

$$f_2 = \{(x, y): y = \tfrac{1}{2}(-x - \sqrt{12 - 3x^2})\},$$

depending upon which square root is specified. In either case, the domain of the function is $|x| \leq 2$.

It is because of examples such as the preceding one that we have an "intuitive" feeling that an equation $F(x, y) = 0$ generally implies one or more functional relationships. Actually, however, this is not always true. For instance, the equation

$$x^2 + y^2 + 1 = 0$$

is true for no real values of $x$ and $y$, so that it does not imply the existence of any real function.

The exact situation is beyond the scope of this book to describe. Instead, we accept the fact that, under circumstances usually met in the applications, an equation $F(x, y) = 0$ defines one or more differentiable functions, a particular one of which may be chosen by making additional specifications. A function whose existence is implied by an equation $F(x, y) = 0$ is called an **implicit function.**

Since it frequently happens that the equation $F(x, y) = 0$ cannot conveniently be solved for $y$, it becomes desirable to find $D_x y$ directly from the given equation. We may argue as follows

$$F(x, y) = 0 \Rightarrow y = f(x),$$

where $f(x)$ is such that substitution of it for $y$ in the equation $F(x, y) = 0$ reduces this equation to an identity; that is,

(1) $$F[x, f(x)] = 0$$

*for all x in the domain of f.* For example, if the expression for $y$ in the preceding definition of $f_1$ is substituted into the left member of the original equation

$$x^2 + xy + y^2 - 3 = 0,$$

we get

$$x^2 + x\left(\frac{-x + \sqrt{12 - 3x^2}}{2}\right) + \left(\frac{-x + \sqrt{12 - 3x^2}}{2}\right)^2 - 3$$

$$= x^2 - \tfrac{1}{2}x^2 + \tfrac{1}{2}x\sqrt{12 - 3x^2} + \tfrac{1}{4}x^2 - \tfrac{1}{2}x\sqrt{12 - 3x^2} + \frac{12 - 3x^2}{4} - 3,$$

which simplifies to zero as Equation (1) indicates.

As a consequence of Equation (1), it follows that

$$D_x F[x, f(x)] = 0.$$

The next example illustrates how this result can be used to find $D_x y$.

---

*Example 6.5a.* Find $D_x y$ from the equation

$$x^2 + xy + y^2 - 3 = 0.$$

The preceding discussion shows that

$$D_x(x^2 + xy + y^2 - 3) = 0$$

if $y = f(x)$ is implied by the given equation. Thus, we have

$$2x + D_x(xy) + D_x(y^2) = 0.$$

The term $xy$ may now be differentiated by the product rule and the term $y^2$ by the general power rule, keeping in mind that $y$ stands for the value at $x$ of one of the implicit functions determined by the given equation. Accordingly,

$$2x + (y + x \, D_x y) + 2y \, D_x y = 0.$$

This equation may now be solved for $D_x y$ by first collecting terms:

$$(x + 2y) \, D_x y = -(2x + y).$$

Then

$$D_x y = -\frac{2x + y}{x + 2y}, \qquad x \neq -2y.$$

---

In order to evaluate $D_x y$ for any given value of $x$, it is necessary to find the value of $y$ such that $F(x, y) = 0$. Thus, in the preceding problem let it be required to evaluate $D_x y$ for $x = 1$. Since, for $x = 1$ the given equation,

$$x^2 + xy + y^2 - 3 = 0,$$

becomes

$$y^2 + y - 2 = 0,$$

we have $y = -2$ or $y = 1$. Thus, $(1, 1)$ and $(1, -2)$ are points on the graph of the given equation. Notice that $(1, 1) \in f_1$ and $(1, -2) \in f_2$, where $f_1$ and $f_2$ are the designations we gave the two functions implied by the equation. Then at the point $(1, 1)$,

$$D_x y = -\frac{2+1}{1+2} = -1,$$

and at the point $(1, -2)$,

$$D_x y = -\frac{2-2}{1-4} = 0.$$

These results are illustrated in Figure 6.5a.

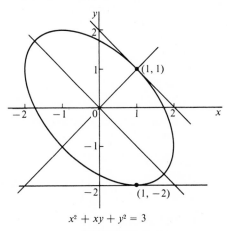

$$x^2 + xy + y^2 = 3$$

**FIGURE 6.5a**

Even though it may be impossible to solve the equation $F(x, y) = 0$ for $y$ explicitly in any simple form in terms of $x$, it is usually possible to obtain accurate numerical approximations to the solutions of $F(x_0, y) = 0$ for a specified numerical value of $x_0$. The existence of more than one such solution generally indicates that $F(x, y) = 0$ implies the existence of more than one function.

The process of taking the derivative with respect to $x$ of both members of $F(x, y) = 0$, while regarding $y$ as the value of the function implied by the equation, is called *implicit differentiation*. We can employ implicit differentiation to find higher derivatives, as in the next example.

---

*Example 6.5b.* Find $D_x^2 y$ for $x = 1$ if

$$x^2 + xy + y^2 - 3 = 0.$$

In Example 6.5a, we had

$$2x + y + x\,D_x y + 2y\,D_x y = 0.$$

We regard this equation along with the given equation as defining the value of $y$ and the value of $D_x y$, and we differentiate both members of the last equation with respect to $x$ to get

$$2 + D_x y + (D_x y + x\,D_x^2 y) + 2[(D_x y)^2 + y\,D_x^2 y] = 0.$$

Notice carefully the way in which the product terms are handled:

$$D_x(x\,D_x y) = (D_x x)(D_x y) + x\,D_x(D_x y)$$

and
$$D_x(y\, D_x y) = (D_x y)(D_x y) + y\, D_x(D_x y).$$

Note that $(D_x y)^2$ and $D_x^2 y$ are entirely different!

By collecting terms and solving for $D_x^2 y$, we find
$$D_x^2 y = -\frac{2 + 2\, D_x y + 2(D_x y)^2}{x + 2y}, \qquad x \neq -2y.$$

The simplest procedure to follow next is to substitute the values we found previously for $y$ and $D_x y$. Thus, at $(1, 1)$, where $D_x y = -1$,
$$D_x^2 y = -\frac{2 - 2 + 2}{1 + 2} = -\frac{2}{3},$$

and at $(1, -2)$, where $D_x y = 0$,
$$D_x^2 y = -\frac{2}{1 - 4} = \frac{2}{3}.$$

An alternative procedure for finding $D_x^2 y$ is to differentiate directly the expression found for $D_x y$. Thus,
$$
\begin{aligned}
D_x^2 y &= -D_x \left(\frac{2x + y}{x + 2y}\right) \\
&= -\frac{(x + 2y)\, D_x(2x + y) - (2x + y)\, D_x(x + 2y)}{(x + 2y)^2} \\
&= -\frac{(x + 2y)(2 + D_x y) - (2x + y)(1 + 2\, D_x y)}{(x + 2y)^2} \\
&= -\frac{3y - 3x\, D_x y}{(x + 2y)^2}.
\end{aligned}
$$

The expression for $D_x y$ may be substituted into the preceding result to obtain $D_x^2 y$ in terms of $x$ and $y$ alone. This gives
$$
\begin{aligned}
D_x^2 y &= -\frac{3y + 3x\,\dfrac{2x + y}{x + 2y}}{(x + 2y)^2} \\
&= -\frac{6(x^2 + xy + y^2)}{(x + 2y)^3}.
\end{aligned}
$$

But for all points $(x, y)$ on the graph of the given equation we have $x^2 + xy + y^2 = 3$. Hence,
$$D_x^2 y = \frac{-18}{(x + 2y)^3}, \qquad x \neq -2y.$$

Although the two expressions we found for $D_x^2 y$ are different in appearance, it is easy to show that substitution of the formula for $D_x y$ into the first expression reduces it to the second.

## Exercises 6.5

In each of Numbers 1 to 4, find whether or not the given equation describes one or more implicit functions. *Hint*: Complete the squares in $x$ and $y$.

1. $x^2 + y^2 - 2x + 4y + 6 = 0.$
2. $x^2 + y^2 - y + 1 = 0.$
3. $4x^2 + 9y^2 + 8x - 18y + 25 = 0.$
4. $4x^2 - 9y^2 + 8x + 18y - 17 = 0.$

In each of Numbers 5 to 10, use implicit differentiation to find the indicated derivative.

5. $4x^2 + y^2 = 16$; $D_x y$. Check by solving for $y$ first.
6. $x^2 - y^2 = 10$; $D_y x$. Check by solving for $x$ first.
7. $x^2 + y^2 - 10x + 4y = 0$; $D_x y$.
8. $x^2 - y^2 + 2xy = 10$; $D_y x$.
9. $x^3 - t^3 + 3t = 0$; $D_x t$.
10. $u + v + u^2 v^2 = 3$; $D_u v$.

In each of Numbers 11 to 16, find the slope of the curve at the given point.

11. $x^3 + y^3 - 2xy = 5$; $(1, 2)$.
12. $x^2 + y^2 - 4x - 6y = 0$; $(0, 0)$.
13. $(x + y)^2 - 3x - 2y = 0$; $(-1, 2)$.
14. $bx^2 = y^2(b - y)$, with $b > 0$; at the point where $y = b/2$, with $x > 0$.

15. $x = \dfrac{2a^3}{2a^2 - y^2}$; $(2a, -a)$.

16. $x^2 = \dfrac{b^3}{b - y}$; $(-b, 0)$.

In each of Numbers 17 to 22, use implicit differentiation to find the indicated derivative.

17. $x^2 - 2y^2 = 4$; $D_x^2 y$.
18. $xy = 50$; $D_x^2 y$.

19. $\dfrac{w}{z} - \dfrac{z}{w} = 1$; $D_z^2 w$.

20. $x^2 + y^2 = 3 - 2xy$; $D_x^2 y$.
21. $x^{2/3} + y^{2/3} = a^{2/3}$; $D_x^2 y$.
22. $u^{1/2} + s^{1/2} = a^{1/2}$; $D_s^2 u$.

In each of Numbers 23 to 26, find the value of $D_x^2 y$ at the points where $D_x y = 0$.

23. $x^3 + y^3 = a^3$.
24. $2\sqrt{x} + 3\sqrt{y} = 8$.

25. $x^2 + 2xy - y^2 + 8 = 0$.
26. $x^2 = y^4 - y^2$.

## 6.6 PARAMETRIC EQUATIONS

In Section 3.2, we discussed briefly the parametric equations of a straight line passing through a given point and having a given direction. Thus

$$x = 2 + 2t, \quad y = -1 + 6t$$

are parametric equations of the line passing through the point $(2, -1)$ and having direction numbers $[2, 6]$. Compare Example 3.2a.

In this section we shall discuss more general parametric representations, which will usually have graphs more complicated than a straight line. Suppose that $f$ and $g$ are two real-valued functions whose domains are $\mathcal{D}_f$ and $\mathcal{D}_g$, respectively, and suppose that $\mathcal{D}_f \cap \mathcal{D}_g$ is not empty. Then

$$S .=. \ \{(x, y): x = f(t), y = g(t), t \in \mathcal{D}_f \cap \mathcal{D}_g\}$$

is a set of points with a graph in the $xy$ plane. The equations

$$x = f(t), \quad y = g(t), \quad t \in \mathcal{D}_f \cap \mathcal{D}_g,$$

are called *parametric* equations of the graph and $t$ is called the **parameter.**

For example,

$$x = t, \quad y = \sqrt{1 - t^2}, \qquad |t| \leq 1,$$

are parametric equations of the upper half of the circle $x^2 + y^2 = 1$. This follows at once, since

$$(x^2 + y^2 = 1, x = t, |t| \leq 1, y \geq 0) \Rightarrow y = \sqrt{1 - t^2}.$$

Parametric equations occur most commonly in the discussion of curvilinear motion, where $x$ and $y$ may be considered to be the usual distances from the coordinate axes and the parameter $t$ is the time. Frequently, the equations $x = f(t)$ and $y = g(t)$ are called the **equations of motion.** The graph of the set of points $\{(x, y)\}$ is the **path** of the motion.

We often employ parametric equations to simplify the calculation of the coordinates of points on a given curve. For instance, points on the curve $4y^3 = 27x^2$ are easily found by putting $x = 2t^3$, which gives $y^3 = 27t^6$ and thus $y = 3t^2$, since $t, y \in \mathfrak{R}$. A three-column table with headings $t$, $x$, $y$ and a table of squares and cubes enable us to write down quite rapidly and in an obvious way the coordinates of points on the curve.

We shall postpone further discussion of curves represented in parametric form until Chapter 7. For the present, we wish to consider the calculation of $D_x y$ and $D_x^2 y$ when $x$ and $y$ are given in terms of a parameter, say $t$. We assume that the parametric equations

$$x = f(t), \quad y = g(t), \qquad t \in \mathfrak{D}_f \cap \mathfrak{D}_g,$$

imply the existence of at least one differentiable function $F$ such that $y = F(x)$. This would be true, for example, if $g$ were a differentiable function and $f$ had a differentiable inverse, so that $t = f^{-1}(x)$ and thus $y = g[f^{-1}(x)]$. Generally, we are faced with the same problems that occur in the discussion of implicit functions.

This discussion suggests the following theorem.

**Theorem 6.6a.** Let $f$ and $g$ be differentiable functions on an interval $t_1 < t < t_2$ and let $f$ have a differentiable inverse on this interval. Then at each point where $f'(t) \neq 0$, the equations

$$x = f(t) \quad \text{and} \quad y = g(t)$$

imply that there exists a differentiable function $F$ such that

$$y = F(x) \quad \text{and} \quad D_x y = \frac{g'(t)}{f'(t)} = \frac{D_t y}{D_t x}.$$

PROOF: Suppose that $t_1 < t_0 < t_2$ and $f'(t_0) \neq 0$. Then

$$x_0 = f(t_0) \quad \text{and} \quad y_0 = g(t_0)$$

are values of $x$ and $y$ corresponding to the value $t_0$. Also, we assumed that $f$ has an inverse, so that

$$t_0 = f^{-1}(x_0),$$

and thus

$$y_0 = g[f^{-1}(x_0)].$$

This procedure may be followed for each value $t_0$ in the given interval. From the assumption that $f^{-1}$ is a function, it follows that for each $x$ value corresponding to a $t$ value in the interval $t_1 < t < t_2$, there is exactly one value $f^{-1}(x)$, so that $g[f^{-1}(x)]$ furnishes one value of $y$. Thus,

$$F(x) = g[f^{-1}(x)]$$

defines a function.

At $t_0$ the equation $y = g(t)$ gives

$$D_x y = g'(t_0) D_x t$$

by the chain rule (Theorem 6.3a). Suppose further that $f'(t_0) \neq 0$. Then the equation $x = f(t)$ gives, upon differentiation with respect to $x$,

$$1 = f'(t_0) D_x t,$$

and we may solve for $D_x t$ to obtain

$$D_x t = 1/f'(t_0).$$

Therefore, at $t_0$,

$$D_x y = \frac{g'(t_0)}{f'(t_0)}.$$

Since $t_0$ is any value between $t_1$ and $t_2$ such that $f'(t_0) \neq 0$, the proof of the theorem is complete.

In Theorem 6.6a, it was assumed that $f$ is a differentiable function with a differentiable inverse on an interval $t_1 < t < t_2$. Frequently, in dealing with the inverse of a function, it is desirable to avoid the assumption that the inverse function $f^{-1}$ is differentiable. This assumption may be dropped provided the function $f$ itself satisfies suitable conditions, as in

**Theorem 6.6b.** Let $y = f(x)$ define a strictly increasing (decreasing) differentiable function $f$ on an interval $a < x < b$. Then, on each subinterval $x_1 < x < x_2$ over which $f'(x) \neq 0$, $f$ has a differentiable inverse function $f^{-1}$ and

$$D_y f^{-1}(y) = \frac{1}{D_x f(x)}.$$

PROOF: Since $f$ is differentiable on the interval $a < x < b$, it is continuous by Theorem 6.1a. Hence, by Theorem 4.5h, $f^{-1}$ exists and is continuous and strictly increasing (decreasing) over the same interval. By the definition of the inverse function,

$$y = f(x) \Rightarrow x = f^{-1}(y)$$

and

$$y + k = f(x + h) \Rightarrow x + h = f^{-1}(y + k).$$

Since $f$ and $f^{-1}$ are both strictly increasing (decreasing), it follows that $k \neq 0 \Leftrightarrow h \neq 0$. Using the definition of the derivative, we may write

$$D_y f^{-1}(y) = \lim_{k \to 0} \frac{f^{-1}(y+k) - f^{-1}(y)}{k} = \lim_{k \to 0} \frac{x+h-x}{k}$$

$$= \lim_{k \to 0} \frac{h}{k} = \lim_{k \to 0} \frac{1}{k/h}.$$

Because $f^{-1}$ is continuous, it is true that $h \to 0$ as $k \to 0$. Accordingly, since $k = f(x+h) - f(x)$,

$$\lim_{k \to 0} \frac{1}{k/h} = \lim_{h \to 0} \frac{1}{\dfrac{f(x+h) - f(x)}{h}}$$

$$= \frac{1}{\displaystyle\lim_{h \to 0} \frac{f(x+h) - f(x)}{h}} = \frac{1}{D_x f(x)}.$$

This result not only demonstrates the existence of $D_y f^{-1}(y)$, but also provides a method for finding it.

Note that under the hypotheses of Theorem 6.6b,

$$D_y x = \frac{1}{D_x y} \quad \text{if} \quad D_x y \neq 0.$$

---

*Example 6.6a.* Verify that Theorem 6.6a applies to the following equations and find $D_x y$ in terms of $t$:

$$x = t^2 + 2, \quad y = t + 1/t.$$

Writing $x .=. f(t) = t^2 + 2$ and $y .=. g(t) = t + 1/t$, we see that

$$\mathfrak{D}_f \cap \mathfrak{D}_g = \mathfrak{R} - \{0\}$$

(or all values of $t$ except $t = 0$) and that $f$ and $g$ are both differentiable on the common domain. Furthermore, the first equation has the solutions

$$t = \sqrt{x-2} \quad \text{and} \quad t = -\sqrt{x-2},$$

each of which defines a differentiable function for $x > 2$. Thus, either of the functions

$$f_1^{-1} = \{(x, t): t = \sqrt{x-2}, x > 2\},$$

or

$$f_2^{-1} = \{(x, t): t = -\sqrt{x-2}, x > 2\}$$

may be chosen as a differentiable inverse of $f$. (The particular choice would have to be dictated by another condition perhaps such as $t \geq 0$.) This completes the verification that the hypotheses of Theorem 6.6a are satisfied.

Accordingly, the theorem assures us that the two given equations do define a differentiable function with the value at $x$,

$$y = g[f_1^{-1}(x)] \quad \text{for } t > 0$$

and

$$y = g[f_2^{-1}(x)] \quad \text{for } t < 0.$$

Furthermore, whichever of the two functions is chosen, we have

$$D_x y = \frac{g'(t)}{f'(t)} = \frac{1 - 1/t^2}{2t}$$

$$= \frac{1}{2t} - \frac{1}{2t^3}.$$

As a check, we take the case where $t > 0$. Then

$$t = \sqrt{x - 2} \quad \text{and} \quad y = \sqrt{x - 2} + \frac{1}{\sqrt{x - 2}}$$

$$= (x - 2)^{1/2} + (x - 2)^{-1/2}.$$

Thus

$$D_x y = \tfrac{1}{2}(x - 2)^{-1/2} - \tfrac{1}{2}(x - 2)^{-3/2}$$

$$= \frac{1}{2t} - \frac{1}{2t^3},$$

as before.

---

To find $D_x^2 y$ when $x$ and $y$ are given in the parametric form $x = f(t)$, $y = g(t)$, we need only observe that Theorem 6.6a gives $D_x y$ in terms of the parameter $t$, say $D_x y = h(t)$. Hence, $D_x y$ and $x$ are both expressed in parametric form, and we may apply Theorem 6.6a with $y$ replaced by $D_x y$ to obtain

$$D_x(D_x y) = \frac{D_t(D_x y)}{D_t x}.$$

As an alternative, we may use the chain rule to differentiate $D_x y$ with respect to $x$ to get

$$D_x^2 y = D_x(D_x y) = D_t(D_x y)D_x t = \frac{D_t(D_x y)}{D_t x}.$$

---

*Example 6.6b.* Find $D_x^2 y$ for $x = t^2 + 2$ and $y = t + (1/t)$.

In Example 6.6a, we found that

$$D_x y = \frac{1}{2t} - \frac{1}{2t^3}.$$

Hence

$$D_x^2 y = \frac{D_t\left(\dfrac{1}{2t} - \dfrac{1}{2t^3}\right)}{D_t x} = \frac{-\dfrac{1}{2t^2} + \dfrac{3}{2t^4}}{2t}$$

$$= \frac{3}{4t^5} - \frac{1}{4t^3}.$$

---

Higher order derivatives may also be found in this manner. In general,

$$D_x^n y = \frac{D_t(D_x^{n-1} y)}{D_t x}.$$

It is frequently impossible for us to verify in an elementary fashion (say by using Theorem 6.6b) that $x = f(t)$ defines a function with a differentiable inverse. We shall assume (unless the contrary is stated) that this portion of the hypothesis of Theorem 6.6a is satisfied in the problems we consider. A more practical statement must await a deeper consideration of implicit functions than is possible at this point.

---

*Example 6.6c.* Find the points where the curve described by the following equations has a zero slope:

$$x = 3t/(1 + t^3), \quad y = 3t^2/(1 + t^3).$$

We have

$$D_t x = \frac{3[(1 + t^3) - 3t^3]}{(1 + t^3)^2} = \frac{3(1 - 2t^3)}{(1 + t^3)^2},$$

$$D_t y = \frac{3[2t(1 + t^3) - 3t^4]}{(1 + t^3)^2} = \frac{3(2t - t^4)}{(1 + t^3)^2},$$

so that

$$D_x y = \frac{D_t y}{D_t x} = \frac{2t - t^4}{1 - 2t^3}.$$

Then

$$D_x y = 0 \quad \text{for } t = 0 \text{ and for } t = 2^{1/3}.$$

For $t = 0$, we find $x = 0$, $y = 0$ and for $t = 2^{1/3}$ we find $x = 2^{1/3}$, $y = 4^{1/3}$. So the points where there is a zero slope are $(0, 0)$ and $(2^{1/3}, 4^{1/3})$.

## Exercises 6.6

In Numbers 1 to 6, show that $D_x y = 1/D_y x$ for all points at which the two derivatives are defined and $D_y x \neq 0$.

1. $y^2 = x$.
2. $y = x^2 - 3$.
3. $x = y^2 + 1$.

4. $x = y^3$.
5. $y = (x^2 - 2)^{1/2}$.
6. $x^2 + y^2 = a^2$.

In Numbers 7 to 12, find the coordinates of the point or points (if there are any) on the given curve where the slope of the curve is zero.

7. $x = 2t^2 - 9$, $y = t + \dfrac{1}{t}$.

8. $x = \dfrac{t^2}{t^2 - 1}$, $y = \dfrac{t}{t^2 - 1}$.

9. $x = \sqrt{t^2 - 1}$, $y = \sqrt{t^2 + 1}$.

10. $x = \dfrac{1}{t + 1}$, $y = \dfrac{1}{t - 1}$.

11. $x = t^{1/2} - 2t^{-1/2}$, $y = t^{1/2} + 2t^{-1/2}$.

12. $x = \dfrac{3}{1 + t^3}$, $y = \dfrac{3t}{1 + t^3}$.

In Numbers 13 to 16, find an equation of the line tangent to the curve at the indicated point.

13. $x = t^2 - 1$, $y = t^3 + 1$; $t = 2$.
14. $x = at$, $y = bt - ct^2$; $t = 0$.
15. $x = u/(1 + u^2)$, $y = u^2/(1 + u^2)$; $u = 1/2$.
16. $x = r^2 - 8r$, $y = r^{2/3}$; $r = 8$.

In Numbers 17 to 20, find $D_x y$ and $D_x^2 y$ in terms of the given parameter.

17. $x = 2u^2$, $y = 3u^3$.

18. $x = \sqrt{1 - v^2}$, $y = \sqrt{1 + v^2}$.

19. $x = at^{1/2}$, $y = bt + ct^2$.

20. $x = t/(t^2 - 1)$, $y = t^2/(t^2 - 1)$.

In each of the following problems, find the interval over which the hypotheses of Theorem 6.6a are satisfied. (The numbers refer to the preceding problems.)

21. Number 7.

22. Number 9.

23. Number 10.

24. Number 11.

## 6.7 DIFFERENTIALS

Whenever the derivative of a function $f$ exists, we have

$$D_x y = \lim_{\Delta x \to 0} \frac{\Delta y}{\Delta x} \Rightarrow \frac{\Delta y}{\Delta x} = D_x y + \eta,$$

where $\lim_{\Delta x \to 0} \eta = 0$. Hence,

(1) $$\Delta y = (D_x y)\, \Delta x + \eta\, \Delta x.$$

As we saw in Section 6.3, the right side of Equation (1) is an expression for the change or *increment* $\Delta y$ in $y$ corresponding to the increment $\Delta x$ in $x$. For example, if $y = x^3$, so that $D_x y = 3x^2$, then

$$\Delta y = (x + \Delta x)^3 - x^3 = 3x^2\, \Delta x + 3x(\Delta x)^2 + (\Delta x)^3$$
$$= (D_x y)\, \Delta x + [3x\, \Delta x + (\Delta x)^2]\, \Delta x.$$

Hence, for $y = x^3$, the $\eta$ of Equation (1) is given by

$$\eta = 3x\, \Delta x + (\Delta x)^2,$$

and it is clear that for any fixed value of $x$, $\eta$ can be made arbitrarily small by keeping $\Delta x$ sufficiently small.

In general, we may consider the increment in $y$ for any value of $x$ and any increment $\Delta x$. The fact that $\lim_{\Delta x \to 0} \eta = 0$ means that for any arbitrary $\epsilon > 0$, there is an $h$ such that

$$\Delta x \in \mathfrak{N}^*(0, h) \Rightarrow \eta \in \mathfrak{N}(0, \epsilon).$$

At a point $(x, y)$, we have $y = f(x)$, and

$$\Delta y = f'(x)\, \Delta x + \eta\, \Delta x.$$

If $f'(x) \neq 0$, then for each given $\theta > 0$, we can find a corresponding $h$ small enough that $|\eta| < \theta|f'(x)|$. In this sense, we can make the term $\eta\, \Delta x$ remain negligible in comparison with $f'(x)\, \Delta x$; that is, we can make $f'(x)\, \Delta x$ as good an approximation to the increment $\Delta y$ as we like by restricting $\Delta x$ to a sufficiently small neighborhood of zero.

For instance, in the preceding illustration, where $y = x^3$, at the point where $x = 3$, we have

$$f'(3) = 27 \quad \text{and} \quad \eta = 9\Delta x + (\Delta x)^2.$$

If it is required to have

$$|\eta| < (0.001)|f'(3)| = 0.027$$

or

$$|9\Delta x + (\Delta x)^2| < 0.027,$$

we can display a neighborhood of zero to which $\Delta x$ should be restricted. First, let us agree to keep $|\Delta x| < 1$ so that

$$|9\Delta x + (\Delta x)^2| = |\Delta x||9 + \Delta x| < 10|\Delta x|.$$

Then surely

$$|\eta| < 0.027 \quad \text{if} \quad |\Delta x| < 0.0027.$$

The preceding discussion serves as the basis for

**Definition 6.7a.** Let $f$ be a differentiable function. At any point $x$, where $f'(x) \neq 0$, the product $f'(x)\,\Delta x$ is called the **principal part** with respect to $x$ of the increment $\Delta y$, and is denoted by the symbol "dy." Thus,

$$dy .=. f'(x)\,\Delta x.$$

It is important to notice that the increments of the functional values so far considered have been with respect to the independent variable of the function. The treatment in the case of an intermediate variable is exemplified in the next discussion.

Suppose that we consider a composite function $F = f(g)$ defined by the chain

$$y = f(x), \quad x = g(t),$$

where $t$ is the final independent variable, $x$ is an intermediate variable, and

$$y = F(t).$$

We may apply Definition 6.7a to both $y$ and $x$ to get

$$dy = F'(t)\,\Delta t$$

and

$$dx = g'(t)\,\Delta t.$$

The chain rule applied to $F = f(g)$ gives

$$F'(t) = f'(x)g'(t),$$

so that

$$dy = f'(x)g'(t)\,\Delta t.$$

Consequently, since

$$dx = g'(t)\,\Delta t,$$

it follows that

$$dy = f'(x)\,dx.$$

In order to handle the independent variable itself, let us apply this definition to the identity function $f$, defined by $y = x$. The result is

$$dy = \Delta x.$$

However, since $y = x$, it is desirable to be able to substitute $x$ for $y$ and thus to have $dy = dx$, so that in this case we are led to write

$$dx .=. \Delta x.$$

The symbols $dx$, $dy$, and so on are called **differentials**. For $dy$ we may read the "differential of $y$." The entire discussion of the differential up to this point is summarized in the following definition.

**Definition 6.7b.** Let a differentiable function $f$ be defined by $y = f(x)$. The differential of $y$ is always

$$dy \ .=. \ f'(x) \, dx,$$

and, if $x$ is the final independent variable, then

$$dx \ .=. \ \Delta x.$$

A geometric interpretation of Definition 6.7b appears in Figure 6.7a. Since

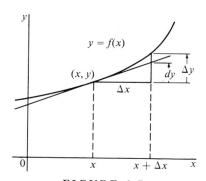

**FIGURE 6.7a**

the slope of the tangent line to the graph of $f$ at $x$ is $f'(x)$, the quantity $f'(x) \, \Delta x$ (or $f'(x) \, dx$) is the increment up to the tangent line corresponding to the increment $\Delta y$ up to the curve itself. The figure gives a visual indication that $dy$ becomes a better and better approximation to $\Delta y$ as $\Delta x$ is taken smaller and smaller.

---

*Example 6.7a.* What is the increment in $y$ and the differential of $y$ for an increment $\Delta x = 1$ at $x = 2$, if $y = x^2$? For an increment $\Delta x = 0.01$?

If $y = x^2$, $x = 2$, and $\Delta x = 1$, then

$$y + \Delta y = (x + \Delta x)^2,$$

so that

$$\Delta y = (x + \Delta x)^2 - x^2 = (2 + 1)^2 - (2)^2 = 9 - 4 = 5.$$

Furthermore, by Definition 6.7a,

$$dy = 2x \, dx = (2)(2)(1) = 4.$$

If $y = x^2$, $x = 2$, and $\Delta x = 0.01$, then

$$\Delta y = (x + \Delta x)^2 - x^2 = (2.01)^2 - 2^2 = 0.0401$$

and

$$dy = 2x \, dx = (2)(2)(0.01) = 0.0400.$$

*Example 6.7b.* A large, rubber weather balloon is 4 feet in diameter at sea level. After rising a certain distance in the atmosphere it swells to 4 feet, 2 inches in diameter. What is (a) the exact, (b) the approximate change in volume of the enclosed gas?

(a) The volume at sea level is $\frac{4}{3}\pi(24)^3$ cubic inches, and at the higher altitude it is $\frac{4}{3}\pi(25)^3$ cubic inches. The exact increase in volume is

$$\frac{4}{3}\pi(25)^3 - \frac{4}{3}\pi(24)^3 = \frac{4}{3}\pi(25-24)(25^2 + 25\cdot24 + 24^2)$$

$$= \frac{4}{3}\pi(1801) = (7.54)(10^3) \text{ cubic inches.}$$

(b) The approximate increase in volume can be obtained by finding the differential of the volume:

$$dv = 4\pi r^2 \, dr.$$

For $r = 24$ inches, $dr = 1$ inch, $dv = 4\pi(24)^2(1) = (7.24)(10^3)$ cubic inches.

---

*Example 6.7c.* Suppose a square of side $x$ has its side increased by an amount $dx = \Delta x$. Draw the original and the enlarged squares and interpret the increases in the area in terms of the increment of the area and the differential (see Figure 6.7b).

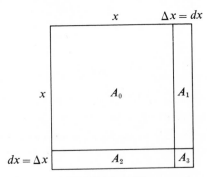

**FIGURE 6.7b**

For the original area, we have $A_0 = x^2$. The enlarged area is

$$A = (x + \Delta x)^2 = x^2 + 2x\,\Delta x + (\Delta x)^2.$$

The term $x^2$ is, of course, $A_0$. The term $2x\,\Delta x$ corresponds to the two areas $A_1$ and $A_2$. The term $(\Delta x)^2$ corresponds to $A_3$. The *increment*, $A_1 + A_2 + A_3$, is equivalent to $2x\,\Delta x + (\Delta x)^2$, and the differential of the area, $dA = 2x\,dx$, corresponds to $A_1 + A_2$.

---

It cannot be emphasized too strongly that the differential is defined for arbitrary $\Delta x$ or $dx$. It is only when the differential is to be used for approximating increments that $dx$ is required to be reasonably small.

As a consequence of the differential notation,

$$dy = f'(x) \, dx,$$

it is natural to divide by $dx$ and to write

$$\frac{dy}{dx} = f'(x).$$

This notation, which is due to Leibniz, is commonly used to designate the derivative, and we shall employ it often in the future. This notation may also be used for higher ordered derivatives. For example, by applying the definition of the differential to $f'$, we get

$$\frac{df'}{dx} = f''(x),$$

which may be written

$$\frac{d\left(\dfrac{dy}{dx}\right)}{dx} = f''(x).$$

The symbol $d\left(\dfrac{dy}{dx}\right)/dx$ is usually written as $d^2y/dx^2$, where it is to be understood that the symbols $d^2y$ and $dx^2$ do not have individual meanings in this notation. Similarly, we may write

$$\frac{d^n y}{dx^n} = f^{(n)}(x) = \frac{d\left(\dfrac{d^{n-1}y}{dx^{n-1}}\right)}{dx}$$

to denote the $n$th derivative of $f$.

It is sometimes convenient to have a basic derivative formula restated in differential form, as in the next example.

---

*Example 6.7d.* Suppose $u = f(x)$ and $v = g(x)$, where $f$ and $g$ are differentiable functions on a common domain. Express the differential of the product $uv$ in terms of the differentials of $u$ and $v$.

By the definition of the differential we have

$$\begin{aligned}
d(uv) &= D_x(uv)\, dx \\
&= (u\, D_x v + v\, D_x u)\, dx \\
&= u(D_x v)\, dx + v(D_x u)\, dx.
\end{aligned}$$

But

$$dv = (D_x v)\, dx \quad \text{and} \quad du = (D_x u)\, dx,$$

so that

$$d(uv) = u\, dv + v\, du.$$

---

*Example 6.7e.* Use differentials to find $D_x y$ from the equation $x^2 + xy + y^2 = 3$.

We make use of the fact that the derivative may be regarded as the quotient of the differentials $dy$ and $dx$ by finding the differentials of both members of the given equation and then solving for the ratio $dy/dx$. Thus,

$$d(x^2 + xy + y^2) = 0,$$

or

$$2x\,dx + x\,dy + y\,dx + 2y\,dy = 0,$$

or

$$(x + 2y)\,dy + (2x + y)\,dx = 0.$$

Hence,

$$D_x y = \frac{dy}{dx} = -\frac{2x + y}{x + 2y}.$$

Notice in Example 6.7e that the product $xy$ was differentiated by making use of the result of Example 6.7d. The verb "to differentiate" means to find either the differential or the derivative. It is usually clear from the context which of these is intended.

## Exercises 6.7

In each of Numbers 1 to 4, calculate the increment and the differential of $y$.

1. $y = x^2$; $x = 3$, $\Delta x = dx = 0.5$.
2. $y = x - 3$; $x = 5$, $\Delta x = dx = 0.1$.
3. $y = \sqrt{x}$; $x = 4$, $\Delta x = dx = 0.04$.
4. $y = 3x^3 - 9x$; $x = 1$, $\Delta x = dx = 1$.

In each of Numbers 5 to 10, use differentials to find $D_x y$.

5. $x^2 + y^2 = 4$.
6. $x^2 y + y^2 = 2x$.
7. $x^3 + 3xy + y^3 = 5$.
8. $x^4 - x^2 y^2 + y = 13$.
9. $x = t/(t^2 - 1)$, $y = (t^2 + 1)/(t^2 - 1)$.
10. $x = 3u$, $y = \sqrt{4 - u^2}$.

11. Use the differential to find an approximate value of $s$ for $t = 2.01$ if $s = t/(t^2 + 1)$.
12. Use the differential to find an approximate value of $y$ for $x = 10.01$ if

$$y = x^3 - 2x^2 + 1000.$$

13. Use the differential to find an approximate value of $\sqrt{9.04}$. *Hint:* Let $y = \sqrt{x}$. Then take $x = 9$, $\Delta x = 0.04$.
14. Find an approximate value of $\sqrt[3]{1027}$. See Number 13.
15. Find an approximate value of $(99)^{-1}$. See Number 13.
16. Find an approximate value of $\sqrt[3]{1004} - \sqrt[3]{996}$.
17. The length of a metal rod as a function of temperature is given by $L = L_0(1 + \alpha t)$, where $L_0$ is the initial length of the rod and $t$ is the temperature. Assuming that all three dimensions depend on the temperature in the same way, find a formula for the volume of a rectangular metal bar as a function of the temperature. Find the differential of the volume.
18. In Number 17, if the volume of the metal bar is increased by 0.1% when the temperature is changed from 100° to 110°, find the approximate value of $\alpha$.
19. A man contracts to dip-paint 10,000 circular metal signs each 2 feet in diameter. When they are delivered he discovers they are 1 inch in diameter oversize. Approximately what percentage of additional paint will be required?

20. A cone-shaped tank, vertex down, is 4 feet in diameter and 6 feet deep. If it is filled to a depth of 3 feet with water, approximately how much additional water will be required to raise the water level 2 inches?

21. What is the approximate percentage increase in the volume of wood per foot of log if the circumference of a tree increases from 12 feet to 12 feet 6 inches?

22. The image distance $q$ and the object distance $p$ of a simple thin lens are related by the equation

$$\frac{1}{p} + \frac{1}{q} = \frac{1}{f},$$

where $f$ is the focal length of the lens. Suppose a slide projector with a focal length of 3 inches, 10 feet away from the screen, is moved to 12 feet away from the screen. How far must the slide be moved in relation to the lens? (To simplify the problem, consider that focusing is accomplished by moving the slide, rather than the lens—as is usually done.)

23. Archimedes' principle states that a floating body displaces a volume of liquid equal in weight to the weight of the body. Suppose a hollow ball 10 centimeters in diameter sinks to a depth of 2 centimeters in water (1 gram per cubic centimeter). Now suppose 5 grams of lead is introduced into the interior of the ball. To what depth will it now sink? *Note*: If the sphere is submerged to a depth $h \leq 2r$, the volume of the submerged portion is

$$V = \tfrac{1}{3}\pi h^2(3r - h).$$

24. The formula for the period (time in seconds for a complete swing) of a simple pendulum is given by the formula $T = 2\pi\sqrt{L/g}$, where $L$ is the length of the pendulum in feet and $g = 32.16$ feet per second per second. The pendulum on a certain clock was intended to make one complete swing every 2 seconds, but the clock gains 2 minutes per day. Find the approximate change in the length of the pendulum that is necessary to correct the inaccuracy.

25. Express the differential of a sum $u + v$, where $u$ and $v$ are differentiable functions on a common domain, in terms of the differentials of $u$ and $v$.

26. Express the differential of the quotient $u/v$, where $u$ and $v$ are as in Number 25, in terms of the differentials of $u$ and $v$.

---

# Summary of Chapter 6

---

It is very important that the student develop a facility with techniques of differentiation in order that he be able to proceed into studies in which the ideas or concepts are of primary concern. Without this facility, he is likely to get bogged down in mechanical details and consequently miss the importance of the fundamental concepts. It is, therefore, appropriate that he understand clearly the following important results:

(1) what is meant by saying that a function is differentiable over an interval (Section 6.1);

(2) the relationship between the differentiability and continuity of a function (Section 6.1);

(3) the meaning of "derivative from the right (or left)" (Section 6.1);

(4) the product and quotient rules for differentiation (Section 6.2);

(5) the chain rule for the differentiation of a composite function (Section 6.3);

(6) the meaning of the second and higher order derivatives (Section 6.4);

(7) the interpretation of the second derivative as acceleration and rate of change of slope (Section 6.4);

(8) the differentiation of implicit functions (Section 6.5);

(9) the differentiation of functions defined by parametric equations (Section 6.6);

(10) the differentiation of the inverse of a function and the relationship of this derivative to the derivative of the original function (Section 6.6);

(11) the concept of the differential and its use in approximating increments (Section 6.7).

# Chapter 7    Further Applications of the Derivative

## 7.1 INCREASING AND DECREASING FUNCTIONS

It has already been noted several times that an important aspect of scientific investigation is the study of the way in which one quantity depends on another. For example, if $s = 16t^2$ gives the distance passed over by an object falling under the influence of gravity, then it is of interest to study exactly the manner in which $s$ increases as $t$ increases. We shall find that the derivative is an invaluable aid in many problems of this type.

More generally, we shall be concerned with the behavior of a function $f$ with values $y = f(x)$ as $x$ increases. Geometrically, this means that we shall be interested in the behavior of the curve given by the equation $y = f(x)$ as we view it from left to right.

In order to sketch a curve without plotting a great many points, it is desirable to obtain as much information about the curve as possible from the function. One important piece of information that can frequently be obtained tells us whether the curve is rising or falling over a particular interval.

Suppose that at a point $(x_0, y_0)$, the derivative $f'(x_0)$ is positive. Then the tangent line at the point slopes *up* from left to right as at the points $A$ and $C$ in Figure 7.1a. If the value of $x$ is slightly increased, it appears from the figure that the curve rises and that the value of $y$ increases.

Similarly, if $f'(x_0)$ is negative, the tangent line at $(x_0, y_0)$ slopes down from left to right as at $B$ in Figure 7.1a. If the value of $x$ is slightly increased, the curve falls and the value of $y$ decreases.

This discussion suggests the following definitions and theorems.

**Definition 7.1a.** A function $f$ is said to be *increasing on an open interval* if, for every pair of points $x_1$ and $x_2$ of the interval,

$$x_1 < x_2 \Rightarrow f(x_1) < f(x_2).$$

The student should formulate for himself the definition of a function *decreas-*

*ing on an open interval.* Figure 7.1a illustrates the graph of a decreasing function on the interval $p < x < q$ and an increasing function in the interval $q < x < r$.

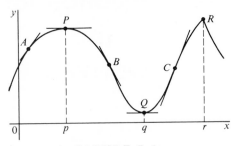

**FIGURE 7.1a**

A function that does not decrease (or does not increase) on an interval $a < x < b$ is said to be **monotonic** on that interval. If the function is always increasing (or decreasing) on the interval, then it is called a **strictly monotonic** function on that interval. For example, a function with a graph such as that in Figure 7.1b is monotonic but not strictly monotonic on the interval $a < x < b$.

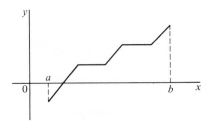

**FIGURE 7.1b**

**Theorem 7.1a.** Let $x_0$ be a point where $f$ has a nonzero derivative. Then there exists no neighborhood of $x_0$ such that $f(x_0)$ is either the least or the greatest value of $f$ on the neighborhood; that is, every neighborhood (no matter how small) of $x_0$ contains a point, say $x_1$, such that $f(x_1) < f(x_0)$ and also a point, say $x_2$, such that $f(x_2) > f(x_0)$.

PROOF: By the definition of the derivative, we have

$$f'(x_0) = \lim_{x \to x_0} \frac{f(x) - f(x_0)}{x - x_0},$$

so that there must be some $\mathfrak{N}^*(x_0, h)$ such that the value of the difference quotient itself is arbitrarily close to $f'(x_0)$ for all $x \in \mathfrak{N}^*(x_0, h)$.

Thus, if $f'(x_0) > 0$, then

$$x \in \mathfrak{N}^*(x_0, h) \Rightarrow \frac{f(x) - f(x_0)}{x - x_0} > 0.$$

But this neighborhood extends both to the left and to the right of $x_0$. Let $x_1 \in \mathfrak{N}^*(x_0^-, h)$. Then $x_1 - x_0 < 0$ and the preceding inequality implies that

$$f(x_1) < f(x_0).$$

Similarly, if $x_2 \in \mathfrak{N}^*(x_0^+, h)$, then $x_2 - x_0 > 0$ and so

$$f(x_2) > f(x_0).$$

The proof for the case where $f'(x) < 0$ is effected simply by a reversal of the inequality signs.

The points $A$, $B$, $C$ in Figure 7.1a illustrate Theorem 7.1a.

**Theorem 7.1b.** Let $x_0$ be a point such that $f(x_0)$ is either the least or the greatest value of $f$ on some neighborhood of $x_0$. Then $f'(x_0) = 0$ or else $f$ has no derivative at $x_0$.

PROOF: If $f$ has a derivative at $x_0$, then, in order not to contradict Theorem 7.1a, we must have $f'(x_0) = 0$. If $f$ has no derivative at $x_0$, then the conclusion of the theorem is, of course, satisfied.

Points $P$, $Q$, and $R$ in Figure 7.1a furnish illustrations of the preceding theorem. At $P$ and $Q$, the curve has horizontal tangents so that the derivative is zero, and at $R$ the derivative fails to exist.

**Theorem 7.1c.** Let $f$ be a differentiable function on an open interval $a < x < b$. Then $f'(x) > 0$ on the interval implies $f$ is increasing on the interval, and $f'(x) < 0$ on the interval implies $f$ is decreasing on the interval.

PROOF: Let $x_1$ and $x_2$ be any two points in the interval such that $x_1 < x_2$, and suppose $f'(x) > 0$. Then we must show that

$$f(x_1) < f(x_2).$$

Consider the closed interval $x_1 \leq x \leq x_2$. Since $f$ is differentiable, it must be continuous, and hence, by Theorem 4.7g, must have a maximum value on this closed interval. Furthermore, $f'(x) > 0$, so that by Theorem 7.1a this maximum cannot occur at any interior point.

Suppose that the maximum is at $x_1$. Then for all $x$ in the interior of the interval, $x - x_1 > 0$ and $f(x) - f(x_1) \leq 0$, so that

$$\frac{f(x) - f(x_1)}{x - x_1} \leq 0,$$

which implies that $f'(x_1) \leq 0$. (Why?) But $f'(x_1) > 0$ by hypothesis. This contradiction shows that the maximum must occur at $x_2$; that is,

$$f(x_1) < f(x_2).$$

The proof for the case $f'(x) < 0$ is quite similar to that for $f'(x) > 0$ and is therefore left to the reader.

---

*Example 7.1a.* Find the intervals on which $y = x^2 + 1$ is increasing or decreasing.

Since $y' = 2x$, $y$ is increasing for $x > 0$ and decreasing for $x < 0$, by Theorem 7.1c.

---

*Example 7.1b.* Discuss the graph of

$$y = \frac{x}{1 - x^2}.$$

Since

$$y' = \frac{1 + x^2}{(1 - x^2)^2} > 0 \quad \text{for all } x, \; |x| \neq 1,$$

we conclude, by Theorem 7.1c, that the graph is rising everywhere. The given equation shows that $x = 1$ and $x = -1$ are vertical asymptotes, and $y = 0$ is a horizontal asymptote. The equation also shows that $(0, 0)$ is the only intercept (see Figure 7.1c).

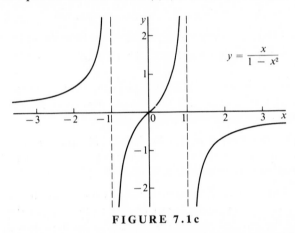

$$y = \frac{x}{1 - x^2}$$

**FIGURE 7.1c**

*Example 7.1c.* The motion of a particle in a straight line is given by the formula

$$s = t + \frac{1}{t},$$

where $s$ is in feet and $t$ in seconds. For what values of $t$ is $s$ increasing (the particle moving to the right)?

Since

$$D_t s = 1 - \frac{1}{t^2} = \frac{t^2 - 1}{t^2},$$

we see that

$$\frac{t^2 - 1}{t^2} > 0 \quad \text{for } t^2 > 1,$$

that is, for $t < -1$ or $1 < t$. Thus, $s$ increases for $t < -1$ and for $t > 1$.

## Exercises 7.1

In Numbers 1 to 10, determine the open intervals of the domain for which $f$ is an increasing function; a decreasing function. In each case $f. =. \{(x, y)\}$.

1. $y = \sqrt{|x|}$.
2. $y = x^2 - 5x + 6$.

3. $y = \frac{x + 1}{x - 1}$.

4. $f(x) = x^2 + \frac{1}{x^2}$.

5. $y = x^3$.
6. $f. =. \{(x, y): x^2 + y^2 = a^2, y \geq 0\}$
7. $y = x^3 + x^2 - x - 2$.

8. $y = |x|^3$.
9. $f.=. \{(x, y): x = t - 2, y = t^2 + 1\}$. (Check by eliminating $t$.)
10. $f.=. \left\{(x, y): x = t + \dfrac{1}{t}, y = t - \dfrac{1}{t}\right\}$.

11. Choose $x_0 = 0$ and show that the function defined in Number 1 illustrates Theorem 7.1b.
12. Find the vertex of the parabola described by the equation in Number 2. Use this point to illustrate Theorem 7.1b.
13. Show that the points where $x = \pm a$ in Number 6 furnish an illustration of Theorem 7.1b.
14. Apply Theorem 7.1a to show that the function $f$ defined by $f(x) = 1/x^3$ can have no greatest or least value.
15. Find the greatest and least values of $y$ if

$$y = \frac{x}{x^2 + 4}, \qquad 0 \leq x \leq 1.$$

16. Suppose the domain of $f$ is the set $\mathfrak{R}$ of all real numbers and

$$f(x) = \frac{x}{x^2 + 4}.$$

At what points might $f$ have its greatest or least values? Can you determine what actually does occur?

## 7.2 CONCAVITY AND THE SIGN OF THE SECOND DERIVATIVE

Let us consider the curve shown in Figure 7.2a. In a neighborhood of such points as $A$ and $B$, the curve lies below its tangent line, and in going from $A$

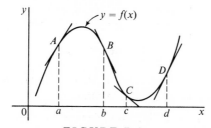

**FIGURE 7.2a**

to $B$ the tangent line turns in the clockwise direction. Similarly, in a neighborhood of $C$ or $D$, the curve lies above its tangent line, and in going from $C$ to $D$ the tangent line turns in the counterclockwise direction. Furthermore, if the tangent line turns counterclockwise as we go to the right, the slope of the tangent line increases, and if the tangent line turns clockwise, the slope decreases. Since the slope of the tangent line at any point $(x, y)$ is given by $f'(x)$, it appears that the sign of $D_x f'(x) = f''(x)$, provided $f''$ exists, may be used to distinguish the behavior of the curve at a point such as $A$ from that at a point such as $C$.

**Theorem 7.2a.** Let $f$ be a twice differentiable function on the interval $a < x < b$.

(i) If $f''(x) > 0$ for $a < x < b$, then the slope of the graph of $f$ is an increasing function and the tangent to the graph turns counterclockwise as $x$ increases.

(ii) If $f''(x) < 0$ for $a < x < b$, then the slope of the graph of $f$ is a decreasing function and the tangent of the graph turns clockwise as $x$ increases.

PROOF: The proof follows at once from the discussion in Section 7.1.

Suppose that $f$ is a twice differentiable function on an interval $a < x < b$. Then $f'$ is a continuous function on this interval and the graph of $f$ has a tangent line at each of its points. If $(x_1, y_1)$ is such a point, then the equation of the tangent line is, as we have seen,

$$y - y_1 = f'(x_1)(x - x_1)$$

or

$$y = f(x_1) + f'(x_1)(x - x_1),$$

since $y_1 = f(x_1)$. The equation of the tangent defines a linear function, say $t$, such that

$$t(x) = f(x_1) + f'(x_1)(x - x_1)$$

is the directed distance from the $x$-axis to the tangent line measured parallel to the $y$-axis (see Figure 7.2b).

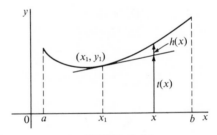

FIGURE 7.2b

The following theorem shows how the sign of $f''(x)$ determines whether the graph of $f$ lies above or below its tangent line.

**Theorem 7.2b.** Let $f$ be a twice differentiable function on the interval $a < x < b$. Let $x_1$ be a point in this interval, and let $t$ be the linear function defined by

$$t(x) = f(x_1) + f'(x_1)(x - x_1).$$

(i) If $f''(x) > 0$ on the interval, then for each $x_1$ there is a $\mathfrak{N}^*(x_1, k)$ such that $x \in \mathfrak{N}^*(x_1, k) \Rightarrow f(x) > t(x)$.

(ii) If $f''(x) < 0$ on the interval, then for each $x_1$ there is a $\mathfrak{N}^*(x_1, k)$ such that $x \in \mathfrak{N}^*(x_1, k) \Rightarrow f(x) < t(x)$.

Note that in (i) the geometric interpretation of the final inequality is that the curve given by $y = f(x)$ lies above its tangent line over the $\mathfrak{N}^*(x_1, k)$ and in (ii) the curve lies below its tangent line.

PROOF: Consider the function $h = f - t$, where $h(x) = f(x) - t(x)$. (Geometrically, this is the directed distance *from* the tangent line *to* the graph of $f$ measured parallel to the $y$-axis. See Figure 7.2b.)

From the definition of $t$, we have

$$h(x) = f(x) - f(x_1) - f'(x_1)(x - x_1),$$

where $f(x_1)$ and $f'(x_1)$ are the constants obtained by evaluating $f$ and $f'$ at $x_1$. Clearly, $h(x_1) = 0$, and

$$h'(x) = f'(x) - f'(x_1).$$

Since $f''(x) > 0$ means that $f'(x)$ is increasing with increasing $x$, it is true that, for all $x$ in the interval,

$$x > x_1 \Rightarrow f'(x) > f'(x_1) \Rightarrow h'(x) > 0$$

and

$$x < x_1 \Rightarrow f'(x) < f'(x_1) \Rightarrow h'(x) < 0.$$

But $h'(x) > 0$ implies that $h(x)$ is increasing with $x$, so that

$$x > x_1 \Rightarrow h(x) > h(x_1) = 0.$$

Similarly, $h'(x) < 0$ implies $h(x)$ is decreasing with $x$, so that

$$x < x_1 \Rightarrow h(x) > h(x_1) = 0.$$

This completes the proof of (i). The proof of (ii) differs from this only in minor details and is left for the reader.

**Definition 7.2a.** The graph of a function is said to be *concave up* over an interval if the graph lies above its tangent line in the sense of Theorem 7.2b. The graph is said to be *concave down* if it lies below its tangent line.

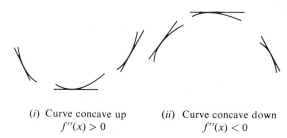

(*i*) Curve concave up      (*ii*) Curve concave down
$f''(x) > 0$              $f''(x) < 0$

**FIGURE 7.2c**

In view of this definition, Theorem 7.2b may be restated as follows:
(i) *Over any interval where* $f''(x) > 0$, *the graph of $f$ is concave up.*
(ii) *Over any interval where* $f''(x) < 0$, *the graph of $f$ is concave down.*
Figure 7.2c illustrates schematically the possibilities for (i) and (ii).

*Example 7.2a.* Examine the concavity of the graph of the function $f$, where $f(x) .=. x^2 - 4x^{1/2}$.

We first find

$$f'(x) = 2x - 2x^{-1/2}$$

and

$$f''(x) = 2 + x^{-3/2}.$$

The domain of $f$ is $x \geq 0$ (why?) and the domains of $f'$ and $f''$ are both $x > 0$. For $x > 0$, it is clear that $f''(x) > 0$. Hence, the graph is concave upward for $x > 0$. The reader may examine the function in more detail near $x = 0$ to see that as $x \to 0^+$, the curve approaches tangency to the $y$-axis at the origin. Since $f(0) = 0$, the origin is on the curve, but the curve does not extend to the left of the origin. (See Figure 7.2d.)

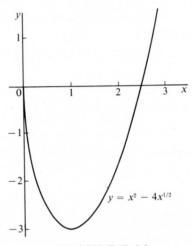

$$y = x^2 - 4x^{1/2}$$

**FIGURE 7.2d**

---

*Example 7.2b.* Find where the curve

$$24y = x^3 - 6x^2 - 36x + 16$$

is concave up and where it is concave down.

We first find

$$24y' = 3x^2 - 12x - 36 = 3(x + 2)(x - 6),$$

and

$$24y'' = 6x - 12 = 6(x - 2).$$

Hence,

$$y'' > 0 \quad \text{for } x > 2,$$

so that the curve is concave up for $x > 2$.

Similarly, $y'' < 0$ for $x < 2$, so that the curve is concave down for $x < 2$ (see Figure 7.2e).

---

In Example 7.2b, we find that $y'' = 0$ for $x = 2$ and the point $(2, -3)$ on the curve separates a portion of the curve that is concave up from a portion that is concave down. At such a point, the tangent line must cross the curve, as Figure 7.2e illustrates. Points of this kind are useful guides in curve sketching

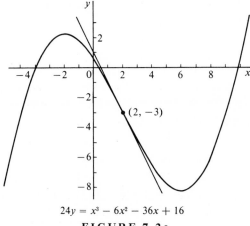

$$24y = x^3 - 6x^2 - 36x + 16$$

**FIGURE 7.2e**

**Definition 7.2b.** A point on a curve at which there exists a unique tangent line and which separates a portion of the curve that is concave up from a portion that is concave down is called an **inflection point.** The tangent to the curve at an inflection point is called an **inflectional tangent.**

**Definition 7.2c.** If there is a deleted neighborhood of a point $x_0$ such that a given function is positive on one half of the neighborhood and negative on the other half, then the function is said to *change sign* at $x_0$.

For example, the quadratic function $q$, defined by

$$q(x) = (x - 1)(x + 2),$$

changes sign at $x = -2$ and at $x = 1$.

**Theorem 7.2c.** On a curve $y = f(x)$, let $(x_0, y_0)$ be a point where the curve has a unique tangent line. The point $(x_0, y_0)$ is an inflection point of the curve if $f$ has a continuous second derivative in some $\mathfrak{N}^*(x_0)$ and $f''$ changes sign at $x_0$.

PROOF: The reader should note that the hypothesis of this theorem is satisfied only if $f''(x_0) = 0$ or else $f''(x_0)$ does not exist. The proof of the theorem follows directly from Definition 7.2b and the connection between the sign of $f'(x)$ and the concavity of the graph of $f$. The details are left for the exercises.

---

*Example 7.2c.* Find an equation of the inflectional tangent to the curve in Example 7.2b.

The discussion preceding Definition 7.2b shows that $(2, -3)$ is the inflection point. In Example 7.2b, we found

$$24y' = 3(x + 2)(x - 6).$$

For $x = 2$, we get $y' = -2$, which is the slope of the required line. Thus, an equation of the inflectional tangent is

$$y + 3 = -2(x - 2),$$

or

$$y = -2x + 1.$$

---

*Note:* It is instructive to show directly that this line actually crosses the curve at $(2, -3)$. We may do this by subtracting the ordinate of the line from that of the curve. Thus, we get

$$
\begin{aligned}
h(x) &= \tfrac{1}{24}(x^3 - 6x^2 - 36x + 16) - (-2x + 1) \\
&= \tfrac{1}{24}(x^3 - 6x^2 + 12x - 8) \\
&= \tfrac{1}{24}(x - 2)^3
\end{aligned}
$$

for the directed vertical distance from the line to the curve. The result shows at once that $h(x)$ changes sign at $x = 2$.

---

*Example 7.2d.* Examine the curve $y = (x - 2)^{1/3}$ for inflection points.

We first find the derivatives

$$D_x y = \tfrac{1}{3}(x - 2)^{-2/3}$$

and

$$D_x^2 y = -\tfrac{2}{9}(x - 2)^{-5/3}.$$

In this example, there is no value of $x$ such that $D_x^2 y = 0$; however, $D_x^2 y$ fails to exist

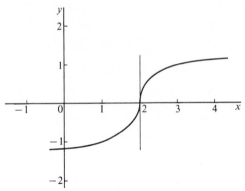

**FIGURE 7.2f**

for $x = 2$. The point $(2, 0)$ is on the curve (why?), and it is evident from the formula for $D_x^2 y$ that the second derivative function is continuous except at $x = 2$. Furthermore,

$$D_x^2 y > 0 \quad \text{for } x < 2,$$

and

$$D_x^2 y < 0 \quad \text{for } x > 2.$$

Accordingly, the curve is concave up for $x < 2$ and concave down for $x > 2$, so that $(2, 0)$ is an inflection point. We see also that

$$D_x y \to \infty \quad \text{as } x \to 2$$

so that the inflectional tangent is vertical (see Figure 7.2f).

## Exercises 7.2

For each of Numbers 1 to 8, find the intervals in which the curve is concave up and those in which it is concave down. Also find the inflection points.

1. $y = 3x^5 - 10x^3$.
2. $y = 3x^5 + 30x^4 + 110x^3 + 180x^2$.
3. $y = 4x^3 - x^4$.
4. $y = 4x^3 - 3x^5$.
5. $y = x - x^{-1}$.
6. $y = 3x^2 - 4x^{5/2}$.
7. $y = a^2x/(x^2 + a^2)$, $a > 0$.
8. $y = \left(\dfrac{x}{x+1}\right)^2$.

9. Let the equation of a "cubic curve" be

$$y = ax^3 + bx^2 + cx + d.$$

Prove that this curve always has one inflection point and that this point is a point of symmetry of the curve. *Hint*: If $(h, k)$ is the inflection point, the substitution

$$x = x' + h, \quad y = y' + k,$$

will yield the equation of the curve referred to a new set of axes with the origin at the inflection point. Then the usual test for symmetry with respect to the origin may be used.

10. Find conditions on the coefficients so that

$$y = ax^4 + bx^3 + cx^2 + dx + e$$

has no inflection point (if possible).

★11. Construct an equation $y = ax^4 + bx^3 + cx^2 + dx + e$ so that the corresponding curve is concave down for $-1 < x < 2$, is concave up everywhere else, and that passes through the points $(0, 1)$, $(2, 0)$, and $(-1, 0)$. *Hint*: Start by writing $f''(x) = A(x - x_1)(x - x_2)$, with $x_1$ and $x_2$ chosen to satisfy the concavity conditions.

In each of Numbers 12 to 20, assume that $f$ has a continuous second derivative. Sketch a curve showing the behavior of the graph of $f$ over a $\mathfrak{N}(a, h)$, if the prescribed behavior is possible. If not possible, explain why.

12. $f''(a) = 0; f'(a) = 0; x \in \mathfrak{N}^*(a, h) \Rightarrow f'(x) > 0$.
13. $f''(a) = 0; f'(a) = 0; x \in \mathfrak{N}^*(a, h) \Rightarrow f'(x) < 0$.
14. $f''(a) > 0; x \in \mathfrak{N}(a, h) \Rightarrow f'(x) > 0$.
15. $f''(a) < 0; x \in \mathfrak{N}(a, h) \Rightarrow f'(x) > 0$.
16. $f''(a) = 0; f'(a) > 0; x \in \mathfrak{N}^*(a^-, h) \Rightarrow f''(x) < 0; x \in \mathfrak{N}^*(a^+, h) \Rightarrow f''(x) > 0$.
17. $f''(a) = 0; f'(a) < 0; x \in \mathfrak{N}^*(a^-, h) \Rightarrow f''(x) < 0; x \in \mathfrak{N}^*(a^+, h) \Rightarrow f''(x) > 0$.
18. $f''(a) = 0; x \in \mathfrak{N}^*(a^-, h) \Rightarrow f'(x) < 0; x \in \mathfrak{N}^*(a^+, h) \Rightarrow f'(x) > 0$.
19. $f''(a) = 0; f'(a) = 1, x \in \mathfrak{N}^*(a, h) \Rightarrow f'(x) < 0$.
20. $f''(a) > 0; x \in \mathfrak{N}^*(a, h) \Rightarrow f''(x) < 0$.
21. Show that the curve $y = (x^2 + a^2)^{k/2}$, $k \neq 0$, has two inflection points for $k < 1$ and no inflection points for $k \geq 1$.

## 7.3 MAXIMA AND MINIMA

Many mathematical problems are concerned with finding the maximum (greatest) or the minimum (least) value of a function, and the derivative is often a useful tool in such problems. It also frequently happens that we are concerned with the greatest or least value over a certain neighborhood in the domain of the function rather than with the absolutely greatest or least value over the entire domain. The next definition makes this idea more precise.

**Definition 7.3a.** A function $f$ is said to have a **relative maximum** at a point $x_0$ of the domain of $f$ if there is a neighborhood $\mathfrak{N}(x_0)$ such that $f(x_0) \geq f(x)$ for each $x \in \mathfrak{N}(x_0)$.

A **relative minimum** is defined in a similar manner. The greatest value (if there is one) of a function on its entire domain is sometimes called an *absolute maximum*. The least value is called an *absolute minimum*. We shall frequently use the terms maximum and minimum to refer to either a relative or an absolute maximum or minimum since it will be clear from the context which is intended. The maxima and minima of a function are called the **extremes** of the function. Note that the existence of a relative maximum (or minimum) at $x_0$ implies that the function is defined in some neighborhood of $x_0$. If $x_0$ is an end point of the domain of $f$, then the neighborhood is a left or a right neighborhood, and the extreme is sometimes called an *end point extreme*. Figure 7.3a illustrates some of the ways in which extremes can occur.

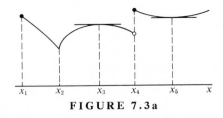

**FIGURE 7.3a**

The graph shown in Figure 7.3a is that of a function with a relative maximum at each of the points where $x = x_1$, $x_3$, and $x_4$, and with a relative minimum for each of $x = x_2$ and $x_5$. The extreme at $x_1$ is an end point maximum. The extreme at $x_2$ is an absolute minimum. There is no absolute maximum as the curve is indicated to be rising indefinitely for $x > x_5$.

The figure also suggests that if $f(x_0)$ is an extreme and $f'(x_0)$ exists, then $f'(x_0) = 0$. This seems to be so at $x = x_3$ and at $x = x_5$. At $x_1$, $x_2$, and $x_4$, the derivative apparently does not exist. (Only one-sided derivatives can exist at such points.) The following theorem covers these conjectures.

**Theorem 7.3a.** If a function has an extreme $f(x_0)$, then either

(i) $f'(x_0) = 0$, or else

(ii) $f'(x_0)$ does not exist.

PROOF: If $f(x_0)$ is an end point extreme, then $f$ can have only a one-sided derivative at $x_0$; the derivative itself does not exist. Suppose that $x_0$ is in the interior of the domain. By Theorem 7.1a, if $f'(x_0)$ exists and is different from zero, then $f(x_0)$ is not an extreme, which is contrary to the hypothesis. Accordingly, either $f'(x_0) = 0$ or else $f'(x_0)$ does not exist.

It is important to realize that the converse of Theorem 7.3a is not true. For example, the function $f$ defined by $f(x) = x^3$ has a zero derivative for $x = 0$, since $f'(x) = 3x^2$. Yet $f$ has no extreme at $x = 0$ as $f'(x) > 0$ for $x \neq 0$, so that $f$ is an increasing function over its entire domain, the set of all real numbers. The student may easily verify that the curve $y = x^3$ has a point of inflection with a horizontal tangent at $(0, 0)$. As an illustration of an instance where the nonexistence of the derivative does not imply an extreme, the reader may refer to Example 7.2d.

In summary, the preceding paragraph shows that neither $f'(x_0) = 0$ nor the failure of $f'(x_0)$ to exist is a sufficient condition for $f(x_0)$ to be an extreme. However, it does follow from Theorem 7.3a that an extreme of a function can occur only (i) at an end point of its domain or (ii) at an interior point where the derivative either is zero or else fails to exist. Accordingly, points where $f'(x) = 0$, or where $f'(x)$ fails to exist, and end points of the domain are called **critical points of the domain** of $f$.

A direct consequence of the preceding discussion is stated in

**Theorem 7.3b.** If the function $f$ is continuous on a closed interval $a \leq x \leq b$ and if $f(a) = f(b)$, then there exists at least one critical point $x_c$ in the open interval $a < x < b$.

PROOF: If $f$ is a constant function, then $f'(x) = 0$ for all $x$ in the open interval. In this case, any such point may be taken as the $x_c$ of the theorem. If $f$ is not a constant function, then, as a consequence of the continuity of $f$, it must attain both a maximum and a minimum value on the closed interval (see Theorem 4.7g). But since $f(a) = f(b)$ and $f(x)$ is not a constant, one of these extremes must occur at a point inside the interval. By Theorem 7.3a this point is a critical point of the domain, and the proof is complete.

If, in addition to the continuity of $f$ on the closed interval $a \leq x \leq b$, it is known that $f'$ exists on the open interval, then for the $x_c$ of Theorem 7.3b, we have $f'(x_c) = 0$. We state this result as

**Theorem 7.3c.** *Rolle's Theorem.* If the function $f$ is continuous on the closed interval $a \leq x \leq b$, with $f(a) = f(b)$, and if $f'(x)$ exists everywhere on the open interval $a < x < b$, then there is at least one number $x_c$, $a < x_c < b$, such that $f'(x_c) = 0$.

PROOF: This is a direct consequence of the preceding two theorems. The details are left to the reader.

---

*Example 7.3a.* Show that the function $f$ defined by

$$f(x) = |1 - x^2|, \qquad -2 \leq x \leq 2,$$

illustrates Theorems 7.3b and 7.3c.

Since

$$f(x) = \begin{cases} 1 - x^2 & \text{for } |x| < 1, \\ x^2 - 1 & \text{for } 1 \leq |x| \leq 2, \end{cases}$$

it follows that $f$ is continuous on $-2 \leqq x \leqq 2$. Moreover,

$$f'(x) = \begin{cases} -2x & \text{for } |x| < 1, \\ 2x & \text{for } 1 < |x| < 2. \end{cases}$$

Hence,

$$f'(x) = 0 \quad \text{for } x = 0,$$

and $f'(x)$ does not exist at $x = -1$ or at $x = 1$. (Why?)

Thus, we have an example in which both types of critical points occur. This illustrates Theorem 7.3b. Furthermore, since $f(1) = f(-1)$ and $f'(x)$ exists for $-1 < x < 1$, we may regard the function on the interval $-1 \leqq x \leqq 1$ as an illustration of Rolle's Theorem (see Figure 7.3b).

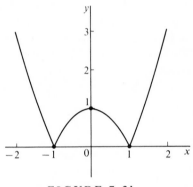

**FIGURE 7.3b**

---

We shall next give conditions that are sufficient for a continuous function to have an extreme at a critical point in the interior of the domain. The first set of conditions is an easy consequence of the interpretation of the sign of the derivative.

**Theorem 7.3d.** Let $f$ be a continuous function over a $\mathfrak{N}(x_c, h)$, where $x_c$ is a critical point of the domain of $f$, and let $f'(x)$ exist for $x \in \mathfrak{N}^*(x_c, h)$. Then

    (i) $f'(x) > 0$ for $x \in \mathfrak{N}^*(x_c^-, h)$ and $f'(x) < 0$ for $x \in \mathfrak{N}^*(x_c^+, h) \Rightarrow f(x_c)$ is a maximum;

    (ii) $f'(x) < 0$ for $x \in \mathfrak{N}^*(x_c^-, h)$ and $f'(x) > 0$ for $x \in \mathfrak{N}^*(x_c^+, h) \Rightarrow f(x_c)$ is a minimum;

    (iii) $f'(x)$ of constant sign for $x \in \mathfrak{N}^*(x_c, h) \Rightarrow f(x_c)$ is not an extreme.

PROOF: For (i), the given conditions imply that $f$ is an increasing function over the left neighborhood of $x_c$ and a decreasing function over the right neighborhood. Hence $f(x_c)$ must be the greatest value that the function assumes over $\mathfrak{N}(x_c, h)$. Thus, $f(x_c)$ is a maximum.

The argument for (ii) and (iii) is similar to that for (i) and is consequently left to the reader.

Theorem 7.3d is frequently called the **first derivative test** for maxima and minima. Its use is illustrated in the next three examples.

*Example 7.3b.* Find the extremes of the function defined by

$$f(x) = 2x^3 + 3x^2 - 12x.$$

For this function,

$$f'(x) = 6x^2 + 6x - 12 = 6(x^2 + x - 2) = 6(x + 2)(x - 1).$$

If $f'(x) = 0$, then $x = -2$ or $1$. Since $f'$ is continuous for all $x$, the only possible extremes are at these critical values of $x$.

We also find that

$$f'(x) > 0 \quad \text{for } x < -2 \text{ and for } x > 1$$

and

$$f'(x) < 0 \quad \text{for } -2 < x < 1.$$

Consequently, there is a left neighborhood $\mathfrak{N}^*(-2^-)$ such that $f'(x) > 0$ for $x \in \mathfrak{N}^*(-2^-)$, and there is a right neighborhood $\mathfrak{N}^*(-2^+)$ such that $f'(x) < 0$ for $x \in \mathfrak{N}^*(-2^+)$. This means that $f(-2) = 20$ is a relative maximum of $f$ (see Figure 7.3c).

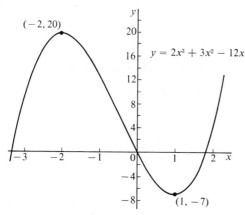

**FIGURE 7.3c**

Similarly, there is a left neighborhood $\mathfrak{N}^*(1^-)$ such that $f'(x) < 0$ for $x \in \mathfrak{N}^*(1^-)$ and there is a right neighborhood $\mathfrak{N}^*(1^+)$ such that $f'(x) > 0$ for $x \in \mathfrak{N}^*(1^+)$. This shows that $f(1) = -7$ is a relative minimum of the function (see Figure 7.3c).

To summarize, we see that $f'(-2) = 0$, and $f'(x)$ changes sign from plus to minus as $x$ increases through the value $-2$. The point $(-2, 20)$ is a maximum point on the graph of $f$. Also $f'(1) = 0$, and $f'(x)$ changes sign from minus to plus as $x$ increases through the value 1. The point $(1, -7)$ is a minimum point on the graph.

---

*Example 7.3c.* Find the extremes of the function defined by $f(x) = x^{2/3}$.

In this example,

$$f'(x) = \tfrac{2}{3}x^{-1/3}, \qquad x \neq 0.$$

The domain of the function is all $x \in \mathfrak{R}$, yet there is no value of $x$ for which $f'(x) = 0$. The only possible critical value of $x$ is $x = 0$, for which $f'(x)$ does not exist. Since

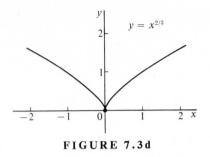

**FIGURE 7.3d**

$f'(x) < 0$ for $x < 0$, and $f'(x) > 0$ for $x > 0$, $f(0) = 0$ is a relative minimum of the function. The graph of the function is shown in Figure 7.3d.

An obvious modification of the first derivative test applies in the case of end point extremes. For example, if the interval is $a \leq x \leq b$, and there is a $\mathfrak{N}^*(a^+, h)$ over which $f'(x) > 0$, then $f(a)$ is an end point minimum. Why? The reader should supply the corresponding statements for $f'(x) < 0$ and also for the right end point $x = b$.

*Example 7.3d.* The velocity of a particle in feet per second is given by

$$v(t) = t^2 - 4t + 5, \qquad t \geq 0,$$

where $t$ is in seconds. Find the instants at which the velocity is a relative maximum or a relative minimum.

For the equation $v(t) = t^2 - 4t + 5$, we have

$$v'(t) = 2t - 4 = 2(t - 2).$$

If $v'(t) = 0$, then $t = 2$. The critical points are $t = 0$ (an end point) and $t = 2$.

We see that $v'(t) < 0$ for $0 \leq t < 2$ and $v'(t) > 0$ for $t > 2$. Hence, it follows that $v$ has an end point maximum $v(0) = 5$ feet per second and a relative minimum $v(2) = 1$ foot per second. Explain. The graph of the function $v$ is shown in Figure 7.3e.

Before considering a second test for maxima and minima, we need the following refinement of Theorem 7.1c on increasing and decreasing functions.

**Theorem 7.3e.** Let $f$ be defined on an open interval $a < x < b$ and let $f$ have a continuous first derivative at the point $x_0$ in this interval. Then,
    (i) $f'(x_0) > 0 \Rightarrow$ there exists a $\mathfrak{N}(x_0, h)$ over which $f$ is an increasing function;
    (ii) $f'(x_0) < 0 \Rightarrow$ there exists a $\mathfrak{N}(x_0, h)$ over which $f$ is a decreasing function.
PROOF: Since the derivative $f'$ is by hypothesis continuous at $x_0$, it follows from Theorem 4.7c that

$$f'(x_0) > 0 \Rightarrow \text{there exists a } \mathfrak{N}(x_0, h) \text{ such that } f'(x) > 0 \text{ for all } x \in \mathfrak{N}(x_0, h).$$

Hence, by Theorem 7.1c, $f$ is an increasing function on this neighborhood.

This completes the proof of (i). The modification of this argument needed to prove (ii) is left for the reader.

The next theorem is the **second derivative test** for maxima and minima.

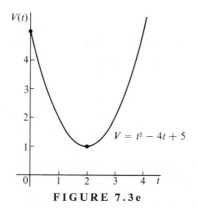

FIGURE 7.3e

**Theorem 7.3f.** Let $f$ be defined on the open interval $a < x < b$ and let $f'(x_c) = 0$, where $x_c$ is a point in the interval. Then, if $f$ has a continuous second derivative at $x_c$,

(i) $f''(x_c) > 0 \Rightarrow f(x_c)$ is a minimum;
(ii) $f''(x_c) < 0 \Rightarrow f(x_c)$ is a maximum.

PROOF: The hypothesis $f''(x_c) > 0$ in (i) implies the existence of a neighborhood of $x_c$ over which $f'$ is an increasing function (by Theorem 7.3e). Since $f'(x_c) = 0$, then over the left neighborhood it must be that $f'(x) < 0$ and over the right neighborhood $f'(x) > 0$. Thus the first derivative test shows that $f(x_c)$ is a minimum.

The proof of (ii) is similar and so is left for the reader.

---

*Example 7.3e.* Find the extremes of the function $f$ defined by $f(x) = 3x^4 + 4x^3$.

For this function, we find

$$f'(x) = 12x^3 + 12x^2 = 12x^2(x + 1).$$

If $f'(x) = 0$, then $x = -1$ or $x = 0$. Since $f'$ is continuous for all $x$, there can be no other critical points. We also have

$$f''(x) = 36x^2 + 24x = 12x(3x + 2),$$

which shows that $f''$ is continuous for all $x$.

At $x = -1$, we find $f''(-1) = (-12)(-1) > 0$ so that $f(-1) = -1$ is a minimum.

At $x = 0$, we have $f''(0) = 0$ so that the second derivative test does not apply. However, $f''(x)$ changes sign as $x$ passes through the value zero. Therefore, $(0, 0)$ is an inflection point. The fact that $f'(0) = 0$ means that the inflectional tangent is parallel to the $x$-axis. The graph of the function is shown in Figure 7.3f.

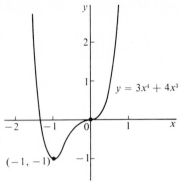

$y = 3x^4 + 4x^3$

$(-1, -1)$

**FIGURE 7.3f**

*Example 7.3f.* Find the extremes of the function $f.=. \{(x, y)\}$, where $x$ and $y$ are given by the parametric equations

$$x = t^3 - 1, \qquad y = t^2 + t.$$

Using the procedure of Section 6.6 for finding derivatives of functions defined by parametric equations, we obtain

$$D_x y = \frac{D_t y}{D_t x} = \frac{2t + 1}{3t^2} = \tfrac{2}{3}t^{-1} + \tfrac{1}{3}t^{-2},$$

and, letting $y'$ denote $D_x y$, we get

$$D_x^2 y = \frac{D_t y'}{D_t x} = \frac{-\tfrac{2}{3}t^{-2} - \tfrac{2}{3}t^{-3}}{3t^2} = -\tfrac{2}{9}(t^{-4} + t^{-5}).$$

These results show that $D_x y$ and $D_x^2 y$ are both continuous for all nonzero values of $t$. Furthermore,

$$D_x y = 0 \Leftrightarrow \tfrac{2}{3}t^{-1} + \tfrac{1}{3}t^{-2} = 0$$
$$\Leftrightarrow \tfrac{1}{3}t^{-2}(2t + 1) = 0 \Leftrightarrow t = -\tfrac{1}{2}.$$

For $t = -\tfrac{1}{2}$, $D_x^2 y = -\tfrac{2}{9}(16 - 32) > 0$. Therefore, by Theorem 7.3f, the function $f$ has a minimum for this value of $t$. Since $x = -\tfrac{9}{8}$ and $y = -\tfrac{1}{4}$, then $(-\tfrac{9}{8}, -\tfrac{1}{4})$ is a minimum point on the graph of $f$ and $-\tfrac{1}{4}$ is the minimum value of $f$.

At $t = 0$, $D_x y$ and $D_x^2 y$ do not exist. However, the fact that

$$D_x y = \tfrac{1}{3}t^{-2}(2t + 1)$$

shows that $D_x y$ does not change sign at $t = 0$, so that the function $f$ has neither a maximum nor a minimum value at $t = 0$.

## Exercises 7.3

In each of Numbers 1 to 4, use the first derivative test and find the extremes of the function defined by the given formula.

1. $f(x) = 1 - 2x - x^2$, $-3 \le x \le 3$.
2. $g(x) = x^2 - x^4$, $-2 \le x \le 2$.
3. $F(x) = 4/(x^2 + 4)$.
4. $H(x) = x^{1/2} + x^{-1/2}$.

In each of Numbers 5 to 8, use the second derivative test and find the extremes of the function defined by the given formula.

5. $h(x) = x^3 - 6x^2 + 12x - 8$.
6. $A(x) = 12x^5 + 45x^4 + 40x^3$.

7. $f(x) = x^2/\sqrt{x^2 + 4}$.
8. $g(x) = a^2x/(x^2 + a^2)$.

In each of Numbers 9 to 20, use any convenient test and find the maximum and minimum points on the given curve.

9. $y = x^{2/3} + 4$, $-2 \leq x \leq 3$.
10. $y = x^3 - 5x^5$.
11. $y = |x^3 - 1|$.
12. $y = x^2 - |3x - 2| + 1$.
13. $y = x^3/(x^2 + 4)$.
14. $x = 1 + (y - 2)^{1/2}$.

15. $y = x - (x - 1)^{3/2}$.
16. $y = 4x - 3(x + 1)^{4/3}$.
17. $x = 1 - 3t$, $y = 9t^2 - 12t + 6$.
18. $x = t^{-2}$, $y = t^2 + t$.
19. $x = t^{-2}$, $y = t^2 - t + 1$.
20. $x = 1 + t$, $y = t^2 - 4t + 5$.

21. Determine conditions on $a$, $b$, $c$, and $d$ so that the function defined by
$$f(x) = ax^3 + bx^2 + cx + d$$
will have a minimum at $x = 0$ and a maximum at $x = 1$.

22. Show that the function defined by $f(x) = x^k - kx$, $k \neq 1$, always has a maximum at $x = 1$ for $0 < k < 1$ and a minimum at $x = 1$ for $k > 1$.

23. Discuss the maximum and minimum points of the curve $y = x^m(1 - x)^n$, where $m$ and $n$ are positive integers greater than 1. Consider various combinations such as $m$ and $n$ both even, both odd, and so on.

★24. Let $f$ be a function that is differentiable at every point of an interval $a \leq x \leq b$ and let $f'(a)$ and $f'(b)$ have opposite signs. Prove that there is a critical point of the domain in the open interval $a < x < b$. *Hint*: Use an indirect proof.

★25. Let $f$ be a continuous function on $a \leq x \leq b$ with just one critical point $x_c$ in $a < x < b$. Suppose that $f(a)$ and $f(b)$ are both less than $f(x_c)$. Prove that $f(x_c)$ is a maximum. *Hint*: Consider the two intervals $a < x < x_c$ and $x_c < x < b$. Can $f$ have an extreme in either of these intervals?

26. If $f'(a) = 0$, $f''(a) = 0$, and $f''(x) > 0$ for $x$ in some deleted neighborhood of $a$, prove that $f(a)$ is a minimum of the function $f$.

★27. For each of the following sets of conditions make a sketch of the graph of a continuous function $f$ near the point where $x = a$, if possible. If the information is not consistent, explain.

(a) $f'(a)$, $f''(a)$ both fail to exist;
$$x \in \mathfrak{N}^*(a^-, h) \Rightarrow f''(x) > 0;$$
$$x \in \mathfrak{N}^*(a^+, h) \Rightarrow f''(x) < 0.$$

(b) $f'(a)$, $f''(a)$ both fail to exist;
$$x \in \mathfrak{N}^*(a^-, h) \Rightarrow f'(x) > 0, f''(x) < 0;$$
$$x \in \mathfrak{N}^*(a^+, h) \Rightarrow f'(x) > 0, f''(x) > 0.$$

# 7.4 THE MEAN VALUE THEOREM FOR DERIVATIVES

A geometric interpretation of Rolle's Theorem (Theorem 7.3c) is as follows. Let $y = f(x)$ be the equation of a curve with $f$ continuous on the closed interval $a \leq x \leq b$ and having a derivative everywhere on the open interval $a < x < b$.

If $f(a) = f(b)$, then there is at least one point $(\xi, f(\xi))$, with $a < \xi < b$, where the tangent to the curve is horizontal (see Figure 7.4a).

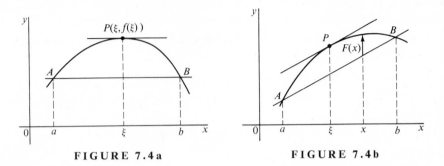

| FIGURE 7.4a | FIGURE 7.4b |

Clearly, if the curve $APB$ were turned so that the line $AB$ became not parallel to the $x$-axis, the geometric content of Rolle's Theorem would still be true; that is, the tangent line through $P$ would still be parallel to the secant line $AB$. This apparently evident result has an important analytic formulation which is given in

**Theorem 7.4a.** *The Mean Value Theorem for Derivatives.* Let $f$ be a continuous function on the closed interval $a \leqq x \leqq b$, and let $f'$ exist everywhere on the open interval $a < x < b$. Then there is at least one point $\xi$ in the open interval such that

(1)
$$f'(\xi) = \frac{f(b) - f(a)}{b - a}.$$

PROOF: The geometric discussion of the preceding paragraphs gives a good hint for the proof of this theorem. Consider Figure 7.4b; let $F(x)$ be the directed distance, measured parallel to the $y$-axis, from the secant $AB$ to the curve. Since the distance from the $x$-axis to the curve is $y = f(x)$, and that to the secant line is

$$y = f(a) + \frac{f(b) - f(a)}{b - a}(x - a),$$

$F(x)$ is the difference between these and is given by

$$F(x) = f(x) - f(a) - \frac{f(b) - f(a)}{b - a}(x - a).$$

But $F(a) = 0$ and $F(b) = 0$. Also, because of the conditions on $f$, $F$ is a continuous function on $a \leqq x \leqq b$ and $F'$ exists on $a < x < b$. Thus, Rolle's Theorem applies to $F$, and so there is a number $\xi$ in $a < x < b$ such that $F'(\xi) = 0$. Hence, by differentiating $F$, we find

$$F'(\xi) = 0 = f'(\xi) - \frac{f(b) - f(a)}{b - a},$$

so that

$$f'(\xi) = \frac{f(b) - f(a)}{b - a},$$

as was to be shown.

Equation (1) is often written in the form obtained by solving for $f(b)$

(2) $$f(b) = f(a) + (b - a)f'(\xi), \qquad a < \xi < b.$$

Furthermore, the same theorem clearly applies to any closed interval from $a$ to $x$ on which $f$ is continuous if $f$ is differentiable (at least on the open interval). Therefore,

(3) $$f(x) = f(a) + (x - a)f'(\xi),$$

where $\xi$ is between $a$ and $x$.

Replacing $a$ by $x$ and $x$ by $x + h$, we get $h = x - a$, and Equation (3) becomes

(4) $$f(x + h) = f(x) + hf'(x + \theta h), \quad \text{where } 0 < \theta < 1.$$

Note that the last formula simply replaces the $\xi$ of the preceding formulas by $x + \theta h$, which is between $x$ and $x + h$ for $0 < \theta < 1$ regardless of the sign of $h$.

---

*Example 7.4a.* Find the value (or values) of $\xi$ which the Mean Value Theorem predicts if

$$f(x) = x^3 - x, \qquad a = 0, b = 3.$$

We find

$$f(a) = 0, \quad f(b) = 24, \quad \text{and} \quad f'(x) = 3x^2 - 1.$$

Therefore, for the required value $\xi$, we must have

$$3\xi^2 - 1 = \frac{24 - 0}{3 - 0} = 8,$$

so that

$$\xi^2 = 3.$$

Since the number $\xi$ must lie in the interval $0 < x < 3$, the positive root of this equation must be used. Hence $\xi = \sqrt{3}$.

---

*Example 7.4b.* Use the Mean Value Theorem to estimate the value of $\sqrt{110}$.

Let $f(x) .=. \sqrt{x}$ and use the Mean Value Theorem in the form

$$f(x + h) = f(x) + hf'(x + \theta h), \qquad 0 < \theta < 1.$$

Then, since

$$f'(x) = \frac{1}{2\sqrt{x}} \quad \text{and} \quad f'(x + \theta h) = \frac{1}{2\sqrt{x + \theta h}},$$

we have

$$\sqrt{x + h} = \sqrt{x} + \frac{h}{2\sqrt{x + \theta h}}.$$

With $x = 100$ and $h = 10$, this formula gives

(5)
$$\sqrt{110} = 10 + \frac{5}{\sqrt{100 + 10\theta}}.$$

Since $f(x)$ increases with $x$ (why?), we have

(6)
$$\sqrt{100} < \sqrt{100 + 10\theta} < \sqrt{110}.$$

Accordingly, the left portion of (6) along with (5) shows that

$$\sqrt{110} < 10 + \frac{5}{\sqrt{100}} = 10.5.$$

Similarly, the right portion of (6) along with (5) gives

$$\sqrt{110} > 10 + \frac{5}{\sqrt{110}} = 10 + \frac{\sqrt{110}}{22}$$

or

$$\frac{21}{22}\sqrt{110} > 10,$$

so that

$$\sqrt{110} > \frac{220}{21} = 10.476^{+}.$$

A combination of the two results now shows that

$$10.476 < \sqrt{110} < 10.5.$$

---

The following basic theorem is an easy but quite important consequence of the Mean Value Theorem.

**Theorem 7.4b.** If two functions are both continuous on the closed interval $a \le x \le b$ and have the same derivative on the open interval $a < x < b$, then the difference of the two functions is a constant function.

PROOF: Let the two functions be denoted by $F$ and $G$, respectively. By hypothesis

$$F'(x) = G'(x) \quad \text{on } a < x < b.$$

Write $H(x) = F(x) - G(x)$, so that

$$H'(x) = 0 \quad \text{on } a < x < b.$$

Then, by the Mean Value Theorem in the form given by (3), we have

$$H(x) = H(a) + (x - a)H'(\xi)$$
$$= H(a), \text{ a constant,}$$

since $H'$ has the value zero at every point of the interval. This completes the proof.

Note that this theorem guarantees the uniqueness to within an additive constant of the inverse derivative (when it exists) of a given function. We used this result repeatedly in Section 5.5.

## Exercises 7.4

In each of Numbers 1 to 4, find the value of $\xi$ that is guaranteed by the Mean Value Theorem, Equation (1):

1. $f(x) = 1 - x^2$, $a = 0$, $b = 2$.
2. $f(x) = \sqrt{x}$, $a = 1$, $b = 9$.

3. $f(x) = x^3 - 3x^2$, $a = 1$, $b = 4$.
4. $f(x) = x/(x - 4)$, $a = 5$, $b = 8$.

In each of Numbers 5 to 8, find the value of $\theta$ that is guaranteed by the Mean Value Theorem, Equation (4):

5. $f(x) = x^3$, $x = 1$, $h = 2$.
6. $f(x) = 1/x$, $x = 1$, $h = 3$.

7. $f(x) = \sqrt{1 - x^2}$, $x = 0$, $h = 1$.
8. $f(x) = x + \sqrt{x}$, $x = 1$, $h = 8$.

9. If $f(x) = ax^2 + bx + c$, show that the value of $\theta$ guaranteed by the Mean Value Theorem, Equation (4), is $\frac{1}{2}$ for all values of $x$ and $h$. Give a geometric interpretation of this fact.
10. Does the Mean Value Theorem apply if $f(x) = 1/x$, $a = -1$, $b = 3$? Explain.
11. Does the Mean Value Theorem apply if $f(x) = x^{1/3}$, $a = -1$, $b = 1$? Explain.
12. Use the Mean Value Theorem to estimate

$$\text{(a) } \sqrt{40}; \quad \text{(b) } \sqrt{66}; \quad \text{(c) } \sqrt[3]{27.2}; \quad \text{(d) } \sqrt[5]{35}.$$

13. If $f(x) = x^{1/3}$, $x = 0$, $h > 0$, show that the value of $\theta$ guaranteed by the Mean Value Theorem, Equation (4), is independent of the value of $h$.
14. Does the result of Number 13 apply to other powers of $x$? Explain.

## 7.5 APPLICATIONS TO CURVE SKETCHING

We have already discussed a number of techniques and ideas useful in making a rapid sketch of the graph of an equation. With the additional techniques available, since we have studied the properties of the derivative, it is now possible to extend the discussion of curve sketching. It is desirable to minimize the plotting of points other than crucial points on the graph. With practice it is possible to produce accurate sketches using only a few plotted points.

Our previous techniques were limited to the following items.

(1) Finding where the curve cuts the axes.
(2) Determining if any simple symmetry exists.
(3) Finding horizontal and vertical asymptotes if there are any.

We shall add three items to this list.

(4) Finding the extent of the curve—that is, the set of values of $x$ for which $y$ is real and the set of values of $y$ for which $x$ is real.
(5) Investigating maximum and minimum points and determining intervals over which the curve rises or falls.
(6) Investigating concavity and inflection points.

The following examples show how these techniques can be employed.

*Example 7.5a.* Discuss and sketch the graph of

$$y = \frac{x}{x^2 + 1}.$$

The first line of the following items may be determined by inspection.

(1) Intercepts: $x = 0 \Leftrightarrow y = 0$.

(2) Symmetry: the graph possesses symmetry with respect to the origin; replacement of $(x, y)$ by $(-x, -y)$ yields the original equation, and hence $(-x, -y)$ satisfies the equation if $(x, y)$ does.

(3) Asymptotes: $y = 0$ is a horizontal asymptote.

(4) There are no restrictions on the values of $x$. However, if we solve for $y$, we obtain

$$x = \frac{1 \pm \sqrt{1 - 4y^2}}{2y}.$$

This formula shows that for $x$ to be real we must have

$$1 - 4y^2 \geq 0 \quad \text{or} \quad 4y^2 \leq 1.$$

Hence $|2y| \leq 1$, and

$$|y| \leq \tfrac{1}{2} \quad \text{or} \quad -\tfrac{1}{2} \leq y \leq \tfrac{1}{2}.$$

This is the interval of permissible values of $y$.

(5) Since

$$y' = \frac{1 - x^2}{(x^2 + 1)^2},$$

it is easy to see that the curve has a tangent with slope 1 at the origin. Furthermore, since $y' = 0$ for $x = \pm 1$, the curve has horizontal tangents at $(-1, -\tfrac{1}{2})$ and $(1, \tfrac{1}{2})$. The denominator of $y'$ is positive, so that the sign of $y'$ is the same as the sign of $1 - x^2$. We find

$$y' > 0 \quad \text{for } -1 < x < 1,$$

and

$$y' < 0 \quad \text{for } x < -1 \text{ and } x > 1.$$

Thus, the curve is falling in the interval $x < -1$, rising in the interval $-1 < x < 1$, and falling in the interval $x > 1$. Therefore $(-1, -\tfrac{1}{2})$ is a minimum point and $(1, \tfrac{1}{2})$ is a maximum point.

(6) The second derivative is calculated, after simplification, to be

$$y'' = \frac{2x(x^2 - 3)}{(x^2 + 1)^3}.$$

Points where $y'' = 0$ are found to be $(0, 0)$, $(\sqrt{3}, \tfrac{1}{4}\sqrt{3})$, and $(-\sqrt{3}, -\tfrac{1}{4}\sqrt{3})$. That these are points of inflection may be shown by investigating the sign changes in $y''$. In fact, $y'' > 0$ for $2x(x^2 - 3) > 0$, or for $x(x - \sqrt{3})(x + \sqrt{3}) > 0$. The solution of this inequality is $-\sqrt{3} < x < 0$ and $\sqrt{3} < x$. Also, $y'' < 0$ for $x < -\sqrt{3}$ and $0 < x < \sqrt{3}$. The curve is thus concave down for $x < -\sqrt{3}$ and $0 < x < \sqrt{3}$, and concave up for $-\sqrt{3} < x < 0$ and $\sqrt{3} < x$.

Before sketching the curve, we try to display all of the preceding information at once, as in Figure 7.5a.

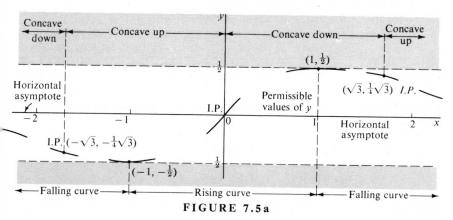

FIGURE 7.5a

With this much information given, it should be clear how the graph must appear. The desired curve, which is shown in Figure 7.5b, is known as a *serpentine*.

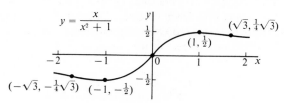

$$y = \frac{x}{x^2 + 1}$$

FIGURE 7.5b

*Example 7.5b.* Discuss and sketch the curve

$$x^3 + xy^2 + ay^2 - 3ax^2 = 0, \qquad a > 0.$$

(1) From the equation it follows that if $x = 0$, then $y = 0$, and if $y = 0$, then $x^3 - 3ax^2 = 0$ so that $x = 0$ or $x = 3a$. Hence the curve crosses the axes at $(0, 0)$ and at $(3a, 0)$.

(2) Since $y$ appears to even powers only, the curve must be symmetric to the $x$-axis. This is the only simple symmetry that the curve has.

(3) We solve for $y$ to obtain

$$y = \pm x \sqrt{\frac{3a - x}{x + a}},$$

which shows that there is a vertical asymptote at $x = -a$, provided that $x = -a$ is within or on the boundary of the extent of the curve. As we shall see in (4), the extent of the curve is $-a < x \leq 3a$, so that the curve lies to the right of and is asymptotic to the line $x = -a$.

(4) To determine the extent of the curve—that is, the set of values of $x$ for which $y$ is real—it is necessary to solve the inequality

$$\frac{3a - x}{x + a} \geq 0.$$

The reader may show that the required solution is

$$-a < x \leq 3a.$$

Solving for $x$ in terms of $y$ involves solving a general cubic equation. Since a cubic equation with real coefficients always has one or three real roots, it is clear that for each real value of $y$ there is always at least one corresponding real value of $x$ and there may be three such values. Consequently there is no restriction on the extent of the curve in the $y$-direction.

(5) Before we investigate the existence of maximum and minimum points on the curve, let us consider the two separate equations

$$y_1 = x \sqrt{\frac{3a - x}{x + a}},$$

and

$$y_2 = -x \sqrt{\frac{3a - x}{x + a}}.$$

These two formulas represent two "branches" of the curve. The two equations can now be properly associated with functions rather than relations and the theorems of calculus can more easily be applied. Because of the symmetry of the curve, one branch is symmetric to the other with respect to the $x$-axis, so that we may restrict the discussion to $y_1$. Since

$$y_1' = \frac{3a^2 - x^2}{\sqrt{(x + a)^3(3a - x)}},$$

we see that

$$x = \sqrt{3}a$$

is a critical value of $x$. (Why is $x = -\sqrt{3}a$ not a critical value?) The nature of the point at $x = \sqrt{3}a$ can be investigated easily by determining the intervals over which the curve is rising or falling. The reader may show that for

$$-a < x < \sqrt{3}a, \qquad y_1' > 0,$$

and for

$$\sqrt{3}a < x < 3a, \qquad y_1' < 0,$$

so that the curve is rising and falling, respectively, over these intervals. This shows, of course, that the point $x = \sqrt{3}a$, $y = 1.2a$ (approx.) is a maximum point.

It has already been shown that $x = -a$ is a vertical asymptote. The fact that $|y_1'| \to \infty$ as $x \to -a^+$ is consistent with this result. However, at $x = 3a$ something new shows up; namely, as $x \to 3a^-$, $y_1' \to -\infty$. This indicates that there is a vertical tangent at $(3a, 0)$ or that the curve approaches the $x$-axis vertically as $x \to 3a^-$.

(6) The reader may show that

$$y_1'' = -\frac{12a^3}{(3a - x)^{3/2}(x + a)^{5/2}}.$$

From this we see that no points of inflection occur and that the curve is concave down everywhere.

Figure 7.5c displays all of the preceding information for $y_1$. In Figure 7.5d we see the completed graph. The curve is known as a *trisectrix* because of the property that

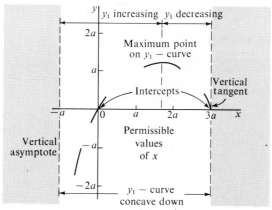

**FIGURE 7.5c**

the angle $\alpha$ shown in the figure is one-third of angle $\beta$ if $x > 0$, $y > 0$ for $P(x, y)$. The concave down portion of the curve corresponds to $y_1$ and the concave up portion, which is obtained by symmetry, corresponds to $y_2$.

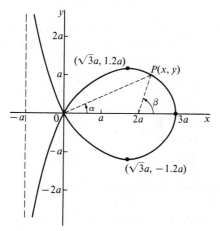

**FIGURE 7.5d**

*Example 7.5c.* Discuss and sketch the graph of

$$y = \frac{x(x - 3)}{(x + 3)^2}.$$

(1) When $x = 0$, then $y = 0$, and when $y = 0$, then $x(x - 3) = 0$, so that $x = 0$ or $x = 3$. The intercepts are 0 on both axes and 3 on the $x$-axis.

(2) There is no simple type of symmetry. (Why?)

(3) Since for positive $h$ sufficiently small,

$$x \in \mathfrak{N}(-3, h) \Rightarrow x(x - 3) > 0,$$

we see that as $x \to -3^-$, $y \to \infty$, and as $x \to -3^+$, $y \to \infty$. Thus, both portions of the curve are asymptotic to the upper part of the line $x = -3$. This kind of asymptotic behavior is characteristic of equations in which a factor such as $x + 3$ appears to an even power in the denominator. Also, we see that as $x \to \infty$, $y \to 1^-$, and as $x \to -\infty$, $y \to 1^+$. (Why?) This shows that $y = 1$ is a horizontal asymptote.

(4) The extent of the curve in the $x$-direction is unlimited since $y$ is real for all real $x$, $x \ne -3$. Solving for $x$, we obtain

$$x = -\frac{3}{2}\left\{\frac{2y + 1 \pm \sqrt{8y + 1}}{y - 1}\right\},$$

which indicates that $x$ is real only for

$$8y + 1 \geq 0$$

or

$$y \geq -\tfrac{1}{8}.$$

The extent of the curve in the $y$-direction is thus $y \geq -\tfrac{1}{8}$.

(5) In order to search for maximum and minimum points, we need to find the derivative of $y$ with respect to $x$. The reader may show that

$$y' = \frac{9(x - 1)}{(x + 3)^3},$$

from which we see that the curve has a horizontal tangent at $(1, -\tfrac{1}{8})$. To find the intervals over which the curve is rising or falling, it is necessary to find the values of $x$ for which $y' > 0$ or $y' < 0$. The reader may show that

$$\frac{9(x - 1)}{(x + 3)^3} > 0 \quad \text{for } x < -3 \text{ and for } 1 < x,$$

and that

$$\frac{9(x - 1)}{(x + 3)^3} < 0 \quad \text{for } -3 < x < 1.$$

Therefore, $(1, -\tfrac{1}{8})$ is a minimum point since the curve on the left is falling and on the right is rising. Note that $y'$ is undefined at $x = -3$ and $y'$ changes sign there; for $x < -3$, $y' > 0$ and for $x > -3$, $y' < 0$, and $|y'| \to \infty$ as $x \to -3$. This substantiates the asymptotic behavior noted in (3).

(6) In order to find points of inflection and determine the type of concavity we investigate the behavior of $y''$. Since

$$y'' = 18\frac{3 - x}{(x + 3)^4},$$

we see that there is an inflection point at $(3, 0)$. In fact, it is easy to see that

$$y'' > 0 \quad \text{for } x < -3 \text{ and for } -3 < x < 3,$$

and that

$$y'' < 0 \quad \text{for } 3 < x,$$

from which we further deduce that the curve is concave up for $x < -3$ and $-3 < x < 3$, and is concave down for $3 < x$.

It is sometimes helpful in sketching a curve to find the slope of the curve at crucial points such as points where the curve cuts the axes and points of inflection. In this example we find

$$y' = -\tfrac{1}{3} \quad \text{at } (0, 0),$$

and

$$y' = +\tfrac{1}{12} \quad \text{at } (3, 0).$$

We now display the preceding information in Figure 7.5e.

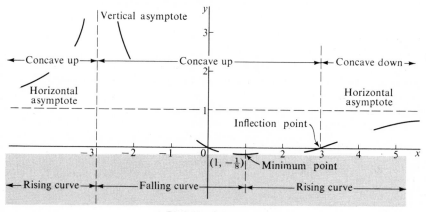

**FIGURE 7.5e**

The completed graph is shown in Figure 7.5f.

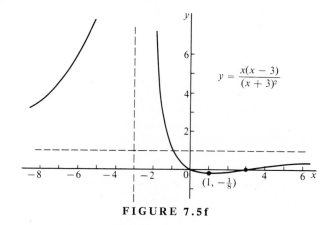

$$y = \frac{x(x-3)}{(x+3)^2}$$

**FIGURE 7.5f**

*Example 7.5d.* Discuss and sketch the curve defined by the parametric equations

$$x = t^3 + 1, \qquad y = t^2 - 2t.$$

(1) For $y = 0$, we have $t = 0$ or $t = 2$, so that $x = 1$ or $x = 9$. For $x = 0$, we have $= -1$, so that $y = 3$. Thus the curve cuts the axes at $(1, 0)$, $(9, 0)$, and $(0, 3)$.
(2) There is no simple symmetry.

(3) and (4) Since $x$ and $y$ are continuous functions of $t$ for all real values of $t$ and the range of $x$ consists of all real numbers, there can be no vertical asymptotes. More-over, $y \to \infty$ as $|t| \to \infty$, so that there can be no horizontal asymptotes. In the formula for $y$, we complete the square in $t$ to get $y = (t-1)^2 - 1$, which shows that $y \geq -1$.

(5) We have

$$D_x y = \frac{D_t y}{D_t x} = \frac{2t - 2}{3t^2} = \tfrac{2}{3}(t^{-1} - t^{-2})$$

and

$$D_x^2 y = \frac{D_t(D_x y)}{D_t x} = \frac{\tfrac{2}{3}(-t^{-2} + 2t^{-3})}{3t^2} = \tfrac{2}{9}(2t^{-5} - t^{-4}).$$

This shows that $D_x y = 0 \Leftrightarrow t^{-1} - t^{-2} = 0 \Leftrightarrow t^{-2}(t - 1) \Leftrightarrow t = 1$, and $D_x y$ does not exist for $t = 0$.

Since $D_x^2 y > 0$ for $t = 1$, this value of $t$ corresponds to a minimum point $(2, -1)$. The fact that $D_t x = 3t^2$ is positive for all nonzero values of $t$ shows that $x$ is an increasing function of $t$. Moreover, $D_x y < 0$ for $t < 1$, and $D_x y > 0$ for $t > 1$. There-fore, the curve falls for $x < 2$ and rises for $x > 2$.

(6) From the formula for $D_x^2 y$, it follows that

$$D_x^2 y = 0 \Leftrightarrow 2t^{-5} - t^{-4} = 0 \Leftrightarrow t^{-5}(2 - t) = 0 \Leftrightarrow t = 2.$$

Also, $D_x^2 y < 0$ for $t < 0$ and for $t > 2$, and $D_x^2 y > 0$ for $0 < t < 2$.

These results mean that the curve is concave down for $x < 1$ and for $x > 9$, and concave up for $1 < x < 9$. Thus, the point $(1, 0)$ where $t = 0$ is an inflection point. The inflectional tangent is vertical there since $|D_x y| \to \infty$ as $t \to 0$. The point $(9, 0)$ where $t = 2$, is an inflection point with the tangent having a slope $1/6$.

The curve is shown in Figure 7.5g.

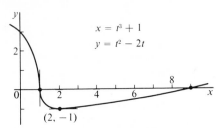

$$x = t^3 + 1$$
$$y = t^2 - 2t$$

**FIGURE 7.5g**

## Exercises 7.5

In Numbers 1 to 24, discuss and sketch the graph of the given equation(s). Make your discussion as complete as possible. Do not plot any more than the crucial points if you can avoid it.

1. $y = x^4 - 8x^2$.
2. $y = 3x^5 - 5x^3$.
3. $y = \sqrt{x^2 - 9}$.
4. $y = -\sqrt{9 - x^2}$.
5. $y = x^2 + |x|$.
6. $y = |x| + |x^2 - 1|$.

7. $y = \dfrac{x - 1}{x + 1}$.

8. $y = \dfrac{x}{\sqrt{x - 9}}$.

9. $y = x\sqrt{x^2 - 4}$.
10. $xy^2 + 4x = y$.

11. $y = \dfrac{|x|}{x^2 + 1}$.

12. $y = \dfrac{x^2}{\sqrt{x^2 + 2}}$.

13. $y = (2x + 10)(x - 3)^{2/3}$.

★14. $x^2y + xy^2 = 16$.

15. $y = \dfrac{x(5 - x)}{(x + 2)^2}$.

16. $y = \dfrac{x(x + 2)}{(x - 2)^2}$.

17. $y = \dfrac{8a^3}{x^2 + 4a^2}$ (the Witch of Agnesi).

★18. $x^3 + y^3 = 6xy$ (the Folium of Descartes). *Hint:* Let $y = tx$, and get parametric equations $x = f(t)$, $y = g(t)$.

19. $x^3 + ax^2 + xy^2 - ay^2 = 0$, $a > 0$ (the strophoid). *Hint:* Let $y = tx$, and get parametric equations $x = f(t)$, $y = g(t)$.

20. $(x - 3)y^2 = x^2(x + 6)$.

21. $x = t - 2$, $y = t^2 + 1$.

22. $x = t^2 + 1$, $y = t^3 - 1$.

23. $x = \frac{1}{2}t^2 - 6$, $y = \frac{1}{2}t^3 - 6t$.

24. $x = t^{-2}$, $y = t^2 + 1$.

★25. Let $y_1 = f(x)$ and $y_2 = g(x)$ be the equations of two curves symmetric to each other with respect to the $x$-axis.
   (a) How are the functions $f$ and $g$ related?
   (b) Prove that a maximum value of $y_1$ is a minimum value of $y_2$.
   (c) Prove that if $y_1 = f(x)$ is concave down for $a < x < b$, then $y_2 = g(x)$ is concave up for the same interval.

26. For what value of $a$ will the curve $y = 9x^{-1} + a(x - 3)$ have a minimum point at $x = 3$?

# 7.6 APPLICATIONS OF MAXIMA AND MINIMA

One of the important reasons for studying the calculus is its usefulness in applications. The scientist and the engineer may appreciate the inherent beauty of the subject, but for them its principal attraction lies in its use as a tool for furthering the study of natural phenomena. In any such application, the user of mathematics attempts to build what is sometimes called a "mathematical model" of the phenomenon under consideration. Often this takes the form of an equation involving the observable quantities, or variables. The interpretation of this equation may yield new insight into the phenomenon under investigation or the equation may be used to predict results under certain combinations of values of the variables.

Almost always the phenomenon, when examined closely, is too complex to be accurately described in any simple way, but sometimes simplifying or "idealizing" the problem still gives worthwhile results. For instance, the exact equations describing the flight of a stone would be virtually impossible to write and solve if one were to account for such things as air drag caused by the shape and surface conditions of the stone, the rotation of the stone, the variations in the earth's gravitational field, the rotation of the earth beneath the flying stone, stray winds, or the attraction of the moon. However, for most purposes, all such effects, including air friction, can be neglected without seriously affecting the accuracy of prediction of the trajectories of thrown stones. In general, the degree of idealization permitted usually depends upon the accuracy desired.

In this section the discussion will be restricted to simple applications that do not require extensive background in the sciences. Furthermore, the problems to be considered are generally simplified to a greater degree than is desirable in actual practice. A few are obviously contrived for the benefit of the reader, but these should not be thought of as any the less valuable, since the main purpose of these problems is to give experience in constructing and interpreting mathematical models from given information.

These exercises concern the finding of maxima or minima of physically meaningful quantities. Although it is difficult to give detailed, universal rules for the solution of such problems, a few general remarks on procedure are in order.

(1) Determine the quantity to be maximized or minimized.
(2) Express this quantity in terms of a single independent variable, using any constraint equations connecting the variables to eliminate unwanted variables in favor of the chosen variable. This procedure will lead to an equation that defines a function. Be sure to specify the domain of this function.
(3) Find the derivative of the function described in (2), and then find the critical points of the domain. Do not omit the end points or the points where the derivative fails to exist.
(4) Determine the nature of suspected extremes by appropriate tests.
(5) Check the results in all possible ways to see that every condition of the problem is satisfied. In particular, make sure that domain restrictions are observed.

The following examples illustrate the procedures for solving problems of this type.

---

*Example 7.6a.* Find the area of the largest rectangle that can be inscribed in a right triangle of sides 5, 12, and 13 inches, respectively, if one vertex of the rectangle is on the longest side of the triangle (see Figure 7.6a).

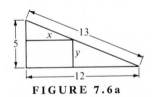

**FIGURE 7.6a**

It seems intuitively evident that the rectangle has maximum area for some configuration near that in the figure, for as $x \to 12$, $y \to 0$ and $A \to 0$, and as $y \to 5$, $x \to$ and $A \to 0$. Moreover, the area of the rectangle shown is far from being zero.

With the variables $x$ and $y$ shown in the figure, we can express the area as $A = xy$. To express $A$ as a function of only one of these variables we must find an equation involving $x$ and $y$ from which we can substitute for one variable in terms of the other. By using similar triangles, we may write the proportion

$$\frac{y}{5} = \frac{12 - x}{12},$$

from which it follows that

$$y = \tfrac{5}{12}(12 - x).$$

Thus,

$$A = \tfrac{5}{12}(12 - x)x = \tfrac{5}{12}(12x - x^2), \qquad 0 \leq x \leq 12.$$

Hence

$$\frac{dA}{dx} = \tfrac{5}{12}(12 - 2x),$$

and the critical value $x = 6$ results from the equation $dA/dx = 0$. This critical value yields a maximum for $A$ because

$$\frac{d^2 A}{dx^2} = -\tfrac{5}{6} < 0.$$

For $x = 6$, we find

$$y = \tfrac{5}{12}(12 - 6) = \tfrac{5}{2} \text{ inches}$$

and

$$A = (6)(\tfrac{5}{2}) = 15 \text{ square inches.}$$

It is evident that the end point values $x = 0$ and $x = 12$ give the minimum value $A = 0$.

An alternative way of handling $dA/dx$ is to employ the ideas of implicit differentiation. Thus, from $A = xy$, it follows that

$$\frac{dA}{dx} = y + x\frac{dy}{dx}.$$

But the equation defining the relationship between $x$ and $y$ may be written as

$$5x + 12y = 60,$$

and differentiated to obtain

$$5 + 12\frac{dy}{dx} = 0.$$

By solving this equation for $dy/dx$ and substituting the result into the formula for $dA/dx$, we get

$$\frac{dA}{dx} = y + x(-\tfrac{5}{12}).$$

Thus, if $dA/dx = 0$, then

$$y = \tfrac{5}{12}x,$$

which may be substituted into the equation $5x + 12y = 60$ to give

$$5x + 12(\tfrac{5}{12}x) - 60 = 0,$$

an equation which leads to the same critical value, $x = 6$, we obtained before.

---

A more difficult example, in which the existence of a maximum at other than an end point depends upon the parameters of the problem, follows next.

*Example 7.6b.* Find the point on the ellipse

$$\frac{x^2}{a^2} + \frac{y^2}{b^2} = 1, \quad a > 0, b > 0,$$

that is farthest from $(0, -b)$ (see Figure 7.6b).

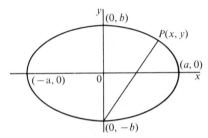

**FIGURE 7.6b**

The distance from $P(x, y)$ to $(0, -b)$ is

$$d = \sqrt{x^2 + (y + b)^2}.$$

Since $d \geq 0$, then $d$ and $d^2$ must have extreme values for the same values of $x$ and $y$. (Why?) Hence, let us try to find the maximum of

$$z \overset{.}{=}. \ d^2 = x^2 + (y + b)^2.$$

We can eliminate $x$ by using the fact that $P(x, y)$ is a point on the ellipse. Thus, $b^2x^2 + a^2y^2 = a^2b^2$, and upon solving this equation for $x^2$ and substituting the result into the expression for $z$, we get

$$z = f(y) = a^2 - \frac{a^2}{b^2} y^2 + (y + b)^2, \quad -b \leq y \leq b.$$

Consequently,

$$D_y z = -2\frac{a^2}{b^2} y + 2(y + b),$$

and

$$D_y z = 0 \Rightarrow y = \frac{b^3}{a^2 - b^2}.$$

Let us next investigate this critical value. If $a > b > 0$, then

$$\frac{b^3}{a^2 - b^2} > 0.$$

Furthermore,

$$D_y^2 z = -2\frac{a^2}{b^2} + 2.$$

This result indicates that we have a maximum if $-(a^2/b^2) + 1 < 0$ or $a > b$. Everything appears to be in order until we ask whether the value of $y$ for the indicated maximum is an element of the set of permissible values of $y$; that is, $-b \leq y \leq b$. Since

$$y = \frac{b^3}{a^2 - b^2} > 0,$$

we must determine whether

$$\frac{b^3}{a^2 - b^2} \leq b.$$

If this last inequality is true, then, since $0 < b < a$, we may divide by $b$ to obtain

$$\frac{b^2}{a^2 - b^2} \leq 1$$

or

$$b^2 \leq a^2 - b^2.$$

This inequality yields

$$a \geq \sqrt{2}b, \qquad a > 0, b > 0.$$

By retracing our steps, we can show that if $a \geq \sqrt{2}b$, $a > 0$, and $b > 0$, then

$$\frac{b^3}{a^2 - b^2} \leq b.$$

That is, the critical value of $y$ is in the range of $y$, provided that $a > \sqrt{2}b$, $a > 0$, $b > 0$.

Hence no maximum value of $z$ with $D_y z = 0$ occurs unless the ellipse is sufficiently elongated. If the ellipse is nearly circular, the point of maximum distance from $(0, -b)$ is at $(0, +b)$, which is an end point of the domain of $f$. The same is true if the ellipse degenerates into a circle ($a = b$), or if it is elongated in the $y$ direction ($b > a$). In summary, we may say that a maximum distance from $(0, -b)$ to $P(x, y)$ occurs when $P$ is at the points for which $y = b^3/(a^2 - b^2)$ when $a \geq \sqrt{2}b$, or at $(0, b)$ for $a < \sqrt{2}b$.

---

A type of problem to which the foregoing procedures do not apply directly is one which involves a function whose domain is a set of discrete values rather than an interval. In some cases, it is possible to approximate the behavior of such a function by means of a differentiable function on which the methods of calculus may be used. After finding the extremes of the new function, it is necessary only to check a few values of the independent variable in the neighborhoods of the critical values to determine which ones actually locate the desired extremes. These remarks are illustrated in the next example.

---

*Example 7.6c.* A manufacturer of boxes produces and sells them in unbroken lots of 1000 at \$4.98 per box with \$0.05 per box reduction in price for each thousand ordered (provided two or more lots are ordered). If the boxes cost him \$3.66 each to make, find the number of thousands in an order that will yield the maximum gross profit.

Let $n$ be the number of thousands of boxes ordered. Then the price per box is $(4.98 - 0.05n)$, and the total number of dollars received is

$$1000(4.98 - 0.05n)n.$$

The manufacturer's gross profit is

$$P = 1000(4.98 - 0.05n)n - 3.66n(1000)$$
$$= 1320n - 50n^2, \qquad n \in \mathfrak{N}.$$

We now replace $n$, the discrete variable, by $x$, a continuous variable, and differentiate

$$P = 1320x - 50x^2$$

to get

$$D_x P = 1320 - 100x.$$

For $D_x P = 0$, we have $x = 13.2$, which yields a maximum for $P$ as may be verified by calculating $D_x^2 P$. This answer indicates that we should investigate $n = 13$ and $n = 14$. Since $P = \$8710$ for $n = 13$ and $P = \$8680$ for $n = 14$, and $P$ increases with increasing $x$ for $x < 13.2$ and decreases with increasing $x$ for $x > 13.2$, we see that $n = 13$ gives the maximum profit.

## Exercises 7.6

1. Find two numbers whose sum is 12 and whose product is a maximum.
2. Find two positive numbers whose sum is 12 and the product of whose squares is a maximum.
3. A line segment $A$ units long joins the points $P(0, y)$ and $Q(x, 0)$. Find $x$ and $y$ such that the line segment, the $x$-axis, and the $y$-axis form a triangle of maximum area.
4. Show that a square is the rectangle of largest area with a specified (constant) perimeter.
5. Show that a square is the rectangle of minimum perimeter for a specified (constant) area.
6. Find the largest rectangle with one side on the $x$-axis and inscribed in the area bounded by the $x$-axis and the curve whose equation is $y = 27 - x^2$.
7. A sheet of tin 16 inches wide by 21 inches long is to be used to make an open rectangular box by cutting a square from each corner of the sheet and folding up the sides. What should be the length of the side of the cut-out square to furnish a box of maximum volume?
8. Find the point on the parabola $y^2 = 4x$ that is nearest the point $(0, -3)$.
9. An open rectangular box with a square base is to have a fixed volume $V$. What must be the relation between the inside dimensions if the inside surface area is to be a minimum?
10. What is the area of the largest isosceles triangle that can be inscribed in a circle of radius $a$?
11. What is the altitude of the circular cylinder of greatest volume that can be inscribed in a circular cone of radius $a$ and height $h$?
12. Find the rectangle of maximum perimeter that can be inscribed in the ellipse $x^2/a^2 + y^2/b^2 = 1$.
13. A window consists of a rectangle surmounted by a semicircle. Find the shape that would give the most light for a fixed perimeter.
14. A container manufacturer wishes to design a closed cylindrical can with a specified fixed volume $V$, but of such radius $r$ and height $h$ that the amount of tinplate used in making the container is a minimum. Find the ratio of the height to the radius that he should use.
15. Work Number 14 if the can is to have an open top.
16. Find the area of the rectangle of maximum area that can be inscribed in the ellipse $4x^2 + 9y^2 = 36$.

17. The electromotive force of a battery is $E$ volts and the internal resistance is $r$ ohms. The formula $I = E/(R + r)$ gives the current $I$ (amperes) that will flow when a resistor of $R$ ohms is connected across the battery terminals. If the formula $P = I^2R$ gives the power $P$ (watts) developed in the resistor, find the value of $R$ for which the power will be a maximum.

18. A rancher wishes to build a small corral against the side of a steep, straight cliff in order to save on fencing. Determine the proportions of the rectangular corral that will require the least amount of fence for a given area.

19. The strength of a wooden beam of rectangular cross section is proportional to the width of the beam and the square of its depth. Determine the proportions of the strongest beam that can be sawed from a round log.

20. The amplitude $I$ of the alternating current flowing in an electric circuit with inductance $L$, capacitance $C$, and resistance $R$ in series is given by

$$I = \frac{V}{\sqrt{R^2 + \left(L\omega - \dfrac{1}{\omega C}\right)^2}},$$

where $V$ is the amplitude of the alternating voltage and $\omega$ is $2\pi f$, where $f$ (cycles per second) is the frequency of the voltage. Show that $I$ is a maximum when

$$f = \frac{1}{2\pi\sqrt{LC}} \text{ cycles per second.}$$

21. A loan shark, whose monthly interest charge is limited by law to 3%, finds that the amount of money people will invest with him is proportional to the interest rate that he will pay them. If he can lend out all the money that people will invest with him, find the interest rate that he should pay them in order to maximize his monthly profit.

★22. A manufacturer of electronic assemblies finds that for no more than 1000 assemblies per week the cost for labor and parts is $A per assembly. In addition he has fixed costs (overhead) of $C regardless of the number assembled. If he exceeds 1000 assemblies per week, then overtime and inefficiencies due to crowding, and so on, raise the cost per assembly by $B for each assembly over one thousand. (If he produces 1003 assemblies, the cost for the 1001st unit is $A + $B, the cost for the 1002nd unit is $A + $2B, and the cost for the 1003rd unit is $A + $3B. One would expect $B$ to be very small, of course.) If he can sell all that he can produce at a fixed price of $P per assembly, $P > A$, find the number per week that he should try to produce to maximize his gross profit $F$. *Hint*: Set up expressions for $F$, for $n \leq 1000$, and $n \geq 1000$. For the case of $n \geq 1000$, see what conditions must be satisfied in order to have a solution. Investigate carefully what happens at $n = 1000$.

23. In connecting a water line to a building at $A$ (see Figure 7.6c), the contractor finds that he must connect to a certain point $C$ on the water main which lies under the paved parking lot of a shopping center. It will cost him $20.00 per foot to dig, lay pipe, fill, and resurface the parking lot, but only $12.00 per foot to lay pipe along the edge. Find the distance from the store water inlet (point $A$) to the point $B$, where he should turn the water line and go directly to point $C$ in order to minimize his cost.

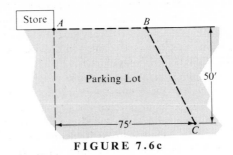

**FIGURE 7.6c**

★24. Work Number 23 with the dimensions 50 feet by 75 feet replaced by $a$ feet by $b$ feet.

## 7.7 TIME-RATE PROBLEMS

A number of applications of the derivative are concerned with the rate of change of one or more related quantities with respect to time. The relationship between these quantities ordinarily may be expressed by means of one or more equations, and differentiation of both members of each such equation with respect to time gives an equation relating the time-rates of change. This procedure is illustrated in the following examples.

---

*Example 7.7a.* Car $A$ is traveling east at 30 miles per hour and car $B$ is traveling north at 22.5 miles per hour. Both cars are traveling toward a junction $O$ of two roads as indicated in Figure 7.7a. (a) At what rate are the cars approaching each other at

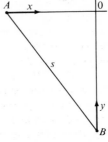

**FIGURE 7.7a**

the instant when car $A$ is 300 feet and car $B$ is 400 feet from the junction? (b) What is the rate of change of the speed of one car with respect to the other?

(a) Let $s$ be the distance between the two cars so that the value of $D_t s$ will be the answer to this question. We have (see Figure 7.7a)

$$s^2 = x^2 + y^2,$$

so that, by differentiation with respect to $t$, we get

$$s\, D_t s = x\, D_t x + y\, D_t y.$$

For $x = 300$ and $y = 400$, $s = 500$. Also

$$D_t x = -44 \text{ feet per second}$$

and

$$D_t y = -33 \text{ feet per second.}$$

Hence,

$$D_t s = \frac{(300)(-44) + (400)(-33)}{500}$$

$$= -52.8 \text{ feet per second.}$$

The minus sign indicates that $s$ is decreasing with the time.

(b) By differentiating both members of the equation

$$s \, D_t s = x \, D_t x + y \, D_t y$$

with respect to $t$, we obtain

$$s \, D_t^2 s + (D_t s)^2 = x \, D_t^2 x + (D_t x)^2 + y \, D_t^2 y + (D_t y)^2.$$

But $D_t x$ and $D_t y$ are both constant in this problem, so that $D_t^2 x = 0$ and $D_t^2 y = 0$. Accordingly, for $x = 300$ and $y = 400$, we have

$$500 \, D_t^2 s + (-52.8)^2 = (-44)^2 + (-33)^2,$$

and

$$D_t^2 s = -0.47 \text{ (approx.) foot per second per second.}$$

The negative sign indicates that the speed of one car relative to the other is decreasing algebraically at the instant in question. However, since by (a) the relative speed is negative, the absolute value of the speed must be increasing.

---

*Example 7.7b.* An optical tracking device has a lens of focal length 6 inches that forms the image of a moving object on a small screen. If the object is moving away at a speed of 20 feet per second, how fast must the lens be moving and in what direction in order to keep the object in focus at the instant when it is 50 feet away from the lens? The simple lens equation is

$$\frac{1}{u} + \frac{1}{v} = \frac{1}{f},$$

where $u$ is the object distance, $v$ the image distance, and $f$ the focal length, all measured in the same units.

By differentiation with respect to $t$, we get from the lens equation

$$-\frac{1}{u^2} D_t u - \frac{1}{v^2} D_t v = 0,$$

or

$$D_t v = -\frac{v^2}{u^2} D_t u.$$

With $f = \frac{1}{2}$ (foot) and $u = 50$ (feet), the lens equation becomes

$$\frac{1}{50} + \frac{1}{v} = 2,$$

so that

$$v = \frac{50}{99}.$$

Since $D_t u = 20$, we get

$$D_t v = -\left(\frac{50}{99}\right)^2 \left(\frac{1}{50}\right)^2 (20)$$

$$= -\frac{20}{9801} \text{ foot per second}$$

$$= -0.024 \text{ (approx.) inch per second.}$$

Thus the lens must be moving toward the screen at the rate of approximately 0.024 inch per second.

## Exercises 7.7

1. As a spherical rubber balloon is being inflated, its volume increases at the rate of $2\pi$ cubic inches per second. At what rate is the surface area changing?

2. A storage tank is in the shape of an inverted circular cone with a diameter of 8 feet and a height of 6 feet. At what rate is water running out of the tank when the depth is 3 feet and is decreasing at the rate of 6 inches per minute?

3. A man 6 feet tall walks at the rate of 4 miles per hour toward a street light that hangs 16 feet directly above the sidewalk. At what rate is the end of his shadow moving? Is the end of his shadow accelerating?

4. In Number 3, if the light is located at a height of 16 feet above the street and 20 feet from the walk, find the rate at which the end of the man's shadow moves. At what rate is the man's shadow getting shorter?

5. A rope 32 feet long is attached to a weight and passed over a pulley 16 feet above the ground. The other end of the rope is pulled away along the ground at the rate of 3 feet per second. At what rate does the weight rise at the instant when the other end of the rope is 12 feet from its initial point?

6. A plane 2 miles above the ground is flying due south at a speed of 600 miles per hour. It flies directly over a car going due east at 60 miles per hour. How fast is the distance between the plane and the car increasing 1 minute later?

7. A swimming pool is 100 feet long, 30 feet wide, 12 feet deep at one end and 2 feet deep at the other. If water is being let into the pool at the rate of 500 cubic feet per minute, at what rate is the surface rising when the greatest depth is 6 feet? 10 feet?

8. One end of a spring is fastened to a point 10 inches up on the $y$-axis and the lower end just reaches the origin. The lower end is then pulled along the $x$-axis at the rate of 2 inches per minute. At what rate is the spring being stretched at the instant when the lower end reaches the point 8 inches from the origin?

9. The two ends of a rubber strip are fastened at the points $(-3, 0)$ and $(3, 0)$, respectively. If the midpoint of the strip is moved up the $y$-axis at the rate of 4 inches per minute, at what rate is the strip being stretched at the end of 2 minutes?

10. Two stones are dropped from the edge of a cliff, one 5 seconds after the other. At what rate does the subsequent distance between the stones increase before the first stone hits the ground? *Hint*: The formula $s = \frac{1}{2}gt^2$ gives the distance passed through in $t$ seconds by a freely falling body.

11. Two ships leave from the same point. The first leaves at 9 A.M. and sails due east at a speed of 10 miles per hour. The second leaves at 10 A.M. and sails 30° east

of north at a speed of 15 miles per hour. At what rate are the ships separating at noon?

12. A mass of air is expanding isothermally in accordance with Boyle's Law, $pv = C$, where $p$ is the pressure, $v$ is the volume, and $C$ is a constant. At a certain instant the pressure is 50 pounds per square inch and the volume is 100 cubic inches. If the volume is decreasing at the rate of 4 cubic inches per second, how is the pressure changing?

13. A train leaves a station at a certain time and travels north at the rate of 60 miles per hour. A second train leaves the same station one hour later and goes east at a rate of 40 miles per hour. At what rate are the trains separating 3 hours after the second train leaves the station? Is the rate of change of distance between the two trains a constant? Explain.

# Summary of Chapter 7

The important ideas in this chapter are not so much the methods used in solving particular problems as the general principles that are illustrated by the various methods used in those problems. These general principles and the fundamental ideas relating to them are

(1) the definition of increasing and decreasing functions over an open interval, and of monotonic functions (Section 7.1);

(2) the condition that a function be increasing or decreasing expressed mathematically in terms of the derivative (Section 7.2);

(3) concavity of a curve and its relationship to the second derivative (Section 7.2);

(4) points of inflection and conditions that a point be a point of inflection expressed in terms of the derivatives (Section 7.2);

(5) maximum and minimum points, relative extremes, and conditions for an extreme (Section 7.3);

(6) critical points of a curve (Section 7.3);

(7) the first derivative test and the second derivative test for maxima and minima (Section 7.3);

(8) the Mean Value Theorem for Derivatives, and the application of this important theorem in proving that two functions having the same derivative over an interval differ by a constant (Section 7.4);

(9) the use of the first and second derivatives in curve sketching (Section 7.5);

(10) applications of maxima and minima and the use of implicit differentiation for cases involving a side condition (Section 7.6);

(11) applications of the derivative to time-rate problems (Section 7.7).

# Chapter 8 The Definite Integral

## 8.1 THE SUMMATION NOTATION

Two fundamental geometric problems, which eventually led to the development of many important mathematical concepts, are those of finding the circumference of a circle and the area enclosed by a circle. Similar problems arise in connection with finding the area of any plane figure bounded by a curved line, or in finding the volume of any solid bounded by a curved surface. When mathematical techniques were developed to handle these problems, it was found that these same techniques could be used to solve a variety of physical problems, such as that of finding the work done by a force acting through a given distance, or that of finding the force exerted on a dam by the water contained by the dam.

In this chapter, we shall develop the mathematical techniques for solving such problems. In order to do this, we must constantly be concerned with sums of quantities, such as the sum of areas of rectangles, expressed in the form

$$a_1 + a_2 + \cdots + a_n.$$

Since such expressions occur so frequently and are clumsy to use extensively, mathematicians have developed a more compact and efficient notation for them.

**Definition 8.1a.** Let $\{a_1, a_2, \ldots, a_n\}$ be a set of $n$ numbers. Then

$$\sum_{k=1}^{n} a_k .=. a_1 + a_2 + \cdots + a_n.$$

The notation $\sum_{k=1}^{n} a_k$ is simply a shorthand form for the sum indicated by the symbol

$$a_1 + a_2 + \cdots + a_n$$

and is read "the sum of $a_k$ from $k = 1$ to $k = n$." This notation is called the *summation notation*. The symbol $\Sigma$ is the Greek letter capital sigma. The subscript $k$ on the sigma is called the *index* of the summation, and the subscript 1 and the superscript $n$ indicate the range of the index.

For example, we may write

(a) $\displaystyle\sum_{k=1}^{n} k^2 = 1^2 + 2^2 + 3^2 + \cdots + n^2,$

(b) $\displaystyle\sum_{k=1}^{5} x^k = x + x^2 + x^3 + x^4 + x^5,$ or

(c) $\displaystyle\sum_{k=1}^{n} \frac{2k}{1+k} = 1 + \frac{4}{3} + \frac{3}{2} + \frac{8}{5} + \cdots + \frac{2n}{1+n}.$

The reader should note the basic properties

$$\sum_{k=1}^{n} (a_n + b_n) = \sum_{k=1}^{n} a_n + \sum_{k=1}^{n} b_n$$

and

$$\sum_{k=1}^{n} ca_n = c \sum_{k=1}^{n} a_n,$$

which result directly from the fundamental laws of addition and multiplication.

Any convenient letter may be used for the index of a summation. For example, the expressions

$$\sum_{k=5}^{n} k^2, \quad \sum_{p=1}^{n} p^2, \quad \sum_{\sigma=1}^{n} \sigma^2$$

all represent

$$1^2 + 2^2 + 3^2 + \cdots + n^2.$$

It is also convenient on occasion to have the range of the index begin with 0 or some integer other than 1. The definition can be modified accordingly. Ordinarily the index does not include negative integers in its range, but there is no reason why negative integers need be excluded. Expressions in which the index may take on negative integral values simply do not occur as frequently as expressions with the index having positive integral values. For example, we may have

$$\sum_{k=5}^{7} \frac{1}{k} = \frac{1}{5} + \frac{1}{6} + \frac{1}{7},$$

$$\sum_{k=0}^{5} a^k = a^0 + a^1 + a^2 + a^3 + a^4 + a^5,$$

or

$$\sum_{k=-2}^{2} 2^k = 2^{-2} + 2^{-1} + 2^0 + 2^1 + 2^2$$

$$= \tfrac{1}{4} + \tfrac{1}{2} + 1 + 2 + 4.$$

Some additional examples will help to illustrate this notation.

(a) The equation $1 + 2 + 3 + \cdots + n = \tfrac{1}{2}n(n+1)$ becomes

$$\sum_{k=1}^{n} k = \tfrac{1}{2}n(n+1).$$

(b) The expression

$$\sqrt{1 - \frac{1}{n^2}} + \sqrt{1 - \frac{2^2}{n^2}} + \sqrt{1 - \frac{3^2}{n^2}} + \cdots + \sqrt{1 - \frac{n^2}{n^2}}$$

may be written as

$$\sum_{k=1}^{n} \sqrt{1 - \frac{k^2}{n^2}}.$$

(c) The expression

$$\frac{1}{10} + \frac{1}{14} + \frac{1}{18} + \frac{1}{22} + \frac{1}{26}$$

becomes

$$\sum_{k=0}^{4} \frac{1}{10 + 4k} \quad \text{or} \quad \sum_{p=2}^{6} \frac{1}{2 + 4p}.$$

This last illustration shows that a given expression may be represented in more than one way by the summation notation.

(d) $\displaystyle\sum_{k=1}^{n} (A_k + 4) = (A_1 + 4) + (A_2 + 4) + \cdots + (A_n + 4)$

$$= 4n + \sum_{k=1}^{n} A_k.$$

(e) $\displaystyle\sum_{k=-n}^{n} (k^2 + kn) = \sum_{k=-n}^{n} k^2 = 2 \sum_{k=1}^{n} k^2.$

(f) $\displaystyle\sum_{k=1}^{n} \frac{1}{k} = \sum_{k=0}^{n-1} \frac{1}{k+1} = \sum_{k=0}^{n-1} \frac{1}{n-k}.$

The second summation in (*f*) amounts only to a renumbering of the terms, beginning with $k = 0$ rather than with $k = 1$; the last summation is the same as the second with the terms written in reverse order.

As a further illustration of the use of the summation notation, we shall prove the binomial theorem by means of mathematical induction.

**Theorem 8.1a.** *The Binomial Theorem.* Let $n \in \mathfrak{N}$. Then

$$(a + b)^n = \sum_{k=0}^{n} \binom{n}{k} a^{n-k} b^k,$$

where

$$\binom{n}{k} .=. \frac{n(n-1) \cdots (n-k+1)}{k!}, \qquad k = 1, 2, \ldots, n,$$

and

$$\binom{n}{0} .=. 1.$$

PROOF: For $n = 1$, the preceding formula becomes

$$a + b = \sum_{k=0}^{1} \binom{1}{k} a^{1-k} b^k = \binom{1}{0} a + \binom{1}{1} b = a + b,$$

which is of course correct.

Now assuming that the formula is valid for a particular value of $n$, say $s$, we have

$$(a + b)^{s+1} = (a + b)(a + b)^s = (a + b) \sum_{k=0}^{s} \binom{s}{k} a^{s-k} b^k$$

$$= a \sum_{k=0}^{s} \binom{s}{k} a^{s-k} b^k + b \sum_{k=0}^{s} \binom{s}{k} a^{s-k} b^k$$

$$= \sum_{k=0}^{s} \binom{s}{k} a^{s+1-k} b^k + \sum_{k=0}^{s} \binom{s}{k} a^{s-k} b^{k+1}.$$

In the first of these summations, let us write the first term separately, and in the second summation let us write the last term separately. Thus,

(1) $\quad (a + b)^{s+1} = a^{s+1} + \sum_{k=1}^{s} \binom{s}{k} a^{s+1-k} b^k + \sum_{k=0}^{s-1} \binom{s}{k} a^{s-k} b^{k+1} + b^{s+1}.$

Next, the second summation can be rewritten by replacing the index $k$ by $k - 1$ to get

$$\sum_{k=0}^{s-1} \binom{s}{k} a^{s-k} b^{k+1} = \sum_{k=1}^{s} \binom{s}{k-1} a^{s+1-k} b^k.$$

This allows the two summations in Equation (1) to be combined in the form

$$\sum_{k=1}^{s} \left[ \binom{s}{k} + \binom{s}{k-1} \right] a^{s+1-k} b^k = \sum_{k=1}^{s} \binom{s+1}{k} a^{s+1-k} b^k,$$

since

$$\binom{s}{k} + \binom{s}{k-1} = \frac{s(s-1) \cdots (s-k+1)}{k!} + \frac{s(s-1) \cdots (s-k+2)}{(k-1)!}$$

$$= \frac{s(s-1) \cdots (s-k+2)}{(k-1)!} \left( \frac{s-k+1}{k} + 1 \right)$$

$$= \frac{s(s-1) \cdots (s-k+2)}{(k-1)!} \cdot \frac{s+1}{k}$$

$$= \frac{(s+1)(s)(s-1) \cdots (s+1-k+1)}{k!} = \binom{s+1}{k}.$$

Accordingly, we use the fact that

$$\binom{s+1}{0} = 1 \quad \text{and} \quad \binom{s+1}{s+1} = 1$$

to write Equation (1) with a single summation on the right:

$$(a + b)^{s+1} = \sum_{k=0}^{s+1} \binom{s+1}{k} a^{s+1-k} b^k.$$

This shows that the validity of the binomial formula for $(a + b)^s$ implies its validity for $(a + b)^{s+1}$, and, since the formula has been shown to hold for $n = 1$, the proof by mathematical induction is complete.

## Exercises 8.1

1. Write each of the following expressions in the summation notation.

   (a) $2 + 4 + 8 + \cdots + 2^n$.

   (b) $7 + 8 + 10 + \cdots + \left[7 + \dfrac{n(n+1)}{2}\right]$.

   (c) $a_1 + 2a_2 + 3a_3 + \cdots + na_n$.

   (d) $\dfrac{1}{n+1} + \dfrac{1}{n+2} + \cdots + \dfrac{1}{n+n}$.

2. If $a_1 .=. 6$ and $a_{k+1} .=. a_k + k$, show that

$$\sum_{k=1}^{n} a_k = 6n + \sum_{k=1}^{n} \frac{(k-1)k}{2}.$$

3. Write out the expressions represented by

   (a) $\displaystyle\sum_{\alpha=1}^{4} a_\alpha$;

   (b) $\displaystyle\sum_{\beta=1}^{5} 2^\beta$;

   (c) $\displaystyle\sum_{k=1}^{5} \frac{1}{(n-k)}$;

   (d) $\displaystyle\sum_{\alpha=1}^{4} \frac{\alpha}{n-\alpha}$;

   (e) $\displaystyle\sum_{k=1}^{4} \frac{(-1)^k + 1}{2}$;

   (f) $\displaystyle\sum_{k=5}^{10} \frac{1}{k}$.

4. Show that $\displaystyle\sum_{k=p}^{n} a_k = \sum_{k=1}^{n} a_k - \sum_{k=1}^{p-1} a_k, \ p < n$.

5. Show that $\displaystyle\sum_{\alpha=1}^{n} a_\alpha = \sum_{\beta=p}^{n+p-1} a_{\beta-p+1}$.

6. Show that $\displaystyle\sum_{k=-n}^{n} k^2 = 2 \sum_{k=1}^{n} k^2$.

7. Show that $\displaystyle\sum_{k=-n}^{n} \frac{k}{n} = 0$.

8. Show that $\displaystyle\sum_{k=-n}^{n} \sqrt{1 - \left(\frac{k}{n}\right)^2} = 1 + 2 \sum_{k=1}^{n} \sqrt{1 - \left(\frac{k}{n}\right)^2}$.

9. Choose $a = b = 1$ in the binomial theorem and evaluate $\displaystyle\sum_{k=0}^{n} \binom{n}{k}$. Can you evaluate $\displaystyle\sum_{k=0}^{n} (-1)^k \binom{n}{k}$?

10. Use the results of Number 9 to evaluate $\displaystyle\sum_{k=0}^{[\![n/2]\!]} \binom{n}{2k}$.

11. Expand the following expressions using the binomial theorem:

    (a) $(2a - 3b^2)^6$;

    (b) $\left(\dfrac{a}{2} - \dfrac{2}{a^2}\right)^7$;

    (c) $\left(\dfrac{x}{3} - \dfrac{3y}{2}\right)^6$;

    (d) $(x^2 - x + 1)^4$.

12. Evaluate each of the following to five significant digits, using the binomial theorem:

$$\text{(a) } (1.02)^5; \quad \text{(b) } (1.01)^8; \quad \text{(c) } (0.98)^7.$$

13. In each of the following find the indicated term of the expansion without writing all the preceding terms:

   (a) $(2a^{-1} + a^2)^{11}$; 7th term;

   (b) $\left(3x + \dfrac{2}{x^2}\right)^{13}$; 8th term;

   (c) $(x - \frac{1}{2}y^2)^{17}$; 9th term.

14. Find the coefficient of $x^{14}$ in $\left(x^3 + \dfrac{1}{x^2}\right)^{13}$.

15. Find the coefficient of $y^{-12}$ in $\left(\dfrac{1}{4y^3} - \dfrac{2y^2}{3}\right)^{14}$.

16. Find the term that involves no $u$ in $\left(\dfrac{2}{u^4} + \dfrac{u^2}{4}\right)^{12}$.

17. The coefficients in the binomial theorem for successive values of $n$ starting with $n = 1$ may be written in the form of an interesting array called Pascal's triangle. This array is

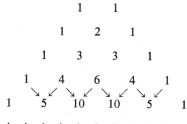

Note that, after the first line, every coefficient except the 1's in a given line may be obtained by adding the two coefficients on the preceding line on either side of the required coefficient as is indicated by the arrows in the array. This is a consequence of what formula that was obtained in this section? Notice that the second number in each line is the value of the exponent for that line. Complete the triangle through the eighth line.

★18. If you did Number 17, you may have observed that the coefficients in lines 1, 3, and 7 are all odd numbers. It is an interesting problem to conjecture for which lines this is so and then to prove that your conjecture is correct.

★19. Find a closed formula in terms of $n$ for the value of

$$\sum_{k=1}^{n} k(k!), \quad n = 2, 3, 4, \ldots .$$

## 8.2 SEQUENCES

Over two thousand years ago the Greek mathematicians became interested in the problem of finding the circumference of a circle having a given radius.

At that time the exact formula, $C = 2\pi r$, which is so familiar to us today, was unknown. For that matter, even though the formula is now well known, very few persons who are not mathematicians understand the profound reasoning underlying its discovery. What is the number denoted by $\pi$? What do we mean when we speak of the "circumference of" or "distance around" a circle?

These are the questions the ancient Greeks attempted to answer. Even though they did not have the benefit of many of the mathematical tools that we use today, they were able to discover the formula $C = 2\pi r$ by reasoning in a manner essentially equivalent to that discussed in the next paragraphs.

Since it was apparently easy to assign a length to a straight line segment, the Greeks hit upon the idea of approximating the circumference of a circle by means of a sum of lengths of straight line segments, and they were able to do this with any desired degree of accuracy. Knowing how to find the perimeter of a regular polygon of $2^n$ sides inscribed in the circle, they simply considered perimeters of polygons of a successively greater number of sides. Thus, for a square inscribed in a circle of radius $r$, the perimeter is

$$p = 8r \sin \frac{\pi}{4}.$$

For an inscribed octagon, the perimeter is

$$p = 16r \sin \frac{\pi}{8}.$$

For a regular sixteen-sided polygon inscribed in a circle,

$$p = 32r \sin \frac{\pi}{16},$$

and in general, for a polygon of $2^n$ equal sides inscribed in a circle of radius $r$,

$$p = 2^{n+1}r \sin \frac{\pi}{2^n}, \qquad n = 2, 3, 4, \ldots.$$

The idea is that as $n$ gets larger, $p$ becomes more nearly equal to the circumference of the circle. Of course, this idea is based on the assumption that the expression $2^{n+1}r \sin (\pi/2^n)$ has a limit as $n \to \infty$. If this limit exists, it would naturally be called the circumference of the circle. It seems intuitively evident that the limit does exist. In fact, we shall show later that

$$\lim_{n \to \infty} \frac{\sin (\pi/2^n)}{\pi/2^n} = 1,$$

from which it follows that $\lim_{n \to \infty} p = 2\pi r$.

The elements of the set of numbers $\{2^{n+1}r \sin (\pi/2^n), n = 1, 2, 3, \ldots\}$ may be regarded as having a definite order, since each element of the set is associated with a natural number. In fact, these numbers may be considered as values in the range of a function whose domain is $\mathfrak{N}$.

**Definition 8.2a.** An *infinite sequence* is a function whose domain is the set $\mathfrak{N}$ of natural numbers. If $s_n$ denotes the value of the function for the number $n \in \mathfrak{N}$, then $s_n$ is called the *nth term* of the sequence. A sequence is usually denoted by the set of its *terms*, $\{s_n\}$.

A sequence is characterized by the fact that its elements are ordered, that is, its elements occur in a definite succession, a consequence of the order properties of the natural numbers. The term $s_n$ is said to *precede* the term $s_{n+1}$, and $s_{n+1}$ is called the *successor* of $s_n$, so that the sequence has a first term, a second term, and a third term, and so on. Accordingly, the notation $\{s_n\}$ is to be interpreted as a symbol for the *ordered* set of numbers

$$\{s_1, s_2, \ldots, s_n, s_{n+1}, \ldots\},$$

which is analogous to the concept of an ordered pair of numbers.

In order to specify a sequence, it is necessary that some rule of formation for its terms be given. Some examples of sequences are:

(a) $\left\{1, \frac{1}{2}, \frac{1}{3}, \frac{1}{4}, \ldots, \frac{1}{n}, \ldots\right\}$ or $\left\{s_n = \frac{1}{n}, n \in \mathfrak{N}\right\}$;

(b) $\left\{1, 0, 1, 0, \ldots, \frac{1 - (-1)^n}{2}, \ldots\right\}$ or $\left\{s_n = \frac{1 - (-1)^n}{2}, n \in \mathfrak{N}\right\}$;

(c) $\left\{1, \frac{1}{2}, -1, \frac{1}{3}, 1, \frac{1}{4}, -1, \ldots s_n, \ldots\right\}$, where

$$s_{2k-1} = (-1)^{k+1}, \quad s_{2k} = \frac{1}{k + 1}, \quad k \in \mathfrak{N}.$$

Notice in the third example that the terms of the sequence are described by means of two formulas.

Since the terms of a sequence constitute a set of "points," it proves useful to modify the definition of a "cluster point" for sequences.

**Definition 8.2b.** A number $a$ is called a **cluster point of a sequence** $\{s_n\}$ if every arbitrary neighborhood $\mathfrak{N}(a, \epsilon)$ contains infinitely many terms of the sequence.

In Example (a), 0 is a cluster point. This is seen from the fact that if $n > 1/\epsilon$, then all terms $1/n, 1/(n + 1), \ldots$, lie in $\mathfrak{N}(0, \epsilon)$. In Example (b), both 0 and 1 are cluster points of $\{s_n\}$; in (c), the cluster points of the sequence are $-1$, 0, and 1.

The last two examples illustrate the fact that an infinite sequence can have more than one cluster point. However, certain special sequences having only one cluster point are particularly important in many mathematical considerations.

**Definition 8.2c.** If $\{s_n\}$ is an infinite sequence having a cluster point $S$ such that for each neighborhood of $S$, $\mathfrak{N}(S, \epsilon)$, there is some integer $N_0$ for which $s_n \in \mathfrak{N}(S, \epsilon)$ for all $n \geq N_0$, then we say that $\{s_n\}$ **converges** to the limit $S$ and write

$$\lim_{n \to \infty} s_n = S,$$

or

$$s_n \to S \quad \text{as } n \to \infty.$$

To illustrate, consider the following example.

---

*Example 8.2a.* What is the limit, if it exists, of each of the following sequences?

(a) $\left\{ 1, \dfrac{3}{2}, \dfrac{7}{4}, \dfrac{15}{8}, \ldots, \dfrac{2^{n+1} - 1}{2^n}, \ldots \right\}, n = 0, 1, 2, \ldots$

(b) $\{s_n\}$ where $s_n = (-1)^n \left( 1 - \dfrac{1}{n} \right), n = 1, 2, \ldots$

(c) $\{s_n\}$ where $s_n = 1 + \dfrac{(-1)^n}{n}, n = 1, 2, \ldots$

In (a) it appears that 2 is a limit. To verify this conjecture, let $\mathfrak{N}(2, \epsilon)$ be an arbitrary neighborhood of 2. We want to know if there is some integer $N_0$ for which $s_n \in \mathfrak{N}(2, \epsilon)$ for all $n \geq N_0$. Hence, let us consider

$$|s_n - 2| = \left| \frac{2^{n+1} - 1}{2^n} - 2 \right| = \frac{1}{2^n}.$$

In order to have $s_n \in \mathfrak{N}(2, \epsilon)$ we need $|s_n - 2| < \epsilon$, and this will indeed be the case if $n$ is large enough to have $1/2^n < \epsilon$. For example, if $\epsilon = 1/1000$, $N_0$ can be taken as 10, since $1/2^{10} = 1/1024 < 1/1000$, and for $n > 10$, $1/2^n < 1/2^{10}$.

In (b) the sequence has two cluster points, $+1$ and $-1$, so that it has no limit in the sense of Definition 8.2c, and therefore the sequence does not converge. In (c) it appears that $s_n \to 1$ as $n \to \infty$. To verify this, consider

$$|s_n - 1| = \left| \frac{(-1)^n}{n} \right| = \frac{1}{n}.$$

Since $1/n < \epsilon$ if $n > N_0$, where

$$N_0 = [\![ 1/\epsilon ]\!],$$

it follows that

$$\lim_{n \to \infty} s_n = 1.$$

---

If the terms of an infinite sequence do not decrease as $n$ increases, that is, if $s_{n+1} \geq s_n$ for all $n$, the sequence is said to be *nondecreasing*. Similarly, if $s_{n+1} \leq s_n$ for all $n$, then the sequence is said to be *nonincreasing*. Nondecreasing and nonincreasing sequences will be of particular interest to us in the succeeding sections of this chapter. Furthermore, we shall be concerned for the most part with bounded infinite sequences—that is, with sequences having the property that there exist two numbers, $a$ and $b$, such that

$$a \leq s_n \leq b \quad \text{for all } n.$$

As in the case of functions in general, $a$ is called a *lower bound* and $b$ is called an *upper bound* of the sequence (see Section 4.7).

We state without proof the following basic theorem, which should appear highly plausible to the reader.

**Theorem 8.2a.** A bounded infinite sequence has a least upper bound, and a greatest lower bound.

As illustrations, we refer to the sequences given in Example 8.2a. These illustrations show that the greatest lower bound and the least upper bound need not themselves be elements of the sequence.

(a) Since

$$s_n = \frac{2^{n+1} - 1}{2^n} = 2 - \frac{1}{2^n},$$

and $1/2^n$ is arbitrarily small for all sufficiently large values of $n$, the sequence has the least upper bound 2. It also has the greatest lower bound 1, since the greatest value of $1/2^n$ occurs for $n = 0$.

(b) Since

$$s_n = (-1)^n \left(1 - \frac{1}{n}\right), \qquad n = 1, 2, \ldots,$$

and $1/n$ is arbitrarily small for all sufficiently large values of $n$, the sequence has the least upper bound 1 and the greatest lower bound $-1$.

(c) Since

$$s_n = 1 - \frac{1}{n}, \qquad n = 1, 2, \ldots,$$

the sequence has the least upper bound 1 and the greatest lower bound 0.

For bounded nondecreasing (nonincreasing) sequences we have the following major results which are indispensable tools in the succeeding discussions.

**Theorem 8.2b.** A bounded nondecreasing infinite sequence converges to its least upper bound. That is, if $B$ is the least upper bound of $\{s_n\}$, then $\lim_{n \to \infty} s_n = B$.

PROOF: Consider an arbitrary left neighborhood of $B$, say $\mathfrak{N}(B^-, \epsilon)$. There must be at least one element, say $s_m$, of the sequence $\{s_n\}$ in this neighborhood, otherwise $B - \epsilon$ is an upper bound of the sequence, contrary to the hypothesis that $B$ is the *least* upper bound. However, the sequence is nondecreasing, so that

$$s_m \leqq s_{m+1} \leqq s_{m+2} \leqq \cdots.$$

Consequently, $s_n \in \mathfrak{N}(B^-, \epsilon)$ for all $n \geqq m$, which, by Definition 8.2c, means that

$$\lim_{n \to \infty} s_n = B.$$

**Theorem 8.2c.** A bounded nonincreasing infinite sequence converges to its greatest lower bound. That is, if $A$ is the greatest lower bound of $\{s_n\}$, then $\lim_{n \to \infty} s_n = A$.

PROOF: The proof is left as an exercise for the reader.

---

*Example 8.2b.* Show that the sequence $\{s_n\}$, where

$$s_n = \sum_{k=n}^{2n} \frac{1}{k} = \frac{1}{n} + \frac{1}{n+1} + \frac{1}{n+2} + \cdots + \frac{1}{2n},$$

converges to a limit $A$ such that $A \geqq \frac{1}{2}$.

We first show that the sequence $\{s_n\}$ has a lower bound $a \geq \frac{1}{2}$. For this purpose, we observe that

$$s_n = \frac{1}{n} + \frac{1}{n+1} + \frac{1}{n+2} + \cdots + \frac{1}{2n}$$

is the sum of $n+1$ terms, the smallest of which is $1/(2n)$. Accordingly, for all $n$, the sum of these terms must be greater than the number of terms times the smallest of them; that is,

$$s_n > (n+1)\left(\frac{1}{2n}\right) = \frac{1}{2} + \frac{1}{2n} > \frac{1}{2}.$$

Next, it can be shown that the sequence is a decreasing one. Consider the difference

$$s_n - s_{n+1} = \sum_{k=n}^{2n} \frac{1}{k} - \sum_{k=n+1}^{2n+2} \frac{1}{k}$$

$$= \frac{1}{n} + \sum_{k=n+1}^{2n} \frac{1}{k} - \left(\sum_{k=n+1}^{2n} \frac{1}{k} + \frac{1}{2n+1} + \frac{1}{2n+2}\right)$$

$$= \frac{1}{n} - \frac{1}{2n+1} - \frac{1}{2n+2} = \frac{3n+2}{n(2n+1)(2n+2)}.$$

Since this last fraction is positive for all $n \in \mathfrak{N}$, it follows that $s_n > s_{n+1}$.

We have thus demonstrated that $\{s_n\}$ is a decreasing sequence with a lower bound $\frac{1}{2}$ (not necessarily the greatest lower bound). Hence, by Theorems 8.2a and 8.2c, the sequence converges to a number $A$ which is not less than $\frac{1}{2}$; that is,

$$\lim_{n \to \infty} s_n = A \geq \frac{1}{2}.$$

## Exercises 8.2

In each of Numbers 1 to 12, write out the first five terms, find the cluster points, and find the limit, if it exists, for the sequence whose general term is given.

1. $s_n = \dfrac{n}{n+3}$.

2. $s_n = \dfrac{n^2 + 2n + 1}{2n^2 - 2n + 1}$.

3. $s_n = (-1)^n 2^{-n}$.

4. $s_n = \cos n\pi$.

5. $s_n = (-1)^n \left(1 - \dfrac{(-1)^n}{2^n}\right)$.

6. $s_n = \dfrac{1 + (-1)^n}{2} 2^n$.

7. $s_n = a^n, \ a \in \mathfrak{R}$.

8. $s_{2k-1} = \dfrac{1}{2} \sin \dfrac{k\pi}{2}, \ s_{2k} = (-1)^k \left(1 - \dfrac{1}{k}\right), \ k = 1, 2, 3, \ldots$

9. $s_n = \dfrac{2^{-n} - 2^n}{2^{-n} + 2^n}$.

10. $s_n = \sin \dfrac{n\pi}{2} + \cos \dfrac{n\pi}{2}$.

11. $s_n = \dfrac{(n-1)^3 - (n+1)^3}{n^2}$.

12. $s_{2k-1} = k, \ s_{2k} = \dfrac{(-1)^k}{2}, \ k = 1, 2, 3, \ldots$

In each of Numbers 13 and 14, find how many terms of the given sequence are *not* included in the neighborhood of the limit of the sequence, for the given $\epsilon$.

13. $\left\{ s_n = \dfrac{(-1)^n}{2^n} \right\}$, $\epsilon = \dfrac{1}{1000}$.    14. $\left\{ s_n = \dfrac{n+1}{2n+3} \right\}$, $\epsilon = \dfrac{1}{100}$.

Use Theorem 8.2b or Theorem 8.2c to show, in Numbers 15 to 18, that the given sequence converges.

15. $\left\{ s_n = \dfrac{2n+1}{2n+3} \right\}$.    17. $\left\{ s_n = \displaystyle\sum_{k=1}^{n} \dfrac{1}{2^k} \right\}$.

16. $\left\{ s_n = \dfrac{3^n+1}{3^n} \right\}$.    18. $\left\{ s_n = \displaystyle\sum_{k=n+1}^{2n} \dfrac{1}{k} \right\}$.

# 8.3 AREA AS THE LIMIT OF AN APPROXIMATION

Archimedes (287–212 B.C.) was an outstanding person in many different respects. In addition to being the discoverer of a number of important principles in mechanics and the inventor of many ingenious devices, he was a profound mathematician. So advanced were some of his mathematical inventions that they lay forgotten or not understood for over 1800 years. The method devised by Archimedes to measure the area of a parabolic segment, for example, was not revitalized until about 1650 A.D. Apparently, Archimedes was the first person to use "limiting processes" in mathematical work. (See E. T. Bell, *The Development of Mathematics*, McGraw-Hill, New York, 1940, pages 69–72.)

Suppose we consider the problem of finding the "area" of a circle. There are really two distinct ideas associated with this problem. One is concerned with explaining what is meant by the "area" of a circle. The other deals with devising a method for finding the area.

Perhaps the concept of the "area" of a circle is clear on an intuitive basis. However, it is not necessarily evident what one means when he says "the area of a circle of radius 2 inches is $4\pi$ square inches." It is not possible to fit together squares of any size, no matter how small, that will exactly cover the area bounded by a closed curved line. There will always be overlapping (see Figure 8.3a) or there will be portions of area that are not covered by the squares. A clarification of both of these problems is provided by the following discussion.

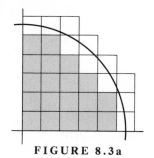

**FIGURE 8.3a**

Since we can easily determine the area of a triangle, let us inscribe a regular polygon of $n$ sides in a circle of radius $r$, and then calculate the area of the

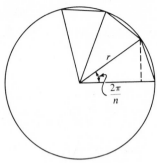

**FIGURE 8.3b**

polygon by partitioning it into $n$ congruent triangles (see Figure 8.3b). The area of one of the triangles is given by

$$T_n = \frac{1}{2} r^2 \sin \frac{2\pi}{n}.$$

Hence, the area of the polygon is

$$A_n = nT_n = \frac{n}{2} r^2 \sin \frac{2\pi}{n}.$$

Although this expression does not give an "area" that satisfies our intuitive concept of the area enclosed by the circle, it does give an "approximation" to that "intuitive area." Evidently, the larger the value of $n$, the more closely the approximation fits the "intuitive area." Consequently, if the sequence of approximations $\{A_n\}$ has a limit as $n$ increases without bound, it seems reasonable to *define* the area of the circle to be that limit number. Thus,

$$\text{area of the circle} \ .=. \ \lim_{n \to \infty} A_n$$

$$= \lim_{n \to \infty} \frac{n}{2} r^2 \sin \frac{2\pi}{n}$$

$$= \lim_{n \to \infty} \pi r^2 \frac{\sin \dfrac{2\pi}{n}}{\dfrac{2\pi}{n}}.$$

We shall prove, in Chapter 10, that $\lim_{x \to 0} (\sin x)/x = 1$, which implies that

$$\lim_{n \to \infty} \frac{\sin 2\pi/n}{2\pi/n} = 1,$$

since $2\pi/n \to 0$ as $n \to \infty$. Thus, we arrive at the familiar formula $A = \pi r^2$ for the area of a circle.

The delightful result of this approximation process immediately suggests a number of entertaining possibilities. For instance, perhaps this method can be used to define the "area" enclosed by any closed curve. Perhaps a similar process can be used in defining the volume of a solid having curved faces, such as a cone or a sphere. However, a certain amount of caution is needed. How do we know that different approximation methods will always lead to the same limit? If the method of approximation is of any value at all, it must lead to unambiguous results.

For example, the area of the circle could be approximated in an entirely different way by means of rectangular strips. Will the use of such strips lead to the same formula for the area of a circle? In order to attempt an answer to this question we consider the first quadrant portion of a circle whose center is at the origin (see Figure 8.3c).

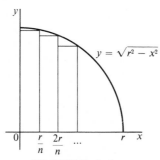

FIGURE 8.3c

Let us partition the radius along the $x$-axis into $n$ equal parts each of length $r/n$ units. The points of subdivision are then $0, r/n, 2r/n, 3r/n, \ldots, nr/n = r$. Now, construct rectangles over each of the subintervals of the partition, as shown in Figure 8.3c. Since the points on the circle are described by the formula $f(x) = \sqrt{r^2 - x^2}$, the height of each rectangle can be determined by finding the value of $f(x)$ at the right hand end of each subinterval. Thus, the height of the first rectangle is $f(r/n)$, of the second, $f(2r/n)$, of the third, $f(3r/n)$, and the height of the $k$th rectangle is $f(kr/n)$. Hence the area of the $k$th rectangle is

$$R_k = \frac{r}{n} f\left(\frac{kr}{n}\right) = \frac{r}{n}\sqrt{r^2 - \frac{k^2 r^2}{n^2}}.$$

The sum of all these areas gives

$$A_n = \sum_{k=1}^{n} R_k = \sum_{k=1}^{n} \frac{r}{n} f\left(\frac{kr}{n}\right) = \sum_{k=1}^{n} \frac{r}{n}\sqrt{r^2 - \frac{k^2 r^2}{n^2}}$$

as the $n$th approximation to the area of the quarter circle.

As before, it appears that the larger the value of $n$, the better will be the approximation to the "intuitive area" which is defined as $\lim_{n\to\infty} A_n$. Hence, the desired area is

$$A .=. \lim_{n\to\infty} \sum_{k=1}^{n} \frac{r}{n} f\left(k\frac{r}{n}\right) = \lim_{n\to\infty} \sum_{k=1}^{n} \frac{r}{n} \sqrt{r^2 - \frac{k^2 r^2}{n^2}}.$$

Unfortunately, we are not in a position to try to evaluate the limit, even if it exists, at this time. Indeed, this result illustrates the fact that this method of approximation may lead to a serious and difficult problem in evaluating limits, a problem that must be solved if the method is to be of any value to us.

However, let us continue exploring the idea of approximating area by applying the rectangular strip method to an area bounded by a simple type of curve such as $f(x) = x^2$, the $x$-axis, and the line $x = 1$, as shown in Figure 8.3d.

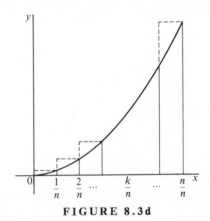

**FIGURE 8.3d**

The interval between 0 and 1 is partitioned into $n$ equal parts by the points $1/n, 2/n, 3/n, \ldots, (n-1)/n$. Rectangles are constructed to cover the area being considered as shown in the figure. The width of each rectangle is $1/n$ units, and the height of the $k$th rectangle can be found by evaluating the function at the point $k/n$, $k = 1, 2, \ldots, n$. The area of the $k$th rectangle is then

$$R_k = \frac{1}{n} f\left(\frac{k}{n}\right),$$

and the approximation of the area by the $n$ rectangles is given by

$$A_n = \sum_{k=1}^{n} R_k = \sum_{k=1}^{n} \frac{1}{n} f\left(\frac{k}{n}\right) = \sum_{k=1}^{n} \frac{1}{n}\left(\frac{k}{n}\right)^2.$$

Evidently the quantity we visualize as the "area" enclosed by the given curve is the limit of $A_n$ as $n \to \infty$. Hence we may write

$$\text{area} .=. \lim_{n\to\infty} \sum_{k=1}^{n} \frac{1}{n} f\left(\frac{k}{n}\right) = \lim_{n\to\infty} \sum_{k=1}^{n} \frac{1}{n}\left(\frac{k}{n}\right)^2,$$

provided the indicated limit exists. Although the last expression may appear difficult to evaluate, it can be handled very nicely with the aid of a simple formula in algebra. First, observe that

$$A_n = \sum_{k=1}^{n} \frac{1}{n} \frac{k^2}{n^2} = \frac{1}{n^3} \sum_{k=1}^{n} k^2 = \frac{1}{n^3} [1^2 + 2^2 + 3^2 + \cdots + n^2].$$

Now the expression in the brackets can be simplified since

$$1^2 + 2^2 + 3^2 + \cdots + n^2 = \frac{n}{6}(n+1)(2n+1).$$

(See Appendix B.) Hence,

$$A_n = \frac{1}{n^3} \left[ \frac{n}{6}(n+1)(2n+1) \right]$$
$$= \frac{1}{3} + \frac{1}{2n} + \frac{1}{6n^2},$$

and

$$\lim_{n \to \infty} A_n = \lim_{n \to \infty} \left( \frac{1}{3} + \frac{1}{2n} + \frac{1}{6n^2} \right) = \frac{1}{3}.$$

Thus we have actually obtained a number representing the number of units of area enclosed by the given curves.

As a summary of the results of our investigation so far, we have found that in some cases the method of approximation yields a complete answer, whereas in other cases it may lead to a difficult limit problem. Furthermore, although we have obtained some concrete results, we have not yet demonstrated that the results obtained by the approximation process are unique—that is, that they do not depend upon the way in which the approximations are set up. Finally, although we have considered only problems involving areas, the approximation method is valuable in the investigation of volumes and in a number of other practical problems of a similar nature, some of which will be considered in the next section.

One other point worthy of mention in the last two illustrations is that in the first we used rectangles enclosed entirely within the area, as illustrated in Figure 8.3c, and in the second we used rectangles that extended beyond the confines of the area, as illustrated in Figure 8.3d. When an approximation is formed as in the first case, it is called an **inner sum** and is denoted by $s_n$. In the second case the approximation is called an **outer sum** and is denoted by $S_n$.

## Exercises 8.3

1. Find the area enclosed by the lines $y = 2x + 3$, $x = 0$, $x = 2$, and the x-axis by the method of approximations.
2. Use the method of approximations to obtain the area enclosed by the curves $y = \frac{1}{4}x^2$, $x = 2$, $x = 4$, and the x-axis.
3. Use the method of approximations to find the area enclosed by the parabola $x^2 + y - 9 = 0$ and the lines $x = 0$, $x = 2$, and $y = 0$.

4. Use the method of approximations to find the area enclosed by the curves $y = \sqrt{x}$, $y = 1$, $y = 3$, and the $y$-axis.

5. In Figure 8.3d, the approximations were obtained by using outer sums. Use inner sums to approximate the area shown and show that as $n \to \infty$ the same result is obtained for the area as was obtained previously.

6. For the area in Number 2, show that inner sums and outer sums lead to the same value.

7. Assuming that the two methods discussed in this section for finding the area of a circle will lead to the same formula, show that

$$\lim_{n \to \infty} \sum_{k=1}^{n} \frac{1}{n} \sqrt{1 - \frac{k^2}{n^2}} = \frac{\pi}{4}.$$

8. (a) Obtain an approximation for the area bounded by $f(x) = x^3$ and the $x$-axis between $x = 0$ and $x = 2$ by using an outer sum $S_n$ and an inner sum $s_n$.

(b) Show that $s_n < \frac{2^4}{4} < S_n$. See the hint in Part (d).

(c) If the area in (a) is between $x = 0$ and $x = b$, show that $s_n < \frac{b^4}{4} < S_n$.

(d) From (b) or (c) try to deduce the limit of $s_n$ and $S_n$ as $n \to \infty$, and thus obtain the area. *Hint*:

$$\sum_{\alpha=1}^{n} \alpha^3 = \frac{n^2(n+1)^2}{4}.$$

(See Appendix B.)

## 8.4 OTHER APPLICATIONS OF THE LIMIT OF AN APPROXIMATION

The process used to define an area by the method of Section 8.3 is not confined to areas. It may be used in connection with a number of physical problems. The process is characterized by four distinct steps whenever the problem is in some way associated with a function $f$ defined on an interval.

(1) The interval is partitioned into subintervals.

(2) Each term of the approximating sum is determined by evaluating the function $f$ at an appropriate point and multiplying this value by the length of the corresponding subinterval.

(3) The approximation is obtained by adding together the values of the products so formed.

(4) The limit of the sum is found, provided the limit exists.

The next examples will illustrate this process applied to several different types of problems.

---

*Example 8.4a.* Determine the volume of a cone by the method of approximation

Suppose the height of the cone is $h$ units and the radius of the base is $r$ units. We shall assume that the volume of a cylinder is known and approximate the volume by a set of cylinders as shown in Figure 8.4a.

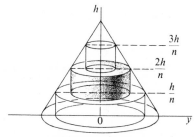

**FIGURE 8.4a**

The altitude of the cone is partitioned into $n$ equal parts by the points

$$\frac{h}{n}, \frac{2h}{n}, \frac{3h}{n}, \ldots, \frac{(n-1)h}{n}.$$

The radius $R_k$ of the $k$th cylinder can be found by using proportional parts of similar triangles. This gives

$$\frac{R_k}{r} = \frac{h - \frac{kh}{n}}{h}.$$

Hence, the volume of the $k$th cylinder is

$$C_k = \frac{h}{n} \cdot \pi R_k^2 = \frac{\pi h}{n} \cdot \left[ \frac{h - \frac{kh}{n}}{h} \right]^2 \cdot r^2 = \frac{\pi h r^2}{n} \left( 1 - \frac{k}{n} \right)^2$$

$$= \frac{h}{n} f\left( \frac{k}{n} \right),$$

where

$$f\left( \frac{k}{n} \right) = \pi r^2 \left( 1 - \frac{k}{n} \right)^2.$$

Thus the $n$th approximation to the volume of the cone is

$$V_n = \sum_{k=1}^{n} C_k = \sum_{k=1}^{n} \frac{\pi h r^2}{n} \left( 1 - \frac{k}{n} \right)^2,$$

$$= \frac{\pi h r^2}{n^3} \sum_{k=1}^{n} (n - k)^2.$$

Since

$$\sum_{k=1}^{n} (n - k)^2 = (n - 1)^2 + (n - 2)^2 + \cdots + 2^2 + 1^2 + 0^2$$

$$= 1^2 + 2^2 + 3^2 + \cdots + (n - 1)^2 = \sum_{\alpha=1}^{n-1} \alpha^2$$

$$= \frac{1}{6} (n - 1)(n)(2n - 1) \qquad \text{(Appendix B)},$$

then

$$V_n = \frac{\pi h r^2}{n^3} \frac{n}{6} (n - 1)(2n - 1).$$

Hence the exact volume $V$ of the cone is *defined* to be

$$V = \lim_{n \to \infty} V_n = \lim_{n \to \infty} \frac{\pi h r^2}{6n^3} (2n^3 - 3n^2 + n)$$

$$= \lim_{n \to \infty} \frac{\pi h r^2}{6} \left( 2 - \frac{3}{n} + \frac{1}{n^2} \right)$$

$$= \frac{\pi h r^2}{3},$$

which is the usual formula for the volume of a cone.

---

The next example illustrates the use of the method of approximation in a problem that is not entirely geometrical.

---

*Example 8.4b.* What is the total force acting on one side of a rectangular gate $a$ units wide and $b$ units high, if the gate is submerged vertically in a lake so that its upper edge is $H$ units below the surface of the lake (Figure 8.4b)?

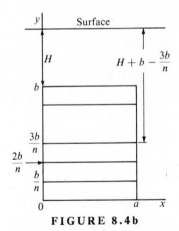

**FIGURE 8.4b**

It is an accepted experimental fact that the force acting on a submerged object depends on the depth of the object. In this case, since different portions of the gate are at different depths, the problem does not have an immediately obvious solution. However, the force on one side of the gate can be approximated by partitioning the gate into horizontal strips of equal width and considering all portions of a particular strip to be at the same depth.

In order to describe the problem easily, let us choose an origin at a lower corner of the gate, as shown in Figure 8.4b. The points of division along the $y$-axis are $b/n$, $2b/n, \ldots, (n - 1)b/n$. The length of each strip is $a$, so that the area of the $k$th strip is $ab/n$.

The force $F$ acting on a *horizontal* area $A$ submerged $h$ units below the surface of a liquid of specific weight $\rho$ is given by

$$F = \rho h A.$$

This force is simply the weight of the column of liquid standing above the area, and is obtained by multiplying the specific weight $\rho$ by the volume $hA$. This formula can be used to approximate the force on the $k$th strip by assuming all points of the strip to be at nearly the same depth as its upper edge. The resulting force on the strip is

$$f_k = \rho \frac{ba}{n}\left(H + b - \frac{kb}{n}\right).$$

Accordingly, the total force on the gate is approximately

$$F_n = \sum_{k=1}^{n} f_k = \sum_{k=1}^{n} \rho \frac{ba}{n}\left(H + b - \frac{kb}{n}\right)$$

$$= \rho \frac{ba}{n^2} \sum_{k=1}^{n} [(H + b)n - kb]$$

$$= \rho \frac{ba}{n^2}\left[n^2(H + b) - b \sum_{k=1}^{n} k\right]$$

$$= \rho \frac{ba}{n^2}\left[n^2(H + b) - b \frac{n}{2}(n + 1)\right].$$

It seems intuitively clear that this approximation to the total force is better and better for narrower and narrower strips. Hence, the exact force acting on one side of the gate may be defined as

$$\lim_{n \to \infty} F_n = \lim_{n \to \infty} \rho \frac{ba}{n^2}\left[n^2(H + b) - b\left(\frac{n^2}{2} + \frac{n}{2}\right)\right]$$

$$= \rho ba\left(H + b - \frac{b}{2}\right)$$

$$= \rho ba\left(H + \frac{b}{2}\right).$$

The reader should note that in this example, as well as in the succeeding problems of the same type, the calculated force is in addition to the force due to atmospheric pressure at the liquid surface.

---

It is interesting to consider the same problem using a circular gate instead of a rectangular one.

---

*Example 8.4c.* Find the force on one side of a circular gate of radius $a$ submerged so that its center is $H$ units, $H > a$, below a liquid surface.

Figure 8.4c shows a coordinate system and strips introduced in order to set up the expressions for the force acting on a typical strip. The vertical axis has been labeled the $x$-axis simply to show that the choice of axes is arbitrary. The vertical diameter of the circle is partitioned into $2n$ parts by the points

$$\pm \frac{a}{n}, \pm \frac{2a}{n}, \pm \frac{3a}{n}, \ldots, \pm \frac{ka}{n}, \ldots, \pm \frac{(n-1)a}{n}.$$

In this case the length of each rectangular strip may be expressed as twice the value of $f(x)$ at the point on the upper edge of the strip for the portion of the area above the $y$-axis and at the point on the lower edge of the strip for the portion of the area below the $y$-axis.

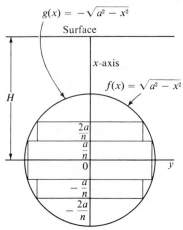

**FIGURE 8.4c**

Thus, for the $k$th strip, we get an area of

$$2\frac{a}{n}f\left(\frac{ka}{n}\right), \qquad \text{where } f(x) = \sqrt{a^2 - x^2}.$$

This time, in order to take into account the negative values of $x$, we let $k$ take on values from $-n$ to $n$, and get for the $n$th approximation of the force on the gate

$$F_n = 2\sum_{k=-n}^{n}\rho\frac{a}{n}f\left(\frac{ka}{n}\right)\left(H - \frac{ka}{n}\right)$$

$$= 2\sum_{k=-n}^{n}\rho\frac{a}{n}\left(H - \frac{ka}{n}\right)\sqrt{a^2 - \frac{k^2a^2}{n^2}}.$$

Although the evaluation of the limit of this expression poses a formidable looking problem, it can be resolved with the aid of Exercises 8.3, Number 7. We may write

$$F .=. \lim_{n\to\infty} 2\sum_{k=-n}^{n}\frac{a\rho}{n}\left[H - \frac{ka}{n}\right]\sqrt{a^2 - \frac{k^2}{n^2}a^2}$$

$$= \lim_{n\to\infty}\left[2a^2\rho H\sum_{k=-n}^{n}\frac{1}{n}\sqrt{1 - \frac{k^2}{n^2}} - 2a^3\rho\sum_{k=-n}^{n}\frac{k}{n^2}\sqrt{1 - \frac{k^2}{n^2}}\right]$$

$$= 2a^2\rho H \lim_{n\to\infty}\sum_{k=-n}^{n}\frac{1}{n}\sqrt{1 - \frac{k^2}{n^2}},$$

since the second sum in the brackets is always zero. Thus, $F = \pi\rho a^2 H$ is obtained by using the fact that

$$\lim_{n\to\infty}\sum_{k=-n}^{n}\frac{1}{n}\sqrt{1 - \frac{k^2}{n^2}} = \frac{\pi}{2}.$$

In the preceding examples, the expression for each term in the $n$th approximation may be interpreted as the product of an interval length and the value of some function at a point in the interval. Thus, in Example 8.2a, the term

$$C_k = \frac{\pi h r^2}{n} \left(1 - \frac{k}{n}\right)^2$$

may be considered as the product of the interval length $h/n$ and the functional value

$$f(x) = \pi r^2 (1 - x)^2$$

evaluated at $x = k/n$. A similar statement also applies in Examples 8.4b and 8.4c.

## Exercises 8.4

1. Use the method of approximations to develop the formula for the volume of a right circular cylinder by using prisms inscribed in the cylinder.
2. Set up an approximation for the volume of a sphere, and then use a limiting process to find the volume.
3. Use outer sums to approximate the volume of a cone and show that in the limit the same result is obtained as in Example 8.4a.
4. If a square of side $b$ is submerged vertically in a liquid with the top edge of the square at the surface of the liquid, find the force on one side of the square.
. Find the force on one side of the square of Number 4 if the square is submerged with a diagonal parallel to the surface of the liquid and the top vertex at the surface.
6. Determine the force on one side of a triangle of height $h$ units and having a base $b$ units, if it is submerged vertically in a liquid so that its vertex is above its base and is $H$ units below the surface, and its base is parallel to the surface.
. Work Number 6 if the base of the triangle is $H$ units below the surface and the vertex is below the base.
8. The amount of work done by a constant force $F$ acting over a distance $s$ is defined to be

$$W = Fs,$$

where $F$ is in pounds, $s$ in inches, and $W$ in inch-pounds. Suppose the amount of force required to compress a spring $s$ inches is $F = 12s$ pounds. Determine an approximation for the amount of work done in compressing the spring 3 inches, and find its limit.
. Express the approximations in Examples 8.4b and 8.4c in the form

$$F_n = \sum_{k=1}^{n} f(x_k)\, \Delta x_k,$$

where $\Delta x_k$ represents the width of the $k$th strip and $f(x_k)$ is the value of an appropriately chosen function at a point in the $k$th interval.

## 8.5 THE DEFINITE INTEGRAL

In each of the examples in the two preceding sections, we have been concerned with the same four steps. Namely, an interval was partitioned into $n$ parts or subintervals, a function was evaluated at a point in each subinterval, the sum of the products of the functional value and the length of the corresponding subinterval was formed, and when possible, the limit of this sum was determined. Since this process has occurred in connection with a number of practical problems, it appears worthwhile to try to express these ideas in as general a way as possible, and, in order for the results to be useful, we must eventually show that the end result does not depend on the particular mode of subdivision or partition that is chosen. Furthermore, we should hope to discover some method or techniques that will enable us to "short cut" much of the work associated with finding the limit of an approximating sum.

With the idea of making the approximating process as general as possible let us restate the four steps used in the process in purely mathematical form for an arbitrary function $f$, defined on a closed interval $a \leq x \leq b$. The first essential generalization that is possible is to allow partitions having unequal subintervals. The only reason for our having used equal subintervals was to have reasonable simplicity for the algebraic manipulations. However, if the approximating process is to be meaningful, we should expect to obtain the same end result regardless of the partitioning scheme. Consequently, let $f$ be defined for all $x$ such that $a \leq x \leq b$, and let an arbitrary partition of the interval $a \leq x \leq b$ be given by the distinct points

$$a = x_0 < x_1 < x_2 < x_3 < \cdots < x_{n-1} < x_n = b,$$

as in Figure 8.5a.

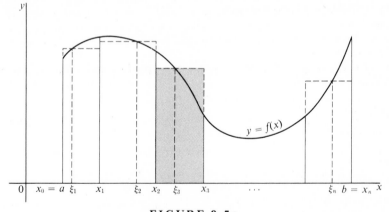

FIGURE 8.5a

Another place where considerable generalization is possible occurs in connection with the point in a particular subinterval at which the function is evaluated. In the examples in the two previous sections, the function was always evaluated at an end point of the subinterval. Actually, there is no reason, other than simplifying the calculations, why the function cannot be evaluated at any point within the interval. This statement is clearly supported by the geometric in

rpretation of the limit of the approximation as the number of units of area
ounded by the curve, the x-axis and the ordinates $x = a$ and $x = b$. Again,
the approximation process is of any value, the final result should not depend
n the points at which $f(x)$ is evaluated. Indeed, there are some instances in
hich it is simpler to evaluate $f(x)$ at an interior point rather than at an end
oint of a subinterval. Hence, let $\xi_\alpha$, where $x_{\alpha-1} \leq \xi_\alpha \leq x_\alpha$, denote the chosen
alue of $x$ in the $\alpha$th subinterval at which $f$ is to be evaluated, as illustrated in
igure 8.5a.

For an approximation, we have the expression

$$A_n = \sum_{\alpha=1}^n f(\xi_\alpha)(x_\alpha - x_{\alpha-1}),$$

here $x_\alpha - x_{\alpha-1}$ denotes the length of the $\alpha$th subinterval. In order to simplify
e expression for $A_n$, it is convenient to write

$$\Delta x_\alpha = x_\alpha - x_{\alpha-1}.$$

hen we have

$$A_n = \sum_{\alpha=1}^n f(\xi_\alpha)\, \Delta x_\alpha.$$

Although a geometric interpretation of $A_n$ is given in Figure 8.5a, $A_n$ in no
ay depends on the geometry; $A_n$ can be calculated independently of any
ometrical interpretation, as we shall see.

The final step is to investigate the limit of the approximating sum. If the limit
ists, it is given a special name, and is denoted by a special symbol.

**efinition 8.5a.** Let $\delta .=. \max \Delta x_\alpha$. If

$$\lim_{\delta \to 0} \sum_{\alpha=1}^n f(\xi_\alpha)\, \Delta x_\alpha$$

ists, and is the same for every sequence of partitions and for every choice of
e $\xi_\alpha$'s in their respective subintervals it is called the **definite integral** of $f$ from
to $b$, and is denoted by the symbol

$$\int_a^b f(x)\, dx.$$

otice that the condition $\delta \to 0$ implies that every $\Delta x_\alpha$ must approach zero;
s condition is necessary, since otherwise it would be possible to obtain
ferent limits by holding one subinterval fixed and partitioning only the re-
ining ones. It is evident that the number of subintervals increases without
und as $\delta \to 0$.

All that has been done thus far is simply to give a name and a symbolic
tation to the process discussed and illustrated in Sections 8.3 and 8.4. We
w recast some of the examples in those sections to illustrate this symbolic
tation.

---

*Example 8.5a.* Express the area enclosed by the curves $f(x) = x^2$, the x-axis,
d the line $x = 1$ (Figure 8.3d) in terms of a definite integral.

Using the notation of Definition 8.5a with $f(x) = x^2$, $a = 0$, and $b = 1$, we have

$$A = \lim_{\delta \to 0} \sum_{\alpha=1}^{n} f(\xi_\alpha) \Delta x_\alpha = \lim_{\delta \to 0} \sum_{\alpha=1}^{n} \xi_\alpha^2 \Delta x_\alpha = \int_0^1 x^2 \, dx.$$

From the result of the evaluation carried out for $f(x) = x^2$ in Section 8.3, we must have

$$\int_0^1 x^2 \, dx = \tfrac{1}{3}.$$

It is instructive to consider a variation of this problem.

*Example 8.5b.* Evaluate $\int_a^b x^2 \, dx$. (Assume that the limit exists.)

Since

$$\int_a^b x^2 \, dx = \lim_{\delta \to 0} \sum_{\alpha=1}^{n} f(\xi_\alpha) \Delta x_\alpha,$$

where $f(x) = x^2$, let us choose a partition of the interval from $a$ to $b$ into $n$ equal subintervals. (We may choose any particular partition we wish; if the limit exists, must be the same regardless of what particular partition is used.) The partition points are then

$$a + \frac{b-a}{n}, a + 2\left(\frac{b-a}{n}\right), a + 3\left(\frac{b-a}{n}\right), \ldots,$$

$$a + \alpha\left(\frac{b-a}{n}\right), \ldots, a + (n-1)\left(\frac{b-a}{n}\right),$$

where the length of each subinterval is $(b-a)/n$. Then, choosing

$$\xi_\alpha = a + \frac{\alpha(b-a)}{n},$$

we have

$$\int_a^b x^2 \, dx = \lim_{n \to \infty} \sum_{\alpha=1}^{n} \frac{b-a}{n}\left[a + \alpha \frac{(b-a)}{n}\right]^2.$$

But

$$\sum_{\alpha=1}^{n} \frac{b-a}{n}\left[a + \alpha \frac{b-a}{n}\right]^2 = \sum_{\alpha=1}^{n}\left[a^2\left(\frac{b-a}{n}\right) + 2a\alpha\left(\frac{b-a}{n}\right)^2 + \alpha^2\left(\frac{b-a}{n}\right)^3\right]$$

$$= na^2\left(\frac{b-a}{n}\right) + 2a\left(\frac{b-a}{n}\right)^2 \sum_{\alpha=1}^{n} \alpha + \left(\frac{b-a}{n}\right)^3 \sum_{\alpha=1}^{n} \alpha^2$$

$$= a^2(b-a) + 2a\left(\frac{b-a}{n}\right)^2 \frac{n(n+1)}{2} + \left(\frac{b-a}{n}\right)^3 \frac{n}{6}(n+1)(2n+1)$$

and, taking the limit as $n \to \infty$, we get

$$\int_a^b x^2 \, dx = a^2(b-a) + 2a(b-a)^2\left(\frac{1}{2}\right) + (b-a)^3\left(\frac{1}{3}\right)$$

$$= a^2b - a^3 + ab^2 - 2a^2b + a^3 + \frac{b^3}{3} - ab^2 + a^2b - \frac{a^3}{3}$$

$$= \frac{b^3}{3} - \frac{a^3}{3}.$$

As is to be expected, even these simple problems lead to a considerable amount of work. It would be desirable to find some method of evaluating definite integrals that would circumvent the work of the direct evaluation. In fact, in many cases a direct evaluation of a definite integral appears to be impossible.

---

*Example 8.5c.* Express the formula for $F$ in Example 8.4c in terms of a definite integral.

We had

$$F = \lim_{n \to \infty} 2 \sum_{k=-n}^{n} \frac{a\rho}{n} \left( H - \frac{ka}{n} \right) \sqrt{a^2 - \frac{k^2 a^2}{n^2}}.$$

By taking $x_k = ka/n$, $\Delta x_k = a/n$, and $f(x) = 2\rho(H - x)\sqrt{a^2 - x^2}$, so that $-a \leq x \leq a$, we may write

$$F = \int_{-a}^{a} 2\rho(H - x)\sqrt{a^2 - x^2}\, dx.$$

---

In order to investigate the feasibility of devising some procedure for handling definite integrals, it is necessary that we develop systematically whatever properties of the definite integral we can see easily, and to study the conditions under which the limit of a sum actually exists. This will be the major effort in the next three sections of this chapter.

## Exercises 8.5

Evaluate each of the definite integrals of Numbers 1 to 6 by using the definition in terms of the limit of a sum.

1. $\int_0^1 c\, dx.$

2. $\int_a^b x\, dx.$

3. $\int_0^2 mx\, dx.$

4. $\int_a^b (cx + e)\, dx.$

5. $\int_0^2 3x^2\, dx.$

6. $\int_0^1 (x - x^2)\, dx.$

7. Evaluate $\int_0^1 x\, dx$ by using a partitioning of the interval from 0 to 1 into unequal parts by the points

$$x_0 = 0, \quad x_\alpha = \frac{\alpha^2}{n^2}, \quad \alpha = 1, 2, \ldots, n.$$

*Note:*

$$\sum_{\alpha=1}^{n} \alpha^3 = \frac{n^2(n+1)^2}{4}, \quad \sum_{\alpha=1}^{n} \alpha^2 = \frac{n}{6}(n+1)(2n+1).$$

8. Express $\int_1^2 \frac{1}{x}\, dx$ as the limit of a sum.

9. Express $\lim_{n \to \infty} \sum_{k=1}^{n} \frac{1}{n+k}$ as a definite integral. *Hint:* Consider the function $f$ where $f(x) = \frac{1}{x}$.

10. Express $\lim\limits_{n \to \infty} \sum\limits_{k=1}^{n} \dfrac{k^2 b^3}{n^3}$ as a definite integral. *Hint*: Consider the function for which $y = x^2$.

11. Show that $\int_a^b k \, dx = k(b - a)$, where $k$ is a nonzero constant.

## 8.6 UPPER AND LOWER SUMS

The use of inner and outer sums as approximations to the definite integral was discussed briefly in Section 8.3. That discussion suggests the following general treatment of the definite integral. In order to clarify the ideas, we shall resort to a geometric interpretation of the discussion in terms of areas, although the concepts actually depend in no way upon this geometric interpretation. The next definition formalizes the intuitive idea of a partition introduced earlier.

**Definition 8.6a.** Let $\mathfrak{D}$ be the interval $\{x: a \leq x \leq b\}$. The set of points

$$\mathcal{P}_n := \{x_0, x_1, \ldots, x_n\},$$

where $x_0 = a$, $x_n = b$, $x_{\alpha-1} < x_\alpha$, $\alpha = 1, 2, \ldots, n$, is called a **partition** of the interval $\mathfrak{D}$.

Clearly, a partition $\mathcal{P}_n$ of an interval divides the interval into $n$ subintervals

$$x_{\alpha-1} \leq x \leq x_\alpha, \qquad \alpha = 1, 2, \ldots, n.$$

Suppose that $f$ is defined and bounded on $\mathfrak{D}$, and let $\mathcal{P}_n$ be a partition of $\mathfrak{D}$. Let us consider a typical subinterval $x_{\alpha-1} \leq x \leq x_\alpha$ (see Figure 8.6a).

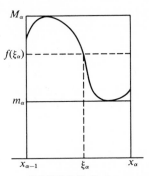

**FIGURE 8.6a**

In setting up the expression for the definite integral of $f$, we choose an arbitrary point, $\xi_\alpha$, in the subinterval, and form the product

$$f(\xi_\alpha) \, \Delta x_\alpha.$$

Since $f$ is bounded on $a \leq x \leq b$, it is bounded on every subinterval. Hence it has a greatest lower bound and a least upper bound on the $\alpha$th subinterval.

If these bounds are denoted by $m_\alpha$ and $M_\alpha$, respectively, then it follows that, for any $\xi_\alpha$, where $x_{\alpha-1} \leq \xi_\alpha \leq x_\alpha$,

$$m_\alpha \leq f(\xi_\alpha) \leq M_\alpha$$

and

$$m_\alpha \, \Delta x_\alpha \leq f(\xi_\alpha) \, \Delta x_\alpha \leq M_\alpha \, \Delta x_\alpha.$$

(See Figure 8.6a.) Hence, we have the inequality

$$(1) \qquad \sum_{\alpha=1}^{n} m_\alpha \, \Delta x_\alpha \leq \sum_{\alpha=1}^{n} f(\xi_\alpha) \, \Delta x_\alpha \leq \sum_{\alpha=1}^{n} M_\alpha \, \Delta x_\alpha.$$

The quantity

$$s_n \,.=. \sum_{\alpha=1}^{n} m_\alpha \, \Delta x_\alpha$$

is called a **lower sum** of $f(x)$ over the interval $a \leq x \leq b$, and the quantity

$$S_n \,.=. \sum_{\alpha=1}^{n} M_\alpha \, \Delta x_\alpha$$

is called an **upper sum** of $f(x)$ over $a \leq x \leq b$. Inequality (1) is equivalent to the statement that, based on a given partition, every approximating sum

$$A_n = \sum_{\alpha=1}^{n} f(\xi_\alpha) \, \Delta x_\alpha$$

must satisfy the inequality

$$(2) \qquad s_n \leq A_n \leq S_n.$$

Notice that for a given $n$, infinitely many different pairs of $s_n$'s and $S_n$'s can be formed by varying the points of subdivision. However, we can show that under certain conditions on $f(x)$, and for every sequence of lower and upper sums,

$$\lim_{\delta \to 0} s_n, \quad \text{where } \delta = \max \Delta x_\alpha,$$

exists and is independent of the particular sequence of sums considered; and, similarly, that for every sequence of upper sums (not necessarily corresponding to the preceding lower sums),

$$\lim_{\delta \to 0} S_n$$

exists in the same sense. Then, if

$$\lim_{\delta \to 0} s_n = \lim_{\delta \to 0} S_n,$$

we may conclude that the definite integral, $\int_a^b f(x) \, dx$, exists and is independent of both the mode of subdivision and the choice of the points $\xi_\alpha$ at which $f(x)$ is evaluated in each subinterval. This discussion is summarized in

**Theorem 8.6a.** $\qquad \int_a^b f(x) \, dx$ exists $\Leftrightarrow \lim_{\delta \to 0} s_n = \lim_{\delta \to 0} S_n.$

PROOF: The proof follows from the definition of the definite integral and the fact that every approximating sum $A_n$ must satisfy Inequality (1).

It may appear that $\int_a^b f(x)\,dx$ exists for almost any function that is defined and bounded on the interval $a \leq x \leq b$, but a simple example will show that this is not the case.

---

*Example 8.6a.* Let

$$f(x) .=. \begin{cases} 0 & \text{if } 0 \leq x \leq 1 \text{ and } x \text{ is a rational number,} \\ 1 & \text{if } 0 \leq x \leq 1 \text{ and } x \text{ is an irrational number.} \end{cases}$$

Prove that $\int_0^1 f(x)\,dx$ does not exist.

For any mode of subdivision it follows that, in each subinterval, $m_\alpha = 0$ and $M_\alpha = 1$. Hence, for every lower sum we have $s_n = 0$, and for every upper sum, $S_n = 1$, so that

$$\lim_{\delta \to 0} s_n \neq \lim_{\delta \to 0} S_n.$$

---

In view of this example, one is tempted to ask for what type of functions does $\int_a^b f(x)\,dx$ exist? In general, the problem of demonstrating the conditions under which the existence of the definite integral is guaranteed is a complex and difficult one. One of the simplest conditions is given in the following theorem.

**Theorem 8.6b.** Let $f$ be a continuous function on the interval $a \leq x \leq b$. Then

$$\int_a^b f(x)\,dx \text{ exists.}$$

Because the proof of this theorem is involved and requires a number of preliminary results, it is presented after Theorem 8.7d in the next section.

## ⋆8.7 THE EXISTENCE OF $\int_a^b f(x)\,dx$

It is convenient to introduce a number of additional concepts in order to facilitate the discussion of the proof of Theorem 8.6b. The first of these is given in

**Definition 8.7a.** Let $\mathcal{P}_n$ be a partition of the interval $a \leq x \leq b$, and let $\mathcal{Q}_k .=. \{q_1, q_2, \ldots, q_k\}$ be a different partition of the same interval, that is such that at least one $q_i$ is not an $x_j$. Then the set $\mathcal{P}_n \cup \mathcal{Q}_k$, which is also a partition of $a \leq x \leq b$, is called a **refinement** of the partition $\mathcal{P}_n$.

The upper and lower sums of a refinement of a partition $\mathcal{P}_n$ have an important relationship to the upper and lower sums of $\mathcal{P}_n$, as shown in

**Theorem 8.7a.** Let $f$ be a function defined and bounded on the interval $a \leq x \leq b$. Let $\mathcal{P}_n$ be a partition of $a \leq x \leq b$, and let $\mathcal{R}_p = \mathcal{P}_n \cup \mathcal{Q}_k$ be a refinement of $\mathcal{P}_n$. Then

$$s_n \leq s_p \quad \text{and} \quad S_p \leq S_n.$$

PROOF: We shall prove that $s_n \leqq s_p$, and leave the proof that $S_p \leqq S_n$ for the reader. Since $\mathcal{R}_p$ is a partition of $a \leqq x \leqq b$, and one or more of the points of $\mathcal{Q}_k$ are distinct from those in $\mathcal{P}_n$, let us consider a typical subinterval $x_{\alpha-1} \leqq x \leqq x_\alpha$ that contains one or more points, $q_i$ of $\mathcal{Q}_k$. The greatest lower bound, $m_{\alpha_1}$, of $f(x)$ on the interval $x_{\alpha-1} \leqq x \leqq q_1$ is not less than the greatest lower bound, $m_\alpha$ of $f(x)$ on $x_{\alpha-1} \leqq x \leqq x_\alpha$. That is,

$$m_{\alpha_1} \geqq m_\alpha.$$

(See Figure 8.7a.) Similarly, on the interval $q_1 \leqq x \leqq q_2$, $m_{\alpha_2} \geqq m_\alpha$. For each subinterval of the interval $x_{\alpha-1} \leqq x \leqq x_\alpha$ formed by the points $q_i$ of $\mathcal{Q}_k$ a

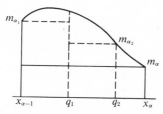

**FIGURE 8.7a**

similar statement may be made. Hence, if $q_1$ is the only point of $\mathcal{Q}_k$ in the $\alpha$th subinterval, then

$$
\begin{aligned}
m_\alpha(x_\alpha - x_{\alpha-1}) &= m_\alpha(x_\alpha - q_1 + q_1 - x_{\alpha-1}) \\
&= m_\alpha(x_\alpha - q_1) + m_\alpha(q_1 - x_{\alpha-1}) \\
&\leqq m_{\alpha_2}(x_\alpha - q_1) + m_{\alpha_1}(q_1 - x_{\alpha-1}).
\end{aligned}
$$

If there are additional points of $\mathcal{Q}_k$ in the $\alpha$th interval, a similar partition of the $\alpha$th interval into subintervals can be made.

In any case, each term in

$$s_n = \sum_{\alpha=1}^{n} m_\alpha(x_\alpha - x_{\alpha-1})$$

either is unaltered or else is replaced by a sum of terms greater than or equal to it, so that

$$\sum_{\alpha=1}^{n} m_\alpha(x_\alpha - x_{\alpha-1}) \leqq \sum_{\beta=1}^{p} \bar{m}_\beta(\bar{x}_\beta - \bar{x}_{\beta-1}),$$

where the $\bar{x}_\beta$'s are points in the partition $\mathcal{R}_p$. Hence

$$s_n \leqq s_p.$$

This result shows that for a sequence of refinements, the lower sums form a sequence of nondecreasing numbers. Furthermore, we show in the next theorem that every upper sum is greater than or equal to any lower sum.

**Theorem 8.7b.** For a given function $f$ defined and bounded on the interval $a \leqq x \leqq b$, and for any two positive integers $m$ and $n$,

$$s_m \leqq S_n.$$

PROOF: Geometrically, the result appears evident (see Figure 8.7b).

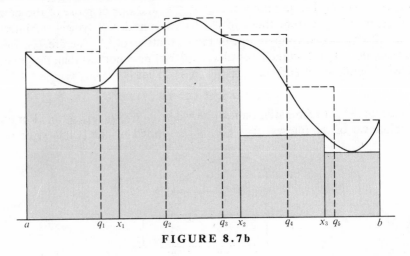

**FIGURE 8.7b**

However, it is easy to give an analytic proof. Let the partition for the lower sum $s_m$ be

$$\mathcal{P}_m .=. \{x_0, x_1, \ldots, x_m\},$$

and for the upper sum $S_n$ let the partition be

$$\mathcal{Q}_n .=. \{q_0, q_1, \ldots, q_n\}.$$

The set of points $\mathcal{P}_m \cup \mathcal{Q}_n$ forms a partition that either is the same as or is a refinement of each of the partitions $\mathcal{P}_m$ and $\mathcal{Q}_n$. Let $s_p$ and $S_p$ be the sums corresponding to the partition $\mathcal{P}_m \cup \mathcal{Q}_n$. By Theorem 8.7a and Inequality (2) of Section 8.6, it follows that

$$s_m \leqq s_p \leqq S_p \leqq S_n.$$

In order to arrive at the main result of this section, we need the following rather more sophisticated property of continuous functions.

**Theorem 8.7c.** If $f$ is a continuous function on a closed interval $a \leqq x \leqq b$ then for any given $\epsilon > 0$, no matter how small, there is a partition $\mathcal{P}_n$ such that for $n$ sufficiently large,

$$M_\alpha - m_\alpha < \epsilon$$

on each subinterval of the partition.

PROOF: Since $f$ is continuous on a closed interval $a \leqq x \leqq b$, $M_\alpha$ and $m_\alpha$ exist on any closed subinterval of $a \leqq x \leqq b$. Choose any partition. Suppose there is a subinterval for which $M_\alpha - m_\alpha \geqq \epsilon$. Partition the subinterval into two equal parts. If $M_\alpha - m_\alpha \geqq \epsilon$ on either of these new subintervals, divide the subinterval into two equal parts again, and repeat this process until $M_\alpha - m_\alpha < \epsilon$ on all resulting subintervals, if possible. Otherwise, consider the process continued indefinitely. In the latter case, there is obtained a se quence of intervals having a point $c$ in common. It follows that every sub-interval containing $c$ has the property $M_\alpha - m_\alpha \geqq \epsilon$. But, since $f$ is continuous at $c$, there is a $\mathfrak{N}(c, h)$ such that

$$x \in \mathfrak{N}(c, h) \Rightarrow f(x) \in \mathfrak{N}[f(c), \epsilon/2].$$

That is, for all $x$ such that $c - h < x < c + h$,

$$f(c) - \epsilon/2 < f(x) < f(c) + \epsilon/2,$$

and over this interval $M_\alpha - m_\alpha < \epsilon$, which contradicts the conclusion that $M_\alpha - m_\alpha \geqq \epsilon$. Hence the process cannot continue indefinitely, and a partition can be found such that $M_\alpha - m_\alpha < \epsilon$ over every subinterval.

The preceding theorem is fundamental in the proof of the next two results, which complete this section.

**Theorem 8.7d.** If $f$ is a continuous function on $a \leqq x \leqq b$, then

$$\lim_{\delta \to 0} s_n \quad \text{and} \quad \lim_{\delta \to 0} S_n$$

both exist and are independent of any particular sequence of partitions.

PROOF: Choose a sequence of lower sums, $\{s_n\}$, such that

$$s_1 \leqq s_2 \leqq s_3 \leqq \cdots \leqq s_n \leqq \cdots.$$

Such a choice is always possible through the use of refinements. Since every $s_n \leqq S_m$, the set

$$\{s_1, s_2, \ldots, s_n, \ldots\}$$

is a bounded nondecreasing infinite sequence, and by Theorem 8.2b it must have a limit, say $s$.

Suppose $\{\sigma_n\}$ is any other sequence of lower sums with $\{\Sigma_n\}$ as the corresponding sequence of upper sums. Then, by Theorem 8.7b, we have $\sigma_n \leqq S_n$ and $s_n \leqq \Sigma_n$. Consequently, for each $n$, either

$$0 \leqq \sigma_n - s_n \leqq S_n - s_n = \sum_{\alpha=1}^{n} (M_\alpha - m_\alpha)\,\Delta x_\alpha$$

or else

$$0 \leqq s_n - \sigma_n \leqq \Sigma_n - \sigma_n = \sum_{\beta=1}^{n} (M_\beta - m_\beta)\,\Delta x_\beta.$$

In either case, if $n$ is sufficiently large,

$$M_\alpha - m_\alpha < \frac{\epsilon}{b-a} \quad \text{and} \quad M_\beta - m_\beta < \frac{\epsilon}{b-a}$$

for every $\alpha$ or $\beta$, by Theorem 8.7c, with $\epsilon$ replaced by $\epsilon/(b - a)$. Hence,

$$|\sigma_n - s_n| < \sum_{\alpha=1}^{n} \frac{\epsilon}{b-a}\,\Delta x_\alpha = \frac{\epsilon}{b-a} \sum_{\alpha=1}^{n} \Delta x_\alpha,$$

or

$$|\sigma_n - s_n| < \epsilon.$$

This means that the sequence $\{\sigma_n\}$ must also have the limit $s$. Hence all sequences of lower sums have the same limit $s$.

The proof that $\lim_{\delta \to 0} S_n$ exists is similar and is left for the reader.

We can now prove Theorem 8.6b, which stated that if $f$ is continuous on the interval $a \leq x \leq b$, then

$$\int_a^b f(x) \, dx \text{ exists.}$$

To show this, we need only demonstrate that

$$\lim_{\delta \to 0} s_n = \lim_{\delta \to 0} S_n.$$

Consider

$$S_n - s_n = \sum_{\alpha=1}^n (M_\alpha - m_\alpha) \, \Delta x_\alpha$$

$$\leq \frac{\epsilon}{b - a} \sum_{\alpha=1}^n \Delta x_\alpha = \epsilon,$$

since, by Theorem 8.7c,

$$M_\alpha - m_\alpha < \frac{\epsilon}{b - a}$$

on every subinterval of the partition for $n$ sufficiently large and the $\Delta x_\alpha$'s sufficiently small. Thus, for this partition,

$$S_n \leq s_n + \epsilon,$$

and by Theorem 8.7d, $\lim_{\delta \to 0} S_n$ and $\lim_{\delta \to 0} s_n$ both exist, so that

$$s_n \leq S_n \leq s_n + \epsilon$$

implies that

$$\lim_{\delta \to 0} S_n = \lim_{\delta \to 0} s_n.$$

## Exercises 8.7

1. Prove the second part of Theorem 8.7a.
2. In the proof of Theorem 8.7c, under the assumption that the subdivision process must be continued indefinitely, explain why every subinterval containing $c$ must have the property $M_\alpha - m_\alpha \geq \epsilon$.
3. Prove the second part of Theorem 8.7d.
4. Let $f(x)$ be continuous on $a \leq x \leq b$ except at the point $c$, where it has a finite jump $h$; that is,

$$\lim_{x \to c^+} f(x) - \lim_{x \to c^-} f(x) = h.$$

   Prove that the definite integral from $a$ to $b$ of $f$ exists.
5. Prove that if $\lim_{\delta \to 0} s_n$ exists, then $s_p \leq \lim_{\delta \to 0} s_n$ for any partition $\mathcal{P}_p$.

## 8.8 PROPERTIES OF THE DEFINITE INTEGRAL

When the definite integral of a function $f$ exists over an interval, the function is said to be **integrable**. We have shown in the preceding section that functions continuous on closed intervals are integrable, but we have not yet given an simple way to evaluate such integrals. In order to arrive at such a means of evaluation, it is necessary first to investigate some elementary properties of the integral.

The definition of the definite integral has been stated for the case where $a < b$. It is desirable to extend the definition to include the case where $a > b$. In order to make such an extension, it is sufficient simply to change the order of the points in the partitions that are used.

**Definition 8.8a.** Let $\mathcal{D}$ be the interval $\{x: b \leq x \leq a\}$. The set of points

$$\mathcal{P}_n .=. \{x_0, x_1, \ldots, x_n\},$$

where $x_0 = a$, $x_n = b$, $x_{\alpha-1} > x_\alpha$, $\alpha = 1, 2, \ldots, n$, is a **partition** of the interval from $a$ to $b$.

**Definition 8.8b.** If $b < a$, then $\int_a^b f(x)\,dx$ is defined as in Definition 8.5a except that all partitions are to be from $a$ to $b$ and $\delta .=. \max |\Delta x_\alpha|$, where $\Delta x_\alpha = x_\alpha - x_{\alpha-1}$.

Crudely speaking, these conventions indicate that one always starts with the lower end point indicated on the symbol $\int_a^b$ and progresses to the upper end point in choosing partition points.

The preceding definitions allow us to establish an important elementary property of the definite integral.

**Theorem 8.8a.** If the function $f$ is integrable on the interval $a \leq x \leq b$, then

$$\int_a^b f(x)\,dx = -\int_b^a f(x)\,dx.$$

PROOF: Let $\mathcal{P}_n$ be a partition for $\int_a^b f(x)\,dx$ for which

$$a = x_0 < x_1 < x_2 < \cdots < x_n = b.$$

The same partition may be used for $\int_b^a f(x)\,dx$ if the points are properly relabeled. We have

$$b = \bar{x}_0 > \bar{x}_1 > \bar{x}_2 > \cdots > \bar{x}_n = a,$$

where $\bar{x}_k = x_{n-k}$, $k = 0, 1, 2, \ldots, n$. Thus, in an approximating sum for $\int_a^b f(x)\,dx$, the interval lengths are of the form

$$\Delta x_\alpha = x_\alpha - x_{\alpha-1},$$

and for $\int_b^a f(x)\,dx$, the interval lengths are of the form

$$\Delta \bar{x}_\alpha = \bar{x}_\alpha - \bar{x}_{\alpha-1} = x_{n-\alpha} - x_{n-\alpha+1},$$

which is the negative of one of the $\Delta x_\alpha$'s. Hence, for a given partition, the $\Delta x_\alpha$ in an approximating sum $A_n$ for $\int_a^b f(x)\,dx$ is simply the negative of the corresponding $\Delta \bar{x}_\alpha$ in an approximating sum for $\int_b^a f(x)\, dx$. The theorem follows directly as a consequence of this reversal in sign.

With the relationship between the symbols $\int_a^b$ and $\int_b^a$ established by Theorem 8.8a for the case $a \neq b$, it is appropriate to ask about a symbol such as $\int_a^a$. In none of the preceding definitions has the interval been allowed to degenerate to zero length. However, it turns out later that it is most desirable to have a definition for this case. From the geometric point of view, it is appropriate to have $\int_a^a f(x)\, dx$ equal to zero, since, if the integral can be interpreted as an area, then as $b \to a$ the area must approach zero. Accordingly, we make the following definition.

**Definition 8.8c.**
$$\int_a^a f(x)\, dx \,.=. \, 0.$$

The next four theorems are simple consequences of the definition of the definite integral and their proofs are left for the reader.

**Theorem 8.8b.** If $f$ is integrable on the interval $a \leqq x \leqq b$, then for each $\xi$ such that $a < \xi < b$,
$$\int_a^b f(x)\, dx = \int_a^\xi f(x)\, dx + \int_\xi^b f(x)\, dx.$$

**Theorem 8.8c.** If $k$ is a constant and $f$ is integrable on the interval $a \leqq x \leqq b$, then
$$\int_a^b k f(x)\, dx = k \int_a^b f(x)\, dx.$$

**Theorem 8.8d.** If $f$ and $g$ are integrable on the interval $a \leqq x \leqq b$, then
$$\int_a^b [f(x) + g(x)]\, dx = \int_a^b f(x)\, dx + \int_a^b g(x)\, dx.$$

**Theorem 8.8e.** If $f(x) \leqq g(x)$ on $a \leqq x \leqq b$ and if $f$ and $g$ are integrable on this interval, then
$$\int_a^b f(x)\, dx \leqq \int_a^b g(x)\, dx.$$

There is one additional property of the definite integral that is of fundamental importance in the development of some of the most significant results in the theory of integration. Although this property has a simple geometric interpretation in terms of area, the reader is again cautioned not to assume that every definite integral arises from an area, since it may not. As has been indicated earlier—and it is repeated here for emphasis—the definite integral can be used to *define* areas, volumes, work done by a variable force, and many other geometric and physical concepts.

**Theorem 8.8f.** *The Mean Value Theorem for Integrals.* Let $f$ be continuous on $a \leqq x \leqq b$. Then there is a value of $x$, say $\xi$, such that $a < \xi < b$, and

$$\int_a^b f(x)\,dx = f(\xi)(b-a).$$

PROOF: Before proceeding with the proof, it is useful to consider a geometric interpretation of the theorem. If the integral can be interpreted as an area enclosed by $y = f(x)$, $x = a$, $x = b$, and the $x$-axis, the theorem simply asserts that there is a rectangle of width $b - a$ and height $f(\xi)$ that has the same area. The diagram in Figure 8.8a illustrates a case in which each of

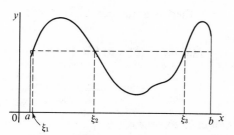

**FIGURE 8.8a**

three different values, $\xi$, in the interval $a \leq x \leq b$ satisfies the requirements of the theorem. However, the theorem asserts only that there is *at least* one such point.

Since $f(x)$ is continuous over a closed interval, it has a least value, $m$, and a greatest value $M$. Thus, for all $x$ such that $a \leq x \leq b$,

$$m \leq f(x) \leq M.$$

It follows by Theorem 8.8e that

$$\int_a^b m\,dx \leq \int_a^b f(x)\,dx \leq \int_a^b M\,dx,$$

or that

$$m(b - a) \leq \int_a^b f(x)\,dx \leq M(b - a).$$

Hence,

$$m \leq \frac{1}{b - a}\int_a^b f(x)\,dx \leq M.$$

The last inequality says that the number

$$\frac{1}{b - a}\int_a^b f(x)\,dx$$

has a value between the least value and the greatest value of $f(x)$ on the closed interval. It follows by the Intermediate Value Theorem that there is a point $\xi$, $a < \xi < b$, at which $f(x)$ takes on this value, so that

$$f(\xi) = \frac{1}{b - a}\int_a^b f(x)\,dx,$$

and

$$\int_a^b f(x)\, dx = (b - a)f(\xi).$$

*Note*: If $a > b$, then, by virtue of Theorem 8.8a, the Mean Value Theorem is still valid, but $a > \xi > b$. This statement of the theorem may conveniently be combined with the original statement as follows.

**Theorem 8.8g.** $f$ is continuous on the interval of integration

$$\Rightarrow \quad \text{there is a number } \theta, \quad 0 < \theta < 1,$$

such that

$$\int_a^b f(x)\, dx = (b - a)f[a + \theta(b - a)].$$

## Exercises 8.8

1. Complete the proof of Theorem 8.8a.
2. Prove Theorem 8.8b.
3. Verify Theorem 8.8b for $f(x) = x^2$, $a = 2$, $b = 7$, and $\xi = 5$.
4. In Theorem 8.8b, prove that the point $\xi$ need not be between $a$ and $b$ for the theorem to hold if all three integrals exist.
5. Verify the statement of Number 4 for $f(x) = x^2$, $a = 2$, $b = 7$, and $\xi = 9$.
6. Prove Theorem 8.8c.
7. Prove Theorem 8.8d.
8. Verify Theorem 8.8d for $f(x) = x$, $g(x) = x^2$, $a = 2$, and $b = 6$.
9. Prove Theorem 8.8e.
10. Find the $\xi$ of Theorem 8.8r if $f(x) = x^2$, $a = 2$, and $b = 5$.

## 8.9 THE INDEFINITE INTEGRAL

The reader should realize that the letter denoting the variable of integration in definite integral is immaterial to the evaluation of the integral. In other words the integrals

$$\int_a^b f(x)\, dx \quad \text{and} \quad \int_a^b f(u)\, du$$

have exactly the same value. Hence, we may freely change the letter used for the variable of integration if it is convenient to do so.

It is clear that the value of the definite integral of a function ordinarily depends on the end points of the interval of integration. In particular, if the value of the upper limit is changed, we would expect the value of the integral to be changed. Geometrically, this is clear whenever the integral can be interpreted as an area (see Figure 8.9a).

This observation suggests that the concept of the definite integral can be used to describe a function by considering one of the end points of the interval of integration as a variable.

**Theorem 8.9a.** If $f$ is an integrable function on the interval

$$\mathcal{D} \ .=. \ \{x: a \leq x \leq b\},$$

and if $t$ is an arbitrary point in the interval, then

$$\int_a^t f(x) \, dx$$

describes a function of $t$ with domain $\mathcal{D}$.

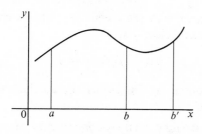

**FIGURE 8.9a**

PROOF: Since $f$ is integrable, then for a given value of $t \in \mathcal{D}$, say $t_0$, $\int_a^{t_0} f(x) \, dx$ exists. Thus to each $t$ in $\mathcal{D}$, there corresponds a unique value $\int_a^t f(x) \, dx$. Hence, the set of ordered pairs,

$$\left\{ \left( t, \int_a^t f(x) \, dx \right) \right\},$$

is, by definition, a function with domain $\mathcal{D}$.

**Definition 8.9a.** The integral $\int_a^t f(x) \, dx$ is called the **indefinite integral** of the function $f$, and the expression $f(x)$ is called the **integrand** of the integral.

Since the indefinite integral of a function $f$ describes another function, say $F$, it is reasonable to inquire as to the nature of this second function. The next theorem states one of the simplest properties of $F$.

**Theorem 8.9b.** Let $f$ be a bounded integrable function on the interval

$$\mathcal{D} \ .=. \ \{x: a \leq x \leq b\}.$$

If

$$F(t) \ .=. \ \int_a^t f(x) \, dx, \qquad t \in \mathcal{D},$$

then $F$ is continuous on $\mathcal{D}$.

PROOF: To show that $F$ is continuous, we need only show that, for $a < t_0 < b$,

$$\lim_{t \to t_0} F(t) = F(t_0).$$

Hence let us consider

$$F(t) - F(t_0) = \int_a^t f(x) \, dx - \int_a^{t_0} f(x) \, dx$$

$$= \int_{t_0}^t f(x) \, dx \qquad \text{(by Theorem 8.8a)}.$$

Since $f$ is bounded, it has a greatest lower bound, say $m$, and a least upper bound, say $M$, and, on the entire interval, it is true that

$$m \leq f(x) \leq M.$$

Thus, by Theorem 8.8e, if $t > t_0$, then

$$(t - t_0)m \leq \int_{t_0}^{t} f(x)\, dx \leq (t - t_0)M,$$

and the same statement with the inequality signs reversed holds if $t_0 < t$. These inequalities make it clear that

$$\lim_{t \to t_0} \int_{t_0}^{t} f(x)\, dx = 0.$$

Hence, $F$ is continuous at $t_0$. The reader should show that $F$ has one-sided continuity at $a$ and $b$.

A more subtle and startling result is contained in the next theorem, which shows the close connection between the two basic concepts, the integral and the derivative.

**Theorem 8.9c.** *The Fundamental Theorem of Integral Calculus.* Let $f$ be continuous on the interval $a \leq x \leq b$. If

$$F(t) .=. \int_{a}^{t} f(x)\, dx, \qquad a \leq t \leq b,$$

then

$$D_t F(t) = f(t).$$

(In other words, the theorem states that the derivative of a function defined by an indefinite integral of a continuous function is the integrand function.)

PROOF: We may determine the derivative of $F$ directly from the definition. We have

$$F(t + h) - F(t) = \int_{a}^{t+h} f(x)\, dx - \int_{a}^{t} f(x)\, dx$$

$$= \int_{t}^{t+h} f(x)\, dx \qquad \text{(by Theorems 8.8a and b)}$$

$$= hf(t + \theta h), \quad 0 < \theta < 1 \quad \text{(by Theorem 8.8g)},$$

or

$$\frac{F(t + h) - F(t)}{h} = f(t + \theta h).$$

Since

$$D_t F(t) = \lim_{h \to 0} \frac{F(t + h) - F(t)}{h} = \lim_{h \to 0} f(t + \theta h),$$

and since $f$ is continuous, we obtain

$$\lim_{h \to 0} f(t + \theta h) = f(t),$$

which completes the proof of the theorem.

This tremendously important relation between the two distinct concepts—the derivative on the one hand and the integral on the other—first of all demonstrates the essential unity of the calculus. As a most profitable by-product, it often provides a simple method for the evaluation of a definite integral without direct recourse to the definition of the integral. This method is essentially contained in

**Theorem 8.9d.** Let $G$ be an inverse derivative of a continuous function $f$. Then

$$\int_a^b f(x)\,dx = G(b) - G(a).$$

PROOF: Let

(1)
$$F(t) .=. \int_a^t f(x)\,dx.$$

Then

$$D_t F(t) = f(t) = D_t G(t).$$

Since the derivatives of $F$ and $G$ are the same, then, by Theorem 7.4b, $F(t)$ and $G(t)$ can differ only by a constant; that is,

(2)
$$F(t) = G(t) + C.$$

From (1) and (2), we have

$$\int_a^b f(x)\,dx = F(b) = G(b) + C.$$

It also follows from (1) that

$$F(a) = \int_a^a f(x)\,dx = 0,$$

so that from (2),

$$0 = G(a) + C,$$

or

$$C = -G(a).$$

Consequently,

$$\int_a^b f(x)\,dx = G(b) - G(a).$$

In connection with the evaluation of the definite integral by means of Theorem 8.9d, it is customary to use the notation

$$[G(x)]_a^b .=. G(b) - G(a).$$

As illustrations of the use of Theorem 8.9d, consider the following examples.

---

*Example 8.9a.* Evaluate $\int_2^3 (x^2 - 2x)\,dx$.

If $f(x) = x^2 - 2x$, then an inverse derivative of $f(x)$ is

$$G(x) = \frac{x^3}{3} - x^2.$$

Therefore, by Theorem 8.9d,

$$\int_2^3 (x^2 - 2x)\, dx = \left[ \frac{x^3}{3} - x^2 \right]_2^3$$

$$= \left( \frac{3^3}{3} - 3^2 \right) - \left( \frac{2^3}{3} - 2^2 \right) = \frac{4}{3}.$$

Notice that $G(x)$ could have been taken as $\frac{1}{3}x^3 - x^2 + C$, where $C$ is an arbitrary constant. However, the specific value of this constant will never affect the value of the definite integral. (Why?)

---

*Example 8.9b.* Evaluate $\int_{-2}^3 |x + 1|\, dx$.

Here, it is not convenient to try to find $D_x^{-1}|x + 1|$ directly. Instead, $f(x) = |x + 1|$ is rewritten as

$$f(x) = \begin{cases} x + 1, & x \geq -1, \\ -x - 1, & x < -1. \end{cases}$$

Then, by Theorem 8.8b,

$$\int_{-2}^3 |x + 1|\, dx = \int_{-2}^{-1} (-x - 1)\, dx + \int_{-1}^3 (x + 1)\, dx,$$

where the point of division is taken as the point at which the formula for $f(x)$ is changed. The two integrals on the right are evaluated as follows:

$$\int_{-2}^{-1} (-x - 1)\, dx = \left[ \frac{-x^2}{2} - x \right]_{-2}^{-1} = \frac{1}{2},$$

$$\int_{-1}^3 (x + 1)\, dx = \left[ \frac{x^2}{2} + x \right]_{-1}^3 = 8.$$

Consequently,

$$\int_{-2}^3 |x + 1|\, dx = 8 + \frac{1}{2} = \frac{17}{2}.$$

---

It is because of Theorem 8.9c that the integral sign without any indicated limits is so widely used to denote an inverse derivative. We shall yield to this almost universal custom and shall hereafter usually employ the integral sign notation, with the explicit understanding that

$$\int f(x)\, dx .=. D_x^{-1} f(x).$$

This means that $\int f(x)\, dx$ is simply a symbol to denote the general inverse derivative of $f(x)$; that is,

$$\int f(x)\, dx .=. G(x) + C,$$

where $G'(x) = f(x)$ and $C$ is an arbitrary constant, the so-called **constant of integration.**

The primary problem in evaluating a definite integral is finding, when possible, an inverse derivative of the integrand. As we shall see later, it is not uncommon to encounter a function that has no "elementary" function as an inverse derivative. However, in many of the simpler cases it is possible to find an inverse derivative with the aid of the chain rule,

$$D_x f(u) = D_u f(u) \, D_x u = f'(u) \, D_x u,$$

from which we get

$$f(u) = \int f'(u) \, D_x u \, dx = \int f'(u) \, du.$$

This formula presents the possibility of sometimes grouping terms in an appropriate way so that the integral appears in the form $\int f'(u) \, du$. The following examples illustrate this idea.

---

*Example 8.9c.* Evaluate

$$F(t) .=. \int_0^t x\sqrt{a^2 - x^2} \, dx, \qquad |t| \leq a.$$

We note that $D_x(a^2 - x^2) = -2x$; then, by letting $u = a^2 - x^2$, we get $du = -2x \, dx$ and

$$\int x\sqrt{a^2 - x^2} \, dx = \int -\frac{1}{2} u^{1/2} \, du = -\frac{1}{2} \int u^{1/2} \, du$$

$$= -\frac{1}{2} \frac{u^{3/2}}{3/2} + C = -\frac{1}{3}(a^2 - x^2)^{3/2} + C.$$

The first term of this result may be taken as the desired inverse derivative, say $G(x)$, of the given integrand. Hence,

$$\int_0^t x\sqrt{a^2 - x^2} \, dx = \left[ -\frac{1}{3}(a^2 - x^2)^{3/2} \right]_0^t = -\frac{(a^2 - t^2)^{3/2}}{3} + \frac{a^3}{3}.$$

---

*Example 8.9d.* Evaluate

$$p(t) .=. \int_a^t \frac{1}{\sqrt{x}\,(1 - \sqrt{x})^2} \, dx, \qquad 1 < a < t.$$

Since $D_x(-\sqrt{x}) = -\frac{1}{2}x^{-1/2}$, the grouping $-2(1 - \sqrt{x})^{-2}(-\frac{1}{2}x^{-1/2})$ is suggested. This form can be treated by letting $u = 1 - \sqrt{x}$ and using the fact that

$$\int u^{-2} \, du = -u^{-1} + C,$$

so that an inverse derivative is seen to be

$$G(x) = \frac{2}{1 - \sqrt{x}}.$$

Hence,

$$p(t) = [G(x)]_a^t = \frac{2}{1 - \sqrt{t}} - \frac{2}{1 - \sqrt{a}}.$$

## Exercises 8.9

Evaluate the given definite integral in each of Numbers 1 to 16.

1. $\int_0^2 (x^2 - 2x)\, dx.$

9. $\int_0^a (a^{2/3} - x^{2/3})^3\, dx.$

2. $\int_0^1 (x^3 - \frac{1}{2}x)\, dx.$

10. $\int_{2b}^{3b} \frac{x\, dx}{(x^2 - b^2)^3}.$

3. $\int_1^2 (x^2 - \sqrt{x})\, dx.$

11. $\int_0^1 \frac{x^3}{(1 + x^4)^2}\, dx.$

4. $\int_0^4 \sqrt{5u}\, du.$

5. $\int_1^4 (s - 1)(\sqrt{s} + 2)\, ds.$

12. $\int_0^{\sqrt{3}} \frac{x\, dx}{(4 - x^2)^{3/2}}.$

6. $\int_{-4}^{-1} \sqrt{x^4 + x^2}\, dx.$

13. $\int_{-2}^4 |x - 2|\, dx.$

7. $\int_0^4 \frac{dx}{\sqrt{1 + 2x}}.$

14. $\int_{-2}^2 \sqrt{2 + |x|}\, dx.$

15. $\int_{-1}^1 \sqrt{|x|} - x\, dx.$

8. $\int_0^{2a} \frac{x\, dx}{\sqrt{a^2 + x^2}}.$

16. $\int_2^4 \frac{6s^2 + 4}{\sqrt{s^3 + 2s}}\, ds.$

In each of Numbers 17 to 22, evaluate the given indefinite integral.

17. $\int_4^t \sqrt{2|x| + 1}\, dx.$

20. $\int_0^t (x^4 + 2)^3 x^3\, dx.$

18. $\int_1^t \frac{(x - 1)^2}{\sqrt{x}}\, dx,\, t > 0.$

21. $\int_0^t (|2x| + x)\, dx.$

22. $\int_0^t (|x - 1| + |x|)\, dx.$

19. $\int_1^x \frac{t^{1/2} + t^{1/4}}{t}\, dt,\, 0 < x.$

Use the Fundamental Theorem of Integral Calculus to obtain the desired derivative in each of Numbers 23 to 28.

23. $D_x \int_0^x \sqrt{1 + t^4}\, dt.$

26. $D_x \int_x^{\pi/2} \sin 2u\, du.$

24. $D_t \int_0^t \cos \theta\, d\theta.$

27. $D_x \int_{-x}^x \frac{dt}{1 + t}.$

25. $D_s \int_s^a \frac{a - u}{a + u}\, du.$

28. $D_x \int_0^{x^2} \frac{dt}{1 + t}.$

29. If $D_x f(x) = G(x)$, show that, for $n \neq -1$,

$$\int [f(x)]^n G(x)\, dx = \frac{[f(x)]^{n+1}}{n + 1} + C$$

and

$$\int_a^b [f(x)]^n G(x)\, dx = \frac{[f(b)]^{n+1} - [f(a)]^{n+1}}{n + 1}.$$

30. If $\int_a^b f(t)\, dt = G(b) - G(a)$, find $\int_a^b f(ct)\, dt$, where $c$ is a nonzero constant.
31. Consider the set of all integrable functions on an interval $a \leqq x \leqq b$. Is this set closed with respect to addition? Explain.

## 8.10 APPLICATIONS TO AREAS

The concept of the definite integral was strongly motivated by the problem of finding areas bounded by curves. This application of the definite integral will be discussed in detail now, and other applications will be discussed in the following section.

---

*Example 8.10a.* Calculate the area enclosed by the curve $y = 2/x^2$, the $x$-axis, and the ordinates $x = 1$ and $x = 4$.

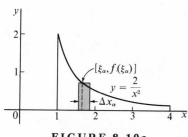

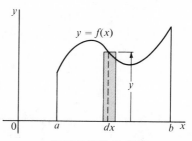

**FIGURE 8.10a**        **FIGURE 8.10b**

From our earlier discussion we know that the desired area is defined by an expression of the form

$$\lim_{\delta \to 0} \sum_{\alpha=1}^{n} f(\xi_\alpha)\, \Delta x_\alpha = \int_a^b f(x)\, dx.$$

(See Figure 8.10a.) Hence we may go directly to the definite integral and write, for the area $A$,

$$A .=. \int_1^4 \frac{2}{x^2}\, dx.$$

An inverse derivative of $2/x^2$ is $-2/x$. Hence

$$A = \left[ -\frac{2}{x} \right]_1^4 = -\frac{1}{2} + 2 = \frac{3}{2}\ (\text{l.u.})^2.$$

(The abbreviation "l.u." will be used for *linear units*.)

---

The integral needed for calculating an area is often set up by considering a typical subinterval of "width" $dx$, as shown in Figure 8.10b. The area of a rectangular strip of height $f(x) = y$ and "width" $dx$ is denoted by

$$dA = f(x)\, dx \quad \text{or} \quad y\, dx.$$

The process of forming the sum of the elements of area and taking the limit is summarized by simply writing

$$A = \int_a^b y\,dx \quad \text{or} \quad \int_a^b f(x)\,dx.$$

Thus, the definite integral for the area can be set up directly without actually having to go through all the intermediate steps.

If a curve crosses the $x$-axis, some care must be taken in setting up an integral to find an area, as is illustrated in the following example.

---

*Example 8.10b.* Find the area enclosed by the curve $f(x) = x^2 - x - 2$, the $x$-axis, and the lines $x = 0$, $x = 3$.

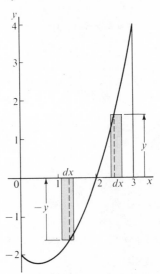

**FIGURE 8.10c**

The problem is illustrated in Figure 8.10c. For that portion of the graph of $f$ that lies below the $x$-axis, a typical "element of area," $dA$, is given by

$$dA = -f(x)\,dx.$$

Because $f(x)$ is negative, it is necessary to represent the length of the element by $-f(x)$ in order to get a positive quantity as a measure of area. Thus the area $A$ can be expressed as

$$A = \int_0^2 [-f(x)]\,dx + \int_2^3 f(x)\,dx$$

$$= \int_0^2 [-(x^2 - x - 2)]\,dx + \int_2^3 (x^2 - x - 2)\,dx$$

$$= \left[-\left(\frac{x^3}{3} - \frac{x^2}{2} - 2x\right)\right]_0^2 + \left[\frac{x^3}{3} - \frac{x^2}{2} - 2x\right]_2^3$$

$$= \frac{10}{3} + \frac{11}{6} = \frac{31}{6} \text{ (l.u.)}^2.$$

The reader should observe that

$$\int_0^3 (x^2 - x - 2)\,dx = \left[\frac{x^3}{3} - \frac{x^2}{2} - 2x\right]_0^3 = -\frac{3}{2},$$

being negative, does not properly represent an area. If an area is bounded by a curve $y = f(x)$ and the $x$-axis from $x = a$ to $x = b$, $a < b$, then the area is always given by

$$A .=. \int_a^b |f(x)|\,dx.$$

The problem of finding an area need not be restricted to an area bounded, in part, by the $x$-axis. The technique used in the preceding examples can be extended to areas enclosed by any simple curves.

*Example 8.10c.* Find the area enclosed by the curves $f(x) = x + 1$ and $g(x) = (x - 1)^2$ (see Figure 8.10d).

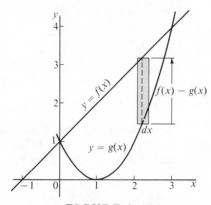

**FIGURE 8.10d**

In this case, a typical element of area $dA$ of "width" $dx$ extends from one curve to the other. Hence, the length of the element is given by

$$f(x) - g(x).$$

[The length must be positive; that is, $g(x) - f(x)$ *cannot* be used as a measure of the length of the element when $g(x) < f(x)$.]

The process of summing over elements of this type and taking the proper limit of the sum leads to the integral

$$A = \int_0^3 [f(x) - g(x)]\,dx$$

for the area. Thus,

$$A = \int_0^3 [(x + 1) - (x - 1)^2]\,dx$$

$$= \int_0^3 [3x - x^2]\,dx$$

$$= \left[\frac{3x^2}{2} - \frac{x^3}{3}\right]_0^3 = \frac{9}{2}\;(\text{l.u.})^2.$$

Although each of the three preceding examples has illustrated the definite integral when the partitioning is carried out along the $x$-axis, there is no reason why the same process cannot be used along the $y$-axis. In that case the roles of the variables are interchanged. In some problems, it is more convenient to use this procedure.

---

*Example 8.10d.* Find the area enclosed by the curves

$$(y - 1)^2 = x, \quad y = x - 1.$$

(See Figure 8.10e.)

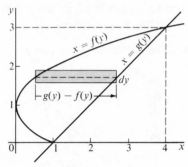

**FIGURE 8.10e**

The equation $(y - 1)^2 = x$ describes not a function, but a relation. However, if $y$ is regarded as the independent variable, we may say that the equation describes a function $\{(y, f(y))\}$. A typical element of area $dA$ is then given by

$$dA = [g(y) - f(y)] \, dy,$$

where the "width" of the element is taken as $dy$. It follows that

$$A = \int_0^3 [(y + 1) - (y - 1)^2] \, dy,$$

which, except for the use of $y$ rather than $x$ for the variable of integration, is exactly the same integral as occurred in Example 8.10c.

---

Suppose we attempt to calculate the area in Example 8.10d by using elements of area of width $dx$. What difficulties would we encounter? (See Exercises 8.10, Number 17.)

## Exercises 8.10

In each of Numbers 1 to 12, find the area enclosed by the given curves. Make a sketch and show a typical element of area.

1. $y = 9 - x^2$; $x = -3$; $x = 3$; $y = 0$.
2. $y = x^3 + 2x$; $x = -2$; $y = 0$.
3. $y = x^{1/2} - x^{-1/2}$; $x = 1$; $x = 4$; $y = 0$.
4. $x^{1/2} + y^{1/2} = a^{1/2}$; $x = 0$; $y = 0$.

5. $y = \dfrac{x}{(x^2 + 1)^2}$; $x = -2$; $x = 3$; $y = 0$.

6. $y = x(x^2 - 1)$; $x = -2$; $x = 3$; $y = 0$.
7. $4y = x^3$; $y = x$, $x \geq 0$.
8. $4y = x^3$; the tangent to this curve at $x = -2$.
9. $4x = 4 - y^2$; $2x = 4 - y^2$.
10. $x = y^3 - 4y$; $x = 5y$, $y \geq 0$.
11. $y = x(x^2 - 1)$; $y = 3x$.
12. $y = x\sqrt{4 - x^2}$, $y = 0$.

In each of Numbers 13 to 16, find in two ways the area enclosed by the given curves.

13. $2x = 2 + y^3$; $x = -3$; $y = 2$.
14. $2y = (x - 1)^3$; $y = 4$; $x = -2$.
15. $27y = 2x^3$; the tangent to the curve at $x = 3$.
16. $y^2 = x^3$, $y = x$.
17. In Example 8.10d, use elements of area of width $dx$ and try to calculate the area.
18. Find $m$ in terms of $a$ so that the segment of the parabola $y = ax - x^2$ cut off by the line $y = mx$ has an area one-eighth that of the segment cut off by the $x$-axis.

## 8.11 APPLICATIONS TO VOLUMES

The techniques used to calculate areas can also frequently be used to calculate volumes, forces, work, and other quantities that often arise in physical problems. A few of the simpler applications to volume will be considered at this time; other applications will be deferred to a later section.

*Example 8.11a.* Find the volume of a right pyramid having a height of $h$ units and a square base $a$ units on a side (see Figure 8.11a).

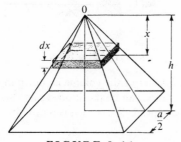

**FIGURE 8.11a**

The volume can be approximated by means of square slabs as indicated in the figure. If the origin is taken at the vertex 0, and the $x$-axis is along the altitude of the pyramid, then the element of volume $dV$ of a typical slab of side $s$ is given by

$$dV = s^2\, dx.$$

The volume of the pyramid is therefore

$$V .=. \int_0^h s^2\, dx.$$

In order to evaluate the integral, we must be able to express $s$ in terms of $x$. By considering similar triangles as indicated in the diagram, we may write

$$\frac{s/2}{x} = \frac{a/2}{h},$$

or

$$s = \frac{a}{h} x.$$

Hence,

$$V = \int_0^h \frac{a^2}{h^2} x^2 \, dx$$

$$= \left[ \frac{a^2 x^3}{3h^2} \right]_0^h = \frac{1}{3} a^2 h \ (\text{l.u.})^3.$$

The success of the procedure in the preceding example depends upon our being able to establish a functional relationship between the variables used to measure the element of volume. The same technique works easily for volumes of revolution—that is, for volumes generated by revolving an area about an axis.

*Example 8.11b.* Find the volume of the solid obtained by revolving the area enclosed by $y = x^2$, $x = 1$, and $y = 0$ about the $x$-axis (see Figure 8.11b).

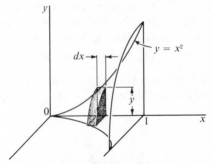

**FIGURE 8.11b**

In the diagram, only one quarter of the volume is shown in order to keep the figure as simple as possible. The volume can be partitioned into "slices," as indicated in the figure. The volume, $dV$, of a typical slice, which is a cylindrical disk, is

$$dV = \pi r^2 \, dx,$$

where $r$ is the radius of the disk. Evidently the radius $r$ is actually measured by the $y$-coordinate of the curve in this case, so that

$$dV = \pi y^2 \, dx$$

and

$$V .=. \pi \int_0^1 x^4 \, dx$$

$$= \frac{\pi}{5} \ (\text{l.u.})^3.$$

In order to illustrate a variation of this problem, we consider the same area revolved about a different line.

---

*Example 8.11c.* Find the volume of the solid generated by revolving the area in Example 8.11b about the line $x = 1$ (see Figure 8.11c).

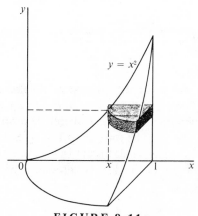
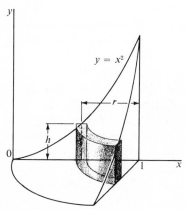

FIGURE 8.11c                                    FIGURE 8.11d

The typical element of volume, $dV$, is taken parallel to the plane of the base of the solid, so that

$$dV = \pi r^2 \, dy.$$

The radius of the element is the length $1 - x$. Since $x = \sqrt{y}$,

$$dV = \pi (1 - \sqrt{y})^2 \, dy.$$

Thus,

$$V = . \pi \int_0^1 (1 - \sqrt{y})^2 \, dy = \frac{\pi}{6} \text{ (l.u.)}^3.$$

---

In general, it appears that the definite integral is useful in finding the volume of any solid having a cross section whose area can be expressed in terms of the perpendicular distance of the section from some fixed plane. In any such case, the integral can be set up by using the "slice" method illustrated in the preceding three examples.

In the case of volumes of revolution, it is sometimes convenient to set up an integral using cylindrical shell elements rather than cylindrical disk elements, such as were used in Examples 8.11b and 8.11c. Thus, consider once again the volume described in Example 8.11c, but regard the volume as the limit of the sum of cylindrical shells of which a portion of a typical one is shown in Figure 8.11d. In order to simplify the computational details, let $r$ be the radius from the line $x = 1$, which is the axis of the cylindrical shell, to the midpoint of the wall of the shell. Then, if the division along the $x$-axis is of length $\Delta x$, the volume of the shell is

$$\pi (r + \tfrac{1}{2} \Delta x)^2 h - \pi (r - \tfrac{1}{2} \Delta x)^2 h = 2\pi r h \, \Delta x.$$

Thus, the volume of the solid is

$$V .=. \int_0^1 2\pi rh \, dx,$$

where

$$r = 1 - x \quad \text{and} \quad h = y = x^2.$$

Accordingly,

$$V = 2\pi \int_0^1 (1 - x)x^2 \, dx = 2\pi \int_0^1 (x^2 - x^3) \, dx = \frac{\pi}{6} (\text{l.u.})^3,$$

which agrees with the result of Example 8.11c.

We have now given two different definitions for the volume of a solid of revolution, one obtained by the use of cylindrical disks in the approximation sum and the other obtained by the use of cylindrical shells. It is therefore proper to inquire if these two definitions are consistent. The answer to this question is yes, although we shall not prove it here. At the present point in his development, it is sufficient for the student to be aware of this logical question and to depend on his geometric intuition to answer it.

## Exercises 8.11

1. Use a definite integral to obtain the formula for the volume of a regular tetrahedron (a triangular pyramid with equilateral triangles for its faces).

2. The base of a certain solid is the parabolic segment enclosed between the parabola $y^2 = 4x$ and the line $x = 4$. Every section of the solid perpendicular to the $x$-axis is an isosceles right triangle with its hypotenuse in the plane of the base. Find the volume of the solid.

3. The base of a certain solid is the portion of the $xy$-plane for which $x^2 + y^2 \leq 1$. If every section of the solid perpendicular to the $y$-axis is a square, find the volume of the solid.

4. A horn-shaped solid has the $xy$-plane for a plane of symmetry and the section of the solid in the $xy$-plane is bounded by the two parabolic arcs $y = \sqrt{x}$ and $y = 2\sqrt{x}$ and by the line $x = 4$. If every section of the solid perpendicular to the $xy$-plane and parallel to the $y$-axis is a circle, find the volume of the solid.

5. Use the method of cylindrical disks to obtain the formula for the volume of a sphere of radius $b$.

6. Use the method of cylindrical shells to obtain the formula for the volume of a right circular cone of radius $b$ and height $h$.

7. Find the volume formed by revolving the area bounded by the $x$-axis and the elliptic arc

$$\frac{x^2}{a^2} + \frac{y^2}{b^2} = 1, \quad y \geq 0,$$

about the $x$-axis.

8. Find the volume of the solid obtained by revolving the area enclosed by $y = 2\sqrt{x}$, $x = 1$, and $y = 0$ about

    (a) the $x$-axis;  (b) the line $x = 1$;  (c) the line $x = 0$.

9. Find the volume of the solid obtained by revolving the area enclosed by $x^2 = 4ay$, $y = 0$, and $x = 2a$ about

(a) the x-axis;  (c) the line $x = 2a$;
(b) the line $y = a$;  (d) the line $y = 4a$.

10. Find the volume of the wedge-shaped solid formed by passing two planes through the center of a sphere if the planes intersect at an angle $\alpha$.

11. Find the volume of a pyramid having a cross section that is a regular polygon of $n$ sides.

12. Find the volume of the intersection of two cylinders of equal radii when their · axes intersect at right angles.

13. The area bounded by the line $y = x$ and the parabola $y^2 = 4x$ is revolved about the y-axis. Find the volume that is generated.

14. The first quadrant area formed by the two curves $y^2 = x$ and $y^2 = x^3$ is revolved about the x-axis. Find the volume that is generated.

15. Find the volume generated by revolving the area in Number 14 about (a) the line $x = 1$; (b) the line $y = 2$.

⋆16. Find the volume generated by revolving the area in Number 13 about the line $y = x$.

## 8.12 AVERAGES

The concept of an average or a weighted mean is important in many statistical and physical problems. For example, a weighted average is often used to compute the average grade on an examination. Suppose there are 5 grades of 70, 10 grades of 75, 8 grades of 80, 6 grades of 85, and 4 grades of 90. Then the average grade $g$ is given by

$$g = \frac{5(70) + 10(75) + 8(80) + 6(85) + 4(90)}{5 + 10 + 8 + 6 + 4}.$$

This kind of average is called a **weighted average** and the number of occurrences of each grade is called a **weight factor.**

In general, if the numbers $x_1, x_2, x_3, \ldots, x_n$ have weight factors $w_1, w_2, \ldots, w_n$, respectively, then the number

$$\bar{x} . = . \frac{\sum\limits_{\alpha=1}^{n} w_\alpha x_\alpha}{\sum\limits_{\alpha=1}^{n} w_\alpha}$$

s called the weighted average of the numbers $x_\alpha$. This concept of weighted average can easily be generalized to define the concept of the average value of a quantity $u$ with respect to a variable $t$, where $u$ is a continuous function of $t$. The definite integral is an ideal tool for accomplishing this generalization.

For instance, suppose the temperature $u$ of a furnace is regulated so that $\cdot = f(t)$, where $t$ is time in hours. Is it possible to find a number that can reasonably be called an average temperature for the period $a \leq t \leq b$? An approximate average temperature can be obtained by partitioning the time interval into subintervals $\Delta t_1$, $\Delta t_2$, ... , $\Delta t_n$, and making spot temperature checks at times $t_1^*$, $t_2^*$, ... , $t_n^*$ in each of the time periods, respectively. (See Figure 8.12a).

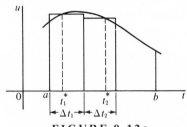

**FIGURE 8.12a**

Using the value $f(t_\alpha^*)$ as the temperature over the time interval $\Delta t_\alpha$, an approximate average temperature $\bar{u}_n$ is given by

$$\bar{u}_n = \frac{\sum\limits_{\alpha=1}^{n} f(t_\alpha^*)\, \Delta t_\alpha}{\sum\limits_{\alpha=1}^{n} \Delta t_\alpha} = \frac{\sum\limits_{\alpha=1}^{n} f(t_\alpha^*)\, \Delta t_\alpha}{b - a}.$$

Evidently, if $\lim_{n\to\infty} \bar{u}_n$ exists, it would be suitable as an average value of $f(t)$ over the interval in question. But the limit of the numerator of $\bar{u}_n$ defines $\int_a^b f(t)\, dt$, so that the following definition is suggested.

**Definition 8.12a.** The average value of a function $f(t)$ with respect to $t$, over the interval $a \leqq t \leqq b$, is $\bar{y}$, where

$$\bar{y} . =. \frac{\int_a^b f(t)\, dt}{b - a}.$$

---

*Example 8.12a.* Find the average height above the $x$-axis of the curve described by $y = x^2(2 - x)$, $0 \leqq x \leqq 2$.

From the definition of average value, we get

$$\bar{y} = \frac{\int_0^2 x^2(2 - x)\, dx}{2 - 0}$$

$$= \frac{1}{2}\left[\frac{2x^3}{3} - \frac{x^4}{4}\right]_0^2 = \frac{2}{3}.$$

---

The average of a quantity $f(x)$ may also be defined with respect to any variable $t$ for which $x = g(t)$.

**Definition 8.12b.** The average of the functional values $f(x)$ with respect to a variable $t$, where $x = g(t)$, over the interval $a \leq t \leq b$ is

$$\bar{y} = \frac{\int_a^b f(x)\, dt}{b - a} = \frac{\int_a^b f[g(t)]\, dt}{b - a}.$$

---

*Example 8.12b.* Find the average value of $y = x^2(2 - x)$, $0 \leq x \leq 2$, with respect to the quantity $x^2$.

By letting $x = \sqrt{t}$, so that $y = t(2 - \sqrt{t})$, we reduce the problem to that of finding the average value of $y$ with respect to $t$ for $0 \leq t \leq 4$. Thus,

$$\bar{y} = \frac{\int_0^4 y\, dt}{4 - 0} = \frac{1}{4} \int_0^4 t(2 - \sqrt{t})\, dt = \frac{4}{5}.$$

---

An important application of the concept of average value occurs in physics and engineering in connection with the concepts of **center of mass** and **centroid**. To illustrate these ideas let us consider a simple physical problem, in which a weight $w$ is suspended on a rigid horizontal rod that is supported at a point $P$ (Figure 8.12b.)

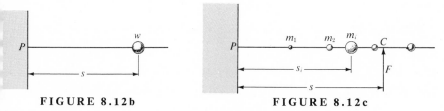

**FIGURE 8.12b**               **FIGURE 8.12c**

Experience indicates that the farther away the weight is from the support point $P$, the greater will be the tendency of the rod to turn about $P$. This "turning tendency" was first expressed in mathematical form by Archimedes, who enunciated the idea in connection with the law of the lever. The turning effect of the weight is called a turning *moment*, and is defined as the product of the weight and its distance from the reference point or reference axis. That is, the *moment M* due to a force $F$ acting at a distance $s$ from a reference point $P$ is

$$M = Fs.$$

A fundamental law of mechanics states that if a plane system of parallel forces acting on a rigid body is in equilibrium, then
(1) the sum of all of the forces must be zero, and
(2) the algebraic sum of the moments relative to an arbitrary reference point in the plane of all the forces must be zero.

Consider a system of $n$ particles of mass $m_i$ on a rod of negligible weight, with the $i$th particle located at a distance $s_i$ from a reference point $P$, and suppose the rod is hinged to a rigid support at $P$ (see Figure 8.12c). Suppose we wish to find the distance, $s$, from $P$, at which a vertical force of magnitude $F$ should be applied on the rod in order to prevent the rod from turning down due to the weight of the masses $m_i$, and to keep the system in equilibrium. It is known from physics that the weight of a mass $m$ is proportional to the mass and that the constant of proportionality is the gravitational constant $g$ (approximately 32 feet per second per second). Hence, the force due to the $i$th mass is $F_i = m_i g$, and the preceding laws of mechanics yield the two equations

$$\sum_{i=1}^{n} m_i g - F = 0 \quad \text{and} \quad \sum_{i=1}^{n} m_i g s_i - Fs = 0.$$

The distance $s$ is a kind of weighted average, since the first of the preceding equations states, in effect, that the force $F$ must equal the sum of the forces due to the masses $m_i$. That is,

$$F = \sum_{i=1}^{n} g m_i,$$

so that the second equation yields the result

$$s = \frac{\displaystyle\sum_{i=1}^{n} m_i g s_i}{\displaystyle\sum_{i=1}^{n} m_i g} = \frac{\displaystyle\sum_{i=1}^{n} m_i s_i}{\displaystyle\sum_{i=1}^{n} m_i}.$$

The point $C$ located by the distance $s$ from $p$ is called the *center of mass*.

Although the above discussion pertains to individual masses, it is easy to extend the argument to a continuously distributed mass. Consider a rod of mass $M$ and length $L$. Choose one end of the rod as a reference point $P$ and partition the rod into elements of mass $\Delta m_i$, $i = 1, 2, \ldots, n$, located at a dis-

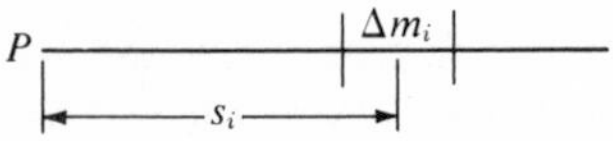

**FIGURE 8.12d**

tance $s_i$ from $P$ (Figure 8.12d). Then the center of mass of the rod is at the point $\bar{s}$ units distant from $P$, where

$$\bar{s} = \frac{\displaystyle\lim_{\delta \to 0} \sum_{i=1}^{n} s_i \, \Delta m_i}{\displaystyle\lim_{\delta \to 0} \sum_{i=1}^{n} \Delta m_i},$$

or

$$\bar{s} = \frac{\displaystyle\int_{s=0}^{s=L} s \, dm}{\displaystyle\int_{s=0}^{s=L} dm}.$$

If the rod is of uniform density $k$ (mass units per unit length), then

$$dm = k \, ds$$

and

$$\bar{s} = \frac{k \int_0^L s \, ds}{k \int_0^L ds} = \frac{k \dfrac{L^2}{2}}{kL} = \frac{L}{2}.$$

Thus, the center of mass of the rod is at the center of the rod, as is to be expected.

A further extension of these ideas to two (or even three) dimensions is reasonable. Consider a plate of uniform density $\rho$ (mass units per unit volume) and thickness $h$, as indicated in Figure 8.12e. It is assumed that the plate has

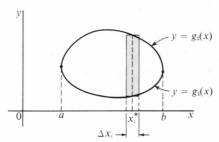

**FIGURE 8.12e**

a shape that can be described in terms of simple functions. There are two averages to be found in order to locate the center of mass: an average $x$ value, $\bar{x}$, and an average $y$ value, $\bar{y}$. To find the average $x$ value, partition the plate into vertical strips. The mass of the $i$th strip is approximately $\rho \, \Delta V_i$, where $\Delta V_i$ is the volume of the $i$th strip. Now suppose that the edge of the plate can be described by the equations

$$y = g_1(x) \quad \text{and} \quad y = g_2(x),$$

as shown in the figure. Then

$$\Delta V_i = h \, \Delta x_i [g_2(x_i^*) - g_1(x_i^*)],$$

and the moment of the $i$th mass with respect to the $y$-axis is

$$M_i = x_i^* \, \Delta m_i$$
$$= x_i^* \rho h [g_2(x_i^*) - g_1(x_i^*)] \, \Delta x_i.$$

In this case the $y$-axis is used as a reference line since it is parallel to the strip, a fact that allows us to use a fixed measurement of distance between the axis and the strip. The approximate average $x$ value, $\bar{x}_n$, is given by

$$\bar{x}_n = \frac{\displaystyle\sum_{i=1}^n M_i}{\displaystyle\sum_{i=1}^n \Delta m_i}$$

$$= \frac{\displaystyle\sum_{i=1}^n x_i^* \rho h [g_2(x_i^*) - g_1(x_i^*)] \, \Delta x_i}{\displaystyle\sum_{i=1}^n \rho h [g_2(x_i^*) - g_1(x_i^*)] \, \Delta x_i}.$$

In the limit this expression becomes

$$\bar{x} = \frac{\int_a^b x\rho h[g_2(x) - g_1(x)]\, dx}{\int_a^b \rho h[g_2(x) - g_1(x)]\, dx}$$

$$= \frac{\int_a^b x\, dm}{\int_a^b dm},$$

or

$$M\bar{x} = \int_a^b x\, dm,$$

where $M$ is the total mass of the plate.

An average $y$ value can be obtained in a similar way. In that case the boundary of the plate must be described by two equations,

$$x = h_1(y) \quad \text{and} \quad x = h_2(y),$$

so that

$$M\bar{y} = \int_{y=c}^{y=d} y\, dm.$$

If the density $\rho$ and the thickness $h$ are constants, the equations for $\bar{x}$ and $\bar{y}$ may be written as

$$A\bar{x} = \int_{x=a}^{x=b} x\, dA \quad \text{and} \quad A\bar{y} = \int_{y=c}^{y=d} y\, dA,$$

where $A$ is the area of the face of the plate. In this case, a physical problem has been expressed in terms of a purely geometric problem—that of finding average $x$- and $y$-coordinates, $\bar{x}$ and $\bar{y}$, respectively, for a geometric area. The point $(\bar{x}, \bar{y})$ is called the *centroid* of the area. Thus, we shall speak of finding moments of areas just as we speak of finding moments of masses.

The succeeding examples in this section will illustrate the preceding discussion.

*Example 8.12c.* Find the centroid of a rectangular area (Figure 8.12f).

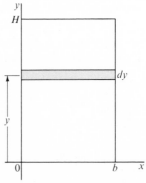

**FIGURE 8.12f**

Suppose the rectangle is $H$ units high and $b$ units wide. Let 0 be an origin at the lower left corner. To find the average $y$ value, $\bar{y}$, choose a rectangular strip parallel to the $x$-axis. Then

$$dA = b\,dy$$

and

$$A\bar{y} = \int_0^H yb\,dy = \left[\frac{by^2}{2}\right]_0^H = \frac{bH^2}{2}.$$

Since $A = bH$, we have

$$\bar{y} = \frac{bH^2}{2bH} = \frac{H}{2}.$$

Similarly, the average $x$ value is found to be $b/2$. Hence the centroid is at the point $(b/2, H/2)$.

---

In general, it appears that the centroid of an area must be on a line of symmetry of the area, if such a line exists. This conjecture is easy to prove.

**Theorem 8.12a.** Let the line $L$ be a line of symmetry of an area $A$. Then the centroid of the area lies on $L$.

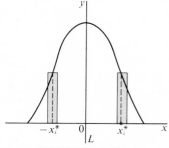

FIGURE 8.12g

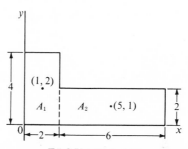

FIGURE 8.12h

PROOF: Choose an origin on $L$ as in Figure 8.12g. We want to show that $\bar{x} = 0$. Consider a vertical element of area $\Delta A_i$ at an approximate distance $x_i^*$ from the $y$-axis. Because the curve is symmetric, there is a corresponding element of area at $-x_i^*$. Hence the moments due to these elements are

$$x_i^* \,\Delta A_i \quad \text{and} \quad -x_i^* \,\Delta A_i.$$

The sum of these terms is 0. It follows that $\bar{x} = 0$. (Why?)

The information contained in the preceding theorem considerably simplifies the problem of finding the centroid of an area that can be partitioned into areas having lines of symmetry.

---

*Example 8.12d.* Find the centroid of the area shown in Figure 8.12h.

The area is divided into two rectangles as indicated in the figure, and the total area is

$$A = A_1 + A_2 = 8 + 12 = 20 \text{ (l.u.)}^2.$$

The centroid, $(\bar{x}_1, \bar{y}_1)$, of rectangle $A_1$ is at the point $(1, 2)$, as indicated by the preceding example. Similarly, the centroid of $A_2$ is $(\bar{x}_2, \bar{y}_2) = (5, 1)$. Since the moment of a plane area with respect to any axis is the product of the area and the perpendicular distance of the centroid of the area from the axis, the sum of the moments with respect to the $y$-axis is

$$A\bar{x} = A_1\bar{x}_1 + A_2\bar{x}_2 = (8)(1) + (12)(5) = 68 \ (\text{l.u.})^3.$$

Similarly, the sum of the moments with respect to the $x$-axis is

$$A\bar{y} = A_1\bar{y}_1 + A_2\bar{y}_2 = (8)(2) + (12)(1) = 28 \ (\text{l.u.})^3.$$

Therefore, the required coordinates are

$$\bar{x} = \frac{68}{20} = \frac{17}{5} \quad \text{and} \quad \bar{y} = \frac{28}{20} = \frac{7}{5}.$$

---

*Example 8.12e.* Find the centroid of the area bounded by the parabola $y = x^2$ and the line $y = 4$.

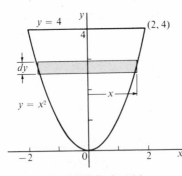

**FIGURE 8.12i**

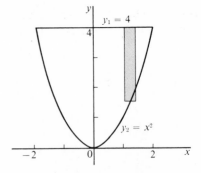

**FIGURE 8.12j**

If the rectangular strip is taken parallel to the $x$-axis, as in Figure 8.12i, then the moment of the strip with respect to the $x$-axis is $y \, dA = y(2x \, dy)$ and

$$A\bar{y} = \int_0^4 (2x)y \, dy.$$

Since $x = y^{1/2}$,

$$A\bar{y} = \int_0^4 2y^{3/2} \, dy$$

$$= \left[\frac{4}{5} y^{5/2}\right]_0^4$$

$$= \frac{128}{5} \ (\text{l.u.})^3.$$

Also,

$$A = 2 \int_0^4 y^{1/2} \, dy = 2 \left[\frac{2}{3} y^{3/2}\right]_0^4 = \frac{32}{3} \ (\text{l.u.})^2,$$

so that

$$\bar{y} = \left(\frac{128}{5}\right)\left(\frac{3}{32}\right) = \frac{12}{5}.$$

The $y$-axis is a line of symmetry, and therefore $\bar{x} = 0$.

*Example 8.12f.* Find the centroid of the area described in Example 8.12e by using vertical strips.

The $y$-coordinate of the centroid of the rectangular strip shown in Figure 8.12j is $\frac{1}{2}(y_1 + y_2)$, where $y_1 = 4$ and $y_2 = x^2$. The area of the strip is $(y_1 - y_2)\,dx$ and the moment with respect to the $x$-axis is therefore

$$\tfrac{1}{2}(y_1 + y_2)(y_1 - y_2)\,dx = \tfrac{1}{2}(y_1^2 - y_2^2)\,dx.$$

Thus

$$A\bar{y} = 2\int_0^2 \tfrac{1}{2}(y_1^2 - y_2^2)\,dx.$$

Use is made of symmetry so that the limits on the definite integrals are 0 to 2 and each integral is multiplied by a factor of 2. Since $y_1 = 4$ and $y_2 = x^2$, the expression for $A\bar{y}$ becomes

$$A\bar{y} = \int_0^2 (16 - x^4)\,dx = \frac{128}{5} \ \text{(l.u.)}^3.$$

It follows that

$$\bar{y} = \left(\frac{128}{5}\right)\left(\frac{3}{32}\right) = \frac{12}{5}.$$

## Exercises 8.12

1. Find the average ordinate ($y$ value) of the parabola $ay = 2ax - x^2$ from $x = 0$ to $x = 2a$, with respect to $x$.
2. Find the average width parallel to the $x$-axis of the area bounded by the curves $y^2 = x^3$ and $y = x$, with respect to $y$.
3. Find the average $y$ value of the curve $y^2 = x^3$ with respect to $x^3$ from $x = 0$ to $x = 2$.
4. Find the average value of $y^2$ with respect to $x$ for the upper half of the circle $x^2 + y^2 = r^2$.
5. Find the average value of $y^2$ with respect to $x^2$ for the upper half of the circle $x^2 + y^2 = r^2$.
6. Find the centroid of the area shown in Figure 8.12k.

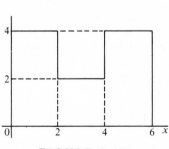

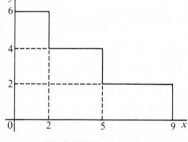

FIGURE 8.12k          FIGURE 8.12l

7. Find the centroid of the area shown in Figure 8.12l.
8. Show that the centroid of any triangle is at the intersection of the medians.

In each of Numbers 9 to 20, find the centroid of the area bounded by the given curves

9. $x^2 + y^2 = a^2$, $y = 0$ (upper half).
10. $x^2 + y^2 = a^2$, $x = 0$, $y = 0$ (first quadrant). Compare the result with that o
Number 9.

11. $y = x$, $y = x^2$.
12. $y^2 = 6y + 3x$, $x = 0$.
13. $y^3 = x$, $y = x^2$.
14. $x^2 - y - 4x = 0$, $y = 0$.

15. $y = x^2$, $y = x + 2$.
16. $y^2 + 4x = 0$, $x^2 + 4y = 0$.
17. $x^2 = 4y$, $2y = x + 4$.
18. $y = x^4$, $y + x^2 - 2 = 0$.

19. $y = x^3 - 8x$, $y = x$ (to the right of the $y$-axis).
20. $y + x = 0$, $y = x + x^2$.

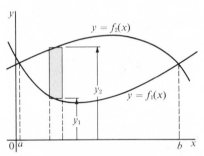

**FIGURE 8.12m**

21. In Figure 8.12m, the area $A$ bounded by the two curves $y = f_1(x)$ and $y = f_2(x)$
is to be revolved about the $x$-axis to generate a volume. Show that this volume i
given by

$$V = 2\pi \bar{y} A,$$

where $\bar{y}$ is the $y$-coordinate of the centroid of the area. *Hint*:

$$V = \pi \int_a^b (y_2^2 - y_1^2)\, dx = 2\pi \int_a^b \left( \frac{y_2 + y_1}{2} \right)(y_2 - y_1)\, dx.$$

The formula $V = 2\pi \bar{y} A$ may be stated in words as follows:
*The volume formed by revolving a plane area about an axis in its plane and no
cutting the area is given by the product of the area and the distance passed over b
the centroid of the area.*
This statement is known as Pappus' Theorem for Volumes of Revolution.

Use Pappus' Theorem in each of Numbers 22 to 26.

22. Find the volume of the torus generated by revolving the area of a circle of radius
about an axis $b$ units from the center of the circle, $b > a$.
23. The centroid of a triangle is at the intersection of the medians. A right triang
with legs 3 units and 4 units long, respectively, is revolved about a line in its plan
This line is parallel to its hypotenuse and 6 units from the hypotenuse on the sid
opposite the vertex of the right angle. Find the volume generated.
24. Locate the centroid of the area of a semicircle of radius $a$.

25. The cross section of a solid metal ring is a square that is $\frac{1}{2}$ inch on a side. The radius of the ring measured from its axis to the center of the square is 2 inches. Find the volume of material in the ring.

26. Find the volume of a right circular cone of radius $a$ and altitude $h$.

## 8.13 APPLICATIONS TO PHYSICAL PROBLEMS

A basic concept in mechanics that lends itself to analysis by means of the limit of a sum is that of the work done by a force $F$ that is directed along an axis and that moves an object through a distance $s$ on this axis. If $F$ is a constant force, then the work done is given by $W = Fs$. However, if $F$ is not constant, then the problem of calculating the work done leads to the employment of the definite integral.

Let $F(x)$ describe the force acting on an object at the point $x$ in moving the object from a point $a$ to a point $b$ on the $x$-axis, where $a \leq x \leq b$. The work done by the force in moving the object through a small interval $\Delta x_i = x_i - x_{i-1}$, $a \leq x_{i-1} < x_i \leq b$, may be approximated by $F(x_i^*) \Delta x_i$, where $x_{i-1} \leq x_i^* \leq x_i$. Consequently, if we form a partition of the interval from $a$ to $b$ into $n$ subintervals by the points

$$a = x_0, x_1, x_2, \ldots, x_n = b,$$

then the total work done is approximated by the sum

$$W_n = \sum_{i=1}^{n} F(x_i^*) \Delta x_i.$$

It is therefore appropriate to *define* the total work done by a force $F(x)$ acting over the interval from $a$ to $b$ by

$$W = \lim_{\delta \to 0} \sum_{i=1}^{n} F(x_i^*) \Delta x_i = \int_a^b F(x) \, dx.$$

A simple example of work done by a varying force is provided by the stretching or compressing of a spring. According to Hooke's Law, the force $F$ required to stretch or compress a spring is proportional to the amount of extension or compression, $x$, of the spring; that is,

$$F(x) = kx.$$

The constant $k$ is called the spring constant and has dimensions of pounds per foot.

---

*Example 8.13a.* A force of 10 pounds is required to compress a spring of natural length of 20 inches to a length of 19 inches. What is the work done in stretching the spring from a length of 24 inches to a length of 30 inches?

Since the foot-pound is an appropriate unit of work to use here, we convert measurements in inches to feet, and, from Hooke's Law, we have

$$F(\tfrac{1}{12}) = 10 = \tfrac{1}{12}k.$$

Hence the spring constant is $k = 120$ pounds per foot, and the work done in stretching the spring from 24 inches to 30 inches is given by the integral

$$W = \int_{1/3}^{5/6} 120x \, dx,$$

where the appropriate conversion of inches to feet has been made. It follows that

$$W = [60x^2]_{1/3}^{5/6} = 35 \text{ foot-pounds.}$$

Another type of work problem occurs in finding the work done in pumping water out of a tank.

*Example 8.13b.* A tank in the shape of an inverted right circular cone 12 feet high and with a base radius of 6 feet is filled with water. Find the work done in pumping the water to the top of the tank. (Water weighs approximately 62.5 pounds per cubic foot.)

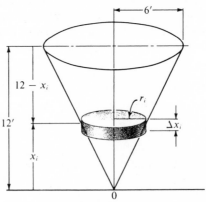

**FIGURE 8.13a**

The work done in pumping the water to the top of the tank may be approximated by considering the volume to consist of $n$ thin disk-shaped elements, and finding the work done in pumping the water in each element to the top of the tank. Let the origin be chosen at the vertex of the cone (Figure 8.13a) and let $x$ measure the upward distance along the axis of the tank. Then the work done in pumping the water in the $i$th disk to the top of the tank is given by

$$\Delta W_i = (12 - x_i)(62.5\pi r_i^2 \, \Delta x_i),$$

where $r_i$ is the radius of the disk.

We can express $r_i$ in terms of $x_i$ by considering the ratios of corresponding sides of similar triangles. Thus,

$$r_i = \tfrac{1}{2}x_i,$$

so that

$$\Delta W_i = (62.5\pi)\tfrac{1}{4}(12 - x_i)x_i^2 \, \Delta x_i.$$

The sum of such contributions will provide an approximation for the work done. Hence

$$W_n = \sum_{i=1}^{n} \frac{62.5\pi x_i^2}{4} (12 - x_i) \, \Delta x_i.$$

By using the limit of this sum, we obtain a suitable definition for the work done in terms of a definite integral, which gives

$$W = \int_0^{12} \frac{62.5\pi}{4}(12 - x)x^2\,dx = 27{,}000\pi \text{ foot-pounds.}$$

The complete details of finding an approximating sum and then passing to the limit are not necessary once the fundamental ideas are grasped. Instead, the definite integral may be set up directly by considering a typical element, as illustrated in the next example.

*Example 8.13c.* A plate in the form of a parabolic segment is submerged vertically in water with the axis vertical. The base of the plate is 12 feet across and is at a depth of 10 feet, while the vertex is at a depth of 30 feet. Find the force exerted by the water on one face of the plate (see Figure 8.13b).

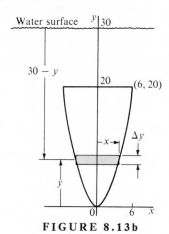

**FIGURE 8.13b**

If the origin and axes are chosen as in the figure, then a typical element of area on the face of the plate has dimensions $2x$ by $\Delta y$. An approximation to the force on this element is given by

$$\Delta F = 62.5(30 - y)2x\,\Delta y.$$

In order to express $x$ in terms of $y$, we need to know the equation of the parabola. For the chosen axes, the equation must be of the form $x^2 = ay$ and the curve passes through the point $(6, 20)$; therefore we find $a = 9/5$ and $x = (3/\sqrt{5})y^{1/2}$. It follows that

$$\Delta F = 62.5(30 - y)\frac{6}{\sqrt{5}}y^{1/2}\,\Delta y,$$

and the total force on the face of the plate is given by

$$F = \int_0^{20} \frac{6}{\sqrt{5}}(62.5)(30 - y)y^{1/2}\,dy$$

$$= \frac{375}{\sqrt{5}}\int_0^{20}(30y^{1/2} - y^{3/2})\,dy = 180{,}000 \text{ pounds.}$$

(The reader should compare this abbreviated setup of the integral with the treatment of that in Example 8.3b.)

## Exercises 8.13

1. A spring is stretched 3 inches by a force of 25 pounds. How much work is required to stretch the spring an additional 3 inches?

2. A spring 8 feet long is stretched to a length of 10 feet by a force of 120 pounds. What is the work done in stretching the spring from a length of 9 feet to a length of 12 feet?

3. A force of 10 pounds stretches a spring 1 inch. What is the percentage increase in the work done in stretching the spring from 10 inches to 12 inches over the work done in stretching it from its natural length of 8 inches to 10 inches?

4. A tank in the shape of a vertical right circular cylinder with a base radius of 8 feet and a height of 24 feet is filled with water. Find the work required to pump the water to the top of the tank.

5. In Number 4, find the work required to pump the water to a point 6 feet above the top of the tank.

6. A tank is in the shape of an inverted right circular cone of base radius 10 feet and a height of 20 feet, with its axis vertical. If the tank is filled with a liquid of specific gravity 0.9, find the work required to pump the liquid to a point 10 feet above the tank.

7. A spherical tank of radius 20 feet is full of water. What is the work done in pumping the water to the top of the tank?

8. In Number 7, what is the work done in pumping the water to a point 20 feet above the tank?

9. A trough 20 feet long has a cross section in the shape of an isosceles trapezoid with a lower base 4 feet long, an upper base 10 feet long, and an altitude of 4 feet. How much work is done in filling the trough with water if the bottom of the trough is located 20 feet above the pump and the water is pumped in through a valve in the bottom of the tank?

10. A tank is in the form of a right circular cylinder with a horizontal axis and has a base radius $r$ feet and a length $L$ feet. Set up an integral for the work done in filling the tank with water from a point $a$ feet ($a > r$) below the center of the tank if the water is pumped in through a valve in the bottom of the tank.

11. Set up an integral for the force exerted on the circular end of a cylindrical tank with its axis horizontal if the tank is filled with water, and if the radius of the tank is 4 feet.

12. A vertical dam in the shape of a parabolic segment with its vertex down is 10 feet deep and 100 feet across the top. Find the force on the face of the dam if the water level is at the top of the dam.

13. A triangular gate of altitude $h$ feet and base $b$ feet is submerged vertically in water so that the base is below the vertex and parallel to the surface of the water. If the vertex is $h$ feet below the surface, find the force exerted on one side of the gate.

14. A plate in the shape of a parabolic segment is submerged vertically in water with the axis parallel to the surface. If the plate has a base 8 feet long and a vertex

4 feet from the base, and is submerged so that its highest point is at the surface, find the force exerted on one side of the plate.

15. In Number 14, suppose the plate is submerged vertically with its vertex at the surface and the base below it. What is the force exerted on one side of the plate?

16. Prove that the force exerted on one side of a plane surface entirely submerged vertically in a fluid is equal to the product of the area of the surface, the depth of the centroid, and the specific weight of the fluid.

17. A particle on the $x$-axis is attracted toward the origin by a force of magnitude

$$F = \frac{kx}{(a^2 + x^2)^{3/2}}.$$

Find the work done by the force if it moves the particle from a distance $2a$ to a distance $a$ from the origin.

18. Two masses attract each other with a force that is proportional to the product of their masses and inversely proportional to the square of the distance between them. A rod of length $a$ units is located on the $x$-axis between the origin and the point where $x = a$. If the rod has a uniform density $\mu$ mass units per unit length, find the force of attraction of the rod on a particle of unit mass located at the point $(2a, 0)$.

19. The weight of an object varies inversely as the square of its distance from the center of the earth. How much work is done in propelling a space capsule weighing 2000 pounds to a height of 400 miles? Take the radius of the earth to be 4000 miles and disregard the resistance of the atmosphere.

20. Find the work done in lifting a mine bucket weighing 500 pounds from a depth of 500 feet to a depth of 300 feet if the hoist cable weighs 3 pounds per foot.

21. A piston compresses a gas in a cylinder from an initial volume of 100 cubic inches to a volume of 40 cubic inches. If the initial pressure is 80 pounds per square inch and if the process is such that the pressure $p$ and the volume $v$ obey the equation $pv^{1.4} = C$, find the work done by the piston. *Hint:* If the piston moves a small distance $\Delta x$, show that the work done is approximately $p \, \Delta v$.

22. A rod extends along the $x$-axis from $x = 1$ to $x = 3$. If the mass per unit length is proportional to the distance from the origin, calculate the total mass of the rod.

23. If it takes 50% more work to stretch a spring from 11 inches to 12 inches than it does to stretch it from 10 inches to 11 inches, what is the natural length of the spring?

24. The *impulse* due to a constant force $F$ (pounds) acting during time $t$ (seconds) is defined to be $Ft$ (pound-seconds).
   (a) Define the impulse if the force is a variable, say $F(t)$.
   (b) A freight car backs slowly into a heavy spring bumper and comes to rest after compressing the springs 2 inches. The speed of the car is $\frac{1}{12}(2 - t)$ feet per second, where $t = 0$ at the instant of contact with the bumper. If the modulus of the spring bumper is 72,000 pounds per inch, find the total impulse that the car delivers to the bumper.

25. The force of attraction between two mass particles is proportional to the product of their masses and inversely proportional to the square of the distance between them. Let a mass $m$ be distributed uniformly along the portion of the $x$-axis between $x_1$ and $x_2$, $x_2 > x_1$. What is the force of attraction of this mass on a particle of mass $m$ placed at the point $x_3$ on the axis with $x_3 > x_2$?

*26. The dimensions of a parabolic dam are shown in Figure 8.13c. At what depth on the axis of the parabola would a single force have to be placed in order to be

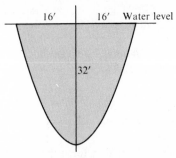

**FIGURE 8.13c**

mechanically equivalent to the total force on the dam? *Hint*: Consider the equilibrium conditions for a system of parallel forces.

## 8.14 SECTIONALLY CONTINUOUS FUNCTIONS

Although most of the discussion of the preceding few sections has been devoted to functions that are continuous on a closed interval, there are a number of physics and engineering problems in which it is important to consider functions with certain types of discontinuities. In the simpler applications, these discontinuities are finite and the functions are continuous except for a finite number of finite discontinuities on a closed interval.

**Definition 8.14a.** A function $f$ is said to be **sectionally** (or **piecewise**) **continuous** on a closed interval $a \leqq x \leqq b$ if

    (i) it is discontinuous at only a finite number of points in the interval,

    (ii) at each point $x_1$ of discontinuity (interior to the interval) $\lim_{x \to x_1^-} f(x)$ and $\lim_{x \to x_1^+} f(x)$ both exist, and

    (iii) $\lim_{x \to a^+} f(x)$ and $\lim_{x \to b^-} f(x)$ both exist.

For example, the graph of the function $f$ defined by

$$f(x) = U(x) - U(x - 1), \qquad 0 < x \leqq 2 \qquad \text{and} \qquad f(x) = 0,$$

where $U$ is the unit step function (Definition 2.5b), is shown in Figure 8.14a.

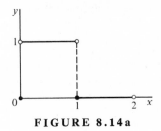

**FIGURE 8.14a**

This function has two finite discontinuities, one at $x = 0$ and the other at $x = 1$. Since $f$ is defined at every point of the interval, $0 \leq x \leq 2$, and $\lim_{x \to 0^+} f(x) = 1$, $\lim_{x \to 1^-} f(x) = 1$, $\lim_{x \to 1^+} f(x) = 0$, and $\lim_{x \to 2^-} f(x) = 0$, the function is sectionally continuous on the interval.

On the other hand, the function $f$ defined by

$$f(x) = (x - 1)^{-2}, \quad 0 \leq x < 1, \quad 1 < x \leq 2,$$
$$f(1) = 0,$$

is *not* sectionally continuous. Although this function is continuous in the half-open intervals $0 \leq x < 1$ and $1 < x \leq 2$, neither $\lim_{x \to 1^-} f(x)$ nor $\lim_{x \to 1^+} f(x)$ exists. In fact, the function has an infinite discontinuity at $x = 1$.

In order to examine the definite integral of a function that is sectionally continuous on an interval $a \leq x \leq b$, let us first consider a specific example. Let

$$f(x) .=. \begin{cases} x^2 & \text{for } 0 \leq x < 1, \\ \frac{3}{2} & \text{for } x = 1, \\ 2 & \text{for } 1 < x \leq 2. \end{cases}$$

(See Figure 8.14b.) It appears clear intuitively from the geometric interpretation of the integral as an area that $\int_0^2 f(x)\, dx$ ought to exist, since it would measure the area below the curve $y = f(x)$ and above the x-axis from $x = 0$ to $x = 2$.

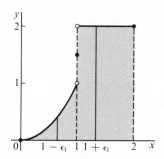

**FIGURE 8.14b**

Let us divide the interval $0 \leq x \leq 2$ into three parts by choosing a number $\epsilon_1, 0 < \epsilon_1 < 1$, and inserting the points $1 - \epsilon_1$ and $1 + \epsilon_1$. (The choice of $\epsilon_1$ will be made more specific later.) Then $f$ is continuous on $0 \leq x \leq 1 - \epsilon_1$ and on $1 + \epsilon_1 \leq x \leq 2$. For any partition of the respective intervals taken in order from left to right, let the lower approximation sums be $s_1$, $s_2$, $s_3$, and the upper sums be $S_1$, $S_2$, $S_3$. For the entire interval, we have

$$s = s_1 + s_2 + s_3 \quad \text{and} \quad S = S_1 + S_2 + S_3.$$

For every $\epsilon_1$, $0 < \epsilon_1 < 1$, the given function is continuous on the two intervals $0 \leq x \leq 1 - \epsilon_1$ and $1 + \epsilon_1 \leq x \leq 2$. Hence, if the norm of the partition is $\delta = \max \Delta x_i$, then

$$\lim_{\delta \to 0} s_1 = \lim_{\delta \to 0} S_1 \quad \text{and} \quad \lim_{\delta \to 0} s_3 = \lim_{\delta \to 0} S_3.$$

This means that for every $\epsilon > 0$ there is a partition fine enough that

$$S_1 - s_1 < \frac{\epsilon}{3} \quad \text{and} \quad S_3 - s_3 < \frac{\epsilon}{3}.$$

Consequently,

$$S - s \leq \frac{\epsilon}{3} + \frac{\epsilon}{3} + S_2 - s_2.$$

Since $f$ is continuous on the interval $1 - \epsilon_1 \leq x \leq 1 + \epsilon_1$ except at the one poin $x = 1$, and $f(1) = \frac{3}{2}$, the difference between the maximum value and the min imum value of $f(x)$ in this interval is bounded. In this example, this differenc is not greater than 2. Therefore, $S_2 - s_2$ is not greater than 2 times the lengtl of the interval; that is,

$$S_2 - s_2 \leq 4\epsilon_1.$$

This shows that if $\epsilon_1$ is chosen less than $\epsilon/12$, then

$$S - s \leq \epsilon,$$

and thus the definite integral $\int_0^2 f(x)\, dx$ exists.

It is important to note that the preceding discussion indicates that

$$\int_0^2 f(x)\, dx = \lim_{\epsilon \to 0^+} \left[ \int_0^{1-\epsilon} x^2\, dx + \int_{1+\epsilon}^2 2\, dx \right]$$

$$= \lim_{\epsilon \to 0} \left\{ \left[ \frac{x^3}{3} \right]_0^{1-\epsilon} + [2x]_{1+\epsilon}^2 \right\}$$

$$= \lim_{\epsilon \to 0^+} \left[ \frac{1}{3}(1 - \epsilon)^3 + 4 - 2(1 + \epsilon) \right] = \frac{7}{3}.$$

Furthermore, it is easy to verify that

$$\lim_{\epsilon \to 0^+} \int_0^{1-\epsilon} x^2\, dx = \int_0^1 x^2\, dx = \frac{1}{3},$$

and

$$\lim_{\epsilon \to 0^+} \int_{1+\epsilon}^2 2\, dx = \int_1^2 2\, dx = 2,$$

so that

$$\int_0^2 f(x)\, dx = \int_0^1 x^2\, dx + \int_1^2 2\, dx = \frac{7}{3}.$$

Notice that the value of the integral is independent of the value of $f(1)$. Thus even if $f$ were undefined at $x = 1$, it would still be reasonable to define th definite integral of $f$ on the basis of the preceding three equations.

Every function that is sectionally continuous on a finite interval and ha only one discontinuity there can be treated in exactly the same manner as tha of the preceding discussion. Consequently, we are led to the following extensio of the definite integral.

**Definition 8.14b.** Let $f$ be a sectionally continuous function on the closed interval $a \leq x \leq b$ with a single discontinuity at $c$, $a < c < b$. Let

$$g(x) \mathrel{.=.} f(x) \quad \text{for } a \leq x < c,$$
$$g(c) \mathrel{.=.} \lim_{x \to c^-} f(x),$$

and

$$h(x) \mathrel{.=.} f(x) \quad \text{for } c < x \leq b,$$
$$h(c) \mathrel{.=.} \lim_{x \to c^+} f(x).$$

Then the definite integral of $f(x)$ from $x = a$ to $x = b$ is

$$\int_a^b f(x)\, dx \mathrel{.=.} \int_a^c g(x)\, dx + \int_c^b h(x)\, dx.$$

The discussion preceding Definition 8.14b applies equally well to a sectionally continuous function having more than one discontinuity. We shall therefore omit a formal general definition of the integral of a function that is sectionally continuous on a finite closed interval, but shall illustrate by the following examples how such integrals may be treated.

---

*Example 8.14a.* A particle moves along the $x$-axis with an acceleration $a = f(t)$ feet per second per second, where $f(t) = t - k$, $k \leq t < k + 1$, $k = 0, 1, 2, \ldots$. If the particle starts from rest at the origin, find its velocity after $T$ seconds.

Using the fact that $a = dv/dt$, we have

$$v = \int_0^T f(t)\, dt + C.$$

This form of the indefinite integral is convenient, since we have the initial condition that $v = 0$ when $T = 0$. This gives

$$0 = \int_0^0 f(t)\, dt + C \Rightarrow C = 0,$$

so that

$$v = \int_0^T f(t)\, dt.$$

To evaluate this integral, let us suppose that

$$k \leq T < k + 1.$$

Then,

$$v = \int_0^1 t\, dt + \int_1^2 (t - 1)\, dt + \int_2^3 (t - 2)\, dt + \cdots + \int_k^T (t - k)\, dt$$

$$= \sum_{p=0}^{k-1} \int_p^{p+1} (t - p)\, dt + \int_k^T (t - k)\, dt.$$

A typical integral in the sum is

$$\int_p^{p+1} (t - p)\, dt = \left[ \frac{(t - p)^2}{2} \right]_p^{p+1}$$

$$= \frac{1}{2}(1 - 0) = \frac{1}{2}.$$

Therefore,

$$v = \sum_{p=0}^{k-1}\frac{1}{2} + \left[\frac{(t-k)^2}{2}\right]_k^T$$

$$= \left[\frac{k}{2} + \frac{(T-k)^2}{2}\right] \text{ feet per second.}$$

---

*Example 8.14b.* Suppose a force $F$ directed along the $x$-axis moves an object from the origin to a point 3 feet to the right. Calculate the work done if the force $F$ (in pounds) is given by

$$F(x) = \sum_{k=0}^{n}(-1)^k x U(x-k), \qquad n > 3,$$

where $U$ is the unit step function and $x$ is in feet. A graph of $F$ is shown in Figure 8.14c.

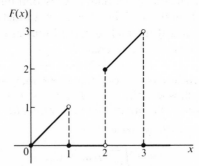

**FIGURE 8.14c**

The work done by the force $F$ (see Section 8.13) is

$$W = \int_0^3 F(x)\,dx = \int_0^3 x[U(x) - U(x-1) + U(x-2)]\,dx$$

$$= \int_0^1 x\,dx + \int_1^2 0\,dx + \int_2^3 x\,dx$$

$$= \left[\frac{x^2}{2}\right]_0^1 + \left[\frac{x^2}{2}\right]_2^3 = 3 \text{ foot-pounds.}$$

## Exercises 8.14

In each of Numbers 1 to 4, find the value of the given integral.

1. $\int_{-2}^{2} f(x)\,dx$, where $f(x) .=. \begin{cases} -1, & -2 \leq x \leq 0, \\ x, & 0 < x \leq 2. \end{cases}$

2. $\int_{-2}^{2} f(x)\,dx$, where $f(x) .=. \begin{cases} 1/x^2, & -2 \leq x \leq -1, \\ 2 - x, & -1 < x \leq 2. \end{cases}$

3. $\int_{0}^{6} g(x)\,dx$, where $g(x) .=. \begin{cases} 4 - x^2, & 0 \leq x < 2, \\ x, & 2 \leq x \leq 6. \end{cases}$

4. $\displaystyle\int_0^4 g(x)\,dx$, where $g(x)\,.=.\begin{cases} -x, & 0 \le x \le 1, \\ 1 - x^2, & 1 < x < 2, \\ 6 - x, & 2 \le x \le 4. \end{cases}$

5. Find the value of $\displaystyle\int_0^n f(x)\,dx$ if

$$f(x) = \sqrt{x - n + 1}, \qquad n - 1 \le x < n, n = 1, 2, 3, \ldots.$$

6. Find the value of $\displaystyle\int_0^{x_1} f(x)\,dx$ where $f(x)$ is given in Number 5.

7. If $U(x)$ is the unit step function, find the value of

$$\int_0^n f(x)\,dx, \qquad \text{where } f(x) = \sum_{p=0}^n U(x - p).$$

8. In Example 8.14b, find the work done if the object moves from the origin to a point $n$ feet away.

9. A particle, starting from rest at the origin, moves along the $x$-axis. Its acceleration is given by

$$f(t) = U(t) + \sum_{p=1}^n (-1)^p 2U(t - p), \qquad 0 \le t \le n,$$

where $n$ is a positive integer and $U$ is the unit step function. Make a graph of the acceleration, and find the velocity of the particle at time $T \le n$. Make a graph of the velocity function.

10. An elevator weighing 2000 pounds is suspended by cables weighing a total of 10 pounds per foot. If the elevator starts from the ground floor with 10 passengers of average weight of 160 pounds each, and two passengers get off at the 5th floor, 3 at the 8th floor, 4 at the 12th floor, and 1 at the 20th floor, find the work done. Assume that each floor is 10 feet above the next lower floor. (Express the work done as an integral of a function that is expressible in terms of the unit step function.)

# Summary of Chapter 8

The first fundamental concept of calculus is the derivative and the associated limit process. This chapter is concerned with the second fundamental concept of calculus, the definite integral, and the limit process associated with it. The following concepts are essential preparation for a study of the definite integral:

(1) the summation notation (Section 8.1);
(2) an infinite sequence (Section 8.2);
(3) cluster point of a sequence (Section 8.2);
(4) convergence and divergence of a sequence (Section 8.2);
(5) nonincreasing and nondecreasing sequences (Section 8.2);
(6) upper and lower bounds of a sequence (Section 8.2);
(7) theorems pertaining to bounded sequences (Section 8.2).

The concept of an $n$th approximation to a physical or geometrical quantity (Sections 8.3, 8.4) dates as far back as the ancient Greek mathematicians. Although the concept of the *limit* of a sequence of approximations was evidently known to Archimedes, it was not seriously considered again until the late 16th and early 17th centuries. The definite integral, as the limit of a sequence of approximating sums, is the culmination of those ideas (Section 8.5). In this connection, the concept of upper and lower sums is important (Section 8.6).

The following ideas are also essential to a proper understanding of the definite integral:

(8) the definition of area by means of the definite integral (Section 8.5);
(9) conditions on a function $f$ for the existence of the definite integral (Section 8.7);
(10) properties of the definite integral (Section 8.8);
(11) the Mean Value Theorem (Section 8.8).

Stemming from the concept of the definite integral is the extremely important and closely allied concept of the indefinite integral and its properties (Section 8.9). Associated with this concept is the Fundamental Theorem of Integral Calculus, which expresses a relationship between the two distinct concepts of the derivative and the indefinite integral (Section 8.9).

In view of the importance of the definite and indefinite integrals, a student must develop an understanding of the applications to

(12) areas (Section 8.10);
(13) volumes of revolution by using "shells" and "disks" (Section 8.11);
(14) averages, moments, and centroids (Section 8.12);
(15) physical problems such as those involving work (Section 8.13);
(16) sectionally continuous functions (Section 8.14).

# Chapter 9    Exponential and Logarithmic Functions

## 9.1 THE EXPONENTIAL FUNCTION AND THE LOGARITHMIC FUNCTION

The meaning of the symbol $a^x$, where $a$ is a given positive number, has previously been given for rational but not for irrational values of $x$. We know, for example, the meaning of $2^{3/5}$, but we have not defined $2^{\sqrt{2}}$ or $2^{\pi}$. Since it is desirable in many applications to have $2^x$ defined for every real value of $x$, if possible, and even to have $2^x$ define a differentiable function, we now raise the question as to whether it is possible to define $a^x$ if $x$ is an irrational number. That the answer is in the affirmative can be shown with the help of the concept of the limit of a sequence.

An irrational number was defined to be a number with an infinite nonrepeating decimal representation. Consequently, let

$$x = x_0.x_1x_2x_3 \ldots x_n \ldots$$

be such a decimal, where $x_0$ is a positive integer and each $x_k$, $k = 1, 2, 3, \ldots$, is a digit. Now, let $\alpha > 1$, and consider the sequence $\{b_n\}$, where

$$b_1 = a^{x_0}, \quad b_2 = a^{x_0.x_1}, \quad \ldots, \quad b_n = a^{x_0.x_1x_2 \ldots x_{n-1}}, \quad \ldots.$$

We shall show that this sequence has a limit, and shall define this limit to be the value of $a^x$ for the irrational number $x$.

For any rational number $p \geq 0$, it is true that

$$a > 1 \Rightarrow a^p \geq 1 \qquad \text{(Theorem 1.10g).}$$

Accordingly,

$$b_n \geq b_{n-1}, \qquad n = 2, 3, \ldots,$$

since

$$b_n = a^{x_0.x_1x_2 \ldots x_{n-2}x_{n-1}}$$

$$= a^{x_0.x_1x_2 \ldots x_{n-2}}(a^{x_{n-1}/10^{n-1}})$$

and

$$a^{x_{n-1}/10^{n-1}} \geq 1.$$

Furthermore,

$$x = x_0.x_1x_2 \ldots x_n \ldots < x_0 + 1,$$

so that

$$b_n < a^{x_0+1} \quad \text{for } n = 1, 2, 3, \ldots.$$

Thus, the sequence $\{b_n\}$ is a bounded nondecreasing sequence, and therefore, by Theorem 8.2b, has a limit. This limit will be denoted by $a^x$.

A similar discussion applies for $0 < a < 1$, since the corresponding sequence would be bounded and nonincreasing. As a consequence of these results, we see that to each number $x > 0$ there corresponds exactly one real number $a^x$ for any given $a$ such that $0 < a < 1$ or $a > 1$. For example, the number $2^\pi$ is the limit of the sequence

$$2^3, \ 2^{3.1}, \ 2^{3.14}, \ 2^{3.141}, \ 2^{3.1415}, \ 2^{3.14159}, \ldots,$$

where the exponents are the successive "partial" decimals in the infinite decimal representation of the number $\pi$. Similar results hold for $x < 0$.

We may summarize the preceding discussion by saying that for each fixed value of $a$ such that $0 < a < 1$ or $a > 1$, the formula $f(x) = a^x$ describes a function with the domain $\mathcal{R}$.

**Definition 9.1a.** The function $f$ for which

$$f(x) = a^x, \qquad a > 1 \quad \text{or} \quad 0 < a < 1,$$

is called the **exponential function** to the base $a$.

Another notation, which is frequently used in dealing with the exponential function, is

$$\exp_a(x) = a^x.$$

Thus, one might write $\exp_2(\pi)$ for $2^\pi$. This notation is particularly useful whenever the exponent is a complicated expression that is difficult to print in the customary exponent position.

It can be shown that the usual rules for rational exponents also hold for irrational exponents. However, we shall not undertake to show this at the present time but shall use these rules without proof. We shall also need some elementary inequalities involving exponents in order to investigate the properties of the exponential function.

**Theorem 9.1a.** $\qquad a > 1$ and $x > 0 \Rightarrow a^x > 1$.

PROOF: This theorem has already been proved for rational values of $x$ (see Theorem 1.10g). Now consider $x$ irrational and, as before, let

$$x = x_0.x_1x_2 \ldots.$$

Suppose $y = x_0.x_1x_2 \ldots x_k$ is any nonzero "partial" decimal in the infinite decimal representation of $x$. Then $y$ is a rational number and

$$a^y > 1 \qquad \text{(by Theorem 1.10g)}.$$

The proof of the existence of

$$\lim_{n \to \infty} \exp_a (x_0.x_1x_2 \ldots x_n)$$

showed that as we take more and more digits from the representation of $x$, the corresponding sequence of powers of $a$ is nondecreasing. Thus it follows that if

$$a^x .=. \lim_{n \to \infty} \exp_a (x_0.x_1x_2 \ldots x_n),$$

then

$$a^x > 1.$$

**Theorem 9.1b.** $\qquad a > 1$ and $x < 0 \Rightarrow 0 < a^x < 1.$

PROOF: This theorem follows from the preceding theorem and the fact that if $x = -y$, then

$$a^x = a^{-y} .=. \frac{1}{a^y}.$$

The details are left to the reader.

**Theorem 9.1c.** $\qquad 0 < x < y$ and $a > 1 \Rightarrow a^x < a^y.$

PROOF: If $x < y$, there is a positive number $s$ such that

$$x + s = y.$$

Also,

$$a > 1 \Rightarrow a^s > 1 \qquad \text{(by Theorem 9.1a).}$$

Hence

$$a^{x+s} = a^x a^s > a^x,$$

or

$$a^y > a^x.$$

This result shows that if $f(x) = a^x$, $a > 1$, then $f$ is an increasing function on its entire domain.

As an aid toward visualizing the preceding results, Figure 9.1a shows the

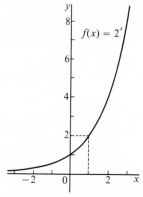

**FIGURE 9.1a**

graph of the function defined by $f(x) = 2^x$. The smooth appearance of the curve will be justified by the later work of this chapter, which in part deals with the derivative of the exponential function.

Figure 9.1a illustrates the following properties which are consequences of the definition of the exponential function given by $f(x) = a^x$, $a > 1$:

(1) $f(0) = 1$;
(2) $f(1) = a$;
(3) $\lim_{x \to -\infty} f(x) = 0$;

(4) as $x \to +\infty$, $f(x) \to +\infty$.

Since for $a > 1$ the exponential function, $f .=. \{(x, a^x)\}$, is an increasing function on its entire domain, it must have an inverse that is also a function. (Why?) The inverse function, $f^{-1}$, is the set of number pairs $\{(a^x, x)\}$. In the usual functional notation, we let $u = a^x$ and denote the same set of number pairs by $\{(u, f^{-1}(u))\}$.

**Definition 9.1b.** If $f .=. \{(x, a^x)\}$ and if $u = a^x$, then the inverse function, $f^{-1}$, which is the set of pairs $\{(u, f^{-1}(u))\}$, is called the **logarithm function** to the base $a$ and is denoted by $\log_a$.

In particular, if $u = a^x$, then $\log_a u .=. f^{-1}(u) = x$, and $x$ is called the **logarithm** of $u$ to the base $a$. The reader should keep in mind that the exponential function, $\exp_a$, is defined only when $0 < a < 1$ or $1 < a$, so that the inverse function, $\log_a$, is also defined only for such values of $a$. Furthermore, since $a^x > 0$ for all $x$, $\log_a u$ is defined only if $u > 0$.

The concept of the logarithm may be expressed by saying that *the logarithm of a number u to the base a is the exponent of that power of a which equals the number u.* Thus, if $2^4 = 16$, then $\log_2 16 = 4$. Similarly, if

$$\log_3 N = 2,$$

then $N$ must be 9, since $3^2 = N = 9$. Again,

$$\log_a 8 = \tfrac{3}{2} \Rightarrow a^{3/2} = 8 \Rightarrow a = 4.$$

The graph of the equation $y = \log_2 x$, which is shown in Figure 9.1b, can be obtained from that of $y = 2^x$ in Figure 9.1a by reflecting the curve with

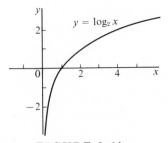

**FIGURE 9.1b**

respect to the line $y = x$. The general appearance of the graph of $y = \log_a x$, $a > 1$, is the same as that for the base 2.

Corresponding to the properties of the exponential function, we have for $f(x) = \log_a x$, $a > 1$:

(1) $f(1) = 0$;
(2) $f(a) = 1$;
(3) as $x \to 0^+$, $f(x) \to -\infty$;
(4) as $x \to +\infty$, $f(x) \to +\infty$.

Logarithms of numbers were first used by John Napier, a Scottish mathematician (1550–1617), as a computational aid. Using 10 as a base, he laboriously and without mechanical aids compiled the first table of logarithms, which was published in 1614.

The following elementary theorems establish those properties of logarithms of numbers that make the logarithms useful in computational as well as theoretical problems.

**Theorem 9.1d.** $\qquad \log_a MN = \log_a M + \log_a N$.

That is, *the logarithm of the product of two numbers is the sum of logarithms of the factors.*

PROOF: Let $\qquad x = \log_a M, \quad y = \log_a N$.
Then, by definition,
$$a^x = M \quad \text{and} \quad a^y = N,$$
so that
$$a^x a^y = a^{x+y} = MN$$
and
$$\log_a MN = x + y.$$

If $x$ and $y$ are replaced by the appropriate expressions, then we have
$$\log_a MN = \log_a M + \log_a N.$$

**Theorem 9.1e.** $\qquad \log_a \dfrac{M}{N} = \log_a M - \log_a N$.

PROOF: Left as an exercise.

**Theorem 9.1f.** $\qquad \log_a M^p = p \log_a M$.

PROOF: Left as an exercise.

**Theorem 9.1g.** $\qquad a^{\log_a N} = N$.

PROOF: Left as an exercise.

**Theorem 9.1h.** $\qquad (\log_a b)(\log_b a) = 1$.

PROOF: Left as an exercise.

The next theorem is commonly known as the Rule for Change of Base.

**Theorem 9.1i.** $\qquad \log_b N = \dfrac{\log_a N}{\log_a b}$.

PROOF: Left for the reader with the hint: $N = a^x = b^y$. What is $\log_a N$?

Although logarithms originally were introduced as an aid in computational problems, they are no longer so important in this respect because most computational problems can be handled more efficiently by desk calculators or modern computers. Of considerably greater importance are the fundamental properties of logarithms as expressed in the preceding theorems. The following examples illustrate how those properties may be used in a noncomputational manner as well as in a computational manner.

---

*Example 9.1a.* Prove that

$$\log_a \sqrt{\frac{MN^3}{P}} = \tfrac{1}{2}(\log_a M + 3 \log_a N - \log_a P).$$

The procedure is a straightforward application of the first three theorems:

$$\log_a \sqrt{\frac{MN^3}{P}} = \log_a \left(\frac{MN^3}{P}\right)^{1/2} = \tfrac{1}{2} \log_a \frac{MN^3}{P}$$
$$= \tfrac{1}{2}(\log_a MN^3 - \log_a P)$$
$$= \tfrac{1}{2}(\log_a M + \log_a N^3 - \log_a P)$$
$$= \tfrac{1}{2}(\log_a M + 3 \log_a N - \log_a P).$$

---

In computational practice, we use decimal approximations, usually obtained from a book of tables, for the logarithms of numbers. For example, we may have

$$\log_{10} 20 \approx 1.30103,$$

where the sign $\approx$ is used to emphasize the fact that $\log_{10} 20$ is approximately equal to 1.30103. The next example illustrates the idea.

---

*Example 9.1b.* If $\log_{10} 2 \approx 0.30103$ and $\log_{10} 3 \approx 0.47712$, find (a) $\log_{10} 24$; (b) $\log_{10} 1/5$; (c) $\log_{10} \sqrt{6}$.

Using the preceding theorems, we obtain

(a)
$$\log_{10} 24 = \log_{10} 2^3 \cdot 3 = 3 \log_{10} 2 + \log_{10} 3$$
$$\approx 3(0.30103) + 0.47712 = 1.38021.$$

(b)
$$\log_{10} \tfrac{1}{5} = \log_{10} \tfrac{2}{10}$$
$$= \log_{10} 2 - \log_{10} 10$$
$$\approx 0.30103 - 1 = -0.69897.$$

(c)
$$\log_{10} \sqrt{6} = \tfrac{1}{2} \log_{10} 6$$
$$= \tfrac{1}{2}(\log_{10} 2 + \log_{10} 3)$$
$$\approx \tfrac{1}{2}(0.30103 + 0.47712) = 0.38908.$$

---

*Example 9.1c.* Show that

$$\log_a \frac{-1 + \sqrt{x^2 + 1}}{x} = -\log_a \frac{1 + \sqrt{x^2 + 1}}{x}.$$

To do this, we rationalize the numerator of the argument of the logarithm to obtain

$$\log_a \left( \frac{-1 + \sqrt{x^2 + 1}}{x} \cdot \frac{1 + \sqrt{x^2 + 1}}{1 + \sqrt{x^2 + 1}} \right) = \log_a \frac{-1 + x^2 + 1}{x(1 + \sqrt{x^2 + 1})}$$

$$= \log_a \frac{x}{1 + \sqrt{x^2 + 1}} = \log_a \left( \frac{1 + \sqrt{x^2 + 1}}{x} \right)^{-1}$$

$$= -\log_a \frac{1 + \sqrt{x^2 + 1}}{x}.$$

# Exercises 9.1

Solve for $x$ in Numbers 1 to 8.

1. $2^x = 3$.
2. $3(3^x) = 6$.
3. $2^{x+1} = 3^x$.
4. $\log_{1/2} 8 = x$.

5. $\log_3 x = -2$.
6. $\log_x 81 = -4$.
7. $3(3^x) = 27^{2x}$.
8. $(2^{2x+1})(4^{x+3}) = 8^{2x}$.

9. Prove Theorem 9.1e.
10. Prove Theorem 9.1f.

11. Prove Theorem 9.1g.
12. Prove Theorem 9.1h.

Solve for $x$ in terms of $y$ in Numbers 13 to 16.

13. $y = 5^{-x}$.
14. $3y = 3^x$.

15. $3^y = 2^{3x+1}$.
16. $y = \frac{1}{2}(10^{2x} + 10^{-2x})$.

In Numbers 17 to 20, transform the left side of the equation into the right.

17. $\log_a \sqrt{x^5} + \log_a \sqrt[3]{x^2} + \log_a \sqrt[4]{x} + \log_a \sqrt{x^3} + \log_a \sqrt[12]{x} = \log_a x^5$.

18. $\log_{10} \frac{x^3 \cdot 10^{2x}}{10^{x^2}} = 3 \log_{10} x + 2x - x^2$.

19. $\log_a \sqrt[3]{2\sqrt{x}} = \frac{1}{3} \log_a 2 + \frac{1}{6} \log_a x$.
20. $\log_a 9 + \log_a 8 + \log_a 2 - \log_a 16 - \log_a 3 = \log_a 3$.

In Numbers 21 to 30, find the value of each logarithm. Use $\log_{10} 2 \approx 0.30103$ and $\log_{10} 3 \approx 0.47712$.

21. $\log_{10} 5$.
22. $\log_{10} \sqrt{18}$.
23. $\log_{10} \frac{1}{5}$.
24. $\log_{10} 900$.
25. $\log_{10} 150$.

26. $\log_{10} 12$.
27. $\log_{10} \sqrt{45}$.
28. $\log_{10} \frac{1}{54}$.
29. $\log_{10} \sqrt[3]{60}$.
30. $\log_{10} 24$.

Sketch the graph of each equation in Numbers 31 to 34.

31. $y = 2^{-x}$.
32. $y = \log_{1/2} x$.

33. $y = (2^x + 2^{-x})/2$.
34. $y = \log_3 (x - 3)$.

## 9.2 THE DERIVATIVE OF THE LOGARITHM FUNCTION

A number of questions concerning the exponential and the logarithm functions remain unanswered. For example, we tacitly assumed that $y = a^x$ and $y = \log_a x$ each describe continuous functions, but we have yet to prove it. Furthermore, if the functions are continuous, are they differentiable? The problem of answering these questions turns out to be more formidable than might be expected.

For instance, if we want to investigate the differentiability of the logarithm function, we naturally appeal to the definition of the derivative. Thus, if

$$f(x) = \log_a x, \qquad x > 0,$$

then

$$\frac{f(x + h) - f(x)}{h} = \frac{1}{h} [\log_a (x + h) - \log_a x]$$

$$= \frac{1}{h} \log_a \left( \frac{x + h}{x} \right)$$

$$= \frac{1}{h} \log_a \left( 1 + \frac{h}{x} \right).$$

It appears that we are faced with the difficult problem of investigating the limit as $h \to 0$. The form of the problem can be changed slightly by writing

$$\frac{f(x + h) - f(x)}{h} = \frac{1}{x} \cdot \frac{x}{h} \log_a \left( 1 + \frac{h}{x} \right)$$

$$= \frac{1}{x} \log_a \left( 1 + \frac{h}{x} \right)^{x/h}.$$

Assuming that the logarithm is a continuous function, we now get

$$\lim_{h \to 0} \frac{1}{x} \log_a \left( 1 + \frac{h}{x} \right)^{x/h} = \frac{1}{x} \log_a \left[ \lim_{h \to 0} \left( 1 + \frac{h}{x} \right)^{x/h} \right],$$

so that the limit to be evaluated is essentially

$$\lim_{h \to 0} \left( 1 + \frac{h}{x} \right)^{x/h}.$$

The replacement of $h/x$ by $t$ and the fact that $t \to 0$ as $h \to 0$ for every fixed $x > 0$ leads to the result

$$\lim_{h \to 0} \left( 1 + \frac{h}{x} \right)^{x/h} = \lim_{t \to 0} (1 + t)^{1/t},$$

and shows that the limit (if it exists) does not depend on the value of $x$.

If, indeed, $\lim_{t \to 0} (1 + t)^{1/t}$ does exist and is $A \neq 1$, we could then write

$$D_x \log_a x = \frac{1}{x} \log_a A, \qquad \log_a A \neq 0,$$

and we could also obtain an inverse derivative,

$$\frac{\log_a x}{\log_a A} = D_x^{-1}\left(\frac{1}{x}\right).$$

Unfortunately, this is all speculation. However, the last result does strongly suggest that there may be some connection between $\log_a x$ and $D_x^{-1}(1/x)$, or between $\log_a x$ and the indefinite integral

$$\int_1^x \frac{dt}{t}.$$

From the results in Section 8.9, we know that the indefinite integral

$$L(x) .=. \int_1^x \frac{dt}{t}, \qquad x > 0,$$

describes a continuous function that has a derivative,

$$D_x L(x) = \frac{1}{x}.$$

This result shows that $L(x)$ fills the gap left by the inverse derivative formula

$$\int x^n \, dx = \frac{x^{n+1}}{n+1} + C, \qquad n \neq -1,$$

with the new formula

$$\int x^{-1} \, dx = L(x) + C.$$

The fact that $L'(x) = 1/x$ indicates that $L$ is an increasing function for $x > 0$ and that the tangent to the graph of $L$ approaches a vertical position as $x \to 0^+$ and becomes more and more nearly horizontal as $x \to \infty$. Indeed, the definition of $L(x)$ must describe the function $L$ completely, and further investigation should reveal its connection with the logarithm function.

For example, if $c$ is a constant, we have

$$L(cx) = \int_1^{cx} \frac{dt}{t}.$$

By using the chain rule for differentiation, we get

$$D_x L(cx) = \frac{1}{cx} D_x(cx) = \frac{1}{x},$$

or

$$D_x L(cx) = D_x L(x).$$

Hence, $L(cx)$ and $L(x)$ differ by a constant (why?), so that

$$L(cx) = L(x) + k.$$

From the integral expression for $L(x)$, it follows that $L(1) = 0$. Hence, the preceding equation gives

$$L(c) = L(1) + k \quad \text{and} \quad k = L(c).$$

Therefore, the function defined by the indefinite integral $\int_1^x \frac{dt}{t}$ has the property

(1) $$L(cx) = L(x) + L(c),$$

which is one of the basic properties of the logarithm function. Of course, we have no guarantee that a function having this property is necessarily a logarithm function, so we must not yet draw a conclusion in this respect.

Another important property of $L(x)$ can be obtained from (1) by putting $x = c$ to get

$$L(c^2) = 2L(c).$$

In general, we may conclude, by mathematical induction, that

$$L(c^n) = nL(c), \qquad n \in \mathfrak{N}.$$

Now suppose that $c > 1$. Then $L(c) > 0$, and evidently, as $n \to \infty$, $L(c^n) \to \infty$. Since $L(1) = 0$ and since $L(c^n)$ can be made arbitrarily large, $L(x)$ must take on every positive real value because it is a continuous function. For instance, from the Intermediate Value Theorem in Section 4.7 on continuous functions, we know that there exists a value of $x$ for which $L(x) = 1$. This value of $x$ is important enough to deserve special recognition.

**Definition 9.2a.** The number $e$ is that number for which $L(e) = 1$.

It will be left as an exercise for the reader to show that for $0 < x < 1$, $L(x) < 0$ and as $x \to 0^+$, $L(x) \to -\infty$. This, along with the preceding results, shows that the range of $L$ is the set of all real numbers.

It has been shown that

(2) $$L(c^p) = pL(c)$$

holds when $p$ is a positive integer. The reader can extend the result to include values of $p$ that are negative integers. The next theorem generalizes the result further.

**Theorem 9.2a.** If $q \in \mathfrak{N}$, and if $c > 0$, then

$$L(c^{1/q}) = \frac{1}{q} L(c).$$

PROOF: Let $x = c^{1/q}$, so that $c = x^q$. Then

$$L(c) = L(x^q) = qL(x),$$

so that

$$L(x) = \frac{1}{q} L(c),$$

or

$$L(c^{1/q}) = \frac{1}{q} L(c).$$

The reader should extend this result to include any rational number $p/q$.

Continuing this line of exploration, we can try to extend the Relation (2) to hold when $p$ is an irrational number, say $r$. Since $L(x)$ is an increasing function that takes on every real value, there is some number $a$ for which

$$L(a) = rL(c).$$

Now, let $r$ have the usual decimal form

$$r = x_0.x_1x_2 \ldots x_n \ldots ,$$

where $x_0$ is an integer and each $x_i$ is a digit. Then, with

$$r_n = x_0.x_1x_2 \ldots x_n,$$

we have

$$\lim_{n\to\infty} r_nL(c) = rL(c) = L(a).$$

Since $r_n$ is a rational number,

$$r_nL(a) = L(a^{r_n}),$$

so that

$$\lim_{n\to\infty} r_nL(c) = \lim_{n\to\infty} L(c^{r_n}).$$

Thus,

$$rL(c) = L(c^r) = L(a),$$

follows from the definition of the exponential $c^r$ and the fact that the function $L$ is continuous.

From the last equations, we have

$$a = c^r, \quad \text{or} \quad r = \log_c a = \frac{L(a)}{L(c)},$$

which identifies $L$ as a logarithm function. In particular, if $c$ is the number $e$ for which $L(e) = 1$, then $L(a) = r$, and

$$r = \log_e a.$$

Hence

$$L(a) = \log_e a.$$

We have now identified the function $L$ as the logarithm function defined by

$$L(x) = \log_e x.$$

The properties of $L$ as determined by the integral definition show that the logarithm function is a continuous, increasing function on its entire domain, the set of positive real numbers. As a consequence, the inverse function exists and is the exponential function $f$, where

$$f(x) .=. e^x.$$

It follows (see Theorem 4.7h) that the exponential function is *continuous* on its entire domain $\mathcal{R}$, the range of the logarithm function.

We now have the tools necessary for the solution of one of the problems raised but not solved earlier in this chapter and thereby to prove the following theorem.

**Theorem 9.2b.** $$\lim_{t\to 0} (1 + t)^{1/t} = e.$$

PROOF: We may write, by Theorems 9.1f and 9.1g,

$$(1 + t)^{1/t} = \exp_e \left[ \frac{1}{t} \log_e (1 + t) \right].$$

Hence, by reason of the continuity of the exponential function,

$$\lim_{t \to 0} (1 + t)^{1/t} = \lim_{t \to 0} \exp_e \left[ \frac{1}{t} \log_e (1 + t) \right]$$

$$= \exp_e \left\{ \lim_{t \to 0} \left[ \frac{1}{t} \log_e (1 + t) \right] \right\}.$$

Since $\log_e 1 = 0$, we have

$$\lim_{t \to 0} \frac{1}{t} \log_e (1 + t) = \lim_{t \to 0} \frac{\log_e (1 + t) - \log_e 1}{t},$$

which is exactly the definition of $L'(1)$. But

$$L'(x) = 1/x \Rightarrow L'(1) = 1,$$

so that

$$\lim_{t \to 0} (1 + t)^{1/t} = \exp_e 1 = e^1 = e,$$

and the proof of the theorem is complete.

It can be shown that

$$e \approx 1 + \frac{1}{1!} + \frac{1}{2!} + \frac{1}{3!} + \cdots + \frac{1}{n!},$$

and that the larger the value of $n$, the more accurate is the approximation for $e$. We shall discuss this fact more fully in our work with infinite series. The value of $e$ to 12 decimal places is given by

$$e \approx 2.718281828459.$$

With the knowledge that $\lim_{t \to 0} (1 + t)^{1/t} = e$, we are able to justify the conjectures entertained at the beginning of this section. The number $e$ is, of course, the number that we earlier called $A$.

**Theorem 9.2c.** $\qquad\qquad D_x \log_a x = \dfrac{1}{x} \log_a e.$

PROOF: By Theorem 9.1i,

$$\log_a x = (\log_a e)(\log_e x).$$

Therefore,

$$D_x(\log_a x) = (\log_a e) D_x(\log_e x)$$

$$= \frac{1}{x} \log_a e.$$

It has already been shown that if the base of the logarithm function is taken to be $e$, then the expression for the derivative of the function is in its simplest form. This is important enough to bear repetition:

$$D_x \log_e x = \frac{1}{x}.$$

It is because of this simplicity that $e$ is called the **natural base** for logarithms and that logarithms to this base are called **natural logarithms.** In order to indicate a logarithm to the base $e$, we shall henceforth use the symbol "ln," which has received wide acceptance in recent years.

An easy application of the chain rule suffices to prove the next result. The details are left for the reader.

**Theorem 9.2d.** If $u = f(x)$ defines a differentiable function such that $f(x) > 0$ on some domain, then on this domain

$$D_x \ln u = \frac{1}{u} D_x u.$$

---

*Example 9.2a.* Find $F'(x)$ if $F(x) = \ln \sqrt{1 - x^2}$, $|x| < 1$.

First, let us write

$$F(x) = \ln (1 - x^2)^{1/2} = \frac{1}{2} \ln (1 - x^2).$$

Thus,

$$F'(x) = \frac{1}{2} D_x \ln (1 - x^2)$$

$$= \frac{1}{2} \cdot \frac{1}{1 - x^2} D_x(1 - x^2) \qquad \text{(Theorem 9.2d)}$$

$$= \frac{-x}{1 - x^2}.$$

---

*Example 9.2b.* Find $f'(x)$ if $f(x) = \log_{10} (x^3\sqrt{1 - x^2})$.

Using the properties of logarithms, we first write

$$f(x) = 3 \log_{10} x + \frac{1}{2} \log_{10} (1 - x^2).$$

Thus,

$$f'(x) = \frac{3}{x} \log_{10} e + \frac{1}{2} \left( \frac{1}{1 - x^2} \right)(-2x) \log_{10} e$$

$$= (\log_{10} e)\left( \frac{3}{x} - \frac{x}{1 - x^2} \right).$$

---

*Example 9.2c.* If $x > 0$ is the thickness of the insulation of a submarine cable, it is found that the speed with which a signal can be transmitted along the cable varies directly as $(\ln x)/x^2$. Find the value of $x$ that would give the maximum speed.

Let $V(x) = k(\ln x)/x^2$, where $k$ is the constant of proportionality. Then

$$V'(x) = k \frac{x^2 \left( \frac{1}{x} \right) - (\ln x)(2x)}{x^4}$$

$$= \frac{k(1 - 2 \ln x)}{x^3}.$$

For $V'(x) = 0$, we have

$$1 - 2 \ln x = 0,$$

or

$$x = e^{1/2}.$$

The student may check by either the first derivative test or the second derivative test to show that this value of $x$ actually yields a maximum value for $V(x)$.

## Exercises 9.2

Find $y'$ in Numbers 1 to 15.

1. $y = \dfrac{\ln x}{x^3}$.

2. $y = \log_{10} x^2$.

3. $y = (\ln x^3)^2$.

4. $y = \log_{10} x^2 \sqrt{1 + x^3}$.

5. $y = \dfrac{x^2}{\ln x^3}$.

6. $y = \sqrt{x} \log_{10} x^3$.

7. $xy + \ln xy = 3$.

8. $y = \ln (\ln x)$.

9. $y = \ln \dfrac{x}{4 + x^2}$.

10. $3xy^2 - \ln x = 5$.

11. $x = t + t \ln t,\ y = t - t \ln t$.

12. $y = \ln (x \ln x)$.

13. $y = \ln (x + \sqrt{x^2 + 1})$.

14. $x = s^2 \ln s,\ y = s + \ln s$.

15. $y = \ln \dfrac{x^2 - 1}{x^2 + 1}$.

Find $y'$ and $y''$ in Numbers 16 to 19.

16. $y = \ln (x^2 - 4)$.

17. $y = x^2 \ln 3x$.

18. $xy + \ln x = 1$.

19. $x = \ln s,\ y = s^2$.

Discuss and sketch the curves in Numbers 20 to 26.

20. $y = \log_{1/2} x$.

21. $y = x \ln x$.

22. $y = \ln (x^2 + 1)$.

23. $y + 2 = \log_3 x$.

24. $y = \ln |x|$.

25. $y = \dfrac{3 \ln x}{x}$.

26. $y = \ln |x^2 - 1|$.

27. If $\ln y = kt$, where $k$ is a constant and $t$ is the time, show that the instantaneous rate of change of $y$ is proportional to $y$ itself. This is an important law of variation in many physical problems such as that of radioactive decay.

28. For values of $x$ that are large in comparison with the value of $h$, show that the difference between $\ln (x + h)$ and $\ln x$ is approximately $h/x$. What would be the approximate percentage error made in using $\ln 1000$ in place of $\ln 1002$?

29. Show that $(1/101) < \ln 1.01 < (1/100)$. *Hint:* Apply the Mean Value Theorem for Derivatives to $f(x) = \ln x$.

30. The capacitance of a certain type of coaxial cylindrical condenser is given by the formula

$$C = \frac{kL}{\ln (r_o/r_i)},$$

where $k$ is a constant, $L$ is the length, and $r_o$ and $r_i$ are the outside and inside radii, respectively, of the condenser. The radii of a certain condenser are 4 centimeters and 2 centimeters, respectively. What approximate percentage change would occur in the capacitance if the outside radius were increased to 4.02 centimeters, all other dimensions remaining unaltered?

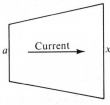

**FIGURE 9.2a**

★31. For a wedge-shaped electrical conductor (see Figure 9.2a) the resistance is given by

$$R = k \frac{\ln (x/a)}{x - a},$$

where $k$ is a constant depending on the length and width of the wedge and the physical properties of the material. Show that $R$ decreases with $x$ for $x > a$.

# 9.3 THE DERIVATIVE OF THE EXPONENTIAL FUNCTION

As we already know, the fact that a function is continuous does not guarantee it to be differentiable. Our investigation of the exponential function leads next to the question of differentiability.

Let $f(x) = a^x$ and let us try to find $f'(x)$ directly from the definition. First, the difference quotient is

$$\frac{f(x + h) - f(x)}{h} = \frac{a^{x+h} - a^x}{h} = a^x \left( \frac{a^h - 1}{h} \right).$$

Hence

$$f'(x) = \lim_{h \to 0} a^x \left( \frac{a^h - 1}{h} \right) = a^x \lim_{h \to 0} \left( \frac{a^h - 1}{h} \right).$$

The evaluation of the last limit, if it exists at all, is the entire key to the problem. It is interesting to note that if the limit does exist, it is $f'(0)$.

It is, of course, not surprising that there is a close connection between the preceding limit and the limit that arose in the problem of differentiating the logarithm function. In the expression

$$\frac{a^h - 1}{h},$$

let $a^h - 1 = k$. Then $h = \log_a (1 + k)$, and we obtain

$$\frac{a^h - 1}{h} = \frac{k}{\log_a (1 + k)}$$

$$= \frac{1}{\frac{1}{k} \log_a (1 + k)}$$

$$= \frac{1}{\log_a (1 + k)^{1/k}}.$$

Since $h \to 0 \Leftrightarrow k \to 0$, we have

$$\lim_{h \to 0} \frac{a^h - 1}{h} = \lim_{k \to 0} \frac{1}{\log_a (1 + k)^{1/k}}$$

$$= \frac{1}{\log_a e} = \ln a.$$

We have thus proved

**Theorem 9.3a.** $\qquad D_x a^x = a^x \ln a, \qquad a > 0, a \neq 1.$

By putting $a = e$, we have the following important special case.

**Theorem 9.3b.** $\qquad\qquad\qquad D_x e^x = e^x.$

Notice that the function $\{(x, e^x)\}$ is unaltered by differentiation.

By a direct application of the chain rule, we can easily prove

**Theorem 9.3c.** If $u = f(x)$ defines a differentiable function, then

$$D_x e^u = e^u D_x u.$$

---

*Example 9.3a.* Find $D_x e^{x^2}$.

Using Theorem 9.3c, we obtain

$$D_x e^{x^2} = e^{x^2} D_x x^2$$
$$= 2x e^{x^2}.$$

---

*Example 9.3b.* Find $D_x \exp_{10} \sqrt{1 - x^2}$.

With the aid of Theorem 9.3a, we find

$$D_x \exp_{10} \sqrt{1 - x^2} = (\exp_{10} \sqrt{1 - x^2})(\ln 10) D_x \sqrt{1 - x^2}$$

$$= (\exp_{10} \sqrt{1 - x^2})(\ln 10) \left( \frac{-x}{\sqrt{1 - x^2}} \right).$$

---

*Example 9.3c.* Find $D_t \ln (1 + e^{-t})$.

We have

$$D_t \ln (1 + e^{-t}) = \frac{1}{1 + e^{-t}} D_t (1 + e^{-t})$$

$$= \frac{-e^{-t}}{1 + e^{-t}}$$

$$= -\frac{1}{e^t + 1}.$$

---

**Theorem 9.3d.** If $x > 0$ and $k$ is real, then

$$D_x(x^k) = k x^{k-1}.$$

PROOF: It has already been shown under milder restrictions on $x$ that this formula holds if the exponent is a positive integer. In the present case, we have

$$x^k = e^{k \ln x},$$

so that, by Theorem 9.3c,

$$D_x x^k = e^{k \ln x} D_x(k \ln x)$$

$$= (x^k)\left(\frac{k}{x}\right) = kx^{k-1}.$$

This completes the proof of a formula that we have used many times.

## Exercises 9.3

Find the indicated derivative in Numbers 1 to 20.

1. $y = e^{x^3}$; $y'$.

2. $s = \dfrac{e^x}{x}$; $D_x s$.

3. $x = 3^{2y}y$; $D_y x$.

4. $xy + e^{xy} = 4$; $D_x y$.

5. $t = \exp_5 \sqrt{4 + u^2}$; $D_u t$.

6. $x = e^{t+1}$; $y = e^{t^2}$; $D_x y$.

7. $\ln xy + e^{xy} = x$; $D_x y$.

8. $e^{2t} + e^{2s} = e^{ts}$; $D_s t$.

9. $w = e^{u + \ln u}$; $D_u w$.

10. $x = e^{2t}$, $y = \ln t$; $D_x y$.

11. $y = e^{x \ln x}$; $D_x y$.

12. $s = \dfrac{e^u}{u^2 + 1}$; $D_u s$.

13. $y = e^2$; $D_x y$.

14. $x = e^{y^e}$; $D_y x$.

15. $v = e^w \ln w$; $D_w v$.

16. $y = e^{1/\ln x}$; $D_x y$.

17. $y = \ln \dfrac{e^{3x} + 1}{e^{3x} - 1}$; $D_x y$.

18. $w = e^{e^s}$; $D_s w$.

19. $y = \log_{10}(e^x + e^{-x})$; $D_x y$.

20. $s = x \exp_4 \sqrt{1 + x^2}$; $D_x s$.

Find $y'$ and $y''$ in Numbers 21 to 24.

21. $y = x^3 e^{-x^2}$.

22. $y = e^x \ln x$.

23. $y = e^{x^2 - x}$.

24. $e^{xy} = x$.

In each of Numbers 25 to 32, discuss and sketch the graph of the given equation.

25. $y = e^{-x^2}$.

26. $y = \dfrac{e^x + e^{-x}}{2}$.

27. $y = \dfrac{e^x - e^{-x}}{2}$.

28. $y = \dfrac{e^x - e^{-x}}{e^x + e^{-x}}$.

29. $y + 1 = 2^x$.

30. $y = 2(2^x)$.

31. $y = 2^{|x|}$.

32. $y = xe^{-x}$.

In Numbers 33 to 36, use the differential to find the approximate value of the given expression.

33. $e^{1.03}$.

34. $e^{-1.98}$.

35. $8^{1.98}$.

36. $(\frac{1}{2})^{2.03}$.

37. Use the Mean Value Theorem for Derivatives in the form of Equation (4), Theorem 7.4a, to show that $2.7726 < e^{1.02} < 2.7737$.

38. If $k$ is a fraction in lowest terms with an odd integer for its denominator, then $f(x) = x^k$ defines a real function whose domain is all real values of $x$ except possibly $x = 0$. Show that, even if $x < 0$,

$$D_x(x^k) = kx^{k-1}.$$

*Hint*: Write $x = -z$, so that $x^k = (-1)^k z^k$.

39. Find an equation of the line that is tangent to the curve $y = e^{-2x}$ and that is parallel to the line $x + y = 2$.
40. A rectangle has its base on the $x$-axis and two vertices on the curve $y = e^{-x^2}$. Show that the rectangle has a maximum area when the two vertices on the curve are at the inflection points.

## 9.4 INVERSE DERIVATIVES LEADING TO EXPONENTIAL AND LOGARITHMIC FUNCTIONS

Formulas for the inverse derivatives of the exponential and logarithmic functions follow immediately from the work of the preceding two sections. From the formula $D_u \ln u = 1/u$, we have

**Theorem 9.4a.** $\quad \displaystyle\int \frac{du}{u} = \ln u + C, \quad u > 0.$

This formula fills a gap by taking care of the exceptional case $n = -1$ in the formula for $D_x^{-1} x^n$.

---

*Example 9.4a.* Find $\displaystyle\int \frac{x\,dx}{x^2 - 1}$, $x > 1$.

If we let $u = x^2 - 1$, then $du = 2x\,dx$. Thus,

$$\int \frac{x\,dx}{x^2 - 1} = \frac{1}{2} \int \frac{2x\,dx}{x^2 - 1} = \frac{1}{2} \ln(x^2 - 1) + C.$$

---

In the next example we shall find the area bounded by the $x$-axis, the lines $x = -3$ and $x = -2$, and the curve $xy = 1$. This is a meaningful problem but Theorem 9.4a is not applicable. Let us see if we can modify the theorem so that it will be applicable.

Since the result of Theorem 9.4a applies only for $u > 0$, we now consider the case $u < 0$. We let $u = -w$ so that $w > 0$ and

$$\int \frac{du}{u} = \int \frac{-dw}{-w} = \int \frac{dw}{w} = \ln w + C = \ln(-u) + C.$$

This result, which may be written $\ln |u| + C$, is combined with that of Theorem 9.4a in

**Theorem 9.4b.** $\quad \displaystyle\int \frac{du}{u} = \ln |u| + C, \quad u > 0 \quad \text{or} \quad u < 0.$

*Example 9.4b.* Find the area bounded by the x-axis, the lines $x = -3$ and $x = -2$, and the curve $xy = 1$ (see Figure 9.4a).

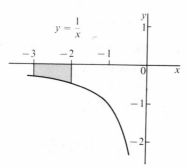

$y = \dfrac{1}{x}$

**FIGURE 9.4a**

Since the area lies below the x-axis, we have

$$\text{area} = -\int_{-3}^{-2} \frac{dx}{x}$$
$$= -[\ln |x|]_{-3}^{-2}$$
$$= -[\ln 2 - \ln 3]$$
$$= (\ln \tfrac{3}{2})\ (\text{l.u.})^2.$$

---

*Example 9.4c.* The rate of decrease of mass of a radioactive substance is proportional to the mass present. If the half-life (the time for half of the mass to decompose) is 10 minutes, how much of a given sample of $x_0$ grams will remain undecomposed at the end of $t$ minutes?

Let $x =$ amount of mass present at time $t$ (minutes). Then the rate of change of the mass is $D_t x$, so that, by the hypothesis,

$$D_t x = -kx,$$

or, by Theorem 6.6b,

$$-D_x t = \frac{1}{kx}.$$

Notice that we have regarded $k$ as a positive physical constant and have written $-kx$ since $x$ is supposed to be decreasing. We thus find

$$-kt = \int \frac{dx}{x},$$

and

$$-kt = \ln x + C.$$

We can now evaluate the constant $C$ by using the fact that $x = x_0$ when $t = 0$. Hence,

$$0 = \ln x_0 + C,$$

or

$$C = -\ln x_0.$$

Thus, we obtain

$$-kt = \ln x - \ln x_0,$$

or

$$-kt = \ln \frac{x}{x_0}.$$

We can now find $k$ by using the known half-life, which tells us that when

$$t = 10, \quad x = \tfrac{1}{2}x_0.$$

Therefore,

$$-10k = \ln \frac{\frac{1}{2}x_0}{x_0} = -\ln 2,$$

so that

$$-\frac{t}{10}\ln 2 = \ln \frac{x}{x_0}.$$

By solving for $x$, we get the desired formula

$$x = x_0 \exp\left[-(t/10)\ln 2\right] = x_0 \exp_2\left(-t/10\right).$$

---

Another inverse derivative formula arises from the result

$$D_u e^u = e^u,$$

which gives the next theorem.

**Theorem 9.4c.**
$$\int e^u \, du = e^u + C.$$

---

*Example 9.4d.* Find

$$\int x^2 e^{x^3} \, dx.$$

If $u = x^3$, then $D_x u = 3x^2$. Hence

$$\int x^2 e^{x^3} \, dx = \frac{1}{3}\int 3x^2 e^{x^3} \, dx = \frac{1}{3}e^{x^3} + C.$$

---

In a similar manner, since $D_u a^u = a^u \ln a, \, a > 0$, we have

**Theorem 9.4d.**
$$\int a^u \, du = \frac{a^u}{\ln a} + C, \qquad a > 0, \qquad a \neq 1.$$

---

*Example 9.4e.* Find the volume formed by revolving about the $x$-axis the are
bounded by the $x$-axis, the line $x = 1$, and the curve $y = \sqrt{x}e^{-x^2}$.

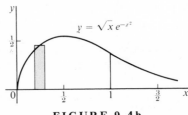

$$y = \sqrt{x}\,e^{-x^2}$$

**FIGURE 9.4b**

This curve touches the y-axis at the origin and lies above the x-axis (see Figure 9.4b). Using the cylindrical disk method of Example 8.11b, we find

$$V = \pi \int_0^1 y^2 \, dx = \pi \int_0^1 xe^{-2x^2} \, dx$$

$$= -\frac{\pi}{4} \int_0^1 -4xe^{-2x^2} \, dx = -\frac{\pi}{4} \left[ e^{-2x^2} \right]_0^1$$

$$= \frac{\pi}{4} (1 - e^{-2}) \text{ (l.u.)}^3.$$

---

*Example 9.4f.* Find

$$\int \frac{x \, dx}{x + 1}.$$

A problem of this type, in which the integrand is a rational fraction, with the degree of its numerator equal to or greater than the degree of its denominator, can always be handled by first dividing numerator by denominator. Thus

$$\frac{x}{x + 1} = 1 - \frac{1}{x + 1}$$

and

$$\int \frac{x \, dx}{x + 1} = \int \left( 1 - \frac{1}{x + 1} \right) dx = x - \ln |x + 1| + C.$$

## Exercises 9.4

In each of Numbers 1 to 20, find the indicated inverse derivative.

1. $\displaystyle\int \frac{x^2 \, dx}{1 + x^3}.$

2. $\displaystyle\int \frac{dt}{2t + 3}.$

3. $\displaystyle\int \frac{x \, dx}{\sqrt{1 - x^2}}.$

4. $\displaystyle\int \frac{2x \, dx}{4x + 3}.$

5. $\displaystyle\int xe^{-x^2} \, dx.$

6. $\displaystyle\int \sqrt{3^x} \, dx.$

7. $\displaystyle\int \frac{e^x - e^{-x}}{e^x + e^{-x}} \, dx.$

8. $\displaystyle\int \frac{s \, ds}{1 - s^2}.$

9. $\displaystyle\int \frac{t^3 + t}{t^2 - 1} \, dt.$

10. $\displaystyle\int \frac{e^w \, dw}{(e^w + 1)^2}.$

11. $\displaystyle\int \frac{e^{1/x}}{x^2} \, dx.$

12. $\displaystyle\int \frac{\ln t \, dt}{t}.$

13. $\displaystyle\int 3^{3x} \, dx.$

14. $\displaystyle\int e^y 3^{-y} \, dy.$

15. $\displaystyle\int \frac{1}{1 + e^t} \, dt.$

16. $\displaystyle\int \frac{e^x \, dx}{e^x + 1}.$

17. $\int e^{2+3x} \, dx.$

19. $\int \dfrac{y \, dy}{(1 + y^2)^2}.$

18. $\int \dfrac{e^{2x} + 1}{e^{2x}} \, dx.$

20. $\int \dfrac{2x + 3}{2x - 3} \, dx.$

Evaluate the definite integrals in Numbers 21 to 30.

21. $\displaystyle\int_{-4}^{-2} \dfrac{3x \, dx}{1 + x^2}.$

26. $\displaystyle\int_{1}^{4} \dfrac{\ln x}{x} \, dx.$

22. $\displaystyle\int_{0}^{2} \dfrac{v \, dv}{2v^2 + 1}.$

27. $\displaystyle\int_{-3}^{-1} x e^{x^2} \, dx.$

23. $\displaystyle\int_{0}^{1} \dfrac{dx}{\sqrt{1 + x}}.$

28. $\displaystyle\int_{2}^{6} x e^{-3 \ln x} \, dx.$

24. $\displaystyle\int_{1}^{3} e^2 \, dx.$

29. $\displaystyle\int_{-5}^{-3} \dfrac{dx}{2x + 3}.$

25. $\displaystyle\int_{-1}^{0} \dfrac{t \, dt}{t - 1}.$

30. $\displaystyle\int_{0}^{1} 2^{3x} \, dx.$

Find the area bounded by the x-axis and the given curves in Numbers 31 to 34.

31. $y = \dfrac{x}{1 + x^2}, \ x = 1, \ x = 3.$

33. $y = \dfrac{1}{x + 1}, \ x = -4, \ x = -2.$

32. $y = 3^{-x}, \ x = -4, \ x = -2.$

34. $y = x e^{-x^2}, \ x = 1, \ x = 3.$

35. The number of bacteria in a culture increases at a rate proportional to the number present. If it takes 20 minutes for the original number to double, when will the colony be five times its original size?

36. A cubical tank 10 feet on an edge is filled with water. A slow leak in the bottom of the tank allows the water to escape, and a reasonable assumption is that the rate of leakage at each instant is proportional to the depth of the water remaining in the tank at that instant. Suppose that 5% of the water leaks out in 2 hours; how much will leak out in 6 hours?

37. If four percent of a given amount of radium decomposes in 100 years, find the half-life.

38. When a gas expands from a volume $v_1$ to a volume $v_2$, the work $W$ done by the gas is given by the formula

$$W = \int_{v_1}^{v_2} p \, dv,$$

where $p$ is the pressure. If $pv = c$ (a constant), find the work done.

39. Find the centroid of the area bounded by

$$xy = 4, \quad y = 0, \quad x = 1, \quad x = 2.$$

40. Find the volume generated by revolving about the x-axis the area bounded by

$$y = e^{-x}, \quad y = 0, \quad x = 0, \quad x = 1.$$

## 9.5 LOGARITHMIC DIFFERENTIATION

Logarithms may frequently be used to good advantage in differentiating complicated products, quotients, or exponential expressions. This idea is illustrated in the following examples.

*Example 9.5a.* Find $D_x x^x$.

Notice that the exponent here is not a constant, so that the formula for $D_x x^n$ does not apply. However, we may write $y = x^x$, take the logarithms of both sides, and then differentiate implicitly. Thus,

$$\ln y = x \ln x,$$

$$\frac{1}{y}(y') = 1 + \ln x,$$

$$y' = y(1 + \ln x) = x^x(1 + \ln x).$$

*Example 9.5b.* Find

$$D_x\left[\frac{\sqrt{1 - x^2}\,(1 + x^3)^2}{(1 + x^2)^4}\right].$$

In this example it would be possible to differentiate the expression in its present form but the work can be greatly simplified by using logarithms. Let

$$y = \frac{\sqrt{1 - x^2}\,(1 + x^3)^2}{(1 + x^2)^4}.$$

Then

$$\ln y = \tfrac{1}{2} \ln (1 - x^2) + 2 \ln (1 + x^3) - 4 \ln (1 + x^2)$$

and

$$\frac{1}{y}(y') = \frac{-x}{1 - x^2} + \frac{6x^2}{1 + x^3} - \frac{8x}{1 + x^2},$$

or

$$y' = \frac{\sqrt{1 - x^2}\,(1 + x^3)^2}{(1 + x^2)^4}\left[-\frac{x}{1 - x^2} + \frac{6x^2}{1 + x^3} - \frac{8x}{1 + x^2}\right].$$

## Exercises 9.5

Find the indicated derivative in Numbers 1 to 12.

1. $y = x^{\ln x}$; $D_x y$.
2. $s = r^{r^2}$; $D_r s$.
3. $y = xe^{-x}$; $D_x y$.
4. $y = (w^2 + 2)^3(1 - w^4)^{1/3}$; $D_w y$.
5. $x = \dfrac{y^5\sqrt[3]{1 - y^2}}{\sqrt{1 + 3y}}$; $D_y x$.
6. $y = \dfrac{e^{2x}\sqrt{1 - x^2}}{x^4}$; $D_x y$.

7. $u = (\ln 2v)^v$; $D_v u$.
8. $r = x^{\ln 2x}$; $D_x r$.
9. $y = \sqrt[4]{\dfrac{x^2 + 4}{\sqrt{1 + x^2}\,(x^3 + 2)}}$; $D_x y$.
10. $y = x^{\sqrt[3]{x}}$; $D_x y$.
11. $w = u^{1/u}$; $D_u w$.
12. $s = r^{\exp(-r^2)}$; $D_r s$.

13. If $y = u^v$, where $u$ and $v$ are differentiable functions of $x$, find a formula for $D_x y$.

14. The period of a simple pendulum is given quite accurately for small oscillations by the formula $T = 2\pi\sqrt{L/g}$, where $T$ is the number of seconds taken for a complete oscillation, $L$ is the length of the pendulum in feet, and $g$ is the gravitational acceleration in feet per second per second. A pendulum clock is adjusted to keep accurate time when its pendulum is 12 inches long. Approximately how much time would the clock lose per day if the pendulum were set $\frac{1}{24}$ inch too long? *Hint*: The number of seconds lost per second is approximately $dT/T$.

★15. Since $D_x \ln f(x) = f'(x)/f(x)$, the latter fraction is frequently called the *logarithmic derivative* of $f(x)$. Suppose $f(x)$ is a polynomial of degree $n$ with the zeros $\alpha_1, \alpha_2, \ldots, \alpha_n$. Show that

$$\sum_{k=1}^{n} \lim_{x \to \alpha_k} (x - \alpha_k) D_x \ln f(x) = n.$$

*Hint*: Use Theorem 1.9d.

---

# Summary of Chapter 9

---

Chapter 9 is concerned with the introduction of the exponential and logarithmic functions and their properties. The student should understand the method of defining $a^x$, $a > 0$, $a \neq 1$, for any real number $x$ by means of the limit of a sequence (Section 9.1). The logarithm function is defined as the inverse of the exponential function (Section 9.1). Of course, the student must know the fundamental properties of the two functions (Section 9.1).

Finding the derivative of the logarithm function poses a particularly difficult limit problem, whose solution leads to the number $e$. It is desirable to understand how the number $e$ arises and its importance in mathematics (Section 9.2). Also, the derivative of the exponential and logarithmic functions should be firmly implanted in the student's mind (Sections 9.2, 9.3). There are many functions whose inverse derivatives lead to exponential or logarithmic functions and it is necessary to have considerable facility with these forms (Section 9.4).

Logarithms may frequently be used to good advantage in differentiating complicated products, quotients, or exponential expressions (Section 9.5).

# Chapter 10 The Calculus of Trigonometric and Hyperbolic Functions

## 10.1 CONTINUITY OF THE SINE FUNCTION

Although the reader may be familiar with the trigonometric functions in connection with the solution of triangles, he has probably not studied the analytic
properties of these functions. For example, it seems intuitively evident that the
sine and cosine functions are continuous everywhere, but it remains to be demonstrated that they actually satisfy the definition of continuity.

Since $\cos x = \pm\sqrt{1 - \sin^2 x}$, the continuity of the cosine function can be
deduced from that of the sine function. Hence, it suffices to investigate the continuity of the sine function. To prepare for this, we shall establish some inequalities between an angle $\theta$, $\sin \theta$, and $\tan \theta$ that will prove to be of considerable importance in later work. Using the definition of the sine function and

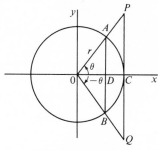

**FIGURE 10.1a**

he fact that a chord of a circle is shorter than the arc it subtends, we see from
Figure 10.1a, where $\theta$ is an acute angle, that

$$0 < \text{chord } AB < \text{arc } ACB.$$

That is,

$$0 < 2r \sin \theta < 2r\theta$$

or
$$0 < \sin \theta < \theta.$$

Furthermore,
$$\text{area of sector } AOC < \text{area of triangle } POC.$$

That is,
$$\tfrac{1}{2}r^2\theta < \tfrac{1}{2}r^2 \tan \theta$$

or
$$\theta < \tan \; \theta.$$

These two results are combined in the following inequality:

(1) $$0 < \theta < \frac{\pi}{2} \Rightarrow 0 < \sin \theta < \theta < \tan \theta.$$

**Theorem 10.1a.** If $f(x) = \sin x$, then $f$ is continuous at $x = 0$.

PROOF: By Inequality (1), we know for $0 < x < \pi/2$ that
$$0 < \sin x < x.$$

Since $\sin (-x) = -\sin x$, it follows from the inequality that
$$\lim_{x \to 0} \sin x = 0.$$

Furthermore, $\sin 0 = 0$, so that the sine function is continuous at $x = 0$.

Using this result we can prove

**Theorem 10.1b.** The cosine function is continuous at $x = 0$.

PROOF: Since $\cos x = \sqrt{1 - \sin^2 x}$, $-\pi/2 \leq x \leq \pi/2$, we may regard $\cos x$ as a composite of
$$y = f(x) .=. 1 - \sin^2 x \quad \text{and} \quad g(y) .=. \sqrt{y}.$$

We have previously proved (Example 4.4b) that $\lim_{x \to a} \sqrt{x} = \sqrt{a}$ for $a > 0$, which means that the square root function is continuous for $x > 0$. It has just been shown that $\lim_{x \to 0} \sin x = 0$, so that an application of Theorem 4.6d, which concerns the interchange of taking a limit and the formation of a functional value, gives
$$\lim_{x \to 0} \cos x = \lim_{x \to 0} \sqrt{1 - \sin^2 x}$$
$$= \sqrt{\lim_{x \to 0} (1 - \sin^2 x)}$$
$$= 1.$$

Since $\cos 0 = 1$, we have proved that the cosine function is continuous at $x = 0$.

We are now in a position to show quite simply that the sine function is continuous for all values of $x$.

**Theorem 10.1c.** The sine function is continuous at $x = a$, where $a$ is any real number.

PROOF: Consider $\sin (a + h) = \sin a \cos h + \cos a \sin h$. Then

$$\lim_{h \to 0} \sin (a + h) = \lim_{h \to 0} \sin a \cos h + \lim_{h \to 0} \cos a \sin h$$

$$= \sin a. \quad \text{(Why?)}$$

Hence, the sine function is continuous at $x = a$.

---

*Example 10.1a.* Evaluate $\lim_{x \to 0} (\csc x - \cot x)$.

We write

$$\lim_{x \to 0} (\csc x - \cot x) = \lim_{x \to 0} \left( \frac{1}{\sin x} - \frac{\cos x}{\sin x} \right)$$

$$= \lim_{x \to 0} \frac{1 - \cos x}{\sin x} = \lim_{x \to 0} \frac{(1 - \cos x)(1 + \cos x)}{\sin x (1 + \cos x)}$$

$$= \lim_{x \to 0} \frac{\sin^2 x}{\sin x (1 + \cos x)} = \lim_{x \to 0} \frac{\sin x}{1 + \cos x} = 0.$$

---

The continuity of the other trigonometric functions may be determined from theorems concerning continuous functions. For example, since the tangent function is described by

$$\tan x = \frac{\sin x}{\cos x},$$

it follows that this function is continuous everywhere except at the points where the cosine is zero, that is, at the odd multiples of $\pi/2$. Explain.

It is now possible to obtain a result that is basic in the investigation of derivatives of the trigonometric functions.

**Theorem 10.1d.**
$$\lim_{x \to 0} \frac{\sin x}{x} = 1.$$

PROOF: Since the denominator has a limit zero, Theorem 4.5e on the limit of a quotient does not apply. Consequently, it is necessary to investigate the limit from another point of view.

From $\sin (-x) = -\sin x$, we get

$$\frac{\sin (-x)}{(-x)} = \frac{\sin x}{x},$$

so that it is sufficient to consider the fraction $(\sin x)/x$ for $x > 0$ only. According to Inequality (1),

$$0 < x < \frac{\pi}{2} \Rightarrow 0 < \sin x < x < \tan x,$$

and since $\sin x > 0$ for this set of values of $x$, we may divide by $\sin x$ to get

$$1 < \frac{x}{\sin x} < \frac{1}{\cos x}.$$

Thus, by taking reciprocals, we obtain

$$1 > \frac{\sin x}{x} > \cos x.$$

By Theorem 10.1b, $\lim_{x \to 0} \cos x = 1$. Hence the preceding inequality shows that

$$\lim_{x \to 0} \frac{\sin x}{x} = 1,$$

as was to be proved.

Using the results of this theorem, we can evaluate limits of many expressions that involve a quotient of a sine function and the variable argument.

---

*Example 10.1b.* Evaluate

$$\lim_{x \to 0} \frac{\sin 2x}{x}.$$

If $u = 2x$, then $u \to 0$ as $x \to 0$, and

$$\lim_{x \to 0} \frac{\sin 2x}{x} = \lim_{u \to 0} \frac{\sin u}{u/2} = 2 \lim_{u \to 0} \frac{\sin u}{u} = 2.$$

## Exercises 10.1

In Numbers 1 to 6, find the limit if it exists.

1. $\lim\limits_{x \to 0} \dfrac{\cos 2x}{x}$.

2. $\lim\limits_{x \to 0} \dfrac{\sin 2x}{3x}$.

3. $\lim\limits_{x \to 0} \dfrac{\tan x}{x}$.

4. $\lim\limits_{x \to \pi/2} \dfrac{\cot x}{x - \pi/2}$.

5. $\lim\limits_{x \to \pi/2} (\sec x - \tan x)$.

6. $\lim\limits_{x \to \pi} \dfrac{\sin x}{\pi - x}$.

7. Prove that the cosine function is continuous at every point.

For the function described by each of the following equations, determine the points of continuity and discontinuity and describe the discontinuities.

8. $y = \dfrac{\sin x}{1 - \cos x}$.

9. $u = \cot v$.

10. $u = \dfrac{\sin v}{|\sin v|}$.

11. $y = \csc x$.

12. $g(x) = \begin{cases} \dfrac{\sin 2x}{x}, & x \neq 0, \\ 1, & x = 0. \end{cases}$

13. $r = \sec s$.

14. $f(x) = \dfrac{x}{\sin x}$.

## 10.2 DERIVATIVES OF THE TRIGONOMETRIC FUNCTIONS

Although the sine and cosine functions are continuous on their entire domain, this is no guarantee that they are differentiable. However, that they are differentiable is easily established.

**Theorem 10.2a.** $$D_x \sin u = \cos u\, D_x u.$$

PROOF: $$D_x \sin x = \lim_{h \to 0} \frac{\sin(x+h) - \sin x}{h}.$$

By Formula 25 of Appendix B, we have

$$\sin(x+h) - \sin x = 2 \cos(x + h/2) \sin h/2,$$

so that

$$\lim_{h \to 0} \frac{\sin(x+h) - \sin x}{h} = \lim_{h \to 0} \cos(x + h/2) \frac{\sin h/2}{h/2} = \cos x$$

or

$$D_x \sin x = \cos x.$$

The chain rule then yields the more general form

$$D_x \sin u = \cos u\, D_x u.$$

The derivatives of the other trigonometric functions can be obtained from Theorem 10.2a with the aid of some of the fundamental trigonometric identities.

**Theorem 10.2b.** $$D_x \cos u = -\sin u\, D_x u.$$

PROOF: $$D_x \cos x = D_x \sin(\pi/2 - x)$$
$$= D_v \sin v\, D_x v = \cos v\, D_x v,$$

where $v = \pi/2 - x$. Hence

$$D_x \cos x = [\cos(\pi/2 - x)](-1)$$
$$= -\sin x,$$

and application of the chain rule gives

$$D_x \cos u = -\sin u\, D_x u.$$

**Theorem 10.2c.** $$D_x \tan u = \sec^2 u\, D_x u.$$

PROOF: $$D_x \tan u = D_x \frac{\sin u}{\cos u} = \frac{\cos u \cos u\, D_x u - \sin u(-\sin u)\, D_x u}{\cos^2 u}$$

$$= \frac{(\cos^2 u + \sin^2 u)}{\cos^2 u} D_x u$$

$$= \sec^2 u\, D_x u.$$

**Theorem 10.2d.** $$D_x \cot u = -\csc^2 u\, D_x u.$$

PROOF: The proof of this result is left for the reader.

**Theorem 10.2e.** $$D_x \sec u = \sec u \tan u\, D_x u.$$

PROOF: $$D_x \sec u = D_x (\cos u)^{-1}$$
$$= -(\cos u)^{-2}(-\sin u)\, D_x u$$
$$= \sec u \tan u\, D_x u.$$

**Theorem 10.2f.** $$D_x \csc u = -\csc u \cot u\, D_x u.$$

PROOF: The proof is left for the reader.

The following examples illustrate the application of some of the derivative formulas to composite functions involving trigonometric functions.

---

*Example 10.2a.* If $y = (\tan x^2)^3$, find $D_x y$.

The quantity $(\tan x^2)^3$ may be treated like $u^3$, so that

$$\begin{aligned} D_x y &= 3(\tan x^2)^2 \, D_x(\tan x^2) \\ &= 3(\tan x^2)^2(\sec^2 x^2) \, D_x x^2 \\ &= 6x(\tan x^2)^2 \sec^2 x^2. \end{aligned}$$

---

*Example 10.2b.* If $y = 1/(1 + \cos \theta)$, find $D_\theta y$.

We may write

$$y = (1 + \cos \theta)^{-1},$$

so that

$$\begin{aligned} D_\theta y &= (-1)(1 + \cos \theta)^{-2} \, D_\theta(1 + \cos \theta) \\ &= (-1)(1 + \cos \theta)^{-2}(-\sin \theta) \\ &= \frac{\sin \theta}{(1 + \cos \theta)^2}. \end{aligned}$$

---

*Example 10.2c.* Find $D_x \ln \tan 3x$.

We have

$$\begin{aligned} D_x \ln \tan 3x &= \frac{1}{\tan 3x} \, D_x \tan 3x \\[2mm] &= \frac{1}{\tan 3x} \, (\sec^2 3x)(D_x 3x) \\[2mm] &= \frac{3}{\tan 3x} \, (\sec^2 3x) \\[2mm] &= \frac{3}{\sin 3x \cos 3x} = 6 \csc 6x. \end{aligned}$$

---

*Example 10.2d.* Find $D_x^2 y$ if $x = \sin^4 t$, $y = \cos^4 t$.

Using the formula $D_x y = D_t y / D_t x$, we obtain

$$D_x y = \frac{-4 \cos^3 t \sin t}{4 \sin^3 t \cos t} = -\cot^2 t, \qquad t \neq \frac{n\pi}{2}, \, n \in \mathcal{I}.$$

The second derivative of $y$ with respect to $x$ is given by

$$D_x^2 y = \frac{D_t(D_x y)}{D_t x}$$

$$= \frac{2 \cot t \csc^2 t}{4 \sin^3 t \cos t} = \frac{1}{2} \csc^6 t, \qquad t \neq \frac{n\pi}{2}, \, n \in \mathcal{I}.$$

## Exercises 10.2

1. Prove Theorem 10.2d.
2. Prove Theorem 10.2f.
3. Derive the formula for $D_x \cos x$ by direct use of the definition of the derivative.
4. Derive the formula for $D_x \tan x$ by direct use of the definition of the derivative.

In each of Numbers 5 to 14, the indicated derivative should be read off by inspection.

5. $y = \cos 5x$; $D_x y$.
6. $y = \tan (2 + 3x)$; $D_x y$.
7. $u = \sin t^2$; $D_t u$.
8. $v = \cot (1 + s^2)$; $D_s v$.
9. $w = \ln \cot \theta$; $D_\theta w$.
10. $s = \sin (1/t^2)$; $D_t s$.
11. $z = \csc e^w$; $D_w z$.
12. $x = \csc 3y$; $D_y x$.
13. $y = e^{\sin x}$; $D_x y$.
14. $r = \cot e^u$; $D_u r$.

Find the indicated derivative in each of Numbers 15 to 38.

15. $y = \sin^4 3x$; $D_x y$.
16. $y = \sin^2 x \cos^3 x$; $D_x y$.
17. $r = \tan^2 4x$; $D_x r$.
18. $s = \cot^2 (1 - x)$; $D_x s$.
19. $u = \ln \cos 3w$; $D_w^2 u$.
20. $y = \tan 5x$; $D_x^2 y$.
21. $w = \sin^2 (1 - 2z)$; $D_z^2 w$.
22. $s = e^{-t} \sin 3t$; $D_t^2 s$.
23. $x = \cos mt \sin nt$; $D_t^2 x$.
24. $v = \ln \tan e^t$; $D_t v$.
25. $y = \sqrt{\sin t^2}$; $D_t y$.
26. $r = \sec^2 3\theta$; $D_\theta^2 r$.
27. $y + x \sec y = \pi$; $D_x y$.
28. $y = (\sin x)^{\cos x}$; $D_x y$.
29. $\cos x + \cos y = 1$; $D_x^2 y$.
30. $x \sin y - y \sin x = 1$; $D_x y$.

31. $x = \sin 2t$, $y = 1 + \cos t$; $D_x y$.
32. $x = \tan t$, $y = \sin^2 t$; $D_x y$.
33. $x = a(u - \sin u)$,
    $y = a(1 - \cos u)$; $D_x y$.
34. $x = a(\sin \theta - \theta \cos \theta)$,
    $y = a(\cos \theta + \theta \sin \theta)$; $D_x^2 y$.
35. $x = a \sin^3 t$,
    $y = a \cos^3 t$; $D_x y$.
36. $x = a \cos t$,
    $y = b \sin t$; $D_x^2 y$.
37. $y = \sin x$; $D_x^{35} y$.
38. $y = \cos^2 x$; $D_x^{10} y$.

39. show that $D_x^n \cos x = \cos \left( x + \dfrac{n\pi}{2} \right)$.

40. Show that $D_x^n \sin x = \sin \left( x + \dfrac{n\pi}{2} \right)$.

# 10.3 APPLICATIONS OF THE DERIVATIVES OF THE TRIGONOMETRIC FUNCTIONS

With the aid of the derivative formulas of the preceding section, it is frequently possible to give an analysis of the salient features of the graph of an equation involving trigonometric functions. Such equations occur frequently in electric circuit analysis, in mechanical vibration analysis, and in other applications. The first two of these applications will be discussed later in connection with the subject of differential equations, and we shall illustrate the application to maximum and minimum problems in this section.

---

*Example 10.3a.* Determine the maxima and minima and the points of inflection of the curve described by

$$y = A \sin (ax + b), \quad A > 0, a > 0.$$

We already have discussed the fact that the sine and cosine are periodic functions. Thus, we know that

$$\sin (ax + b) = \sin (ax + b + 2\pi),$$

so that $\sin (ax + b) = \sin [a(x + 2\pi/a + b/a)]$. Thus,

$$f\left(x + \frac{2\pi}{a}\right) = f(x),$$

which shows the period to be $2\pi/a$.

To find relative maxima and minima, we have

$$D_x y = Aa \cos (ax + b),$$

which is zero if

$$ax + b = \frac{2n + 1}{2} \pi, \quad n \in \mathcal{I}$$

or if

$$x = \frac{2n + 1}{2a} \pi - \frac{b}{a}.$$

It is clear that the maximum values of $y$ occur for

$$x = \frac{\pi}{2a} - \frac{b}{a}, \ \frac{5\pi}{2a} - \frac{b}{a}, \ \cdots,$$

and are all equal to $A$. Similarly, the minimum values of $y$ occur when

$$x = \frac{3\pi}{2a} - \frac{b}{a}, \ \frac{7\pi}{2a} - \frac{b}{a}, \ \cdots,$$

and are all equal to $-A$. The quantity

$$\tfrac{1}{2}(y_{\max} - y_{\min})$$

is called the **amplitude** of a periodic function. Another term often associated with a periodic function is the **frequency** $\mu .=. 1/T$, where $T$ is the period. The factor $a$ in $A \sin (ax + b)$ is often called the **angular frequency** which will be discussed later. The quantity $b/a$ is called the **phase shift** of the function. It measures the amount by which the curve

$$y = A \sin (ax + b)$$

is "shifted" from the curve

$$y = A \sin ax,$$

as illustrated in Figure 10.3a.

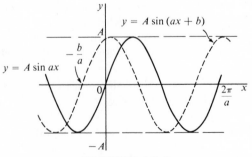

FIGURE 10.3a

Points of inflection are determined from

$$D_x^2 y = -Aa^2 \sin (ax + b),$$

which is zero if

$$ax + b = n\pi, \qquad n \in \mathcal{I},$$

or if

$$x = \frac{n\pi - b}{a}.$$

Each of these values actually corresponds to a point of inflection. Why?

---

*Example 10.3b.* Discuss and sketch the curve

$$y = \sin^2 x + 2 \cos x, \qquad -\pi \leq x \leq \pi.$$

This curve is symmetric with respect to the *y*-axis. Explain.

Since

$$\begin{aligned} y' &= 2 \sin x \cos x - 2 \sin x \\ &= 2 \sin x(\cos x - 1), \end{aligned}$$

and

$$\begin{aligned} y'' &= 2 \cos^2 x - 2 \sin^2 x - 2 \cos x \\ &= 4 \cos^2 x - 2 \cos x - 2 \\ &= 2(2 \cos x + 1)(\cos x - 1), \end{aligned}$$

we find

$$y'' = 0 \Rightarrow x = \pm 2\pi/3, \qquad x = 0.$$

Also,

$$y'' > 0 \quad \text{for } -\pi < x < -2\pi/3 \text{ and } 2\pi/3 < x < \pi,$$

and

$$y'' < 0 \quad \text{for } -2\pi/3 < x < 2\pi/3, \quad x \neq 0.$$

Thus, the curve is concave up for $-\pi < x < -2\pi/3$ and for $2\pi/3 < x < \pi$. The curve is concave down for $-2\pi/3 < x < 2\pi/3$. Since $y' = 0$ for $x = 0, \pm\pi$, the concavity indicates that $(0, 2)$ is a maximum point and that $(\pm\pi, -2)$ are end point minima. The points $(\pm 2\pi/3, -1/4)$ are inflection points. The sketch is shown in Figure 10.3b.

In this example, if $x$ were unrestricted, it would be quite easy to extend the curve by making use of the periodicity of the trigonometric functions. The curve in Figure 10.3b is actually one complete cycle.

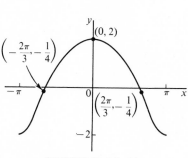

**FIGURE 10.3b**

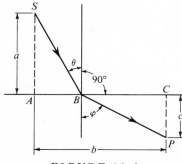

**FIGURE 10.3c**

The next example illustrates an important type of physical application of the trigonometric functions.

---

*Example 10.3c.* A ray of light, emitted from a source $S$ in a medium in which the velocity of light is $v_1$, reaches a point $P$ in a second medium in which the velocity of light is $v_2$ (Figure 10.3c). Suppose that the media are separated by a plane interface and that the time taken by the light to go from $S$ to $P$ is a minimum. Show that the angle of incidence $\theta$ is related to the angle of refraction $\varphi$ by the equation

$$\frac{\sin \theta}{\sin \varphi} = \frac{v_1}{v_2}.$$

This is known as Snell's law of refraction. Principles of *least time* and *least action* are of great importance in many physical problems.

Let the interface between the two media be $ABC$, where $B$ is the point where the ray passes through the interface. Then, with the labeling in the figure, we have

$$SB = a \sec \theta, \quad BP = c \sec \varphi,$$

and

$$AB + BC = a \tan \theta + c \tan \varphi = b.$$

The time $T$ taken for the ray to pass from $S$ to $P$ is

$$T = \frac{SB}{v_1} + \frac{BP}{v_2},$$

or

$$T = \frac{a}{v_1} \sec \theta + \frac{c}{v_2} \sec \varphi,$$

which is the quantity to be minimized.

Since it seems clear that the elimination of $\varphi$ or $\theta$ will result in a quite unwieldy expression in the remaining variable, we shall use implicit differentiation. Upon choosing $\theta$ as the independent variable, we have

$$(1) \qquad D_\theta T = \frac{a}{v_1} \sec \theta \tan \theta + \frac{c}{v_2} \sec \varphi \tan \varphi \, D_\theta \varphi.$$

From the equation relating $a$, $b$, $c$, we get the condition

$$(2) \qquad a \sec^2 \theta + c \sec^2 \varphi \, D_\theta \varphi = 0,$$

since $a$, $b$, $c$ are all constant.

To find the value of $\theta$ for minimum $T$, we put $D_\theta T = 0$ to get

$$(3) \qquad \frac{a}{v_1} \sec \theta \tan \theta + \frac{c}{v_2} \sec \varphi \tan \varphi \, D_\theta \varphi = 0.$$

By solving each of Equations (2) and (3) for $D_\theta \varphi$ and equating the results, we obtain

$$-\frac{a \sec^2 \theta}{c \sec^2 \varphi} = -\frac{a v_2 \sec \theta \tan \theta}{c v_1 \sec \varphi \tan \varphi},$$

or

$$(4) \qquad \frac{v_1}{v_2} = \frac{\sin \theta}{\sin \varphi}.$$

In order to show that this result actually corresponds to a minimum value of $T$, we eliminate $D_\theta \varphi$ between Equations (1) and (2) to get

$$D_\theta T = \frac{a}{v_1} \sec \theta \tan \theta - \frac{a}{v_2} \sin \varphi \sec^2 \theta$$

$$= a \sec^2 \theta \left( \frac{\sin \theta}{v_1} - \frac{\sin \varphi}{v_2} \right).$$

From this equation, it is evident that

$$D_\theta T < 0 \quad \text{for } \sin \theta < \frac{v_1}{v_2} \sin \varphi$$

and

$$D_\theta T > 0 \quad \text{for } \sin \theta > \frac{v_1}{v_2} \sin \varphi.$$

Accordingly, $D_\theta T$ changes sign from minus to plus as $\theta$ passes through the critical value determined by (4) and the condition

$$a \tan \theta + c \tan \varphi = b.$$

Therefore, this critical value corresponds to a minimum value of $T$.

Although it seems physically evident that there always exists such a critical value of $\theta$, the more mathematically inclined reader may assure himself of this fact by writing $x = \tan \theta$, $y = \tan \varphi$, so that $\sin \theta = x/\sqrt{x^2 + 1}$ and $\sin \varphi = y/\sqrt{y^2 + 1}$. It is ther not difficult to show that the resulting equations have graphs that always intersect at exactly one point in the first quadrant.

## Exercises 10.3

In each of Numbers 1 to 10, discuss and sketch the curve described by the given equation.

1. $y = 2 \cos \frac{1}{2}x$, $0 \leq x \leq 4\pi$.
2. $y = \frac{1}{2} \tan 4x$, $0 \leq x \leq \pi$.
3. $y = 4 \sin (2x - \pi)$, $0 \leq x \leq \pi$.
4. $y = \begin{cases} \cos x, & 0 < x < \pi, \\ \cos (x - \pi), & \pi < x < 2\pi. \end{cases}$
5. $y = \begin{cases} \sin x, & 0 < x < \pi, \\ \cos x, & \pi < x < 2\pi. \end{cases}$

6. $y = 5|\sin 4x|$, $0 \leq x \leq \pi$.
7. $y = 5 \sin |2x|$, $-\pi \leq x \leq \pi$.
8. $y = |\cos 2x|$, $0 \leq x \leq \pi$.
9. $y = 2 - \cos 2x$.
10. $y = 1 + \sin \pi(x - 1)$.

The graph of an equation of the form

$$y = f(x) + g(x)$$

may be conveniently obtained by the method of *composition of ordinates*. For example, the graph of

$$y = \sin 2x + 2 \cos x$$

may be obtained by first sketching the two curves

$$y = \sin 2x \quad \text{and} \quad y = 2 \cos x$$

on the same set of axes. Points on the required curve may then be found by adding geometrically the ordinates of the two component curves for the same value of $x$.

In each of Numbers 11 to 16, use this method to sketch the curve described by the given equation. Find the maximum, minimum, and inflection points for each curve.

11. $y = 2x - \sin x$.

12. $y = x + \cos x; 0 \leq x \leq 2\pi$.

13. $y = \sin x + \cos x; 0 \leq x \leq 2\pi$.

14. $y = \sin 2x + 2 \cos x$.

15. $y = x - 2 + \sin 2x$.

16. $y = \cos^2 x - 2 \cos x; 0 \leq x \leq 2\pi$.

In each of Numbers 17 to 19, use composition of ordinates to sketch the given curve. Find the maximum and minimum points.

17. $y = \frac{1}{2} \cos 2x - \cos x$.

★18. $y = \frac{4}{3} \sin 3x + 3 \cos 2x$.

★19. $y = 2 \cos 3x - 3 \cos 2x$.

20. What is the period of the curve $y = 2 \cos 2x + \sin 3x$? Is a curve of the form $y = a \cos mx + b \sin nx$, $m, n \in \mathfrak{N}$, necessarily periodic? Explain.

★21. Is the curve $y = \sin x + \sin \sqrt{2}x$ periodic? Explain.

22. A line segment of length 20 units is to lie in the first quadrant and is to be terminated by the coordinate axes. Locate the line so that its perpendicular distance from the origin is a maximum.

23. Given a circle of radius $r$, what is the altitude of the isosceles triangle with least area that can be circumscribed about the circle?

24. An irrigation ditch is to have a cross section in the shape of an isosceles trapezoid with the equal sides and the bottom each of length $L$. What should be the width across the top for maximum carrying capacity—that is, for maximum cross-sectional area? *Hint*: Let $\theta$ be the angle of inclination of one of the sloping sides.

25. A metal solid of revolution consists of two cylinders with a common axis. Figure 10.3d shows a cross section of the solid through its axis. Suppose the solid is to be put into a lathe and turned down to a cone with the elements of the cone passing through the edge of the base of the upper cylinder as indicated in the figure. Find the dimensions of the cone of largest volume and the dimensions of the cone of smallest volume that can be turned from the solid.

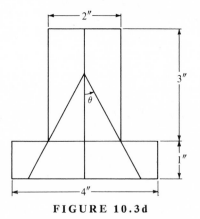

**FIGURE 10.3d**

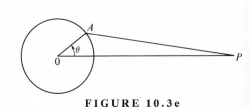

**FIGURE 10.3e**

26. A steel ball bearing of radius $b$ is to fit into a hollow conical bearing so that the ball is barely but entirely inside the cone. Find the dimensions of the cone of smallest volume for which this is possible.
27. A thin rod of length $4b$ and with perfectly smooth ends passes through the center of a small heavy ball that is fixed on the rod a distance $b$ from one end. The rod is placed in a smooth hollow hemisphere of radius $4b$ and is allowed to come to its equilibrium position. Find the angle that the rod makes with the horizontal when it finally comes to rest. Assume that the weight of the rod is negligible in comparison with that of the ball. *Hint*: The center of the ball will be as low as possible.
28. A perfectly smooth cable is passed over two smooth pegs in the same horizontal plane and $2b$ units apart. One end of the cable is then passed through a loop in the other end and is attached to a weight $W$. If the weight is assumed to pull the cable taut, find the angle between the two portions of the cable where it passes over one of the pegs. *Hint*: The weight will hang as low as possible.
29. A particle $P$ starts at $A(a, 0)$ and moves counterclockwise on a circle of radius $a$ and with center at the origin. If $P$ makes one complete revolution every 12 seconds, find the rate at which the length of the segment $AP$ is changing at the end of 2 seconds; at the end of 4 seconds; at the end of 8 seconds.
30. The crankshaft of an engine is turning at the rate of 30 revolutions per second. At what rate is the piston $P$ (Figure 10.3e) moving if the arm $OA$ is 1.5 inches long and the connecting rod $AP$ is 6 inches long? What is the rate at the instant when $\theta = 150°$?
31. The hour hand of a watch is 10 millimeters long and the minute hand is 12 millimeters long. At what rate are the ends of the hands approaching each other at 4 o'clock?

# 10.4 INVERSE DERIVATIVES
## OF TRIGONOMETRIC FUNCTIONS

It follows directly from the corresponding differentiation formulas that

(1)
$$\int \sin x \, dx = -\cos x + C,$$

(2)
$$\int \cos x \, dx = \sin x + C.$$

---

*Example 10.4a.* Find $\int \sin 3x \, dx$.

We note that $\int \sin 3x \, dx$ is $\cos 3x$ except for a constant factor. Since $D_x \cos 3x = -3 \sin 3x$, the constant factor is $-\frac{1}{3}$. Consequently,

$$\int \sin 3x \, dx = -\frac{1}{3} \cos 3x + C.$$

---

*Example 10.4b.* Find the area bounded by the curve $y = \sin 2x$, the line $x = \pi/4$, and that portion of the x-axis between 0 and $\pi/4$.

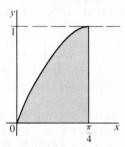

**FIGURE 10.4a**

The area lies entirely above the x-axis, as Figure 10.4a indicates. Thus we have

$$A = \int_0^{\pi/4} \sin 2x \, dx.$$

Since,

$$D_x^{-1} \sin 2x = -\tfrac{1}{2} \cos 2x,$$

it follows that

$$
\begin{aligned}
A &= -\tfrac{1}{2}[\cos 2x]_0^{\pi/4} \\
&= -\tfrac{1}{2}[\cos (\pi/2) - 1] \\
&= \tfrac{1}{2} \text{ (l.u.)}^2.
\end{aligned}
$$

By reading the corresponding derivative formulas in reverse, we have the following additional inverse derivative formulas:

(3)
$$\int \sec^2 x \, dx = \tan x + C,$$

(4)
$$\int \csc^2 x \, dx = -\cot x + C,$$

(5)
$$\int \sec x \tan x \, dx = \sec x + C,$$

(6)
$$\int \csc x \cot x \, dx = -\csc x + C.$$

The preceding six formulas include the inverse derivatives of only two of the six simple trigonometric functions. It is, however, not difficult to obtain the remaining desired formulas.

The definition of $\tan x$ in terms of $\sin x$ and $\cos x$ is the clue to the inverse derivative of $\tan x$. Since

$$\tan x = \frac{\sin x}{\cos x} = \frac{-D_x(\cos x)}{\cos x},$$

we may use the formula

$$D_x^{-1}\left(\frac{D_x u}{u}\right) = \ln |u| + C$$

to obtain

(7)
$$\int \tan x \, dx = -\ln |\cos x| + C$$
$$= \ln |\sec x| + C.$$

Using the same approach with cot $x$, we obtain

(8)
$$\int \cot x \, dx = \ln |\sin x| + C$$
$$= -\ln |\csc x| + C.$$

---

*Example 10.4c.* Evaluate $\int_{3\pi/8}^{\pi/2} \tan 2\theta \, d\theta$.

We use Formula (7) to obtain

$$\int_{3\pi/8}^{\pi/2} \tan 2\theta \, d\theta = \frac{1}{2} \int_{3\pi/8}^{\pi/2} \tan 2\theta \, (2d\theta)$$

$$= -\frac{1}{2} [\ln |\cos 2\theta|]_{3\pi/8}^{\pi/2}$$

$$= -\frac{1}{2} \ln |\cos \pi| + \frac{1}{2} \ln \left|\cos \frac{3\pi}{4}\right|$$

$$= \frac{1}{2} \ln \frac{1}{\sqrt{2}} = -\frac{1}{4} \ln 2.$$

---

In order to derive a formula for the inverse derivative of sec $x$, we examine the two derivative formulas that involve sec $x$; that is,

$$D_x \sec x = \sec x \tan x,$$
$$D_x \tan x = \sec^2 x.$$

We note that if the corresponding members of these two equations are added, the expression sec $x$ + tan $x$ appears on both sides of the resulting equation. Thus,

$$D_x(\tan x + \sec x) = \sec x (\sec x + \tan x),$$

so that

$$\sec x = \frac{D_x(\sec x + \tan x)}{\sec x + \tan x}.$$

Therefore,

(9)
$$\int \sec x \, dx = \ln |\sec x + \tan x| + C.$$

In a similar manner we may obtain the result

(10)
$$\int \csc x \, dx = \ln |\csc x - \cot x| + C$$
$$= \ln |\tan \tfrac{1}{2}x| + C.$$

---

*Example 10.4d.* Evaluate

$$\int_{\pi/2}^{\pi} \frac{dx}{\sin x/2}.$$

Since $1/\sin u = \csc u$, Formula (10) may be used to get

$$\int_{\pi/2}^{\pi} \frac{dx}{\sin x/2} = 2 \int_{\pi/2}^{\pi} \tfrac{1}{2} \csc \tfrac{1}{2}x \, dx$$

$$= 2[\ln |\csc \tfrac{1}{2}x - \cot \tfrac{1}{2}x|]_{\pi/2}^{\pi}$$

$$= -2 \ln (\sqrt{2} - 1) = 2 \ln (\sqrt{2} + 1) = \ln (3 + 2\sqrt{2}).$$

## Exercises 10.4

In Numbers 1 to 20, find the indicated inverse derivatives.

1. $\displaystyle\int \cos \frac{2x}{3} \, dx.$

2. $\displaystyle\int s \sin s^2 \, ds.$

3. $\displaystyle\int \frac{dx}{\tan 2x}.$

4. $\displaystyle\int e^{3x} \cot e^{3x} \, dx.$

5. $\displaystyle\int \frac{\sin 3r}{\cos^2 3r} \, dr.$

6. $\displaystyle\int \frac{dy}{\sec 2y}.$

7. $\displaystyle\int \sin (2 - 3t) \, dt.$

8. $\displaystyle\int \sec 2x \tan 2x \, dx.$

9. $\displaystyle\int \frac{dw}{\sin^2 2w}.$

10. $\displaystyle\int \tan (3y + 4) \, dy.$

11. $\displaystyle\int \frac{dx}{\cos 3x}.$

12. $\displaystyle\int \frac{du}{\cos^2 2u}.$

13. $\displaystyle\int e^{\sin y} \cos y \, dy.$

14. $\displaystyle\int \frac{\sin \omega x}{\sqrt{1 + \cos \omega x}} \, dx.$

15. $\displaystyle\int \csc 4y \cot 4y \, dy.$

16. $\displaystyle\int \sin^3 2z \cos 2z \, dz.$

17. $\displaystyle\int x \sin (1 + x^2) \, dx.$

18. $\displaystyle\int \frac{\cos 3w - \sin 3w}{\cos 3w} \, dw.$

19. $\displaystyle\int \frac{\sin 3\theta}{1 + \cos 3\theta} \, d\theta.$

20. $\displaystyle\int \frac{x}{\sin x^2} \, dx.$

Evaluate the definite integrals in Numbers 21 to 30.

21. $\displaystyle\int_0^{\pi/2} (w^2 + \sin 2w) \, dw.$

22. $\displaystyle\int_{\pi/8}^{\pi/6} \tan 2\theta \, d\theta.$

23. $\displaystyle\int_0^{1/3} \sin \pi w \, dw.$

24. $\displaystyle\int_0^{\sqrt{\pi/2}} x \cos x^2 \, dx.$

25. $\displaystyle\int_0^{\pi/2} \sec \frac{x}{2} \tan \frac{x}{2} \, dx.$

26. $\displaystyle\int_0^{2\pi} |\sin t - \cos t| \, dt.$

27. $\displaystyle\int_0^{2\pi} |\sin 2t| \, dt.$

28. $\displaystyle\int_{\pi/6}^{\pi/3} \sin^2 2s \cos 2s \, ds.$

29. $\displaystyle\int_{\pi}^{4\pi/3} \sin (\pi - x) \, dx.$

30. $\displaystyle\int_0^{\pi/3} \frac{du}{\cos^2 u/2}.$

31. Derive Formula 10.
32. Find the area bounded by the $x$-axis and one arch of the curve $y = \sin(x/3)$.
33. Find the area bounded by the $x$-axis and the curve $y = |\cos(x/2)|$ from $x = 0$ to $x = 2\pi$.
34. Find the first quadrant area under the curve $y = \cos x - \sin x$ from $x = 0$ to the first point where the curve cuts the positive $x$-axis.
35. Find the area bounded by the $x$-axis and one arch of the curve $y = a \sin bx$.
36. Find the area in the first quadrant enclosed by the $x$-axis and the curves $y = \tan x$ and $y = \cot x$, between $x = 0$ and $x = \pi/2$.
37. Find the volume of revolution formed by revolving the curve $y = \csc x$ between $x = \pi/4$ and $x = \pi/2$ about the $x$-axis.
38. Find the volume formed by revolving the curve $y = \cot 2x$ between $x = \pi/8$ and $x = \pi/4$ about the $x$-axis. *Hint*: Use the formula $\cot^2 u = \csc^2 u - 1$.
39. The area bounded by $y = 1$, the $y$-axis, and $y = \tan 3x$ is revolved about the line $y = 1$ to generate a solid. Find the volume of this solid. (See the hint in Number 38.)
40. The area bounded by $y = 2$ and the portion of $y = \sec 2x$ for which $|x| \leq \pi/6$ is revolved about the line $y = 2$. Find the volume of the solid of revolution so generated.
41. In a certain type of "nonlinear" spring (not obeying Hooke's Law), the force $F$ necessary to produce a deflection $x$ is

$$F = A \sin kx,$$

where $A$ and $k$ are constants dependent upon the particular spring, and where $|kx| < \pi/2$. Find the work done in compressing such a spring from its natural length by an amount $\xi$, where $0 \leq \xi < \pi/2k$.

## 10.5 INVERSE TRIGONOMETRIC FUNCTIONS

In studying the inverses of the trigonometric functions, we encounter a practical difficulty that did not arise in the case of the exponential function $\{(x, a^x)\}$, where the inverse relation $\{(x, \log_a x)\}$ is also a function. Let the inverse of the sine function $\{(x, \sin x)\}$ be designated by $\{(x, \sin^{-1} x)\}$, where $\{\sin^{-1} x\}$ is the set of numbers that satisfy the equation $x = \sin y$. Then it follows, for instance, that $\sin^{-1}(\frac{1}{2})$ must satisfy the equation $\frac{1}{2} = \sin y$ so that $y$ can have any one of the values $\pi/6, 5\pi/6, 2\pi + \pi/6, 2\pi + 5\pi/6, \ldots$. Obviously, $\sin^{-1} x$ is not single-valued, and hence describes a relation rather than a function.

In order to avoid the ambiguity arising from the multiple-valued relations, we define what are sometimes called the **principal-valued** inverse trigonometric functions. These definitions simply eliminate all but a small portion of the range of the inverse trigonometric relations, so that the remaining parts yield functions.

In order to make the inverse functions as useful as possible, it is desirable to choose, as part of the definition, the set of values corresponding to the usually tabulated values. This requirement dictates that the range of the principal inverse sine function, for example, include the values from 0 to $\pi/2$. As a second desirable property, continuity of the inverse function should be attained. In Figure 10.5a, there appears the graph of $y = \sin^{-1} x$ with the heavy portion of the

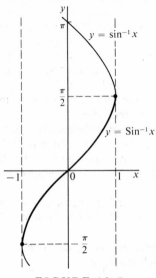

**FIGURE 10.5a**

curve corresponding to the customary principal value portion of the inverse sine. The inverse function whose range is $-\pi/2 \le y \le \pi/2$ is designated with a capital letter $\{(x, \text{Sin}^{-1} x)\}$. Thus, we make the following definition.

**Definition 10.5a.** The **principal inverse sine** function is the function

$$\{(x, y)\colon x = \sin y, \; -\pi/2 \le y \le \pi/2\}.$$

The value of this function at $x$ is denoted by $\text{Sin}^{-1} x$.

(In many books, especially the older ones, the archaic notations, arcsin $x$ and Arcsin $x$ are used in place of $\sin^{-1} x$ and $\text{Sin}^{-1} x$.)

---

*Example 10.5a.* Find $\sin^{-1} (-\tfrac{1}{2})$ and $\text{Sin}^{-1} (-\tfrac{1}{2})$.

If we let $y = \sin^{-1} (-\tfrac{1}{2})$, then we may write

$$\sin y = -\tfrac{1}{2},$$

and thus

$$y = n\pi + \frac{(-1)^{n+1}\pi}{6}, \qquad n \in \mathcal{I}.$$

For

$$y = \text{Sin}^{-1} (-\tfrac{1}{2}),$$

we have only

$$y = -\frac{\pi}{6}.$$

---

It has already been shown that the sine function is continuous on its entire domain, and, since the sine function is a strictly increasing function on the interval $-\pi/2 \le x \le \pi/2$, it follows, by Theorem 4.7h, that the principal inverse sine function is also a continuous strictly increasing function on its domain $-1 \le x \le 1$. These characteristics are, of course, verified by the graph in Figure 10.5a. Note that the domain of $\{(x, \text{Sin}^{-1} x)\}$ is exactly the same as that of $\{(x, \sin^{-1} x)\}$.

The inverse relation for $\{(x, \cos x)\}$ is denoted by $\{(x, \cos^{-1} x)\}$, where $\cos^{-1} x$ is the set of real numbers $y$ that satisfy the equation $x = \cos y$. The domain of the inverse relation is $-1 \le x \le 1$, and the range is the set of all real numbers. The graph is shown in Figure 10.5b.

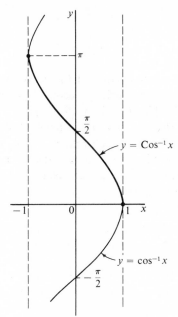

**FIGURE 10.5b**

In choosing a subset of $\{(x, \cos^{-1} x)\}$ that will be a function, we adopt the convention of restricting the range so that $0 \le y \le \pi$. As in the case of the inverse sine, the criteria used for making this choice are that, if possible, the function should be continuous and should include the points where $0 \le y \le \pi/2$ (that is, the customarily tabulated portion of the function), and that the function should have the same domain as the relation. With this in mind, we make the following definition.

**Definition 10.5b.** The **principal inverse cosine** function is the function

$$\{(x, y): x = \cos y, 0 \le y \le \pi\}.$$

The value of this function at $x$ is denoted by $\text{Cos}^{-1} x$.

*Example 10.5b.* Find $\cos^{-1}(-\tfrac{1}{2})$ and $\text{Cos}^{-1}(-\tfrac{1}{2})$.

Let $y = \cos^{-1}(-\tfrac{1}{2})$, so that

$$\cos y = -\tfrac{1}{2}$$

and

$$y = 2n\pi \pm \tfrac{2}{3}\pi, \qquad n \in \mathcal{I}.$$

For

$$y = \text{Cos}^{-1}(-\tfrac{1}{2}),$$

we have only

$$y = \tfrac{2}{3}\pi.$$

---

*Example 10.5c.* Find $\sin \text{Cos}^{-1}\tfrac{1}{3}$.

If we let $\theta = \text{Cos}^{-1}\tfrac{1}{3}$, the problem is to find $\sin \theta$. Since $\text{Cos}^{-1}\tfrac{1}{3}$ is the inverse function, it follows that $\theta$ must be between 0 and $\pi/2$. and thus

$$\sin \theta = \sqrt{1 - \cos^2 \theta}$$
$$= \sqrt{1 - \tfrac{1}{9}}$$
$$= \tfrac{2}{3}\sqrt{2}.$$

---

As is indicated by the heavy portion of the curve in Figure 10.5b, the prin
cipal inverse cosine function is a strictly decreasing continuous function on its
domain. This is assured by Theorem 4.7h. (Why?)

The inverse relation for $\{(x, \tan x)\}$ is denoted by $\{(x, \tan^{-1} x)\}$, where
$\tan^{-1} x$ is the set of real numbers such that $x = \tan y$. The domain of the in
verse relation is the set of all real numbers and the range is the set of all real
numbers except those values of $y$ for which $\cos y = 0$. The graph of the inverse
relation is shown in Figure 10.5c.

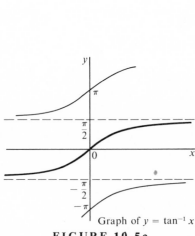

Graph of $y = \tan^{-1} x$

FIGURE 10.5c

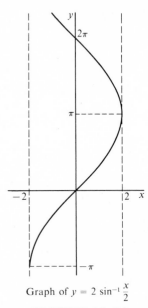

Graph of $y = 2 \sin^{-1} \dfrac{x}{2}$

FIGURE 10.5d

The same criteria as those used for the inverse sine and cosine functions lead to the following definition for the inverse tangent function.

**Definition 10.5c.** The **principal inverse tangent** function is the function

$$\{(x, y): x = \tan y, \; -\pi/2 < y < \pi/2\}.$$

The value of this function at $x$ is denoted by $\text{Tan}^{-1} x$.

---

*Example 10.5d.* Find $\text{Tan}^{-1} \tan (3\pi/4)$.

Since $\tan 3\pi/4 = -1$,

$$\text{Tan}^{-1} \tan (3\pi/4) = \text{Tan}^{-1} (-1) = -\pi/4.$$

---

The construction of the graphs of the inverse relations for the remaining three trigonometric functions is left for the exercises.

---

*Example 10.5e.* Sketch $y = 2 \sin^{-1} \frac{1}{2}x$.

We have

$$\tfrac{1}{2}y = \sin^{-1} \tfrac{1}{2}x,$$

so that

$$\tfrac{1}{2}x = \sin \tfrac{1}{2}y,$$

and

$$x = 2 \sin \tfrac{1}{2}y.$$

The graph is a sine curve along the $y$-axis with an amplitude of 2 and a period of $2\pi/\frac{1}{2} = 4\pi$. See Figure 10.5d.

## Exercises 10.5

In each of Numbers 1 to 12, evaluate the given expression.

1. $\sin^{-1} (-\sqrt{3}/2)$.
2. $\tan^{-1} \sqrt{3}$.
3. $\cos^{-1} (1/\sqrt{2})$.
4. $\cos^{-1} (-1)$.
5. $\text{Tan}^{-1} (-1)$.
6. $\text{Sin}^{-1} (-1)$.

7. $\text{Cos}^{-1} (-\sqrt{3}/2)$.
8. $\text{Tan}^{-1} (-1/\sqrt{3})$.
9. $\text{Sin}^{-1} \cos (\pi/2)$.
10. $\text{Cos}^{-1} \cos (5\pi/3)$.
11. $\text{Cos}^{-1} \sin (-\pi/4)$.
12. $\text{Sin}^{-1} \tan (\pi/4)$.

In each of Numbers 13 to 15, define and sketch the *inverse relation* of the given function.

13. $\{(x, \cot x)\}$.
14. $\{(x, \sec x)\}$.
15. $\{(x, \csc x)\}$.

16. Make restrictions on the range of each of the relations in Numbers 13 to 15 so that the relation will be a function.
17. Is it true that $\text{Sin}^{-1} (-x) = -\text{Sin}^{-1} x$? Explain.
18. Is it true that $\text{Cos}^{-1} (-x) = \text{Cos}^{-1} x$? Explain.

In each of Numbers 19 to 22, solve for $x$ in terms of $y$.

19. $y = \frac{1}{2} \tan^{-1} 2x$.
20. $y = 5 \sin^{-1} (2/x)$.

21. $y + 1 = 2 \cos^{-1} (x + 1)$.
22. $y = \frac{1}{2} \text{Sin}^{-1} \sqrt{2x}$.

In each of Numbers 23 to 26, discuss and sketch the graph of the given equation

23. $y = \frac{1}{2} \sin^{-1} 3x$.

24. $y = 2 \cos^{-1} (x/3)$.

25. $y = 3 \operatorname{Tan}^{-1} (x - 1)$.

26. $y = \operatorname{Sin}^{-1} \sqrt{x}$.

In each of Numbers 27 to 34, simplify the given expression.

27. $\tan \operatorname{Sin}^{-1} x$.

28. $\sec \operatorname{Tan}^{-1} (1/x)$.

29. $\sec \operatorname{Sin}^{-1} \sqrt{4 - x^2}$.

30. $\sin \operatorname{Tan}^{-1} (3/\sqrt{x^2 - 9})$.

31. $\sin [2 \operatorname{Cos}^{-1} (21/29)]$.

32. $\cos [2 \operatorname{Sin}^{-1} (3/5)]$.

33. $\tan [\frac{1}{2} \operatorname{Sin}^{-1} (24/25)]$.

34. $\sin [\frac{1}{2} \operatorname{Tan}^{-1} (5/12)]$.

In each of Numbers 35 to 40, find (a) $\sin \theta$, (b) $\cos \theta$, (c) $\tan \theta$. Do not use tables

35. $\theta = \operatorname{Sin}^{-1} (\frac{1}{3}) + \operatorname{Cos}^{-1} (\frac{2}{3})$.

36. $\theta = \operatorname{Tan}^{-1} 1 + \operatorname{Cos}^{-1} (\frac{1}{2})$.

37. $\theta = \operatorname{Tan}^{-1} (\frac{3}{4}) - \operatorname{Sin}^{-1} (\frac{1}{2})$.

38. $\theta = \operatorname{Tan}^{-1} (\frac{1}{7}) - 2 \operatorname{Tan}^{-1} (\frac{1}{3})$.

39. $\theta = 2 \operatorname{Sin}^{-1} (\frac{3}{5}) - \operatorname{Cos}^{-1} (\frac{12}{13})$.

40. $\theta = \operatorname{Cos}^{-1} (\frac{3}{5}) + 2 \operatorname{Tan}^{-1} (\frac{5}{12})$.

Solve for $x$ in each of Numbers 41 to 48. Do not use tables.

41. $\operatorname{Tan}^{-1} x + \operatorname{Tan}^{-1} (\frac{3}{5}) = \pi/4$.

42. $\operatorname{Sin}^{-1} (\frac{3}{5}) + \operatorname{Sin}^{-1} x = \operatorname{Tan}^{-1} (\frac{56}{33})$.

43. $\operatorname{Tan}^{-1} (\frac{1}{3}) + \operatorname{Tan}^{-1} x = \operatorname{Tan}^{-1} (-1)$.

44. $2 \operatorname{Tan}^{-1} (\frac{1}{3}) + \operatorname{Tan}^{-1} x = \pi/4$.

45. $\operatorname{Tan}^{-1} (\frac{1}{2}) + \operatorname{Tan}^{-1} (\frac{1}{3}) = \operatorname{Tan}^{-1} x$.

46. $\operatorname{Sin}^{-1} x = \operatorname{Cos}^{-1} (\frac{1}{5}) + \operatorname{Cos}^{-1} (\frac{2}{5})$.

47. $\operatorname{Tan}^{-1} x = \operatorname{Tan}^{-1} h + \operatorname{Tan}^{-1} k$.

48. $\operatorname{Sin}^{-1} x = 2 \operatorname{Sin}^{-1} a - \operatorname{Sin}^{-1} b$.

## 10.6 THE CALCULUS OF THE INVERSE TRIGONOMETRIC FUNCTIONS

To find the derivative of the inverse sine function $\{(x, y): y = \operatorname{Sin}^{-1} x\}$, let u
write

$$x = \sin y, \qquad -\pi/2 \leqq y \leqq \pi/2,$$

so that

$$D_y x = \cos y.$$

If $-\pi/2 < y < \pi/2$, then Theorem 6.6b guarantees that $D_x y$ exists and

$$D_x y = \frac{1}{D_y x} = \frac{1}{\cos y}.$$

Furthermore, for these values of $y$, $\cos y > 0$ and

$$\cos y = \sqrt{1 - \sin^2 y} = \sqrt{1 - x^2}, \qquad |x| < 1.$$

Thus,

$$D_x \operatorname{Sin}^{-1} x = \frac{1}{\sqrt{1 - x^2}}, \qquad |x| < 1.$$

Furthermore, an application of the chain rule yields the formula

(1) $$D_x \operatorname{Sin}^{-1} u = \frac{1}{\sqrt{1 - u^2}} D_x u, \qquad |u| < 1.$$

The inverse differential formula corresponding to (1) is

(2)
$$\int \frac{du}{\sqrt{1 - u^2}} = \text{Sin}^{-1} u + C, \qquad |u| < 1.$$

Formula (2) may be replaced by the following more general formula, which may be verified by differentiation:

(3)
$$\int \frac{du}{\sqrt{a^2 - u^2}} = \text{Sin}^{-1} \frac{u}{a} + C, \qquad |u| < a.$$

The only other inverse trigonometric function of particular interest in differentiation and integration techniques is the inverse tangent function given by $\{(x, y): y = \text{Tan}^{-1} x\}$. Here we may write

$$x = \tan y, \qquad -\pi/2 < y < \pi/2,$$

to obtain

$$D_y x = \sec^2 y.$$

As before, if $-\pi/2 < y < \pi/2$, then Theorem 6.6b guarantees that $D_x y$ exists and

$$D_x y = \frac{1}{D_y x} = \frac{1}{\sec^2 y}.$$

Since $\sec^2 y = 1 + \tan^2 y = 1 + x^2$, we have the formula

$$D_x \text{Tan}^{-1} x = \frac{1}{1 + x^2}.$$

This result is generalized by use of the chain rule to give

(4)
$$D_x \text{Tan}^{-1} u = \frac{1}{1 + u^2} D_x u.$$

The following inverse differential formula may now be verified by direct differentiation:

(5)
$$\int \frac{du}{a^2 + u^2} = \frac{1}{a} \text{Tan}^{-1} \frac{u}{a} + C, \qquad a \neq 0.$$

---

*Example 10.6a.* Find

$$\int \frac{dx}{\sqrt{4 - 9x^2}} \quad \text{and} \quad \int \frac{x\,dx}{\sqrt{4 - 9x^2}}.$$

In the first case, we have

$$\int \frac{dx}{\sqrt{4 - 9x^2}} = \frac{1}{3} \int \frac{3\,dx}{\sqrt{(2)^2 - (3x)^2}}$$

$$= \frac{1}{3} \text{Sin}^{-1} \frac{3x}{2} + C.$$

In the second case, the formula for $\int u^n \, du$ must be used (why?), and we obtain

$$\int \frac{x \, dx}{\sqrt{4 - 9x^2}} = -\frac{1}{18} \int (4 - 9x^2)^{-1/2}(-18x \, dx)$$

$$= -\frac{1}{9} \sqrt{4 - 9x^2} + C.$$

*Example 10.6b.* Find

$$\int \frac{dx}{4 + 9x^2} \quad \text{and} \quad \int \frac{x \, dx}{4 + 9x^2}.$$

In the first case, we have

$$\int \frac{dx}{4 + 9x^2} = \frac{1}{3} \int \frac{3 \, dx}{(2)^2 + (3x)^2}$$

$$= \frac{1}{6} \text{Tan}^{-1} \frac{3x}{2} + C.$$

In the second case, the formula for $\int du/u$ must be used (why?), and we have

$$\int \frac{x \, dx}{4 + 9x^2} = \frac{1}{18} \int \frac{18x \, dx}{4 + 9x^2}$$

$$= \frac{1}{18} \ln (4 + 9x^2) + C.$$

The student should study the preceding two examples carefully and be able to distinguish among the cases where the different formulas apply.

## Exercises 10.6

1. Verify Formula (3).
2. Verify Formula (5).
3. Obtain a formula for $D_x \text{Cos}^{-1} u$, where $0 < \text{Cos}^{-1} u < \pi$.
4. Show that

$$D_x \text{Sec}^{-1} u = \frac{1}{u\sqrt{u^2 - 1}} D_x u,$$

where $0 < \text{Sec}^{-1} u < \frac{1}{2}\pi$ for $u > 1$, and $-\pi < \text{Sec}^{-1} u < -\frac{1}{2}\pi$ for $u < -1$.

Find the indicated derivative in each of Numbers 5 to 16.

5. $r = \text{Tan}^{-1} (s/2)$; $D_s r$.
6. $y = \text{Sin}^{-1} 2x$; $D_x y$.
7. $w = \text{Sin}^{-1} \sqrt{2u}$; $D_u w$.
8. $y = \text{Tan}^{-1} e^x$; $D_x y$.
9. $y = e^{2x} \text{Tan}^{-1} e^{2x}$; $D_x y$.
10. $s = \text{Sin}^{-1} \ln u$; $D_u s$.
11. $y = 3x \text{Sin}^{-1} 2x$; $D_x y$.
12. $w = x \text{Tan}^{-1} (1/x)$; $D_x w$.

13. $t = \ln \text{Tan}^{-1} \frac{1}{2}s$; $D_s t$.
14. $x = \dfrac{\text{Sin}^{-1} t}{t}$; $D_t x$.
15. $u = \dfrac{v}{\text{Tan}^{-1} 2v}$; $D_v u$.
16. $y = \text{Sin}^{-1} \dfrac{x}{1 + x^2}$; $D_x y$.

In each of Numbers 17 to 26, find the indicated inverse derivative.

17. $\int \dfrac{4}{4 + s^2}\, ds.$

22. $\int \dfrac{u^3\, du}{4 + u^4}.$

18. $\int \dfrac{t\, dt}{9 + t^4}.$

23. $\int \dfrac{t\, dt}{1 + t}.$

19. $\int \dfrac{x\, dx}{\sqrt{1 - 4x^2}}.$

24. $\int \dfrac{x^2\, dx}{x^2 + 1}.$

20. $\int \dfrac{dx}{\sqrt{9 - 16x^2}}.$

25. $\int \dfrac{\cos u\, du}{1 + \sin^2 u}.$

21. $\int \dfrac{e^v\, dv}{1 + 4e^{2v}}.$

26. $\int \dfrac{s\, ds}{\sqrt{16 - 9s^4}}.$

In each of Numbers 27 to 30, evaluate the given definite integral.

27. $\displaystyle\int_0^1 \dfrac{dx}{\sqrt{4 - x^2}}.$

29. $\displaystyle\int_0^1 \dfrac{dx}{e^x + e^{-x}}.$

28. $\displaystyle\int_{-3}^3 \dfrac{du}{9 + u^2}.$

30. $\displaystyle\int_0^{1/2} \dfrac{x\, dx}{\sqrt{1 - 4x^4}}.$

1. Find the area bounded by the curve $y = 1/(4 + x^2)$, the $x$-axis, and the lines $x = -2$ and $x = 0$.
2. Find the area bounded by the curve $y = 8/(4 + 9x^2)$, the $x$-axis, the $y$-axis, and the line $x = 2/3$.
3. Discuss and sketch the graph of $y = \text{Sin}^{-1}\sqrt{2x - x^2}$.
4. Discuss and sketch the graph of $y = \text{Sin}^{-1}(1/\sqrt{2x})$.
5. Show that

$$D_x \text{Tan}^{-1}\left(\dfrac{1 + x}{1 - x}\right) = \dfrac{1}{1 + x^2}.$$

Explain how to reconcile this with the fact that

$$\int \dfrac{dx}{1 + x^2} = \text{Tan}^{-1} x + C.$$

6. Show that

$$D_x\left[\dfrac{1}{2} \text{Sin}^{-1}\left(\dfrac{1 - x^2}{1 + x^2}\right)\right] = \begin{cases} -(1 + x^2)^{-1} & \text{for } x \geq 0, \\ (1 + x^2)^{-1} & \text{for } x < 0. \end{cases}$$

Explain how to reconcile this with the fact that

$$\int \dfrac{dx}{1 + x^2} = \text{Tan}^{-1} x + C.$$

7. Find $D_{xy}$ if $\text{Tan}^{-1}(y/x) - \ln\sqrt{x^2 + y^2} = 1$, and determine for what values of $x$, if any, the derivative function is discontinuous.
8. Show that the area under the curve $y = a/(b^2 + c^2 x^2)$ from $x = 0$ to $x = t$ is bounded as $t \to \infty$.

39. Find the area enclosed by $x = 0$, $y = 0$, $y = 1/\sqrt{9 - 4x^2}$, and $x = 3\sqrt{3}/4$.
40. Find the volume generated by revolving the area bounded by $x = 0$, $y = 0$, $x = 4/5$, and $y = 1/\sqrt{16 + 25x^2}$ about the $x$-axis.
41. A flagpole 15 feet high stands at the edge of the roof of a building so that the foot of the pole is 60 feet above an observer's eye level. How far from the building should the observer stand so that the pole subtends the maximum possible angle at his eye?
42. A line is drawn from the point $(-1, 0)$ to a point $(x, y)$ on the curve $y = 2\sqrt{x}$. Find the maximum inclination that this line can have.
43. Use the Mean Value Theorem for Derivatives to show that

$$0.7952 < \text{Tan}^{-1} 1.02 < 0.7954.$$

44. Use the Mean Value Theorem for Derivatives to show that

$$0.1 < \text{Sin}^{-1} 0.1 < 0.10051.$$

45. In Example 7.7a, find the rate at which the angle $OAB$ is changing.
46. In Exercises 7.7, Number 5, find the rate at which the angle between the rope and the ground is changing.
47. In Exercises 7.7, Number 9, find the rate at which the angle between the two parts of the strip is changing.
48. A balloon is released 500 feet away from an observer. If the balloon rises at the rate of 100 feet per minute, what is the rate at which the angle of elevation of the observer's line of sight is increasing, 6 minutes after the balloon is released?
49. In Number 48, suppose that while the balloon is rising a wind carries it directly away from the observer at a rate of 75 feet per minute. At what rate is the angle of elevation of the observer's line of sight increasing, 6 minutes after the balloon is released?
50. A searchlight is trained on a plane that flies directly above the light at an altitude of 2 miles and at a speed of 400 miles per hour. How fast must the light be turning 2 seconds after the plane passes directly overhead?

## 10.7 THE HYPERBOLIC FUNCTIONS

Certain combinations of the exponential functions occur frequently enough in engineering and physics that they have been given special names. The two most important such combinations are called the **hyperbolic sine** (sinh) and the **hyperbolic cosine** (cosh). They are

(1) $$\sinh u . = . \frac{e^u - e^{-u}}{2},$$

and

(2) $$\cosh u . = . \frac{e^u + e^{-u}}{2}.$$

These functions are called hyperbolic functions because they are related geometri rically to the hyperbola in much the same way that the trigonometric functions are related to a circle. It is easily shown from Equations (1) and (2) that

$$\cosh^2 u - \sinh^2 u = 1.$$

This fundamental identity suggests that the hyperbola

$$x^2 - y^2 = 1$$

may be represented in parametric form by the equations

$$x = \cosh u, \quad y = \sinh u.$$

The relationship between the parameter $u$, $\cosh u$, $\sinh u$, and the hyperbola may then be given a geometric interpretation similar to that given to the relationship between $\theta$, $\cos \theta$, $\sin \theta$, and the unit circle. For the unit circle in Figure 10.7a, the area of the sector $AOP$, where $A$ is the point $(1, 0)$, $O$ is the origin,

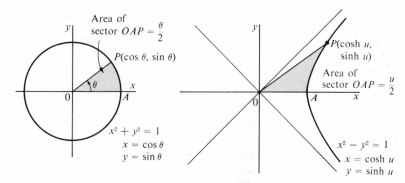

**FIGURE 10.7a**

and $P$ is the point $(\cos \theta, \sin \theta)$, is $\theta/2$ (l.u.)$^2$. For the hyperbola $x^2 - y^2 = 1$, if $A$ is the point $(1, 0)$ and $P$ the point $(\cosh u, \sinh u)$, then the area of the sector $AOP$ is $u/2$ (l.u.)$^2$. (The proof that the area of the hyperbolic sector $AOP$ is $u/2$ is deferred to Exercises 12.3, Number 41.)

The other hyperbolic functions are defined with reference to the hyperbolic sine and hyperbolic cosine by analogy with the definitions of the trigonometric functions; that is,

(3)
$$\tanh u .=. \frac{\sinh u}{\cosh u} = \frac{e^u - e^{-u}}{e^u + e^{-u}},$$

(4)
$$\coth u .=. \frac{\cosh u}{\sinh u} = \frac{e^u + e^{-u}}{e^u - e^{-u}},$$

(5)
$$\operatorname{sech} u .=. \frac{1}{\cosh u} = \frac{2}{e^u + e^{-u}},$$

(6)
$$\operatorname{csch} u .=. \frac{1}{\sinh u} = \frac{2}{e^u - e^{-u}}.$$

The graph of $y = \sinh x$ can be obtained by sketching the curves $y = e^x/2$ and $y = e^{-x}/2$ and then subtracting the ordinates (see Figure 10.7b). The graph of $y = \cosh x$ can be obtained in a similar manner by adding ordinates (see Figure 10.7c).

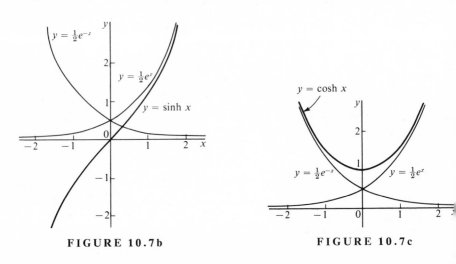

**FIGURE 10.7b**                    **FIGURE 10.7c**

If a uniform, perfectly flexible, and inextensible cable is suspended between two points, under its own weight the cable forms a curve called a *catenary*. A close approximation to a catenary is the curve formed by an electric transmission cable suspended between two poles, and the calculations for the length of wire needed for a given project are based on the length of the catenary. If the origin is taken at a distance $a$ below the lowest point of the curve, then it can be shown that the equation of the curve is

$$y = a \cosh \frac{x}{a}.$$

Thus, Figure 10.7c illustrates the catenary for $a = 1$.

To obtain the graph of $y = \tanh x$, note that

$$\lim_{x \to \infty} \tanh x = \lim_{x \to \infty} \frac{e^x - e^{-x}}{e^x + e^{-x}} = \lim_{x \to \infty} \frac{1 - e^{-2x}}{1 + e^{-2x}} = 1,$$

and also that

$$\lim_{x \to -\infty} \tanh x = \lim_{x \to -\infty} \frac{e^{2x} - 1}{e^{2x} + 1} = -1.$$

The graph is shown in Figure 10.7d. Notice that the range of the hyperbolic tangent function is $-1 < y < 1$.

There are numerous identities involving the hyperbolic functions which are quite similar to the corresponding identities involving trigonometric functions.

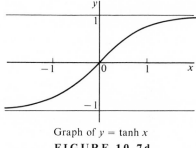

Graph of $y = \tanh x$

**FIGURE 10.7d**

These identities for the hyperbolic functions can easily be proved by direct use of the definitions of the functions, as in the next example.

---

*Example 10.7a.* Prove that

$$\sinh (x + y) = \sinh x \cosh y + \cosh x \sinh y.$$

In this problem, we may make use of the definitions of the hyperbolic functions to write $\sinh x \cosh y + \cosh x \sinh y$

$$= \left(\frac{e^x - e^{-x}}{2}\right)\left(\frac{e^y + e^{-y}}{2}\right) + \left(\frac{e^x + e^{-x}}{2}\right)\left(\frac{e^y - e^{-y}}{2}\right)$$

$$= \tfrac{1}{4}(e^{x+y} - e^{-x+y} + e^{x-y} - e^{-x-y} + e^{x+y} + e^{-x+y} - e^{x-y} - e^{-x-y})$$

$$= \tfrac{1}{2}(e^{x+y} - e^{-x-y})$$

$$= \sinh (x + y).$$

---

Similar expressions may be obtained for $\sinh (x - y)$, $\cosh (x + y)$, and $\cosh (x - y)$. (See Exercises 10.7, Numbers 4 and 5.) Identities such as these are occasionally helpful in simplifying more cumbersome expressions involving the hyperbolic functions, as will be illustrated later.

The derivatives of the hyperbolic sine and' hyperbolic cosine are easily obtained from their definitions. Thus,

(7) $$D_x \sinh x = D_x \frac{e^x - e^{-x}}{2} = \frac{e^x + e^{-x}}{2} = \cosh x,$$

and

(8) $$D_x \cosh x = D_x \frac{e^x + e^{-x}}{2} = \frac{e^x - e^{-x}}{2} = \sinh x.$$

The derivation of the formulas for the derivatives of the other hyperbolic functions is left for the exercises.

The following example illustrates the application of some of these ideas.

---

*Example 10.7b.* Find the maximum, minimum, and inflection points, and sketch the curve $y = 5 \cosh x - 4 \sinh x$.

We have

$$y' = 5 \sinh x - 4 \cosh x$$

and

$$y'' = 5 \cosh x - 4 \sinh x = y.$$

It follows from the first of these equations that

$$y' = 0 \Rightarrow \tanh x = \frac{4}{5},$$

and a book of tables gives the value $x = 1.1$ (approximately). Also, since

$$\tanh x = \frac{\sinh x}{\cosh x} \quad \text{and} \quad 1 + \sinh^2 x = \cosh^2 x,$$

we find

$$\tanh x = \frac{4}{5} \Rightarrow \sinh x = \frac{4}{3} \quad \text{and} \quad \cosh x = \frac{5}{3}.$$

Hence, at the critical point, where $x = 1.1$, we obtain $y'' = 3 > 0$, so that the curve is concave up and the point (1.1, 3) is a minimum point.

Since $\cosh x \geq 1$ and $\cosh x > \sinh x$, it follows that $y'' > 0$ for all values of $x$, and the curve is concave upward everywhere with no inflection points. It can be shown (see Exercises 10.7, Number 5) that

$$\cosh (a - b) = \cosh a \cosh b - \sinh a \sinh b.$$

This result suggests that we write

$$5 \cosh x - 4 \sinh x = k \cosh x \cosh b - k \sinh x \sinh b.$$

Then,

$$k \cosh b = 5 \quad \text{and} \quad k \sinh b = 4 \Rightarrow k^2 \cosh^2 b - k^2 \sinh^2 b = k^2 = 9$$
$$\Rightarrow k = 3,$$

since $\cosh b > 0$. Thus, $\cosh b = 5/3$, $\sinh b = 4/3$, and

$$5 \cosh x - 4 \sinh x = 3 \cosh (x - b).$$

It follows that the given curve is simply a hyperbolic cosine curve with its minimum point at $(b, 3) = (1.1, 3)$ (see Figure 10.7e).

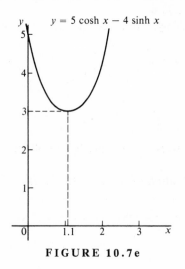

FIGURE 10.7e

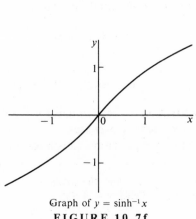

Graph of $y = \sinh^{-1} x$

FIGURE 10.7f

The inverse of the function $\{(x, y): y = \sinh x\}$ is the relation described by $\{(x, y): y = \sinh^{-1} x\}$. Since to each value of the range of the hyperbolic sine function there corresponds only one value of the domain, this inverse is also a function (see Figure 10.7f).

It would seem that $\sinh^{-1} x$ might be expressed as a logarithmic function, since $\sinh x$ is defined in terms of the exponential function. This conjecture is easily verified by writing

$$y = \sinh^{-1} x$$

in the form

$$x = \sinh y = \frac{e^y - e^{-y}}{2}$$

and solving for $y$. Upon multiplying each side by $e^y$ and solving the resulting quadratic equation in $e^y$, we get

$$2xe^y = e^{2y} - 1,$$
$$e^{2y} - 2xe^y - 1 = 0,$$

and

$$e^y = x + \sqrt{x^2 + 1}.$$

Only the positive sign is used in front of the radical, since $e^y > 0$. Thus, by taking logarithms, we find $y = \ln(x + \sqrt{x^2 + 1})$, or

(9) $$\sinh^{-1} x = \ln(x + \sqrt{x^2 + 1}).$$

The inverse of the hyperbolic cosine function is not a function but may be made one by restricting the range so that $y \geq 0$, as is indicated by the heavy portion of the curve in Figure 10.7g.

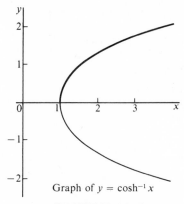

Graph of $y = \cosh^{-1} x$

**FIGURE 10.7g**

If $\cosh^{-1} x$ is expressed in terms of logarithms, the result is

(10) $$\cosh^{-1} x = \ln(x \pm \sqrt{x^2 - 1}), \qquad x \geq 1.$$

The inverse hyperbolic cosine *function* is obtained by choosing the positive sign in front of the radical. Thus,

$$(10')\qquad\qquad \text{Cosh}^{-1} x = \ln (x + \sqrt{x^2 - 1}), \qquad x \geq 1.$$

By differentiating Formulas (9) and (10'), we obtain

$$(11)\qquad\qquad D_x \sinh^{-1} u = \frac{D_x u}{\sqrt{u^2 + 1}}$$

and

$$(12)\qquad\qquad D_x \text{Cosh}^{-1} u = \frac{D_x u}{\sqrt{u^2 - 1}}, \qquad u > 1.$$

---

*Example 10.7c.* Find

$$\int \frac{dx}{\sqrt{9x^2 + 4}}.$$

It follows from Formula (11) that

$$\int \frac{dx}{\sqrt{9x^2 + 4}} = \frac{1}{2} \int \frac{dx}{\sqrt{(3x/2)^2 + 1}}$$

$$= \frac{1}{3} \int \frac{3/2 \, dx}{\sqrt{(3x/2)^2 + 1}}$$

$$= \frac{1}{3} \sinh^{-1} \frac{3x}{2} + C.$$

## Exercises 10.7

In each of Numbers 1 to 13, verify the given identity.

1. $\cosh^2 x - \sinh^2 x = 1.$
2. $1 - \tanh^2 x = \text{sech}^2 x.$
3. $\coth^2 x - 1 = \text{csch}^2 x.$
4. $\sinh (x - y) = \sinh x \cosh y - \cosh x \sinh y.$
5. $\cosh (x - y) = \cosh x \cosh y - \sinh x \sinh y.$
6. $\sinh 2x = 2 \sinh x \cosh x.$
7. $\cosh 2x = \cosh^2 x + \sinh^2 x.$

8. $\sinh \dfrac{x}{2} = \pm \sqrt{\dfrac{\cosh x - 1}{2}}.$

9. $\cosh \dfrac{x}{2} = \sqrt{\dfrac{\cosh x + 1}{2}}.$

10. $\tanh \dfrac{x}{2} = \dfrac{\sinh x}{1 + \cosh x}.$

11. $\sinh x + \sinh y = 2 \sinh \frac{1}{2}(x + y) \cosh \frac{1}{2}(x - y).$
12. $\cosh x + \cosh y = 2 \cosh \frac{1}{2}(x + y) \cosh \frac{1}{2}(x - y).$

13. $\tanh (x + y) = \dfrac{\tanh x + \tanh y}{1 + \tanh x \tanh y}.$

In each of Numbers 14 to 21, verify the differentiation formula.

4. $D_x \tanh u = \text{sech}^2 u \, D_x u.$

5. $D_x \coth u = -\text{csch}^2 u \, D_x u.$

6. $D_x \text{sech} \, u = -\text{sech} \, u \tanh u \, D_x u.$

7. $D_x \text{csch} \, u = -\text{csch} \, u \coth u \, D_x u.$

8. Formula (11).

19. Formula (12).

20. $D_x \tanh^{-1} u = \dfrac{D_x u}{1 - u^2}, \; |u| < 1.$

21. $D_x \coth^{-1} u = \dfrac{D_x u}{1 - u^2}, \; |u| > 1.$

In each of Numbers 22 to 25, sketch the graph of the function defined by the given equation.

22. $y = \coth x.$

23. $y = \text{sech} \, x.$

24. $y = \text{csch} \, x.$

25. $y = 2 \sinh (x - 3).$

In each of Numbers 26 to 39, find the indicated inverse derivative.

26. $\displaystyle\int x \cosh \tfrac{1}{2} x^2 \, dx.$

27. $\displaystyle\int \sinh 3x \cosh 3x \, dx.$

28. $\displaystyle\int \sinh^2 x \, dx.$

29. $\displaystyle\int \tanh 2x \, dx.$

30. $\displaystyle\int \text{sech} \, x \, dx.$

31. $\displaystyle\int \tanh^3 x \, dx.$

32. $\displaystyle\int \sinh^3 3u \, du.$

33. $\displaystyle\int \dfrac{dx}{\sqrt{4x^2 - 9}}.$

34. $\displaystyle\int \dfrac{4 \, dx}{\sqrt{4x^2 + 9}}.$

35. $\displaystyle\int \dfrac{dx}{4 - x^2}, \; |x| < 2.$

36. $\displaystyle\int \dfrac{x \, dx}{\sqrt{4x^2 - 9}}.$

37. $\displaystyle\int \dfrac{dx}{9x^2 - 16}, \; |3x| > 4.$

38. $\displaystyle\int \dfrac{x^2 \, dx}{x^2 - 4}, \; |x| > 2.$

39. $\displaystyle\int \dfrac{x \, dx}{4 - 9x^2}, \; |3x| < 2.$

40. Derive Formula (10).

41. Find the volume formed by revolving about the $x$-axis the area under the catenary $y = a \cosh x/a$ from $x = 0$ to $x = a$.

42. Find the maximum and minimum points of the curve

$$y = a \cosh x + b \sinh x, \qquad a > 0, b > 0.$$

43. Sketch the curve $x = 3 \cosh t, y = 4 \sinh t$.

## 10.8 EVALUATION OF LIMITS BY L'HÔPITAL'S RULE

On a number of occasions, we have encountered problems in which it was necessary to evaluate limits of the form $\lim_{x \to a} f(x)/g(x)$. In some cases we have been able to use the theorem on limits, which states that

$$\lim_{x \to a} \frac{f(x)}{g(x)} = \frac{\lim\limits_{x \to a} f(x)}{\lim\limits_{x \to a} g(x)}$$

provided the latter two limits exist and $\lim_{x \to a} g(x) \neq 0$. In the event that $\lim_{x \to a} g(x) = 0$ and $\lim_{x \to a} f(x) = 0$ also, it is sometimes possible to evaluate $\lim_{x \to a} f(x)/g(x)$. For example, it has already been shown that

$$\lim_{x \to 2} \frac{x^2 - 4}{x - 2} = 4 \quad \text{and} \quad \lim_{x \to 0} \frac{\sin x}{x} = 1.$$

However, there are many examples of expressions of the form $f(x)/g(x)$ for which a limit exists but for which we have not yet developed a technique for finding the limit. For instance, does $\lim_{x \to 1} [(\ln x)/(x - 1)]$ exist, and, if it does, what is the limit?

In order to develop a general method for evaluating limits of this form, we find it convenient first to refer back to Rolle's Theorem and the Mean Value Theorem for Derivatives and to derive from those ideas a somewhat more generalized version of the Mean Value Theorem.

The Mean Value Theorem for Derivatives was given for functions described by an equation of the form $y = f(x)$. If a function is described in parametric form, then the theorem assumes the following somewhat different aspect.

**Theorem 10.8a.** Suppose that $x = f(t)$ and $y = g(t)$ define two functions on the interval $a \leq t \leq b$ such that

(1) $f$ and $g$ are continuous on $a \leq t \leq b$,
(2) $f$ and $g$ are differentiable over $a < t < b$,
(3) $g(a) \neq g(b)$,
(4) $g'(t) \neq 0$ for $a < t < b$.

Then there is a value of $t$, say $t_1$, in $a < t < b$ such that

$$\frac{f(b) - f(a)}{g(b) - g(a)} = \frac{f'(t_1)}{g'(t_1)}.$$

PROOF: The proof of the theorem is based on Rolle's Theorem and is similar to the proof of the original Mean Value Theorem. Let

$$\varphi(t) = f(t) - f(a) - \left[ \frac{f(b) - f(a)}{g(b) - g(a)} \right] [g(t) - g(a)].$$

It is then easy to verify that $\varphi(a) = \varphi(b) = 0$, so that Rolle's Theorem may be used. Hence, there is a point, $t_1$, such that $\varphi'(t_1) = 0$. Thus

$$0 = f'(t_1) - \left[ \frac{f(b) - f(a)}{g(b) - g(a)} \right] g'(t_1),$$

and the theorem follows.

The preceding theorem provides a simple way of proving the next theorem which can frequently be used for the evaluation of limits.

**Theorem 10.8b.** *L'Hôpital's Rule.* Let two functions $f$ and $g$ have continuous derivatives on some $\mathfrak{N}^*(a, h)$, where $g'(x) \neq 0$, and let $f(a) = g(a) = 0$. Then

(i) $$\lim_{x \to a} \frac{f'(x)}{g'(x)} \text{ exists} \Rightarrow \lim_{x \to a} \frac{f(x)}{g(x)} = \lim_{x \to a} \frac{f'(x)}{g'(x)}$$

and

(ii) $$\frac{f'(x)}{g'(x)} \to \infty \text{ as } x \to a \Rightarrow \frac{f(x)}{g(x)} \to \infty \text{ as } x \to a.$$

PROOF: The proof will be given for (i). The details of (ii) are left for the reader.

In $\mathfrak{N}^*(a^+, h)$, $g'(x) \neq 0$, so that Theorem 10.8a may be applied for the interval $a < x < a + h$. In this interval, there is an $x_1$ such that $a < x_1 < x$, and

$$\frac{f(x) - f(a)}{g(x) - g(a)} = \frac{f'(x_1)}{g'(x_1)} \quad \text{or} \quad \frac{f(x)}{g(x)} = \frac{f'(x_1)}{g'(x_1)},$$

and, since $\lim_{x \to a} f'(x)/g'(x)$ exists,

$$\lim_{x \to a^+} \frac{f'(x_1)}{g'(x_1)} = \lim_{x \to a^+} \frac{f'(x)}{g'(x)} = \lim_{x \to a^+} \frac{f(x)}{g(x)}.$$

In a similar way, the limit from the left can be shown to exist, and consequently

$$\lim_{x \to a} \frac{f'(x)}{g'(x)} = \lim_{x \to a} \frac{f(x)}{g(x)}.$$

The following examples illustrate the use of L'Hôpital's Rule.

---

*Example 10.8a.* Find

$$\lim_{x \to 0} \frac{x \cos x - \sin x}{x}.$$

If $f(x) = x \cos x - \sin x$ and $g(x) = x$, it follows that $f(0) = 0$ and $g(0) = 0$. Also we have

$$f'(x) = \cos x - x \sin x - \cos x = -x \sin x,$$

and

$$g'(x) = 1.$$

The conditions of Theorem 10.8b are satisfied, so that

$$\lim_{x \to 0} \frac{x \cos x - \sin x}{x} = \lim_{x \to 0} \frac{-x \sin x}{1} = \frac{0}{1} = 0,$$

a result that makes use of the continuity of the derivatives.

---

*Example 10.8b.* Evaluate

$$\lim_{x \to 0^+} \frac{\sin x}{\sqrt{x}}.$$

If $f(x) = \sin x$ and $g(x) = \sqrt{x}$, then $f(0) = g(0) = 0$, and

$$f'(x) = \cos x, \quad g'(x) = \frac{1}{2\sqrt{x}}.$$

Again the conditions of Theorem 10.8b are satisfied, so that

$$\lim_{x \to 0^+} \frac{\sin x}{\sqrt{x}} = \lim_{x \to 0^+} \frac{\cos x}{1/(2\sqrt{x})} = \lim_{x \to 0^+} 2\sqrt{x} \cos x = 0.$$

If an application of L'Hôpital's Rule should lead to a form $\lim_{x \to a} f'(x)/g'(x)$ where both $f'(a)$ and $g'(a)$ are 0, then the rule may be applied to the ratio $f'(x)/g'(x)$, provided that the functions $f'$ and $g'$ satisfy the conditions of the theorem.

*Example 10.8c.* Evaluate

$$\lim_{x \to 0} \frac{xe^x - x}{\sin^2 2x}.$$

Since the conditions of Theorem 10.8b are satisfied, we have

$$\lim_{x \to 0} \frac{xe^x - x}{\sin^2 2x} = \lim_{x \to 0} \frac{e^x + xe^x - 1}{4 \sin 2x \cos 2x} = \lim_{x \to 0} \frac{e^x + xe^x - 1}{2 \sin 4x}.$$

The numerator and denominator of the last expression are both 0 when $x = 0$, so that the limit cannot yet be determined. However, the expressions $e^x + xe^x - 1$ and $2 \sin 4x$ both satisfy the conditions of Theorem 10.8b. Hence, a further application of this theorem yields

$$\lim_{x \to 0} \frac{e^x + xe^x - 1}{2 \sin 4x} = \lim_{x \to 0} \frac{2e^x + xe^x}{8 \cos 4x} = \frac{1}{4}.$$

It is clear that Theorem 10.8b may be used successively as often as is necessary, provided the appropriate conditions are satisfied at each stage of the application.

The following extension of L'Hôpital's Rule is stated without proof.

**Theorem 10.8c.** If $f$ and $g$ both have continuous derivatives for all sufficiently large values of $x$, and $f(x) \to 0$, $g(x) \to 0$ as $x \to \infty$, then

(i)
$$\lim_{x \to \infty} \frac{f'(x)}{g'(x)} \text{ exists} \Rightarrow \lim_{x \to \infty} \frac{f(x)}{g(x)} = \lim_{x \to \infty} \frac{f'(x)}{g'(x)}$$

and

(ii)
$$\frac{f'(x)}{g'(x)} \to \infty \text{ as } x \to \infty \Rightarrow \frac{f(x)}{g(x)} \to \infty \text{ as } x \to \infty.$$

*Example 10.8d.* Evaluate

$$\lim_{x \to \infty} \frac{1/x^2}{\sin^2 (2/x)}.$$

Since the conditions of Theorem 10.8c are satisfied, we have

$$\lim_{x \to \infty} \frac{1/x^2}{\sin^2 (2/x)} = \lim_{x \to \infty} \frac{-2/x^3}{-(4/x^2) \sin (2/x) \cos (2/x)}$$

$$= \lim_{x \to \infty} \frac{1/x}{\sin (4/x)}$$

$$= \lim_{x \to \infty} \frac{-1/x^2}{-(4/x^2) \cos (4/x)}$$

$$= \lim_{x \to \infty} \frac{1}{4 \cos (4/x)} = \frac{1}{4}.$$

(Notice that in addition to the algebraic simplifications, L'Hôpital's Rule has been applied twice. This limit can be evaluated without L'Hôpital's Rule. Do you see how to do it?)

The following case of L'Hôpital's Rule is also given without proof.

**Theorem 10.8d.** Suppose that $f(x)$ and $g(x)$ both increase without limit as $x$ approaches $a$ and that $f'$ and $g'$ are both continuous on some $\mathfrak{N}^*(a, h)$. Then

(i)
$$\lim_{x \to a} \frac{f'(x)}{g'(x)} \text{ exists} \Rightarrow \lim_{x \to a} \frac{f(x)}{g(x)} = \lim_{x \to a} \frac{f'(x)}{g'(x)}$$

and

(ii)
$$\frac{f'(x)}{g'(x)} \to \infty \text{ as } x \to a \Rightarrow \frac{f(x)}{g(x)} \to \infty \text{ as } x \to a.$$

Furthermore, the same rule applies without other changes as $x \to \infty$, provided $f'$ and $g'$ are continuous for all sufficiently large values of $x$.

*Example 10.8e.* Evaluate

$$\lim_{x \to \infty} \frac{\ln x}{\ln (a + x)}.$$

Using Theorem 10.8d, we get

$$\lim_{x \to \infty} \frac{\ln x}{\ln (a + x)} = \lim_{x \to \infty} \frac{1/x}{1/(a + x)} = \lim_{x \to \infty} \frac{a + x}{x} = 1.$$

# Exercises 10.8

Evaluate each of the following limits, if the limit exists. Make algebraic simplifications when possible before using L'Hôpital's Rule.

1. $\lim\limits_{x \to 0} \dfrac{\sin kx}{x}$.

2. $\lim\limits_{x \to \pi/2} \dfrac{\frac{1}{2}\pi - x}{\cos 3x}$.

3. $\lim\limits_{x \to 0} \dfrac{e^x - e^{-x}}{x^2}$.

4. $\lim\limits_{t \to 0} \dfrac{1 - \cos t}{\sin t}$.

5. $\lim\limits_{x \to a} \dfrac{a - x}{\ln (a - x)}$.

6. $\lim\limits_{x \to 0^+} \dfrac{e^{-1/x}}{x}$.

7. $\lim\limits_{t \to \infty} \dfrac{t}{\ln t}$.

8. $\lim\limits_{u \to \infty} \dfrac{e^u}{u^2}$.

9. $\lim\limits_{y \to \infty} \dfrac{y^3}{e^y}$.

10. $\lim\limits_{s \to \infty} \dfrac{\ln (as + b)}{\ln (cs + d)}$.

11. $\lim\limits_{\varphi \to 0} \dfrac{\sin \varphi - \varphi}{\tan \varphi - \varphi}$.

12. $\lim\limits_{x \to 0} \dfrac{1 - x}{\cos x}$.

13. $\lim\limits_{x \to \infty} \dfrac{\ln x}{\sqrt{x}}$.

14. $\lim\limits_{x \to \pi/2} \dfrac{\tan 3x}{\tan 5x}$.

15. $\lim\limits_{x \to 0} \dfrac{a^x - b^x}{x}$.

16. $\lim\limits_{x \to 0^-} \dfrac{\ln (1 - x)}{\sin x}$.

17. $\lim\limits_{t \to 0} \dfrac{\mathrm{Sin}^{-1} t}{t}$.

18. $\lim\limits_{y \to a} \dfrac{y^n - a^n}{y - a}$.

19. $\lim\limits_{\theta \to 0} \dfrac{\theta - \theta \cos \theta}{\sin^3 2\theta}$.

20. $\lim\limits_{x \to 0} \dfrac{e^{2x^2} - 1}{\sin^2 x}$.

21. $\lim\limits_{x \to 0} \dfrac{e^x - \sin x - 1}{1 - \cos 2x}$.

22. $\lim\limits_{t \to 0} \dfrac{t - \sin^2 t}{1 - \cos 2t}$.

## 10.9 FURTHER EVALUATION OF LIMITS

In the preceding section we saw that the limit of a fraction $f(x)/g(x)$, where both $f(x)$ and $g(x) \to 0$ or else increase without limit, can be evaluated with the aid of L'Hôpital's Rule. These limits are conveniently referred to as $0/0$ or $\infty/\infty$ forms. There are a number of other forms that can be changed algebraically into one of these forms so that L'Hôpital's Rule may be applied.

Suppose $f(x) \to 0$ and $g(x) \to \infty$ as $x \to a$. Then, $\lim_{x \to a} f(x)g(x)$ may be designated as a $0 \cdot \infty$ form. Such a form is easily changed into a $0/0$ form or an $\infty/\infty$ form by writing

$$f(x)g(x) = \frac{f(x)}{1/g(x)} \quad \text{or} \quad f(x)g(x) = \frac{g(x)}{1/f(x)},$$

and then L'Hôpital's Rule may often be used.

*Example 10.9a.* Evaluate $\lim_{x \to 0^+} x \ln \sin x$.

Since

$$x \ln \sin x = \frac{\ln \sin x}{1/x},$$

we have a form to which L'Hôpital's Rule applies. Hence,

$$\lim_{x \to 0^+} \frac{\ln \sin x}{1/x} = \lim_{x \to 0^+} \frac{\cos x / \sin x}{-1/x^2}$$

$$= \lim_{x \to 0^+} (-x) \frac{x}{\sin x} \cos x = 0.$$

Another form that can be changed algebraically into one to which L'Hôpital's Rule may be applied is $f(x) - g(x)$, where $f(x)$ and $g(x)$ both $\to \infty$ as $x \to a$. The procedure is illustrated in the following example.

*Example 10.9b.* Evaluate

$$\lim_{x \to 0} \left[ \frac{1}{x} - \frac{1}{\sin x} \right].$$

Since

$$\frac{1}{x} - \frac{1}{\sin x} = \frac{\sin x - x}{x \sin x},$$

L'Hôpital's Rule may be applied to give

$$\lim_{x \to 0} \frac{\sin x - x}{x \sin x} = \lim_{x \to 0} \frac{\cos x - 1}{\sin x + x \cos x}$$

$$= \lim_{x \to 0} \frac{-\sin x}{2 \cos x - x \sin x} = 0.$$

Exponential forms may also be analyzed, as in the following example, by first taking logarithms to obtain a form of one of the types already discussed.

*Example 10.9c.* Evaluate $\lim_{x \to 0^+} (\cos 2x)^{1/x}$.

Let $y = (\cos 2x)^{1/x}$, so that $\ln y = (1/x) \ln \cos 2x$. Then, by L'Hôpital's Rule, we get

$$\lim_{x\to 0^+} \ln y = \lim_{x\to 0^+} \frac{\ln \cos 2x}{x}$$

$$= \lim_{x\to 0^+} \frac{-2 \sin 2x}{\cos 2x} = 0.$$

Since $\ln y \to 0$ as $x \to 0^+$, then $y \to 1$, so that

$$\lim_{x\to 0^+} (\cos 2x)^{1/x} = 1.$$

The reader is cautioned against falling into the trap of saying that since $\cos 2x \to 1$ as $x \to 0$, then

$$(\cos 2x)^{1/x} \to 1$$

because "any power of 1 is 1." Since we are concerned only with values of $x$ in a *deleted* neighborhood of 0, $\cos 2x$ is never actually equal to 1 for values of $x \in \mathfrak{N}^*(0, \epsilon)$, if $\epsilon < \pi/4$.

An expression of the type $\lim_{x\to a} [f(x)]^{g(x)}$, for which one of the following is true,

(a) $g(x) \to 0$, $f(x) \to 0$, as $x \to a$,
(b) $g(x) \to 0$, $f(x) \to \infty$, as $x \to a$,
(c) $g(x) \to \infty$, $f(x) \to 1$, as $x \to a$,

can often be evaluated by the process described in the preceding example.

## Exercises 10.9

Evaluate each of the following limits, if possible.

1. $\lim_{x\to\infty} xe^{1/x}$.

2. $\lim_{x\to 0^+} x \ln x$.

3. $\lim_{x\to 0^+} x^x$.

4. $\lim_{y\to\infty} y^2 e^{-y}$.

5. $\lim_{x\to\pi/2} (\sec x - \tan x)$.

6. $\lim_{x\to 0} (\csc 2x - \cot x)$.

7. $\lim_{x\to 0^+} x \ln \sin x$.

8. $\lim_{\theta\to 0} \theta \csc 3\theta$.

9. $\lim_{t\to 0} \left(\frac{1}{t^2} - \frac{1}{\sin^2 t}\right)$.

10. $\lim_{u\to 0^+} \left(\frac{1}{u} + \ln u\right)$.

11. $\lim_{x\to 1} \left(\frac{1}{x-1} - \frac{1}{\ln x}\right)$.

12. $\lim_{\theta\to\pi/2} \left(2 \sec^2 \theta - \frac{1}{1-\sin \theta}\right)$.

13. $\lim_{x\to 0^+} (1 - \sin x)^{1/x}$.

14. $\lim_{\varphi\to 0} (\cos 2\varphi)^{1/\varphi^2}$.

15. $\lim_{t\to\pi/2} (\sin t)^{\tan t}$.

16. $\lim_{x\to\infty} (1 + e^{-x^2})^x$.

17. $\lim_{x\to 0} (1/x)^{\sin x}$.

18. $\lim_{h\to\infty} \left(1 + \frac{b}{h}\right)^h$.

19. $\lim_{x\to 0} (x + e^x)^{a/x}$.

20. $\lim_{x\to 1^-} x^{1/(1-x)}$.

## 10.10 THE NEWTON-RAPHSON METHOD OF SOLVING EQUATIONS

It is quite common in mathematics and in its applications to be required to find a root of an equation $f(x) = 0$, where there is no elementary method for solving the equation in an exact form. For instance, although quadratic equations can be solved by means of the quadratic formula, there are no corresponding formulas for polynomial equations of degree higher than the fourth. Even the third and fourth degree equations are usually solved more conveniently by approximation methods rather than by the use of the complicated general formulas that are available. Equations involving trigonometric, inverse trigonometric, logarithmic, or exponential functions may be deceptively simple in appearance without being amenable to any practical method of exact solution. One example will suffice to illustrate the truth of this statement.

---

*Example 10.10a.* A wire 10 inches long is to be bent into a circular arc with a chord 8 inches long. Find the radius of the arc (see Figure 10.10a).

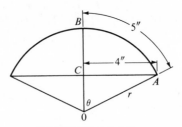

**FIGURE 10.10a**

From the geometry of the figure, we see that the length of arc $AB$ is given by $r\theta$, and that the half-chord $AC$ is given by $r \sin \theta$. Hence,

$$r\theta = 5 \quad \text{and} \quad r \sin \theta = 4,$$

so that, by eliminating $r$, we obtain the equation

$$4\theta = 5 \sin \theta.$$

Once this equation is solved, the radius $r$ can easily be found from the equation $r\theta = 5$. However, at this stage of our discussion we can solve this equation only by trial and error methods using a table of trigonometric functions for angles in radians. From such a table, we find for $\theta = 1.13$ that $\sin \theta = 0.9044$, which is very nearly $\frac{4}{5}(1.13)$. Consequently, $\theta$ is approximately 1.13 radians and $r = 5/1.13 = 4.42$ inches.

---

A better method than simply guessing and verifying the guess by means of a table is desirable even in as easy a problem as the preceding one, and it is quite necessary in more complicated problems. A simple and often effective procedure for approximating a root of an equation is known as the **Newton-Raphson method,** which we shall discuss next.

Suppose we wish to find a root of $f(x) = 0$. Then, as was pointed out in Sec-
ion 3.4, an equivalent problem is that of finding where the graph of the func-
ion $f$ crosses the $x$-axis (see Figure 10.10b). If $f$ is a continuous function, then, by

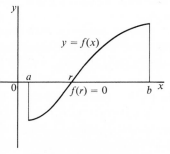

FIGURE 10.10b

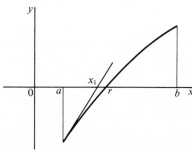

FIGURE 10.10c

he Intermediate Value Theorem, at least one root $r$ of the equation must be
ocated between every two numbers $a$ and $b$ for which $f(a)$ and $f(b)$ have oppo-
ite signs. For simplicity, let us assume that $f(a) < 0$ and $f(b) > 0$. Suppose
urther that $f$ is differentiable and $f'(x) \neq 0$ for any $x$ in the interval $a \leq x \leq b$.
The equation of a line tangent to the curve at $(a, f(a))$ is easily found to be

$$\frac{y - f(a)}{x - a} = f'(a)$$

or

$$y = f(a) + f'(a)(x - a).$$

The point where this tangent line crosses the $x$-axis is found by putting $y = 0$,
and the corresponding value of $x$ is

$$x_1 = a - \frac{f(a)}{f'(a)}.$$

Now, if the curve $y = f(x)$ is concave down over the interval $a \leq x \leq b$, so
hat the tangent line lies above the curve, and if $f(a) < 0$, then $x_1$ is between $a$
nd the root $r$; that is, $x_1$ is *nearer* than $a$ is to the root $r$. This situation is illus-
rated in Figure 10.10c. Thus, the number $x_1$ may be taken as an approximation
o the root $r$ of the equation. By repeating this procedure with $x_1$ in place of $a$,
 second approximation $x_2$ may be obtained, where

$$x_2 = x_1 - \frac{f(x_1)}{f'(x_1)}.$$

This process may be repeated as many times as is necessary in order to obtain
an approximation to $r$ to any desired degree of accuracy.

In order to be assured that the successive points $x_1, x_2, \ldots$, approach $r$, we
must impose certain conditions on the function $f$ in the neighborhood of the
oot $r$. In the preceding discussion, one of four possible cases was illustrated.
A complete statement is given in the following theorem.

**Theorem 10.10a.** Let $f$ be a function with a continuous second derivative on an interval $a \leq x \leq b$ and such that $f(a)$ and $f(b)$ have opposite signs and neither $f'(x)$ nor $f''(x)$ is zero for any $x$ in the interval.

(i) If the sign of $f''(x)$ is the same as that of $f(a)$, and $x_1 = a - [f(a)/f'(a)]$, then $a < x_1 < r$.

(ii) If the sign of $f''(x)$ is opposite to that of $f(a)$, and $x_1 = b - [f(b)/f'(b)]$, then $r < x_1 < b$.

PROOF: The proof, which depends simply on the interpretation of the sign of $f''(x)$, is left to the reader.

By the use of the appropriate part of Theorem 10.10a, we may show that a sequence of approximations $\{x_n\}$, where

$$x_{n+1} = x_n - \frac{f(x_n)}{f'(x_n)},$$

approaches the root $r$ as $n \to \infty$. Frequently, only a few steps are needed to obtain a good approximation to the root.

We can even show that, under fairly simple conditions, the number of accurate decimal places is at least doubled at each successive step. Thus, suppose that $r$ is a root of $f(x) = 0$, where $a < r < b$, and suppose that $f(a) < 0$, $f(b) > 0$, $f'(x) \neq 0$, and $f''(x) < 0$. Then the conditions of (i) of Theorem 10.10a are met. Let $x_{n+1}$ be the $(n+1)$th approximation to $r$ obtained by using the Newton-Raphson formula, so that

$$x_1 = a - \frac{f(a)}{f'(a)},$$

and

$$x_{n+1} = x_n - \frac{f(x_n)}{f'(x_n)}, \quad n \in \mathfrak{N}.$$

By Theorem 10.10a, $x_n < x_{n+1} < r$, and the difference $r - x_n$ is a positive number, say $h$. We have

$$r - x_{n+1} = r - x_n + \frac{f(x_n)}{f'(x_n)} = h + \frac{f(x_n)}{f'(x_n)}.$$

Also, by the Mean Value Theorem for Derivatives,

$$f(r) = f(x_n) + hf'(x_n + \theta_1 h), \quad 0 < \theta_1 < 1,$$

and, since $f(r) = 0$,

$$f(x_n) = -hf'(x_n + \theta_1 h).$$

By applying the Mean Value Theorem to $f'$, we obtain

$$f'(x_n + \theta_1 h) = f'(x_n) + \theta_1 hf''(x_n + \theta_2\theta_1 h), \quad 0 < \theta_2 < 1.$$

Hence

$$f(x_n) = -h[f'(x_n) + \theta_1 hf''(x_n + \theta_1\theta_2 h)],$$

so that

$$\frac{f(x_n)}{f'(x_n)} = -h - \theta_1 h^2 \frac{f''(x_n + \theta_1\theta_2 h)}{f'(x_n)}.$$

Accordingly,

$$r - x_{n+1} = -\theta_1 h^2 \frac{f''(x_n + \theta_1\theta_2 h)}{f'(x_n)},$$

and, since $0 < \theta_1 < 1$,

$$|r - x_{n+1}| < Mh^2,$$

where $M = \max |f''(x)|/\min |f'(x)|$ for $x$ between $x_n$ and $r$.

The final result can be obtained in the same way if any one of the other sets of conditions in Theorem 10.10a is assumed.

It follows that if we have a root $r$ in an interval of length $h$ for which $M < 1$, then the error in each approximation after the first is less than the square of the error in the preceding approximation. Now suppose that at some stage of the procedure we get the root correct to $k \geqq 1$ decimal places, so that the error is not greater than $5 \times 10^{-k-1}$. Then the error in the next step will be not greater than

$$25 \times 10^{-2k-2} < 5 \times 10^{-2k-1}.$$

That is, the number of correct decimal places is doubled. In practice, it is convenient to choose for $h$ the length of any interval which contains $r$ and one of whose end points is $x_n$.

---

*Example 10.10b.* Find, correct to three decimal places, the real root of the equation

$$\ln x + x - 2 = 0.$$

If $f(x) .=. \ln x + x - 2$, then $f$ is a continuous function with continuous derivatives for $x > 0$. Using tables, we find

$$f(1) = -1 \quad \text{and} \quad f(2) = 0.69315,$$

indicating that the root lies between 1 and 2. Furthermore,

$$f'(x) = \frac{1}{x} + 1 \quad \text{and} \quad f''(x) = -\frac{1}{x^2}.$$

Since $f''(x) < 0$ for all $x$, the curve is concave down and Case (i) of Theorem 10.10a applies. Hence, an approximation to the root is

$$x_1 = 1 - \frac{f(1)}{f'(1)} = 1.5.$$

By Theorem 10.10a, we know that the root $r$ is greater than 1.5, and less than 2. A second approximation is

$$x_2 = 1.5 - \frac{f(1.5)}{f'(1.5)} = 1.5 - \frac{(-0.09453)}{5/3}$$

$$= 1.5567 \text{ (approx.)}.$$

In order to obtain an idea of the accuracy of this result, we make use of the fact that $r - x_2 < Mh^2$, where

$$M = \frac{\max |f''(x)|}{\min |f'(x)|} \quad \text{for } 1.5 \leqq x \leqq 2,$$

and

$$h = r - x_1.$$

For values of $x$ from 1.5 to 2, we find that

$$\max |f''(x)| = \frac{1}{(1.5)^2} = \frac{4}{9}$$

and

$$\min |f'(x)| = \frac{1}{2} + 1 = \frac{3}{2}.$$

Hence, $M = 8/27 < 0.3$. This bound on the value of $M$ may be used from this point on, since the value of $M$ can only decrease if the interval containing the root is diminished. To get an estimate for $h$ so that $h$ is reasonably small, we need to determine a value of $x$ near $r$ such that $f(x) > 0$. Because the second approximation is less than 1.6, the latter value may prove to be satisfactory. In fact, with the aid of tables, we find that $f(1.6) = 0.07 > 0$. Therefore, we may take $h = 1.6 - 1.5 = 0.1$, and get

$$r - x_2 < Mh^2 < (0.3)(0.1)^2 = 0.003,$$

so that $r < 1.5597 < 1.56$. Since, by Theorem 10.10a, $x_2 < r$, we have

$$1.5567 < r < 1.56.$$

A third approximation is found to be

$$x_3 = 1.556 - \frac{f(1.556)}{f'(1.556)}$$

$$= 1.556 - \frac{-0.001882}{1.64267} = 1.557145.$$

An estimate for the error of this approximation is given by

$$r - x_3 < (0.3)(0.0033)^2 < 0.0000033,$$

where the value of $h$ is taken as the difference between the two previously given bounds on $r$.

Thus, we may say with certainty that

$$1.557145 < r < 1.5571483,$$

and to three decimals, we have $r = 1.557$. As this example illustrates, the accuracy of the approximation increases rapidly after the root has been located in an interval of length 0.1 or less.

---

A second example will illustrate the method further.

---

*Example 10.10c.* Find the real root of

$$x^3 - 2x - 5 = 0$$

to four decimal places.

If $f(x) = x^3 - 2x - 5$, then $f(2) = -1$ and $f(3) = 16$, so that a root lies between 2 and 3, since $f$ is continuous. Also,

$$f'(x) = 3x^2 - 2 \quad \text{and} \quad f''(x) = 6x.$$

Since, $f''(x) > 0$ over the interval between 2 and 3, and since $f'(x) \neq 0$ over this interval, we may use Theorem 10.10a, Case (ii). However, rather than using $b = 3$, it appears that we ought to choose a value for $b$ nearer 2—because $f(3)$ is so much larger than $|f(2)|$. Substitution of $x = 2.1$ into $f(x)$ shows that $f(2.1) > 0$, so that we may take $b = 2.1$. Then,

$$x_1 = 2.1 - \frac{f(2.1)}{f'(2.1)} = 2.095 \text{ (approx.).}$$

For the interval $2 \leq x \leq 2.1$, max $|f''(x)| = 12.6$, and min $|f'(x)| = 10$, and we have

$$|r - 2.095| < \left(\frac{1}{10}\right)^2\left(\frac{12.6}{10}\right) < 0.013,$$

so that

$$2.082 < r < 2.095.$$

Since it is awkward to round off 2.095 any further, let us make a second approximation using this value. Then,

$$x_2 = 2.095 - \frac{f(2.095)}{f'(2.095)} = 2.095 - \frac{0.005075}{11.167075} = 2.094552 \text{ (approx.).}$$

Furthermore, $f(2.094) < 0$, so that $2.094 < r < 2.095$. Therefore,

$$|r - 2.094552| < (0.001)^2(1.26) = 0.00000126,$$

where the value of $h$ in this case is taken as 0.001, since $r$ is in the interval from 2.094 to 2.095. Hence the approximation $x_2 = 2.09455$ is accurate to the fifth decimal place. Calculations show that

$$f(2.094552) = 0.00000578,$$

and

$$f(2.094550) = -0.000016,$$

so that the root $r > 2.09455$ and thus $r = 2.0946$, correct to four decimal places.

In the preceding example, the reader should observe that in rounding off an approximation $x_n$, he must round off to a larger number in order to assure that $f(x_n)$ will be of the same sign as $f(x_{n-1})$. Rounding off to a smaller number may lead to an "overcorrection." When an approximation $x_n$ is an overcorrection, then $f(x_n)$ will be of opposite sign from that of $f(x_{n-1})$. Normally, however, the overcorrection will cause no trouble. In general, in rounding off an approximation $x_n$, when $x_n$ is greater than the root $r$, we should round off to a larger value, and when $x_n$ is less than the root $r$, we should round off to a smaller value.

## Exercises 10.10

For each of Numbers 1 to 10, use the Newton-Raphson Method to find the indicated root of the given equation to three decimal places.

1. $2 \ln x + x = 0$; the real root.
2. $x^4 + 4x + 1 = 0$; the negative root of smaller absolute value.
3. $x^3 - 3x - 3 = 0$; the real root.
4. $2 \sin x = x$; the positive root.
5. $e^x + x - 2 = 0$; the real root.
6. $\theta + \cos 2\theta = 0$; the real root.

7. $e^x = \tan x$; the smallest positive root.
8. $3 \sin x = x^2$; the positive root.
9. $x^4 + x^3 + x^2 = 1$; the smallest positive root.
10. $x + \text{Tan}^{-1} x - 1 = 0$; the smallest positive root.
11. In a certain circle, a chord 9 inches long subtends an arc 12 inches long. Find, in radians correct to three decimal places, the central angle which the chord subtends.
12. The area of one end of a tank in the form of a right circular cylinder is 75 square feet. The axis of the tank is horizontal and the tank is partially filled with water. Find the depth of the water if one-third of the area of the end of the tank is covered with water.
13. A wire 12 inches long is bent into a circular arc whose chord is 10 inches. What is the radius of the arc?
14. Two buildings are on opposite sides of an alley. A ladder 16 feet long extends from the foot of one building to the wall of the second building. Another ladder 20 feet long extends from the foot of the second building to the wall of the first building. If the ladders cross at a point 4 feet above the alley, find the width of the alley. *Hint*: You should get a fourth degree polynomial equation to solve for the height to which a ladder reaches up the side of the building. Use this distance to calculate the width of the alley.
15. A sector of a circle is cut from a piece of paper and rolled up without overlapping to form a right circular cone. What should be the central angle of the sector so that this angle is 1.5 times the vertex angle of the cone?
16. Find the maximum point on the curve $y = x \sin x$, $x > 0$, that is closest to the origin.

---

## Summary of Chapter 10

---

The trigonometric and hyperbolic functions and their inverses play an important role in many mathematical studies. It is therefore important that the student have a thorough knowledge of and facility with them, as well as an understanding of the general techniques, in regard to the following points:

(1) the continuity of the sine and cosine functions (Section 10.1);
(2) the derivatives of the trigonometric functions and their applications (Sections 10.2, 10.3);
(3) the inverse derivatives of the trigonometric functions (Section 10.4);
(4) the inverse trigonometric functions (Section 10.5);
(5) the derivatives of the inverse trigonometric functions (Section 10.6);
(6) the hyperbolic and inverse hyperbolic functions and their derivatives (Section 10.7);
(10) L'Hôpital's Rule for the evaluation of limits and its applications (Sections 10.8, 10.9);
(11) the Newton-Raphson Method for the approximation of roots of equations (Section 10.10).

# Chapter 11    Vectors and Complex-Valued Functions

## 11.1 VECTORS

The study of physical problems is a rich source of many mathematical concepts, which are particularly valuable because they in turn lead to simple methods of describing and analyzing other physical situations. In this section, we shall introduce one such concept from mathematical physics.

In physics, we are often concerned with an entity called a **force.** It has been found, as a result of many experiments, that a force is characterized by a magnitude, a direction, and a rule of combination with other forces. The first two characteristics suggest that a force can be represented geometrically by a directed line segment such as $OP$ in Figure 11.1a. The length of the line segment

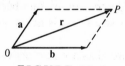

**FIGURE 11.1a**

proportional to the magnitude of the force and the direction of the segment the direction in which the force acts. Directed line segments used for such a representation may be called **arrows** and are frequently denoted by symbols such as **a, b, r,** and so on. (In this book, boldface type will be used to denote these directed quantities. In writing by hand, it is customary to use a half-arrow over a letter or a wavy line under the letter, as $\vec{a}$ or $\underset{\sim}{a}$ for the same purpose.)

It is known from experiment that two forces, **a** and **b**, acting at a common point, are equivalent to a single **resultant** force, **r**. Furthermore, this single force correctly represented by the diagonal of the parallelogram having the arrows representing **a** and **b** as its sides (see Figure 11.1a). The force **r** is called the sum the forces **a** and **b**, and we write

$$\mathbf{r} = \mathbf{a} + \mathbf{b}.$$

Notice that this equation uses the plus sign in a different sense from that of ordinary algebraic addition. The plus sign here means that the quantities represented by **a** and **b** are combined by the **parallelogram law of composition.**

**Definition 11.1a.** Quantities that can be represented by arrows and that combine according to the parallelogram law are called **vectors.**

Examples of such quantities are forces, displacements, and velocities. (There are also other quantities that can be represented by arrows, but that do not combine according to the parallelogram law.)

Although we now have a geometrical representation for vectors, we do not yet have a convenient analytical representation for them. However, that it is possible to represent vector quantities by sets of numbers is already suggested by our earlier considerations in locating points in a two-dimensional space by means of ordered pairs of numbers. To illustrate, recall that the symbol (4, 3) represents a certain point $P$, with respect to an origin $O$ (see Figure 11.1b).

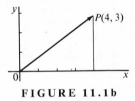

**FIGURE 11.1b**

This pair of numbers determines, with reference to $O$, a direction and a magnitude, the direction being given by the direction numbers $[4k, 3k]$ and the magnitude by the length of the line segment from $O$ to $P$. Hence, it appears reasonable to interpret an ordered pair of numbers $(a_1, a_2)$, where $a_1$ and $a_2$ are not both zero, as an arrow whose *tip* is at the point $(a_1, a_2)$ and whose *tail* is at the origin.

Finally, $(a_1, a_2)$ may be regarded as a vector provided a condition for equality and a definition for addition of ordered pairs that is equivalent to the parallelogram rule can be prescribed. Since distinct ordered pairs are associated with distinct points, the following definition is reasonable.

**Definition 11.1b.** $(a_1, a_2) = (b_1, b_2) \Leftrightarrow a_1 = b_1$ and $a_2 = b_2$.

The geometrical illustration in Figure 11.1c suggests the definition for addition.

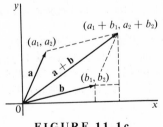

**FIGURE 11.1c**

**Definition 11.1c.** $(a_1, a_2) + (b_1, b_2) .=. (a_1 + b_1, a_2 + b_2).$

Thus, if

$$\mathbf{a} = (2, 4), \quad \mathbf{b} = (-3, 2),$$

then

$$\mathbf{a} + \mathbf{b} = (2, 4) + (-3, 2)$$
$$= (2 - 3, 4 + 2) = (-1, 6).$$

It follows at once that if $\mathbf{a} = (a_1, a_2)$ is a vector, then the magnitude of $\mathbf{a}$, denoted by $|\mathbf{a}|$, is given by the number

$$[a_1^2 + a_2^2]^{1/2}.$$

The vector $\mathbf{0} .=. (0, 0)$ is called the **zero vector**. This vector has magnitude zero but does not have direction.

The representation of vectors by pairs of real numbers implies that some properties of vectors can be deduced from properties of real numbers. This idea is illustrated in the proofs of the following three theorems.

**Theorem 11.1a.** The addition of vectors obeys the commutative law:

$$\mathbf{a} + \mathbf{b} = \mathbf{b} + \mathbf{a}.$$

PROOF: Let $\mathbf{a} = (a_1, a_2)$ and $\mathbf{b} = (b_1, b_2)$. Then

$$\mathbf{a} + \mathbf{b} = (a_1 + b_1, a_2 + b_2),$$

and

$$\mathbf{b} + \mathbf{a} = (b_1 + a_1, b_2 + a_2).$$

By the commutative law of addition for real numbers, we have

$$a_1 + b_1 = b_1 + a_1, \quad a_2 + b_2 = b_2 + a_2,$$

so that

$$\mathbf{a} + \mathbf{b} = \mathbf{b} + \mathbf{a},$$

as was to be shown.

**Theorem 11.1b.** Vector addition is associative:

$$(\mathbf{a} + \mathbf{b}) + \mathbf{c} = \mathbf{a} + (\mathbf{b} + \mathbf{c}).$$

PROOF: The proof is a simple consequence of the definition of addition for vectors and the associative law for real numbers, and is left for the reader.

Let $\mathbf{a} = (a_1, a_2)$. Then by the definition of addition we may write $2(a_1, a_2) = (a_1, a_2) + (a_1, a_2) = (2a_1, 2a_2)$. If this process is repeated $k - 1$ times, we arrive at a relation $k(a_1, a_2) = (ka_1, ka_2)$, where $k$ is an integer. This suggests the more general relationship given by

**Definition 11.1d.** If $k$ is a real number, then

$$k(a_1, a_2) .=. (a_1, a_2)k .=. (ka_1, ka_2).$$

*Note*: The first part of this definition is equivalent to the statement

$$k\mathbf{a} = \mathbf{a}k.$$

The real number $k$ is often called a **scalar** and the operation defined in Definition 11.1d is called **scalar multiplication.**

**Theorem 11.1c.** $\qquad k(\mathbf{a} + \mathbf{b}) = k\mathbf{a} + k\mathbf{b}, \qquad k \in \mathcal{R}.$

PROOF: This result follows directly from Definition 11.1d and Definition 11.1c. The details are left for the reader.

It is not difficult to see that the multiplication of a vector by a positive real number does not alter the direction of the vector, but it may change the magnitude or the length of the vector. Multiplication of a vector by a negative number reverses the direction of the vector and may also change the magnitude. Multiplication of a vector by zero always yields the zero vector.

Vector subtraction may be defined by means of the following two definitions.

**Definition 11.1e.** $\qquad -\mathbf{a} .=. (-1)\mathbf{a}.$

**Definition 11.1f.** $\qquad \mathbf{a} - \mathbf{b} .=. \mathbf{a} + (-\mathbf{b}).$

The vector sum and difference of $\mathbf{a}$ and $\mathbf{b}$ are shown in Figure 11.1d.

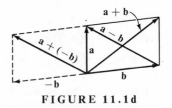

**FIGURE 11.1d**

Figure 11.1d illustrates an important fact about vectors. Since $\mathbf{a} - \mathbf{b}$ is a vector $\mathbf{x}$ such that $\mathbf{a} = \mathbf{b} + \mathbf{x}$, it may be represented in the diagram as the vector that extends from the tip of $\mathbf{b}$ to the tip of $\mathbf{a}$. But $\mathbf{x}$ is also the vector $\mathbf{a} + (-\mathbf{b})$ which is shown in the diagram. We know that $\mathbf{a} - \mathbf{b}$ and $\mathbf{a} + (-\mathbf{b})$ are the same vector $\mathbf{x}$, yet they appear as two different line segments in the figure. Evidently, the location of the arrow in the diagram is unimportant only the magnitude and direction are of fundamental importance insofar as a vector is concerned. (*Note:* There are certain applications in which the location of the arrow *is* important and attention will be called to this fact when it is necessary.)

For example, the vector $\mathbf{a} = (3, 1)$ can be written as the sum or difference of

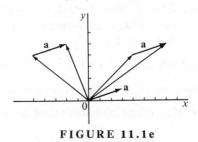

**FIGURE 11.1e**

two other vectors in infinitely many ways. Thus, $\mathbf{a} = (7, 5) - (4, 4)$ or $\mathbf{a} = (-2, 5) - (-5, 4)$, and $\mathbf{a}$ may be drawn as shown in Figure 11.1e. In other words, we may regard a given vector to be represented by an arrow of the correct length and direction but located anywhere in the plane, simply by writing the vector as the difference of two appropriate vectors.

In view of Definition 11.1d and the rule for addition of vectors, we may write an arbitrary vector $\mathbf{a}$ in a special form as follows:

$$\mathbf{a} = (a_1, a_2) = (a_1, 0) + (0, a_2)$$
$$= a_1(1, 0) + a_2(0, 1).$$

In other words, *every* vector in two-dimensional space may be expressed as a sum of just the two vectors $(1, 0)$ and $(0, 1)$, each multiplied by a properly chosen scalar. Since each of the two vectors $(1, 0)$ and $(0, 1)$ has a magnitude of one unit, it is called a **unit vector.** The following notation is customarily employed:

$$\mathbf{i} .=. (1, 0), \quad \mathbf{j} .=. (0, 1),$$

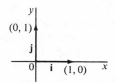

**FIGURE 11.1f**

and the vectors $\mathbf{i}$ and $\mathbf{j}$ may be represented as in Figure 11.1f. In terms of these two vectors, we may now write any vector $\mathbf{a} = (a_1, a_2)$ as

$$\mathbf{a} = a_1\mathbf{i} + a_2\mathbf{j}.$$

The numbers $a_1$ and $a_2$ are called the *components of* $\mathbf{a}$ *with respect to the* $\mathbf{i}$ *and* $\mathbf{j}$ *vectors*. The $\mathbf{i}$ and $\mathbf{j}$ vectors are called a **base set** or simply a **basis,** because every other vector may be written in terms of these two vectors in the manner just indicated. These ideas will be of considerable value later in obtaining important results in a simple way.

## Exercises 11.1

1. If $\mathbf{a} .=. (2, 4)$, $\mathbf{b} .=. (4, -3)$, $\mathbf{c} .=. (-3, 2)$, determine

    (a) $\mathbf{a} + \mathbf{b}$,             (d) $|\mathbf{c} - \mathbf{b}|$,
    (b) $\mathbf{b} - \mathbf{a}$,             (e) $2\mathbf{a} + 3\mathbf{b}$,
    (c) $|\mathbf{c}|$,               (f) $|3\mathbf{a} - \mathbf{b}|$.

2. Suppose a vector $\mathbf{v}$ has its tail at the point $\mathbf{a} .=. (-2, -3)$ and its tip at $\mathbf{b} .=. (3, 9)$. Express $\mathbf{v}$ in terms of $\mathbf{a}$ and $\mathbf{b}$. Is this the same as the vector $\mathbf{p} = (5, 12)$? Explain.

3. Suppose the sides of a closed polygon represent vectors arranged tip to tail. What is the sum of these vectors?

4. The resultant of $\mathbf{a} .=. (3, 2)$ and $\mathbf{b}$ is $\mathbf{r} .=. (8, 8)$. What is the magnitude of $\mathbf{b}$?

5. If $\mathbf{a} \doteq 2\mathbf{i} + 3\mathbf{j}$ and $\mathbf{b} \doteq 4\mathbf{i} - \mathbf{j}$, determine

(a) $\mathbf{a} + \mathbf{b}$,

(b) $\mathbf{a} - \mathbf{b}$,

(c) $2\mathbf{a} - 3\mathbf{b}$,

(d) $|\mathbf{a}| \cdot |\mathbf{b}|$,

(e) $|\mathbf{a} + \mathbf{b}|$,

(f) $|\mathbf{a}| + |\mathbf{b}|$,

(g) $|3\mathbf{a} - 2\mathbf{b}|$,

(h) $|3\mathbf{a}| - |2\mathbf{b}|$.

6. In general, does $|\mathbf{a} + \mathbf{b}| = |\mathbf{a}| + |\mathbf{b}|$?

7. Demonstrate *geometrically* the associative law for vector addition.

8. Do vectors form a group with respect to addition?

9. Prove Theorem 11.1b.

10. Prove Theorem 11.1c.

11. Find a unit vector parallel to the resultant of the vectors $\mathbf{a} \doteq 2\mathbf{i} + 5\mathbf{j}$ and $\mathbf{b} \doteq 3\mathbf{i} - \mathbf{j}$.

12. Demonstrate graphically that $-(\mathbf{a} - \mathbf{b}) = -\mathbf{a} + \mathbf{b}$.

13. Show that $|\mathbf{a} - \mathbf{b}| \geq ||\mathbf{a}| - |\mathbf{b}||$.

14. Show that $|\mathbf{a} + \mathbf{b} + \mathbf{c}| \leq |\mathbf{a}| + |\mathbf{b}| + |\mathbf{c}|$.

15. If $\mathbf{a} \doteq -2\mathbf{i} + 3\mathbf{j}$, $\mathbf{b} \doteq 3\mathbf{i} - 4\mathbf{j}$, and $\mathbf{c} \doteq -\mathbf{i} - \mathbf{j}$, find $|2\mathbf{a} - 3\mathbf{b} - \mathbf{c}|$.

16. The vectors $\mathbf{i}$ and $\mathbf{j}$ form a base set for vectors in two dimensions. Is this the only base set possible? If you think not, give an example.

17. Do the vectors in a base set need to be unit vectors?

18. A rotation of a body through a given angle about a given line as axis can be represented by an arrow of length proportional to the angle and pointing along the axis in the direction from which the angle appears to be counterclockwise. Are such arrows vectors? That is, can such arrows be combined like vectors so that the associative and commutative laws are obeyed? *Hint*: Consider the simple case of a rotation through 90° about the $x$-axis followed by a rotation through 90° about the $y$-axis.

## 11.2 APPLICATIONS OF VECTORS

Vectors are indispensable in analyzing problems involving velocities, accelerations, and forces. Some of the simpler applications to velocity problems and force problems are discussed in this section.

Since a velocity is completely characterized by a magnitude and a direction, it is ideally represented by a vector whose magnitude represents the speed and whose direction is that of the velocity. This idea is illustrated in the following examples.

---

*Example 11.2a.* A man can row a boat at a rate of 4 mph in still water. If he attempts to row straight across a river 100 yards wide, and flowing at a rate of 3 mph, where will he land on the opposite shore? What will be the actual speed of the boat?

If the origin of coordinates is chosen at the starting point of the boat, then the rate of rowing is represented by the vector $\mathbf{a} = 4\mathbf{i}$, and the rate of the stream is represented by the vector $\mathbf{b} = -3\mathbf{j}$, as shown in Figure 11.2a. The resulting direction of travel is therefore that of the vector

$$\mathbf{r} = \mathbf{a} + \mathbf{b} = 4\mathbf{i} - 3\mathbf{j},$$

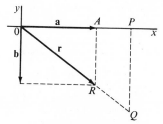

**FIGURE 11.2a**

which has the direction $[4, -3]$. The rate of travel in this direction is $|\mathbf{r}| = 5$ mph. Furthermore, triangle $OAR$ is similar to triangle $OPQ$, so that

$$\frac{PQ}{OP} = \frac{AR}{OA} = \frac{3}{4}.$$

Since $OP = 100$,

$$PQ = (100)\left(\frac{3}{4}\right) = 75 \text{ yards.}$$

Thus the boat lands 75 yards downstream.

---

The next example offers a slight variation of the problem in the preceding example.

---

*Example 11.2b.* A wind is blowing from the south at 50 mph. The pilot of a plane, whose speed in still air is 130 mph, wants to fly due east. In what direction should he head the plane?

If the plane were to head due east, the wind would cause it to drift north. Hence, the plane must head in a southeasterly direction in order to compensate for the wind.

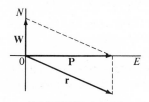

**FIGURE 11.2b**

Since the wind is due north, let its velocity be represented by the vector $\mathbf{W} = 50\mathbf{j}$, and let

$$\mathbf{r} = x\mathbf{i} + y\mathbf{j}$$

represent a vector of magnitude 130 mph in the direction in which the plane heads (see Figure 11.2b). Since it is required that the plane actually travel due east, the vector $\mathbf{p} = u\mathbf{i}$ may be used to represent the resultant velocity of the plane. Hence, we must have

$$\mathbf{W} + \mathbf{r} = \mathbf{p} \Rightarrow 50\mathbf{j} + x\mathbf{i} + y\mathbf{j} = u\mathbf{i}$$
$$\Rightarrow x\mathbf{i} + (y + 50)\mathbf{j} = u\mathbf{i} + 0\mathbf{j}$$
$$\Rightarrow x = u, \text{ and } y + 50 = 0, \text{ or } y = -50.$$

Furthermore, since
$$|\mathbf{r}| = \sqrt{x^2 + y^2} = 130,$$
we have
$$\sqrt{x^2 + 50^2} = 130.$$
It follows that
$$x = 120, \quad \mathbf{p} = 120\mathbf{i}.$$

This result means that if the plane heads in the direction given by [12, −5], then i
will actually travel due east at a speed of 120 mph.

---

*Example 11.2c.* Two forces, $\mathbf{F}_1$ and $\mathbf{F}_2$, are acting on an object. If $\mathbf{F}_1$ is 12 pound
and acts in the northeast direction and $\mathbf{F}_2$ is 6 pounds and acts in the northwest direc
tion, find their resultant.

If the origin is chosen at the object, then
$$\mathbf{F}_1 = 6\sqrt{2}\mathbf{i} + 6\sqrt{2}\mathbf{j},$$
and
$$\mathbf{F}_2 = -3\sqrt{2}\mathbf{i} + 3\sqrt{2}\mathbf{j},$$

as shown in Figure 11.2c. The resultant vector $\mathbf{r}$ is simply the sum of $\mathbf{F}_1$ and $\mathbf{F}_2$, so tha
$$\mathbf{r} = (6\sqrt{2}\mathbf{i} + 6\sqrt{2}\mathbf{j}) + (-3\sqrt{2}\mathbf{i} + 3\sqrt{2}\mathbf{j})$$
$$= 3\sqrt{2}\mathbf{i} + 9\sqrt{2}\mathbf{j}.$$

Thus, the direction of $\mathbf{r}$ is given by [1, 3], and its magnitude is
$$|\mathbf{r}| = [(3\sqrt{2})^2 + (9\sqrt{2})^2]^{1/2} = 6\sqrt{5} \text{ pounds.}$$

---

Problems involving a set of forces that are in equilibrium often make us
of the following fundamental law of mechanics.

**Law 11.2a.** If a rigid mechanical system is at rest, then the vector sum of all th
external forces acting on the system is zero.

An application of this law is illustrated in

---

*Example 11.2d.* An object weighing 7000 pounds is suspended by two cables. Rela
tive to the horizontal and vertical directions, one cable is in the [4, 3] direction and th
other is in the [−12, 5] direction. What is the tension in each of the cables?

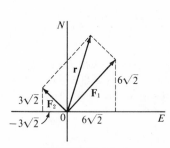

FIGURE 11.2c

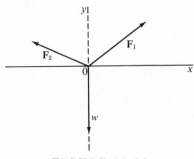

FIGURE 11.2d

It is convenient to introduce a coordinate system with the origin at the object and the cables in the $xy$-plane, as shown in Figure 11.2d. If $F_1$ is the force along the cable in the [4, 3] direction, $F_2$ the force along the cable in the [−12, 5] direction, and $w$ the downward force due to the weight of the object, then, by Law 11.2a, the sum of these forces must be zero; that is,

$$F_1 + F_2 + w = 0.$$

Since the vector $F_1$ is in the [4, 3] direction, its components are proportional to 4 and 3. Thus we may write

$$F_1 = 4ki + 3kj.$$

Similarly,

$$F_2 = -12mi + 5mj,$$

and

$$w = -7000j.$$

Hence, from

$$F_1 + F_2 + w = 0,$$

we get

$$(4k - 12m)i + (3k + 5m - 7000)j = 0,$$

and

$$4k - 12m = 0 \quad \text{and} \quad 3k + 5m - 7000 = 0.$$

It follows that

$$k = 3m \quad \text{and} \quad 3(3m) + 5m = 7000,$$

so that

$$m = 500 \quad \text{and} \quad k = 1500.$$

Thus,

$$F_1 = 6000i + 4500j$$

and

$$F_2 = -6000i + 2500j.$$

The tension in the first cable is

$$|F_1| = \sqrt{(6000)^2 + (4500)^2} = 7500 \text{ pounds},$$

and the tension in the second cable is

$$|F_2| = \sqrt{(6000)^2 + (2500)^2} \doteq 6500 \text{ pounds}.$$

## Exercises 11.2

In each of Numbers 1 to 3, find the resultant of the given set of vectors.

1. 10 units upward, 8 units to the right, 3 units downward.
2. 5 units in the northeast direction, 7 units in the northwest direction.
3. 3 units in the northeast direction, 6 units in the east direction, 5 units in the southeast direction.
4. Find the resultant of a force of 200 pounds acting in the [3, 4] direction and a force of 500 pounds acting in the [−8, 15] direction.
5. Find the resultant of a force of 50 pounds acting in the [−5, −12] direction, a force of 100 pounds acting in the [3, −4] direction, and a force of 75 pounds acting in the [8, 15] direction.

6. A plane is headed west at right angles to a 50 mph wind blowing from the north. If the plane's speed with no wind is 700 mph, find the actual speed and direction of flight.

7. A ship sailing north meets an ocean current flowing from west to east at a speed of 4 knots. If the ship's speed in still water is 25 knots, find the resultant speed and direction.

8. A man pushes a lawn mower with a force of 50 pounds acting in the direction of the handle. If the handle is held at a 30° angle with the horizontal, what part of the force actually is used in pushing the lawn mower in the horizontal direction? What is the useful part of the force if the handle is held at 45°? at 60°?

9. Two men were pushing a heavy box across a floor. One man pushed on the box in an easterly direction with a force of 60 pounds and the other pushed in a northerly direction with a force of 25 pounds. Find the magnitude and direction of the resultant force. If the second man had pushed in a northeasterly direction with the same force, what would be the resultant force on the box?

10. A boat can travel 9 mph in still water. In what direction should the boat head in order to reach a point 20 miles below its starting point on the opposite bank of a river that is $2\sqrt{65}$ miles wide and that flows at a rate of 6 mph?

11. If the wind blows in a southeasterly direction at 40 mph, in what direction should a pilot fly a plane at 120 mph in order that the plane will travel straight east?

12. A car is stuck in the mud. The enterprising driver ties a rope to the car and to a tree 40 feet in front of the car. Assuming that the rope is initially taut and won't stretch, what force can the driver apply to pull the car straight forward if he can displace the center of the rope 1 foot with a force of 100 pounds in a direction perpendicular to the rope?

13. A crane is holding a 3-ton beam above the ground. There is a 6-foot length of cable between the beam and the top of the crane. What force would be required to push the beam 2 feet sideways? If the cable is lengthened 12 feet, what force would be required to push the beam 2 feet sideways?

14. A boom 20 feet long is attached to the base of a vertical pole 20 feet high, and is supported at its upper end by a cable passing through a pulley at the top of the pole. Find the tension in the cable when the boom supports a weight of 500 pounds from its upper end when it is in a direction of [3, 4] relative to the horizontal and vertical directions. Neglect the weight of the boom.

## 11.3 THE TRIGONOMETRIC FORM OF A COMPLEX NUMBER

In Section 1.8, a complex number was defined to be an ordered pair of real numbers that obeys certain rules of equality, addition, and multiplication. In Section 11.1, a vector in a two-dimensional space was defined to be an ordered pair of real numbers, the rules for equality and addition being the same as for complex numbers. The multiplication of a vector by a scalar corresponds exactly to the multiplication of a complex number by a real number. Therefore it is both interesting and useful to associate the complex number $(a, b)$ or $a + ib$ with the vector $(a, b)$. Thus, we may regard the arrow that represents vector $(a, b)$ as a geometric representation of the complex number $a + ib$. For example, in Figure 11.3a the arrow labeled **a**, which represents the vector

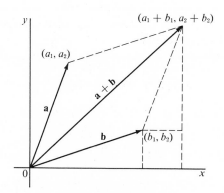

**FIGURE 11.3a**

$\mathbf{a} .=. (a_1, a_2)$, may also represent the complex number $a_1 + ia_2$. Figure 11.3a illustrates further that the geometric representation of the sum of two vectors $(a_1, a_2)$ and $(b_1, b_2)$ is the same as the representation of the sum of two complex numbers $a_1 + ia_2$ and $b_1 + ib_2$.

Since the number-pair $(a, b)$ may also be represented as a point with $x$-coordinate $a$ and $y$-coordinate $b$ in the $xy$-plane, the complex number $a + ib$ may be associated with the point $(a, b)$. We shall find that both the point representation and the vector representation of a complex number are useful, and we may employ either of these at our convenience.

The absolute value of a real number may be interpreted geometrically as the distance between the origin and the point representing the number on the number scale. The absolute value of a complex number (sometimes called the modulus) is defined in a similar manner.

**Definition 11.3a.** The quantity

$$|a + ib| .=. \sqrt{a^2 + b^2}$$

is called the **absolute value** or **modulus** of the complex number $a + ib$.

Notice that this definition agrees with the definition of the magnitude $|\mathbf{a}|$ of the vector **a**, and with the meaning of $|x|$ when $x$ is real.

In the work that follows the letter $z$ will be used to represent a complex number. The conjugate of the number $z = a + ib$ was previously defined as the number $a - ib$. The conjugate of $z$ will be denoted by $\bar{z}$. The absolute value of $z = a + ib$ is then given by

(1) $$|z|^2 = a^2 + b^2 = (a + ib)(a - ib) = z\bar{z}.$$

The following two theorems will be helpful. Proofs are left for the exercises.

**Theorem 11.3a.** The conjugate of the sum of two complex numbers is the sum of their conjugates; that is,

$$\overline{z_1 + z_2} = \bar{z}_1 + \bar{z}_2.$$

**Theorem 11.3b.** The conjugate of the product of two complex numbers is the product of their conjugates; that is,

$$\overline{z_1 z_2} = \bar{z}_1 \bar{z}_2.$$

We are ready now to prove two theorems concerning absolute values.

**Theorem 11.3c.**          $|z_1 z_2| = |z_1||z_2|.$

PROOF:

$$
\begin{aligned}
|z_1 z_2|^2 &= (z_1 z_2)(\overline{z_1 z_2}) & \text{(By (1))} \\
&= (z_1 z_2)(\bar{z}_1 \bar{z}_2) & \text{(By Theorem 11.3b)} \\
&= (z_1 \bar{z}_1)(z_2 \bar{z}_2) & \text{(Why?)} \\
&= |z_1|^2 |z_2|^2. & \text{(Why?)}
\end{aligned}
$$

Thus

$$|z_1 z_2| = |z_1||z_2|.$$

**Theorem 11.3d.**          $\left|\dfrac{z_1}{z_2}\right| = \dfrac{|z_1|}{|z_2|}, \quad z_2 \neq 0.$

PROOF: Let          $z = \dfrac{z_1}{z_2},$

then

$$zz_2 = z_1,$$

and

$$|zz_2| = |z_1|,$$

and, by Theorem 11.3c,

$$|z||z_2| = |z_1|.$$

Thus,

$$|z| = \frac{|z_1|}{|z_2|}, \quad z_2 \neq 0.$$

---

*Example 11.3a.* Verify geometrically that $|z_1 + z_2| \leq |z_1| + |z_2|$.

The inequality is apparent from Figure 11.3b, since the length of any side of a triangle is less than or equal to the sum of the lengths of the other two sides.

---

From the geometric interpretation we may obtain a useful trigonometric form for a complex number. In Figure 11.3c, let the modulus of the nonzero complex number $a + ib$ be represented by the letter $r$ and let $\theta$ be the angle from the positive $x$-axis to the line $OP$. The angle $\theta$ is called the *argument* (or *amplitude*) of the complex number. Since

$$a = r \cos \theta \quad \text{and} \quad b = r \sin \theta,$$

we may write

$$
\begin{aligned}
a + ib &= r \cos \theta + ir \sin \theta \\
&= r(\cos \theta + i \sin \theta).
\end{aligned}
$$

The fact that $\cos \theta + i \sin \theta = \cos (\theta + 2n\pi) + i \sin (\theta + 2n\pi)$, $n \in \mathcal{I}$ shows that any integral multiple of $2\pi$ may be added to the argument of a complex number to obtain another representation of the number.

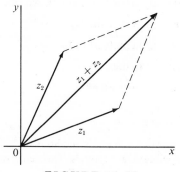

FIGURE 11.3b

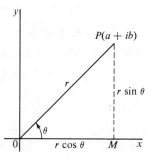

FIGURE 11.3c

The trigonometric form is useful for finding the product of two complex numbers, $z_1$ and $z_2$. If $z_1 = r_1(\cos \theta_1 + i \sin \theta_1)$ and $z_2 = r_2(\cos \theta_2 + i \sin \theta_2)$, then

$$z_1 z_2 = r_1 r_2 [(\cos \theta_1 \cos \theta_2 - \sin \theta_1 \sin \theta_2) + i(\sin \theta_1 \cos \theta_2 + \cos \theta_1 \sin \theta_2)]$$

or

(2) $$z_1 z_2 = r_1 r_2 [(\cos (\theta_1 + \theta_2) + i \sin (\theta_1 + \theta_2)].$$

Similarly, the reciprocal of a nonzero complex number may be expressed in trigonometric form as follows:

$$\frac{1}{r(\cos \theta + i \sin \theta)} = \frac{(\cos \theta - i \sin \theta)}{r(\cos \theta + i \sin \theta)(\cos \theta - i \sin \theta)}$$

$$= \frac{1}{r} (\cos \theta - i \sin \theta)$$

or

(3) $$\frac{1}{r(\cos \theta + i \sin \theta)} = \frac{1}{r} [\cos (-\theta) + i \sin (-\theta)].$$

This formula and Formula (2) for a product may be used to obtain a formula for expressing the quotient of two complex numbers in trigonometric form:

$$\frac{r_1(\cos \theta_1 + i \sin \theta_1)}{r_2(\cos \theta_2 + i \sin \theta_2)} = \frac{r_1}{r_2} (\cos \theta_1 + i \sin \theta_1) \left( \frac{1}{\cos \theta_2 + i \sin \theta_2} \right)$$

$$= \frac{r_1}{r_2} (\cos \theta_1 + i \sin \theta_1)[\cos (-\theta_2) + i \sin (-\theta_2)]$$

(4) $$\frac{r_1(\cos \theta_1 + i \sin \theta_1)}{r_2(\cos \theta_2 + i \sin \theta_2)} = \frac{r_1}{r_2} [\cos (\theta_1 - \theta_2) + i \sin (\theta_1 - \theta_2)].$$

The product formula leads to an interesting result if $z_1 = z_2$. Let $r_1 = r_2 = r$ and $\theta_1 = \theta_2 = \theta$. Then we have

$$[r(\cos \theta + i \sin \theta)]^2 = r^2(\cos 2\theta + i \sin 2\theta).$$

If each side of this equation is multiplied by $r(\cos \theta + i \sin \theta)$, we obtain

$$[r(\cos \theta + i \sin \theta)]^3 = r^3(\cos 3\theta + i \sin 3\theta).$$

The following general result is obtained by mathematical induction.

**Theorem 11.3e.** *De Moivre's Theorem.* If $n \in \mathfrak{N}$, then

(5) $$(\cos \theta + i \sin \theta)^n = \cos n\theta + i \sin n\theta.$$

---

*Example 11.3b.* Express $(\sqrt{3} + i)^8$ in the form $a + ib$.

The complex number $\sqrt{3} + i$ has an argument of $\pi/6$ and a modulus of 2. Writing the number in trigonometric form and applying De Moivre's Theorem, we have

$$
\begin{aligned}
(\sqrt{3} + i)^8 &= [2(\cos 30° + i \sin 30°)]^8 \\
&= 2^8(\cos 240° + i \sin 240°) \\
&= 256\left(-\frac{1}{2} - i\frac{\sqrt{3}}{2}\right) \\
&= -128 - i\,128\,\sqrt{3}.
\end{aligned}
$$

---

*Example 11.3c.* Express $(-1/2 - i\sqrt{3}/2)^{50}$ in the form $a + ib$.

Writing the number in trigonometric form and applying De Moivre's Theorem, we obtain

$$
\begin{aligned}
(-1/2 - i\sqrt{3}/2)^{50} &= [1(\cos 240° + i \sin 240°)]^{50} \\
&= 1^{50}(\cos 12{,}000° + i \sin 12{,}000°) \\
&= \cos 120° + i \sin 120° \\
&= -1/2 + i\sqrt{3}/2.
\end{aligned}
$$

---

In order to verify that De Moivre's Theorem is true if $n$ is a negative integer, we write $n = -m$, with $m$ a positive integer. Then, we have

$$
\begin{aligned}
(\cos \theta + i \sin \theta)^n &= \frac{1}{(\cos \theta + i \sin \theta)^m} \\
&= \frac{1}{\cos m\theta + i \sin m\theta} \qquad \text{(By Formula 5)} \\
&= \cos(-m\theta) + i \sin(-m\theta) \qquad \text{(By Formula 3)} \\
&= \cos n\theta + i \sin n\theta.
\end{aligned}
$$

## Exercises 11.3

1. Prove Theorem 11.3a.
2. Prove Theorem 11.3b.

3. Verify geometrically that $|z_1 + z_2| \geq ||z_1| - |z_2||$.

4. Prove that $\overline{z_1 z_2 z_3} = \bar{z}_1 \bar{z}_2 \bar{z}_3$.

5. Show that if $z_2 z_3 \neq 0$, then

$$\left| \frac{z_1}{z_2 z_3} \right| = \frac{|z_1|}{|z_2||z_3|}.$$

⋆6. Give an algebraic proof that

$$|z_1 + z_2| \leq |z_1| + |z_2|.$$

*Hint*: $|z_1 + z_2|^2 = (z_1 + z_2)(\bar{z}_1 + \bar{z}_2)$. After multiplying out the right side, use Cauchy's Inequality, Exercises 1.10, Number 14.

In Numbers 7 to 16, perform the indicated operations and express the answers in the form $a + ib$.

7. $[3(\cos 37° + i \sin 37°)][2(\cos 23° + i \sin 23°)]$.

8. $\dfrac{12(\cos 52° + i \sin 52°)}{4(\cos 7° + i \sin 7°)}$.

9. $[\frac{1}{2}(\cos 10° + i \sin 10°)]^6$.

10. $(1 + i)^8$.

11. $(1/2 + i\sqrt{3}/2)^{100}$.

12. $[2(\cos 36° + i \sin 36°)]^5$.

13. $[2(\cos 15° + i \sin 15°)]^{-4}$.

14. $(\sqrt{2}/2 - i\sqrt{2}/2)^{60}$.

15. $(-1/2 + i\sqrt{3}/2)^{-50}$.

16. $(-\sqrt{2}/2 - i\sqrt{2}/2)^{100}$.

## 11.4 COMPLEX-VALUED FUNCTIONS

The domain and range of a function have thus far been restricted to subsets of the field of real numbers. However, the definition of a function can be extended so that the range is a subset of the field of complex numbers.

**Definition 11.4a.** A function $f$ whose domain is a subset of $\mathcal{R}$ and whose range is a subset of $\mathcal{C}$ and is such that

$$f(t) = g(t) + ih(t),$$

where $g$ and $h$ are real-valued functions of the real variable $t$, is called a **complex-valued function** of the real variable $t$.

That is, a complex-valued function $f$ is a set of ordered pairs $\{(t, w)\}$, for which $t \in \mathcal{R}$ and $w \in \mathcal{C}$ such that $(t_0, w_1) \in f$ and $(t_0, w_2) \in f \Rightarrow w_1 = w_2$.

In general, a complex number $a + ib$ may be interpreted geometrically as a vector from the origin to the point $(a, b)$. Therefore, a complex-valued function has a range that is a collection of vectors whose $x$- and $y$-components are $g(t)$ and $h(t)$, respectively. Thus, the function $f$ defined by $f(t) = g(t) + ih(t)$ may be regarded as having for its graph a curve in the $xy$-plane whose equations are given in parametric form by

$$x = g(t), \quad y = h(t).$$

The curve is traced by the end of the vector $f(t)$.

For example, if

$$f(t) = t + it^2,$$

then we may let $x = t$ and $y = t^2$ to obtain $y = x^2$, which is the equation of the parabola shown in Figure 11.4a.

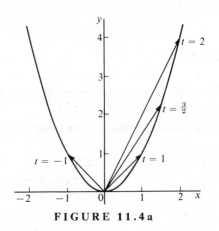

**FIGURE 11.4a**

In order to discuss limits and continuity of a complex-valued function, we must extend the neighborhood concept.

**Definition 11.4b.** A neighborhood, $\mathfrak{N}(P, \epsilon)$, of a complex number $P = a + ib$, is the set of points

$$\{(x + iy): (x - a)^2 + (y - b)^2 < \epsilon^2\}.$$

That is, a neighborhood of $P$ is the set of points inside a circle of radius $\epsilon$ and center at $P$ (see Figure 11.4b).

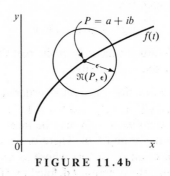

**FIGURE 11.4b**

With this extension it is possible to formulate the limit concept for a complex valued function in the same way that the ordinary limit concept was formulated.

**Definition 11.4c.** Let $f(t) .=. g(t) + ih(t)$. Then $\lim_{t \to t_0} f(t) = P$ means that given an $\epsilon > 0$, there is a $\mathfrak{N}^*(t_0, h)$ such that

$$t \in \mathfrak{N}^*(t_0, h) \Rightarrow f(t) \in \mathfrak{N}(P, \epsilon).$$

Interpreted geometrically, this statement says that for all values of $t$ sufficiently near $t_0$, the graph of $f(t)$ will lie within a circle of radius $\epsilon$ about $P$.

The definition of continuity follows.

**Definition 11.4d.** A complex-valued function $f$ is said to be continuous at a point $t_0$ if

$$\lim_{t \to t_0} f(t) = f(t_0).$$

A complex-valued function is continuous on $a \leqq t \leqq b$ if it is continuous at every point in the interval.

**Theorem 11.4a.** A complex-valued function $f$, where $f(t) .=. g(t) + ih(t)$, is continuous at a point $t_0 \Leftrightarrow g$ and $h$ are continuous at $t_0$.

PROOF: First, if $f$ is continuous at $t_0$, then for each $\epsilon > 0$ there is a $\mathfrak{N}(t_0, h)$ such that

$$t \in \mathfrak{N}(t_0, h) \Rightarrow f(t) \in \mathfrak{N}[f(t_0), \epsilon].$$

That is,

$$[g(t) - g(t_0)]^2 + [h(t) - h(t_0)]^2 < \epsilon^2.$$

It follows that

$$[g(t) - g(t_0)]^2 < \epsilon^2$$

or that

$$|g(t) - g(t_0)| < \epsilon.$$

Therefore, if $f$ is continuous at $t_0$, then $g$ is continuous at $t_0$. A similar argument holds for the function $h$.

For the second part of the proof, we show that if $g$ and $h$ are continuous at $t_0$, then $f$ is continuous at $t_0$. For a given $\epsilon$ there is a $\delta_1$ such that

$$t \in \mathfrak{N}(t_0, \delta_1) \Rightarrow g(t) \in \mathfrak{N}[g(t_0), \epsilon/\sqrt{2}],$$

and there is a $\delta_2$ such that

$$t \in \mathfrak{N}(t_0, \delta_2) \Rightarrow h(t) \in \mathfrak{N}[h(t_0), \epsilon/\sqrt{2}].$$

Let

$$\mathfrak{N}(t_0, \delta) = \mathfrak{N}(t_0, \delta_1) \cap \mathfrak{N}(t_0, \delta_2).$$

Then, for $t \in \mathfrak{N}(t_0, \delta)$,

$$|g(t) - g(t_0)| < \epsilon/\sqrt{2}$$

or

$$[g(t) - g(t_0)]^2 < \epsilon^2/2$$

and

$$|h(t) - h(t_0)| < \epsilon/\sqrt{2}$$

or

$$[h(t) - h(t_0)]^2 < \epsilon^2/2,$$

so that

$$t \in \mathfrak{N}(t_0, \delta) \Rightarrow [g(t) - g(t_0)]^2 + [h(t) - h(t_0)]^2 < \epsilon^2$$
$$\Rightarrow f(t) \in \mathfrak{N}[f(t_0), \epsilon],$$

which shows that $f$ is continuous at $t_0$.

The derivative of a complex-valued function $f$ is easily defined.

**Definition 11.4e.** If $f(t) .=. g(t) + ih(t)$, then
$$D_t f .=. g'(t) + ih'(t),$$
provided the latter two derivatives exist.

Thus, if $f(t) = \cos 4t + i\sqrt{t}$, $t \geq 0$, then
$$f'(t) = -4 \sin 4t + i/(2\sqrt{t}), \qquad t > 0.$$

The importance of the derivative concept for a complex-valued function will become apparent a little later.

It is not difficult to show that all the usual rules for derivatives hold for complex-valued functions. For example, if $p$ and $q$ are complex-valued functions, then
$$D_t[p(t)q(t)] = p(t) \, D_t q(t) + q(t) \, D_t p(t).$$

Suppose
$$p(t) = u(t) + iv(t) = u + iv$$
and
$$q(t) = w(t) + iz(t) = w + iz.$$

Then
$$p(t)q(t) = [uw - vz] + i[vw + uz]$$
and
$$\begin{aligned}
D_t[p(t)q(t)] &= uw' + u'w - vz' - v'z + i(vw' + wv' + uz' + zu') \\
&= (u + iv)w' + i(u + iv)z' + (w + iz)u' + i(w + iz)v' \\
&= (u + iv)(w' + iz') + (w + iz)(u' + iv') \\
&= p(t) \, D_t q(t) + q(t) \, D_t p(t).
\end{aligned}$$

The inverse derivative of a complex-valued function is also defined in a manner similar to that for a real-valued function.

**Definition 11.4f.** If there is a complex-valued function $F$ such that $F'(t) = f(t)$, then $F$ is an inverse derivative of $f$, and we write
$$D_t^{-1} f(t) = F(t) + C \quad \text{or} \quad \int f(t) \, dt = F(t) + C.$$

As a consequence of this definition, if $f(t) = g(t) + ih(t)$, then
$$\int f(t) \, dt = \int g(t) \, dt + i \int h(t) \, dt.$$

Toward the end of the 18th century, the Swiss mathematician Euler discovered that he could extend the definition of the exponential function in a highly useful manner. Consider the complex-valued function $\varphi$ defined by
$$\varphi(\alpha) = \cos \alpha + i \sin \alpha.$$

We have
$$\begin{aligned}
\varphi(\alpha)\varphi(\beta) &= (\cos \alpha + i \sin \alpha)(\cos \beta + i \sin \beta) \\
&= (\cos \alpha \cos \beta - \sin \alpha \sin \beta) + i(\cos \alpha \sin \beta + \cos \beta \sin \alpha) \\
&= \cos (\alpha + \beta) + i \sin (\alpha + \beta).
\end{aligned}$$

or

(2) $$\varphi(\alpha)\varphi(\beta) = \varphi(\alpha + \beta).$$

The functional property expressed by the last equation is characteristic of the ordinary exponential function. For if

$$f(x) = e^{ax}, \qquad a, x \in \mathcal{R},$$

then

$$f(x)f(y) = e^{ax}e^{ay} = e^{a(x+y)},$$

or

$$f(x)f(y) = f(x + y).$$

Does this similarity of properties imply that $\varphi$ is an exponential type function? In seeking the answer to this question, we first compare other properties of $\varphi(\alpha)$ and $f(x)$. For example, we know that

$$D_x e^{ax} = a e^{ax},$$

or, in functional form,

$$D_x f(x) = af(x).$$

But

$$D_\alpha \varphi(\alpha) = -\sin \alpha + i \cos \alpha$$

or $D_\alpha \varphi(\alpha) = i \,[\cos \alpha + i \sin \alpha]$, so that

(3) $$D_\alpha \varphi(\alpha) = i\varphi(\alpha).$$

This relationship resembles in a remarkable way the relationship expressed in $D_x f(x) = af(x)$ with $a = i$. Indeed, if we wrote

$$\varphi(\alpha) = e^{i\alpha},$$

and agreed to apply to $e^{i\alpha}$ the rules of exponents and the derivative formula which are valid for the ordinary real exponential function, then it would appear that Equations (2) and (3) are satisfied. Thus, it looks as if a meaning can be given to the exponential form $e^{i\alpha}$ in terms of the complex-valued function defined by $\cos \alpha + i \sin \alpha$.

We have just shown that $\varphi$ is a complex-valued function that satisfies properties (2) and (3). Can we be sure there is no other function satisfying these same properties? In other words, is $\varphi(\alpha)$ *uniquely* determined by properties (2) and (3)?

Suppose $g$ is another complex-valued function with these properties. That is, let $g$ be a function for which

$$g(\alpha)g(\beta) = g(\alpha + \beta)$$

and

$$D_\alpha g(\alpha) = ig(\alpha).$$

Then

$$\frac{D_\alpha g(\alpha)}{g(\alpha)} = \frac{D_\alpha \varphi(\alpha)}{\varphi(\alpha)},$$

or

$$\frac{D_\alpha g(\alpha)}{g(\alpha)} - \frac{D_\alpha \varphi(\alpha)}{\varphi(\alpha)} = 0$$

and

$$\varphi(\alpha) \, D_\alpha g(\alpha) - g(\alpha) \, D_\alpha \varphi(\alpha) = 0.$$

Hence

$$\frac{\varphi(\alpha) \, D_\alpha g(\alpha) - g(\alpha) \, D_\alpha \varphi(\alpha)}{\varphi(\alpha)^2} = 0,$$

or

$$D_\alpha \left( \frac{g(\alpha)}{\varphi(\alpha)} \right) = 0,$$

so that

$$\frac{g(\alpha)}{\varphi(\alpha)} = c, \qquad c \text{ a constant.}$$

Thus,

$$g(\alpha) = c\varphi(\alpha)$$

and, in particular,

$$g(0) = c\varphi(0).$$

From (2), we have $\varphi(\alpha)\varphi(0) = \varphi(\alpha)$ when $\beta = 0$, so that $\varphi(0) = 1$. Similarly since $g$ obeys the same functional relationship as $\varphi$ does, $g(0) = 1$. Hence $c = 1$, and it follows that

$$g(\alpha) = \varphi(\alpha).$$

This result shows that the complex-valued function $\varphi$ satisfying Equations (2) and (3) is unique. Accordingly, the preceding discussion strongly suggests the following extension of the meaning of the exponential function to imaginary exponents.

**Definition 11.4g.** $\qquad e^{i\alpha} \, . = . \cos \alpha + i \sin \alpha.$

This remarkable relationship, which is credited to Euler, serves as an important unifying link between the exponential and hyperbolic functions and the trigonometric functions. Through this definition, these apparently unrelated functions will soon appear simply as different combinations of exponential functions.

According to this definition, $e^{i\alpha}$ is a complex number with $\cos \alpha$ as its real part and $\sin \alpha$ as the coefficient of its imaginary part. With an additional definition, it is possible to extend the meaning of the exponential to the field of complex numbers.

**Definition 11.4h.** $\qquad e^{x+iy} \, . = . \, e^x e^{iy}, \qquad x, y \in \mathfrak{R}.$

With the last two definitions, it can be shown that $e^z$, $z \in \mathfrak{C}$, obeys all the usual rules of algebra developed for real numbers. For instance, it is a direct consequence of Equation (2) that

$$e^{i\alpha} e^{i\beta} = e^{i(\alpha + \beta)}.$$

This result may be used to show that

$$e^{z_1}e^{z_2} = e^{z_1+z_2},$$

where $z_1 = x_1 + iy_1$ and $z_2 = x_2 + iy_2$.

Since, by Definition 11.4g,

$$e^{i2\pi} = \cos 2\pi + i \sin 2\pi = 1,$$

it follows that

$$e^{z+i2\pi} = e^z e^{i2\pi} = e^z.$$

Thus, the exponential function satisfies the functional equation

$$f(z + i2\pi) = f(z);$$

that is, the function is periodic with period $i2\pi$.

There are a number of other interesting consequences of the preceding definitions. For example, if $\alpha = \pi$, we get

$$e^{i\pi} + 1 = 0,$$

a simple statement that encompasses in one result the five most important numbers in mathematics. Furthermore, since every complex number may be written in polar form (see Section 11.3), we have

$$a + ib = \sqrt{a^2 + b^2}\left[\frac{a}{\sqrt{a^2 + b^2}} + i\frac{b}{\sqrt{a^2 + b^2}}\right]$$

$$= r(\cos \theta + i \sin \theta) = re^{i\theta},$$

where $r = \sqrt{a^2 + b^2}$, and where $\theta$ is the smallest nonnegative angle such that $\cos \theta = a/r$, and $\sin \theta = b/r$. For example,

$$-\sqrt{3} + i = 2(-\sqrt{3}/2 + i\,1/2) = 2[\cos(5\pi/6) + i \sin(5\pi/6)]$$
$$= 2e^{i5\pi/6}.$$

As we shall see later, the exponential form for complex numbers will simplify considerably some of the work involving complex quantities.

Another interesting relationship is obtained as follows. Since

$$e^{i\alpha} = \cos \alpha + i \sin \alpha,$$

it follows that

$$e^{-i\alpha} = \cos \alpha - i \sin \alpha. \qquad \text{(Why?)}$$

By adding, and dividing by 2, we get

$$\cos \alpha = \frac{e^{i\alpha} + e^{-i\alpha}}{2}.$$

Similarly,

$$\sin \alpha = \frac{e^{i\alpha} - e^{-i\alpha}}{2i}.$$

Upon comparing these expressions with the exponential forms for $\sinh \alpha$ and $\cosh \alpha$, we get

$$\cos \alpha = \cosh i\alpha,$$
$$i \sin \alpha = \sinh i\alpha.$$

It is customary to base the definitions of the trigonometric and hyperbolic functions of complex numbers on the preceding results. Thus, for $z \in \mathbb{C}$, we have

$$\cos z . = . \frac{e^{iz} + e^{-iz}}{2}, \qquad \sin z . = . \frac{e^{iz} - e^{-iz}}{2i},$$

$$\cosh z . = . \frac{e^z + e^{-z}}{2}, \qquad \sinh z . = . \frac{e^z - e^{-z}}{2}.$$

## Exercises 11.4

1. Sketch the graph associated with each of the following complex-valued functions.

   (a) $f(t) = t^2 + it^2$.
   (b) $f(s) = \cos s + i \sin s$.

   (c) $G(u) = \dfrac{u}{1 + u^2} + i \dfrac{u^2}{1 + u^2}$.

   (d) $p(s) = (s^2 - s) + i(s^2 + s)$.

2. For what real values of the variable is each of the following complex-valued functions continuous?

   (a) $f(t) = t + i(t^2 - 1)$.

   (b) $f(s) = \dfrac{1}{s} + i \dfrac{1}{s - 1}$.

   (c) $f(t) = \sec t + i \cot t$.
   (d) $g(t) = \coth t + i \tanh t$.
   (e) $h(s) = \mathrm{Sin}^{-1} s + i \,\mathrm{Cos}^{-1} s, \ |s| \leq 1$.

3. Find the derivative of each of the following.

   (a) $f(s) = \cos 2s + i \sin 2s$.

   (b) $f(t) = \dfrac{t}{1 - t^2} + i \dfrac{1}{1 - t^2}$.

   (c) $g(u) = \cos^2 u + i \sin^2 u$.
   (d) $h(s) = \mathrm{Sin}^{-1} s + i \,\mathrm{Cos}^{-1} s, \ |s| \leq 1$.

4. If $p$ and $q$ are differentiable complex-valued functions, prove that

   (a) $D_t[p + q] = D_t p + D_t q$.
   (b) $D_t p^n = np^{n-1} D_t p, \ n \in \mathcal{I}$. *Hint:* Let $p(t) = r(t)e^{i\theta(t)}$.

   (c) $D_t \left(\dfrac{p}{q}\right) = \dfrac{q \, D_t p - p \, D_t q}{q^2}$. *Hint:* Show first that $D_t \left(\dfrac{1}{q}\right) = -\dfrac{D_t q}{q^2}$.

   (d) $D_t \left\{ \displaystyle\int_a^t p(u) \, du \right\} = p(t)$.

5. Write each of the following numbers in the exponential form $re^{i\theta}$.

   (a) $-2\sqrt{3} - 2i$.
   (b) $\sqrt{2} - \sqrt{2}i$.
   (c) $6 + 8i$.

   (d) $\dfrac{1}{1 + \sqrt{3}i}$.

6. Deduce that $\displaystyle\int \sin \theta \, d\theta = -\cos \theta + C$ and $\displaystyle\int \cos \theta \, d\theta = \sin \theta + C$ by considering $\displaystyle\int e^{i\theta} \, d\theta$ and equating the real and imaginary parts of the resulting expression

7. Evaluate $\int e^{s+is}\, ds$, and then deduce expressions for

$$\int e^s \cos s\, ds \quad \text{and} \quad \int e^s \sin s\, ds.$$

8. Show that $\cosh (x + iy) = \cosh x \cos y + i \sinh x \sin y$.
9. Show that $\sin (x + iy) = \sin x \cosh y + i \cos x \sinh y$.
10. The logarithmic function is defined as the inverse of the exponential function. That is, if $z = e^w$, then $w .=. \ln z$. Every complex number can be written in exponential form, so that

$$z = x + iy = re^{i\theta},$$

where $r = \sqrt{x^2 + y^2}$, $\theta = \tan^{-1} y/x$. Hence we make this definition:

$$\text{Ln } z .=. \text{Ln } r + i\theta, \qquad -\pi < \theta \leq \pi,$$

where Ln $r$ is the natural logarithm of the real number $r$. Thus,

$$\begin{aligned} \text{Ln } (1 + i) &= \text{Ln } [\sqrt{2}\,(\cos \pi/4 + i \sin \pi/4)] \\ &= \text{Ln } \sqrt{2} + i\pi/4. \end{aligned}$$

Find each of the following as a complex number in the form $a + ib$.

(a) Ln $(-1)$.            (c) Ln $i$.
(b) Ln $(2 - 2i)$.

11. In each of the following, determine a complex number of the form $a + ib$, with $a$ and $b$ real, equivalent to the given number.

(a) $\sin i$.            (f) $e^{3+4i}$.
(b) $\cos (1 - i)$.        (g) Ln $2i$.
(c) $\sin (-\pi/4 - i)$.    (h) Ln $(1 + i)$.
(d) $\sinh 2i$.           (i) Ln $(-3)$.
(e) $e^{i\pi/4}$.             (j) $\cosh (2 + i\pi/2)$.

⋆12. On the basis of the definition in Number 10, is it necessarily true that

$$\text{Ln } z_1 z_2 = \text{Ln } z_1 + \text{Ln } z_2,$$

where $z_1$ and $z_2$ are complex numbers? Explain.

## 11.5 ROOTS OF COMPLEX NUMBERS

From De Moivre's Theorem, established in Section 11.3, we have

$$[r(\cos \theta + i \sin \theta)]^n = r^n(\cos n\theta + i \sin n\theta), \qquad n \in \mathcal{I}.$$

By making use of the relationship

$$\cos \theta + i \sin \theta = e^{i\theta},$$

we may write the preceding result in the more compact form

(1) $$(re^{i\theta})^n = r^n e^{in\theta}.$$

This equation makes it possible for us to define the $n$th roots of a complex number in a relatively simple way. As in the case of real numbers, we define an $n$th root of a complex number $r(\cos \theta + i \sin \theta)$ to be a complex number $R(\cos \varphi + i \sin \varphi)$ such that

$$[R(\cos \varphi + i \sin \varphi)]^n = r(\cos \theta + i \sin \theta)$$

or, in exponential form,

$$[Re^{i\varphi}]^n = re^{i\theta}.$$

It follows from Equation (1) that

$$R^n e^{in\varphi} = re^{i\theta},$$

which implies

$$R^n = r \quad \text{and} \quad n\varphi = \theta.$$

Since both $R$ and $r$ are real and nonnegative and $0 \leq \theta < 2\pi$, it follows that

$$R = \sqrt[n]{r} \quad \text{and} \quad \varphi = \theta/n.$$

Thus, an $n$th root of the complex number $re^{i\theta}$ is given by

$$\sqrt[n]{re^{i\theta/n}} = \sqrt[n]{r}[\cos (\theta/n) + i \sin (\theta/n)].$$

However, further investigation reveals that the $n$th root of a complex number given in this way is not the only $n$th root, an observation that may be verified in either of two ways. We find that the problem of determining an $n$th root $z$ of a given complex number $\alpha$ is equivalent to solving the equation

$$z^n - \alpha = 0.$$

According to the theory of equations, this equation must have $n$ roots (not necessarily distinct) in the field of complex numbers. Consequently, we may expect to find values for $z$ other than

$$\sqrt[n]{r}[\cos (\theta/n) + i \sin (\theta/n)].$$

A second verification consists in finding the other $n$th roots of the complex number, which is easily done by making use of the periodicity of the exponential function. Since

$$e^{i\theta} = e^{i(\theta + 2\pi k)}, \quad k \in \mathcal{I},$$

we may write for the $n$th roots of a complex number $\alpha = re^{i\theta}$ the more general form

$$z = \sqrt[n]{r}e^{i(\theta + 2\pi k)/n}.$$

It follows further from the periodicity of the exponential function that $k = 0, 1, 2, \ldots, n - 1$ will yield the only distinct values of

$$\exp [i(\theta + 2k\pi)/n],$$

so that there are exactly $n$ different roots. Furthermore, since all of these roots have the same modulus $\sqrt[n]{r}$, they will, if plotted on the plane of complex numbers, correspond to a set of $n$ equally spaced points on a circle of radius $\sqrt[n]{r}$. This is illustrated in the next example.

*Example 11.5a.* Solve the equation $z^5 + 2\sqrt{3} - 2i = 0$.

If we write this equation in the form

$$z^5 = -2\sqrt{3} + 2i = 4 \exp\left[i\left(\frac{5\pi}{6} + 2k\pi\right)\right],$$

we have

$$z = \left\{4 \exp i\left(\frac{5\pi}{6} + 2k\pi\right)\right\}^{1/5}$$

$$= \sqrt[5]{4} \exp\left[i\left(\frac{\pi}{6} + \frac{2k\pi}{5}\right)\right].$$

The five distinct roots may be obtained by letting $k = 0, 1, 2, 3, 4$ to get

$$z_0 = \sqrt[5]{4} \exp\frac{i\pi}{6} = \sqrt[5]{4}\,(\cos 30° + i \sin 30°),$$

$$z_1 = \sqrt[5]{4} \exp\frac{i17\pi}{30} = \sqrt[5]{4}\,(\cos 102° + i \sin 102°),$$

$$z_2 = \sqrt[5]{4} \exp\frac{i29\pi}{30} = \sqrt[5]{4}\,(\cos 174° + i \sin 174°),$$

$$z_3 = \sqrt[5]{4} \exp\frac{i41\pi}{30} = \sqrt[5]{4}\,(\cos 246° + i \sin 246°),$$

$$z_4 = \sqrt[5]{4} \exp\frac{i53\pi}{30} = \sqrt[5]{4}\,(\cos 318° + i \sin 318°).$$

These roots are represented geometrically in Figure 11.5a.

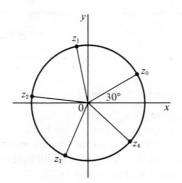

**FIGURE 11.5a**

It is left to the reader to verify that with the preceding result for the $n$th roots of $re^{i\theta}$, we obtain

$$(re^{i\theta})^{p/n} = \sqrt[n]{r^p} \exp\left[i\left(\frac{p\theta}{n} + \frac{2kp\pi}{n}\right)\right], \qquad k = 0, 1, 2, \ldots, n - 1,$$

where $p$ is any integer and $n$ is any positive integer.

## Exercises 11.5

In Numbers 1 to 16, solve the given equation and make a sketch to show the roots graphically.

1. $x^3 - 8 = 0$.
2. $y^5 + 32i = 0$.
3. $x^3 + i = 0$.
4. $y^3 + 27 = 0$.
5. $x^4 + 16 = 0$.
6. $w^6 - 1 = 0$.
7. $z^3 - 8i = 0$.
8. $x^6 + 1 = 0$.

9. $z^2 = 1 - i\sqrt{3}$.
10. $x^4 = 2(-1 + i\sqrt{3})$.
11. $x^3 = -3 + 4i$.
12. $y^5 = 1$.
13. $w^2 = -4(1 + i)$.
14. $x^3 = 2(1 + i)$.
15. $w^8 = 1$.
16. $x^5 + 2\sqrt{3} + 2i = 0$.

17. Solve the equation $w^4 + w^2 + 1 = 0$.
18. Solve the equation $x^6 + x^3 + 1 = 0$.
19. If $w^4 + 2w^3 + 4w^2 + 8w + 16 = 0$, what are the possible values of $w$?
20. Find the integer of smallest absolute value of which $-\sqrt{2} + i\sqrt{2}$ is a root.
21. Find the integer of smallest absolute value of which $\sqrt{3} + i$ is a root.

The $n$ distinct solutions of the equation $z^n = 1$ are called the $n$th *roots of unity*. Numbers 22 to 25 are concerned with certain $n$th roots of unity.

22. Find the sixth roots of unity and show that they form a multiplicative group.
23. Find the fifth roots of unity and show that they form a multiplicative group.
24. Show that, for each $n$, the $n$th roots of unity form a multiplicative group.
25. If $\omega$ is an imaginary fifth root of unity, and if $u = \omega + 1/\omega$, show that $u^2 + u = 1$.

---

## Summary of Chapter 11

---

The reader should understand the following basic items:

    (1) vectors and vector quantities (Section 11.1);
    (2) parallelogram law of composition (Section 11.1);
    (3) representation of vectors in two dimensions by number-pairs (Section 11.1);
    (4) properties of vector addition and scalar multiplication (Section 11.1);
    (5) the set of base vectors, **i** and **j** (Section 11.1);
    (6) the magnitude of a vector (Section 11.1);
    (7) simple applications of vectors to force and velocity problems (Section 11.2);
    (8) the trigonometric form of a complex number (Section 11.3);
    (9) de Moivre's Theorem (Section 11.3);
  (10) the definition of complex-valued functions and their geometric interpretation as vector functions (Section 11.4);
  (11) the definition of $e^{x+iy}$ and the relationships involving this expression (Section 11.4);
  (12) finding roots of complex numbers (Section 11.5).

# Chapter 12    Formal Integration and Applications

## 12.1 REVIEW OF BASIC INVERSE DERIVATIVES

The definite integral has been shown to be of fundamental importance in the mathematical analysis of many practical problems. The evaluation of definite integrals has been based upon the Fundamental Theorem of Integral Calculus, which requires a knowledge of the appropriate inverse derivatives. Thus far, inverse derivatives have been found by inspection or by a simple inversion of a derivative formula. For example, from

$$D_x \sin x = \cos x$$

it follows that

$$\int \cos x \, dx = \sin x + C.$$

However, it should not be expected that every definite integral can be handled simply by finding an inverse derivative in the form of a familiar elementary type of function. For example, the integral

$$\int_1^3 e^{-x^2} \, dx$$

cannot be evaluated in this way because there is no simpler form for the inverse derivative of $e^{-x^2}$ than

$$\int_1^x e^{-t^2} \, dt.$$

(The proof of this is beyond the scope of our work here.)

Meanwhile, we must develop additional techniques for finding inverse derivatives when they can be expressed in terms of the simple functions with which we are already familiar. Most of these techniques are based upon the inverse derivatives that have been obtained in the preceding chapters. Accordingly, it is important for the student to be familiar with the following basic list which summarizes the pertinent inverse derivative formulas that have been discussed previously. The exercises that follow provide a review of the skills associated with the use of these formulas.

(1) $\int u^n \, du = \dfrac{u^{n+1}}{n+1} + C, \, n \neq -1.$

(2) $\int \dfrac{du}{u} = \ln |u| + C.$

(3) $\int e^u \, du = e^u + C.$

(4) $\int a^u \, du = \dfrac{a^u}{\ln a} + C, \, a > 0, \, a \neq 1.$

(5) $\int \sin u \, du = -\cos u + C.$

(6) $\int \cos u \, du = \sin u + C.$

(7) $\int \sec^2 u \, du = \tan u + C.$

(8) $\int \csc^2 u \, du = -\cot u + C.$

(9) $\int \sec u \tan u \, du = \sec u + C.$

(10 $\int \csc u \cot u \, du = -\csc u + C.$

(11) $\int \tan u \, du = \ln |\sec u| + C = -\ln |\cos u| + C.$

(12) $\int \cot u \, du = \ln |\sin u| + C = -\ln |\csc u| + C.$

(13) $\int \sec u \, du = \ln |\sec u + \tan u| + C.$

(14) $\int \csc u \, du = \ln |\csc u - \cot u| + C = \ln |\tan \tfrac{1}{2}u| + C.$

(15) $\int \dfrac{du}{\sqrt{a^2 - u^2}} = \mathrm{Sin}^{-1} \dfrac{u}{a} + C, \, u < a.$

(16) $\int \dfrac{du}{a^2 + u^2} = \dfrac{1}{a} \mathrm{Tan}^{-1} \dfrac{u}{a} + C, \, a \neq 0.$

(17) $\int \dfrac{du}{\sqrt{u^2 + a^2}} = \sinh^{-1} \dfrac{u}{a} + C, \, a > 0.$

(18) $\int \dfrac{du}{\sqrt{u^2 - a^2}} = \mathrm{Cosh}^{-1} \dfrac{u}{a} + C, \, u > a > 0.$

# Exercises 12.1

In each of Numbers 1 to 34, find the inverse derivative.

1. $\int (4x^3 + 8x^2 + 7)\, dx.$

2. $\int \sqrt{2x + 3}\, dx.$

3. $\int \cos t \sin^2 t\, dt.$

4. $\int x \cos x^2\, dx.$

5. $\int w\sqrt{w^2 + 1}\, dw.$

6. $\int v^2 (2 + v^3)^{1/2}\, dv.$

7. $\int \frac{x}{x + 1}\, dx.$

8. $\int \frac{t^3\, dt}{t^2 + 9}.$

9. $\int e^{3u}\, du.$

10. $\int (2^s + s^2)\, ds.$

11. $\int \frac{\sin v}{\cos^2 v}\, dv.$

12. $\int \csc 5w\, dw.$

13. $\int \frac{\tan \sqrt{x}}{\sqrt{x}}\, dx.$

14. $\int x \sec x^2 \tan x^2\, dx.$

15. $\int \frac{w\, dw}{\sqrt{w^2 + 4}}.$

16. $\int \frac{dw}{\sqrt{w^2 + 4}}.$

17. $\int \frac{t\, dt}{t^2 - 9}.$

18. $\int \frac{r^3}{4r^4 + 9}\, dr.$

19. $\int x\, 2^{x^2}\, dx.$

20. $\int x e^{x^2}\, dx.$

21. $\int \frac{u\, du}{\sqrt{u^2 - 4}}.$

22. $\int \frac{du}{\sqrt{u^2 - 4}}.$

23. $\int \frac{dx}{4x^2 + 25}.$

24. $\int \frac{u^2\, du}{u^2 + 4}.$

25. $\int \frac{dy}{\sqrt{4 - y^2}}.$

26. $\int \frac{dx}{\sqrt{3 - 4x^2}}.$

27. $\int u^2 \csc u^3\, du.$

28. $\int \sec^3 \theta \tan \theta\, d\theta.$

29. $\int (\sqrt{2w} + 1)^2\, dw.$

30. $\int \frac{ds}{\sqrt{4s + 9}}.$

31. $\int \sin^3 2x \cos 2x\, dx.$

32. $\int \csc 2w \cot 2w\, dw.$

33. $\int 2^w\, dw.$

34. $\int e^2\, dx.$

In each of Numbers 35 to 44, evaluate the given definite integral.

35. $\displaystyle\int_0^1 \frac{3x\,dx}{\sqrt{x^2+8}}.$

36. $\displaystyle\int_2^{2\sqrt{3}} \frac{dt}{4+t^2}.$

37. $\displaystyle\int_0^{\pi/2} \sin 2t\,dt.$

38. $\displaystyle\int_0^{\pi/2} (\sin x)e^{\cos x}\,dx.$

39. $\displaystyle\int_0^2 3se^{s^2}\,ds.$

40. $\displaystyle\int_0^4 \frac{dx}{\sqrt{2x+1}}.$

41. $\displaystyle\int_{-1/4}^{1/4} \sec^2 \pi x \tan \pi x\,dx.$

42. $\displaystyle\int_{-3\pi/4}^0 \tan \tfrac{1}{3}t\,dt.$

43. $\displaystyle\int_0^{\sqrt{2}/2} \frac{dw}{\sqrt{1-w^2}}.$

44. $\displaystyle\int_0^{\pi/6} \tan^2 2w \sec^2 2w\,dw.$

## 12.2 ADDITIONAL INTEGRALS INVOLVING TRIGONOMETRIC FUNCTIONS

The inverse derivatives of the trigonometric functions were discussed in Section 10.4. By the use of trigonometric identities, many integrals involving products and powers of the trigonometric functions may be reduced to a standard form. Several examples will illustrate the procedure.

*Example 12.2a.* Evaluate

$$\int_0^{\pi/2} \tan^2 \frac{x}{2}\,dx.$$

Replacing $\tan^2 (x/2)$ by its equivalent, $\sec^2 (x/2) - 1$, we obtain

$$\int_0^{\pi/2} \tan^2 \frac{x}{2}\,dx = \int_0^{\pi/2} \left( \sec^2 \frac{x}{2} - 1 \right) dx$$

$$= \left[ 2 \tan \frac{x}{2} - x \right]_0^{\pi/2} = 2 - \frac{\pi}{2}.$$

It is frequently possible to rewrite the integrand as the sum of powers of a trigonometric function multiplied by the differential of that function, as in the next examples.

*Example 12.2b.* Find $\displaystyle\int \cos^3 x\,dx.$

Using the fact that $d \sin x = \cos x\,dx$, we write

$$\int \cos^3 x\,dx = \int (\cos^2 x) \cos x\,dx$$

$$= \int (1 - \sin^2 x) \cos x\,dx$$

$$= \int \cos x\,dx - \int \sin^2 x\,d(\sin x)$$

$$= \sin x - \tfrac{1}{3} \sin^3 x + C.$$

*Example 12.2c.* Find $\int \tan^5 3x \, dx$.

In this problem, we make use of the identity $\tan^2 3x = \sec^2 3x - 1$, and proceed as follows:

$$\int \tan^5 3x \, dx = \int \tan^3 3x \tan^2 3x \, dx$$

$$= \int \tan^3 3x \, (\sec^2 3x - 1) \, dx$$

$$= \tfrac{1}{3} \int \tan^3 3x \, (\sec^2 3x)(3 \, dx) - \int \tan^3 3x \, dx$$

$$= \tfrac{1}{3} \int \tan^3 3x \, d(\tan 3x) - \int \tan 3x \, (\sec^2 3x - 1) \, dx$$

$$= \tfrac{1}{12} \tan^4 3x - \tfrac{1}{3} \int \tan 3x \, d(\tan 3x) + \int \tan 3x \, dx$$

$$= \tfrac{1}{12} \tan^4 3x - \tfrac{1}{6} \tan^2 3x + \tfrac{1}{3} \ln |\sec 3x| + C.$$

Even powers of $\sin u$ and $\cos u$ may be integrated by means of the identities

$$\sin^2 u = \tfrac{1}{2}(1 - \cos 2u),$$
$$\cos^2 u = \tfrac{1}{2}(1 + \cos 2u),$$

as in the following example.

*Example 12.2d.* Find $\int \cos^4 5y \, dy$.

We proceed as follows:

$$\int \cos^4 5y \, dy = \int \left(\frac{1 + \cos 10y}{2}\right)^2 dy$$

$$= \tfrac{1}{4} \int (1 + 2 \cos 10y + \cos^2 10y) \, dy$$

$$= \tfrac{1}{4} \int (1 + 2 \cos 10y + \tfrac{1}{2} + \tfrac{1}{2} \cos 20y) \, dy$$

$$= \tfrac{3}{8}y + \tfrac{1}{20} \sin 10y + \tfrac{1}{160} \sin 20y + C.$$

Although techniques similar to the preceding ones enable us to find the inverse derivatives of many combinations of trigonometric functions, the reader should recognize that such a procedure will not always suffice. For example, $\int \sec^3 x \, dx$ cannot be handled by any of the preceding schemes. However, a method of finding this inverse derivative will be discussed in Section 12.5 on Integration by Parts.

## Exercises 12.2

In each of Numbers 1 to 32, find the inverse derivative.

1. $\int \sin^3 3x \, dx.$

2. $\int \cot^2 2y \, dy.$

3. $\int \dfrac{\tan^2 \theta}{\sin^2 \theta} \, d\theta.$

4. $\int \dfrac{\cos 2x}{\sin x} \, dx.$

5. $\int \dfrac{\tan 2r}{\cos^2 2r} \, dr.$

6. $\int \cos^3 (w/2) \, dw.$

7. $\int \sec^3 3y \tan^5 3y \, dy.$

8. $\int \sin^2 5r \, dr.$

9. $\int \tan^3 2s \, ds.$

10. $\int \sin 2x \tan x \, dx.$

11. $\int \sin^2 y \cos^3 y \, dy.$

12. $\int \tan^4 (s/2) \, ds.$

13. $\int \cos^5 2w \, dw.$

14. $\int \sec^4 3y \, dy.$

15. $\int \dfrac{\cos x}{\sin^3 x} \, dx.$

16. $\int \sin^5 3r \cos^2 3r \, dr.$

17. $\int \sin^2 2x \cos^2 2x \, dx.$

18. $\int \cos^2 2x \sin 4x \, dx.$

19. $\int (\cos x - \cos x \cos 2x) \, dx.$

20. $\int \cos^4 4x \, dx.$

21. $\int \dfrac{\cos 3y \, dy}{1 + \sin 3y}.$

22. $\int \dfrac{dy}{1 + \sin 5y}.$

23. $\int \cot^5 2r \, dr.$

24. $\int \sin^3 (s/2) \cos^2 (s/2) \, ds.$

25. $\int \sqrt{1 + \cos 2x} \, dx.$

26. $\int \sqrt{1 - \cos (w/3)} \, dw.$

27. $\int \dfrac{1 + \cos 2\theta}{\sin 2\theta} \, d\theta.$

28. $\int \dfrac{\cos 2y}{\sin^2 2y} \, dy.$

29. $\int \dfrac{dw}{1 + \sec (w/2)}.$

30. $\int \dfrac{dw}{1 - \cos 7w}.$

31. $\int \cot^6 2u \, du.$

32. $\int \sin^3 3y \cos^5 3y \, dy.$

In each of Numbers 33 to 42, evaluate the definite integral.

33. $\displaystyle\int_0^{\pi/4} \tan^3 x \, dx.$

34. $\displaystyle\int_0^{\pi/2} \sqrt{\cos x} \sin^3 x \, dx.$

35. $\displaystyle\int_0^{\pi/2} \cos^4 3y \, dy.$

36. $\displaystyle\int_0^{\pi/4} (\cos y + \cos^2 y)^2 \, dy.$

37. $\displaystyle\int_0^{\pi/3} \frac{dw}{1 + \sin w}.$

40. $\displaystyle\int_0^{\pi/2} \frac{1 - \sin x}{x + \cos x}\, dx.$

38. $\displaystyle\int_0^{\pi/4} (\sin y - \cos y)^2 \, dy.$

41. $\displaystyle\int_{\pi/4}^{\pi/2} \csc^6 u \, du.$

39. $\displaystyle\int_0^{\pi/2} \sin^3 2v \, dv.$

42. $\displaystyle\int_0^{\pi/6} \tan^4 2z \, dz.$

By using the fact that

$$a \cos\theta + b \sin\theta = \sqrt{a^2 + b^2}\, \cos(\theta - \alpha),$$

where $\alpha = \mathrm{Tan}^{-1}\, b/a$ for $a > 0$, $b > 0$, integrals such as those in Numbers 43 to 46 can be evaluated.

43. $\displaystyle\int_0^t \frac{dx}{4\cos x + 3\sin x}.$

45. $\displaystyle\int_0^x \frac{dy}{(4\sin y - 3\cos y)^2}.$

44. $\displaystyle\int_0^x \frac{d\varphi}{5\cos\varphi - 12\sin\varphi}.$

46. $\displaystyle\int_0^t \frac{d\varphi}{(5\cos\varphi + 12\sin\varphi)^2}.$

If the integrand is a product of two sines or two cosines or a sine and a cosine of different multiples of the same variable, the inverse differentiation can be performed by using the appropriate one of the following trigonometric identities:

$$\sin\alpha\cos\beta = \tfrac{1}{2}\sin(\alpha + \beta) + \tfrac{1}{2}\sin(\alpha - \beta),$$
$$\cos\alpha\cos\beta = \tfrac{1}{2}\cos(\alpha + \beta) + \tfrac{1}{2}\cos(\alpha - \beta),$$
$$\sin\alpha\sin\beta = -\tfrac{1}{2}\cos(\alpha + \beta) + \tfrac{1}{2}\cos(\alpha - \beta).$$

Use these results to evaluate the integrals in Numbers 47 to 50.

47. $\displaystyle\int_0^{\pi/2} \sin 2x \cos 3x \, dx.$

49. $\displaystyle\int_0^{\pi/6} \cos \tfrac{1}{2}x \cos \tfrac{7}{2}x \, dx.$

48. $\displaystyle\int_0^{\pi/4} \sin\theta \sin 3\theta \, d\theta.$

50. $\displaystyle\int_0^{\pi} \cos 2u \sin 4u \, du.$

51. Show that

$$\int \tan^n x \, dx = \frac{\tan^{n-1} x}{n - 1} - \int \tan^{n-2} x \, dx, \qquad n \neq 1.$$

52. Show that

$$\int \cot x \csc^n x \, dx = -\frac{\csc^n x}{n} + C, \qquad n \neq 0.$$

53. Find the area bounded by the curve $y = \tan^2 x$, the $x$-axis, and the line $x = \pi/4$.

54. Find the area bounded by the curve $y = |\sin^3 x|$ and the $x$-axis from $x = 0$ to $x = 2\pi$.

55. Find the area bounded by the curve $y = (\cos 2x - \sin 2x)^2$, the $y$-axis, and the $x$-axis from $x = 0$ to the first point where the curve touches the positive $x$-axis.

56. Find the area bounded by the curve $y = \sec^4 x$ and the lines $x = 0$, $y = 4$, $x = \pi/3$.

57. Calculate the volume formed by revolving the area bounded by $y = \tan x$, $x = 0$, $y = 0$, $x = \pi/4$ about the $x$-axis.

58. Find the volume formed by revolving the area bounded by one arch of the curve $y = \sin \frac{1}{2}x$ and the $x$-axis about the $x$-axis.

59. The quantity of heat (joules) generated by a constant current $I$ (amperes) in a resistance $R$ (ohms) in time $t_0$ (seconds) is $Q = RI^2 t_0$. If the current is not constant but is 60-cycle per second current, so that $I = I_0 \sin 120\pi t$, what quantity of heat is generated in 1 minute?

60. A variable force directed along the positive $x$-axis has a magnitude in pounds $F = F_0 \cos^2 \omega x$. How much work is done by this force in moving a body from $x = 0$ to $x = 2\pi/\omega$ (feet) on the $x$-axis?

## 12.3 THE METHOD OF SUBSTITUTION

In the preceding work, we have often found an inverse derivative of a given function by means of a substitution method based on the chain rule. For instance, in the integral

$$\int x\sqrt{x^2 + 4}\, dx,$$

we observe that $d(x^2 + 4) = 2x\, dx$ and rewrite the integral in the form

$$\tfrac{1}{2} \int \sqrt{x^2 + 4}\, (2x\, dx).$$

If we let $u = x^2 + 4$, then the integral becomes

$$\tfrac{1}{2} \int \sqrt{u}\, du = \tfrac{1}{3}u^{3/2} + C,$$

so that

$$\int x\sqrt{x^2 + 4}\, dx = \tfrac{1}{3}(x^2 + 4)^{3/2} + C.$$

This procedure is justified by considering two differentiable functions defined by $y = F(u)$ and $u = g(x)$ and applying the chain rule to get

$$D_x F(u) = D_u F(u)\, D_x u = D_u F(u)\, g'(x).$$

If $f(u) .=. D_u F(u)$, so that

$$D_x F(u) = f[g(x)]g'(x),$$

then the corresponding inverse derivative formula is

(1) $$\int f[g(x)]g'(x)\, dx = F[g(x)] + C,$$

which may be put in the form

(2) $$\int f(u)\, du = F(u) + C$$

since $u = g(x)$.

The foregoing discussion suggests that a substitution of the type $x = g(u)$ might be used to transform an integral

$$\int f(x)\, dx$$

into the form

$$\int f[g(u)]g'(u)\, du,$$

where the inverse derivative is known, say

$$\int f[g(u)]g'(u)\, du = H(u) + C.$$

If the function $g$ has a corresponding inverse function, then under the appropriate hypotheses, we can justify the result

$$\int f(x)\, dx = H[g^{-1}(x)] + C,$$

which would be obtained by replacing $u$ by $g^{-1}(x)$.

**Theorem 12.3a.** Let $x = g(u)$ be a differentiable function having a differentiable inverse function $u = g^{-1}(x)$. Then, on any interval where $g'(x) \neq 0$,

(3) $$\int f[g(u)]g'(u)\, du = H(u) + C \Rightarrow \int f(x)\, dx = H[g^{-1}(x)] + C.$$

PROOF: By the chain rule we have

$$D_x H(u) = D_u H(u)\, D_x g^{-1}(x) = D_u H(u)\, \frac{1}{g'(u)},$$

and since $D_u H(u) = f[g(u)]g'(u)$, it follows that

$$D_x H[g^{-1}(x)] = f[g(u)]g'(u)\, \frac{1}{g'(u)} = f[g(u)] = f(x).$$

In other words, we have shown that $H[g^{-1}(x)]$ is an inverse derivative of $f(x)$ and that the process of substitution is justified under the appropriate conditions.

The replacement of the variable of integration $x$ in an integral $\int f(x)\, dx$ by means of an equation $x = g(u)$ and the application of Theorem 12.3a to the resulting integral is called the **method of substitution.** This method may be used successfully whenever a substitution $u = g(x)$, $du = g'(x)\, dx$ transforms an integral into a known inverse derivative as in the preceding example. The ability needed to determine useful substitutions comes only with practice and experience.

The example of the first paragraph is a special case of the integral

(4) $$\int (a + bx^n)^{p/q} x^m\, dx.$$

Before reading further, make a guess as to a good substitution and try it.

The substitution should be one that transforms the integrand into a rational algebraic expression, so an obvious conjecture is

(5) $$a + bx^n = y^q.$$

Differentiation of both members of this equation gives

(6) $$nbx^{n-1}\, dx = qy^{q-1}\, dy,$$

and the result of substituting from these two equations into (4) is

$$\frac{q}{nb} \int \left(\frac{y^q - a}{b}\right)^{(m-n+1)/n} y^{p+q-1}\, dy.$$

Thus it appears that if $(m - n + 1)/n$ is an integer, then the new integrand is a rational expression in $y$.

---

*Example 12.3a.* Integrate $\int x^3\sqrt{1 + 2x^2}\, dx$.

Here we have $m = 3$ and $n = 2$, so that $(m - n + 1)/n = 1$. Hence, let $y^2 = 1 + 2x^2$, so that $2y\, dy = 4x\, dx$. Then,

$$\begin{aligned}
\int x^3\sqrt{1 + 2x^2}\, dx &= \int x^2\sqrt{1 + 2x^2}\, x\, dx \\
&= \int [\tfrac{1}{2}(y^2 - 1)](y)(\tfrac{1}{2}y\, dy) \\
&= \tfrac{1}{4} \int (y^4 - y^2)\, dy \\
&= \tfrac{1}{4}(\tfrac{1}{5}y^5 - \tfrac{1}{3}y^3) + C \\
&= \tfrac{1}{60}y^3(3y^2 - 5) + C \\
&= \tfrac{1}{60}(1 + 2x^2)^{3/2}(6x^2 - 2) + C.
\end{aligned}$$

---

If $n = 1$ in the general integral (4), then $(m - n + 1)/n$ is an integer and the substitution $a + bx = y^q$ will always yield a rational integrand.

Frequently an integral involving $ax^2 + bx + c$ may be transformed into one of the standard forms by completing the square in $x$ and then making a substitution.

*Example 12.3b.* Integrate

$$\int \frac{dx}{\sqrt{x^2 + 6x}}.$$

We first complete the square under the radical to get

$$\int \frac{dx}{\sqrt{x^2 + 6x}} = \int \frac{dx}{\sqrt{x^2 + 6x + 9 - 9}} = \int \frac{dx}{\sqrt{(x + 3)^2 - 9}}.$$

Then let $u = x + 3$, so that the integral becomes

$$\begin{aligned}
\int \frac{du}{\sqrt{u^2 - 3^2}} &= \text{Cosh}^{-1}\frac{u}{3} + C \\
&= \text{Cosh}^{-1}\frac{x + 3}{3} + C.
\end{aligned}$$

*Example 12.3c.* Integrate

$$\int \frac{x+3}{x^2+2x+2}\, dx.$$

By completing the square in the denominator of the integrand, we get

$$x^2 + 2x + 2 = (x+1)^2 + 1.$$

Accordingly, let $x + 1 = v$ so that $dx = dv$, and

$$\int \frac{(x+3)\, dx}{x^2+2x+2} = \int \frac{(v+2)\, dv}{v^2+1}$$

$$= \int \frac{v\, dv}{v^2+1} + \int \frac{2\, dv}{v^2+1}$$

$$= \tfrac{1}{2} \ln (v^2+1) + 2 \operatorname{Tan}^{-1} v + C$$

$$= \tfrac{1}{2} \ln (x^2+2x+2) + 2 \operatorname{Tan}^{-1} (x+1) + C.$$

The evaluation of a definite integral can often be made by substitution on the basis of the next theorem.

**Theorem 12.3b.** Let $f$ be a continuous function of $x$ on the closed interval $a \leqq x \leqq b$, and let $x = g(t)$, where $t = c$ when $x = a$, $t = d$ when $x = b$, and $t$ is in the interval from $c$ to $d$ when $x$ is in the interval $a \leqq x \leqq b$. Let $g'$ be continuous on the interval from $c$ to $d$. Then

$$\int_a^b f(x)\, dx = \int_c^d f[g(t)]g'(t)\, dt = \int_c^d h(t)\, dt,$$

where $h(t) = f[g(t)]g'(t)$.

PROOF: Let $F(x) = \int_a^x f(y)\, dy$ and $H(t) = \int_c^t h(s)\, ds$. Then

$$F(b) = \int_a^b f(y)\, dy \quad \text{and} \quad H(d) = \int_c^d h(s)\, ds,$$

so that we need only show that $F(b) = H(d)$. By the Fundamental Theorem of Integral Calculus, we have

$$F'(x) = f(x) \quad \text{and} \quad H'(t) = h(t).$$

Next, using $x = g(t)$, we get

$$F[g(t)] = \int_a^{g(t)} f(y)\, dy$$

and

$$D_t F[g(t)] = F'[g(t)]g'(t)$$
$$= f[g(t)]g'(t)$$
$$= h(t)$$
$$= H'(t).$$

Thus

$$F[g(t)] = H(t) + C.$$

If we substitute $t = c$, then

$$F[g(c)] = H(c) + C.$$

But $g(c) = a$, so that

$$F(a) = H(c) + C.$$

However,

$$F(a) = \int_a^a f(y)\, dy = 0 \quad \text{and} \quad H(c) = \int_c^c h(s)\, ds = 0,$$

so that

$$C = 0 \quad \text{and} \quad F(x) = H(t).$$

Hence, if we let $x = b$, then $t = d$, and we obtain

$$F(b) = H(d),$$

which completes the proof.

---

*Example 12.3d.* Evaluate

$$\int_0^4 \frac{x}{\sqrt{1 + 2x}}\, dx.$$

If $y = \sqrt{1 + 2x}$, then $y^2 = 1 + 2x$, $dx = y\, dy$, and $x = 0 \Rightarrow y = 1$, $x = 4 \Rightarrow y = 3.$
Thus,

$$\int_0^4 \frac{x}{\sqrt{1 + 2x}}\, dx = \frac{1}{2} \int_1^3 \frac{(y^2 - 1)y\, dy}{y}$$

$$= \frac{1}{2} \left[ \frac{y^3}{3} - y \right]_1^3$$

$$= \frac{10}{3}.$$

---

Another way in which Theorem 12.3b is useful is illustrated by the next example, which involves parametric equations.

---

*Example 12.3e.* Find the area bounded by the $x$-axis and the curve $x = t + t^2$, $y = t - t^2$ from $t = 0$ to $t = 1$.

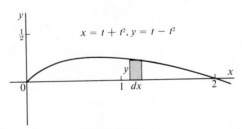

$x = t + t^2, \ y = t - t^2$

**FIGURE 12.3a**

From the given equations, it is seen that $t = 0$ corresponds to the point $(0, 0)$ and $t = 1$ to the point $(2, 0)$. Figure 12.3a shows that the required area is given by

$$A = \int_0^2 y \, dx.$$

Since it is inconvenient to substitute for $y$ in terms of $x$, we substitute for $y$ and $x$ both in terms of $t$. From the equation $x = t + t^2$, it follows that $dx = (1 + 2t) \, dt$, which we use along with the limits on $t$ to obtain

$$A = \int_0^2 y \, dx = \int_0^1 (t - t^2)(1 + 2t) \, dt$$

$$\int_0^1 (t + t^2 - 2t^3) \, dt = \tfrac{1}{3} \text{ (l.u.)}^2.$$

## Exercises 12.3

In each of Numbers 1 to 22, find the inverse derivative.

1. $\displaystyle\int \frac{x \, dx}{\sqrt{x + 4}}.$

2. $\displaystyle\int \frac{dy}{y - \sqrt{y}}.$

3. $\displaystyle\int s^3 \sqrt{9 - s^2} \, ds.$

4. $\displaystyle\int \frac{\sqrt{r - 4}}{r} \, dr.$

5. $\displaystyle\int \frac{dx}{\sqrt{8 + 2x - x^2}}.$

6. $\displaystyle\int \frac{dt}{t^2 - 6t + 12}.$

7. $\displaystyle\int \frac{u \, du}{\sqrt{u^2 - 4u + 8}}.$

8. $\displaystyle\int \frac{(x + 7) \, dx}{x^2 + 4x + 8}.$

9. $\displaystyle\int \frac{(w - 2) \, dw}{w^2 - 4w + 13}.$

10. $\displaystyle\int \frac{dx}{x\sqrt{x^2 - 4}}.$

11. $\displaystyle\int \frac{\sqrt{x^2 - 9}}{3x} \, dx.$

12. $\displaystyle\int \frac{dy}{\sqrt{y^2 - 6y + 5}}.$

13. $\displaystyle\int \frac{dt}{t^2 + 2t + 3}.$

14. $\displaystyle\int \frac{x \, dx}{4 + \sqrt{x + 4}}.$

15. $\displaystyle\int \frac{y^3 \, dy}{(4 + y^2)^{3/2}}.$

16. $\displaystyle\int t(1 + t)^{3/2} \, dt.$

17. $\displaystyle\int \frac{x + 3}{\sqrt[5]{x}} \, dx.$

18. $\displaystyle\int \frac{s \, ds}{\sqrt{s^2 + s}}.$

19. $\displaystyle\int \frac{s^2 \, ds}{\sqrt{s + 1}}.$

20. $\displaystyle\int s\sqrt[3]{s + 1} \, ds.$

21. $\displaystyle\int \frac{y \, dy}{(y + 1)^{2/3}}.$

22. $\displaystyle\int \frac{dx}{x^{1/2} + x^{1/3}}.$

Evaluate the definite integral in each of Numbers 23 to 34.

23. $\int_0^7 \dfrac{s\,ds}{\sqrt[3]{s+1}}.$

24. $\int_0^{2\sqrt{3}} \dfrac{x^3\,dx}{\sqrt{4+x^2}}.$

25. $\int_4^7 \dfrac{dx}{x^2-8x+25}.$

26. $\int_0^5 \dfrac{3y\,dy}{\sqrt{y+4}}.$

27. $\int_0^3 t^5\sqrt{9-t^2}\,dt.$

28. $\int_2^3 \dfrac{dy}{\sqrt{4y-y^2}}.$

29. $\int_1^{\sqrt{2}} \dfrac{t^3\,dt}{\sqrt{4-t^2}}.$

30. $\int_4^9 \dfrac{3\,dx}{x+\sqrt{x}}.$

31. $\int_0^3 y^2(1+y)^{-3/2}\,dy.$

32. $\int_1^4 \dfrac{x\,dx}{x+\sqrt{x}}.$

33. $\int_1^2 \dfrac{dx}{x^2\sqrt{1+x^2}}.$ $\left(\text{Let } x = \dfrac{1}{z}.\right)$

34. $\int_{4/\sqrt{3}}^4 \dfrac{dz}{z^2\sqrt{z^2-4}}.$

35. Find the area bounded by the curve $y = x/\sqrt{1+3x}$ and the lines $y = 0$, $x = 5$
36. Find the area within the loop of the curve $y^2 + x^3 = x^2$.
37. Find the area bounded by the curve $y = x/(1+\sqrt{x})$ and the lines $y = 0$, $x = 9$
38. Find the $x$-coordinate of the centroid of the area of Number 37.
39. Find the volume formed by revolving about the $y$-axis the area of Number 37
40. Find the area bounded by the $y$-axis and the curve $x = t - t^3$, $y = t + t^3$ from $t = 0$ to $t = 1$.
41. Refer to Figure 10.7a and show that the area of the hyperbolic sector $AOP$ is $\frac{1}{2}u$ (l.u.)². *Hint*: Use the parametric equations $x = \cosh u$, $y = \sinh u$.
42. Find the area enclosed by the ellipse $x = a \cos \theta$, $y = b \sin \theta$.

## 12.4 TRIGONOMETRIC AND HYPERBOLIC SUBSTITUTIONS

Formulas (15), (16), (17), and (18) of Section 12.1 express certain integrals in terms of inverse trigonometric or inverse hyperbolic functions. These formulas may be derived using the method of substitution and some of the trigonometric or hyperbolic identities. These substitutions not only furnish a handy method of developing the formulas, but are useful in integrating many other expressions.

*Example 12.4a.* Use a trigonometric substitution to derive a formula for

$$\int \frac{du}{\sqrt{a^2 - u^2}}, \qquad a > 0.$$

Here it would be advantageous to find a substitution that would remove the radical in the denominator. This suggests the use of the identity

$$1 - \sin^2 \theta = \cos^2 \theta,$$

since if we let

$$u = a \sin \theta, \qquad \theta = \text{Sin}^{-1}(u/a),$$

hen

$$\sqrt{a^2 - u^2} = \sqrt{a^2 - a^2 \sin^2 \theta} = a \cos \theta.$$

Notice that $\cos \theta \geq 0$ since we have employed the principal inverse sine function. This agrees with the understanding that the radical sign signifies the principal square root. Furthermore,

$$du = a \cos \theta \, d\theta,$$

o that the integral is transformed as follows:

$$\int \frac{du}{\sqrt{a^2 - u^2}} = \int \frac{a \cos \theta \, d\theta}{a \cos \theta} = \int d\theta$$

$$= \theta + C = \text{Sin}^{-1} (u/a) + C.$$

Since $1 - \tanh^2 \theta = \text{sech}^2 \theta$, the substitution $u = a \tanh \theta$ could also have been used although not as conveniently, as the reader may verify.

---

*Example 12.4b.* Integrate

$$\int \frac{dx}{x^2 \sqrt{4 - x^2}}.$$

Let $x = 2 \sin \theta$, with $\theta = \text{Sin}^{-1} (x/2)$. Then $dx = 2 \cos \theta \, d\theta$, so that

$$\int \frac{dx}{x^2 \sqrt{4 - x^2}} = \int \frac{2 \cos \theta \, d\theta}{4 \sin^2 \theta (2 \cos \theta)}$$

$$= \frac{1}{4} \int \csc^2 \theta \, d\theta$$

$$= -\frac{1}{4} \cot \theta + C.$$

From Figure 12.4a, it is apparent that if $\sin \theta = x/2$, then

$$\cot \theta = \frac{\sqrt{4 - x^2}}{x}.$$

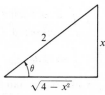

**FIGURE 12.4a**

he specification of the principal inverse sine value for $\theta$ justifies the use of the triangle. hus we find

$$\int \frac{dx}{x^2 \sqrt{4 - x^2}} = \frac{-\sqrt{4 - x^2}}{4x} + C.$$

*Note:* The student should keep in mind that any inverse derivative can always be checked by differentiation

*Example 12.4c.* Use a trigonometric substitution to derive a formula for

$$\int \frac{du}{a^2 + u^2}.$$

The form of the denominator suggests using the identity $1 + \tan^2 \theta = \sec^2 \theta$. Thus we let

$$u = a \tan \theta, \quad \theta = \text{Tan}^{-1} (u/a).$$

Then $du = a \sec^2 \theta \, d\theta$, and the result is

$$\int \frac{du}{a^2 + u^2} = \int \frac{a \sec^2 \theta \, d\theta}{a^2 + a^2 \tan^2 \theta} = \int \frac{a \sec^2 \theta \, d\theta}{a^2 \sec^2 \theta}$$

$$= \frac{1}{a} \int d\theta = \frac{1}{a} \theta + C = \frac{1}{a} \text{Tan}^{-1} \frac{u}{a} + C.$$

The next example illustrates the substitution of a hyperbolic function to simplify the form of an inverse derivative, and brings in an important subtlety pertaining to the form of an inverse derivative.

*Example 12.4d.* Integrate

$$\int \frac{du}{\sqrt{u^2 - a^2}}.$$

We may let $u = a \cosh x$, and make use of the identity $\cosh^2 x - \sinh^2 x = 1$ to obtain

$$\int \frac{du}{\sqrt{u^2 - a^2}} = \int \frac{a \sinh x \, dx}{\sqrt{a^2 \cosh^2 x - a^2}}$$

$$= \int dx = x + C$$

$$= \text{Cosh}^{-1} \frac{u}{a} + C.$$

Or, we could let $u = a \sec \theta$ to obtain

$$\int \frac{du}{\sqrt{u^2 - a^2}} = \int \frac{a \sec \theta \tan \theta \, d\theta}{\sqrt{a^2 \sec^2 \theta - a^2}}$$

$$= \int \sec \theta \, d\theta$$

$$= \ln [\sec \theta + \tan \theta] + C_1$$

$$= \ln [u + \sqrt{u^2 - a^2}] + C_2.$$

This last result is indeed rather startling because it apparently has no resemblance whatsoever to $\text{Cosh}^{-1} (u/a) + C$. Indeed, it appears that we may have obtained a contradiction to Theorem 7.4b, which states that two functions having the same derivative differ at most by a constant. However, let us see if these apparently different expressions are really equivalent. The work in Section 10.7 included a derivation of the formula

$$\text{Cosh}^{-1} x = \ln [x + \sqrt{x^2 - 1}], \quad 1 \le x,$$

so that upon replacing $x$ by $u/a$ in this expression, we can show the equivalence of the two seemingly different results. The reader should find the difference between the two constants $C$ and $C_2$.

The point to be emphasized here is simply that the form obtained for an inverse derivative may very well depend upon the method by which the result was obtained. The fact that a particular result does not agree with a given solution or with a solution obtained by another method does not necessarily imply that the result is not a correct solution. For example, the two expressions

$$2 \,\text{Sin}^{-1} \left( \frac{\sqrt{x}}{2} \right) \quad \text{and} \quad \text{Sin}^{-1} \left( \frac{x - 2}{2} \right).$$

differ only by a constant. (Can you show this?)

---

*Example 12.4e.* Integrate

$$\int \frac{dx}{x^2 \sqrt{x^2 + 4}}.$$

Let $x = 2 \tan \theta$, with $\theta = \text{Tan}^{-1} (x/2)$. Then $dx = 2 \sec^2 \theta \, d\theta$, and

$$\int \frac{dx}{x^2 \sqrt{x^2 + 4}} = \int \frac{2 \sec^2 \theta \, d\theta}{(4 \tan^2 \theta)(2 \sec \theta)}$$

$$= \frac{1}{4} \int \frac{1}{\cos \theta} \left( \frac{\cos^2 \theta}{\sin^2 \theta} \right) d\theta$$

$$= \frac{1}{4} \int \csc \theta \cot \theta \, d\theta$$

$$= -\frac{1}{4} \csc \theta + C$$

$$= -\frac{\sqrt{x^2 + 4}}{4x} + C.$$

To obtain the final step, we may refer to Figure 12.4b, from which it follows that if $\theta = \text{Tan}^{-1} (x/2)$, then $\csc \theta = (\sqrt{x^2 + 4}/x)$.

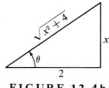

**FIGURE 12.4b**

---

As in the preceding section, the student should not be limited to the specific substitutions suggested, but should try to develop other substitutions to fit special cases. Some of these are suggested in the hints for certain problems.

## Exercises 12.4

1. Use a hyperbolic substitution to derive Formula (17) of Section 12.1.
2. Use a hyperbolic substitution to derive Formula (18) of Section 12.1.

Find the inverse derivative in each of Numbers 3 to 18.

3. $\int \dfrac{x^2}{\sqrt{9 - x^2}}\, dx.$

4. $\int \dfrac{dy}{9 - y^2}.$

5. $\int \sqrt{1 - t^2}\, dt.$

6. $\int \dfrac{dx}{\sqrt{4 + x^2}}.$

7. $\int \dfrac{ds}{s^2\sqrt{4 - s^2}}.$

8. $\int y^3\sqrt{y^2 - 4}\, dy.$

9. $\int \dfrac{y^3\, dy}{4 + y^2}.$

10. $\int \dfrac{w^2\, dw}{\sqrt{2 - 3w^2}}.$

11. $\int \dfrac{dx}{(4 + x^2)^{3/2}}.$

12. $\int \dfrac{dw}{w\sqrt{w^2 - 2}}.$

13. $\int \dfrac{dx}{x\sqrt{x^2 + 4}}.$

14. $\int \dfrac{dt}{\sqrt{4t + t^2}}.$ (Let $t = 4\tan^2 \theta$.)

15. $\int \dfrac{x^3\, dx}{\sqrt{9 - x^2}}.$

16. $\int \dfrac{dy}{\sqrt{y^2 - 4y + 8}}.$

17. $\int \dfrac{dy}{\sqrt{4y - y^2}}.$ (Let $y = 4\sin^2 \theta$.)

18. $\int \dfrac{\sqrt{s^2 - 16}}{s^4}\, ds.$

Evaluate the definite integral in each of Numbers 19 to 26.

19. $\int_0^1 \dfrac{u^2\, du}{\sqrt{4 - u^2}}.$

20. $\int_{\sqrt{3}}^3 \dfrac{x^2\, dx}{9 + x^2}.$

21. $\int_4^8 \dfrac{dy}{(y^2 - 4)^{3/2}}.$

22. $\int_{\sqrt{3}}^3 \dfrac{dx}{x^2\sqrt{x^2 + 9}}.$

23. $\int_4^6 \dfrac{dw}{w\sqrt{w^2 - 4}}.$

24. $\int_2^{2\sqrt{3}} \dfrac{t^3\, dt}{\sqrt{t^2 + 4}}.$

25. $\int_{\sqrt{2}/2}^{\sqrt{3}/2} x^2\sqrt{1 - x^2}\, dx.$

26. $\int_1^3 x^3\sqrt{3 + x^2}\, dx.$

27. Use integration to find the area enclosed by the ellipse $4x^2 + 9y^2 = 36$.
28. Use integration to find the area enclosed by the circle $x^2 + y^2 = 9$.
29. Find the volume of the solid formed by rotating about the $x$-axis the area bounded by the $x$-axis and the curve $y = x(1 - x^3)^{1/3}$.
30. Find the area enclosed by the curve $x^{2/3} + y^{2/3} = a^{2/3}$.
31. Find the area bounded by the $x$-axis, the line $x = 4$, and the curve

$$y = (\sqrt{x^2 - 4})/x^2.$$

32. Find the volume formed when the area of Number 31 is revolved about the $y$-axis.
33. Find the area enclosed by one loop of the curve $x^2 = y^4(1 - y^2)$.
34. Find the area bounded by the $x$-axis and one arch of the cycloid $x = b(t - \sin t)$, $y = b(1 - \cos t)$.
35. Find the area of Number 30 by using the parametric equations $x = a \cos^3 \varphi$, $y = a \sin^3 \varphi$.
36. Find the volume of a spherical segment of one base and of altitude $h$ if the radius of the sphere is $b$.

## 2.5 INTEGRATION BY PARTS

One of the most important techniques frequently used to transform an integral into a more manageable form is based on the formula for the derivative of a product of two differentiable functions, say $u$ and $v$:

$$D_x(uv) = u\,D_x v + v\,D_x u.$$

If we solve this formula for the term $u\,D_x v$ and take inverse derivatives, we obtain, in succession,

$$u\,D_x v = D_x(uv) - v\,D_x u$$

and

(1) $$\int u\,D_x v\,dx = uv - \int v\,D_x u\,dx.$$

Formula (1) is frequently written in terms of the differentials $du$ and $dv$ as follows:

(2) $$\int u\,dv = uv - \int v\,du.$$

Integration by means of (1) or (2) is called **integration by parts.**

Whenever the integrand is regarded as the product of a function $u$ and the derivative of a second function $v$, the formula expresses the integral in terms of a second integral in which the roles of the two factors are interchanged, the function $u$ being replaced by its derivative and the derivative $D_x v$ by the function $v$. Some examples will indicate the possibilities stemming from the use of this formula.

---

*Example 12.5a.* Integrate $\int x \sin x\,dx$.

We let

$$u = x \quad \text{and} \quad D_x v = \sin x,$$

so that

$$D_x u = 1 \quad \text{and} \quad v = -\cos x.$$

Thus, Formula (1) gives

$$\int x \sin x\,dx = -x \cos x - \int -\cos x\,dx$$

$$= -x \cos x + \sin x + C.$$

---

Notice in the preceding example that the constant of integration $C$ was added after the last integration was performed. It is usually convenient to follow this procedure, which is justified because we may regard the problem at the start as that of obtaining *an* inverse derivative, the general result then being obtained by adding the arbitrary constant. (The student may easily verify the fact that omission of a constant of integration in the intermediate step of finding $v$ from $dv$ makes no difference in the final result.)

---

*Example 12.5b.* Integrate $\int x^2 \cos x\, dx$.

In this example, we use the notation of Formula (2) and let

$$dv = \cos x\, dx \quad \text{and} \quad u = x^2,$$

so that

$$v = \sin x, \quad du = 2x\, dx,$$

and

$$\int x^2 \cos x\, dx = x^2 \sin x - 2 \int x \sin x\, dx.$$

Since the last integral is exactly that of Example 12.5a, we obtain

$$\int x^2 \cos x\, dx = x^2 \sin x + 2x \cos x - 2 \sin x + C.$$

---

This example illustrates the possibility of removing a factor $x^n$ by integrating by parts $n$ times, each time taking the power of $x$ as the factor to be differentiated. This scheme is often successful in handling inverse derivatives of the type

$$\int x^n f(x)\, dx.$$

The next example illustrates another type of integral for which repeated integration by parts is useful.

---

*Example 12.5c.* Integrate $\int e^{-x} \sin 2x\, dx$.

Letting

$$u = e^{-x} \quad \text{and} \quad D_x v = \sin 2x,$$

so that

$$D_x u = -e^{-x} \quad \text{and} \quad v = -\tfrac{1}{2} \cos 2x,$$

we get

$$\int e^{-x} \sin 2x\, dx = -\tfrac{1}{2} e^{-x} \cos 2x - \tfrac{1}{2} \int e^{-x} \cos 2x\, dx.$$

In this last integral, we let

$$u = e^{-x} \quad \text{and} \quad D_x v = \cos 2x,$$

so that

$$D_x u = -e^{-x} \quad \text{and} \quad v = \tfrac{1}{2} \sin 2x.$$

Then

$$\int e^{-x} \sin 2x\, dx = -\tfrac{1}{2} e^{-x} \cos 2x - \tfrac{1}{4} e^{-x} \sin 2x - \tfrac{1}{4} \int e^{-x} \sin 2x\, dx.$$

Since the last integral in this equation is the same as the one with which we started, we may solve for it and then complete the problem by adding an arbitrary constant. The final result is

$$\int e^{-x} \sin 2x \, dx = -\tfrac{2}{5} e^{-x} \cos 2x - \tfrac{1}{5} e^{-x} \sin 2x + C.$$

It should be noted that Formula (1) can be put into definite integral form by use of the Fundamental Theorem of Integral Calculus. Thus, we have

(3) $$\int_a^b u \, D_x v \, dx = [uv]_a^b - \int_a^b v \, D_x u \, dx.$$

*Example 12.5d.* Evaluate $\int_0^2 x^2 e^x \, dx$.

We let

$$u = x^2 \quad \text{and} \quad D_x v = e^x,$$

so that

$$D_x u = 2x \quad \text{and} \quad v = e^x.$$

Then,

$$\int_0^2 x^2 e^x \, dx = [x^2 e^x]_0^2 - 2 \int_0^2 x e^x \, dx$$

$$= 4e^2 - 2 \int_0^2 x e^x \, dx.$$

In the last integral, write $u = x$, $D_x v = e^x$, to get $D_x u = 1$, $v = e^x$, and then

$$\int_0^2 x^2 e^x \, dx = 4e^2 - 2[x e^x]_0^2 + 2 \int_0^2 e^x \, dx$$

$$= 4e^2 - 4e^2 + [2e^x]_0^2 = 2(e^2 - 1).$$

# Exercises 12.5

In each of Numbers 1 to 24, find the inverse derivative.

1. $\int w \cos 3w \, dw.$

2. $\int y e^{-y} \, dy.$

3. $\int x^2 \sin x \, dx.$

4. $\int \ln x \, dx.$

5. $\int \operatorname{Tan}^{-1} w \, dw.$

6. $\int s^2 e^{2s} \, ds.$

7. $\int x^3 \cos 2x \, dx.$

8. $\int \operatorname{Sin}^{-1} (y/2) \, dy.$

9. $\int y \ln y \, dy.$

10. $\int e^u \sin 2u \, du.$

11. $\int y \operatorname{Sin}^{-1} y \, dy.$

12. $\int \cos t \sin 3t \, dt.$

13. $\int x \csc^2 x \, dx.$

14. $\int t \sqrt{t+1} \, dt.$

15. $\int e^{2x} \cos 3x \, dx$.

19. $\int \theta \sec^2 \theta \, d\theta$.

16. $\int t^2 \ln t \, dt$.

20. $\int x^2 \sqrt{x - 2} \, dx$.

17. $\int x^3 \tan^{-1} x \, dx$.

21. $\int y^{3/2} \ln 3y \, dy$.

18. $\int \ln^2 y \, dy$.

22. $\int x \sin^2 2x \, dx$.

23. $\int \sec^3 t \, dt$. Hint: Let $dv = \sec^2 t \, dt$ and in the resulting integral use the formula $\tan^2 t = \sec^2 t - 1$.

24. $\int \csc^3 2t \, dt$. Hint: See Number 23.

In Numbers 25 to 32, evaluate the definite integrals.

25. $\int_0^{\pi/2} y \sin y \, dy$.

29. $\int_0^{\pi/4} e^x \sin 2x \, dx$.

26. $\int_0^1 u e^{3u} \, du$.

30. $\int_{-\pi/2}^{\pi/2} w \cos w \, dw$.

27. $\int_0^1 \tan^{-1} x \, dx$.

31. $\int_0^5 x \sqrt{x + 4} \, dx$.

28. $\int_0^{\pi/2} x^2 \cos 2x \, dx$.

32. $\int_0^{1/2} \sin^{-1} x \, dx$.

33. Find the area bounded by the $x$-axis, the curve $y = xe^{-x}$, and the ordinate drawn to the maximum point of the curve.

34. Find the volume formed by revolving about the $x$-axis the area of Number 33.

35. Calculate the area bounded by the $x$-axis, the curve $y = \sin^{-1} 2x$, and the line $x = \sqrt{3}/4$.

36. Calculate the area below the curve $y = \ln x$ and above the $x$-axis from $x = 1$ to $x = 5$.

37. Locate the centroid of the area in Number 36.

38. Find the area bounded by the $x$-axis, the curve $y = xe^{-x}$, and the ordinate drawn to the inflection point of the curve.

39. Find the $x$-coordinate of the centroid of the area bounded by the curve $y = \sin x$ and the lines $y = 0$, $x = \pi/2$.

★40. Calculate $\int x e^x \cos x \, dx$.

★41. In the case where $uv$ is a nonzero constant, say $c$, so that $D_x(uv) = 0$, we find that $v \, D_x u = -u \, D_x v$, and Formula (1) of this section becomes

$$\int u \, D_x v \, dx = c + \int u \, D_x v \, dx.$$

Explain this apparently contradictory result.

## 12.6 WALLIS' FORMULA

The reader has undoubtedly noticed the frequent occurrence of integrals of the type

$$\int_0^{\pi/2} \cos^m \theta \, d\theta, \quad \int_0^{\pi/2} \sin^m \theta \, d\theta, \quad \text{and} \quad \int_0^{\pi/2} \cos^m \theta \sin^n \theta \, d\theta,$$

where $m$ and $n$ are positive integers. For such integrals there is a set of efficient formulas named after the English mathematician John Wallis (1616–1703). Although we shall find it not difficult to derive Wallis' formulas, his own derivation exhibited remarkable ingenuity, being obtained without the aid of the symbolism of modern calculus.

Let us apply integration by parts to the integral

$$\int \cos^m \theta \, d\theta, \quad m = 2, 3, 4, \ldots,$$

by setting

$$dv = \cos \theta \, d\theta, \quad u = \cos^{m-1} \theta,$$

so that

$$v = \sin \theta, \quad du = -(m-1) \cos^{m-2} \theta \sin \theta \, d\theta.$$

Then

$$\int \cos^m \theta \, d\theta = \cos^{m-1} \theta \sin \theta + (m-1) \int \cos^{m-2} \theta \sin^2 \theta \, d\theta.$$

If we replace the factor $\sin^2 \theta$ by $1 - \cos^2 \theta$ in the last integrand, we get

$$\int \cos^m \theta \, d\theta = \cos^{m-1} \theta \sin \theta + (m-1) \int \cos^{m-2} \theta \, d\theta - (m-1) \int \cos^m \theta \, d\theta.$$

Hence, by adding $(m-1) \displaystyle\int \cos^m \theta \, d\theta$ to both members and then dividing by $m$, we obtain the formula

1) $$\int \cos^m \theta \, d\theta = \frac{1}{m} \cos^{m-1} \theta \sin \theta + \frac{m-1}{m} \int \cos^{m-2} \theta \, d\theta.$$

Because this equation expresses the original integral in terms of an integral in which the exponent of $\cos \theta$ is 2 less than its original value, Formula (1) is called a **reduction formula**. Many other examples of such formulas appear in tables of integrals (see Section 12.11).

We next consider the two definite integrals

$$\int_0^{\pi/2} \cos^m x \, dx \quad \text{and} \quad \int_0^{\pi/2} \sin^m x \, dx.$$

In the second integral we make the substitution $x = \pi/2 - v$, to obtain

$$\int_0^{\pi/2} \sin^m x \, dx = \int_{\pi/2}^0 \cos^m v \, (-dv) = \int_0^{\pi/2} \cos^m v \, dv.$$

Thus

$$\int_0^{\pi/2} \cos^m x \, dx = \int_0^{\pi/2} \sin^m x \, dx.$$

Next, from Formula (1), it follows that

$$\int_0^{\pi/2} \cos^m x \, dx = \left[ \frac{1}{m} \cos^{m-1} x \sin x \right]_0^{\pi/2} + \frac{m-1}{m} \int_0^{\pi/2} \cos^{m-2} x \, dx,$$

or

(2)
$$\int_0^{\pi/2} \cos^m x \, dx = \frac{m-1}{m} \int_0^{\pi/2} \cos^{m-2} x \, dx,$$

since the term in brackets is zero at both $x = 0$ and $x = \pi/2$.

If $m - 2 \geq 2$, the preceding result may be applied as a reduction formula to the integral on the right to get

$$\int_0^{\pi/2} \cos^m x \, dx = \frac{(m-1)(m-3)}{m(m-2)} \int_0^{\pi/2} \cos^{m-4} x \, dx.$$

By successive applications of Formula (2), the exponent of cos $x$ may be reduced to 0 if $m$ is even or to 1 if $m$ is odd. Thus

(3)
$$\int_0^{\pi/2} \cos^m x \, dx = \int_0^{\pi/2} \sin^m x \, dx$$

$$= \frac{(m-1)(m-3) \cdots (1) \text{ or } (2)}{m(m-2) \cdots (2) \text{ or } (3)} M,$$

where if $m$ is even and $\geq 2$,

$$M = \int_0^{\pi/2} dx = \frac{\pi}{2},$$

and, if $m$ is odd and $\geq 3$,

$$M = \int_0^{\pi/2} \cos x \, dx = 1.$$

Notice in Formula (3) that the denominator begins with $m$, the original exponent, and the numerator begins with 1 less than the denominator. The remaining factors both above and below are each obtained by subtracting 2 from the preceding factor. This subtraction is stopped when the next factor so constructed would be zero or negative. The factor 2 in the denominator of $\pi/2$ should suggest that this factor comes in when $m$ is even.

---

*Example 12.6a.* Evaluate $\int_0^{\pi/2} \cos^5 x \, dx$.

Formula (3) immediately yields

$$\int_0^{\pi/2} \cos^5 x \, dx = \frac{(4)(2)}{(5)(3)} = \frac{8}{15}.$$

---

*Example 12.6b.* Evaluate $\int_0^{\pi/2} \sin^6 x \, dx$.

In this instance $m$ is even, so that

$$\int_0^{\pi/2} \sin^6 x \, dx = \frac{(5)(3)(1)}{(6)(4)(2)} \left( \frac{\pi}{2} \right) = \frac{5\pi}{32}.$$

A formula corresponding to Formula (3) can be found for

$$\int_0^{\pi/2} \cos^m x \sin^n x \, dx.$$

The derivation is left for the exercises (see Exercises 12.6, Number 40).
If $m$, $n$ are both positive integers $\geq 2$, then

(4) $\displaystyle\int_0^{\pi/2} \cos^m x \sin^n x \, dx$

$$= \frac{[(m-1)(m-3) \cdots (1) \text{ or } (2)][(n-1)(n-3) \cdots (1) \text{ or } (2)]}{(m+n)(m+n-2) \cdots (2) \text{ or } (3)} N,$$

where

$$N = \begin{cases} 1 \text{ unless both } m \text{ and } n \text{ are even,} \\ \pi/2 \text{ if both } m \text{ and } n \text{ are even.} \end{cases}$$

---

*Example 12.6c.* Evaluate $\displaystyle\int_0^{\pi/2} \cos^3 x \sin^2 x \, dx$.

Using Formula (4), we get

$$\int_0^{\pi/2} \cos^3 x \sin^2 x \, dx = \frac{(2)(1)}{(5)(3)} = \frac{2}{15}.$$

---

*Example 12.6d.* Evaluate $\displaystyle\int_0^{\pi/2} \cos^4 x \sin^2 x \, dx$.

Again, by the use of Formula (4), we obtain

$$\int_0^{\pi/2} \cos^4 x \sin^2 x \, dx = \frac{(3)(1)(1)}{(6)(4)(2)} \left(\frac{\pi}{2}\right) = \frac{\pi}{32}.$$

---

Although the limits are 0 and $\pi/2$ in Wallis' formulas, simple considerations allow us to use the formulas if the limits are integral multiples of $\pi/2$. Thus, Formula (4) applies immediately to

$$\int_{k\pi/2}^{(k+1)\pi/2} \cos^m x \sin^n x \, dx$$

if the interval $k\pi/2$ to $(k+1)\pi/2$ is one on which the integrand $\cos^m x \sin^n x$ is positive. If the integrand is negative, only a minus sign needs to be supplied before the right hand side of the formula. It is left to the reader to verify these statements (see Exercises 12.6, Number 41). If the integral extends over more than one interval of length $\pi/2$, it may be written as a sum of integrals of the type of the preceding one and handled as in the next examples.

---

*Example 12.6e.* Evaluate $\displaystyle\int_0^{5\pi/2} \cos^4 x \sin^2 x \, dx$.

In this integral both exponents are even, so the integrand is always nonnegative. Since the interval 0 to $5\pi/2$ is equivalent to 5 intervals of length $\pi/2$, we have

$$\int_0^{5\pi/2} \cos^4 x \sin^2 x \, dx = (5) \frac{(3)(1)(1)}{(6)(4)(2)} \left(\frac{\pi}{2}\right) = \frac{5\pi}{32}.$$

---

*Example 12.6f.* Evaluate $\int_{-3\pi/2}^0 \cos^5 x \sin^3 x \, dx$.

In this problem, we have for the interval

$$\begin{aligned}
-3\pi/2 < x < -\pi, & \quad \text{the integrand is negative,} \\
-\pi < x < -\pi/2, & \quad \text{the integrand is positive,} \\
-\pi/2 < x < 0, & \quad \text{the integrand is negative.}
\end{aligned}$$

Accordingly, it follows that

$$\int_{-3\pi/2}^0 \cos^5 x \sin^3 x \, dx = -\frac{(4)(2)(2)}{(8)(6)(4)(2)} = -\frac{1}{24}.$$

---

It frequently happens that a change of the variable of integration allows us to use Wallis' formulas as in the following examples.

---

*Example 12.6g.* Evaluate $\int_0^\pi \cos^4 3\theta \, d\theta$.

Let $3\theta = x$ or $\theta = x/3$. Then

$$d\theta = dx/3,$$
$$\theta = 0 \implies x = 0 \quad \text{and} \quad \theta = \pi \implies x = 3\pi.$$

Hence

$$\int_0^\pi \cos^4 3\theta \, d\theta = \frac{1}{3} \int_0^{3\pi} \cos^4 x \, dx$$

$$= 2 \int_0^{\pi/2} \cos^4 x \, dx = \frac{3\pi}{8}.$$

---

*Example 12.6h.* Evaluate $\int_0^a x^2 \sqrt{a^2 - x^2} \, dx$.

Let $x = a \sin \theta$ and $\theta = \text{Sin}^{-1}(x/a)$. Then

$$dx = a \cos \theta \, d\theta,$$
$$x = 0 \implies \theta = 0 \quad \text{and} \quad x = a \implies \theta = \pi/2.$$

Thus

$$\int_0^a x^2 \sqrt{a^2 - x^2} \, dx = a^4 \int_0^{\pi/2} \sin^2 \theta \cos^2 \theta \, d\theta$$

$$= \frac{\pi a^4}{16}.$$

# Exercises 12.6

In each of Numbers 1 to 32, evaluate the given integral.

1. $\int_0^{\pi/2} \cos^3 x \, dx$.

2. $\int_0^{\pi/2} \sin^{10} x \, dx$.

3. $\int_0^{\pi/2} \sin^4 \varphi \, d\varphi$.

4. $\int_0^{\pi/2} \cos^7 y \, dy$.

5. $\int_0^{\pi/2} \cos^2 \theta \sin^3 \theta \, d\theta$.

6. $\int_0^{\pi/2} \cos^2 u \sin^2 u \, du$.

7. $\int_0^{\pi/2} \cos^3 w \sin^4 w \, dw$.

8. $\int_0^{\pi/2} \cos^4 t \sin^6 t \, dt$.

9. $\int_0^{\pi} \sin^2 z \, dz$.

0. $\int_0^{3\pi/2} \cos^4 \theta \, d\theta$.

1. $\int_{-\pi/2}^{\pi} \sin^3 u \, du$.

2. $\int_{-\pi/2}^{\pi} \cos^5 y \, dy$.

3. $\int_0^{2\pi} |\cos^3 x| \, dx$.

4. $\int_{-\pi}^{\pi} |\sin^5 \theta| \, d\theta$.

5. $\int_0^{2\pi} \cos^2 v \sin^4 v \, dv$.

6. $\int_{-\pi}^{\pi/2} \cos^3 x \sin^3 x \, dx$.

17. $\int_0^{\pi} \cos^2 t \sin^3 t \, dt$.

18. $\int_0^{2\pi} \cos^4 u \sin^5 u \, du$.

19. $\int_{-\pi/2}^{\pi/2} \cos^2 t \sin^6 t \, dt$.

20. $\int_{-\pi/2}^{\pi} \cos^5 x \sin^2 x \, dx$.

21. $\int_{\pi}^{\pi/4} \sin^7 2\theta \, d\theta$.

22. $\int_0^{\pi/2} \cos^3 5\theta \, d\theta$.

23. $\int_0^{\pi} \sin^6 4\theta \, d\theta$.

24. $\int_{-\pi}^{\pi} \cos^4 (\theta/2) \sin^2 (\theta/2) \, d\theta$.

25. $\int_0^{2\pi} \cos^2 \theta \sin^2 2\theta \, d\theta$.

26. $\int_0^{2\pi} \sin^2 \theta \cos^2 2\theta \, d\theta$.

27. $\int_0^4 \sqrt{16 - x^2} \, dx$.

28. $\int_0^3 (9 - t^2)^{3/2} \, dt$.

29. $\int_0^2 \sqrt{2y - y^2} \, dy$.

30. $\int_0^a u\sqrt{au - u^2} \, du$.

31. $\int_0^a (a^{2/3} - x^{2/3})^{3/2} \, dx$.

32. $\int_0^a w^3 \sqrt{a^2 - w^2} \, dw$.

3. Find the area bounded by one arch of the curve $y = \sin^3 3x$ and the $x$-axis.

4. Find the area bounded by one arch of the curve $y = \sin^6 2x$ and the $x$-axis.

5. Find the volume formed by revolving about the $x$-axis the area bounded by the curve $y = \cos^2 x$, the $y$-axis, and the $x$-axis from $x = 0$ to $x = \pi/2$.

6. Find the volume formed by revolving about the $x$-axis the area bounded by one arch of the curve $y = \sin^2 2x$ and the $x$-axis.

7. Find the area enclosed by one loop of the curve $y^2 = x^4(1 - x^2)^3$.

8. Find the area enclosed by the curve $b^8 x^2 = (b^2 - y^2)^5$.

39. Find a formula for the area enclosed by the loop of the curve $x^2 = y^{2m}(1 - y)^{2n-1}$, where $m$ and $n$ are positive integers.

40. (a) By integration by parts with $dv = \cos^m x \sin x \, dx$, show that

$$\int_0^{\pi/2} \cos^m x \sin^n x \, dx = \frac{n-1}{m+n} \int_0^{\pi/2} \cos^m x \sin^{n-2} x \, dx, \qquad n \geq 2.$$

(b) Let $m$ be an even integer $\geq 2$ and show that repeated application of the preceding formula gives the result of Wallis' formula.

(c) Repeat the procedure in (b) for $m$ an odd integer $\geq 3$.

41. By use of the substitution $x = y + k\pi/2$, show that

$$\int_{k\pi/2}^{(k+1)\pi/2} \cos^m x \sin^n x \, dx$$

can be evaluated by Formula (4).

42. If $k, m, n \in \mathfrak{N}$, evaluate the integral

$$\int_{k\pi/4}^{(k+1)\pi/4} \cos^{2m} 2x \sin^{2n} 4x \, dx.$$

## 12.7 INTEGRATION OF RATIONAL FRACTIONS

An expression of the type $P(x)/Q(x)$, where $P(x)$ and $Q(x)$ are polynomials is called a **rational fraction.** The inverse derivatives of several types of rational fractions have already been discussed.

For example, the inverse derivative of $A/(x - a)^n$ is easily written, since this fraction is the derivative of the constant $A$ times a power of $x - a$, for $n \neq 1$ and of $\ln |x - a|$, if $n = 1$. The inverse derivative of a rational fraction of the type

$$\frac{Ax + B}{x^2 + bx + c},$$

where $x^2 + bx + c$ is irreducible in $\mathfrak{R}$ (that is, has no real linear factors) was found in Example 12.3c.

To find the inverse derivative of a fraction of the type

$$\frac{Ax + B}{(x^2 + bx + c)^n},$$

where $x^2 + bx + c$ is again irreducible, the same procedure as in Example 12.3 may be used. This leads in part to an integral of the form

$$\int \frac{du}{(a^2 + u^2)^n},$$

which may be handled by using the substitution

$$u = a \tan \theta, \quad \theta = \text{Tan}^{-1}(u/a),$$

or by means of Formula 22 in the table of integrals in Appendix C. This formula is another example of a reduction formula, since it reduces the exponent in the integral from $n$ to $n - 1$.

*Example 12.7a.* Integrate

$$\int \frac{(4x + 9)\, dx}{(x^2 + 4x + 13)^2}.$$

Since $D_x(x^2 + 4x + 13) = 2x + 4$, we rewrite the numerator in the form

$$4x + 9 = 2(2x + 4) + 1,$$

and thus obtain

$$\int \frac{(4x + 9)\, dx}{(x^2 + 4x + 13)^2} = \int \frac{2(2x + 4)\, dx}{(x^2 + 4x + 13)^2} + \int \frac{dx}{[(x + 2)^2 + 9]^2}.$$

The first integral on the right is of the form $2 \int u^{-2}\, du$ and so gives $-2u^{-1}$; that is,

$$- \frac{2}{x^2 + 4x + 13}.$$

In the second integral, let

$$x + 2 = 3 \tan \theta, \quad \theta = \mathrm{Tan}^{-1}\left(\frac{x + 2}{3}\right),$$

so that $dx = 3 \sec^2 \theta\, d\theta$. Then

$$\int \frac{dx}{[(x + 2)^2 + 9]^2} = \int \frac{3 \sec^2 \theta\, d\theta}{81 \sec^4 \theta} = \frac{1}{27} \int \cos^2 \theta\, d\theta$$

$$= \frac{1}{27} \int \frac{1 + \cos 2\theta}{2}\, d\theta = \frac{1}{54}\left(\theta + \frac{1}{2} \sin 2\theta\right)$$

$$= \frac{1}{54} \theta + \frac{1}{54} \sin \theta \cos \theta$$

$$= \frac{1}{54} \mathrm{Tan}^{-1}\left(\frac{x + 2}{3}\right) + \frac{1}{54}\left(\frac{x + 2}{\sqrt{x^2 + 4x + 13}}\right)\left(\frac{3}{\sqrt{x^2 + 4x + 13}}\right)$$

$$= \frac{1}{54} \mathrm{Tan}^{-1}\left(\frac{x + 2}{3}\right) + \frac{x + 2}{18(x^2 + 4x + 13)}.$$

The final result is now written as

$$\int \frac{(4x + 7)\, dx}{(x^2 + 4x + 13)^2} = \frac{x - 34}{18(x^2 + 4x + 13)} + \frac{1}{54} \mathrm{Tan}^{-1}\left(\frac{x + 2}{3}\right) + C.$$

---

The preceding discussion suggests that it is possible to find the inverse derivative of any rational fraction *if* the denominator can be factored into linear factors and/or quadratic factors which are irreducible in the field of real numbers, and *if* the fraction can then be "decomposed" into a sum of fractions whose denominators are of the types mentioned earlier in this section.

In order to investigate this possibility, it is necessary to digress briefly to consider the factorization of a polynomial,

$$p(x) \,.=. \, a_0 x^n + a_1 x^{n-1} + \cdots + a_{n-1} x + a_n,$$

where the coefficients are real numbers. The essential theorems for the present purposes were discussed in Section 1.9. Theorems 1.9b, 1.9d, 1.9e, and 1.9f state the basic facts that we need here.

(1) The remainder upon dividing a polynomial $p(x)$ by $x - c$ is a constant $p(c)$ (The Remainder Theorem, Theorem 1.9b). An important consequence of this theorem is that $x - c$ is a factor of $p(x)$ if, and only if, $p(c) = 0$.

(2) A polynomial $p(x)$ of degree $n$ in $\mathfrak{C}$ is reducible to a product of exactly $n$ linear factors in $\mathfrak{C}$ (Theorem 1.9d).

(3) If the value of a polynomial $p(x)$ of degree $n$ is equal to the value of a polynomial $q(x)$ of degree $m$, $m \leq n$, for at least $n + 1$ values of $x$, then the polynomials are identical and have equal values for all values of $x$ (Theorem 1.9e).

(4) If $p(x)$ is a polynomial in the field $\mathfrak{R}$, then

$$p(a + ib) = 0 \implies p(a - ib) = 0 \qquad \text{(Theorem 1.9f).}$$

It follows from Statement (4) that if a polynomial $p(x)$ in the field $\mathfrak{R}$ has a zero $a + ib$, then

$$(x - a - ib)(x - a + ib) = x^2 - 2ax + a^2 + b^2$$

is a factor of the polynomial. Consequently, the preceding facts show that every polynomial in the field $\mathfrak{R}$ can theoretically be factored into linear and/or quadratic factors with real coefficients. Of course, it may not be possible to find the factors in any practical fashion, but if $p(x)$ has numerical coefficients, the factors can always be approximated as accurately as is desired, even if they cannot be found exactly. Thus, the first of the two problems suggested earlier—factoring the denominator of the rational fraction—may be regarded as solved. Let us then consider the second problem—decomposing a rational fraction into a sum of simpler rational fractions, which are customarily called **partial fractions.**

In some of the earlier work in finding inverse derivatives of rational fractions. we encountered fractions in which the degree of the numerator was equal to or greater than the degree of the denominator. In such cases the first operation was to divide and obtain a polynomial plus a "proper" fraction (that is, a fraction in which the numerator is of lower degree than the denominator). In this work we shall assume that this division has been done and also that all common factors have been removed from numerator and denominator.

Let us first consider the case of a linear factor $x - a$ to the power $k$ in the denominator. The next theorem shows that an expansion into partial fractions can be made.

**Theorem 12.7a.** Let $P(x)/Q(x)$ be a proper rational fraction in lowest terms, and let

$$\frac{P(x)}{Q(x)} = \frac{P(x)}{(x - a)^k Q_1(x)},$$

where $Q_1(a) \neq 0$, so that $Q_1(x)$ does not have $x - a$ as a factor. Then there exist $k$ unique constants $A, B, \ldots,$ such that

$$\frac{P(x)}{(x - a)^k Q_1(x)} = \frac{A}{(x - a)^k} + \frac{B}{(x - a)^{k-1}} + \cdots + \frac{P_k(x)}{Q_1(x)}, \qquad A \neq 0.$$

PROOF: The first step will be to show that we can get an expansion of the form

(1)
$$\frac{P(x)}{(x - a)^k Q_1(x)} = \frac{A}{(x - a)^k} + \frac{P_1(x)}{(x - a)^{k-1} Q_1(x)},$$

where $A$ is a constant. With this in mind, consider the difference

$$\frac{P(x)}{(x - a)^k Q_1(x)} - \frac{A}{(x - a)^k} = \frac{P(x) - A Q_1(x)}{(x - a)^k Q_1(x)}.$$

If we can find a value for $A$ such that

$$P(x) - A Q_1(x) = (x - a) P_1(x),$$

then

$$\frac{P(x) - A Q_1(x)}{(x - a)^k Q_1(x)} = \frac{P_1(x)}{(x - a)^{k-1} Q_1(x)},$$

which would lead to the desired form. Since $P(x)$ and $Q_1(x)$ are polynomials, it follows from the Remainder Theorem that $x - a$ is a factor of $P(x) - A Q_1(x)$ if, and only if,

$$P(a) - A Q_1(a) = 0.$$

This equation and the inequality $Q_1(a) \neq 0$ imply that

$$A = \frac{P(a)}{Q_1(a)},$$

and thus a unique $A$ exists such that Equation (1) holds. Furthermore, $A \neq 0$ because $P(a) \neq 0$, since $P(x)$ and $Q(x)$ have no common factors.

Notice also that the new numerator $P_1(x)$ is obtained by dividing $P(x) - A Q_1(x)$ by $x - a$, so that the degree of $P_1(x)$ is at least one less than the degree of $P(x)$. This means that the new fraction is also a proper one. Consequently, the preceding argument may be repeated with

$$\frac{P_1(x)}{(x - a)^{k-1} Q_1(x)}$$

to find the constant $B$, and repeated application will determine the other constants.

The next example illustrates the integration of a rational fraction by means of Theorem 12.7a.

---

*Example 12.7b.* Integrate

$$\int \frac{x^2 + 2}{(x + 2)(x - 1)(x + 3)} \, dx.$$

Using the preceding theorem, we write

$$\frac{x^2 + 2}{(x + 2)(x - 1)(x + 3)} = \frac{A}{x + 2} + \frac{B}{x - 1} + \frac{D}{x + 3}.$$

The constant $A$ is $P(-2)/Q_1(-2)$, where $P(x)$ is the numerator and $Q_1(x)$ is that portion of the denominator of the original fraction that multiplies the factor $(x + 2)$, that is, the denominator with the factor $x + 2$ deleted. Thus,

$$A = \frac{P(-2)}{Q_1(-2)} = \left[\frac{x^2 + 2}{(x - 1)(x + 3)}\right]_{x=-2} = \frac{6}{(-3)(1)} = -2.$$

In determining $B$, we use $a = 1$ and $Q_1(x) = (x + 2)(x + 3)$ to get

$$B = \left[\frac{x^2 + 2}{(x + 2)(x + 3)}\right]_{x=1} = \frac{3}{(3)(4)} = \frac{1}{4}.$$

Finally, we use $a = -3$ and $Q_1(x) = (x + 2)(x - 1)$, to find

$$D = \left[\frac{x^2 + 2}{(x + 2)(x - 1)}\right]_{x=-3} = \frac{11}{(-1)(-4)} = \frac{11}{4}.$$

Substituting the values of the constants into the assumed expansion, we have

$$\int \frac{x^2 + 2}{(x + 2)(x - 1)(x + 3)}\, dx = \int \frac{-2}{x + 2}\, dx + \int \frac{1/4}{x - 1}\, dx + \int \frac{11/4}{x + 3}\, dx$$

$$= -2 \ln |x + 2| + \frac{1}{4} \ln |x - 1| + \frac{11}{4} \ln |x + 3| + C.$$

For a repeated linear factor, such as $(x - a)^k$, $k > 1$, it is frequently a good idea to use a general procedure called the **method of undetermined coefficients,** since, if the preceding method is used, the constants would have to be determined one at a time and the process could become excessively laborious. In order to use the method of undetermined coefficients we need to rely on Theorem 1.9e (the identity theorem for polynomials). The following example illustrates the manner in which this theorem enters the discussion.

*Example 12.7c.* Integrate

$$\int \frac{x - 1}{(x - 2)^2(x + 3)}\, dx.$$

Theorem 12.7a guarantees that there exist unique constants $A$, $B$, $D$ such that

$$\frac{x - 1}{(x - 2)^2(x + 3)} = \frac{A}{(x - 2)^2} + \frac{B}{x - 2} + \frac{D}{x + 3}$$

is an identity in $x$. After multiplying each side by the lowest common denominator (the denominator of the original fraction), we get

(2) $$x - 1 = A(x + 3) + B(x - 2)(x + 3) + D(x - 2)^2.$$

Since both members of this equation are polynomials of degree two or less and must be equal for more than two values of $x$, it follows from Theorem 1.9e that they are equal for all values of $x$. Accordingly, we may choose three arbitrary values of $x$ to substitute into Equation (2) to obtain three equations in the three unknowns $A$, $B$ and $D$. The values of $A$, $B$, and $D$ may be found from these equations.

Usually we choose values for $x$ that will lead to the simplest possible equations. For example, if $x = 2$, we get

$$1 = A(2 + 3) \quad \text{or} \quad A = \tfrac{1}{5}.$$

Similarly, for $x = -3$, we find

$$-4 = D(-5)^2 \quad \text{or} \quad D = -\tfrac{4}{25}.$$

After this method has been used to determine as many of the constants as possible, the coefficients of corresponding powers of $x$ may be equated to determine the other constants. In this case, the coefficient of $x^2$ on the left side is zero and on the right side is $B + D$. Thus,

$$B + D = 0,$$

and since $D = -4/25$, we have

$$B = \frac{4}{25}.$$

Substituting the values of the constants into the assumed expansion, we obtain

$$\int \frac{x - 1}{(x - 2)^2(x + 3)}\, dx = \frac{1}{5} \int \frac{dx}{(x - 2)^2} + \frac{4}{25} \int \frac{dx}{x - 2} - \frac{4}{25} \int \frac{dx}{x + 3}$$

$$= \frac{-1}{5(x - 2)} + \frac{4}{25} \ln |x - 2| - \frac{4}{25} \ln |x + 3| + C.$$

Quadratic factors in the denominator will be discussed in the next section.

## Exercises 12.7

In each of Numbers 1 to 18, find the indicated inverse derivative.

1. $\displaystyle \int \frac{dx}{x^2 - 4}.$

2. $\displaystyle \int \frac{y^2\, dy}{y^2 + y - 6}.$

3. $\displaystyle \int \frac{5w - 2}{w^2 - 4}\, dw.$

4. $\displaystyle \int \frac{1 - t}{t^2 + t}\, dt.$

5. $\displaystyle \int \frac{2x^2 + 3x - 3}{x^3 - x}\, dx.$

6. $\displaystyle \int \frac{-14y + 20}{y^3 + 4y^2 - 5y}\, dy.$

7. $\displaystyle \int \frac{2w^2 + 11w + 8}{w^3 + 4w^2 + 4w}\, dw.$

8. $\displaystyle \int \frac{x^2 + x - 2}{x^3 - 2x^2}\, dx.$

9. $\displaystyle \int \frac{t^2\, dt}{t^2 - 3t + 2}.$

10. $\displaystyle \int \frac{s^3 + s^2 - 6s - 14}{s^2 - s - 6}\, ds.$

11. $\displaystyle \int \frac{x^2 + 5x + 1}{x(x + 1)^2}\, dx.$

12. $\displaystyle \int \frac{y^2 + 15y + 2}{(y - 2)(y + 1)(y + 3)}\, dy.$

13. $\displaystyle \int \frac{24w^2 - 3w - 3}{9w^3 - w}\, dw.$

14. $\displaystyle \int \frac{x^3 + 2x^2 - 4x - 6}{x^2 - 4}\, dx.$

15. $\displaystyle \int \frac{5t^2 + 6t + 2}{t(t + 1)^2}\, dt.$

16. $\displaystyle \int \frac{4t^2 - 30}{t^3 + 3t^2 - 10t}\, dt.$

17. $\displaystyle \int \frac{6w^2 - 5w - 9}{w^3 - 2w^2 - w + 2}\, dw.$

18. $\displaystyle \int \frac{3x^2 - 10x + 6}{x^3 - 7x^2 + 16x - 12}\, dx.$

In each of Numbers 19 to 26 evaluate the given definite integral.

19. $\int_0^2 \dfrac{-x+1}{x^2+3x+2}\,dx.$

23. $\int_0^2 \dfrac{2w^2+6w+2}{w^3+6w^2+11w+6}\,dw.$

20. $\int_2^5 \dfrac{4t+5}{t^2+t-2}\,dt.$

24. $\int_0^3 \dfrac{2x^2+9x+11}{x^3+7x^2+16x+12}\,dx.$

21. $\int_1^4 \dfrac{2w^2+13w+18}{w(w+3)^2}\,dw.$

25. $\int_1^2 \dfrac{2x^2+x+4}{x^3+4x^2}\,dx.$

22. $\int_1^3 \dfrac{2x^2-x-3}{x^3+3x^2}\,dx.$

26. $\int_0^3 \dfrac{t^2+6t+7}{(t+2)^2(t+1)}\,dt.$

27. Find the area bounded by the curve $y = (x-1)/(x^2-5x+6)$ and the lines $x=4$, $x=6$, $y=0$.
28. Find the area bounded by the curve $y = (x-2)/(2x^2+7x+3)$ and the lines $x=0$, $x=4$, $y=0$.
29. Find the area bounded by the curve $y = \sqrt{9+x}/x^2$ and the lines $x=7$, $x=16$, $y=0$.
30. Find the area bounded by the curve $y = \sqrt{x+4}/[x(x+3)]$ and the lines $x=5$, $x=12$, $y=0$.
31. Find the $x$-coordinate of the centroid of the area of Number 27.
32. Find the $x$-coordinate of the centroid of the area of Number 28.
33. Calculate the volume formed by revolving about the $y$-axis the area of Number 27.
34. Calculate the volume formed by revolving about the $y$-axis the area of Number 28.

## 12.8 RATIONAL FRACTIONS WITH QUADRATIC FACTORS

Suppose the denominator $Q(x)$ of the rational fraction $P(x)/Q(x)$ has the imaginary number $a+ib$ as a zero. Then from Theorem 1.9f it is known that $a-ib$ is also a zero. The product of the corresponding factors is

$$[x-(a+ib)][x-(a-ib)] = x^2 - 2ax + a^2 + b^2,$$

and if these are simple factors, the partial fractions expansion is

(1) $\dfrac{P(x)}{(x^2-2ax+a^2+b^2)Q_1(x)} = \dfrac{A}{x-a-ib} + \dfrac{B}{x-a+ib} + \dfrac{P_1(x)}{Q_1(x)}.$

From the proof of Theorem 12.7a, we know that

$$A = \left[\frac{P(x)}{(x-a+ib)Q_1(x)}\right]_{x=a+ib} = \frac{P(a+ib)}{(2ib)Q_1(a+ib)}$$

and

$$B = \left[\frac{P(x)}{(x-a-ib)Q_1(x)}\right]_{x=a-ib} = \frac{P(a-ib)}{(-2ib)Q_1(a-ib)}.$$

Thus,

(2) $\dfrac{A}{x-a-ib} + \dfrac{B}{x-a+ib} = \dfrac{\dfrac{P(a+ib)}{(2ib)Q_1(a+ib)}}{x-a-ib} + \dfrac{\dfrac{P(a-ib)}{(-2ib)Q_1(a-ib)}}{x-a+ib}.$

The numerator of the last fraction is the same as the numerator of the preceding fraction with the exception that each imaginary number has been replaced by its conjugate. To appreciate how this fact can be used, we need two preliminary theorems. The notation $\bar{z}$, introduced in Section 11.3, will be used for the conjugate of the number $z$, so that $z = a + ib \implies \bar{z} = a - ib$.

**Theorem 12.8a.** If $P(x)$ is a polynomial over $\mathcal{R}$ and $z$ is an imaginary number, then

$$P(\bar{z}) = \overline{P(z)}.$$

PROOF: To prove this theorem, we first use the fact that

$$z = r(\cos \theta + i \sin \theta) = re^{i\theta} \implies \bar{z} = r(\cos \theta - i \sin \theta) = re^{-i\theta}.$$

Hence (see Section 11.5),

$$z^n = r^n e^{in\theta} \implies \overline{(z^n)} = r^n e^{-in\theta}.$$

Since $(\bar{z})^n = (re^{-i\theta})^n = r^n e^{-in\theta}$, it follows that

$$\overline{(z^n)} = (\bar{z})^n.$$

Thus, for the polynomial

$$P(x) = a_0 x^n + a_1 x^{n-1} + \cdots + a_n,$$

we have

$$P(\bar{z}) = a_0(\bar{z})^n + a_1(\bar{z})^{n-1} + \cdots + a_n$$
$$= a_0 \overline{z^n} + a_1 \overline{z^{n-1}} + \cdots + a_n,$$
$$= \overline{P(z)},$$

since the $a$'s are real numbers.

As a simple example of this theorem, let $P(x) = x^2 - x + 3$, and let $z = 1 + i$. Then

$$P(z) = P(1 + i) = (1 + i)^2 - (1 + i) + 3 = 2 + i$$

and

$$\overline{P(z)} = 2 - i.$$

But

$$P(\bar{z}) = P(1 - i) = (1 - i)^2 - (1 - i) + 3 = 2 - i,$$

and thus

$$\overline{P(z)} = P(\bar{z}).$$

Another theorem that is needed here is

**Theorem 12.8b.** If $z_1$ and $z_2$ are imaginary numbers, then

$$\overline{\left(\frac{z_1}{z_2}\right)} = \frac{\bar{z}_1}{\bar{z}_2}.$$

PROOF: This theorem can be proved quite simply by making use of the exponential form of the numbers $z_1$ and $z_2$. Thus, let

$$z_1 = r_1 e^{i\theta_1} \quad \text{and} \quad z_2 = r_2 e^{i\theta_2}.$$

Then

$$\frac{z_1}{z_2} = \frac{r_1 e^{i\theta_1}}{r_2 e^{i\theta_2}} = \frac{r_1}{r_2} e^{i(\theta_1 - \theta_2)}$$

and

$$\overline{\left(\frac{z_1}{z_2}\right)} = \frac{r_1}{r_2} e^{-i(\theta_1 - \theta_2)}.$$

Also, we have

$$\frac{\bar{z}_1}{\bar{z}_2} = \frac{r_1 e^{-i\theta_1}}{r_2 e^{-i\theta_2}} = \frac{r_1}{r_2} e^{-i(\theta_1 - \theta_2)}$$

$$= \overline{\left(\frac{z_1}{z_2}\right)}.$$

We now return to Equation (2) and let

$$\frac{P(a + ib)}{2ib Q_1(a + ib)} = A_1 + iB_1.$$

Then, by Theorems 12.8a and 12.8b, the numerator of the last fraction in Equation (2) must be the conjugate of this expression; that is,

$$\frac{P(a - ib)}{(-2ib)Q_1(a - ib)} = A_1 - iB_1.$$

Equation (2) may now be written

$$\frac{A}{x - a - ib} + \frac{B}{x - a + ib} = \frac{A_1 + iB_1}{x - a - ib} + \frac{A_1 - iB_1}{x - a + ib}$$

$$= \frac{2A_1(x - a) - 2b\, B_1}{x^2 - 2ax + a^2 + b^2}.$$

Consequently, we have proved the following theorem.

**Theorem 12.8c.** Let $P(x)/Q(x)$ be a proper rational fraction in lowest terms with real coefficients, and let $Q(x)$ have a simple quadratic factor

$$ax^2 + bx + c$$

with imaginary zeros. Then

$$\frac{P(x)}{Q(x)} = \frac{P(x)}{(ax^2 + bx + c)Q_1(x)} = \frac{Ax + B}{ax^2 + bx + c} + \frac{P_1(x)}{Q_1(x)},$$

where $A$ and $B$ are real.

For the case where the quadratic factor appears with an exponent $k \geq 2$, the proof follows along the same lines as the preceding proof, but is rather more complicated and will not be given. The theorem is as follows.

**Theorem 12.8d.** Let $P(x)/Q(x)$ be a proper rational fraction in lowest terms and let

$$\frac{P(x)}{Q(x)} = \frac{P(x)}{(ax^2 + bx + c)^k Q_1(x)},$$

where $ax^2 + bx + c$ and $Q_1(x)$ are relatively prime. Then,

$$\frac{P(x)}{(ax^2 + bx + c)^k Q_1(x)} = \frac{A_1 x + B_1}{(ax^2 + bx + c)^k} + \frac{A_2 x + B_2}{(ax^2 + bx + c)^{k-1}} + \cdots$$

$$+ \frac{A_k x + B_k}{ax^2 + bx + c} + \frac{P_1(x)}{Q_1(x)},$$

where the degree of $P_1(x)$ is less than the degree of $Q_1(x)$, $A_1$ and $B_1$ are not both zero, and all of the $A$'s and $B$'s are real.

---

*Example 12.8a.* Integrate

$$\int \frac{3x + 7}{(x^2 + 2x + 2)(x^2 + 4)} dx.$$

Using the theorems on partial fractions, we first write

$$\frac{3x + 7}{(x^2 + 2x + 2)(x^2 + 4)} = \frac{Ax + B}{x^2 + 2x + 2} + \frac{Dx + E}{x^2 + 4}.$$

Then, multiplying each side by the denominator on the left, we get

(3) $$3x + 7 = (Ax + B)(x^2 + 4) + (Dx + E)(x^2 + 2x + 2).$$

Equating coefficients of corresponding powers of $x$ in Equation (3), we obtain the set of equations

$$\begin{array}{rl} x^3: & A + D = 0, \\ x^2: & B + 2D + E = 0, \\ x: & 4A + 2D + 2E = 3, \\ x^0: & 4B + 2E = 7. \end{array}$$

The preceding four equations are sufficient to determine the values of the four coefficients, and we find

$$A = 1, \quad B = \frac{3}{2}, \quad D = -1, \quad E = \frac{1}{2}.$$

Consequently,

$$\int \frac{3x + 7}{(x^2 + 2x + 2)(x^2 + 4)} dx = \frac{1}{2} \int \frac{2x + 3}{x^2 + 2x + 2} dx - \frac{1}{2} \int \frac{2x - 1}{x^2 + 4} dx.$$

Since the derivative of $x^2 + 2x + 2$ is $2x + 2$, we write the numerator of the first fraction as

$$2x + 3 = [(2x + 2) + 1]$$

and then split each of the fractions into two fractions to obtain

$$\int \frac{3x + 7}{(x^2 + 2x + 2)(x^2 + 4)}$$

$$= \frac{1}{2} \int \frac{2x + 2}{x^2 + 2x + 2} dx + \frac{1}{2} \int \frac{dx}{(x + 1)^2 + 1} - \frac{1}{2} \int \frac{2x \, dx}{x^2 + 4} + \frac{1}{2} \int \frac{dx}{x^2 + 4}$$

$$= \frac{1}{2} \ln (x^2 + 2x + 2) + \frac{1}{2} \text{Tan}^{-1} (x + 1) - \frac{1}{2} \ln (x^2 + 4) + \frac{1}{4} \text{Tan}^{-1} \frac{x}{2} + C.$$

*Example 12.8b.* Integrate

$$\int \frac{3x^4 + 5x^3 - 2x + 2}{(x^2 + 1)^2(x - 1)} \, dx.$$

Using the theorems on partial fractions, we write

$$\frac{3x^4 + 5x^3 - 2x + 2}{(x^2 + 1)^2(x - 1)} = \frac{Ax + B}{(x^2 + 1)^2} + \frac{Dx + E}{x^2 + 1} + \frac{F}{x - 1}.$$

Multiplying by the denominator on the left, we have

$$3x^4 + 5x^3 - 2x + 2 = (Ax + B)(x - 1) + (Dx + E)(x^2 + 1)(x - 1) + F(x^2 + 1)^2.$$

For $x = 1$, we find

$$8 = 4F \quad \text{or} \quad 2 = F.$$

If we now equate coefficients of corresponding powers of $x$, the resulting equations are

$$D + F = 3,$$
$$-D + E = 5,$$
$$A + D - E + 2F = 0,$$
$$-A + B - D + E = -2,$$
$$-B - E + F = 2.$$

Again, the preceding five equations are sufficient to obtain the five unknowns, but we can make use of the value of $F$ obtained earlier to simplify the work.

Since $F = 2$, then $D = 1$, and $D = 1$ gives $E = 6$. With these results, we get $A = 1$ and finally, $B = -6$. Now the original integral may be written as

$$\int \frac{3x^4 + 5x^3 - 2x + 2}{(x^2 + 1)^2(x - 1)} \, dx$$

$$= \int \frac{x \, dx}{(x^2 + 1)^2} - 6 \int \frac{dx}{(x^2 + 1)^2} + \int \frac{x \, dx}{x^2 + 1} + 6 \int \frac{dx}{x^2 + 1} + 2 \int \frac{dx}{x - 1}$$

$$= -\frac{1}{2(x^2 + 1)} - \left( \frac{3x}{x^2 + 1} + 3 \, \text{Tan}^{-1} \, x \right) + \frac{1}{2} \ln (x^2 + 1)$$

$$+ 6 \, \text{Tan}^{-1} \, x + 2 \ln |x - 1| + C$$

$$= -\frac{6x + 1}{2(x^2 + 1)} + 3 \, \text{Tan}^{-1} \, x + \frac{1}{2} \ln [(x^2 + 1)(x - 1)^4] + C.$$

## Exercises 12.8

In Numbers 1 to 22, find the inverse derivative.

1. $\displaystyle\int \frac{3y^2 + 2y + 1}{(y + 1)(y^2 + 1)} \, dy.$

2. $\displaystyle\int \frac{4w^2 - 3w + 6}{(w^2 + 4)(w - 2)} \, dw.$

3. $\displaystyle\int \frac{(4t^2 + 7t + 30) \, dt}{(t + 3)(t^2 + 4t + 8)}.$

4. $\displaystyle\int \frac{3x^2 + 14x + 12}{(x + 4)(x^2 + 6x + 10)} \, dx.$

5. $\displaystyle\int \frac{2w^2 + 3w + 8}{w(w^2 + 4)} \, dw.$

6. $\displaystyle\int \frac{5s^2 + 4}{s^3 + 8} \, ds.$

7. $\displaystyle\int \frac{3x^2 + 7x - 8}{(x-2)(x^2 + 2x + 10)}\, dx.$

15. $\displaystyle\int \frac{2w^3 + 3w^2 + 11w + 15}{(w+1)(w^2 + 4)}\, dw.$

8. $\displaystyle\int \frac{2t^2 - 1}{t^2(t^2 + 1)}\, dt.$

16. $\displaystyle\int \frac{dy}{y^3 - 8}.$

9. $\displaystyle\int \frac{s^2 + 1}{s^4 + s^2 - 2}\, ds.$

17. $\displaystyle\int \frac{7x^2 + 11x + 15}{x^3 + 4x^2 + 5x}\, dx.$

10. $\displaystyle\int \frac{2w^2 - 2w + 18}{w^3 + 9w}\, dw.$

18. $\displaystyle\int \frac{5y^2 - 3y + 1}{y^3 + y}\, dy.$

11. $\displaystyle\int \frac{-x^2 + 5x - 2}{x^3 - 2x^2 + 2x}\, dx.$

19. $\displaystyle\int \frac{3x^4 + x^2 - 5x + 3}{(x+1)(x^2 + 1)^2}\, dx.$

12. $\displaystyle\int \frac{3t^2 + 3t + 8}{t^3 + 2t^2 + 3t + 6}\, dt.$

20. $\displaystyle\int \frac{2w^4 + 7w^2 - 6w + 2}{(w^2 + 1)^2(w - 2)}\, dw.$

13. $\displaystyle\int \frac{3w^2 + 4w + 5}{w^3 + 2w^2 + 5w - 8}\, dw.$

21. $\displaystyle\int \frac{x\, dx}{x^4 + 4}.$

14. $\displaystyle\int \frac{3t^2 + 24}{t^3 + 6t + 20}\, dt.$

22. $\displaystyle\int \frac{dx}{x^4 + 4}.$

Evaluate the definite integrals in Numbers 23 to 32.

23. $\displaystyle\int_0^3 \frac{3y^2 + 2y + 15}{(y+3)(y^2 + 9)}\, dy.$

28. $\displaystyle\int_0^1 \frac{5y^3 + y^2 + 20y + 12}{y^4 - 16}\, dy.$

24. $\displaystyle\int_1^{\sqrt{3}} \frac{4x^3 + 3x^2 + 2x + 2}{x^3 + x}\, dx.$

29. $\displaystyle\int_0^2 \frac{5w^2 + 12w + 1}{(w+3)(w^2 + 2w + 2)}\, dw.$

25. $\displaystyle\int_{1/\sqrt{3}}^1 \frac{4w^2 - 4w + 2}{w^3 + w}\, dw.$

30. $\displaystyle\int_1^2 \frac{x^2 + 1}{(x+1)(x^2 + 2x + 3)}\, dx.$

26. $\displaystyle\int_{\sqrt{3}/3}^{\sqrt{3}} \frac{3x^3 + 3x^2 + 2}{x^4 + x^2}\, dx.$

31. $\displaystyle\int_1^{\sqrt{3}} \frac{t^4 + 4t^2 + 6}{t^2(t^2 + 3)}\, dt.$

27. $\displaystyle\int_0^1 \frac{3y^2 + 2y - 13}{(y^2 + 1)(y + 5)}\, dy.$

32. $\displaystyle\int_1^2 \frac{-2x - 8}{x^3 + 4x^2 + 8x}\, dx.$

33. Find the area bounded by the curve $y = 1/[x^2(x^2 + 4)]$ and the lines $x = 2$, $x = 2\sqrt{3}$, and $y = 0$.

34. Find the area bounded by the curve $x = 2/[(y^2 + 1)(y^2 + 3)]$ and the lines $y = 0$, $y = \sqrt{3}$, and $x = 0$.

35. Find the area bounded by the curve $y = 12/(8 + x^3)$ and the lines $x = 0$, $x = 2$, $y = 0$.

36. Find the volume obtained by revolving about the $y$-axis the area of Number 35.

## 12.9 IMPROPER INTEGRALS

The definite integral, $\int_a^b f(x)\, dx$, was introduced in Chapter 8 under the assumption that the function $f$ was defined at every point of a finite interval $a \leq x \leq b$. It is possible to relax this restriction on $f$ and on the interval to obtain extensions of the definite integral that are often useful in practical applications.

For example, a fundamental concept in electromagnetic field theory is that of the electric potential at a point in an electromagnetic field due to an electric charge distribution. It is known that two like electric charges, $q_1$ and $q_2$, repel each other with a force $F$ given by

$$F = k\,\frac{q_1 q_2}{r^2},$$

where $r$ is the distance between the charges and $k$ is a constant of proportionality. The electric potential $V_P$ at a point $P$ in an electromagnetic field due to a charge $q$ is defined by the physicist as the work done in bringing a unit charge from "infinity" to the point $P$. Using the definition of work, and letting $r$ be the distance from the charge $q$, we may express the potential at $P$ by the "integral"

$$V_P = \int_\infty^x k\,\frac{q}{r^2}\, dr,$$

where the symbol $\int_\infty^x$ indicates that the charge must "start" at "infinity" and be moved to the point $x$. In this illustration, the integral is not an ordinary one since we are concerned with an infinite interval.

From the mathematician's point of view, this new concept must be given a meaning that is consistent with that of the definite integral. Accordingly, we make the following definition.

**Definition 12.9a.** If $f$ is sectionally continuous on the interval $a \leq x \leq t$, for every $t$ no matter how large, and if

$$\lim_{t \to \infty} \int_a^t f(x)\, dx$$

exists, then

$$\int_a^\infty f(x)\, dx \,.=. \lim_{t \to \infty} \int_a^t f(x)\, dx.$$

The symbol $\int_a^\infty f(x)\, dx$ is called an **improper integral of the first kind,** and if $\lim_{t \to \infty} \int_a^t f(x)\, dx$ exists, then the improper integral is said to **converge;** otherwise, it is said to **diverge.**

*Example 12.9a.* If the integral $\int_1^\infty xe^{-x}\,dx$ converges, find its value.

By definition,

$$\int_1^\infty xe^{-x}\,dx = \lim_{t\to\infty} \int_1^t xe^{-x}\,dx$$

$$= \lim_{t\to\infty}\, [-te^{-t} - e^{-t} + 2e^{-1}].$$

By L'Hôpital's Theorem,

$$\lim_{t\to\infty} te^{-t} = \lim_{t\to\infty} \frac{t}{e^t} = \lim_{t\to\infty} \frac{1}{e^t} = 0,$$

and since $e^{-t} \to 0$ as $t \to \infty$,

$$\lim_{t\to\infty}\, [-te^{-t} - e^{-t} + 2e^{-1}] = 2e^{-1}.$$

Therefore, the improper integral converges and

$$\int_1^\infty xe^{-x}\,dx = 2e^{-1}.$$

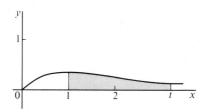

**FIGURE 12.9a**

A geometric interpretation of $\int_1^\infty xe^{-x}\,dx$ may be helpful. The proper integral $\int_1^t xe^{-x}\,dx$ may be interpreted as the area bounded by the curve $y = xe^{-x}$ and the $x$-axis between $x = 1$ and $x = t$, as illustrated in Figure 12.9a. The question of convergence essentially depends on whether the curve $y = xe^{-x}$ approaches the $x$-axis "rapidly enough" as $t \to \infty$ to prevent the area from increasing without bound.

---

In a similar way, improper integrals of the form $\int_{-\infty}^b f(x)\,dx$ or $\int_{-\infty}^\infty f(x)\,dx$ may be defined.

**Definition 12.9b.** If $f(x)$ is sectionally continuous on the interval $t \leq x \leq b$ for every $t \leq b$, and if

$$\lim_{t\to-\infty} \int_t^b f(x)\,dx$$

exists, then

$$\int_{-\infty}^b f(x)\,dx .=. \lim_{t\to-\infty} \int_t^b f(x)\,dx.$$

**Definition 12.9c.** If $f(x)$ is sectionally continuous on $t \le x \le T$ for every $t$ and $T$ and if *both*

$$\int_a^\infty f(x)\, dx \quad \text{and} \quad \int_{-\infty}^a f(x)\, dx$$

exist for every $a$, then

$$\int_{-\infty}^\infty f(x)\, dx \;.=. \int_{-\infty}^a f(x)\, dx + \int_a^\infty f(x)\, dx.$$

This last statement may be written as

$$\int_{-\infty}^\infty f(x)\, dx = \lim_{t \to -\infty} \int_t^a f(x)\, dx + \lim_{T \to \infty} \int_a^T f(x)\, dx,$$

but it is *not* equivalent to

$$\int_{-\infty}^\infty f(x)\, dx = \lim_{t \to \infty} \left[ \int_{-t}^a f(x)\, dx + \int_a^t f(x)\, dx \right].$$

This last limit may exist under circumstances where the preceding one does not. Since $f(x)$ is sectionally continuous on every finite interval, it follows easily that the choice of the point $a$ is unimportant.

---

*Example 12.9b.* Find the value of

$$\int_{-\infty}^\infty \frac{x}{x^2 + 1}\, dx$$

provided that the integral converges.

According to Definition 12.9c, we must select a number $a$ and examine the two improper integrals $\int_{-\infty}^a f(x)\, dx$ and $\int_a^\infty f(x)\, dx$. Since any convenient value of $a$ may be used, let us choose $a = 0$. Then

$$\int_{-\infty}^\infty \frac{x\, dx}{x^2 + 1} = \int_{-\infty}^0 \frac{x\, dx}{x^2 + 1} + \int_0^\infty \frac{x\, dx}{x^2 + 1}$$

and

$$\int_0^\infty \frac{x}{x^2 + 1}\, dx = \lim_{t \to \infty} \int_0^t \frac{x}{x^2 + 1}\, dx$$

$$= \lim_{t \to \infty} \frac{1}{2} \ln (t^2 + 1).$$

Since this limit does not exist,

$$\int_0^\infty \frac{x}{x^2 + 1}\, dx$$

diverges, and consequently

$$\int_{-\infty}^\infty \frac{x}{x^2 + 1}\, dx$$

diverges.

---

It is left as an exercise for the reader to show that

$$\lim_{t \to \infty} \left\{ \int_{-t}^{a} \frac{x}{x^2 + 1} \, dx + \int_{a}^{t} \frac{x}{x^2 + 1} \, dx \right\} = 0.$$

(See Exercises 12.9, Number 16.)

A second type of extension of the definite integral can be made in certain cases to functions having infinite discontinuities on the interval of integration.

**Definition 12.9d.** Let $f$ have an infinite discontinuity at a point $c$ in the interval $a \leq x \leq b$, and suppose $f$ is sectionally continuous elsewhere in the interval. Then, whenever the limits exist we have

(1) $\int_{a}^{c} f(x) \, dx \, . = . \lim_{\epsilon \to 0^{+}} \int_{a}^{c-\epsilon} f(x) \, dx,$

(2) $\int_{c}^{b} f(x) \, dx \, . = . \lim_{\epsilon \to 0^{+}} \int_{c+\epsilon}^{b} f(x) \, dx,$ and

(3) $\int_{a}^{b} f(x) \, dx \, . = . \int_{a}^{c} f(x) \, dx + \int_{c}^{b} f(x) \, dx.$

If the discontinuity of $f$ occurs at an end point of the interval of integration, then the point of discontinuity is approached from *within* the interval, as indicated by requiring that $\epsilon \to 0^{+}$. If the discontinuity occurs at an interior point of the interval, then the two integrals on the right side of Equation (3) must converge independently before we may say that $\int_{a}^{b} f(x) \, dx$ converges. Integrals of the kind defined in Definition 12.9d are called **improper integrals of the second kind.**

---

*Example 12.9c.* Evaluate

$$\int_{1}^{2} \frac{dx}{\sqrt{x - 1}}$$

f the integral converges.

Since $1/\sqrt{x - 1}$ has an infinite discontinuity at $x = 1$, we must consider

$$\lim_{\epsilon \to 0^{+}} \int_{1+\epsilon}^{2} \frac{dx}{\sqrt{x - 1}} = \lim_{\epsilon \to 0^{+}} \left[ \tfrac{1}{2}\sqrt{x - 1} \right]_{1+\epsilon}^{2}$$

$$= \tfrac{1}{2} - \lim_{\epsilon \to 0^{+}} \tfrac{1}{2}\sqrt{\epsilon} = \tfrac{1}{2}.$$

Hence the integral converges to the value $\tfrac{1}{2}$.

---

If we interpret the results of the preceding example geometrically, then

$$\int_{1+\epsilon}^{2} \frac{1}{\sqrt{x - 1}} \, dx$$

represents the area bounded by the curve $y = 1/\sqrt{x-1}$ and the $x$-axis between $1 + \epsilon$ and 2, as illustrated in Figure 12.9b. The question of convergence

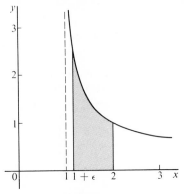

**FIGURE 12.9b**

then depends on whether or not the curve approaches the asymptote $x = 1$
"sufficiently rapidly" as $\epsilon \to 0^+$ that the area will not increase without bound.
An improper integral may involve infinite discontinuities as well as infinite
limits. In this case the integral must be broken up into as many individual
improper integrals as are necessary to isolate each of the discontinuities and
infinite limits. To illustrate, we may write

$$\int_0^\infty \frac{1}{x^2}\,dx = \int_0^a \frac{1}{x^2}\,dx + \int_a^\infty \frac{1}{x^2}\,dx, \qquad a > 0,$$

and examine each of the resulting integrals for convergence. The original integral
converges *only* if each of the component integrals converges. It is left as an
exercise for the reader to show that the point $a$ in the preceding illustration is
immaterial, so long as $a$ separates the improprieties of the original integral.
It is not uncommon to encounter an improper integral of a function having
no elementary inverse derivative. For example, in probability and statistics an
integral of the form

$$\int_0^\infty e^{-x^2}\,dx$$

often occurs. This integral cannot be examined for convergence by the procedures discussed up to this point because $\int e^{-x^2}\,dx$ cannot be expressed in
terms of elementary functions. Consequently, it is necessary that we develop a
means of testing such an integral for convergence or divergence. There are
two elementary theorems that will suffice for our needs in this regard. They are
stated without proof.

**Theorem 12.9a.** Suppose that

$$(1) \ \int_a^t f(x)\, dx \text{ exists for all } t > a,$$

$$(2) \ 0 \leq f(x) \leq g(x) \text{ for all } x > a, \text{ and}$$

$$(3) \ \int_a^\infty g(x)\, dx \text{ converges.}$$

Then $\int_a^\infty f(x)\, dx$ also converges.

This theorem is analogous to the theorem on the convergence of a bounded monotonic increasing sequence, and its proof is carried out in a similar fashion.

**Theorem 12.9b.** If $\int_a^t f(x)\, dx$ and $\int_a^t g(x)\, dx$ both exist for all $t > a$, where $f(x) \geq 0, g(x) > 0$ for all $x > a$, and if

$$\lim_{x \to \infty} \frac{f(x)}{g(x)} = A, \qquad A \neq 0,$$

then the integrals $\int_a^\infty f(x)\, dx$ and $\int_a^\infty g(x)\, dx$ converge or diverge together. If $A = 0$, then $\int_a^\infty f(x)\, dx$ converges if $\int_a^\infty g(x)\, dx$ converges.

This theorem is easily made plausible in the following way: Since

$$\lim_{x \to \infty} f(x)/g(x) = A \neq 0,$$

t follows that for all sufficiently large $x$, $f(x)/g(x) < B$, where the constant $3 > A$. Thus $f(x) < Bg(x)$ and so $\int_a^\infty f(x)\, dx$ converges if $\int_a^\infty Bg(x)\, dx$ does. On the other hand, $f(x)/g(x) > C$, where $0 < C < A$, so that $f(x) > Cg(x)$ and thus $\int_a^\infty f(x)\, dx$ diverges if $\int_a^\infty Cg(x)\, dx$ does.

The following examples illustrate the use of these theorems.

---

*Example 12.9d.* Determine the behavior with respect to convergence of the integral

$$\int_1^\infty \frac{dx}{\sqrt{x^3 + 1}}.$$

Since $\int (x^3 + 1)^{-1/2}\, dx$ cannot be expressed in terms of elementary functions, we must find a function $g$ that is suitable for use in Theorem 12.9a or in Theorem 12.9b. Our choice for $g(x)$ is somewhat arbitrary, as there may be many functions that meet the requirements of either of the theorems. Accordingly, we try to select as simple form as possible for $g(x)$. In this case, since

$$\frac{1}{\sqrt{x^3 + 1}} < \frac{1}{x^{3/2}} \quad \text{for all } x > 1,$$

it appears feasible to let $g(x) = x^{-3/2}$. Since $\int_1^\infty x^{-3/2} \, dx$ converges to the value 2

it follows that $\int_1^\infty (x^3 + 1)^{-1/2} \, dx$ converges by Theorem 12.9a. Although the theorem enables us to show that the integral converges in this case, it does not help us to find the value to which it converges. However, we may be certain that this value is not greater than 2.

---

*Example 12.9e.* Examine the convergence behavior of the integral $\int_1^\infty e^{-x}x^s \, dx$ where $s \in \mathfrak{R}$.

It is easy to show (by the use of L'Hôpital's Theorem, if necessary) that

$$\lim_{x \to \infty} e^{-x}x^k = 0, \quad k \in \mathfrak{R}.$$

Furthermore,

$$\int_1^\infty \frac{dx}{x^2} = \lim_{t \to \infty} \int_1^t \frac{dx}{x^2} = \lim_{t \to \infty} \left(1 - \frac{1}{t}\right) = 1.$$

For any $s$,

$$\lim_{x \to \infty} \frac{e^{-x}x^s}{x^{-2}} = \lim_{x \to \infty} e^{-x}x^{s+2} = 0,$$

so that Theorem 12.9b applies with $f(x) = e^{-x}x^s$ and $g(x) = x^{-2}$, and we conclude that the given integral converges for all $s \in \mathfrak{R}$.

## Exercises 12.9

In each of Numbers 1 to 14 test the improper integral for convergence and evaluate the integral if it converges.

1. $\int_1^\infty \frac{dx}{x}$.

2. $\int_0^\infty \frac{dx}{4 + x^2}$.

3. $\int_0^\infty e^{-x} \cos x \, dx$.

4. $\int_0^2 \frac{dx}{\sqrt{4 - x^2}}$.

5. $\int_1^\infty \frac{\ln x}{x} \, dx$.

6. $\int_{-\infty}^\infty xe^{-x^2} \, dx$.

7. $\int_0^1 \frac{\ln x}{\sqrt{x}} \, dx$.

8. $\int_2^\infty \frac{dx}{x(\ln x)^p}$.

9. $\int_0^1 \ln x \, dx$.

10. $\int_0^\infty \frac{x \, dx}{1 + x^3}$.

11. $\int_{-\infty}^\infty \frac{dx}{x^2 - a^2}$.

12. $\int_{-1}^1 \frac{dx}{x^{2/3}}$.

13. $\int_{-a}^a \frac{x \, dx}{\sqrt{a^2 - x^2}}$.

14. $\int_{-\infty}^\infty e^{-|x|} \, dx$.

15. Show that for every value of $a$,

$$\int_a^\infty \frac{x}{x^2 + 1}\, dx$$

diverges.

16. Verify that

$$\lim_{t \to \infty} \left\{ \int_{-t}^a \frac{x}{x^2 + 1}\, dx + \int_a^t \frac{x}{x^2 + 1}\, dx \right\} = 0,$$

but that

$$\int_{-\infty}^\infty \frac{x}{x^2 + 1}\, dx$$

diverges.

17. If $k \geq 1$, show that

$$\int_0^\infty x^k e^{-x}\, dx = k \int_0^\infty x^{k-1} e^{-x}\, dx.$$

Show further that if $k = n$, a positive integer, then $\int_0^\infty x^n e^{-x}\, dx = n!$.

18. For what values of $k$ is the integral

$$\int_0^\infty \left( \frac{1}{\sqrt{1 + 2x^2}} - \frac{k}{x + 1} \right) dx$$

convergent?

19. The force of attraction between two masses $m_1$ and $m_2$ is $F = k(m_1 m_2/r^2)$, where $r$ is the distance between their centers. Suppose an infinitely long rod of mass $m$ units per unit length lies along the $x$-axis, and suppose a unit mass is placed at $(0, a)$. Find the force of attraction exerted between the rod and the unit mass, by considering that the contribution to the total force of attraction between an element of the rod $dx$ units long and the unit mass is given by $dF = km\, dx/r^2$, where $r = \sqrt{a^2 + x^2}$, and finding the $x$- and $y$-components of this element.

In each of Numbers 20 to 25, test the given improper integral for convergence, but do not try to evaluate any of the integrals.

20. $\int_0^\infty e^{-x^2}\, dx.$

21. $\int_1^\infty x^2 e^{-x^2}\, dx.$

22. $\int_0^1 \frac{\sin x}{x}\, dx.$

23. $\int_0^\infty e^{-x} x^{s-1}\, dx, \; s \geq 1.$

24. $\int_0^1 \frac{\cos t}{t^2}\, dt.$ Hint: Use the fact that $(\cos t)/t \to \infty$, as $t \to 0^+$.

25. $\int_1^2 \frac{x}{\ln x}\, dx.$ Hint: Consider the interval from $1 + \epsilon$ to 2 and let $x = e^u$.

## 12.10 APPROXIMATE INTEGRATION

In many of the practical applications of integration, we often encounter integrals of functions for which the inverse differentiation cannot be performed in terms of elementary functions. In such cases, it is essential to have methods of approximating the value of the definite integral.

Since a definite integral may be interpreted as an area under a curve, any method for finding this area can be used to evaluate the integral. Thus, to obtain an approximate evaluation of $\int_a^b f(x)\,dx$, $f(x) \geq 0$, we need only to approximate the area under the curve $y = f(x)$ and above the x-axis, from $x = a$ to $x = b$.

Let us choose points $x_0, x_1, \ldots, x_n$ so that the interval $a \leq x \leq b$ is divided into $n$ equal parts, and $x_0 = a$, $x_n = b$. Let the corresponding values of the function be $y_0, y_1, \ldots, y_n$, and let $P_0, P_1, \ldots, P_n$ denote the points $(x_0, y_0)$, $(x_1, y_1), \ldots, (x_n, y_n)$ on the curve. A fairly close approximation to the area can

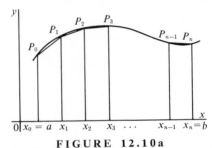

**FIGURE 12.10a**

be made using trapezoids formed by joining adjacent points $P_0, P_1, \ldots, P_n$ with chords, as shown in Figure 12.10a. The area of the kth trapezoid is

$$\tfrac{1}{2}h(y_{k-1} + y_k),$$

where $h = (b - a)/n$, the width of each subinterval. The sum of the areas of the $n$ trapezoids is

$$T_n = \frac{h}{2}(y_0 + y_1) + \frac{h}{2}(y_1 + y_2) + \cdots + \frac{h}{2}(y_{n-1} + y_n)$$

or

(1)
$$T_n = \frac{h}{2}(y_0 + 2y_1 + 2y_2 + \cdots + 2y_{n-1} + y_n).$$

Equation (1) is called the **Trapezoidal Rule** for approximating the integral $\int_a^b f(x)\,dx$.

For an approximation method such as the Trapezoidal Rule to be more useful, it is necessary that a method for estimating the accuracy of the approximation be available. Although it is beyond the scope of our work here to include a derivation, it can be shown that the error, $E_n$, made by using the Trapezoidal Rule with $n$ trapezoids to approximate $\int_a^b f(x)\,dx$ must satisfy the inequality

$$|E_n| \leq \frac{h^2}{12}(b - a) \max |f''(x)|,$$

where max $|f''(x)|$ denotes the maximum value of $f''$ on the interval $a \leq x \leq b$. (For example, see N. Macon, *Numerical Analysis*, Wiley, New York, 1963.)

Another method of approximating the area under a curve $y = f(x)$ is obtained by approximating the curve by a sequence of parabolic arcs, rather than by chords as in the Trapezoidal Rule. In this case, we use a partitioning of the interval $a \leq x \leq b$ as indicated in Figure 12.10a, except that the number of subintervals must be even, say $n = 2m$. A parabolic arc described by an equation of the form

$$y = ax^2 + bx + c$$

is then passed through the points $P_0$, $P_1$, $P_2$, another parabolic arc through the points $P_2$, $P_3$, $P_4$, and so on.

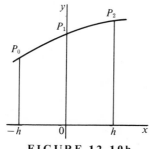

**FIGURE 12.10b**

Consequently, we need to find the area under a typical parabolic arc through three points. For this purpose, let us choose the points as

$$P_0(-h, y_0), \quad P_1(0, y_1), \quad P_2(h, y_2),$$

as shown in Figure 12.10b. Since the equation of the parabolic arc is of the form

$$y = ax^2 + bx + c,$$

the area under the curve is

$$A = \int_{-h}^{h} (ax^2 + bx + c)\, dx$$

$$= \left[ \frac{ax^3}{3} + \frac{bx^2}{2} + cx \right]_{-h}^{h}$$

$$= \frac{2ah^3}{3} + 2ch.$$

Also, since the curve passes through the points $(-h, y_0)$, $(0, y_1)$, $(h, y_2)$, we must have

$$y_0 = ah^2 - bh + c,$$
$$y_1 = c,$$
$$y_2 = ah^2 + bh + c,$$

so that

$$y_0 + y_2 = 2ah^2 + 2c = 2ah^2 + 2y_1.$$

Hence,

$$2ah^2 = y_0 + y_2 - 2y_1$$

and

$$A = \frac{h}{3}(y_0 + y_2 - 2y_1) + 2hy_1,$$

or

$$A = \frac{h}{3}(y_0 + 4y_1 + y_2).$$

This formula for the area under a parabolic arc is known as the **prismoidal formula,** and is independent of the location of the $y$-axis.

The area under a curve $y = f(x)$ is therefore approximated by adding together the areas under successive parabolic arcs along the curve. This area is

$$S = \frac{h}{3}(y_0 + 4y_1 + y_2) + \frac{h}{3}(y_2 + 4y_3 + y_4) + \cdots + \frac{h}{3}(y_{2m-2} + 4y_{2m-1} + y_{2m})$$

or

(2) $$S = \frac{h}{3}(y_0 + 4y_1 + 2y_2 + 4y_3 + 2y_4 + \cdots + 4y_{2m-1} + y_{2m}).$$

Equation (2) is called **Simpson's Rule** for approximating the integral $\int_a^b f(x)\, dx$. The prismoidal formula is, of course, Simpson's Rule with two subdivisions.

If $E_n$ is the error in Simpson's Rule with $n$ subintervals, then it can be shown that

$$|E_n| \leqq \frac{h^4}{180}(b - a)\max|f^{(4)}(x)|, \qquad a \leqq x \leqq b.$$

(The derivation can be found in N. Macon, *Numerical Analysis*, Wiley, New York, 1963.)

---

*Example 12.10a.* Find an approximate value for

$$\int_0^1 \frac{dx}{1 + x^2}$$

(a) by using the Trapezoidal Rule, and (b) by using Simpson's Rule, with eight subintervals in each case.

The work is conveniently arranged in tabular form as follows.

| $x$ | $y = 1/(1 + x^2)$ | | |
|---|---|---|---|
| 0.000 | 1.00000 | | |
| 0.125 | | 0.98461 | |
| 0.250 | | | 0.94118 |
| 0.375 | | 0.87671 | |
| 0.500 | | | 0.80000 |
| 0.625 | | 0.71910 | |
| 0.750 | | | 0.64000 |
| 0.875 | | 0.56637 | |
| 1.000 | 0.50000 | | |
| | 1.50000 | 3.14679 | 2.38118 |

For the Trapezoidal Rule, we have $h = \frac{1}{8}$, and

$$T = \tfrac{1}{16}(1.50000 + 2 \times 3.14679 + 2 \times 2.38118)$$
$$= \tfrac{1}{16}(12.55594)$$
$$= 0.78475.$$

Since the error is given by $|E_8| \le \tfrac{1}{12}h^2 \max |y''(x)|$, we have

$$|E_8| \le \tfrac{1}{768} \times 2 \le 0.0026,$$

so that

$$0.7821 \le \int_0^1 \frac{dx}{1 + x^2} < 0.7874.$$

For Simpson's Rule, we have $h = \frac{1}{8}$ and

$$S = \tfrac{1}{24}(1.50000 + 4 \times 3.14679 + 2 \times 2.38118)$$
$$= \tfrac{1}{24}(18.84952)$$
$$= 0.78540.$$

A calculation of the error, $E_8$, for Simpson's Rule gives

$$|E_8| < 0.00002.$$

In this example, the integral can be evaluated, and we have

$$\int_0^1 \frac{dx}{1 + x^2} = \text{Tan}^{-1} 1 = \frac{\pi}{4} = 0.78540 \ (\text{approx.}).$$

Thus, it appears that Simpson's Rule gives a much more accurate approximation to the value of the integral than does the Trapezoidal Rule.

# Exercises 12.10

In Numbers 1 to 4, use the inverse derivative to evaluate the definite integrals. Then find an approximate value for each integral by using (a) the Trapezoidal Rule, and (b) Simpson's Rule, with four subintervals in each case. Also, use the formulas of this section to estimate the error of each approximation. Compare the results.

1. $\int_0^{0.8} x^3 \, dx.$

2. $\int_1^{1.4} \ln x \, dx.$

3. $\int_0^{\pi/2} \cos x \, dx.$

4. $\int_0^{0.8} e^x \, dx.$

In Numbers 5 to 12, find an approximate value for the given integral by using (a) the Trapezoidal Rule, and (b) Simpson's Rule. Use four subintervals, and round off each answer to four decimal places.

5. $\int_0^{0.8} e^{-x^2} \, dx.$

6. $\int_0^{0.8} \cos x^2 \, dx.$

7. $\int_0^{0.4} \sin x^2 \, dx.$

8. $\int_0^{0.8} \sqrt{1 - x^4} \, dx.$

9. $\int_{0.1}^{0.5} \frac{\cos x}{x} \, dx.$

10. $\int_{0.2}^1 \sqrt{\sin x} \, dx.$

11. $\int_1^{1.8} \sqrt{1 + x^3} \, dx.$

12. $\int_0^{\pi/3} \sqrt{1 - \tfrac{1}{4}\sin^2 x} \, dx.$

13. Use Simpson's Rule to obtain the formula

$$V = \frac{\pi h}{6}(3r_1^2 + 3r_2^2 + h^2)$$

for the volume of a spherical segment of altitude $h$ and base radii $r_1$ and $r_2$. Use two subintervals.

14. Use Simpson's Rule to find the formula for the volume of a right circular cone of altitude $h$ and base radius $a$. Make your own choice as to the number of subintervals to use.

15. Use Simpson's Rule with $n = 4$ to find approximately the area under the probability curve $y = (1/\sqrt{2\pi})e^{-x^2/2}$ from $x = 0$ to $x = 0.4$.

16. Draw a smooth curve through the following points and find an approximation to the area under the curve using Simpson's Rule with $n = 6$:

| $x$ | 0 | 2 | 4 | 6 | 8 | 10 | 12 |
|-----|----|-----|-----|-----|-----|-----|-----|
| $y$ | 10 | 6.8 | 5.3 | 4.5 | 3.6 | 3.3 | 3.1 |

17. If $y = P(x)$, where $P(x)$ is a polynomial of degree three or less, show that Simpson's Rule gives an exact result.

18. The area under the curve $y = \ln x$ from $x = 1$ to $x = 4$ is revolved about the $x$-axis. Find an approximation to the volume of the resulting solid by using Simpson's Rule with $n = 6$.

## 12.11 USE OF A TABLE OF INTEGRALS

The formulas in a table of integrals can be derived with standard techniques, and a table of integrals may consist of as many hundreds of formulas as the compiler wishes to include. The table of integrals in Appendix C is comparatively short and is essentially a sampling of the formulas that are commonly encountered.

Before using a table of integrals, the student should examine the organization of the table and should study the "items to be observed" at the head of the table.

*Example 12.11a.* Integrate

$$\int \frac{dx}{x\sqrt{2 + 3x}}.$$

This form contains $\sqrt{a + bu}$ so we look in the integrals listed under this heading and find that Formula (14) will fit with $a = 2$ and $b = 3$. Thus,

$$\int \frac{dx}{x\sqrt{2 + 3x}} = \frac{1}{\sqrt{2}} \ln \left| \frac{\sqrt{2 + 3x} - \sqrt{2}}{\sqrt{2 + 3x} + \sqrt{2}} \right| + C.$$

*Example 12.11b.* Integrate

$$\int \frac{dy}{y^3(y^2 + 4)}.$$

Formula (21), with $m = 3$ and $a = 2$, may be used as a reduction formula.

$$\int \frac{dy}{y^3(y^2 + 4)} = \frac{-1}{4(2)y^2} - \frac{1}{4} \int \frac{dy}{y(y^2 + 4)}.$$

Now Formula (20) may be used on the last integral to obtain

$$\int \frac{dy}{y^3(y^2 + 4)} = \frac{-1}{8y^2} - \frac{1}{32} \ln \frac{y^2}{y^2 + 4} + C.$$

---

*Example 12.11c.* Integrate $\int w^2 \sqrt{w^2 - 9} \, dw$.

Formula (27) may be used with $a = 3$. The student should note carefully the choices of sign in the use of this formula.

$$\int w^2 \sqrt{w^2 - 9} \, dw = \frac{w}{4}(w^2 - 9)^{3/2} + \frac{9w}{8} \sqrt{w^2 - 9} - \frac{81}{8} \ln |w + \sqrt{w^2 - 9}| + C.$$

---

*Example 12.11d.* Integrate $\int \cos^4 3x \, dx$.

Formula (81) may be used with $m = 4$, $u = 3x$, and $du = 3 \, dx$. Thus $dx = \frac{1}{3} du$, and we may write

$$\int \cos^4 3x \, dx = \frac{1}{3} \int \cos^4 u \, du = \frac{1}{3} \left[ \frac{\cos^3 u \sin u}{4} + \frac{3}{4} \int \cos^2 u \, du \right].$$

The last integral fits Formula (79), and the result is

$$\int \cos^4 3x \, dx = \frac{1}{3} \left[ \frac{\cos^3 u \sin u}{4} + \frac{3}{4} \left( \frac{u}{2} + \frac{1}{4} \sin 2u \right) \right] + C.$$

Substituting $u = 3x$, the final result is

$$\int \cos^4 3x \, dx = \frac{1}{12} \cos^3 3x \sin 3x + \frac{3x}{8} + \frac{1}{16} \sin 6x + C.$$

## Exercises 12.11

In Numbers 1 to 12, derive the indicated formula of the table of integrals.

1. Formula 79.
2. Formula 80.
3. Formula 18.
4. Formula 19.
5. Formula 96.
6. Formula 109.
7. Formula 50.
8. Formula 58.
9. Formula 4.
10. Formula 9.
11. Formula 22.
12. Formula 28.

In Numbers 13 to 32, find the inverse derivative by using the table of integrals.

13. $\int \dfrac{\sqrt{x^2+1}}{x^3}\,dx.$

14. $\int \dfrac{(4x^2-9)^{3/2}}{x}\,dx.$

15. $\int \dfrac{y^3\,dy}{4y^2-1}.$

16. $\int \sqrt{9y^2-4}\,dy.$

17. $\int w^3\sqrt{w^2-4}\,dw.$

18. $\int \dfrac{dt}{t^3(4t^2+9)^{3/2}}.$

19. $\int y^2\sin 2y\,dy.$

20. $\int w^4\cos 3w\,dw.$

21. $\int (\ln 2x)^2\,dx.$

22. $\int \dfrac{x^2\,dx}{\sqrt{4x^2-1}}.$

23. $\int y^2\sqrt{9-4y^2}\,dy.$

24. $\int \dfrac{y^2\,dy}{\sqrt{9-4y^2}}.$

25. $\int \dfrac{(4-y^2)^{3/2}}{y^2}\,dy.$

26. $\int t^2\sqrt{9t^2-16}\,dt.$

27. $\int e^{2x}\sin 3x\,dx.$

28. $\int \operatorname{csch} 3y\,dy.$

29. $\int \dfrac{\sqrt{2+3x}}{5x}\,dx.$

30. $\int \sin^4 2w\,dw.$

31. $\int \sin 2t\cos 3t\,dt.$

32. $\int \dfrac{2x^4+7x^2-4x-2}{(x^2+1)^2(x-2)}\,dx.$

In each of Numbers 33 to 46, evaluate the given definite integral.

33. $\int_0^{\pi/8} \tan^2 2x\,dx.$

34. $\int_0^a t^3(a^2+t^2)^{3/2}\,dt.$

35. $\int_1^4 \dfrac{3w\,dw}{\sqrt{2+3w}}.$

36. $\int_2^3 \dfrac{\sqrt{4x^2-9}}{3x}\,dx.$

37. $\int_0^{\pi/4} \sec^5 w\,dw.$

38. $\int_0^{\pi/4} \tan^5 t\,dt.$

39. $\int_0^4 \sqrt{16-x^2}\,dx.$

40. $\int_0^{\pi/2} e^{-t}\sin 3t\,dt.$

41. $\int_0^1 \operatorname{Tan}^{-1} w\,dw.$

42. $\int_0^1 \dfrac{t^2\,dt}{(9-4t^2)^{3/2}}.$

43. $\int_0^{\pi/4} \cos^4 x\,dx.$

44. $\int_0^1 y^2e^{2y}\,dy.$

45. $\int_0^{1/4} \operatorname{Sin}^{-1} 2w\,dw.$

46. $\int_0^{\pi} u^4\sin u\,du.$

# 12.12 MISCELLANEOUS PROBLEMS

The following exercises are intended not only to review a number of applications of integration but also to test the reader's ability to extend the application to a few situations that have not previously been discussed.

## Exercises 12.12

1. Find the centroid of the area bounded by the x-axis and the arch of the curve $y = \sin^2 x$ from $x = 0$ to $x = \pi$.
2. Find the centroid of the first quadrant area inside the hypocycloid $x = a \cos^3 t$, $y = a \sin^3 t$.
3. Find the centroid of the area bounded by the x-axis and one arch of the cycloid $x = a(t - \sin t)$, $y = a(1 - \cos t)$.
4. Find the centroid of the area bounded by the curve $y = \sec^2 x$, the x-axis, and the two lines $x = 0$ and $x = \pi/4$.
5. Find the average value with respect to $x$ of $y = \ln x$ from $x = 1$ to $x = 3$.
6. Calculate the average value with respect to $x$ of $y = \text{Tan}^{-1} x$ from $x = 0$ to $x = 1$.
7. What is the average value of $y = a(t - \sin t)$ with respect to $x = a(1 - \cos t)$ from $t = 0$ to $t = \pi$?
8. The area bounded by the axes and the first quadrant portion of the hypocycloid $x^{2/3} + y^{2/3} = a^{2/3}$ is revolved about the y-axis. Find the volume so generated.
9. Find the volume formed by revolving about the y-axis the area that is bounded by the curve $a^{1/2}y = x\sqrt{a - x}$, $a > 0$, and the x-axis.
10. The area above the x-axis and under one arch of the cycloid $x = a(t - \sin t)$, $y = a(1 - \cos t)$ is revolved about the y-axis. Find the volume that is formed.
11. The area bounded by the catenary $y = a \cosh x/a$ and the lines $x = 0$, $y = 0$, $x = a$ is revolved about the x-axis. Locate the centroid of the resulting volume.
12. Through the center of a solid sphere of radius 4 inches a cylindrical hole of radius 2 inches is bored. What volume of material remains?
13. Loudspeaker horns are frequently of the so-called *exponential* type, in which the cross-sectional area increases exponentially with the distance from the throat. Find the volume of air in such a horn if it is 4 feet long and has a throat diameter of 2 inches and a mouth diameter of 2 feet.
14. A horn-shaped solid has for a longitudinal section the region between $y = e^x$ and $y = e^{-x}$ from $x = 0$ to $x = 1$. If every section perpendicular to the x-axis is a square with one diagonal in the xy-plane, find the volume.
15. A vertical water gate is in the shape of a semicircle with its base at the surface of the water. Find the total force on the gate if the radius of the circle is 2 feet.
★16. Locate the point at which a single force would have to be placed to be the equivalent of the total force on the water gate of Number 15.
17. A particle of mass $m$ moves along the x-axis so that its distance (feet) from the origin at time $t$ (seconds) is $x = A \sin \omega t$. This type of motion is called *simple harmonic motion*. The particle makes a complete oscillation in $2\pi/\omega$ seconds. During such an oscillation, what is the average of the kinetic energy, $\frac{1}{2}mv^2$, with respect to the time?

18. A 60 cycle per second alternating electric current is described by the equation $I = I_0 \sin 120\pi t$, where $I_0$ is in amperes and $t$ is in seconds. Find the average magnitude (absolute value) of the current with respect to the time.

★19. An alternating electric current $I$ (amperes) is described by the equation $I = I_0 \sin \omega t$, where $t$ is the time in seconds and $\omega$ is a constant. The effective value $I_e$ of the current is defined to be the direct current (a constant) that will produce the same amount of heat per period in a resistance of $R$ ohms as is produced by the alternating current. If the rate at which heat $Q$ (joules) is produced is given by $D_t Q = RI^2$, find $I_e$ in terms of $I_0$.

20. Suppose it is conjectured that the cost of an upper atmosphere sounding rocket is $200 + 12\sqrt{x}$ dollars per mile if the rocket is to be propelled to a height of $x$ miles. On this basis, what would be the cost of a rocket that is to be propelled to a height of 100 miles?

★21. Find the force of attraction of a thin semicircle of wire of radius $a$ and of mass $m$ per unit length on a unit mass particle located at the center of the circle.

★22. A thin circle of wire is of radius $a$ and of mass $m$ per unit length. A unit mass particle is located on the axis of the circle at a distance $R$ from the plane of the circle. Show that the force of attraction of the wire on the particle is $2\pi kmaR(a^2 + R^2)^{-3/2}$.

★23. Use the result of Number 22 to find the force of attraction of a thin disk of radius $b$ and of constant mass $\mu$ per unit area on a particle of unit mass located on the axis of the disk and at the distance $s$ from the disk.

# Summary of Chapter 12

Chapter 12 is primarily devoted to the development of techniques of integration. These techniques include

(1) the recognition of simple inverse derivatives by inspection (Section 12.1);
(2) inverse derivatives of expressions involving trigonometric functions (Section 12.2);
(3) the method of substitution in finding inverse derivatives and in evaluating definite integrals (Section 12.3);
(4) trigonometric and hyperbolic substitutions (Section 12.4);
(5) integration by parts (Section 12.5);
(6) Wallis' formulas and their use (Section 12.6);
(7) integration of rational fractions by means of partial fractions (Sections 12.7 12.8).

An important extension of the concept of the integral includes integrals having infinite limits and integrals of functions having infinite discontinuities (Section 12.9) Also, the student should understand the need for methods of approximating definite integrals and how to use these methods (Section 12.10). Finally, he must understand how to use a table of integrals (Section 12.11).

# Chapter 13    Coordinate Geometry

## 13.1 SETS OF POINTS DETERMINED BY GEOMETRIC CONDITIONS

The first organization of geometric concepts into an axiomatic system was given by Euclid about 300 B.C. Euclid's geometry was a study of geometric figures based on certain axioms suggested by physical considerations. In the early 1600's, the French mathematician René Descartes (1596–1650) introduced the concept of a coordinate system by means of which he was able to translate geometric problems into an algebraic language. The resulting union of algebra and geometry, now known as **analytic** or **coordinate geometry,** proved to be so powerful that it opened the door to an amazing new era of mathematics.

The fundamental ideas of coordinate geometry, such as the representation of points in a plane by ordered pairs of real numbers and the representation of a curve by an algebraic equation, were introduced in some detail in Chapter 2. By means of these representations, we were able to study the straight line in considerable detail and, in particular, we saw how to specify the direction of a straight line by means of the slope or by means of direction numbers. We were also able to analyze properties of curves, to find symmetries, asymptotes, and so on; and with the aid of the calculus, to describe other salient features of a curve. The importance and value of these ideas in the analysis of many physical problems can hardly be overestimated.

In order to see further how these concepts are used, we shall investigate additional simple applications to geometric problems. The set of all ordered pairs of real numbers is called a **space,** and a particular ordered pair in the set is called a **point** in the space. The distance between two points $(x_1, y_1)$ and $(x_2, y_2)$ was found in Theorem 2.2a to be

$$d = [(x_1 - x_2)^2 + (y_1 - y_2)^2]^{1/2}.$$

The expression for $d$ is called the **metric** of the space, and the space is called a **euclidean metric space** of two dimensions. This space is the familiar $xy$-plane.

Suppose we wish to describe analytically a set of points each of which is located twice as far from the $x$-axis as from the $y$-axis. If the distance of an arbitrary point of the set from the $y$-axis is denoted by $d_1$, then the distance of the point from the $x$-axis is $2d_1$ (see Figure 13.1a). In analytic form, we have

$$d_1 = |x| \quad \text{and} \quad 2d_1 = |y|,$$

so that the equations

$$2x = y \quad \text{and} \quad 2x = -y$$

describe the set of points, since the coordinates of each point in the set satisfy one or the other of these equations.

The next example illustrates another simple geometric problem.

---

*Example 13.1a.* Find an analytic description for the set of points located so that the distance of each from the point $(1, 0)$ is equal to its distance from the line $x = 0$.

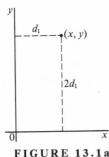

FIGURE 13.1a

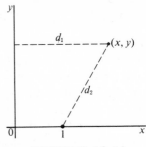

FIGURE 13.1b

As Figure 13.1b shows, $d_1$ represents the distance of the point $(x, y)$ from the $y$-axis, and $d_2$ its distance from the point $(1, 0)$. The condition to be satisfied is that $d_1 = d_2$. From

$$d_1 = |x| \quad \text{and} \quad d_2 = [(x - 1)^2 + y^2]^{1/2},$$

we get

$$|x| = [(x - 1)^2 + y^2]^{1/2},$$
$$x^2 = (x - 1)^2 + y^2.$$

This equation reduces to

$$y^2 = 2x - 1.$$

In other words, every point $(x, y)$ that satisfies the given geometric condition must have coordinates that satisfy the above algebraic condition. But can we be sure that every point whose coordinates satisfy the equation also satisfies the geometric condition? In this case, the desired assurance can be obtained by working backward from the final equation to obtain the result that $d_1 = d_2$. Thus, if

$$y^2 = 2x - 1,$$

then

$$y^2 + x^2 - 2x + 1 = x^2,$$

or

$$y^2 + (x - 1)^2 = x^2.$$

Since the left side of this equation is the square of the distance $d_2$ of the point $(x, y)$ from the point $(1, 0)$, and the right side is the square of the distance $d_1$ of the point from the $y$-axis, we see that $d_1 = d_2$ as required.

The next example shows that it is sometimes necessary to adjoin an inequality to the equation in order to describe the geometric conditions completely.

---

*Example 13.1b.* Find an equation to describe the set of points $\{(x, y)\}$ in the first quadrant such that the product of the coordinates of each point is always 6.

It is easy to write that $xy = 6$. Unfortunately, this equation is satisfied by the co-ordinates of points in the third quadrant, such as $(-2, -3)$, which we wish to exclude. Hence, the equation $xy = 6$ alone is not adequate. Instead we must write

$$xy = 6, \quad x > 0$$

to describe the given set of points.

---

*Example 13.1c.* Find an equation for the set of all points located at a distance of 5 units from the point $(3, 4)$.

Let $P(x, y)$ be a typical point of the set (see Figure 13.1c). The distance of this point from $(3, 4)$ is $d = [(x - 3)^2 + (y - 4)^2]^{1/2}$, which must equal 5. Hence,

$$5 = [(x - 3)^2 + (y - 4)^2]^{1/2}$$

or

$$x^2 - 6x + y^2 - 8y = 0.$$

---

*Example 13.1d.* Find an equation for the set of points such that the product of the slopes of the two lines joining each point of the set to the points $(0, 2)$ and $(0, -2)$ is 1.

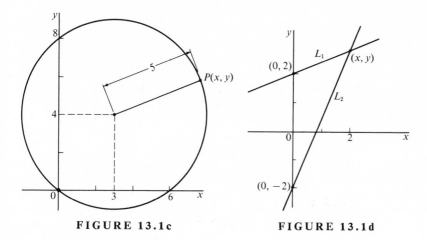

FIGURE 13.1c          FIGURE 13.1d

Referring to Figure 13.1d, where $(x, y)$ is supposed to be a point in the given set, we have, for the slope of $L_1$,

$$m_1 = \frac{y - 2}{x}, \quad x \neq 0,$$

and, for the slope of $L_2$,

$$m_2 = \frac{y + 2}{x}, \quad x \neq 0.$$

Since the given condition is $m_1 m_2 = 1$, we get

$$\left(\frac{y-2}{x}\right)\left(\frac{y+2}{x}\right) = 1,$$

or

$$y^2 - x^2 = 4, \qquad x \neq 0.$$

The final equation is that of a hyperbola with its vertices at $(0, 2)$ and $(0, -2)$, but the vertices themselves are not in the given set of points.

___

The next example illustrates another technique that is helpful in determining equations for sets of points.

___

*Example 13.1e.* Find an equation for the set of midpoints of the chords drawn from the origin to the points of the curve determined by $y^2 = x$.

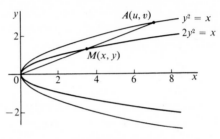

**FIGURE 13.1e**

Figure 13.1e shows the graph of $y^2 = x$ and a typical chord. Let the point $A(u, v)$ be a point of the curve $y^2 = x$, and let the point $M(x, y)$ be the midpoint of the chord $OA$. The coordinates of the point $A$ on the given curve are denoted by $u$ and $v$ in order to distinguish them from the coordinates of a point $M(x, y)$ on the required curve.

It is now necessary to find a connection between the coordinates $(u, v)$ and $(x, y)$. In this case the desired relationship is easily obtained, since it is known that $M$ is the midpoint of the chord. Hence,

$$x = \tfrac{1}{2}u \quad \text{and} \quad y = \tfrac{1}{2}v,$$

or

$$2x = u, \quad 2y = v.$$

Since $u$ and $v$ satisfy the equation $v^2 = u$, we get

$$(2y)^2 = 2x,$$

or

$$2y^2 = x$$

as an equation of the set of points.

___

The preceding example illustrates a device that is frequently convenient in analytic geometry—namely, giving a point on an unknown curve the general coordinates $(x, y)$ and then finding a relationship between these coordinates and the coordinates of a point $(u, v)$ on a known curve.

*Example 13.1f.* Find an equation for the set of all points located 4 units farther from (4,0) than from the line $x = 2$.

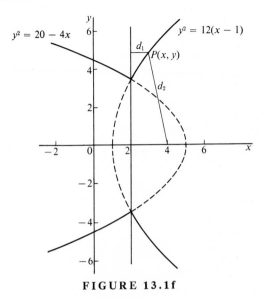

**FIGURE 13.1f**

If $P(x, y)$ is a typical element of the set (Figure 13.1f), then the distances of $P$ from the line and from the point are, respectively,

$$d_1 = \sqrt{(x - 2)^2} \quad \text{and} \quad d_2 = \sqrt{(x - 4)^2 + y^2}.$$

The problem states $d_2 = d_1 + 4$. However, $d_1 \geqq 0$ and $d_2 \geqq 0$, so that care must be used in performing algebraic operations on this equation. Keep in mind that the distances may not be negative and that we must use

$$\sqrt{(x - 2)^2} = \begin{cases} x - 2 & \text{for } x \geqq 2, \\ 2 - x & \text{for } x < 2. \end{cases}$$

Thus, the problem must be considered in two parts. For $x \geqq 2$, we have

$$x - 2 + 4 = \sqrt{(x - 4)^2 + y^2},$$
$$(x + 2)^2 = (x - 4)^2 + y^2,$$
$$y^2 = 12(x - 1).$$

For $x < 2$, we have

$$2 - x + 4 = \sqrt{(x - 4)^2 + y^2},$$
$$(6 - x)^2 = (x - 4)^2 + y^2,$$
$$y^2 = 20 - 4x.$$

Accordingly, we may write for the required set of points:

$$y^2 = \begin{cases} 12(x - 1), & x \geqq 2, \\ 4(5 - x), & x < 2. \end{cases}$$

The graph consists of the heavy solid lines in Figure 13.1f.

## Exercises 13.1

In Numbers 1 to 20, find an equation for the set of points satisfying the given condition, and sketch its graph.

1. Each point is 2 units from the line $x = 3$.
2. Each point is 6 units from the line $y = 4$.
3. The slope of the line joining any point $P$ of the set to $(4, 0)$ is twice the slope of the line through $P$ and the origin.
4. The slope of the line joining any point $P$ of the set to $(4, 0)$ is one-half the slope of the line through $P$ and the origin.
5. The sum of the slopes of the lines joining any point of the set to $(2, 5)$ and $(2, -1)$ is 2.
6. The distance of each point from the line $x = 1$ is equal to its distance above the $x$-axis.
7. The distance of each point from the line $y = 3$ is equal to the $x$-coordinate minus the $y$-coordinate of the point.
8. Each point is 4 units from $(3, 4)$.
9. Each point is 5 units from $(0, 2)$.
10. Each point is equidistant from $(1, 3)$ and $(4, 6)$.
11. Each point is equidistant from $(-2, 3)$ and the line $x = -4$.
12. Each point is equidistant from $(-2, -3)$ and the $y$-axis.
13. Each point is twice as far from $(1, 2)$ as from $(4, 3)$.
14. Each point is twice as far from $(0, 3)$ as from the line $x = 2$.
15. The square of the distance of each point from $(2, 6)$ is equal to the square of its distance from $(1, 2)$.
16. The sum of the squares of the distances of each point from $(-2, -1)$ and $(3, -2)$ is 21.
17. The distance of each point from the line $x = -2$ is equal to the sum of the squares of the coordinates of the point.
18. Each point is 2 units farther from $(4, 0)$ than from the line $x = -2$.
19. Each point is 1 unit farther from $(2, 1)$ than from the line $y = 3$.
20. The sum of the distances of each point from the point $(0, 1)$ and the line $x = -3$ is 5.

21. For Example 13.1f, prove that points on the curve whose equation is $y^2 = 12(x - 1)$ actually do satisfy the conditions of the problem for $x \geq 2$ but not for $x < 2$.
22. For the equation $y^2 = 20 - 4x$, prove results corresponding to those of Number 21; that is, show that for $x \leq 2$ this equation is satisfactory but not for $x > 2$.

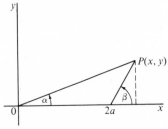

**FIGURE 13.1g**

23. Find an equation of a set of points $\{(x, y)\}$ such that for each point $P(x, y)$, the angle $\alpha$ (see Figure 13.1g) is one third the angle $\beta$. Compare with Figure 7.5d. *Hint*: Use the formulas for $\sin 3\alpha$ and $\cos 3\alpha$ to obtain a second expression for $\tan \beta = y/(x - 2a)$.
24. Find an equation for the set of centers of all the circles that pass through the points $(5, 2)$ and $(3, 0)$.
25. One of the equal sides of an isosceles triangle joins the points $(2, 4)$ and $(1, -3)$. Find an equation that the coordinates of the third vertex must satisfy.
26. A triangle of area 2 has two of its vertices at $(2, 1)$ and $(4, 3)$. Find an equation that the coordinates of the third vertex must satisfy.
27. Find an equation of the set of midpoints of the chords of the curve $4x^2 + 9y = 36$ that are drawn from the point $(0, 4)$.
28. Find an equation of the set of points that divide the chords from the origin to points on the curve $x^2 + y^2 - 2x = 0$ in the ratio (a) 1 to 1; (b) 2 to $-1$.
29. A line segment of length $a$ is drawn from a point on the $x$-axis to a point on the $y$-axis. Find an equation of the set of midpoints of all possible line segments that answer this description.

## 13.2 TRANSLATION OF COORDINATES

As we stated in the preceding section. the set of points $\{(x, y): x, y \in \mathfrak{R}\}$ is called a space of points. Besides being regarded as a point, a pair of real numbers may also be interpreted as a two-dimensional vector determined by the origin and the point $(x, y)$. The magnitude of a vector is then determined by the metric for the space. Since the elements of the space have a dual interpretation, the space itself may be looked upon either as a space of points or as a set of vectors called a **vector space**. The vector space, however, embodies two additional concepts not associated with a space of points: the **sum** of two vectors and the **product** of a vector and a real number. This dual interpretation of the space $\mathcal{V}_2 . =. \ \{(x, y): x, y \in \mathfrak{R}\}$ is a convenient and important analytic tool.

This idea may be illustrated in a simple fashion. In ordinary rectangular coordinates, the coordinates $(x, y)$ locate a point with reference to the $x$- and $y$-axes and relative to the origin. Let us consider the problem of locating a point relative to some point other than the origin, and with reference to a new pair of axes parallel to the $x$- and $y$-axes.

In Figure 13.2a, a new origin $O_n$ is shown with coordinates $(h, k)$ relative to the given origin and axes. The point $P$ has coordinates $(x, y)$ in the given system and $(u, v)$ in the new system. Using the vector interpretation of the space, we have

(1) $$\mathbf{r} = \mathbf{b} + \mathbf{r}_n,$$

where $\mathbf{r} = (x, y)$, $\mathbf{b} = (h, k)$, and $\mathbf{r}_n = (u, v)$. Accordingly, by equating corresponding components on both sides of Equation (1), we get

(2) $$x = u + h, \quad y = v + k,$$

a pair of equations which represent the relationship between the given $xy$-

coordinates and the new $uv$-coordinates. These equations are called the *equations of translation* of coordinates. In effect, these equations describe a shift of the coordinate reference from $O$ to $O_n$, with the new axes parallel to the old ones, as shown in Figure 13.2a.

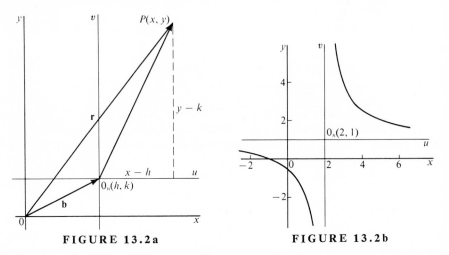

**FIGURE 13.2a**                **FIGURE 13.2b**

The next example illustrates the value of changing coordinates.

---

*Example 13.2a.* Sketch the curve described by

$$xy - x - 2y = 1.$$

Although a straightforward approach of plotting numerous points can always be used, it is desirable to rewrite an equation in as simple a form as possible to aid in the discussion of the curve. In this example an elementary factorization is possible if we add 2 to both members to get

$$xy - x - 2y + 2 = 3,$$
$$(x - 2)(y - 1) = 3.$$

If we put $u = x - 2$ and $v = y - 1$, the equation becomes

$$uv = 3$$

relative to a new origin at $(2, 1)$. This form is easily translated into a graph relative to the $u$- and $v$-axes, as shown in Figure 13.2b.

---

In case the reader feels that the factorization in the preceding example is another variation of the old hat trick, he will be pleased to know that a systematic analytic approach can be used to determine equations of translation once it is known what can be accomplished by translating coordinates. In this example, the result of the translation is an equation in which the first-degree terms are missing.

If the reason for translating axes is to eliminate the first-degree terms in an equation, then we can tackle the problem in a different way. Let

$$x = u + h \quad \text{and} \quad y = v + k,$$

where $h$ and $k$ are numbers to be so chosen that the first-degree terms are eliminated. Upon substituting these expressions for $x$ and $y$ into the equation

$$xy - x - 2y = 1,$$

we get

$$(u + h)(v + k) - (u + h) - 2(v + k) = 1,$$

or

$$uv + hv + uk - u - 2v = 1 + h + 2k - hk.$$

The last result may be rewritten as

$$uv + v(h - 2) + u(k - 1) = 1 + h + 2k - hk.$$

It is immediately apparent that if $h = 2$ and $k = 1$, the first-degree terms will be eliminated from the equation. Hence, the desired equations of translation are

$$x = u + 2, \quad y = v + 1.$$

Let us try the same approach with another kind of equation.

---

*Example 13.2b.* Sketch the curve described by

$$x^2 + y^2 - 2x + 4y = 4.$$

Again, let

$$x = u + h, \quad y = v + k.$$

Then

$$(u + h)^2 + (v + k)^2 - 2(u + h) + 4(v + k) = 4,$$

or

$$u^2 + 2uh + v^2 + 2vk - 2u + 4v = 4 + 2h - 4k - h^2 - k^2,$$

and

$$u^2 + v^2 + 2u(h - 1) + 2v(k + 2) = 4 + 2h - 4k - h^2 - k^2.$$

If $h = 1$ and $k = -2$, the equation becomes

$$u^2 + v^2 = 9.$$

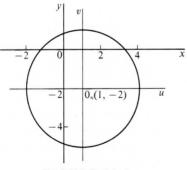

**FIGURE 13.2c**

The curve is shown in Figure 13.2c as a circle of radius 3 units with its center at $(1, -2)$, which is the new origin $O_n$.

In this example, the coordinates of the new origin were obtained by first substituting directly from the general translation equations; $h$ and $k$ were then determined from the requirement that the first-degree terms in the new equation be absent. Although this approach may be necessary in some complicated problems, in many instances the new origin can be found directly by factoring or by completing the squares.

---

*Example 13.2c.* Sketch the graph of $x^2 - 4y^2 + 6x + 12y = 0$.

The terms in the equation are rearranged in order to complete the squares, giving

$$x^2 + 6x + 9 - 4y^2 + 12y - 9 = 0,$$

or

$$(x + 3)^2 - 4(y - \tfrac{3}{2})^2 = 0.$$

If we put

$$u = x + 3 \quad \text{and} \quad v = y - \tfrac{3}{2},$$

the equation becomes

$$u^2 - 4v^2 = 0,$$

or

$$(u - 2v)(u + 2v) = 0.$$

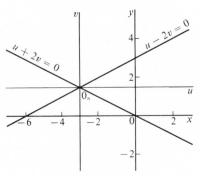

**FIGURE 13.2d**

The graph of this equation is the pair of straight lines shown in Figure 13.2d. The new origin is at $(-3, \tfrac{3}{2})$ relative to the old origin.

---

A translation of a coordinate system in a space is a special type of transformation of the space. In general, we say that a point $(x, y)$ is **mapped** to a point $(u, v)$ by a set of equations if to each point $(x, y)$ there corresponds a point $(u, v)$ as determined by the equations. A mapping of a set of points $\{(x, y)\}$ to a set of points $\{(u, v)\}$ is called a **transformation**. The equations by means of which the mapping is accomplished are called **equations of transformation**. A translation is one of the simplest types of transformation. We shall soon see that the concept of transformation plays an important role in mathematics.

## Exercises 13.2

In Numbers 1 to 4, find the coordinates of the point $P$ if the axes are shifted so that the new origin $(O_n)$ has the coordinates given relative to the old coordinate system.

1. $P(2, 3)$; $O_n(5, 1)$.
2. $P(3, 5)$; $O_n(3, 5)$.
3. $P(-8, 2)$; $O_n(2, 3)$.
4. $P(7, -5)$; $O_n(5, -5)$.

5. A vector $\overrightarrow{OP}$ reaches from the origin to point $P(x, y)$. For the following points $P$, find the vector $\overrightarrow{O_nP}$ if the origin is shifted four units to the right and three units down to the new position $O_n$.

   (a) $P(4, 3)$.
   (b) $P(-4, 3)$.
   (c) $P(-6, 2)$.
   (d) $P(x_1, y_1)$.

   In Numbers 6 to 9, a vector $\overrightarrow{OP}$ reaches from $O$ to $P(x, y)$. If the origin is translated to a new position $O_n(h, k)$, where $h$ and $k$ are measured in the original coordinate system, find the two vectors $\mathbf{a} = \overrightarrow{O_nO}$ and $\mathbf{b} = \overrightarrow{O_nP}$, such that $\mathbf{a} + \overrightarrow{OP} = \mathbf{b}$.

6. $(x, y) = (2, 5)$; $(h, k) = (9, 8)$.
7. $(x, y) = (-3, 4)$; $(h, k) = (4, 5)$.
8. $(x, y) = (-8, -9)$; $(h, k) = (-2, -1)$.
9. $(x, y) = (3, -7)$; $(h, k) = (15, 2)$.

   In Numbers 10 to 13, translate axes so that the straight lines whose equations are given will pass through the origin. State the coordinates of $O_n$ in terms of the old system of coordinates. Give two different translations for each, one in which only the $x$-axis is shifted, and one in which only the $y$-axis is shifted.

10. $y = 2x - 3$.
11. $9x - 5y + 7 = 0$.

12. $m = \dfrac{y - y_1}{x - x_1}$, $(x_1, y_1) \neq (0, 0)$, $m \neq 0$.

13. $\dfrac{x}{a} + \dfrac{y}{b} = 1$.

14. Construct a translation of axes so that the curve $xy = 1/4$ will pass through the new origin and through the point $(1, 1)$ in the new system.

    In each of Numbers 15 to 20, translate axes to remove the first-degree terms in the given equation. State the coordinates of $O_n$ in terms of the old system of coordinates.

15. $x^2 + y^2 - 4x + 9y = 0$.
16. $xy - x + 2y - 5 = 0$.
17. $2xy + x - 2y = 0$.
18. $5x^2 - y^2 + 10x + 2y = 25$.
19. $x^2y + 2xy + 4x + 2x^2 + y = 0$.
20. $x^2 - 2xy + y^2 - x + y = 2$.

    In each of Numbers 21 to 23, construct a translation of the axes such that the given parabola will have its vertex at the new origin.

21. $x^2 - 2y - 10x + 27 = 0$.
22. $4y^2 + x - 16y + 11 = 0$.
23. $y^2 - 5x - 16y = 1$.

24. Show that under a translation of coordinates, the distance between two points is **invariant**—that is, unaltered.

## 13.3 POLAR COORDINATES

The system of rectangular coordinates in analytic geometry may be described as the space $\mathcal{V}_2 = \{(x, y): x, y \in \mathcal{R}\}$ with the metric

$$d = [(x_2 - x_1)^2 + (y_2 - y_1)^2]^{1/2},$$

which gives the distance between the points $(x_1, y_1)$ and $(x_2, y_2)$. Points in the space having the same $y$-coordinate, $b$, lie on a line $\{(x, b)\}$ called a **coordinate curve**. Each such line is parallel to the $x$-axis. Similarly, the line of points having the same $x$-coordinate, $a$, that is, the set $\{(a, y)\}$, is also a coordinate curve, and is parallel to the $y$-axis. These two families of curves are distinguished by defining a curve on which $x$ is variable as an $x$-curve, and one on which $y$ is variable as a $y$-curve. The two families of coordinate curves are illustrated in Figure 13.3a.

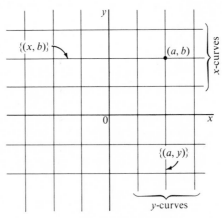

**FIGURE 13.3a**

Coordinate curves are important in the sense that a point $(a, b)$ can be identified as the intersection of two of these curves. For example,

$$\{(a, b)\} = \{(x, b)\} \cap \{(a, y)\}.$$

The idea of locating a point in the plane as the intersection of two coordinate curves immediately suggests an interesting question. Is it possible to use *any* two families of curves as coordinate curves for the purpose of locating points in the space? If so, how should these families of curves be specified?

A simple example shows that any two distinct families of parallel straight lines can be used for this purpose, as illustrated in Figure 13.3b. Using this network, a point is located as the intersection of two oblique lines. A coordinate system of this type is called an **oblique** coordinate system.

As in a translation, each point in the space is designated by a different pair of numbers for each different reference frame. The relationship between a new reference frame and that for rectangular coordinates is usually expressed in analytic form by the equations of transformation. For example, if the $v$-axis in Figure 13.3c makes an angle of 60° with the $u$-axis, then the equations of transformation can be found easily by the use of some simple trigonometry.

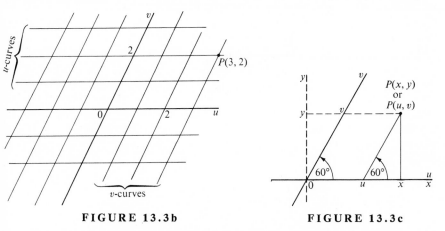

FIGURE 13.3b                    FIGURE 13.3c

If we let the $x$-axis coincide with the $u$-axis, and if the origins coincide, then we have

$$y = v \sin 60° = v\sqrt{3}/2,$$
$$x = u + v \cos 60° = u + v/2$$

as the equations of transformation. The distance formula for the $uv$-system is then obtained by substitution into the distance formula in rectangular coordinates to give

$$d = [(u_2 - u_1)^2 + (u_2 - u_1)(v_2 - v_1) + (v_2 - v_1)^2]^{1/2}.$$

Just as we may use two families of straight lines as coordinate curves, we may also use two families of curved lines or a family of curved lines and a family of straight lines. One natural method of locating a point $P$ relative to a reference point $O$, the origin or **pole**, is to specify the distance of $P$ from $O$ and the angle that the vector $\overrightarrow{OP}$ makes with a fixed reference line, the **polar axis**. In other words, $P$ is located relative to $O$ by the number-pair $(r, \theta)$, where $r = |\overrightarrow{OP}|$ and $\theta$ is an angle, as shown in Figure 13.3d. The two numbers, $r$ and $\theta$,

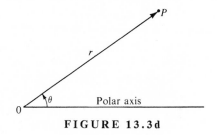

FIGURE 13.3d

are called the polar coordinates of *P*. As will soon be evident, one of the sets of coordinate lines in polar coordinates is a family of circles.

The polar axis from which the angle $\theta$ is measured is chosen as a horizontal ray (half-line) originating at *O*. To establish a consistency of notation for polar coordinates, we shall measure positive values of $\theta$ in a counterclockwise sense, and negative values of $\theta$ in a clockwise sense. Although *r* has been associated with a distance, negative values of *r* may be allowed, provided the sign is that associated with the direction of the vector $\mathbf{r} = \overrightarrow{OP}$, where *P* is a point on the terminal side of the angle $\theta$. For example, in Figure 13.3e several points plotted

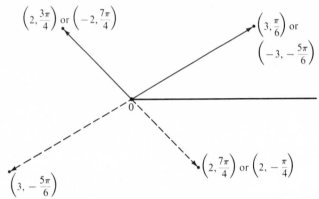

**FIGURE 13.3e**

in polar coordinates are shown. Some of the points are labeled in two ways. Notice that a negative value of *r* indicates that the point is at a distance $|r|$ from the origin, but in a direction exactly opposite that of the terminal ray of the angle $\theta$.

Since we wish to consider an interpretation for each number-pair $(r, \theta)$ in the space $\mathcal{V}_2$, we have included an interpretation for those number-pairs in which *r* or $\theta$ is negative. Although this results in an added multiplicity of representa-

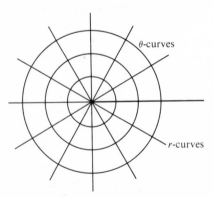

**FIGURE 13.3f**

tions of a point by a number pair, we gain a greater versatility in describing relations and functions in polar coordinates.

Coordinate curves in polar coordinates are obtained as before by considering the sets of points for which either the first coordinate or the second coordinate is fixed. Thus the set of points $\{(r, \theta_0)\}$ is a straight line through the origin making an angle $\theta_0$ with the reference line $\{(r, 0)\}$. The set of points $\{(r_0, \theta)\}$ is a circle of radius $r_0$ having its center at the origin. Hence the coordinate curves are a family of straight lines passing through the origin and a family of concentric circles having centers at the origin, as shown in Figure 13.3f. The curves $r = a$ and $r = -a$ are identical, as are all the curves $\theta = \theta_0 + k\pi,\ k \in \mathcal{I}$.

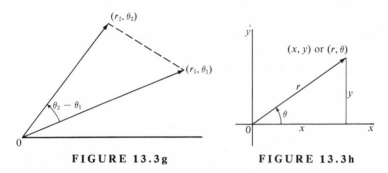

FIGURE 13.3g          FIGURE 13.3h

The distance formula for polar coordinates can easily be found by using the Law of Cosines for the triangle as indicated in Figure 13.3g. We find

$$d = [r_2^2 + r_1^2 - 2r_2 r_1 \cos(\theta_2 - \theta_1)]^{1/2}$$

as the expression for the distance $d$ between the two points $(r_1, \theta_1)$ and $(r_2, \theta_2)$.

When two different coordinate systems are given for a euclidean space, it is useful to have the equations of transformation that connect the two systems. These are easily obtained for polar and rectangular coordinates by superimposing the two coordinate systems so that the origins coincide and the polar reference line lies along the positive $x$-axis, as shown in Figure 13.3h.

It is clear that

(1)
$$\begin{cases} x = r \cos \theta, \\ y = r \sin \theta. \end{cases}$$

By means of these equations we can transform the rectangular coordinates of a point into its polar coordinates, and vice versa. For example, the rectangular coordinates of the point with polar coordinates $(3, \pi/3)$ are

$$x = 3 \cos \pi/3 = \tfrac{3}{2},$$

and

$$y = 3 \sin \pi/3 = \tfrac{3}{2}\sqrt{3}.$$

Similarly, polar coordinates of the point with rectangular coordinates $(x, y)$ may be obtained from the equations

(2)
$$\begin{cases} r^2 = x^2 + y^2, \\ \theta = \tan^{-1}(y/x), \end{cases}$$

where the quadrant of $\theta$ is the same as the quadrant of the point. Thus, for the point $(3, 4)$,

$$r = \sqrt{3^2 + 4^2} = 5, \quad \theta = \mathrm{Tan}^{-1}(4/3),$$

but for the point $(-3, -4)$,

$$r = 5, \quad \theta = \pi + \mathrm{Tan}^{-1}(4/3).$$

Because of the ambiguity of the expression $\theta = \tan^{-1}(y/x)$, it is generally best to determine $\theta$ from the formulas

$$\sin \theta = y/r, \quad \cos \theta = x/r.$$

Using Equations (1), we can easily transform the equation of a curve from rectangular coordinates into polar coordinates, and using Equations (2) we can transform the equation of a curve from polar coordinates into rectangular coordinates.

---

*Example 13.3a.* Transform the equation $x^2 + y^2 = 4x$ into polar coordinates.

We have

$$(r \cos \theta)^2 + (r \sin \theta)^2 = 4r \cos \theta,$$

or

$$r^2(\cos^2 \theta + \sin^2 \theta) = 4r \cos \theta.$$

Since $r \neq 0$, in general, we may divide both sides of the equation by $r$ to give

$$r = 4 \cos \theta.$$

The reader should sketch the curve, which is a circle passing through the origin and having its center at $(2, 0)$ in rectangular coordinates. Note that $(0, \pi/2)$ satisfies the last equation, so that the origin is not omitted when the factor $r$ is divided out.

---

*Example 13.3b.* Transform the equation $r = 2 \cos 2\theta$ into rectangular coordinates

We first rewrite $\cos 2\theta$ in terms of $\cos \theta$ and $\sin \theta$ to get

$$r = 2(\cos^2 \theta - \sin^2 \theta),$$

or

$$r^3 = 2(r^2 \cos^2 \theta - r^2 \sin^2 \theta).$$

Thus, we have

$$\pm (x^2 + y^2)^{3/2} = 2(x^2 - y^2),$$

or

$$(x^2 + y^2)^3 = 4(x^2 - y^2)^2.$$

---

As the last example suggests, many curves can be described much more simply in polar coordinates than in rectangular coordinates.

Although in the preceding discussions we have used only one metric—the euclidean distance between two points—it is worth noting that other metrics are useful in certain advanced applications of mathematics such as the theory of relativity, as well as in more advanced mathematics itself. In general, a metric is a quantity that has certain distance-like properties and is defined in the following manner.

**Definition 13.3a.** Let $s$ be a nonnegative function of the coordinates of two points $A$ and $B$ in the space $\mathcal{V}_2$. If $s(A, B)$ is a real number associated with $A$ and $B$, and if

(a) $s(A, B) = 0 \Leftrightarrow A = B$  (Axiom of identity),
(b) $s(A, B) = s(B, A)$  (Axiom of symmetry),
(c) $s(A, B) + s(B, C) \geq s(A, C)$  (Axiom of triangular inequality),

for all points $A$, $B$, and $C$ in $\mathcal{V}_2$, then $s$ is called a **metric** on the space $\mathcal{V}_2$.

---

*Example 13.3c.* Let $s$ denote a function of the points $A$ and $B$ in the space $\mathcal{V}_2$, and let

$$s(A, B) = 0 \quad \text{if } A = B.$$
$$s(A, B) = 1 \quad \text{if } A \neq B.$$

Show that $s$ is a metric on the space $\mathcal{V}_2$.

To show that $s$ is a metric as required, we must show that $s$ satisfies the three conditions of Definition 13.3a. Clearly, (a) is satisfied, since $s(A, B) = 0$ if $A = B$, and $s(A, B) \neq 0$ if $A \neq B$. Moreover, $s(A, B) = 1$ if $A \neq B$, and $s(B, A) = 1$ if $B \neq A$. Thus, (b) is satisfied. Similarly, it is easily verified that (c) holds, since if $A$, $B$, $C$ are all distinct, the left side of (c) has the value 2 and the right side has the value 1. The reader may verify that (c) also holds if $A$, $B$, $C$ are not all different. This verification completes the demonstration that $s$ is a metric on the space.

## Exercises 13.3

Determine polar coordinates for each of the points given in rectangular coordinates in Numbers 1 to 3.

1. $(-3, 4)$; $(-7, -12)$; $(2, -2)$.
2. $(2, 1)$; $(-2, 1)$; $(-2, -1)$.
3. $(1, -1)$; $(-1, 1)$; $(-1, -1)$.

Determine rectangular coordinates for each of the points given in polar coordinates in Numbers 4 to 7.

4. $(5, \pi/6)$; $(-5, \pi/6)$; $(5, -\pi/6)$.
5. $(1, 3\pi/2)$; $(1, -\pi/2)$; $(-1, \pi/2)$.
6. $(2, \pi/4)$; $(-2, -\pi/4)$; $(2, 3\pi/4)$.
7. $(-3, 2\pi/3)$; $(3, 8\pi/3)$; $(3, 14\pi/3)$.

Transform the equation in each of Numbers 8 to 11 into polar coordinates, and sketch the curve.

8. $x^2 + y^2 - 2x + 4y = 0$.
9. $y^2 = 4x$.
10. $x^2 - y^2 = 4$.

11. $y = \dfrac{x}{x^2 + 1}$.

Transform the equation in each of Numbers 12 to 16 into rectangular coordinates.

12. $r^2 = 4 \cos 2\theta$.

13. $r = 2 \sin \theta$.

14. $r = 3 \cos \theta + 4 \sin \theta$.

15. $r = \cos 3\theta$.

16. $r^2 = \sin \theta$.

17. Find the coordinate curves for the *uv*-coordinate system determined by the transformation

$$\begin{cases} x = u + v, \\ y = u - v. \end{cases}$$

18. Find the distance formula for the transformation in Number 17.

19. The set of points $\{(2, \theta)\}$ is a coordinate curve in polar coordinates. What is the equation of this curve in rectangular coordinates?

20. The set of points $\{(r, 3)\}$ is a coordinate curve in polar coordinates. What is the equation of this curve in rectangular coordinates?

★21. Let $s$ denote a function of the points $A(x_1, y_1)$, $B(x_2, y_2)$, where

$$s^2 = |x_1x_2 + y_1y_2|.$$

Is $s$ a metric on the space $\mathcal{V}_2$? Explain.

★22. Show that $s(A, B) . = . |u_2 - u_1| + |v_2 - v_1|$ is a metric for a space in which the coordinates are $u$ and $v$. This would be a proper definition of distance on a checkerboard if the pieces were allowed to move horizontally or vertically but not diagonally. If $u$ and $v$ are taken as ordinary rectangular coordinates, describe the set of points at "distance" 2 from the origin.

## 13.4 CURVES IN POLAR COORDINATES

Of the various possible coordinate systems, the polar coordinate system is one of the most useful. For instance, it is clear from the preceding section that some sets of points can be described more simply in polar than in rectangular coordinates. As an illustration of this fact, note that the circle described by $x^2 + y^2 = 4$ is given in polar coordinates by $r = 2$.

In some cases, the graph of an equation in polar coordinates can be determined from information about the curve in rectangular coordinates. For example, the equation

$$x^2 - 2x + y^2 = 0$$

can be put into the form

$$(x - 1)^2 + y^2 = 1,$$

from which it is easily seen that the graph is a circle of radius 1 with its center at $(1, 0)$. If the equation is changed into polar coordinates, we get

$$r^2 \cos^2 \theta - 2r \cos \theta + r^2 \sin^2 \theta = 0,$$

or

$$r^2 = 2r \cos \theta,$$

and since $r \neq 0$, in general, we get

$$r = 2 \cos \theta,$$

which describes the circle in polar coordinates. Thus, simply knowing from what form in rectangular coordinates a given equation in polar coordinates is obtained may be sufficient information to determine the graph of the curve.

Information obtained in this way will, of course, not always be helpful, so that we must work directly with the equation in polar coordinates. Frequently, enough information on which to base a sketch of the curve can be obtained from quite simple considerations. It is convenient to regard the system of polar coordinates as being superimposed on a system of rectangular coordinates with the pole at the origin and the polar axis along the positive $x$-axis. The points where the curve cuts the $x$- and $y$-axes are then found by putting the values $n\pi/2$, $n = 0, \pm1, \pm2, \ldots$, for $\theta$ into the equation and calculating the corresponding values of $r$. If trigonometric functions are involved in the equation, the variation in the values of these functions is often useful information in drawing the sketch. This will be illustrated in the examples at the end of this section.

In discussing a curve in polar coordinates, it is often helpful to determine if any simple symmetry exists. As in rectangular coordinates, the principal references for symmetry are the axes and the origin. Unfortunately, the discussion of symmetry in polar coordinates is somewhat more complicated than in rectangular coordinates because of the lack of uniqueness in the polar coordinates of a given point.

Suppose we wish to examine an equation $r = f(\theta)$ to determine if its graph is symmetric relative to the $y$-axis. Then, as shown in Figure 13.4a, if $P(r, \theta)$ is a

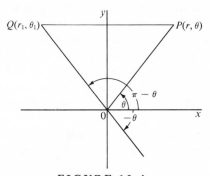

**FIGURE 13.4a**

point on the graph, and if the graph is symmetric relative to the $y$-axis, then there is a second point $Q(r_1, \theta_1)$ on the graph located so that the $y$-axis is the perpendicular bisector of the line segment $PQ$. Conversely, if for each point $P$ there is such a corresponding symmetric point $Q$, then the graph of $r = f(\theta)$ is symmetric relative to the $y$-axis. In terms of the coordinates of $P$, the only possible coordinates of $Q$ are $(r, \pi - \theta + 2n\pi)$ or $(-r, -\theta + 2n\pi)$, $n \in \mathcal{I}$. Consequently, such symmetry exists if the equation reduces to its original form when $r, \theta)$ is replaced by $(r_1, \theta_1)$, where, for some integer $n$, either

$$r_1 = r \quad \text{and} \quad \theta_1 = \pi - \theta + 2n\pi,$$

or

$$r_1 = -r \quad \text{and} \quad \theta_1 = -\theta + 2n\pi.$$

This means that whenever the point $(r, \theta)$ is on the graph of the equation, the point $(r_1, \theta_1)$ is also on the graph, since the equation is satisfied by $(r_1, \theta_1)$ whenever it is satisfied by $(r, \theta)$.

For illustration, consider the equation $r = a \sin 2\theta$. Replacing $(r, \theta)$ by $(r, \pi - \theta)$, we get

$$\begin{aligned} r &= a \sin 2(\pi - \theta) \\ &= a \sin (2\pi - 2\theta) \\ &= a \sin (-2\theta), \end{aligned}$$

or

$$r = -a \sin 2\theta,$$

which is not the original equation. But, if we replace $(r, \theta)$ by $(-r, -\theta)$, we obtain

$$\begin{aligned} -r &= a \sin 2(-\theta) \\ &= a \sin (-2\theta) \\ &= -a \sin 2\theta, \end{aligned}$$

or

$$r = a \sin 2\theta,$$

which is the original equation. Hence, the graph is symmetric with respect to the $y$-axis. Note that only one of the possible sets of coordinates for the point symmetric to $(r, \theta)$ actually works in the symmetry test in this example.

Exactly the same considerations as in the preceding discussion will serve to examine the equation for symmetry of its graph relative to the $x$-axis or to the origin. Thus, for symmetry relative to the $x$-axis, the equation should reduce to its original form after substitution for $(r, \theta)$ of one of the sets $(r, -\theta + 2n\pi$ or $(-r, \pi - \theta + 2n\pi)$. Similarly, for symmetry with respect to the origin, we try substituting for $(r, \theta)$ one of the sets $(-r, \theta + 2n\pi)$ or $(r, \pi + \theta + 2n\pi)$. This symmetry is present if, for some $n \in \mathcal{G}$ one of these substitutions reduces the equation to its original form.

Sometimes, useful information can be obtained from the derivative, $D_\theta r$. As we shall soon see, however, $D_\theta r$ does *not* give the slope of the curve so that we can use it directly to get only relative maximum and minimum values of $r$. Nevertheless, we can find the slope in terms of polar coordinates by making use of the equations of transformation from rectangular to polar coordinates:

$$x = r \cos \theta, \quad y = r \sin \theta.$$

Since $r = f(\theta)$, it follows that

$$\begin{aligned} D_\theta x &= (D_\theta r) \cos \theta - r \sin \theta, \\ D_\theta y &= (D_\theta r) \sin \theta + r \cos \theta, \end{aligned}$$

so that

$$\tan \alpha = D_x y = \frac{D_\theta y}{D_\theta x} = \frac{(D_\theta r) \sin \theta + r \cos \theta}{(D_\theta r) \cos \theta - r \sin \theta},$$

where $\alpha$ is the angle from the $x$-axis to the tangent line, measured in a counter-clockwise sense.

The preceding formula indicates that if $r \to 0$ as $\theta \to \theta_0$, then $\tan \alpha \to \tan \theta_0$. That is, if $D_\theta r$ is a continuous function of $\theta$, then *the tangent lines to the curve at the origin are given by the values of $\theta$ for which $r = 0$.*

---

*Example 13.4a.* Discuss and sketch the graph of the equation $r = a \cos 2\theta$.

(1) The points where the curve cuts the axes are indicated in the following table.

| $\theta$ | 0 | $\pi/2$ | $\pi$ | $3\pi/2$ |
|---|---|---|---|---|
| $r$ | $a$ | $-a$ | $a$ | $-a$ |

(2) Since $\cos(-2\theta) = \cos 2\theta$, substitution of $(r, -\theta)$ for $(r, \theta)$ leaves the equation unchanged. Hence the curve is symmetric with respect to the $x$-axis. Furthermore, substitution of $(r, \pi - \theta)$ also leaves the equation unchanged, since $\cos(2\pi - 2\theta) = \cos 2\theta$. Therefore, the graph is symmetric relative to the $y$-axis. Being symmetric to both axes, the graph must be symmetric with respect to the origin.

(3) By putting $r = 0$, we get $\theta = \pi/4$, $3\pi/4$, $5\pi/4$, and $7\pi/4$ as the directions in which the curve passes through the origin.

(4) As $\theta$ increases from 0 to $\pi/4$, $\cos 2\theta$ decreases from 1 to 0. As $\theta$ increases from $\pi/4$ to $\pi/2$, $\cos \theta$ decreases from 0 to $-1$. The symmetries found in (2) will enable us to construct the remainder of the curve from the portion described as $\theta$ varies from 0 to $\pi/2$.

(5) Since $D_\theta r = -2a \sin 2\theta$, we find

$$D_x y = \frac{-2 \sin 2\theta \sin \theta + \cos 2\theta \cos \theta}{-2 \sin 2\theta \cos \theta - \cos 2\theta \sin \theta}.$$

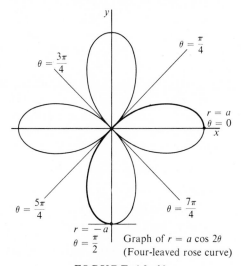

Graph of $r = a \cos 2\theta$
(Four-leaved rose curve)

**FIGURE 13.4b**

At the point where $\theta = \pi/2$, this gives $D_x y = 0$, so that the curve has a horizontal tangent at $(-a, \pi/2)$. As $\theta \to 0^+$, $D_x y \to \infty$, so that the curve has a vertical tangent at $(a, 0)$.

Figure 13.4b shows the graph as constructed from the preceding information.

---

*Example 13.4b.* Sketch the graph of $r = 1 + 2 \cos \theta$.

(1) The points where the curve cuts the axes are given in the following table.

| $\theta$ | 0 | $\pi/2$ | $\pi$ | $3\pi/2$ |
|---|---|---|---|---|
| $r$ | 3 | 1 | $-1$ | 1 |

(2) Since $\cos(-\theta) = \cos \theta$, the curve is symmetric relative to the $x$-axis. The reader may show that no other simple symmetry exists.

(3) By setting $r = 0$, we obtain $\theta = 2\pi/3$ and $\theta = 4\pi/3$ as the directions in which the curve passes through the origin.

(4) As $\theta$ increases from 0 to $\pi$, $r$ decreases from 3 to $-1$. The remainder of the curve will be determined by the symmetry found in (2).

(5) From $D_\theta r = -2 \sin \theta$, we obtain

$$D_x y = \frac{-2 \sin^2 \theta + (1 + 2 \cos \theta) \cos \theta}{-2 \sin \theta \cos \theta - (1 + 2 \cos \theta) \sin \theta}$$

$$= -\frac{\cos \theta + 2 \cos 2\theta}{\sin \theta + 2 \sin 2\theta}.$$

This result shows that $D_x y \to \infty$ as $\theta \to 0^+$ and as $\theta \to \pi^-$. Hence the curve has vertical tangents at the points where $\theta = 0$, $r = 3$ and $\theta = \pi$, $r = -1$.

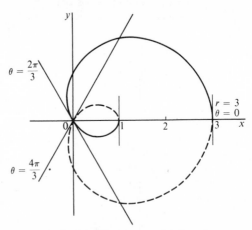

Graph of the Limaçon $r = 1 + 2 \cos \theta$

**FIGURE 13.4c**

With the preceding information, the graph may be sketched to give the curve shown in Figure 13.4c.

*Example 13.4c.* Discuss and sketch the curve $r^2 = 4 \cos 2\theta$.

(1) We see from the equation that $r = \pm 2$ for $\theta = 0$ or $\theta = \pi$, and that $r$ is imaginary for $\theta = \pi/2$ or $\theta = 3\pi/2$.

(2) Since $(-r, \theta)$ and $(r, -\theta)$ both satisfy the equation whenever $(r, \theta)$ does, the curve is symmetric relative to the origin and both axes. This symmetry enables us to confine our further attention to first-quadrant values of $\theta$.

(3) By setting $r = 0$, we find that the tangents to the curve at the origin are $\theta = \pm \pi/4$.

(4) From the variation in the values of the cosine function, we see that as $\theta$ increases from 0 to $\pi/4$, $r$ decreases from 2 to 0. Since $\cos 2\theta$ is negative for $\pi/4 < 0 \le \pi/2$, $r$ is imaginary and the first-quadrant portion of the curve is thus restricted to values of $\theta$ such that $0 \le \theta \le \pi/4$.

(5) It is possible in this problem to obtain additional information by examining the slope of the curve. Since $r^2 = 4 \cos 2\theta$, we find

$$2r \, D_\theta r = -8 \sin 2\theta, \quad D_\theta r = -\frac{4 \sin 2\theta}{r}, \quad r \ne 0.$$

Thus,

$$\tan \alpha = \frac{-\dfrac{4 \sin 2\theta}{r} \sin \theta + r \cos \theta}{-\dfrac{4 \sin 2\theta}{r} \cos \theta - r \sin \theta}$$

$$= \frac{-4 \sin 2\theta \sin \theta + r^2 \cos \theta}{-4 \sin 2\theta \cos \theta - r^2 \sin \theta}$$

$$= \frac{-4 \sin 2\theta \sin \theta + 4 \cos 2\theta \cos \theta}{-4 \sin 2\theta \cos \theta - 4 \cos 2\theta \sin \theta}$$

$$= \frac{\cos 3\theta}{\sin 3\theta}.$$

It follows that the curve will have horizontal tangents at the points where $\cos 3\theta = 0$ or $\theta = \pi/6$, $r = \sqrt{2}$. Similarly, there will be vertical tangents where $\sin 3\theta = 0$ or $\theta = 0$, $r = 2$.

All of the preceding information has been translated into the graph shown in Figure 13.4d.

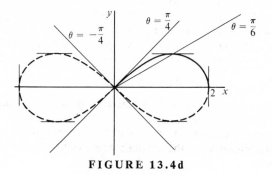

**FIGURE 13.4d**

## Exercises 13.4

In each of Numbers 1 to 12, transform the given equation into rectangular coordinates
Then identify and sketch the curve.

1. $r \sin \theta = -2$.
2. $r \cos \theta = 3$.
3. $r = 5$.
4. $\theta = 3\pi/4$.
5. $r = 4 \cos \theta$.
6. $r + 2 \sin \theta = 0$.

7. $r = \cos \theta + \sin \theta$.
8. $r = 3 \cos \theta - 4 \sin \theta$.
9. $r(\cos \theta - \sin \theta) = 2$.
10. $r(3 \cos \theta + 4 \sin \theta) = 10$.
11. $r^2 - 2\sqrt{2}r(\cos \theta + \sin \theta) = 8$.
12. $r^2 - 4r \cos (\theta - \pi/3) = 6$.

In each of Numbers 13 to 26, discuss the given equation and sketch its graph. You
should calculate the slope in order to find where the curve has vertical or horizonta
tangents.

13. $r - 2 = \sin \theta$.
14. $r = 1 - 2 \sin \theta$.
15. $r = 3 - 6 \cos \theta$.
16. $r = 2 + 3 \sin \theta$.
17. $r = 3 + 2 \cos \theta$.
18. $r = 3 \sin 2\theta$.
19. $r = \sin 4\theta$.

20. $r = 2 \cos 3\theta$.
21. $r = 5 \cos 2\theta$.
22. $r = 2(1 + \sin \theta)$.
23. $r = 4(1 - \cos \theta)$.
24. $r^2 = \sin \theta$.
25. $r = \sin^2 \theta$.
26. $r = \sin^2 2\theta$.

In each of Numbers 27 to 34, sketch the graph of the given equation.

27. $r = 3 \cos (2\theta - \pi/3)$.
28. $r \sin (\theta + \pi/4) = 4$.
29. $r^2 = \sin 2\theta$.
30. $r\theta = 1$ (Hyperbolic Spiral).

31. $r = \theta$ (Spiral of Archimedes).
32. $r = e^\theta$ (Logarithmic Spiral).
33. $r = \ln \theta$.
34. $r = \sec^2 \theta$.

35. Transform the equation

$$(x^2 + y^2)^2 = x^3 - 3xy^2$$

into polar coordinates. Then discuss and sketch the curve.

36. Show that the equation

$$r^2 - 2br \cos (\theta - \alpha) = c$$

describes a circle with center at $(b, \alpha)$ if $b^2 + c > 0$. Find the radius of the circle

37. Find an equation of the set of points each of which is $k$ times as far from th
origin as from the point $(a, 0)$. If $k \neq 1$, use Number 36 to show that the set c
points is a circle. Find the center and the radius.

38. Transform the equation $y = mx + b$ into polar coordinates and write the resu
in the form $r = f(\theta)$. Let $m = \tan \alpha$, and show that

$$r = b \cos \alpha \csc (\theta - \alpha).$$

39. Transform the equation $y = mx$ into polar coordinates. If $m = \tan \alpha$, what is th
relationship between $\alpha$ and $\theta$?

40. Find the slope of the curve $r = 1 + \cos \theta$ at the point where $\theta = \pi/3$.

41. Find the polar coordinates of the points where the curve $r = a \sin 2\theta$ has hor
zontal tangents.

In each of Numbers 42 to 47, find the points of intersection of the given curves and sketch the graphs.

42. $r = 2 \sin \theta$, $r^2 = 4 \cos 2\theta$.

43. $r \cos \theta = 2$, $r = 4$.

44. $r = \cos \theta$, $r = \cos 2\theta$.

45. $r = \cos \theta$, $r^2 = \cos 2\theta$.

46. $r = 3a \cos \theta$, $r = a(1 + \cos \theta)$.

47. $r = 1 + \cos \theta$, $4r(1 + \cos \theta) = 1$.

## 3.5 THE CONIC SECTIONS

A special class of curves, called the conic sections because each curve in the class can be obtained geometrically as the intersection of a cone and a plane, is particularly important in physical problems concerning such things as orbits, trajectories, telescopes, and radar. This class of curves includes the circle, the parabola, the hyperbola, and the ellipse. These curves were briefly treated in Section 3.6.

The conic sections are completely characterized by a simple geometric property of the type discussed in Section 13.1. A conic section can be described as a set of points such that *the distance of each point of the set from a certain fixed point is in a constant ratio to its directed distance from a fixed line.* If a polar coordinate system is chosen so that the origin is at the fixed point and the polar axis is perpendicular to the fixed line at a distance $p$ from the origin, then the set of points $\{P(x, y)\}$ for which

$$\frac{OP}{DP} = e$$

a conic section (see Figure 13.5a).

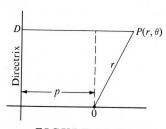

**FIGURE 13.5a**

The fixed line is called a **directrix**, the fixed point is a **focus** and the constant ratio $e$ is called the **eccentricity** of the conic section. Since

$$OP = r,$$

and

$$DP = p + r \cos \theta,$$

the equation of the curve in polar coordinates is

$$\frac{r}{p + r \cos \theta} = e,$$

or

$$r = \frac{ep}{1 - e \cos \theta}.$$

Curves described by this equation are of three types according to the value of $e$. If $e < 1$, the curve is an *ellipse*, if $e = 1$, the curve is a *parabola*, and if $e > 1$, the curve is a *hyperbola*. It will be evident later that these definitions are consistent with those given in Section 3.6.

If $e < 1$, the denominator $1 - e \cos \theta$ can never be 0. Hence, $r$ is defined for every value of $\theta$. Moreover,

$$D_\theta r = \frac{-e^2 p \sin \theta}{(1 - e \cos \theta)^2},$$

and $D_\theta r = 0$ if $\sin \theta = 0$. It is easy to see that $r$ has a relative maximum value of $ep/(1 - e)$ when $\theta = 0$, and a relative minimum value of $ep/(1 + e)$ when $\theta = \pi$. The points $V_1(ep/(1 - e), 0)$ and $V_2(ep/(1 + e), \pi)$ are called the **vertices** of the ellipse. Furthermore, since the point $(r, -\theta)$ satisfies the equation of the curve whenever $(r, \theta)$ does, the curve is symmetric about the polar axis. There is no value of $\theta$ for which $r = 0$, so that the curve does not pass through the origin (Figure 13.5b).

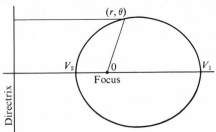

**FIGURE 13.5b**

When $e = 1$, the equation of the curve, a parabola, becomes

$$r = \frac{p}{1 - \cos \theta}.$$

At $\theta = 0$, $r$ is undefined. For every other value of $\theta$, $0 < \theta < 2\pi$, $r$ is defined. Since

$$D_\theta r = \frac{-p \sin \theta}{(1 - \cos \theta)^2},$$

and $D_\theta r = 0$ when $\theta = \pi$ ($\theta = 0$ is excluded), $r$ has a minimum value at $\theta = \pi$ since $r$ is a decreasing function of $\theta$ for $0 < \theta < \pi$, and an increasing function for $\pi < \theta < 2\pi$. The fact that there is no value of $\theta$ such that $r = 0$, means that the curve does not pass through the origin.

The curve is symmetric about the polar axis (Figure 13.5c). The point $V(p/2, \pi)$ is the vertex of the parabola.

If $e > 1$, so that the curve is a hyperbola, we see from the equation

$$r = \frac{ep}{1 - e \cos \theta}$$

that $r$ is undefined when $\cos \theta = 1/e$. There are two values of $\theta$ between $-\pi/2$ and $\pi/2$ that satisfy this condition:

$$\theta_1 = \text{Cos}^{-1}(1/e) \quad \text{and} \quad \theta_2 = -\text{Cos}^{-1}(1/e).$$

This indicates that the curve consists of two disconnected pieces, one described when $\theta_2 < \theta < \theta_1$, and the other when $-\pi \leqq \theta < \theta_2$ or $\theta_1 < \theta \leqq \pi$. For $\theta_2 < \theta < \theta_1$, $1 - e \cos \theta < 0$, hence $r$ is negative. For $-\pi \leqq \theta < \theta_2$ and for $\theta_1 < \theta \leqq \pi$, $r$ is positive.

As $\theta \to \theta_1^-$, $r \to -\infty$ and as $\theta \to \theta_1^+$, $r \to \infty$. Similarly, as $\theta \to \theta_2^+$, $r \to -\infty$ and as $\theta \to \theta_2^-$, $r \to \infty$. Thus, the curve appears to recede from the origin in the directions of $\theta = \theta_1$ and $\theta = \theta_2$ for large values of $r$. We shall show later that the hyperbola actually has two asymptotes, in these respective directions, passing through the point $C$ midway between the vertices $V_1(ep/(1 - e), 0)$ and $V_2(ep/(1 + e), \pi)$. See Figure 13.5d. As in the case of the ellipse and the parabola, the hyperbola is symmetric about the polar axis.

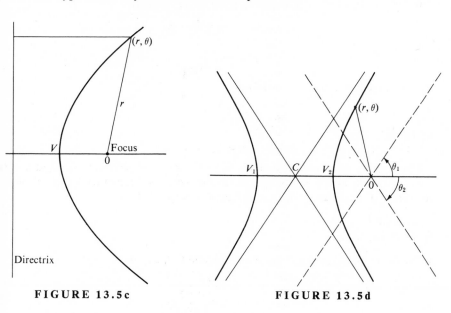

FIGURE 13.5c          FIGURE 13.5d

The circle is also a conic section and may be considered a limiting case of the form

$$r = \frac{ep}{1 - e \cos \theta},$$

in which the directrix is allowed to recede indefinitely far to the left and the eccentricity is allowed to approach zero in such a way that

$$ep \to k \quad \text{as } e \to 0,$$

since in that case

$$r \to k \quad \text{as } e \to 0,$$

and the limiting form of the equation is

$$r = k,$$

which is the equation of a circle.

The equations

$$r = \frac{ep}{1 - e \sin \theta}, \quad r = \frac{ep}{1 + e \cos \theta}, \quad r = \frac{ep}{1 + e \sin \theta}$$

can be obtained from the standard equation $r = ep/(1 - e \cos \theta)$ by replacing $\theta$ by $\pi/2 - \theta$, $\pi - \theta$, and $3\pi/2 - \theta$, respectively. Consequently, these are all equations of conic sections rotated from the position originally described through angles of $\pi/2$, $\pi$, and $3\pi/2$, respectively.

---

*Example 13.5a.* Identify the graph of the equation

$$4r \cos \theta = r - 8.$$

We first solve this equation for $r$ in terms of $\theta$ as follows:

$$r(1 - 4 \cos \theta) = 8,$$

or

$$r = \frac{8}{1 - 4 \cos \theta}.$$

By comparison with the standard form

$$r = \frac{ep}{1 - e \cos \theta},$$

we obtain

$$e = 4, \quad ep = 8, \quad \text{and} \quad p = 2.$$

The graph is therefore a hyperbola, as in Figure 13.5d, with vertices $V_1$ at $\theta = 0$ $r = -\frac{8}{3}$ and $V_2$ at $\theta = \pi$, $r = \frac{8}{5}$. The asymptotes pass through the midpoint of the segment $V_1V_2$ and are parallel to the lines $\theta = \pm \mathrm{Cos}^{-1}(1/4)$.

## Exercises 13.5

In Numbers 1 to 12, convert the given equation to the form

$$r = \frac{ep}{1 \pm e \left\{ \begin{matrix} \sin \theta \\ \cos \theta \end{matrix} \right\}},$$

identify the type of conic section and make a sketch.

1. $2r - 4 = r \sin \theta$.
2. $2r - 6 = r \cos \theta$.
3. $r - r \cos \theta = 2$.
4. $r + r \sin \theta = 5$.

5. $r = \dfrac{4}{1 - 2 \cos \theta}$.

6. $r = \dfrac{2}{\frac{1}{2} + \sin \theta}$.

7. $r = \dfrac{9}{3 + \sin \theta}$.

8. $r = \dfrac{6}{3 + \cos \theta}$.

9. $r - 5 + 2r \cos \theta = 0$.
10. $r - r \sin \theta = 3$.
11. $2r - 2 - r \sin \theta = 0$.
12. $r = \csc^2(\theta/2)$.

13. Show that any equation of the form

$$\frac{1}{r} = a + b \sin\theta \quad \text{or} \quad \frac{1}{r} = a + b \cos\theta, \qquad ab \neq 0,$$

represents a conic section. Determine the eccentricity in terms of $a$ and $b$.

14. Show that all conic sections with equations of the form

$$r = \frac{ep}{1 \pm e \cos\theta}$$

are symmetric about the polar axis.

15. Show that all conic sections with equations of the form

$$r = \frac{ep}{1 \pm e \sin\theta}$$

are symmetric about the 90° line.

16. Consider an equation of the form

$$r = \frac{ep}{1 - e \cos(\theta - \alpha)}.$$

How can this equation be interpreted geometrically?

17. Show that the slope of the parabola $r(1 - \cos\theta) = p$ is given by $\tan\alpha = \tan(\theta/2)$. For the upper half of the parabola, show that $\alpha = \theta/2$ and hence that the tangent line makes equal angles with the horizontal and with the line joining the focus to the point of tangency. This is the famous reflection property of the parabola, on which is based the construction of parabolic mirrors, parabolic reflectors, and radar antennas.

★18. Prove that the eccentricity of an ellipse is given by the formula

$$e = (r_{\max} - r_{\min})/(r_{\max} + r_{\min}),$$

where $r_{\max}$ and $r_{\min}$ are the maximum and minimum distances of the curve from one focus.

19. An artificial earth satellite describes an elliptic orbit with the center of the earth at one focus. The maximum distance of the orbit from the surface of the earth is 400 miles and the minimum distance 150 miles. Assume the earth is a sphere 4000 miles in radius, and find the eccentricity of the orbit of the satellite. (See Number 18.)

20. Show that for every focal chord of a conic section, the sum of the reciprocals of the lengths of the segments into which the focus divides the chord is $2(ep)^{-1}$.

## 13.6 THE CONIC SECTIONS IN RECTANGULAR COORDINATES

Although conic sections can be simply described in polar coordinates, it is also convenient to study them in rectangular coordinate form. If we transform the equation

$$r = \frac{ep}{1 - e \cos\theta}, \quad \text{or} \quad r = e(r \cos\theta + p)$$

into rectangular coordinates, we get

$$\pm(x^2 + y^2)^{1/2} = e(x + p),$$

or, by squaring both members and simplifying,

(1) $$x^2(1 - e^2) - 2e^2px + y^2 = e^2p^2.$$

We shall investigate the cases $e = 1$, $e < 1$, and $e > 1$ in the sections that follow.

## Exercises 13.6

1. Verify the details of the derivation of Equation (1).
2. Find the rectangular coordinate equation for

   (a) $r = \dfrac{ep}{1 + e \cos \theta}$;

   (b) $r = \dfrac{ep}{1 - e \sin \theta}$;

   (c) $r = \dfrac{ep}{1 + e \sin \theta}$.

3. Find the rectangular coordinate equation for the parabola

   $$r = p + r \cos (\theta - \alpha),$$

   then translate the origin to the vertex of the parabola and show that the resulting equation is

   $$(u \sin \alpha - v \cos \alpha)^2 = 2p(u \cos \alpha + v \sin \alpha).$$

## 13.7 THE PARABOLA

For a parabola, $e = 1$, and Equation (1) of Section 13.6 becomes

$$y^2 = e^2p^2 + 2e^2px$$

or

$$y^2 = 2p(x + p/2).$$

If the origin is then translated to $(-p/2, 0)$, the equation of the parabola takes on a characteristic form

$$Y^2 = 2pX,$$

where $X$ and $Y$ refer to the new coordinate system. The details are shown in Figure 13.7a. In the diagram, coordinates are referred to the new origin $O_n$. Thus, relative to $O_n$, the old origin $O$ is the point $(p/2, 0)$, which is the focus of the parabola.

The following example illustrates the convenience of this form.

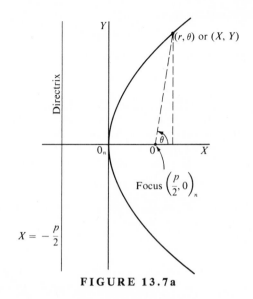

**FIGURE 13.7a**

*Example 13.7a.* Locate the directrix and focus of the curve $y^2 = 6x$.

It is sufficient to compare $y^2 = 6x$ with the general form $y^2 = 2px$, where the letters $X$ and $Y$ have been replaced by the letters $x$ and $y$. For the equation $y^2 = 6x$, we have $p = 3$, so that the focus is at $(\frac{3}{2}, 0)$ and the directrix is the line $x = -\frac{3}{2}$.

---

Let the vertex of the parabola $Y^2 = 2pX$ be at a general point $(h, k)$ with reference to an $xy$-coordinate system in which the $x$-axis is parallel to the $X$-axis and the $y$-axis is parallel to the $Y$-axis. Then

$$x = X + h \quad \text{and} \quad y = Y + k,$$

so that the equation of the curve referred to the $xy$-system is

(1) $$(y - k)^2 = 2p(x - h).$$

If the axis of the parabola is parallel to the $y$-axis rather than the $x$-axis, the roles of $X$ and $Y$ are interchanged and the equation is $X^2 = 2pY$, or in terms of the $xy$-coordinates

(2) $$(x - h)^2 = 2p(y - k).$$

These results show that a quadratic equation in $x$ and $y$ that is of the second degree in only one of the variables and includes no $xy$ term can always be put into one or the other of the standard forms given by Equations (1) and (2) simply by completing the square in the variable that occurs to the second degree.

---

*Example 13.7b.* Find the vertex, focus, and directrix of the parabola

$$x^2 + 4x + 4y = 2.$$

We write the equation in the form

$$x^2 + 4x = -4y + 2$$

and complete the square on $x$ by adding 4 to both sides to get

$$(x + 2)^2 = -4y + 6,$$

or

$$(x + 2)^2 = -4(y - \tfrac{3}{2}).$$

This equation shows that the vertex of the parabola is at the point $(-2, \tfrac{3}{2})$ and that the axis is vertical. Furthermore, the parabola opens downward and $2p = 4$, so that $p = 2$. Therefore, the focus is 1 unit below the vertex, which places it at $(-2, \tfrac{1}{2})$, and the directrix is a horizontal line 1 unit above the vertex with an equation $y = \tfrac{5}{2}$ (see Figure 13.7b).

---

*Example 13.7c.* The focus of a parabolic reflector is 2 inches from its vertex. If the reflector is 6 inches deep, what is its diameter?

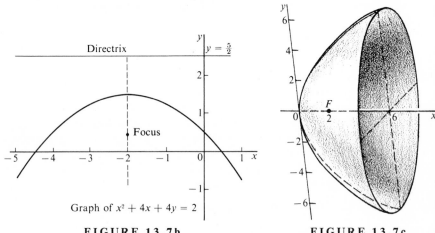

Graph of $x^2 + 4x + 4y = 2$

FIGURE 13.7b                    FIGURE 13.7c

Since the distance from the vertex to the focus is 2, we have $p/2 = 2$, or $p = 4$. If the origin is taken at the vertex, and the axis of the mirror lies along the positive $x$-axis, the equation of the parabolic section in the $xy$-plane is $y^2 = 8x$ (see Figure 13.7c). For $x = 6$, we have $y^2 = 48$, hence $y = \pm 4\sqrt{3}$. Thus, the diameter of the reflector is $8\sqrt{3}$, or approximately 13.9 inches.

## Exercises 13.7

In each of Numbers 1 to 8, find the vertex, the focus, and the directrix of the parabola and sketch the curve.

1. $x^2 = -6y$.
2. $y^2 = -4x$.
3. $4x^2 - y = 0$.
4. $x^2 - 4y = 4$.

5. $y^2 - 4x + 12 = 0$.
6. $2x^2 + 4y + 7 = 0$.
7. $y^2 + 6y + 2x + 13 = 0$.
8. $x^2 + 4x + 6y - 8 = 0$.

9. Find an equation of the set of points each of which is equidistant from the line $y = 2$ and the point $(-3, 0)$.

10. Find an equation of the set of points each of which is equidistant from the line $x = 3$ and the point $(7, -2)$.

11. Find an equation of the line that is tangent to the parabola $y^2 - 4x + 4 = 0$ at the point $(5, -4)$. Sketch the parabola and the tangent line.

12. By using the derivative, show that the maximum point of the parabola $x^2 + 4x + 4y + 8 = 0$ is at the vertex.

13. Find an equation of the line that is tangent to the parabola $(x - 2)^2 = y - 3$ at the point where the parabola intersects the $y$-axis. Sketch the parabola and the tangent line.

14. Find the area of the region bounded by the parabola $x^2 - 4x + 4y - 12 = 0$ and the $x$-axis.

15. Find the area of the region bounded by the parabola $y^2 - 4y - 4x = 0$ and the $y$-axis.

16. Find an equation of the line that is tangent to the parabola $y^2 + 6y + 2x + 7 = 0$ and parallel to the line $2x - 2y + 5 = 0$. Sketch the parabola and the tangent line.

17. Eliminate the parameter, identify, and sketch the curve $x = \cosh^2 t$, $y = 4 \sinh t$.

18. Sketch $x = \cos 2t$, $y = 2 \sin t$. Do these equations give the entire parabola? Explain.

19. Show that the two parabolas $y^2 = 4x$ and $x^2 - 3x + y = 0$ are tangent to each other at one of their common points.

★20. A tangent line is drawn at a point $P$ on the parabola $y^2 = 4px$. Let the point of intersection of the tangent line and the directrix of the parabola be $Q$, and let the focus of the parabola be $F$. Show that the lines $FP$ and $FQ$ are perpendicular to each other.

## 13.8 THE ELLIPSE

If $e \neq 1$, Equation (1) of Section 13.6 may be rewritten as

$$x^2 - \frac{2e^2p}{1 - e^2}x + \frac{y^2}{1 - e^2} = \frac{e^2p^2}{1 - e^2}.$$

Upon completing the square for the $x$ terms and simplifying, we get

$$\left(x - \frac{e^2p}{1 - e^2}\right)^2 + \frac{y^2}{1 - e^2} = \frac{e^2p^2}{(1 - e^2)^2}.$$

The coordinate system can be translated to a new origin at

$$\left(\frac{e^2p}{1 - e^2}, 0\right)$$

to obtain the simpler form

$$X^2 + \frac{Y^2}{1 - e^2} = \frac{e^2p^2}{(1 - e^2)^2},$$

or

(1)
$$\frac{X^2}{\dfrac{e^2p^2}{(1 - e^2)^2}} + \frac{Y^2}{\dfrac{e^2p^2}{1 - e^2}} = 1.$$

If $e < 1$, we let

$$a^2 = \frac{e^2 p^2}{(1 - e^2)^2} \quad \text{and} \quad b^2 = \frac{e^2 p^2}{1 - e^2}$$

to obtain the equation

$$\frac{X^2}{a^2} + \frac{Y^2}{b^2} = 1,$$

which is a characteristic form for the equation of an ellipse.

Since the letters $X$ and $Y$ have now served their purpose, we replace them by $x$ and $y$ and write the equation of the ellipse in the standard form

$$\frac{x^2}{a^2} + \frac{y^2}{b^2} = 1.$$

Notice, since $0 < 1 - e^2 < 1$, that $(1 - e^2)^2 < 1 - e^2$ and hence $a > b$. Observe also that

$$a^2(1 - e^2) = b^2,$$

or

$$a^2 = b^2 + a^2 e^2.$$

The focus is at the point

$$\left(-\frac{e^2 p}{1 - e^2}, 0\right), \quad \text{or} \quad (-ae, 0).$$

The equation of the ellipse shows that the curve is symmetric with reference to the axes and origin, so that there is also a focus at $(ae, 0)$ and a directrix corresponding to this focus. The first directrix is $p$ units to the left of the focus $(-ae, 0)$. Since

$$a = \frac{ep}{1 - e^2},$$

the directrix is the line

$$x = -ae - p = -\frac{e^2 p}{1 - e^2} - p = -\frac{p}{1 - e^2}$$

or

$$x = -\frac{a}{e}.$$

By symmetry the other directrix is the line $x = a/e$ (see Figure 13.8a). The quantities $a$ and $b$, respectively are called the **semimajor** and **semiminor** axes of the ellipse. Note the basic triangle giving the relationship of $a$, $b$, and $ae$ in the figure. Since the ellipse has a center of symmetry—the common midpoint of its axes—the curve is called a **central conic.**

---

*Example 13.8a.* Find the eccentricity and locate the vertices, foci, ends of the minor axes, and directrices of the ellipse

$$\frac{x^2}{16} + \frac{y^2}{9} = 1.$$

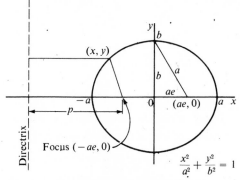

**FIGURE 13.8a**

Since $a = 4$, $b = 3$, the vertices are at $(\pm 4, 0)$, and the ends of the minor axis are are at $(0, \pm 3)$. Furthermore, $a^2e^2 = 16 - 9 = 7$, so that $e = \sqrt{7}/4$. Thus, the foci are at $(\pm\sqrt{7}, 0)$, and the directrices are the lines $x = \pm 16\sqrt{7}/7$.

---

Evidently, the same procedure may be employed to obtain the salient features of the curve if the foci lie on the $y$-axis. For instance, the ellipse

$$\frac{x^2}{9} + \frac{y^2}{16} = 1$$

is identical in shape and size to that in the preceding example, since the equation is obtained merely by interchanging $x$ and $y$, but the semimajor axis is now along the $y$-axis and the semiminor axis along the $x$-axis. Thus, the vertices are at $(0, \pm 4)$ and the foci are at the points $(0, \pm\sqrt{7})$. The directrices are the lines $y = \pm 16\sqrt{7}/7$.

---

*Example 13.8b.* Find the equation of the ellipse having an eccentricity $\frac{1}{2}$, and a focus at the point $(4, 0)$, if the center of the ellipse is at $(0, 0)$.

Since $ae = 4$ and $e = \frac{1}{2}$, then $a = 8$. Moreover, since

$$a^2 = b^2 + a^2e^2,$$

we have

$$64 = b^2 + 16, \quad \text{or} \quad b^2 = 48,$$

and $b = 4\sqrt{3}$. Hence the equation of the ellipse is

$$\frac{x^2}{64} + \frac{y^2}{48} = 1.$$

---

If the center of the ellipse is at some point $(h, k)$ rather than at the origin, the equation is obtained at once by replacing $x$ and $y$ by $x - h$ and $y - k$, respectively, in the preceding standard equations. Thus, if the major axis of the ellipse is horizontal, we get

(2)
$$\frac{(x-h)^2}{a^2} + \frac{(y-k)^2}{b^2} = 1,$$

and if the major axis is vertical,

(3)
$$\frac{(y-k)^2}{a^2} + \frac{(x-h)^2}{b^2} = 1.$$

A quadratic equation of the form
$$Ax^2 + Cy^2 + Dx + Ey + F = 0,$$

where $AC > 0$, can always be put into the form
$$A(x-h)^2 + C(y-k)^2 = G$$

by completing the squares in $x$ and $y$. If $A$, $C$, and $G$ are all of the same sign, then the equation may be written
$$\frac{(x-h)^2}{G/A} + \frac{(y-k)^2}{G/C} = 1,$$

which is of the form (2) or (3). If the sign of $G$ is opposite that of $A$ and $C$, the equation is satisfied by no real points, and if $G = 0$, the equation is satisfied only by the point $(h, k)$. It is customary to describe the last two cases as **degenerate**.

---

*Example 13.8c.* Sketch the curve $9x^2 + y^2 - 36x + 8y + 43 = 0$, and find the foci

By completing the square on the $x$ terms and the $y$ terms, we get
$$9(x^2 - 4x + 4) + (y^2 + 8y + 16) = -43 + 36 + 16 = 9,$$

or

$$(x-2)^2 + \frac{(y+4)^2}{9} = 1,$$

or by putting $u = x - 2$, $v = y + 4$,

$$u^2 + \frac{v^2}{9} = 1.$$

This equation describes an ellipse with its center at $(2, -4)$ in $xy$-coordinates. Since $a = 3$ and $b = 1$, then $9 = 1 + 9e^2$ and $e = 2\sqrt{2}/3$. Hence the foci are on the $v$-axis at the points $(0, \pm 2\sqrt{2})_n$ or at the points $(2, -4 \pm 2\sqrt{2})$ in the $xy$-coordinate system (see Figure 13.8b).

## Exercises 13.8

In each of Numbers 1 to 8, find the eccentricity, the foci, and the directrices, and sketch the curve.

1. $x^2 + 16y^2 = 16$.
2. $9x^2 + 4y^2 = 36$.
3. $x^2 + 4y^2 - 6x + 5 = 0$.
4. $4x^2 + 9y^2 + 18y - 27 = 0$.

5. $9x^2 + 4y^2 + 18x - 8y + 4 = 0$.
6. $x = a \cos\theta$, $y = b \sin\theta$.
7. $x^2 + 4y^2 + 2x + 40y + 97 = 0$.
8. $3x^2 + y^2 + 24x + 2y = 0$.

9. Find an equation of the line that is tangent to the ellipse $x^2 + 4y^2 = 4$ at the point $(1, -\sqrt{3}/2)$. Sketch the ellipse and the tangent line.

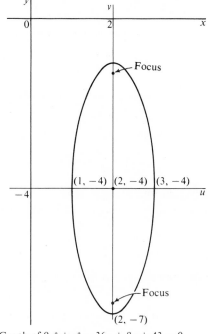

Graph of $9x^2 + y^2 - 36x + 8y + 43 = 0$

**FIGURE 13.8b**

10. Find the equation of the ellipse with vertices at $(-6, 3)$ and $(-1, 3)$ and with one focus at $(-2, 3)$.

11. Find an equation of the set of points such that the sum of the distances from any point of the set to the points $(-2, 2)$ and $(-2, 6)$ is equal to 6.

12. Show for an ellipse that the length of the chord that passes through a focus and is perpendicular to the major axis is $2b^2/a$.

13. An arch in the shape of half an ellipse has a base width of 20 feet and a height of 15 feet. What is the height of the arch at a horizontal distance of 5 feet from the center of the base?

⋆14. Show that the two focal radii (lines from the two foci) of an ellipse to a point on the curve make equal angles with the tangent line at the point.

⋆15. Is it possible for the focal radii to a point on an ellipse to be perpendicular to each other? Explain.

⋆16. If two curves have equations $f(x, y) = 0$ and $g(x, y) = 0$, respectively, then for each pair of values of $m$ and $n$, the equation

$$mf(x, y) + ng(x, y) = 0$$

represents a curve that passes through the intersections (if there are any) of the original two curves. Explain why. This idea should suggest a very easy way of writing an equation of the circle that passes through the intersections of the two ellipses

$$b^2x^2 + a^2y^2 = a^2b^2 \quad \text{and} \quad a^2x^2 + b^2y^2 = a^2b^2.$$

Do you see it?

## 13.9 THE HYPERBOLA

If $e > 1$, then in Equation (1) of the preceding section, we let

$$b^2 = \frac{e^2 p^2}{e^2 - 1},$$

and

$$a^2 = \frac{e^2 p^2}{(1 - e^2)^2}.$$

The equation then takes the form

$$\frac{X^2}{a^2} - \frac{Y^2}{b^2} = 1,$$

which is a characteristic form for the hyperbola.

As in the case of the ellipse, we drop the capital letters and use the standard form

$$\frac{x^2}{a^2} - \frac{y^2}{b^2} = 1.$$

Since the hyperbola is symmetric about the axes and the origin is a center of symmetry, the curve is also a central conic. Furthermore, we have

$$a^2(1 - e)^2 = -b^2,$$

or

$$a^2 + b^2 = a^2 e^2.$$

The focus is at the point $(ae, 0)$, and by symmetry there is also a focus at $(-ae, 0)$. There is a directrix $p$ units to the left of $(ae, 0)$, so that its equation is

$$x = ae - p,$$

or, as in the case of the ellipse,

$$x = \frac{a}{e}.$$

By symmetry, the other directrix is $x = -a/e$.

From the equation of the curve, it is easily seen that there are $x$-intercepts at $\pm a$ and that there are no $y$-intercepts. The $x$-axis, which is cut at two points by the curve, is called the **transverse axis** of the hyperbola. Note also that as $x \to \infty$, $y \to \infty$, and if we consider the equation in the form

$$\frac{b^2}{a^2} - \frac{y^2}{x^2} = \frac{b^2}{x^2},$$

we see that as $x \to \infty$,

$$\left(\frac{y}{x}\right)^2 \to \left(\frac{b}{a}\right)^2.$$

This indicates that the two lines $y = (b/a)x$ and $y = -(b/a)x$ obtained from

$$\left(\frac{y}{x}\right)^2 - \left(\frac{b}{a}\right)^2 = \left(\frac{y}{x} - \frac{b}{a}\right)\left(\frac{y}{x} + \frac{b}{a}\right) = 0$$

are asymptotes to the hyperbola. The details are shown in Figure 13.9a.

---

*Example 13.9a.* Discuss and sketch the curve $9y^2 - 16x^2 = 144$.

By dividing both sides by 144, we may write the given equation in the form

$$\frac{y^2}{16} - \frac{x^2}{9} = 1.$$

This is in the standard form for the equation of a hyperbola with its transverse axis along the $y$-axis. From this equation, we have $a = 4$, $b = 3$, so that

$$a^2e^2 = a^2 + b^2 = 25 \quad \text{and} \quad ae = 5.$$

Thus, the vertices are at $(0, \pm 4)$ and the foci at $(0, \pm 5)$.

The asymptotes are most easily obtained by equating to zero the two factors of the left side of the equation. Thus, we get

$$\frac{y}{4} - \frac{x}{3} = 0 \quad \text{and} \quad \frac{y}{4} + \frac{x}{3} = 0$$

as equations for these asymptotes.

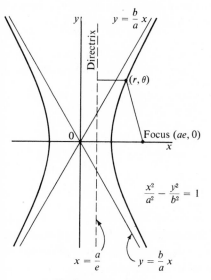

FIGURE 13.9a

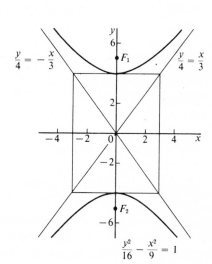

FIGURE 13.9b

The preceding information is an adequate basis on which to construct a good sketch of the curve (see Figure 13.9b). Notice the basic rectangle relating $a$, $b$, $ae$, and the asymptotes.

---

We may write the equation for a hyperbola with its center at $(h, k)$ in the form

(1)
$$\frac{(x - h)^2}{a^2} - \frac{(y - k)^2}{b^2} = 1$$

if the transverse axis is parallel to the *x*-axis, and in the form

(2)
$$\frac{(y - k)^2}{a^2} - \frac{(x - h)^2}{b^2} = 1$$

if the transverse axis is parallel to the *y*-axis.

---

*Example 13.9b.* Sketch the curve $9x^2 - y^2 - 36x + 8y - 5 = 0$. Find the foci, the vertices, and the asymptotes.

By completing the squares in *x* and *y*, we find

$$9(x^2 - 4x + 4) - (y^2 - 8y + 16) = 5 + 36 - 16 = 25,$$

or

(3)
$$\frac{(x - 2)^2}{25/9} - \frac{(y - 4)^2}{25} = 1.$$

Thus, the curve is a hyperbola with its center at (2, 4) and its transverse axis parallel to the *x*-axis.

We have $a = \frac{5}{3}$ and $b = 5$, so that

$$a^2e^2 = \frac{25}{9} + 25 = \frac{250}{9} \quad \text{and} \quad ae = \frac{5\sqrt{10}}{3}.$$

Accordingly, the foci are at the points $(2 + 5\sqrt{10}/3, 4)$ and $(2 - 5\sqrt{10}/3, 4)$. The vertices are at $(\frac{11}{3}, 4)$ and $(\frac{1}{3}, 4)$.

The asymptotes are obtainable in a manner similar to that used in Example 13.9b; that is, by factoring the left side of Equation (3) and setting each factor equal to zero. Thus, we get

$$\frac{x - 2}{5/3} - \frac{y - 4}{5} = 0 \quad \text{and} \quad \frac{x - 2}{5/3} + \frac{y - 4}{5} = 0,$$

or

$$3x - y = 2 \quad \text{and} \quad 3x + y = 10$$

as the required equations (see Figure 13.9c).

---

By using the method of completing the square we may write the equation $Ax^2 + Cy^2 + Dx + Ey + F = 0$, where $AC < 0$, in the form

$$\alpha^2(x - h)^2 - \beta^2(y - k)^2 = \delta.$$

If $\delta \neq 0$, this can be written in one of the standard forms (1) or (2) of the hyperbola. If $\delta = 0$, this is an equation of a pair of straight lines,

$$\alpha(x - h) = \beta(y - k) \quad \text{and} \quad \alpha(x - h) = -\beta(y - k),$$

passing through the point $(h, k)$. The latter case is usually described as being the **degenerate case** of the hyperbola.

In the preceding section we noted the so-called degenerate case of the ellipse. For the parabola, we begin with an equation such as

$$Ax^2 + Dx + Ey + F = 0.$$

If $AE \neq 0$, then this equation actually represents a parabola. If $E = 0$ and $A \neq 0$, then the equation may represent a pair of parallel lines, a single line (counted twice as in $(x + 2)^2 = 0$), or it may be satisfied by no real values of $x$ (as $x^2 + 2x + 2 = 0$). These are all called degenerate cases of the parabola.

It follows from the preceding discussion that the equation

$$Ax^2 + Cy^2 + Dx + Ey + F = 0$$

always represents a conic section or one of the degenerate conics. Conversely, the reader should already have noted that every conic whose principal axis is parallel to one of the coordinate axes has an equation of this general form.

*Example 13.9c.* An alternate definition of the hyperbola is frequently stated as follows: *The hyperbola is the set of points such that the difference of the distances from any point of the set to two given points (the foci) is a constant.* Let the foci be at $(ae, 0)$ and $(-ae, 0)$, $e > 1$, and let the difference of the distances be $2a$. Show that this results in the standard equation of the hyperbola with its center at the origin.

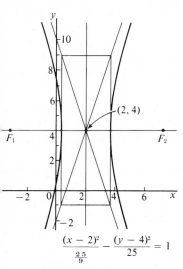

$$\frac{(x - 2)^2}{\frac{25}{9}} - \frac{(y - 4)^2}{25} = 1$$

**FIGURE 13.9c**

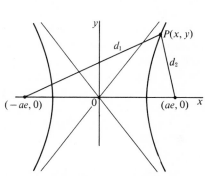

**FIGURE 13.9d**

In Figure 13.9d, $P(x, y)$ represents any point in the required set. Accordingly, we must have

$$|d_1 - d_2| = 2a,$$

or

$$\sqrt{(x + ae)^2 + y^2} - \sqrt{(x - ae)^2 + y^2} = \pm 2a,$$

where the plus or minus depends on whether $d_1 > d_2$ or $d_1 < d_2$. We rewrite the equation in the form

$$\sqrt{(x + ae)^2 + y^2} = \pm 2a + \sqrt{(x - ae)^2 + y^2}$$

and square both sides to get

$$x^2 + 2aex + a^2e^2 + y^2 = 4a^2 \pm 4a\sqrt{(x - ae)^2 + y^2} + x^2 - 2aex + a^2e^2 + y^2,$$

or

$$ex - a = \pm\sqrt{(x - ae)^2 + y^2}.$$

Again, squaring both sides, we obtain

$$e^2x^2 - 2aex + a^2 = x^2 - 2aex + a^2e^2 + y^2,$$

or

$$(e^2 - 1)x^2 - y^2 = a^2(e^2 - 1),$$

or

$$\frac{x^2}{a^2} - \frac{y^2}{a^2(e^2 - 1)} = 1.$$

Thus, writing $b^2 = a^2e^2 - a^2$, we obtain the required form,

$$\frac{x^2}{a^2} - \frac{y^2}{b^2} = 1.$$

---

The definition of the hyperbola given in Example 13.9c is at the basis of a method of range finding. If the exact time of the report of a gun is recorded at each of two listening stations, the difference in time multiplied by the speed of sound in air gives the difference in the distances of the gun from the two stations. Therefore, the gun is on the hyperbola whose foci are the listening stations. The distance between the vertices is the calculated difference in the distances of the gun from the two stations. By using a third listening station, a second hyperbola is found that also passes through the position of the gun, which is then easily located at one of the intersections of the two curves.

Essentially the same idea is used in the method of long-range navigation known as "Loran," in which the difference in the distances from the stations is computed by means of the difference in the times at which radio signals are received from these stations.

A few applications of the conic sections have already been indicated in this and in the preceding sections. By way of summary, it is worth knowing that these curves occur in many other problems in science and engineering. The path of a projectile is closely approximated by a parabola. Parabolic arches are used in building. Loaded cables such as those on a suspension bridge are parabolic in shape. Parabolic mirrors are used in large telescopes because a light ray traveling parallel to the axis of the parabola—that is, parallel to the line through the vertex and the focus—is reflected through the focus. The orbits of planets are elliptical, as are the orbits of satellites. Rays emanating from one focus of an ellipse are reflected by an elliptical surface of rotation through the other focus. Cams having an elliptical shape are necessary for certain kinds of machinery.

## Exercises 13.9

Sketch the curve in each of Numbers 1 to 8. Find the eccentricity, the foci, the vertices, the directrices, and the asymptotes.

1. $y^2 - 4x^2 = 16.$
2. $x^2 - 9y^2 = 1.$
3. $x^2 - 9y^2 = -36.$
4. $x^2 = y^2 + 3.$

5. $x^2 - 9y^2 + 4x - 5 = 0.$
6. $x^2 - 4y^2 - 6x - 16y - 11 = 0.$
7. $4y^2 - 9x^2 + 16y + 18x = 29.$
8. $y^2 - x^2 + 2y - 2x - 1 = 0.$

9. Find an equation of the set of points such that the difference in the distances from any point of the set to the points $(1, 1)$ and $(1, 5)$ is 2.

10. Find an equation of the set of points such that the difference in the distances from any point of the set to the points $(-7, -2)$ and $(-1, -2)$ is 4.

11. Show that the length of the chord drawn through either focus of a hyperbola perpendicular to the line through the two foci is $2b^2/a$.

12. Sketch the curve whose parametric equations are

$$x = a \cosh \theta, \, y = b \sinh \theta, \qquad a \neq b.$$

13. An ellipse and a hyperbola both have their foci at $(12, 0)$ and $(-12, 0)$. If their eccentricities are, respectively, $\frac{2}{3}$ and $\frac{3}{2}$, find their points of intersection.

★14. The hyperbola for which $a = b$ is usually called an **equilateral hyperbola**. Show that the distance from the center to any point on such a hyperbola is a mean proportional between the focal radii to this point.

15. The two hyperbolas

$$\frac{x^2}{a^2} - \frac{y^2}{b^2} = 1 \quad \text{and} \quad \frac{y^2}{b^2} - \frac{x^2}{a^2} = 1$$

are called **conjugate hyperbolas**. Show that if $e_1$ and $e_2$ are the eccentricities of two conjugate hyperbolas, then

$$e_1^2 + e_2^2 = e_1^2 e_2^2.$$

## Summary of Chapter 13

As is frequently the case in elementary mathematics, a student of advanced mathematics is confronted with two situations that are not always independent. He must, in his learning process, develop skills as well as an understanding of concepts and terminology. For this reason he should know what is meant by such terms as *space*, *metric*, and *metric space* (Sections 13.1 and 13.3). He should understand:

(1) how to describe sets of points analytically (Section 13.1);

(2) the process of translating coordinates (Section 13.2);

(3) the significance of coordinate curves in different coordinate systems, particularly in polar coordinates (Section 13.3);

(4) the equations of transformation between rectangular and polar coordinates, and their use (Section 13.3);

(5) the techniques of curve sketching in polar coordinates, including a discussion of symmetry and the determination of lines tangent to the curve at the origin (Section 13.4);

(6) the definition of the conic sections as sets of points satisfying certain geometric conditions, and the meaning of the terms focus, directrix, and eccentricity (Section 13.5);

(7) the conic sections in rectangular coordinates and how to determine the significant characteristics of each type of conic (Sections 13.6, 13.7, 13.8, 13.9);

(8) the use of the conic sections in various kinds of physical situations (Sections 13.7, 13.8, 13.9).

# Chapter 14    Vectors and Three-dimensional Geometry

## 14.1 THE VECTOR EQUATION OF A STRAIGHT LINE IN A PLANE

In the preceding chapters we discussed a number of geometric concepts from an algebraic point of view based on the close connection between geometry and algebra. A natural way of studying geometric properties algebraically is by means of the vector concept, since a vector inherently combines geometric and algebraic properties in one construct. Moreover, it is important for the reader to realize that a mathematical concept may often be approached in several different ways. The use of vectors in the approach to be introduced here will demonstrate a simple but important way of unifying several concepts that were introduced earlier. In this chapter, some of these concepts will be briefly reviewed.

To illustrate these remarks, let us begin our investigation by recalling the equation for a straight line through two points, $(a_1, a_2)$ and $(b_1, b_2)$, which is

$$\frac{y - a_2}{x - a_1} = \frac{b_2 - a_2}{b_1 - a_1},$$

or

$$\frac{y - a_2}{b_2 - a_2} = \frac{x - a_1}{b_1 - a_1}.$$

If the equal ratios in the second form are denoted by a variable $t$, then we obtain

(1)
$$\begin{cases} x - a_1 = t(b_1 - a_1), \\ y - a_2 = t(b_2 - a_2), \end{cases}$$

as parametric equations for the line.

In order to relate these equations to vectors, the reader may recall that two vectors are equal if, and only if, their corresponding components are equal. If Equations (1) are regarded as the result of equating components of two equal vectors, then a vector equation from which these equations would arise is

$$(x - a_1, y - a_2) = (t(b_1 - a_1), t(b_2 - a_2)),$$

since, upon equating the components of this vector equation, we obtain the parametric equations of the line.

Furthermore, the vector equation may be rewritten as

$$(x, y) - (a_1, a_2) = t[(b_1, b_2) - (a_1, a_2)].$$

Thus, if

$$\mathbf{r} .=. (x, y), \quad \mathbf{a} .=. (a_1, a_2), \quad \mathbf{b} .=. (b_1, b_2),$$

then

(2)
$$\mathbf{r} - \mathbf{a} = t(\mathbf{b} - \mathbf{a})$$

is a simple **vector equation** for the straight line passing through the points represented by **a** and **b**.

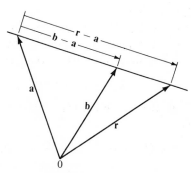

**FIGURE 14.1a**

Geometrically, this equation states that the vector $\mathbf{r} - \mathbf{a}$ is parallel to the vector $\mathbf{b} - \mathbf{a}$, as illustrated in Figure 14.1a. Since these two vectors are parallel, one must be a scalar multiple of the other—a fact expressed by Equation (2), in which the parameter $t$ serves as the scalar multiplier. The following example illustrates this idea.

---

*Example 14.1a.* Find the vector equation of the line that passes through the points $(-1, 2)$ and $(3, 1)$.

If we define $\mathbf{r} = (x, y)$ as a position vector from the origin to any point on the line, then

$$\mathbf{r} - (-1, 2) = t[(3, 1) - (-1, 2)],$$

or

$$\mathbf{r} = (-1, 2) + t(4, -1),$$

is the desired equation. If the corresponding components are equated, then the following parametric equations of the line are obtained:

$$x = -1 + 4t,$$
$$y = 2 - t.$$

---

The reader should note that any other form of the straight line equation can easily be found from a set of parametric equations. For instance, to find the slope-intercept form for the line in the preceding example, we may solve the first of the parametric equations for $t$ and substitute into the second as follows:

$$t = \tfrac{1}{4}x + \tfrac{1}{4} \Rightarrow y = 2 - (\tfrac{1}{4}x + \tfrac{1}{4}).$$

Thus

$$y = -\tfrac{1}{4}x + \tfrac{7}{4}$$

is the required form. An alternative procedure consists in using the fact that $[4, -1]$ are direction numbers of the line, so that its slope is $-\tfrac{1}{4}$. Since the line intersects the $y$-axis for $x = 0$, we find $t = \tfrac{1}{4}$ and hence $y = \tfrac{7}{4}$ by direct substitution in the parametric equations. These values may be used in the form

$$y = mx + b$$

to give the same result as before.

It is worth noting that a vector form of the equation can always be obtained from any other form by first finding two points on the line and then applying the method illustrated in Example 14.1a. Thus, the line

$$2x + 3y = 5$$

is found to pass through the two points $(1, 1)$ and $(-2, 3)$. Hence, a vector equation of this line is

$$\mathbf{r} = (1, 1) + t[(-2, 3) - (1, 1)],$$

or

$$\mathbf{r} = (1, 1) + t(-3, 2).$$

(Suppose two other points on the line were chosen. To what extent could the resulting equation differ from the one just found?)

The equation of a straight line through two points can always be reduced to the form

(3) $$\mathbf{r} = \mathbf{a} + t\mathbf{c},$$

as illustrated in the preceding example. Furthermore, an equation of this form *always* represents a straight line, since the terminus of the vector $\mathbf{r}$ must lie on the line of the vector $\mathbf{c}$, no matter what the value of $t$ is. This is illustrated in Figure 14.1b.

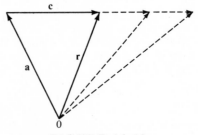

**FIGURE 14.1b**

To illustrate how vector notation can be used to simplify the discussion of a problem in analytic geometry, let us obtain an expression for a vector that divides the line segment from the point $(a_1, a_2)$ to the point $(b_1, b_2)$ in the ratio $k_1/k_2$. Let $\mathbf{a} .=. (a_1, a_2)$ and $\mathbf{b} .=. (b_1, b_2)$. We want to obtain an expression for the vector $\mathbf{r}$ that divides $\mathbf{b} - \mathbf{a}$ into two vectors whose lengths are in the ratio $k_1/k_2$ (see Figure 14.1c).

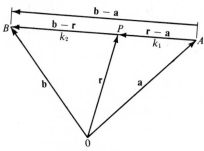

**FIGURE 14.1c**

Since $\mathbf{b} - \mathbf{r}$ is parallel to and has the same positive sense as $\mathbf{b} - \mathbf{a}$, one of these vectors must be a positive scalar multiple of the other. Furthermore, the ratio of $|\mathbf{b} - \mathbf{r}|$ to $|\mathbf{b} - \mathbf{a}|$ is $k_2/(k_1 + k_2)$. (See Figure 14.1c.) Hence,

$$\mathbf{b} - \mathbf{r} = \frac{k_2}{k_1 + k_2}(\mathbf{b} - \mathbf{a}).$$

We can obtain a simpler form than this by solving for $\mathbf{r}$ to get

$$\mathbf{r} = \mathbf{b} - \frac{k_2}{k_1 + k_2}(\mathbf{b} - \mathbf{a}),$$

4)
$$\mathbf{r} = \frac{k_2\mathbf{a} + k_1\mathbf{b}}{k_2 + k_1}.$$

By writing the last equation in terms of components, we have

$$(x, y) = \left(\frac{k_2a_1 + k_1b_1}{k_2 + k_1}, \frac{k_2a_2 + k_1b_2}{k_2 + k_1}\right),$$

so that

$$x = \frac{k_2a_1 + k_1b_1}{k_2 + k_1},$$

$$y = \frac{k_2a_2 + k_1b_2}{k_2 + k_1},$$

which are formulas for the coordinates of the required point of division of the line segment. Note in particular that $AP/PB = k_1/k_2$, so that $k_1/k_2$ is the ratio which $P$ divides the segment *from A to B*.

*Example 14.1b.* Find the point that divides the line segment from $(3, -5)$ to $(8, 10)$ in the ratio 2/3.

We may reason directly that the required point is two-fifths of the way from $(3, -5)$ to $(8, 10)$. Thus, if $\mathbf{r}$ is the vector to this point, then

$$\mathbf{r} - (3, -5) = \tfrac{2}{5}[(8, 10) - (3, -5)],$$
$$= \tfrac{2}{5}(5, 15) = (2, 6),$$

which implies that

$$\mathbf{r} = (3, -5) + (2, 6) = (5, 1).$$

This procedure is actually safer than memorizing and using the formulas that were derived. If these formulas are used in this example, then $(a_1, a_2) = (3, -5)$ and $(b_1, b_2) = (8, 10)$. Thus, with $k_1 = 2$ and $k_2 = 3$, we get, as before,

$$x = \frac{(3)(3) + (2)(8)}{5} = 5,$$

$$y = \frac{(3)(-5) + (2)(10)}{5} = 1.$$

---

Another interesting result that follows at once from the preceding work is a condition that three position vectors terminate at points that lie on a straight line. From Equation (4), we have

$$(k_1 + k_2)\mathbf{r} - k_2\mathbf{a} - k_1\mathbf{b} = 0.$$

If we write $k_1 + k_2 = -k_3$, then we find that

(5) $$k_2\mathbf{a} + k_1\mathbf{b} + k_3\mathbf{r} = 0, \quad k_1 + k_2 + k_3 = 0.$$

These two equations together constitute a condition that must be satisfied when the vectors $\mathbf{a}$, $\mathbf{b}$, and $\mathbf{r}$ terminate on a line. By retracing steps to Equation (4) from (5), we may also conclude that if Equations (5) are satisfied, then the vectors $\mathbf{a}$, $\mathbf{b}$, and $\mathbf{r}$ terminate on a line.

## Exercises 14.1

1. The vertices of a triangle are located at the points $A(1, 3)$, $B(-1, 5)$, $C(6, -2)$. Find the vector sum $\vec{AB} + \vec{BC} + \vec{CA}$ by actually computing and adding the three vectors.
2. Find the position vectors from the origin $O$ to the midpoints of the sides of the triangle $ABC$ in Number 1.
3. Write a vector equation for the line that passes through the origin and through the point $(3, -2)$.
4. Write a vector equation for the line that passes through the point $(3, 4)$ and has direction numbers $[-5, 1]$. At what points does this line intersect the coordinate axes?
5. Write a vector equation for the line that has intercepts $a$ and $b$; that is, the line that passes through the points $(a, 0)$ and $(0, b)$.
6. Do the position vectors $\mathbf{r}_1 = (2, 1)$, $\mathbf{r}_2 = (-1, 5)$, $\mathbf{r}_3 = (302, -399)$ terminate on a straight line? Explain.

7. If the position vector $\mathbf{r} = (x, 3)$ terminates on the line through the two points $(7, 1)$ and $(-3, 4)$, what is the value of $x$?

8. Find a vector equation for the line given by

$$y = -2x - 10.$$

9. Write a vector equation for the line given by (a) $x = -3$; (b) $y = 4$.

10. Find the point that divides the line segment from $(-3, 2)$ to $(6, 5)$ in the ratio $1/2$.

11. Find the point that divides the line segment from $(-2, -5)$ to $(2, 3)$ in the ratio $3/5$.

12. If $M$ is the midpoint of the line segment $AB$, then for any point $O$, we have by Equation (4),

$$\overrightarrow{OM} = \tfrac{1}{2}(\overrightarrow{OA} + \overrightarrow{OB}).$$

This equation says that the diagonals of the parallelogram on $OA$ and $OB$ (as adjacent sides) bisect each other. Explain.

13. If $\mathbf{r}_1, \mathbf{r}_2, \ldots, \mathbf{r}_n$ are position vectors to the vertices $A_1, A_2, \ldots, A_n$ of an $n$-sided closed polygon, prove algebraically that the sum of the vectors

$$\overrightarrow{A_1A_2}, \overrightarrow{A_2A_3}, \ldots, \overrightarrow{A_{n-1}A_n}, \overrightarrow{A_nA_1}$$

is zero. *Hint*: $\overrightarrow{A_1A_2} = \mathbf{r}_2 - \mathbf{r}_1$, $\overrightarrow{A_2A_3} = \mathbf{r}_3 - \mathbf{r}_2$, and so on.

14. Let $ABC$ be any triangle and let $D$, $E$, and $F$, be the midpoints of its sides. If $O$ is any other point, show that

$$\overrightarrow{OA} + \overrightarrow{OB} + \overrightarrow{OC} = \overrightarrow{OD} + \overrightarrow{OE} + \overrightarrow{OF}.$$

Is the corresponding result valid for a polygon of $n$ sides?

15. Suppose a straight line $Ax + By + C = 0$ is given. Show that the vector equation of the line may always be chosen to be of the form

$$\mathbf{r} = (x_1, y_1) + t(B, -A),$$

where $(x_1, y_1)$ is a point on the line and $t$ is a suitably chosen parameter.

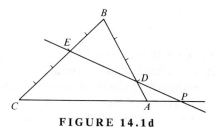

**FIGURE 14.1d**

16. Figure 14.1d shows a straight line cutting across the sides of a triangle $ABC$ and intersecting these sides at $E$, $D$, and $P$, respectively If $D$ divides $AB$ in the ratio $1/3$ and $E$ divides $BC$ in the ratio $2/3$, find the ratio in which $P$ divides $CA$. *Hint*: Let $k_1/k_2$ be the required ratio and let $m_1/m_2$ be the ratio in which $P$ divides $ED$. Write $\mathbf{a}$, $\mathbf{b}$, $\mathbf{c}$, and so on for position vectors from some origin to the points $A$, $B$, $C$, and so on. Then we must have

$$\mathbf{p} = \frac{k_2\mathbf{c} + k_1\mathbf{a}}{k_1 + k_2} = \frac{m_2\mathbf{e} + m_1\mathbf{d}}{m_1 + m_2}.$$

(Why?) By the given data,

$$e = \frac{3b + 2c}{5} \quad \text{and} \quad d = \frac{3a + b}{4}.$$

Now eliminate **b** and then rearrange the resulting equation to get the desired equation between **a**, **c**, **d**, and **e**. You should find that the desired ratio is $-9/2$. The product of the three ratios in this problem is $(1/3)(2/3)(-9/2) = -1$. According to the Theorem of Menelaus, the product of the three ratios into which a straight line divides the sides of a triangle is always $-1$. Can you use the method outlined here to prove this theorem?

## 14.2 THREE-DIMENSIONAL EUCLIDEAN SPACE

Points in a euclidean three-space can be described in much the same way as in a euclidean two-space. In order to accomplish this, three mutually perpendicular planes are first chosen as reference planes. The lines of intersection of these planes are called the **coordinate axes** and are named the $x$-, $y$-, and $z$-axes. The three planes are called **coordinate planes** and are designated as the $xy$-, $yz$-, and $xz$-planes.

If the point of intersection of the planes is taken as the *origin*, and if a common

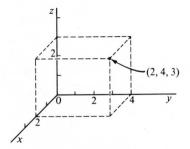

**FIGURE 14.2a**

number scale is associated with each axis, then points in space are located relative to the origin by an ordered number-triple $(x, y, z)$. The numbers in the triple are called the coordinates of the point located $x$ units from the $yz$-plane, $y$ units from the $xz$-plane, and $z$ units from the $xy$-plane. Coordinates are customarily given in the $x$, $y$, $z$ order. See Figure 14.2a.

The three coordinate axes are usually chosen so as to form a right-handed system. In such a system, if one faces in the positive $y$-direction with his head in the positive $z$-direction, then the positive $x$-direction is to his right.

The next theorem shows that the formula for the distance between two points extends easily to the three-dimensional case.

**Theorem 14.2a.** The distance between the two points $P_1(x_1, y_1, z_1)$ and $P_2(x_2, y_2, z_2)$ is given by

$$d(P_1, P_2) = \sqrt{(x_2 - x_1)^2 + (y_2 - y_1)^2 + (z_2 - z_1)^2}.$$

ROOF: Geometrically, this expression is the result of calculating the length of a diagonal of a "box" by means of the Pythagorean Theorem, as indicated

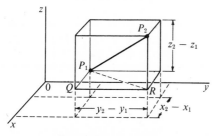

**FIGURE 14.2b**

in Figure 14.2b. By considering the right triangles $P_1QR$ and $P_1RP_2$, the reader may verify that the length of the diagonal is given by the expression in the theorem.

*Example 14.2a.* Show that the triangle with vertices at the points $A(1, 2, 1)$, $B(5, 3, 4)$, nd $C(8, -3, 2)$ is a right triangle and find its area.

The lengths of the sides are

$$d(A, B) = \sqrt{4^2 + 1^2 + 3^2} = \sqrt{26},$$
$$d(A, C) = \sqrt{7^2 + 5^2 + 1^2} = \sqrt{75} = 5\sqrt{3},$$

nd

$$d(B, C) = \sqrt{3^2 + 6^2 + 2^2} = \sqrt{49} = 7.$$

Since $(AC)^2 = (AB)^2 + (BC)^2$, the triangle $ABC$ is a right triangle, and its area is

$$\tfrac{1}{2}(\text{base})(\text{altitude}) = \tfrac{7}{2}\sqrt{26}.$$

Another concept that generalizes easily to the three-dimensional case is nat of direction numbers of a line.

**efinition 14.2a.** An ordered set of three numbers, denoted by $[m, n, p]$, which characterizes the direction of a line in three-dimensional space, is called a set of **direction numbers** of the line.

These numbers specify the number of units change in the $y$- and $z$-direcons for a given number of units change in the $x$-direction. It is clear that set of direction numbers such as $[2, 3, 6]$ specify the same direction as the set $?k, 3k, 6k]$, where $k$ is any real number other than zero.

*Example 14.2b.* Obtain direction numbers for the line through the points $P_1(-2, 3, 4)$ id $P_2(3, -1, 1)$ and show how to obtain other points on this line (see Figure 14.2c). In order to get to the second point from the first, we must move five units in the ɔsitive $x$-direction, four units in the negative $y$-direction, and three units in the negave $z$-direction. Since the direction of the line is fixed, the number-triple $[5, -4, -3]$ ɩaracterizes this particular direction. This same direction is given by any other set of numbers proportional to these, such as $[5k, -4k, -3k]$, with $k \neq 0$. These numbers are therefore direction numbers of the line.

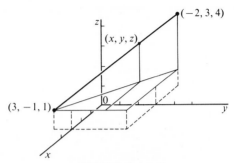

**FIGURE 14.2c**

If $(x, y, z)$ is another point on the line through $P_1$ and $P_2$, then we have the following equal ratios:

$$\frac{x - 3}{5} = \frac{y + 1}{-4} = \frac{z - 1}{-3} = k.$$

Hence, other points on the line can be found by giving $k$ different values. For instance $k = 1$ yields the point $(8, -5, -2)$; $k = -2$ yields $(-7, 7, 7)$; and so on.

By using the ideas illustrated in Example 14.2b, we may locate a point $P$ that divides a line segment $P_1P_2$ in three dimensions in a desired ratio. To illustrate, suppose we wish to find the point $P(x, y, z)$ that divides the line segment $P_2P_1$ in Example 14.2b in the ratio $P_2P/PP_1 = 1/2$. Since $P_2P$ is one-third the length of $P_2P_1$, we know that the difference of the $x$-coordinates of $P_2$ and $P$ and the difference of the $x$-coordinates of $P_2$ and $P_1$ must be in the same ratio $1/3$. This conclusion is easily established by means of similar triangles such as those illustrated in Figure 14.2c. A similar statement may be made for the $y$ and $z$-coordinates. Hence, we have

$$\frac{x - 3}{-5} = \frac{y + 1}{4} = \frac{z - 1}{3} = \frac{1}{3},$$

so that

$$x = 4/3, \quad y = 1/3, \quad z = 2$$

are the coordinates of the desired point. In other words, the point $P$ is that for which $k = -1/3$ in Example 14.2b.

Matters of symmetry in three dimensions are slightly more complicated than they are in two dimensions, since we may wish to consider symmetry with respect to the origin, a coordinate axis, or a coordinate plane. In general, we shall say that a point $P$ is symmetrically located to a point $Q$ with respect to the origin $O$ if $O$ is the midpoint of the line segment $PQ$. The point $P$ is symmetric to $Q$ with respect to a line $L$ if $L$ is a perpendicular bisector of $PQ$

Finally, $P$ is symmetric to $Q$ with respect to a plane $M$ if $M$ is perpendicular to the line segment $PQ$ and bisects it. For example, the point $(2, -1, 3)$ is symmetric to the point $(-2, -1, 3)$ with respect to the $yz$-plane, and to the point $(-2, 1, 3)$ with respect to the $z$-axis.

## Exercises 14.2

1. Find the distance between the following pairs of points.
   (a) $(3, 5, 2), (-2, 3, 1)$.
   (b) $(-2, -1, 4), (3, -1, 0)$.
   (c) $(3, -4, -2), (-2, 3, -5)$.

2. Find direction numbers of the lines determined by the pairs of points in Number 1.
3. Plot the points $P(-2, 3, -4)$, $Q(2, 0, -3)$, $R(3, 4, 5)$. Determine whether or not $PQR$ is a right triangle.
4. Find a point one-third of the distance from the point $(3, 6, 4)$ to the point $(-1, 3, 2)$.
5. Find a point three-fifths of the distance from the point $(-1, -2, 4)$ to the point $(-3, 1, 5)$.
6. Is the straight line joining the points $(-2, -3, 4)$ and $(-1, 2, -1)$ parallel to the straight line joining the points $(3, -7, -1)$ and $(4, -2, -6)$?
7. Prove that the following three points are on a straight line by using the distance formula and also by using direction numbers: $(-1, 3, -4)$, $(5, 0, 5)$, and $(1, 2, -1)$.
8. What are the direction numbers of each of the coordinate axes? What are the direction numbers of a line through the point $(2, -3, 1)$ parallel to the $x$-axis? to the $y$-axis? to the $z$-axis?
9. What are the coordinates of the midpoint of the line segment joining the points $(x_1, y_1, z_1)$ and $(x_2, y_2, z_2)$?
10. Let the points $(2, 3, 5)$, $(2, -1, -1)$, $(-2, 5, 3)$, and $(1, 1, 2)$ be the vertices of a quadrilateral. Show that the midpoints of the sides, when joined in succession, form a parallelogram.
11. Find the coordinates of the point that is symmetric to the point $(2, 5, 3)$ with respect to

    (a) the $yz$-plane,          (d) the origin,
    (b) the $xz$-plane,          (e) the $z$-axis.
    (c) the $xy$-plane,

12. What are the coordinates of the point on the $z$-axis that is equidistant from $(2, 1, 3)$ and $(-4, 5, -2)$?
13. How many lines are there in the $yz$-plane that have each of their points equidistant from the $y$-axis and $z$-axis? Find direction numbers of each line.
14. Describe and sketch the set of points in three-dimensional space satisfying the following conditions.

    (a) $y = 0$.                  (d) $y = 2$ and $z = 3$.
    (b) $y = 0$ and $x = 0$.      (e) $y = z$.
    (c) $z = 3$.

15. Show that for any tetrahedron (a pyramid with triangular faces), the three lines joining the midpoints of the opposite edges bisect each other.

16. Show that for any tetrahedron (see Number 15), the lines from each vertex to the intersection of the medians of the opposite face meet in a point that divides these lines in the ratio of $\frac{1}{3}$.

    *Hint:* Let the origin be taken at one vertex. Then choose axes so that the other vertices are $(3a, 0, 0)$, $(3b, 3c, 0)$, and $(3d, 3e, 3f)$.

17. Let $L_1$ and $L_2$ denote two lines intersecting at a point $P$, and suppose that the direction numbers of $L_i$ are $[l_i, m_i, n_i]$, $i = 1, 2$.

    (a) Show that the angle between the two lines is given by

    $$\theta = \text{Cos}^{-1}\left(\frac{l_1 l_2 + m_1 m_2 + n_1 n_2}{s_1 s_2}\right),$$

    where

    $$s_i^2 = l_i^2 + m_i^2 + n_i^2.$$

    *Hint:* Choose a convenient point $Q$ on $L_1$ and a point $R$ on $L_2$, and use the law of cosines on triangle $PQR$.

    (b) Show that $L_1$ and $L_2$ are perpendicular $\Leftrightarrow l_1 l_2 + m_1 m_2 + n_1 n_2 = 0$.

## 14.3 THREE-DIMENSIONAL VECTORS

The discussion of the vector equation of a straight line in the plane can be extended in a simple and natural way to the vector equation of a line in three dimensions. Indeed, it is in this respect that the vector approach to geometric problems is particularly valuable, since the same vector discussion can frequently be applied regardless of the number of dimensions.

A vector in three dimensions is defined in just the same way as it is in two dimensions.

**Definition 14.3a.** A vector in a three-dimensional space is a quantity that can be represented by an ordered triple of real numbers, denoted by $\mathbf{a} = (a_1, a_2, a_3)$ and that satisfies the following rules.

(a) Equality:

$$(a_1, a_2, a_3) = (b_1, b_2, b_3) \Leftrightarrow a_1 = b_1, \quad a_2 = b_2, \quad a_3 = b_3.$$

(b) Addition:

$$(a_1, a_2, a_3) + (b_1, b_2, b_3) .=. (a_1 + b_1, a_2 + b_2, a_3 + b_3).$$

(c) Multiplication by a scalar:

$$k(a_1, a_2, a_3) .=. (a_1, a_2, a_3)k .=. (ka_1, ka_2, ka_3).$$

Evidently, a vector in three dimensions may always be written as

$$\mathbf{r} = (x, y, z) = x(1, 0, 0) + y(0, 1, 0) + z(0, 0, 1).$$

The three vectors $(1, 0, 0)$, $(0, 1, 0)$, and $(0, 0, 1)$ form a **base** system for three dimensional vectors because every vector $\mathbf{r}$ can be written as a sum of these vectors each multiplied by a suitable scalar. For this reason they are given special names as follows:

$$\mathbf{i} .=. (1, 0, 0), \quad \mathbf{j} .=. (0, 1, 0), \quad \mathbf{k} .=. (0, 0, 1).$$

n terms of this new notation, a typical vector **r** is written as

$$\mathbf{r} = x\mathbf{i} + y\mathbf{j} + z\mathbf{k}.$$

he $x$, $y$, and $z$ are called the **components** of **r** in the **i**, **j**, **k** directions, respectively
ee Figure 14.3a).

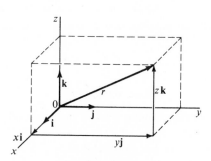

**FIGURE 14.3a**

The **magnitude**, or **length**, $|\mathbf{a}|$, of a three-dimensional vector **a** is also defined
the usual way.

**efinition 14.3b.** If $\mathbf{a} .=. (a_1, a_2, a_3)$, then

$$|\mathbf{a}| .=. (a_1^2 + a_2^2 + a_3^2)^{1/2}.$$

It follows that the vectors **i**, **j**, and **k** are each vectors of unit length. It is on
is account that they are called **unit vectors**. A unit vector can be obtained
om any vector $\mathbf{x} \neq \mathbf{0}$ merely by dividing **x** by its magnitude $|\mathbf{x}|$.

---

*Example 14.3a.* If $\mathbf{a} .=. (-1, -2, 5)$ and $\mathbf{b} .=. (3, 5, -1)$, find a unit vector in the
rection of $\mathbf{b} - \mathbf{a}$.

We have

$$\mathbf{b} - \mathbf{a} = (3, 5, -1) - (-1, -2, 5) = (4, 7, -6).$$

nce

$$|\mathbf{b} - \mathbf{a}| = \sqrt{4^2 + 7^2 + (-6)^2} = \sqrt{101},$$

e desired unit vector is

$$\left(\frac{4}{\sqrt{101}}, \frac{7}{\sqrt{101}}, \frac{-6}{\sqrt{101}}\right).$$

---

The equation of a line in the plane was given in the preceding section as

$$\mathbf{r} = \mathbf{a} + t\mathbf{c},$$

here **c** is a vector on the line and **a** is a position vector to a point on the line.
the vectors in this equation are three-dimensional, then the equation repre-
nts a line in space, since it states that the vector $\mathbf{r} - \mathbf{a}$ is always parallel to
e fixed vector **c**, and $\mathbf{r} - \mathbf{a}$ passes through the tip of the fixed vector **a** (see
gure 14.3b).

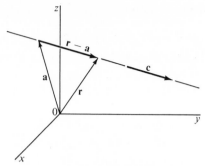

**FIGURE 14.3b**

If we equate corresponding components in the equation $\mathbf{r} = \mathbf{a} + t\mathbf{c}$, then we get

$$x = a_1 + tc_1,$$
$$y = a_2 + tc_2,$$
$$z = a_3 + tc_3$$

as parametric equations of the line. Assuming that none of the $c$'s are zero, we may solve these equations for $t$ and equate the results to get the so-called **symmetric** form of the equation of the line:

$$\frac{x - a_1}{c_1} = \frac{y - a_2}{c_2} = \frac{z - a_3}{c_3}.$$

Since the vector $\mathbf{c}$ determines the direction of the line, the numbers $c_1$, $c_2$, $c$ are direction numbers of the line.

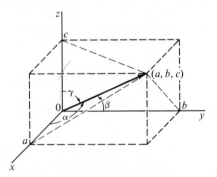

**FIGURE 14.3c**

Suppose we consider a set of direction numbers $[a, b, c]$ as a vector $\mathbf{r} = (a, b, c)$. This vector makes an angle with each of the $x$-, $y$-, and $z$-coordinate axes, as illustrated in Figure 14.3c. It is customary to label the corresponding angles $\alpha$, $\beta$, and $\gamma$. From the geometry illustrated in Figure 14.3c, it is easy to see that these angles can be found by means of their cosines; that is,

$$\cos \alpha = \frac{a}{|\mathbf{r}|}, \quad \cos \beta = \frac{b}{|\mathbf{r}|}, \quad \cos \gamma = \frac{c}{|\mathbf{r}|},$$

where $|\mathbf{r}| = (a^2 + b^2 + c^2)^{1/2}$, and $\alpha$, $\beta$, and $\gamma$ are between 0 and $\pi$, inclusive.

Since the triple of numbers $[\cos \alpha, \cos \beta, \cos \gamma]$ is proportional to the set of direction numbers $[a, b, c]$, they are also direction numbers of the vector $\mathbf{r}$. The following definition is a natural consequence of this observation.

**Definition 14.3c.** The cosines of the angles made by a vector $\mathbf{r}$ with the coordinate axes are called **direction cosines** of the vector. The angles $\alpha$, $\beta$, and $\gamma$ are called the **direction angles** of the vector.

The direction cosines of a given vector form a unique set of direction numbers, except for sign, in that they are the only set of direction numbers that satisfy the condition

$$\cos^2 \alpha + \cos^2 \beta + \cos^2 \gamma = 1.$$

It is clear that direction cosines can be obtained from any set of direction numbers merely by dividing the set of direction numbers by either the positive or the negative square root of the sum of the squares of the direction numbers. For example, for the direction numbers $[2, 3, -6]$, we have $\pm[2^2 + 3^2 + (-6)^2]^{1/2} = \pm 7$. Accordingly,

$$\cos \alpha = \tfrac{2}{7}, \qquad \cos \beta = \tfrac{3}{7}, \qquad \cos \gamma = -\tfrac{6}{7},$$

or

$$\cos \alpha = -\tfrac{2}{7}, \qquad \cos \beta = -\tfrac{3}{7}, \qquad \cos \gamma = +\tfrac{6}{7}.$$

The choice of the square root to be used is often determined by the problem, which may require the use of a specific square root. Direction cosines have a special significance in certain kinds of transformations, which will be considered later.

The next example illustrates some of the ideas we have discussed so far.

*Example 14.3b.* Write the vector equation of a line in three-dimensional space that passes through the point $(1, 3, 2)$ and has direction numbers $[2, -1, 3]$ (see Figure 14.3d). What is the symmetric form of the equations of this line?

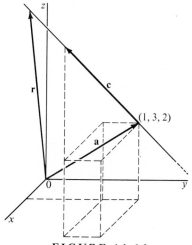

**FIGURE 14.3d**

Let $\mathbf{a}\,.=.\,(1, 3, 2)$, and let $\mathbf{c}\,.=.\,(2, -1, 3)$. Then if $\mathbf{r} = (x, y, z)$, the desired equation is

$$\mathbf{r} = \mathbf{a} + t\mathbf{c}$$

or

$$\mathbf{r} = (1, 3, 2) + t(2, -1, 3).$$

From this equation we can write the parametric equations of the line in the form

$$x = 2t + 1,$$
$$y = -t + 3,$$
$$z = 3t + 2.$$

By solving these three equations for $t$ and equating the results, we obtain the required symmetric equations:

$$\frac{x - 1}{2} = \frac{y - 3}{-1} = \frac{z - 2}{3}.$$

## Exercises 14.3

1. Find the direction angles of the line that makes equal acute angles with the three positive coordinate axes.
2. If $\alpha = 60°$, $\beta = 120°$, what are the possible values of $\gamma$?
3. If $\alpha = 45°$, $\beta = 60°$, what are the possible values of $\gamma$?
4. If $\alpha = 45°$, is it possible for $\beta$ to be $30°$? Explain.
5. If $\alpha = 30°$, what is the possible range of values for $\beta$?
6. What are the direction cosines of each of the coordinate axes?
7. In each of the following, find the direction cosines and the direction angles of the vector $\overrightarrow{P_1P_2}$ if $P_1$ and $P_2$ have the coordinates given.

   (a) $P_1(2, 5, 3)$, $P_2(-3, 4, -1)$.　　(c) $P_1(3, -1, 7)$, $P_2(4, -3, -1)$.
   (b) $P_1(-1, -3, 2)$, $P_2(2, -1, -1)$.　　(d) $P_1(2, -2, -1)$, $P_2(1, 4, -3)$.

8. If $\mathbf{a}\,.=.\,(-1, 0, 2)$, $\mathbf{b}\,.=.\,(2, 3, 6)$, $\mathbf{c}\,.=.\,(2, -2, 1)$, find each of the following:
   (a) $3\mathbf{a} + \mathbf{b}$;
   (b) $|2\mathbf{b} - 3\mathbf{c}|$;
   (c) A unit vector in the direction of $\mathbf{c}$;
   (d) $|\mathbf{b}|\mathbf{a}$;
   (e) $|\mathbf{a}|\mathbf{b}/|\mathbf{b}|$, and describe the vector;
   (f) A vector bisecting the angle between $\mathbf{b}$ and $\mathbf{c}$;
   (g) Direction cosines of $\mathbf{a} + \mathbf{b} - 2\mathbf{c}$.
9. Under what conditions does the following hold?

   $$|\mathbf{a} + \mathbf{b}| = |\mathbf{a}| + |\mathbf{b}|.$$

10. Find the vector equation of a line in three-dimensional space passing through the point $(2, 5, 3)$ and having direction numbers $[-2, 4, -3]$.
11. Find the vector equation of a line in three-dimensional space passing through the points $(-2, -1, 4)$ and $(3, 2, 2)$.
12. Write the symmetric form of the equations of the line in Number 10.
13. Write the symmetric form of the equations of the line in Number 11.
14. Find the position vector $\mathbf{r}$ to the midpoint of the line segment from $A(1, 0, -$ to $B(-3, 6, 7)$.

15. Find the position vector **r** to the point that divides the line segment from $A(5, 2, -1)$ to $B(0, 7, 4)$ in the ratio $3/5$.
16. Find the position vector **r** to the intersection of the medians of the triangle with vertices at $A(1, 5, -2)$, $B(4, -6, 3)$, $C(2, 4, 5)$.

## 14.4 THE DOT PRODUCT

Although we have considered vectors as a kind of algebraic element for which the operations of addition and multiplication by a scalar have been defined, we have not yet attempted to define an operation of "multiplication" of one vector by another. One reason for this is that we have not yet encountered a situation in which a product of vectors appeared to be necessary. We shall soon see, however, that it is convenient to define the product of one vector by another in a special way.

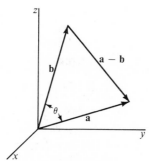

**FIGURE 14.4a**

Let us first consider the relationship between the magnitudes of three vectors that form a triangle, as shown in Figure 14.4a. If $\theta$ is the angle between the vectors, **a** and **b**, then, by the Law of Cosines (see Appendix B),

$$|a - b|^2 = |a|^2 + |b|^2 - 2|a||b| \cos \theta,$$

or

$$(a_1 - b_1)^2 + (a_2 - b_2)^2 + (a_3 - b_3)^2$$
$$= a_1^2 + a_2^2 + a_3^2 + b_1^2 + b_2^2 + b_3^2 - 2|a||b| \cos \theta.$$

From this we get

(1) $$a_1b_1 + a_2b_2 + a_3b_3 = |a||b| \cos \theta,$$

which shows that the expression

(2) $$a_1b_1 + a_2b_2 + a_3b_3$$

describes a fundamental relationship between the vectors **a** and **b**. In particular if **a** is *orthogonal* (perpendicular) to **b**, then $\cos \theta = 0$, and we have

$$a_1b_1 + a_2b_2 + a_3b_3 = 0.$$

Since (2) involves only the components of the vectors **a** and **b**, it is frequently a more convenient form to use than is $|\mathbf{a}||\mathbf{b}| \cos \theta$. Because of its basic importance, the expression in (2) is given a special name.

**Definition 14.4a.** For two vectors, $\mathbf{a} .=. (a_1, a_2, a_3)$ and $\mathbf{b} .=. (b_1, b_2, b_3)$, the expression

$$\mathbf{a} \cdot \mathbf{b} .=. a_1 b_1 + a_2 b_2 + a_3 b_3$$

is called their **scalar, or dot, product.**

By virtue of Equation (1), the dot product $\mathbf{a} \cdot \mathbf{b}$ of two vectors making an angle $\theta$ with each other is the product formed by multiplying the magnitude $|\mathbf{a}|$ of one vector by the **scalar projection,** $|\mathbf{b}| \cos \theta$, of the second vector on the first (see Figure 14.4b). Thus, we also have

(3)
$$\mathbf{a} \cdot \mathbf{b} = |\mathbf{a}||\mathbf{b}| \cos \theta.$$

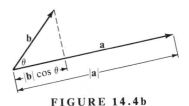

**FIGURE 14.4b**

For dot products involving only the unit vectors $\mathbf{i}$, $\mathbf{j}$, and $\mathbf{k}$, it follows that

$$\mathbf{i} \cdot \mathbf{i} = (1)(1) \cos 0 = 1,$$

and similarly for $\mathbf{j} \cdot \mathbf{j}$ and $\mathbf{k} \cdot \mathbf{k}$. Thus, we may write

$$\mathbf{i} \cdot \mathbf{i} = \mathbf{j} \cdot \mathbf{j} = \mathbf{k} \cdot \mathbf{k} = 1.$$

All the other possible products are zero, as is evident from Equation (3). Since $\mathbf{i}$, $\mathbf{j}$, $\mathbf{k}$ are mutually perpendicular, they are called an **orthogonal set** of vectors.

The dot product is useful in discussing the projection of one vector on another. For example, if

$$\mathbf{a} .=. a_1 \mathbf{i} + a_2 \mathbf{j} + a_3 \mathbf{k},$$

then

$$\mathbf{a} \cdot \mathbf{i} = a_1, \quad \mathbf{a} \cdot \mathbf{j} = a_2, \quad \mathbf{a} \cdot \mathbf{k} = a_3,$$

so that the scalar product of $\mathbf{a}$ by a unit vector $\mathbf{i}$, $\mathbf{j}$, or $\mathbf{k}$ gives the **component** of $\mathbf{a}$ in the direction of the unit vector.

To emphasize the meaning of the terminology used here, let us summarize as follows: The **projection** of a vector $\mathbf{b}$ on a vector $\mathbf{a}$ is a **vector** in the direction of $\mathbf{a}$ whose signed magnitude is $|\mathbf{b}| \cos \theta$, where $\theta$ is the angle between $\mathbf{a}$ and $\mathbf{b}$. The **scalar projection** of $\mathbf{b}$ on $\mathbf{a}$ is the **signed magnitude** of the projection of $\mathbf{b}$ on $\mathbf{a}$. Observe that $|\mathbf{b}| \cos \theta$ may be either positive or negative, depending on the angle $\theta$. The dot product may generally be used in this connection, so that if $\mathbf{e}$ is *any* unit vector, then

$$\mathbf{a} \cdot \mathbf{e}$$

represents the **component** of **a** in the **e** direction. In general, the *component of a vector* **b** *in the direction of a vector* **a** is the scalar projection of **b** on a unit vector in the **a** direction.

Since the scalar projection of **b** on **a** is given by

$$|\mathbf{b}| \cos \theta,$$

where $\theta$ is the angle between **a** and **b**, and since $\mathbf{a}/|\mathbf{a}|$ is a unit vector in the direction of **a**, the projection of **b** in the direction of **a** is

$$|\mathbf{b}| \cos \theta \, \frac{\mathbf{a}}{|\mathbf{a}|}.$$

This may be rewritten as

$$\frac{|\mathbf{a}||\mathbf{b}| \cos \theta}{|\mathbf{a}||\mathbf{a}|} \mathbf{a}$$

or as

$$\left( \frac{\mathbf{a} \cdot \mathbf{b}}{\mathbf{a} \cdot \mathbf{a}} \right) \mathbf{a}.$$

---

*Example 14.4a.* Find the component of the vector

$$\mathbf{a} = 2\mathbf{i} - 2\mathbf{j} + \mathbf{k}$$

in the direction of the vector

$$\mathbf{b} = 6\mathbf{i} + 7\mathbf{j} - 6\mathbf{k}.$$

What is the projection of **a** on **b**? Find the angle between **a** and **b**.

A unit vector in the direction of **b** is

$$\mathbf{u} = \frac{\mathbf{b}}{|\mathbf{b}|} = \frac{6}{11}\mathbf{i} + \frac{7}{11}\mathbf{j} - \frac{6}{11}\mathbf{k}.$$

Consequently, the component of **a** in the direction of **b** is

$$\mathbf{a} \cdot \mathbf{u} = \frac{12}{11} - \frac{14}{11} - \frac{6}{11} = -\frac{8}{11}.$$

The minus sign shows that the angle between **a** and **b** is obtuse. The projection of **a** on **b** is

$$-\frac{8}{11}\mathbf{u} = -\frac{48}{121}\mathbf{i} - \frac{56}{121}\mathbf{j} + \frac{48}{121}\mathbf{k}.$$

For the angle between **a** and **b**, we use

$$\cos \theta = \frac{\mathbf{a} \cdot \mathbf{b}}{|\mathbf{a}||\mathbf{b}|} = \frac{\mathbf{a} \cdot \mathbf{u}}{|\mathbf{a}|} = -\frac{8}{33} \Rightarrow \theta = 104° \text{ (approx.)}.$$

---

Since the scalar product of two vectors **a** and **b** is *not* a vector, this product has *no* analogy in the multiplication of real (or complex) numbers, where the product of two real (or complex) numbers is again a real (or complex) number. Before considering applications of the dot product, it is convenient first to determine some of the properties of the product that are implied by its definition.

**Theorem 14.4a.** The dot product of vectors is commutative; that is

$$\mathbf{a} \cdot \mathbf{b} = \mathbf{b} \cdot \mathbf{a}.$$

PROOF: Left for the reader.

**Theorem 14.4b.** The dot product is distributive with respect to vector addition; that is,

$$\mathbf{a} \cdot (\mathbf{b} + \mathbf{c}) = \mathbf{a} \cdot \mathbf{b} + \mathbf{a} \cdot \mathbf{c}.$$

PROOF: Left for the reader.

There are several common properties of numbers that do not hold for vectors. For example, we may *not* say that the dot product is associative because the expression $(\mathbf{a} \cdot \mathbf{b}) \cdot \mathbf{c}$ is meaningless. Furthermore, if $\mathbf{a} \cdot \mathbf{b} = 0$, it does *not* necessarily follow that $\mathbf{a} = \mathbf{0}$ or $\mathbf{b} = \mathbf{0}$, since $\mathbf{a} \cdot \mathbf{b} = 0$ if $\mathbf{a}$ is perpendicular to $\mathbf{b}$. Similarly, if

$$\mathbf{a} \cdot \mathbf{c} = \mathbf{b} \cdot \mathbf{c},$$

we may *not* conclude that

$$\mathbf{a} = \mathbf{b}$$

because we may rewrite the given equation as

$$\mathbf{a} \cdot \mathbf{c} - \mathbf{b} \cdot \mathbf{c} = 0$$

or

$$(\mathbf{a} - \mathbf{b}) \cdot \mathbf{c} = 0,$$

which is satisfied if $\mathbf{a} - \mathbf{b}$ and $\mathbf{c}$ are orthogonal vectors.

Of particular interest is the fact that if $\mathbf{a} = (a_1, a_2, a_3,)$, then

$$\mathbf{a} \cdot \mathbf{a} = a_1^2 + a_2^2 + a_3^2 = |\mathbf{a}|^2.$$

Thus, the square of the magnitude of a vector is the dot product of the vector and itself. It is customary to denote $\mathbf{a} \cdot \mathbf{a}$ by the symbol $\mathbf{a}^2$.

The concept of the scalar projection of a vector in some specified direction is probably the main factor that motivated the definition of the dot product, for it is this idea that is at the root of the application of the dot product both in geometry and in physics. For example, the work done by a constant force $\mathbf{F}$ whose point of application moves along a directed line segment $\mathbf{s}$ is by definition *the product of the component of* $\mathbf{F}$ *along* $\mathbf{s}$ *and the length of* $\mathbf{s}$; that is, $\mathbf{F} \cdot \mathbf{s}$ exactly. If the physical magnitudes of $\mathbf{F}$ and $\mathbf{s}$ are in pounds and feet, respectively, then the work will be in foot-pounds.

*Example 14.4b.* In the $xy$-plane let a force $\mathbf{F}$ have a magnitude of five pounds and make an angle of $60°$ with the positive $x$-direction. Suppose the point of application of $\mathbf{F}$ moves in a straight line from the origin to the point $(2, 2)$. How much work is done by $\mathbf{F}$? See Figure 14.4c.

The work, which is given by $\mathbf{F} \cdot \mathbf{s}$, can be calculated in two ways.

(a) The force $\mathbf{F}$ can be expressed as

$$\mathbf{F} = (5 \cos 60°, 5 \sin 60°) = (5/2, 5\sqrt{3}/2).$$

Since $\mathbf{s} = (2, 2)$, then

$$\mathbf{F} \cdot \mathbf{s} = \left( \frac{5}{2}, \frac{5}{2} \sqrt{3} \right) \cdot (2, 2) = (5 + 5\sqrt{3}) \text{ ft-lb}.$$

(b) Since the angle that **s** makes with the x-axis is 45°, the angle between **F** and **s** is 15°. Thus,

$$\mathbf{F}\cdot\mathbf{s} = |\mathbf{F}||\mathbf{s}| \cos 15° = (5)(2\sqrt{2}) \cos 15°.$$

By using

$$\cos 15° = \cos (60° - 45°)$$
$$= \cos 60° \cos 45° + \sin 60° \sin 45°$$
$$= \frac{1 + \sqrt{3}}{2\sqrt{2}},$$

we may arrive at the same answer as in (a).

---

*Example 14.4c.* A particle constrained to move along the x-axis is acted on by a force **F** in the xy-plane. The magnitude of **F** is constantly 5 pounds, but its direction changes so that the angle $\theta$ it makes with the x-axis when the particle is at $(x, 0)$ is given by $\theta = \pi x/4$. Find the work done by **F** in moving the particle two feet, from $(0, 0)$ to $(2, 0)$.

Since the vector **F** is variable, the work done by **F** cannot be calculated directly from the basic definition **F**·**s** alone. Instead, it must be calculated by means of the type of argument that leads to the definite integral. If **i** is the usual unit vector along the x-axis, then the scalar component of **F** along the axis is **F**·**i** at each point. Accordingly, the work done by **F** is

$$\int_0^2 \mathbf{F}\cdot\mathbf{i}\, dx = \int_0^2 5 \cos \frac{\pi x}{4}\, dx$$
$$= \left[ \frac{20}{\pi} \sin \frac{\pi x}{4} \right]_0^2 = \frac{20}{\pi} \text{ ft-lb.}$$

---

We shall next consider a number of examples that illustrate the geometric applications of the dot product. The student should again note that the basic idea is the projection of a vector in some specified direction, as in the preceding examples.

---

*Example 14.4d.* Find the perpendicular distance from the point $P(2, -2, 1)$ to the line through the two points $A(1, 0, -1)$ and $B(7, 2, 2)$.

Figure 14.4d indicates the method of solution. We need to find the vector $\mathbf{u} .=. \overrightarrow{AP}$,

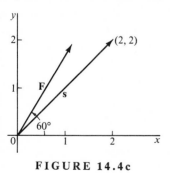

FIGURE 14.4c

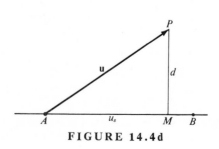

FIGURE 14.4d

its magnitude $|\mathbf{u}|$, and its scalar projection $u_s$ on the vector $\overrightarrow{AB}$. Then the distance $d$ can be found from the right triangle relationship

$$|\mathbf{u}|^2 = u_s^2 + d^2.$$

We have

$$\mathbf{u} = \overrightarrow{AP} = \overrightarrow{OP} - \overrightarrow{OA} = (1, -2, 2)$$

and

$$\overrightarrow{AB} = \overrightarrow{OB} - \overrightarrow{OA} = (6, 2, 3).$$

Hence

$$|\mathbf{u}| = \sqrt{1^2 + (-2)^2 + 2^2} = 3,$$

$$u_s = \frac{\mathbf{u} \cdot \overrightarrow{AB}}{|\overrightarrow{AB}|} = \frac{6 - 4 + 6}{7} = \frac{8}{7},$$

and

$$d = \sqrt{|\mathbf{u}|^2 - u_s^2} = \sqrt{9 - (64/49)} = \frac{1}{7}\sqrt{377}.$$

---

*Example 14.4e.* Find an equation of the line that passes through the point $A(2, 0, 1)$ and intersects the line

$$\mathbf{r} = (1, 2, 3) + t(-2, -1, 1)$$

at right angles.

Let $\mathbf{r}_0$ be the position vector to the point of intersection of the given line and the required line, and let $t_0$ be the corresponding value of the parameter $t$ in the given equation, so that $\mathbf{r}_0 = (1, 2, 3) + t_0(-2, -1, 1)$. If $\mathbf{a} .=. (2, 0, 1)$, then, as shown in

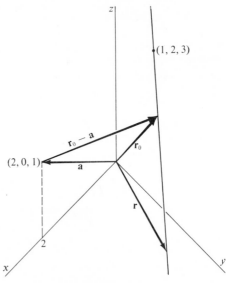

FIGURE 14.4e

Figure 14.4e, the vector $\mathbf{r}_0 - \mathbf{a}$ is perpendicular to every vector along the given line. A vector $(-2, -1, 1)$ along the line is obtained from the given equation. Thus

$$(\mathbf{r}_0 - \mathbf{a}) \cdot (-2, -1, 1) = 0,$$

and since

$$\mathbf{r}_0 - \mathbf{a} = (1, 2, 3) + t_0(-2, -1, 1) - (2, 0, 1)$$
$$= (-1, 2, 2) + t_0(-2, -1, 1),$$

we have

$$[(-1, 2, 2) + t_0(-2, -1, 1)] \cdot (-2, -1, 1) = 0.$$

This equation yields the value $t_0 = -\frac{1}{3}$, so that

$$\mathbf{r}_0 = (1, 2, 3) - \tfrac{1}{3}(-2, -1, 1) = (\tfrac{5}{3}, \tfrac{7}{3}, \tfrac{8}{3}),$$

which may be interpreted as the point of intersection of the given line and the required line. Making use of this point and the point $A$, we may now write the desired equation:

$$\mathbf{r} = (2, 0, 1) + t[(\tfrac{5}{3}, \tfrac{7}{3}, \tfrac{8}{3}) - (2, 0, 1)],$$

or

$$\mathbf{r} = (2, 0, 1) + t(-\tfrac{1}{3}, \tfrac{7}{3}, \tfrac{5}{3}).$$

## Exercises 14.4

1. From Figure 14.4f we see that $\mathbf{c} = \mathbf{a} - \mathbf{b}$. Take the square of both sides of this equation and derive the Law of Cosines. (Recall that the square of a vector $\mathbf{v}$ is the dot product $\mathbf{v} \cdot \mathbf{v}$.)

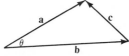

**FIGURE 14.4f**

2. Suppose $\mathbf{a} = a_1\mathbf{i} + a_2\mathbf{j} + a_3\mathbf{k}$ and that $\mathbf{r} = x\mathbf{i} + y\mathbf{j} + z\mathbf{k}$ is the usual position vector from the origin. Show that

$$(\mathbf{r} - \mathbf{a}) \cdot \mathbf{a} = 0$$

is the equation of a plane perpendicular to $\mathbf{a}$ and passing through the point $(a_1, a_2, a_3)$.

3. With $\mathbf{a}$ and $\mathbf{r}$ as in Number 2, show that

$$(\mathbf{r} - \mathbf{a}) \cdot \mathbf{r} = 0$$

is the equation of a sphere.

4. Use the dot product to find the angle between the vectors $\overrightarrow{AB}$ and $\overrightarrow{AC}$ if the points $A$, $B$, $C$ are $A(1, -1, 0)$, $B(3, 1, 1)$, $C(7, 2, 2)$.

5. Use the dot product to show that the triangle with the given vertices is a right triangle.
   (a) $A(-1, 4, -1)$, $B(5, 8, 5)$, $C(11, -4, 7)$.
   (b) $A(3, -1, 2)$, $B(-1, 2, 1)$, $C(1, 4, -1)$.

6. Find the angles of the triangle with vertices $A(2, 2, 2)$, $B(3, -2, 1)$, $C(-2, -3, 2)$.

7. Are the three points $A(-2, -1, 4)$, $B(2, 1, 2)$, $C(-4, -2, 6)$ on a straight line? Explain.

8. If $P(x, y, z)$ and $A(2, 0, 5)$ are on a line perpendicular to the line through $A$ and $B(1, -2, 4)$, what condition must $x$, $y$, $z$ satisfy?

9. If $\mathbf{a} = a_1\mathbf{i} + a_2\mathbf{j}$, $\mathbf{b} = b_1\mathbf{i} + b_2\mathbf{j}$, $\mathbf{r} = x\mathbf{i} + y\mathbf{j}$, describe the set of points $\{(x, y)\}$ given by $(\mathbf{r} - \mathbf{a}) \cdot (\mathbf{r} - \mathbf{b}) = 0$.

10. Write the vector equation of the line that passes through the points $(2, 1, -2)$ and $(3, -2, 4)$.

11. Write the vector equation of the line that passes through the point $(-2, 3, -4)$ and is parallel to the line

$$\mathbf{r} = (1, -1, 2) + t(-3, 2, 1).$$

12. Find the vector equation of the line that passes through the point $(2, 3, -1)$ and intersects the line

$$\mathbf{r} = (2, 2, 1) + t(-1, 1, 0)$$

at right angles.

13. If $\mathbf{a} . = . (-1, 0, 2)$, $\mathbf{b} . = . (2, 3, 6)$, $\mathbf{c} . = . (2, -2, 1)$, find each of the following.
    (a) The projection of $\mathbf{a}$ on $\mathbf{b}$.
    (b) The projection of $\mathbf{c}$ on $2\mathbf{a} - \mathbf{b}$.
    (c) $3\mathbf{a} + \mathbf{b} - 2\mathbf{c}$ in terms of $\mathbf{i}, \mathbf{j}, \mathbf{k}$.
    (d) The projection of $\mathbf{a} - 2\mathbf{b} + \mathbf{c}$ on the $y$-axis.
    (e) The projection of $\mathbf{a} - 2\mathbf{b} + \mathbf{c}$ on the line through the points $(0, 0, 0)$ and $(1, 1, 1)$.

14. Prove Theorem 14.4a.

15. Prove Theorem 14.4b.

16. Find the component of $\mathbf{a}$ in the $\mathbf{b}$ direction if
    (a) $\mathbf{a} = 2\mathbf{i} - 3\mathbf{j} + 6\mathbf{k}$, $\mathbf{b} = 2\mathbf{i} - \mathbf{j} - 2\mathbf{k}$;
    (b) $\mathbf{a} = \mathbf{i} + 2\mathbf{k}$, $\mathbf{b} = -\mathbf{i} - 2\mathbf{j} + 2\mathbf{k}$;
    (c) $\mathbf{a} = a_1\mathbf{i} + a_2\mathbf{j} + a_3\mathbf{k}$, $\mathbf{b} = b_1\mathbf{i} + b_2\mathbf{j} + b_3\mathbf{k}$.

17. Prove that if $\mathbf{a}$ is perpendicular to both $\mathbf{b}$ and $\mathbf{c}$, then $\mathbf{a}$ is perpendicular to $m\mathbf{b} + n\mathbf{c}$ for all scalars $m$ and $n$. Interpret the result geometrically.

18. Prove by use of the dot product that

$$|\mathbf{a} + \mathbf{b}| \leq |\mathbf{a}| + |\mathbf{b}|.$$

*Hint*: Consider the square of each side.

★19. Find the vector equation of the line that intersects both the following lines at right angles.

$$\mathbf{r} = (3, 3, 4) + t(2, 2, 3), \quad \mathbf{r} = (1, 6, -1) + t(-1, 2, 0).$$

20. A force of magnitude 10 pounds makes an angle of $45°$ with the positive $x$-axis. How much work is done if the point of application of the force is moved feet along the $x$-axis? Four feet along the $y$-axis? Four feet along the vector $\mathbf{a} = \mathbf{i} + 2\mathbf{j}$?

21. A unit point charge is located at the point $(0, 5)$. The force of repulsion on a charge of the same sign has the magnitude $\alpha/r^2$, where $r$ is the distance between the charges and $\alpha$ is a constant, and the force is directed along the line joining the two charges.
    (a) Write the vector that describes the force acting on a unit charge of the same sign located at a point $(x, 0)$.
    (b) Find the component of the force in the $x$-direction.
    (c) Calculate the work done in moving the unit charge on the $x$-axis from the point $(10, 0)$ to the origin against the force of repulsion.

22. A spring is attached to a pivot on the *y*-axis 4 inches above the origin, the natural
length of the spring being such that the lower end just touches the origin. If it
takes 10 pounds to stretch the spring one inch, calculate the work done in pulling
the lower end of the spring along the *x*-axis from the origin to a point 3 inches
from the origin. Show that your answer is the same as the work done in merely
stretching the spring downward 1 inch beyond its natural length.

# 14.5 THE VECTOR PRODUCT

As we have seen, the set of all vectors is not closed with respect to scalar multiplication, since the dot product of two vectors is not another vector. This fact
suggests that we attempt to define a kind of multiplication of vectors that will
yield another vector. To provide a practical definition, however, we need to
investigate additional ways in which vectors may be used.

So far, vectors have been discussed in relation to physical quantities having
a magnitude and direction, such as forces and velocities. It is also possible to
assign in a meaningful way a magnitude and a direction to such physical quantities as angular velocities of rotation about an axis and to such geometric
quantities as areas.

Consider, for example, a point *P* on the rim of a rotating wheel of radius *a*
units, as illustrated in Figure 14.5a. If the axis of rotation is *L*, and if *ω* is the

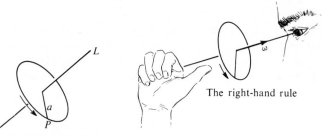

The right-hand rule

**FIGURE 14.5a**          **FIGURE 14.5b**

angular speed of the wheel, then the angular velocity of the point *P* can be represented by a vector *ω* along *L* such that the magnitude of *ω* is the angular
speed *ω*. Clearly, the vector *ω* is uniquely determined by the angular speed *ω*
and the axis of rotation *L*, except for its sense along *L*. (The radius of the wheel
has nothing to do with the *angular speed* of *P*, which would be measured in units
of angle per unit of time.)

In order to determine uniquely a sense for *ω* along *L*, we must adopt some
convention for this purpose. According to the most commonly accepted rule,
the vector *ω* is directed so that if one looks from the tip of *ω* toward its tail, then
the direction of rotation will be counterclockwise (see Figure 14.5b). This rule
is called the "right-hand rule" because if the fingers of the right hand are curled
in the direction of rotation, the thumb points in the positive sense of *ω*.

Now let $O$ be an origin or reference point chosen on $L$, and let $\mathbf{r}$ be a position vector to the point $P$ (see Figure 14.5c). Let $\theta$ denote the angle between $\mathbf{r}$ and $\boldsymbol{\omega}$

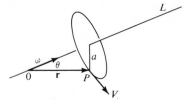

**FIGURE 14.5c**

The *linear speed* of the point $P$ can be found in terms of $\omega$ and the radius $a$ of the wheel. In fact, if $v$ is the linear speed of $P$, then

(1)
$$v = a\omega.$$

The linear velocity of the point $P$ can, of course, be represented by a vector $\mathbf{v}$ whose magnitude is the linear speed $v$. Moreover, since the angular velocity of the wheel about the line $L$ is represented by the vector $\boldsymbol{\omega}$ and the radius of the circle is given by $a = |\mathbf{r}| \sin \theta$, Equation (1) may be rewritten as

$$|\mathbf{v}| = |\boldsymbol{\omega}||\mathbf{r}| \sin \theta.$$

Furthermore, $\mathbf{v}$ is perpendicular to both $\mathbf{r}$ and $\boldsymbol{\omega}$. Thus, the vector $\mathbf{v}$ is completely determined by the two vectors $\mathbf{r}$ and $\boldsymbol{\omega}$ in some way. The question is: How can $\mathbf{v}$ be found when $\mathbf{r}$ and $\boldsymbol{\omega}$ are known?

There is a problem concerning areas that gives rise to the same kind of question. A planar area can be represented by a vector normal to the plane of the area by taking the magnitude of the vector equal to the area being represented, as in Figure 14.5d. For example, consider a parallelogram of sides $a$ and $b$. If $\theta$

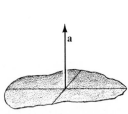

**FIGURE 14.5d**

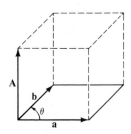

**FIGURE 14.5e**

is the acute angle between the sides (Figure 14.5e), then the area $A$ of the parallelogram is given by

$$A = ab \sin \theta.$$

Consequently, the area enclosed by the parallelogram may be represented by a vector $\mathbf{A}$ perpendicular to the plane of the parallelogram, where

$$|\mathbf{A}| = ab \sin \theta.$$

The parallelogram is uniquely determined by the two vectors **a** and **b**, along its sides. Therefore the area of the parallelogram, represented by **A**, must be determined in some way by the vectors **a** and **b**, because if the direction or the magnitude of either **a** or **b** is changed, the area of the parallelogram is changed.

We agree to regard **a**, **b**, and **A**, in this order, as forming a **right-handed set** of vectors. This means that if one looks from the tip of **A** toward its tail, then the rotation of **a** toward **b** through the angle between **a** and **b** appears counter-clockwise. Note that the angle between the two vectors is always the angle between their positive directions and hence cannot exceed 180°. Another ex-ample of a right-handed set of vectors is the triple **i**, **j**, **k**.

These examples suggest the desirability of having a means of generating a vector from two specified vectors in a way that would give the velocity **v** in the rotation problem and the area **A** in the area problem just discussed. In each of these examples, the vector to be determined turned out to be perpendicular to each of the two given vectors. Furthermore, the magnitude of the vector to be deter-mined is the product of the magnitudes of the given vectors and the sine of the angle between them. Hence, the following definition is pretty well dictated.

**Definition 14.5a.** The **vector,** or **cross, product** of two vectors **a** and **b**, denoted by **a** $\times$ **b**, is defined to be a vector perpendicular to **a** and **b** such that **a**, **b**, and **a** $\times$ **b** (in that order) form a right-handed set of vectors and such that

$$|\mathbf{a} \times \mathbf{b}| = |\mathbf{a}||\mathbf{b}| \sin \theta,$$

where $\theta$ is the angle between **a** and **b** (see Figure 14.5f).

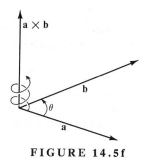

**FIGURE 14.5f**

Returning to the two problems with which this discussion began, we now have the following results:

(1) In the case of the rotating wheel, the linear velocity **v** of a point on the wheel is given by the formula

$$\mathbf{v} = \boldsymbol{\omega} \times \mathbf{r},$$

where $\boldsymbol{\omega}$ is the angular velocity vector and **r** is a vector from an origin on the axis of revolution to the point in question.

(2) In the case of the parallelogram with sides **a** and **b**, the vector area **A** is given by

$$\mathbf{A} = \mathbf{a} \times \mathbf{b},$$

where the orientation is such that **a**, **b**, **A** (in that order) form a right-handed set of vectors.

It follows from the definition that **b** × **a** is a vector in a direction opposite that of **a** × **b**, since the direction of rotation from **b** to **a** is opposite that from **a** to **b**. Thus,

$$\mathbf{a} \times \mathbf{b} = -\mathbf{b} \times \mathbf{a},$$

which shows that the vector product is *not* commutative.

From Definition 14.5a, we find that

$$\mathbf{i} \times \mathbf{i} = \mathbf{j} \times \mathbf{j} = \mathbf{k} \times \mathbf{k} = 0,$$

and that

$$\mathbf{i} \times \mathbf{j} = -\mathbf{j} \times \mathbf{i} = \mathbf{k}, \quad \mathbf{j} \times \mathbf{k} = -\mathbf{k} \times \mathbf{j} = \mathbf{i}, \quad \mathbf{k} \times \mathbf{i} = -\mathbf{i} \times \mathbf{k} = \mathbf{j}.$$

Although the preceding discussion describes the vector **a** × **b** geometrically it does not show how **a** × **b** can be found directly from **a** and **b** in a practical way when these vectors are given in component form. This is the next problem to be attacked.

It is convenient to consider first a product of three vectors. Since **b** × **c** is a vector, it is meaningful to form the dot product of it and another vector **a** to get **a**·(**b** × **c**). The parentheses here are not actually needed, as **a**·**b** is a scalar and so **a**·**b** × **c** can be interpreted in only one way.

Since the product

$$\mathbf{a} \cdot \mathbf{b} \times \mathbf{c}$$

is a scalar, it is usually called the **triple scalar product** of the vectors **a**, **b**, and **c**. Because dot multiplication is a commutative operation, we have

$$\mathbf{a} \cdot \mathbf{b} \times \mathbf{c} = \mathbf{b} \times \mathbf{c} \cdot \mathbf{a}.$$

This product may be interpreted as a scalar quantity whose magnitude is equal to the volume of the parallelepiped formed with **a**, **b**, and **c**, emanating from a common point, as edges. In Figure 14.5g, **b** × **c** is a vector perpendicular to the

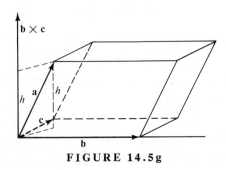

**FIGURE 14.5g**

plane of **b** and **c** and having a magnitude equal to the area of the parallelogram with **b** and **c** as adjacent sides. The magnitude of the component of **a** in the direction of **b** × **c** is the altitude of the parallelepiped. Accordingly, the volume is given by

$$V = |\mathbf{a} \cdot \mathbf{b} \times \mathbf{c}|.$$

The reader may easily verify geometrically that the triple scalar product is positive if the vectors **a**, **b**, and **c** form a right-handed set and negative if they form a left-handed set. Figure 14.5g shows **a**, **b**, and **c** with a right-handed orientation.

The fact that **a** · **b** × **c** is the volume (or its negative) of the parallelepiped on the vectors **a**, **b**, and **c** shows that *the value of the scalar product will be unaltered by a change in the order of the three vectors, provided that the cyclic order of the vectors is preserved.* The arrangements **a, b, c** and **b, c, a,** and **c, a, b** are said to be in the same cyclic order. This order can be indicated by a diagram such as follows:

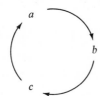

The same geometric interpretation shows that *the dot and the cross may be interchanged without altering the product.* Hence,

$$\mathbf{a} \cdot \mathbf{b} \times \mathbf{c} = \mathbf{a} \times \mathbf{b} \cdot \mathbf{c}.$$

We shall accept the geometric evidence of these properties of the triple scalar product without attempting to give any analytic proof.

The preceding properties of the triple scalar product make it easy to demonstrate the distributive property of cross multiplication with respect to vector addition.

**Theorem 14.5a.** $\mathbf{a} \times (\mathbf{b} + \mathbf{c}) = \mathbf{a} \times \mathbf{b} + \mathbf{a} \times \mathbf{c}.$

PROOF: Let the difference between the two members of this proposed identity be denoted by **d**; that is,

$$\mathbf{d} \mathbin{.=.} \mathbf{a} \times (\mathbf{b} + \mathbf{c}) - \mathbf{a} \times \mathbf{b} - \mathbf{a} \times \mathbf{c}.$$

Then form the dot product of **d** and any other vector **u** to get

$$\mathbf{u} \cdot \mathbf{d} = \mathbf{u} \cdot \mathbf{a} \times (\mathbf{b} + \mathbf{c}) - \mathbf{u} \cdot \mathbf{a} \times \mathbf{b} - \mathbf{u} \cdot \mathbf{a} \times \mathbf{c},$$

or by interchanging the dots and crosses in the triple products,

$$\mathbf{u} \cdot \mathbf{d} = \mathbf{u} \times \mathbf{a} \cdot (\mathbf{b} + \mathbf{c}) - \mathbf{u} \times \mathbf{a} \cdot \mathbf{b} - \mathbf{u} \times \mathbf{a} \cdot \mathbf{c}.$$

The distributive property of dot multiplication (Theorem 14.5b) allows a further revision of the right side so that we obtain

$$\mathbf{u} \cdot \mathbf{d} = \mathbf{u} \times \mathbf{a} \cdot \mathbf{b} + \mathbf{u} \times \mathbf{a} \cdot \mathbf{c} - \mathbf{u} \times \mathbf{a} \cdot \mathbf{b} - \mathbf{u} \times \mathbf{a} \cdot \mathbf{c} = 0.$$

Since **u** is a completely arbitrary vector, it is necessary that $\mathbf{d} = \mathbf{0}$, and the proof of the theorem is complete.

A repeated application of Theorem 14.5a shows that a vector product such as

$$(2\mathbf{i} - 3\mathbf{j} + \mathbf{k}) \times (\mathbf{i} + \mathbf{j} - 2\mathbf{k})$$

can be expanded by multiplying by one term at a time and employing the known cross products of the vectors **i, j, k** to get

$$5\mathbf{i} + 5\mathbf{j} + 5\mathbf{k}.$$

(The reader should check this result.) There is, however, a more elegant way in which to calculate the product.

Let

$$\mathbf{a} .=. a_1\mathbf{i} + a_2\mathbf{j} + a_3\mathbf{k},$$

and

$$\mathbf{b} .=. b_1\mathbf{i} + b_2\mathbf{j} + b_3\mathbf{k}.$$

Then, by multiplication and collection of terms, it is easy to obtain the general result

$$\mathbf{a} \times \mathbf{b} = (a_2b_3 - a_3b_2)\mathbf{i} - (a_1b_3 - a_3b_1)\mathbf{j} + (a_1b_2 - a_2b_1)\mathbf{k}.$$

This formula is not easily recalled as it stands, but is more conveniently represented in a symbolic form to be constructed next.

We shall let the symbol

$$\begin{vmatrix} A_1 & A_2 \\ B_1 & B_2 \end{vmatrix} .=. A_1B_2 - A_2B_1.$$

This symbol is called a **determinant of order two.** For instance,

$$\begin{vmatrix} 1 & 3 \\ -2 & 4 \end{vmatrix} = (1)(4) - 3(-2) = 4 + 6 = 10.$$

The vector product may now be written in the form

$$\mathbf{a} \times \mathbf{b} = \begin{vmatrix} a_2 & a_3 \\ b_2 & b_3 \end{vmatrix}\mathbf{i} - \begin{vmatrix} a_1 & a_3 \\ b_1 & b_3 \end{vmatrix}\mathbf{j} + \begin{vmatrix} a_1 & a_2 \\ b_1 & b_2 \end{vmatrix}\mathbf{k}.$$

The expression on the right side of this equation may be considered to be an expansion of another determinant. The symbol

$$\begin{vmatrix} A_1 & A_2 & A_3 \\ B_1 & B_2 & B_3 \\ C_1 & C_2 & C_3 \end{vmatrix} .=. A_1\begin{vmatrix} B_2 & B_3 \\ C_2 & C_3 \end{vmatrix} - A_2\begin{vmatrix} B_1 & B_3 \\ C_1 & C_3 \end{vmatrix} + A_3\begin{vmatrix} B_1 & B_2 \\ C_1 & C_2 \end{vmatrix},$$

and is called a **determinant of order three.** Note the pattern of the numbers in the second-order determinants. The second-order determinant that multiplies $A_1$ is obtained by striking out the row and column of $A_1$, and similarly for the other terms in the expansion. For example, we have

$$\cdots \begin{vmatrix} 2 & \cdots -1 & \cdots 3 \\ 0 & 1 & 2 \\ 3 & -2 & 1 \end{vmatrix} \cdots \quad = 2 \begin{vmatrix} 1 & 2 \\ -2 & 1 \end{vmatrix} - (-1) \begin{vmatrix} 0 & 2 \\ 3 & 1 \end{vmatrix} + 3 \begin{vmatrix} 0 & 1 \\ 3 & -2 \end{vmatrix}$$

$$= 2(1+4) + (0-6) + 3(0-3)$$
$$= 10 - 6 - 9 = -5.$$

By means of this definition, the vector product may be written as

$$(2) \qquad \mathbf{a} \times \mathbf{b} = \begin{vmatrix} \mathbf{i} & \mathbf{j} & \mathbf{k} \\ a_1 & a_2 & a_3 \\ b_1 & b_2 & b_3 \end{vmatrix}.$$

---

*Example 14.5a.* Use the determinant form of the cross product to verify the multiplication performed in the text, using

$$\mathbf{a} .=. \, 2\mathbf{i} - 3\mathbf{j} + \mathbf{k} \quad \text{and} \quad \mathbf{b} .=. \, \mathbf{i} + \mathbf{j} - 2\mathbf{k}.$$

We have

$$\mathbf{a} \times \mathbf{b} = \begin{vmatrix} \mathbf{i} & \mathbf{j} & \mathbf{k} \\ 2 & -3 & 1 \\ 1 & 1 & -2 \end{vmatrix}$$

$$= \mathbf{i} \begin{vmatrix} -3 & 1 \\ 1 & -2 \end{vmatrix} - \mathbf{j} \begin{vmatrix} 2 & 1 \\ 1 & -2 \end{vmatrix} + \mathbf{k} \begin{vmatrix} 2 & -3 \\ 1 & 1 \end{vmatrix}$$

$$= 5\mathbf{i} + 5\mathbf{j} + 5\mathbf{k},$$

which agrees with the previously obtained result.

---

*Example 14.5b.* A triangular pyramid has one vertex at the origin and the other three vertices at $(4, 0, 0)$, $(0, 2, 0)$, and $(0, 0, 3)$, respectively. If the vector area of each face is represented by an outward-drawn vector normal to that face, find the vector sum of these areas.

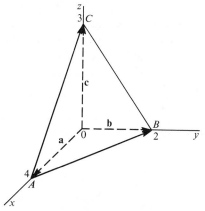

**FIGURE 14.5h**

From Figure 14.5h, it appears that the faces are the triangles determined by vector edges:

$$OAB: \quad \mathbf{a} = 4\mathbf{i}, \mathbf{b} = 2\mathbf{j}.$$
$$OBC: \quad \mathbf{b} = 2\mathbf{j}, \mathbf{c} = 3\mathbf{k}.$$
$$OAC: \quad \mathbf{a} = 4\mathbf{i}, \mathbf{c} = 3\mathbf{k}.$$
$$ABC: \quad \overrightarrow{AB} = 2\mathbf{j} - 4\mathbf{i}, \overrightarrow{AC} = 3\mathbf{k} - 4\mathbf{i}.$$

The vector area of each face is then calculated by using the fact that the area of a triangle is half that of a parallelogram on two of its sides. Thus,

$$A_1 = \tfrac{1}{2}\mathbf{b} \times \mathbf{a} = -4\mathbf{k},$$
$$A_2 = \tfrac{1}{2}\mathbf{c} \times \mathbf{b} = -3\mathbf{i},$$
$$A_3 = \tfrac{1}{2}\mathbf{a} \times \mathbf{c} = -6\mathbf{j},$$

and

$$A_4 = \tfrac{1}{2}\overrightarrow{AB} \times \overrightarrow{AC} = \tfrac{1}{2}\begin{vmatrix} \mathbf{i} & \mathbf{j} & \mathbf{k} \\ -4 & 2 & 0 \\ -4 & 0 & 3 \end{vmatrix}$$

$$= 3\mathbf{i} + 6\mathbf{j} + 4\mathbf{k}.$$

Evidently, $A_1 + A_2 + A_3 + A_4 = \mathbf{0}$.

*Note*: This is a special case of a general result that the reader will be asked to obtain in Exercises 14.5, Number 16.

---

As is true of the scalar product, if

$$\mathbf{a} \times \mathbf{b} = \mathbf{0},$$

it does *not* follow that $\mathbf{a} = \mathbf{0}$ or $\mathbf{b} = \mathbf{0}$, for the product is zero when $\mathbf{a}$ and $\mathbf{b}$ are parallel vectors. In particular, for every vector $\mathbf{a}$,

$$\mathbf{a} \times \mathbf{a} = \mathbf{0}.$$

We have already proved that the vector product is *not* commutative, and that we do have the relationship given by

**Theorem 14.5b.** $\qquad\qquad \mathbf{a} \times \mathbf{b} = -\mathbf{b} \times \mathbf{a}.$

Theorem 14.5b illustrates that the algebra of a set of vectors is very much *unlike* the algebra of ordinary real numbers. Another startling difference in the two algebras occurs in connection with the associative law, in that *the vector product is not associative!* That is,

$$\mathbf{a} \times (\mathbf{b} \times \mathbf{c}) \neq (\mathbf{a} \times \mathbf{b}) \times \mathbf{c}.$$

The reader can easily verify this statement by letting $\mathbf{a} = \mathbf{i}$, $\mathbf{b} = \mathbf{i}$, $\mathbf{c} = \mathbf{j}$, and evaluating the two expressions $\mathbf{a} \times (\mathbf{b} \times \mathbf{c})$ and $(\mathbf{a} \times \mathbf{b}) \times \mathbf{c}$.

## Exercises 14.5

1. Find $\mathbf{a} \times \mathbf{b}$, and make a diagram showing $\mathbf{a}$, $\mathbf{b}$ and $\mathbf{a} \times \mathbf{b}$ if

(a) $\mathbf{a} = (1, 2, -2)$, $\mathbf{b} = (2, 0, 1)$;     (c) $\mathbf{a} = \mathbf{i} - \mathbf{k}$, $\mathbf{b} = 2\mathbf{j} - 3\mathbf{k}$;

(b) $\mathbf{a} = (0, 0, 2)$, $\mathbf{b} = (3, 0, 1)$;     (d) $\mathbf{a} = 2\mathbf{i} - 3\mathbf{j} - \mathbf{k}$, $\mathbf{b} = -\mathbf{i} - 2\mathbf{j} + 3\mathbf{k}$.

2. Verify Theorem 14.5b if $\mathbf{a} = (0, -1, 2)$, $\mathbf{b} = (2, -1, 1)$.

3. Find the area of the parallelogram formed by the vectors

$$\mathbf{a} = 2\mathbf{i} - 3\mathbf{j} \quad \text{and} \quad \mathbf{b} = 4\mathbf{j} + 5\mathbf{k}.$$

4. If $\mathbf{a} = 2\mathbf{i} - \mathbf{j} + 3\mathbf{k}$, $\mathbf{b} = 3\mathbf{i} + 2\mathbf{j} - \mathbf{k}$, and $\mathbf{c} = \mathbf{i} - 3\mathbf{j} + 2\mathbf{k}$, find:
   (a) $\mathbf{a} \times (\mathbf{b} \times \mathbf{c})$;
   (b) $(\mathbf{a} \times \mathbf{b}) \times \mathbf{c}$;
   (c) $(\mathbf{a} + \mathbf{b}) \times (\mathbf{a} - \mathbf{b})$.
5. Find the area of a triangle having vertices at $A(2, 3, -1)$, $B(1, -2, 3)$, $C(-2, 1, 4)$.
6. Use the vector product to prove the Law of Sines.
7. Find a unit vector perpendicular to the plane of the vectors $\mathbf{a}$ and $\mathbf{b}$ if

$$\mathbf{a} = \mathbf{i} + 3\mathbf{j} - 2\mathbf{k} \quad \text{and} \quad \mathbf{b} = 2\mathbf{i} - \mathbf{j} - \mathbf{k}.$$

8. If $\mathbf{a} \times \mathbf{b} = \mathbf{0}$, is it true that $\mathbf{a}$ is parallel to $\mathbf{b}$?
9. Show that the vector product is not associative.
10. Show that $(\mathbf{a} - \mathbf{b}) \times (\mathbf{a} + \mathbf{b}) = 2\mathbf{a} \times \mathbf{b}$.
11. If $\mathbf{a} \times \mathbf{b} = \mathbf{a} \times \mathbf{c}$, does it follow that $\mathbf{b} = \mathbf{c}$? Explain.
12. If $\mathbf{a} = (a_1, a_2, a_3)$, $\mathbf{b} = (b_1, b_2, b_3)$, and $\mathbf{c} = (c_1, c_2, c_3)$, show that

$$\begin{vmatrix} \mathbf{i} & \mathbf{j} & \mathbf{k} \\ a_1 & a_2 & a_3 \\ b_1 + c_1 & b_2 + c_2 & b_3 + c_3 \end{vmatrix} = \begin{vmatrix} \mathbf{i} & \mathbf{j} & \mathbf{k} \\ a_1 & a_2 & a_3 \\ b_1 & b_2 & b_3 \end{vmatrix} + \begin{vmatrix} \mathbf{i} & \mathbf{j} & \mathbf{k} \\ a_1 & a_2 & a_3 \\ c_1 & c_2 & c_3 \end{vmatrix}.$$

13. Find the area of the parallelogram whose vertices are
   (a) $(3, 1, 1)$, $(-1, 1, -2)$, $(0, 4, -5)$, $(-4, 4, -8)$;
   (b) $(1, 3, -2)$, $(4, -1, 3)$, $(2, 1, 2)$, $(5, -3, 7)$.
14. Find all the unit vectors perpendicular to both $(3, -2, -2)$ and $(2, 3, 1)$.
15. Prove the result of Example 14.5b for a pyramid determined by three vectors $\mathbf{a}$, $\mathbf{b}$, and $\mathbf{c}$ concurrent at the origin.
16. Let $P$ denote a triangular prism. Show that the sum of the vector areas of the faces is $\mathbf{0}$, where the vector area of each face is represented by an outward-drawn normal.

## 14.6 MORE ABOUT MULTIPLE VECTOR PRODUCTS

As was indicated earlier, dot multiplication is not an associative operation on vectors because $\mathbf{a} \cdot \mathbf{b}$ is a scalar and $(\mathbf{a} \cdot \mathbf{b}) \cdot \mathbf{c}$ has no meaning. On the other hand, $\mathbf{a} \times \mathbf{b}$ is a vector, so that it is possible to form either a scalar or a vector product with it and another vector $\mathbf{c}$. The vector product

$$(\mathbf{a} \times \mathbf{b}) \times \mathbf{c},$$

which is called a **triple vector product,** has already been mentioned in connection with the fact that the associative law does not hold for vector multiplication; and the triple scalar product played an important role in proving the distributive property of vector multiplication (Theorem 14.5a).

Although several arrangements of scalar and vector multiplications are possible, not all such arrangements are meaningful. For example, the expression $(\mathbf{a} \cdot \mathbf{b})\mathbf{c}$ is meaningful, since $\mathbf{a} \cdot \mathbf{b}$ is a scalar, and the multiplication of $\mathbf{c}$ by a scalar is defined. On the other hand, the expression

$$(\mathbf{a} \cdot \mathbf{b}) \times \mathbf{c}$$

is *not* meaningful because a vector product cannot be formed between a scalar, $\mathbf{a} \cdot \mathbf{b}$, and a vector.

Of the various combinations of symbols, only

$$(\mathbf{a} \cdot \mathbf{b})\mathbf{c}, \quad \mathbf{a} \cdot (\mathbf{b} \times \mathbf{c}), \quad \text{and} \quad \mathbf{a} \times (\mathbf{b} \times \mathbf{c}) \quad \text{or} \quad (\mathbf{a} \times \mathbf{b}) \times \mathbf{c}$$

are meaningful. Just as with the scalar product, the parentheses in the first expression are not really necessary because $\mathbf{a} \cdot \mathbf{b}\mathbf{c}$ may be interpreted in only one meaningful way. The parentheses in $\mathbf{a} \times (\mathbf{b} \times \mathbf{c})$ *are* essential, however, because they denote the order in which the vectors must be combined, and $(\mathbf{a} \times \mathbf{b}) \times \mathbf{c}$ has already been shown to be different from $\mathbf{a} \times (\mathbf{b} \times \mathbf{c})$, in general

The work of Section 14.5 shows that if

$$\mathbf{a} = a_1\mathbf{i} + a_2\mathbf{j} + a_3\mathbf{k},$$
$$\mathbf{b} = b_1\mathbf{i} + b_2\mathbf{j} + b_3\mathbf{k},$$
$$\mathbf{c} = c_1\mathbf{i} + c_2\mathbf{j} + c_3\mathbf{k},$$

then

$$\mathbf{b} \times \mathbf{c} = \begin{vmatrix} \mathbf{i} & \mathbf{j} & \mathbf{k} \\ b_1 & b_2 & b_3 \\ c_1 & c_2 & c_3 \end{vmatrix}$$

$$= \begin{vmatrix} b_2 & b_3 \\ c_2 & c_3 \end{vmatrix} \mathbf{i} - \begin{vmatrix} b_1 & b_3 \\ c_1 & c_3 \end{vmatrix} \mathbf{j} + \begin{vmatrix} b_1 & b_2 \\ c_1 & c_2 \end{vmatrix} \mathbf{k}.$$

Thus,

$$\mathbf{a} \cdot \mathbf{b} \times \mathbf{c} = \begin{vmatrix} b_2 & b_3 \\ c_2 & c_3 \end{vmatrix} a_1 - \begin{vmatrix} b_1 & b_3 \\ c_1 & c_3 \end{vmatrix} a_2 + \begin{vmatrix} b_1 & b_2 \\ c_1 & c_2 \end{vmatrix} a_3,$$

which is the expansion along the first row of the third-order determinant with the $a$'s, the $b$'s, and the $c$'s in the respective rows. Thus, we have arrived at the important result:

$$\mathbf{a} \cdot \mathbf{b} \times \mathbf{c} = \begin{vmatrix} a_1 & a_2 & a_3 \\ b_1 & b_2 & b_3 \\ c_1 & c_2 & c_3 \end{vmatrix}.$$

This determinant is frequently a convenient tool for dealing with the triple scalar product $\mathbf{a} \cdot \mathbf{b} \times \mathbf{c}$.

---

*Example 14.6a.* Use the triple scalar product to show that the three points $(2, -1, 0)$ $(3, 1, 5)$, and $(0, 3, 6)$ all lie on a plane passing through the origin.

Consider the three position vectors

$$\mathbf{r}_1 = (2, -1, 0), \quad \mathbf{r}_2 = (3, 1, 5), \quad \mathbf{r}_3 = (0, 3, 6).$$

If the parallelepiped on these three vectors has zero volume, then the three vectors lie in a plane through the origin. (Why?) Accordingly, since

$$\mathbf{r}_1 \cdot \mathbf{r}_2 \times \mathbf{r}_3 = \begin{vmatrix} 2 & -1 & 0 \\ 3 & 1 & 5 \\ 0 & 3 & 6 \end{vmatrix}$$

$$= (2)(-9) - (-1)(18) + (0)(9) = 0,$$

the required result is demonstrated.

*Example 14.6b.* Find the perpendicular distance between the line through the points $A(1, 1, 1)$ and $B(-1, 3, 0)$ and the line through the points $C(0, 2, 4)$ and $D(0, 0, 1)$.

We know that $\overrightarrow{AB} \times \overrightarrow{CD}$ is a vector perpendicular to both $\overrightarrow{AB}$ and $\overrightarrow{CD}$. Consequently, the magnitude of the projection of $\overrightarrow{AC}$ on $\overrightarrow{AB} \times \overrightarrow{CD}$ will be the desired distance. We have, then,

$$d = \frac{|\overrightarrow{AC} \cdot \overrightarrow{AB} \times \overrightarrow{CD}|}{|\overrightarrow{AB} \times \overrightarrow{CD}|}.$$

Thus,

$$\overrightarrow{AB} \times \overrightarrow{CD} = (-2\mathbf{i} + 2\mathbf{j} - \mathbf{k}) \times (-2\mathbf{j} - 3\mathbf{k})$$
$$= -8\mathbf{i} - 6\mathbf{j} + 4\mathbf{k},$$

and

$$|\overrightarrow{AB} \times \overrightarrow{CD}| = \sqrt{64 + 36 + 16} = 2\sqrt{29},$$
$$\overrightarrow{AC} \cdot \overrightarrow{AB} \times \overrightarrow{CD} = (-\mathbf{i} + \mathbf{j} + 3\mathbf{k}) \cdot (-8\mathbf{i} - 6\mathbf{j} + 4\mathbf{k})$$
$$= 8 - 6 + 12 = 14.$$

Therefore,

$$d = \frac{14}{2\sqrt{29}} = \frac{7}{\sqrt{29}}.$$

Suppose the lines $AB$ and $CD$ in the preceding example were coplanar (lay in the same plane). Would the method used in this example work? If not, where would it break down?

The next example illustrates an application of vectors to the development of an interesting property of determinants.

*Example 14.6c.* Show that a triple scalar product in which two vectors are identical is zero.

This result is obvious geometrically since the triple scalar product represents the volume of a parallelepiped. If two of the three vectors in such a product are identical, then the associated parallelepiped has zero volume. This result can be expressed analytically as

$$\mathbf{a} \times \mathbf{b} \cdot \mathbf{a} = \begin{vmatrix} a_1 & a_2 & a_3 \\ b_1 & b_2 & b_3 \\ a_1 & a_2 & a_3 \end{vmatrix} = 0,$$

which shows that a determinant having two identical rows must have a value zero.

We now return to a consideration of the triple vector product. It is easy to show that $\mathbf{a} \times (\mathbf{b} \times \mathbf{c})$ is a vector in the plane of $\mathbf{b}$ and $\mathbf{c}$. Note first that $\mathbf{b} \times \mathbf{c}$ is perpendicular to the plane of $\mathbf{b}$ and $\mathbf{c}$. Note also that $\mathbf{a} \times (\mathbf{b} \times \mathbf{c})$ is perpendicular to $\mathbf{a}$ and to $\mathbf{b} \times \mathbf{c}$. Hence, the triple vector product must lie in the plane of $\mathbf{b}$ and $\mathbf{c}$. This result is another indication that if $\mathbf{a}$, $\mathbf{b}$, and $\mathbf{c}$ are three vectors not lying in the same plane, then generally

$$\mathbf{a} \times (\mathbf{b} \times \mathbf{c}) \neq (\mathbf{a} \times \mathbf{b}) \times \mathbf{c},$$

since the first of these lies in the plane of $\mathbf{b}$ and $\mathbf{c}$, whereas the second lies in the plane of $\mathbf{a}$ and $\mathbf{b}$.

If three vectors **a**, **b**, and **r** lie in the same plane, we can show as follows that there must exist scalar constants $\alpha$ and $\beta$ such that

$$\mathbf{r} = \alpha\mathbf{a} + \beta\mathbf{b}.$$

Since **a**, **b**, and **r** are in the same plane, then $\mathbf{a} \times \mathbf{b}$ is a vector parallel to $\mathbf{a} \times \mathbf{r}$ because both are normal to the plane. Hence, there is a constant $\beta$ such that

$$\beta\mathbf{a} \times \mathbf{b} = \mathbf{a} \times \mathbf{r};$$

that is,

$$\mathbf{a} \times (\mathbf{r} - \beta\mathbf{b}) = \mathbf{0},$$

so that $\mathbf{r} - \beta\mathbf{b}$ is either the zero vector or else a vector parallel to **a**. In either case there is a constant $\alpha$ (which might be zero) such that

$$\alpha\mathbf{a} = \mathbf{r} - \beta\mathbf{b},$$

or

$$\mathbf{r} = \alpha\mathbf{a} + \beta\mathbf{b}.$$

It is also worthwhile to look at a geometric proof of the same fact. In Figure 14.6a, the vectors **a**, **b**, and **r** are shown. Let **r** be fixed and let its origin and tip

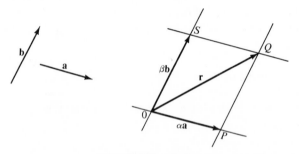

**FIGURE 14.6a**

be labeled $O$ and $Q$, respectively. We know from geometry that there is one and only one line through $O$ parallel to **a**, and similarly for **b**. This is also true for the point $Q$. Thus, there is a unique parallelogram $OPQS$, with **r** as its diagonal and with sides parallel to **a** and **b**, respectively. Since $\overrightarrow{OP}$ is parallel to **a**, it follows that $\overrightarrow{OP} = \alpha\mathbf{a}$, where $\alpha$ is a scalar constant. Similarly, $\overrightarrow{OS} = \beta\mathbf{b}$ so that

$$\mathbf{r} = \alpha\mathbf{a} + \beta\mathbf{b},$$

as before.

If three vectors **r**, **a**, and **b** are related by an equation of the preceding form, then **r** is said to be a **linear combination** of **a** and **b**. Accordingly, since the vector $\mathbf{a} \times (\mathbf{b} \times \mathbf{c})$ is in the plane of **b** and **c**, it must be a linear combination of **b** and **c**. Hence, there exist scalars $\alpha$ and $\beta$ such that

$$\mathbf{a} \times (\mathbf{b} \times \mathbf{c}) = \alpha\mathbf{b} + \beta\mathbf{c}.$$

Upon dotting both sides of this equation with **a**, we get

$$\mathbf{a} \cdot \mathbf{a} \times (\mathbf{b} \times \mathbf{c}) = 0 = \alpha\mathbf{a} \cdot \mathbf{b} + \beta\mathbf{a} \cdot \mathbf{c}.$$

In the trivial case in which **a** is perpendicular to the plane of **b** and **c** (and thus parallel to **b** × **c**), the triple vector product is zero and the two dot products **a** · **b** and **a** · **c** are both zero. In the general case, at least one of these dot products (say **a** · **c**) is not zero. We may then solve the preceding equation for $\beta$ to get

$$\beta = -\alpha \frac{\mathbf{a} \cdot \mathbf{b}}{\mathbf{a} \cdot \mathbf{c}},$$

so that

$$\mathbf{a} \times (\mathbf{b} \times \mathbf{c}) = \alpha\mathbf{b} - \alpha \frac{\mathbf{a} \cdot \mathbf{b}}{\mathbf{a} \cdot \mathbf{c}} \mathbf{c}$$

$$= \frac{\alpha}{\mathbf{a} \cdot \mathbf{c}} [(\mathbf{a} \cdot \mathbf{c})\mathbf{b} - (\mathbf{a} \cdot \mathbf{b})\mathbf{c}],$$

or

(1) $$\mathbf{a} \times (\mathbf{b} \times \mathbf{c}) = \lambda[(\mathbf{a} \cdot \mathbf{c})\mathbf{b} - (\mathbf{a} \cdot \mathbf{b})\mathbf{c}],$$

where $\lambda = \alpha/(\mathbf{a} \cdot \mathbf{c})$.

It now remains for us to determine $\lambda$. We do not know at this point whether or not $\lambda$ depends on **a**, **b**, and **c**. However, in the special case where **c** = **a**, Equation (1) becomes

$$\mathbf{a} \times (\mathbf{b} \times \mathbf{a}) = \lambda[(\mathbf{a} \cdot \mathbf{a})\mathbf{b} - (\mathbf{a} \cdot \mathbf{b})\mathbf{a}],$$

and upon forming the dot product with **b**, we get

$$\mathbf{b} \cdot \mathbf{a} \times (\mathbf{b} \times \mathbf{a}) = \lambda[(\mathbf{a} \cdot \mathbf{a})(\mathbf{b} \cdot \mathbf{b}) - (\mathbf{a} \cdot \mathbf{b})(\mathbf{a} \cdot \mathbf{b})],$$

or

$$(\mathbf{b} \times \mathbf{a}) \cdot (\mathbf{b} \times \mathbf{a}) = \lambda(|\mathbf{a}|^2|\mathbf{b}|^2 - |\mathbf{a}|^2|\mathbf{b}|^2 \cos^2 \theta),$$

where $\theta$ is the angle between **a** and **b**. Since

$$(\mathbf{b} \times \mathbf{a}) \cdot (\mathbf{b} \times \mathbf{a}) = |\mathbf{b} \times \mathbf{a}|^2 = |\mathbf{b}|^2|\mathbf{a}|^2 \sin^2 \theta,$$

the preceding equation may be written

$$|\mathbf{a}|^2|\mathbf{b}|^2 \sin^2 \theta = \lambda|\mathbf{a}|^2|\mathbf{b}|^2 \sin^2 \theta.$$

Thus, $\lambda = 1$ for this special case.

Returning to the general case, we dot multiply both sides of Equation (1) by **b** to get

(2) $$\mathbf{b} \cdot \mathbf{a} \times (\mathbf{b} \times \mathbf{c}) = \lambda[(\mathbf{a} \cdot \mathbf{c})(\mathbf{b} \cdot \mathbf{b}) - (\mathbf{a} \cdot \mathbf{b})(\mathbf{b} \cdot \mathbf{c})].$$

We may obtain another form for the left side of this equation by interchanging the dot and the first cross as follows:

$$\mathbf{b} \cdot \mathbf{a} \times (\mathbf{b} \times \mathbf{c}) = (\mathbf{b} \times \mathbf{a}) \cdot (\mathbf{b} \times \mathbf{c})$$
$$= (\mathbf{a} \times \mathbf{b}) \cdot (\mathbf{c} \times \mathbf{b})$$
$$= \mathbf{a} \cdot \mathbf{b} \times (\mathbf{c} \times \mathbf{b}).$$

Using the result found for the special case, we expand the last triple vector product to get

$$\mathbf{b} \cdot \mathbf{a} \times (\mathbf{b} \times \mathbf{c}) = \mathbf{a} \cdot [(\mathbf{b} \cdot \mathbf{b})\mathbf{c} - (\mathbf{b} \cdot \mathbf{c})\mathbf{b}]$$
$$= (\mathbf{b} \cdot \mathbf{b})(\mathbf{a} \cdot \mathbf{c}) - (\mathbf{b} \cdot \mathbf{c})(\mathbf{a} \cdot \mathbf{b}).$$

By comparing this with Equation (2), we see that $\lambda = 1$ even in the general case, so that always

(3) $$\mathbf{a} \times (\mathbf{b} \times \mathbf{c}) = (\mathbf{a} \cdot \mathbf{c})\mathbf{b} - (\mathbf{a} \cdot \mathbf{b})\mathbf{c}.$$

In many physical and geometrical problems, it is necessary to refer a vector given with respect to the usual *xyz*-coordinate system to some other coordinate system. That is, given a vector

$$\mathbf{u} = x\mathbf{i} + y\mathbf{j} + z\mathbf{k}$$

with respect to the $\mathbf{i}$, $\mathbf{j}$, $\mathbf{k}$ basis, we want its representation relative to some other basis (say, $\mathbf{e}_1$, $\mathbf{e}_2$, $\mathbf{e}_3$) where in the simplest cases the new basis is again a right-handed system of unit orthogonal vectors. The orientation of the new basis is easily checked by considering the triple scalar product $\mathbf{e}_1 \cdot \mathbf{e}_2 \times \mathbf{e}_3$, which, as we have previously noted, is positive for right-handed and negative for left-handed sets of three vectors. It has also been pointed out in Section 14.4 that if $\mathbf{e}$ is a unit vector, then $\mathbf{u} \cdot \mathbf{e}$ is the component of $\mathbf{u}$ in the direction of $\mathbf{e}$. Hence, if $\mathbf{e}$ is given in terms of the $\mathbf{i}$, $\mathbf{j}$, $\mathbf{k}$ basis, it is an easy matter to calculate the component of $\mathbf{u}$ in the direction of $\mathbf{e}$.

---

*Example 14.6d.* (a) Show that the following set of vectors is a right-handed set of unit orthogonal vectors:

$$\mathbf{e}_1 = \frac{1}{\sqrt{3}}(\mathbf{i} + \mathbf{j} + \mathbf{k}),$$

$$\mathbf{e}_2 = \frac{1}{\sqrt{6}}(\mathbf{i} - 2\mathbf{j} + \mathbf{k}),$$

$$\mathbf{e}_3 = \frac{1}{\sqrt{2}}(\mathbf{i} - \mathbf{k}).$$

(b) Express the vector $\mathbf{u} = 5\mathbf{i} - 2\mathbf{j} + 3\mathbf{k}$ in the form

$$\mathbf{u} = u_1\mathbf{e}_1 + u_2\mathbf{e}_2 + u_3\mathbf{e}_3.$$

(a) It is easy to show that $|\mathbf{e}_1| = |\mathbf{e}_2| = |\mathbf{e}_3| = 1$. This requires only the calculation of the three magnitudes. Furthermore,

$$\mathbf{e}_1 \cdot \mathbf{e}_2 = 0 = \mathbf{e}_1 \cdot \mathbf{e}_3 = \mathbf{e}_2 \cdot \mathbf{e}_3,$$

which shows the orthogonality of the three vectors.

Next, we have

$$(\sqrt{3}\mathbf{e}_1) \cdot (\sqrt{6}\mathbf{e}_2) \times (\sqrt{2}\mathbf{e}_3) = \begin{vmatrix} 1 & 1 & 1 \\ 1 & -2 & 1 \\ 1 & 0 & -1 \end{vmatrix} = 6,$$

so that

$$\mathbf{e}_1 \cdot \mathbf{e}_2 \times \mathbf{e}_3 = 1,$$

which means that the set $\mathbf{e}_1$, $\mathbf{e}_2$, $\mathbf{e}_3$ in this order has a right-handed orientation.

(b) Since $\mathbf{e}_1$, $\mathbf{e}_2$, $\mathbf{e}_3$ is an orthogonal set of unit vectors, we see that

$$\mathbf{u} = u_1\mathbf{e}_1 + u_2\mathbf{e}_2 + u_3\mathbf{e}_3 \implies \mathbf{u} \cdot \mathbf{e}_1 = u_1, \quad \mathbf{u} \cdot \mathbf{e}_2 = u_2, \quad \mathbf{u} \cdot \mathbf{e}_3 = u_3.$$

Hence, we calculate

$$\mathbf{u} \cdot \mathbf{e}_1 = (5, -2, 3) \cdot \frac{1}{\sqrt{3}} (1, 1, 1) = 2\sqrt{3},$$

$$\mathbf{u} \cdot \mathbf{e}_2 = (5, -2, 3) \cdot \frac{1}{\sqrt{6}} (1, -2, 1) = 2\sqrt{6},$$

$$\mathbf{u} \cdot \mathbf{e}_3 = (5, -2, 3) \cdot \frac{1}{\sqrt{2}} (1, 0, -1) = \sqrt{2},$$

which leads to the result

$$\mathbf{u} = 2\sqrt{3}\mathbf{e}_1 + 2\sqrt{6}\mathbf{e}_2 + \sqrt{2}\mathbf{e}_3.$$

The student is advised to check this answer by substituting the given expressions for $\mathbf{e}_1$, $\mathbf{e}_2$, and $\mathbf{e}_3$, and combining terms to recover the original form of $\mathbf{u}$.

## Exercises 14.6

In Numbers 1 to 4, find $\mathbf{a} \cdot \mathbf{b} \times \mathbf{c}$ and $\mathbf{a} \times (\mathbf{b} \times \mathbf{c})$. Verify in each case that $\mathbf{a} \times (\mathbf{b} \times \mathbf{c}) = (\mathbf{a} \cdot \mathbf{c})\mathbf{b} - (\mathbf{a} \cdot \mathbf{c})\mathbf{b}$.

1. $\mathbf{a} = \mathbf{i} - 2\mathbf{j} + \mathbf{k}$, $\mathbf{b} = -\mathbf{i} + 5\mathbf{j} - \mathbf{k}$, $\mathbf{c} = 3\mathbf{i} + 3\mathbf{j} + 2\mathbf{k}$.
2. $\mathbf{a} = (1, 1, 1)$, $\mathbf{b} = (-3, 2, 9)$, $\mathbf{c} = (5, 4, 3)$.
3. $\mathbf{a} = (0, 0, 1)$, $\mathbf{b} = (0, 1, 0)$, $\mathbf{c} = (1, 0, 0)$.
4. $\mathbf{a} = (1, 5, -2)$, $\mathbf{b} = (1, 0, 1)$, $\mathbf{c} = (3, 2, 4)$.

5. Find the volume of the parallelepiped that has one vertex at the origin and the three adjacent vertices at $(1, 0, 0)$, $(3, 2, 9)$, $(5, 2, -3)$.
6. Show how to construct a unit vector perpendicular to a vector $\mathbf{a}$ and lying in the plane of the two vectors $\mathbf{a}$ and $\mathbf{b}$. *Hint:* Consider the direction of $\mathbf{a} \times \mathbf{b}$. The required vector is perpendicular to this and to $\mathbf{a}$.

In Numbers 7 to 9, determine whether the given points lie on a plane through the origin.

7. $(1, 1, 1)$, $(2, 3, 5)$, $(6, 9, 7)$.
8. $(1, 6, -2)$, $(5, 4, 8)$, $(3, 5, 3)$.
9. $(3, 9, 1)$, $(6, 2, 8)$, $(1, 1, 4)$.

In Numbers 10 to 13, determine whether the four given points are coplanar.

10. $(1, 1, 6)$, $(2, 3, 5)$, $(8, 4, 6)$, $(2, 1, 3)$.
11. $(1, 3, 5)$, $(4, 9, 14)$, $(6, 7, 8)$, $(5, 8, 11)$.
12. $(4, 6, 2)$, $(3, -2, 8)$, $(-1, -1, 2)$, $(4, -6, 3)$.
13. $(1, 1, 2)$, $(-7, 4, -3)$, $(7, 3, 5)$, $(5, 8, 3)$.

14. Let $\mathbf{a}$, $\mathbf{b}$, and $\mathbf{c}$ be position vectors from the origin to the points $A$, $B$, and $C$, respectively. Show that the vector

$$\mathbf{a} \times \mathbf{b} + \mathbf{b} \times \mathbf{c} + \mathbf{c} \times \mathbf{a}$$

is perpendicular to the plane of $A$, $B$, and $C$. *Hint:* $\mathbf{a} - \mathbf{b}$ and $\mathbf{a} - \mathbf{c}$ are two vectors in the plane.
15. Are

$$\mathbf{e}_1 = (2, 2, 1), \quad \mathbf{e}_2 = (-2, 1, 2), \quad \mathbf{e}_3 = (1, -2, 2)$$

a set of orthogonal vectors? From this set obtain a set of unit vectors $f_1, f_2, f_3$, and write $u = 3i + j - 2k$ in the form

$$u_1f_1 + u_2f_2 + u_3f_3.$$

16. Given the basis

$$e_1 = \frac{1}{7}(2, 3, 6), \quad e_2 = \frac{1}{7}(3, -6, 2), \quad e_3 = \frac{1}{7}(6, 2, -3),$$

express each of the following vectors relative to this basis.

(a) $(1, 0, 0)$;      (b) $(1, 1, 1)$;      (c) $(x, y, z)$.

17. Show that

$$(a \times b) \times c = (a \cdot c)b - (b \cdot c)a.$$

18. Expand the product $(a \times b) \times (c \times d)$ in two ways: (a) by first writing $e = a \times b$ and using the appropriate triple vector product formula (see Number 17); (b) by first writing $f = (c \times d)$ and expanding by the corresponding formula. How do you explain the difference in the final resulting expressions?

19. Show that

$$a \times (b \times c) + b \times (c \times a) + c \times (a \times b) = 0.$$

20. If any three vectors $a$, $b$, and $c$ are given, we may always choose an $x$-axis along the vector $a$ so that $a = a_1i$. We may then choose a $y$-axis so that $b$ is in the $xy$-plane and hence $b = b_1i + b_2j$. The $z$-axis is then, of course, determined so that $c = c_1i + c_2j + c_3k$. Use these expressions for $a$, $b$, and $c$ to derive the result of Number 17. Does this constitute a general proof for the triple vector product formula? Explain.

## 14.7 THE PLANE

Suppose we are required to find an equation describing the plane that passes through a given point $P(p_1, p_2, p_3)$ and that is perpendicular to $OP$, the line from the origin to $P$ (see Figure 14.7a). Let $Q(x, y, z)$ be any point on the plane other than $P$, and let the position vector to $Q$ be denoted by $r$. Since the plane is perpendicular to $OP$ at $P$, we must have

$$\vec{PQ} \cdot \vec{OP} = 0,$$

or if $p .=. \vec{OP}$, then $\vec{PQ} = r - p$, and

(1) $$(r - p) \cdot p = 0.$$

Equation (1) is a vector form of the desired equation. It is evident, since $p - p = 0$, that the point $(p_1, p_2, p_3)$ satisfies this equation. For $r \neq p$, Equation (1) specifies that $\vec{PQ}$ is perpendicular to $\vec{OP}$, which is true if, and only if, the point $Q(x, y, z)$ is on the plane. Hence, all points on the plane (and only these points) satisfy the equation.

It is no more difficult to obtain the equation of a plane that passes through a point $R(a_1, a_2, a_3)$ and is perpendicular to the line $RS$, where $S(b_1, b_2, b_3)$ is a second given point. The reader may show that

(2) $$(\mathbf{r} - \mathbf{a}) \cdot (\mathbf{b} - \mathbf{a}) = 0$$

s the desired equation.

By using the distributive property of dot multiplication, we may rewrite Equation (1) in the form

$$\mathbf{r} \cdot \mathbf{p} = \mathbf{p}^2.$$

Then, upon dividing by $|\mathbf{p}|$, we get

(3) $$\mathbf{r} \cdot \mathbf{u}_p = p,$$

where $\mathbf{u}_p = \mathbf{p}/|\mathbf{p}|$ is a unit vector in the direction of $\mathbf{p}$, and where $p .=. |\mathbf{p}|$. Since $\mathbf{p}$ is a normal from the origin to the plane, $p$ is the perpendicular distance between the origin and the plane. Equation (3) is called the **normal form** of the equation of the plane.

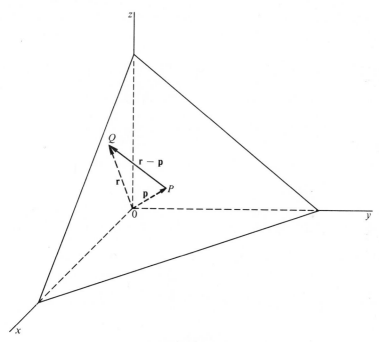

**FIGURE 14.7a**

Since $\mathbf{u}_p$ is a unit vector, it may be written in the form

$$\mathbf{u}_p = \mathbf{i} \cos \alpha + \mathbf{j} \cos \beta + \mathbf{k} \cos \gamma,$$

where $\alpha$, $\beta$, $\gamma$ are the direction angles of the normal $\mathbf{p}$. By writing $\mathbf{r} = x\mathbf{i} + y\mathbf{j} + z\mathbf{k}$, we may expand the scalar product on the left side of Equation (3) to obtain

(4) $$x \cos \alpha + y \cos \beta + z \cos \gamma - p = 0,$$

which is the usual normal form of the equation in rectangular cartesian coordinates.

If Equation (2) is expanded by replacing **r**, **a**, **b** by their respective equivalents in the **i**, **j**, **k** form, the result, after terms are combined, is of the form

$$(5) \qquad Ax + By + Cz + D = 0,$$

which is called a **linear equation** in $x$, $y$, $z$. This argument shows that every plane must have an equation of the form (5), since we may choose any point in a given plane, find a normal to the plane at this point, and repeat the same argument. The reader should note that (4) is also of the form of (5).

We shall show next that every equation of the form (5), for which not all three of $A$, $B$, $C$ are zero, is the equation of a plane. The plan of this demonstration is to try to show that every such equation is reducible to the form of Equation (4). We make use of the fact that any three numbers $A$, $B$, $C$ (not all zero) determine a direction in space, and that by dividing these numbers by one of the square roots of the sum of their squares, we convert them into a set of direction cosines.

Thus, to convert Equation (5) into the normal form, we divide by $\pm\sqrt{A^2 + B^2 + C^2}$, choosing the sign before the radical to be opposite to the sign of $D$ if $D \neq 0$. The equation then appears in the form

$$\frac{Ax + By + Cz}{\pm\sqrt{A^2 + B^2 + C^2}} + \frac{D}{\pm\sqrt{A^2 + B^2 + C^2}} = 0,$$

or, since the coefficients of $x$, $y$, $z$ are now direction cosines,

$$x \cos \alpha + y \cos \beta + z \cos \gamma - p = 0.$$

Notice that the sign before the radical is chosen opposite to that of $D$ (if $D \neq 0$) to make the sign before the $p$ of the final equation negative to agree with Equation (4).

If $D = 0$, $C \neq 0$, the sign before the radical is chosen so that the coefficient of $z$ is positive. If $D = C = 0$, $B \neq 0$, the sign is chosen to make the $y$-coefficient positive, and if $D = C = B = 0$, the sign is chosen to make the $x$-coefficient positive. (To what do these conventions correspond with reference to the positive direction of the normal?) In every case, the equation is reduced to the normal form (4), which was shown to be the equation of a plane. Hence, the linear equation is always that of a plane, and *the coefficients $A$, $B$, and $C$ are always direction numbers of a normal to the plane.*

---

*Example 14.7a.* Reduce the equation

$$2x + 3y - 6z + 14 = 0$$

to the normal form.

We have for the given equation

$$A^2 + B^2 + C^2 = 2^2 + 3^2 + (-6)^2 = 49 \quad \text{and} \quad D = 14.$$

Hence, we divide by $-\sqrt{49} = -7$ to get

$$-\frac{2}{7}x - \frac{3}{7}y + \frac{6}{7}z - 2 = 0.$$

This result indicates that the plane is at a distance of 2 units from the origin and that the direction cosines of the normal are

$$\cos \alpha = -\tfrac{2}{7}, \quad \cos \beta = -\tfrac{3}{7}, \quad \cos \gamma = \tfrac{6}{7}.$$

Since $\cos \gamma > 0$, the plane is reached from the origin by proceeding in the direction of increasing $z$ values on the normal.

---

By using vectors, it is easy to find the perpendicular distance from a given plane to a given point. If we let $\mathbf{r}$ be the position vector from the origin to any point $Q(x, y, z)$ on the plane and let $\mathbf{r}_1$ be the position vector to the given point $P(x_1, y_1, z_1)$. Then $\mathbf{r}_1 - \mathbf{r}$ is the vector $\overrightarrow{QP}$. The component of $\overrightarrow{QP}$ in the direction of the normal to the plane is the required directed distance *from* the plane to the point. Thus,

$$d = (\mathbf{r}_1 - \mathbf{r}) \cdot \mathbf{u}_p = \mathbf{r}_1 \cdot \mathbf{u}_p - \mathbf{r} \cdot \mathbf{u}_p,$$

where $\mathbf{u}_p$ is the unit normal to the plane. Also, since the distance of the plane from the origin is given by $\mathbf{r} \cdot \mathbf{u}_p = p$, we have

$$d = \mathbf{r}_1 \cdot \mathbf{u}_p - p.$$

Then, using

$$\mathbf{r}_1 = \mathbf{i}x_1 + \mathbf{j}y_1 + \mathbf{k}z_1$$

and

$$\mathbf{u}_p = \mathbf{i} \cos \alpha + \mathbf{j} \cos \beta + \mathbf{k} \cos \gamma,$$

we obtain

(5) $$d = x_1 \cos \alpha + y_1 \cos \beta + z_1 \cos \gamma - p.$$

Notice that this result means that the distance is found simply by substituting the coordinates of the given point into the left member of the normal form given in Equation (4).

---

*Example 14.7b.* Find the distance from the plane of Example 14.7a to the point $(4, -3, 1)$.

Using the normal form of the equation of the plane as found in Example 14.7a, we have

$$d = -(\tfrac{2}{7})(4) - (\tfrac{3}{7})(-3) + (\tfrac{6}{7})(1) - 2 = -1.$$

Thus, the distance is one unit and the point is on the same side of the plane as the origin. (Why?)

---

It appears from Figure 14.7b, in which the two planes are viewed on edge, that the acute angle $\theta$ between the planes is the same as the acute angle between their normals. Thus, if the equations of the planes are

$$A_1 x + B_1 y + C_1 z + D_1 = 0, \quad A_2 x + B_2 y + C_2 z + D_2 = 0,$$

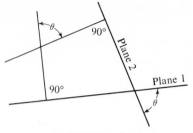

**FIGURE 14.7b**

then the angle $\theta$ can be found from

(7)
$$\cos \theta = \frac{|A_1 A_2 + B_1 B_2 + C_1 C_2|}{\sqrt{(A_1^2 + B_1^2 + C_1^2)(A_2^2 + B_2^2 + C_2^2)}}.$$

---

*Example 14.7c.* Find an equation of the plane that passes through the point $(0, 0, 1)$ is perpendicular to the *xz*-plane, and makes an angle $\text{Cos}^{-1} (\tfrac{1}{3})$ with the plane

$$x + 2y + 2z = 5.$$

Since the required plane is perpendicular to the *xz*-plane, we see that $\beta$, the angl that its normal makes with the *y*-axis, is $90°$. Therefore, $\cos \beta = 0$. Every such plan has an equation of the form

$$Ax + Cz + D = 0.$$

The point $(0, 0, 1)$ is to be òn the plane, so that

$$C + D = 0, \quad \text{or} \quad D = -C.$$

We now have $Ax + Cz - C = 0$ as the equation of a plane satisfying the first tw conditions. To satisfy the third condition, we use Formula (7) to write

$$\left| \frac{A + 2C}{3\sqrt{A^2 + C^2}} \right| = \frac{1}{3}.$$

This gives

$$(A + 2C)^2 = A^2 + C^2,$$

or

$$4AC + 3C^2 = 0.$$

Hence

$$C = 0 \quad \text{or} \quad 4A + 3C = 0.$$

For $C = 0$, we get $Ax = 0$, or since $A$ must be a nonzero constant, we divide b it to get

$$x = 0.$$

For $4A + 3C = 0$, we get $C = -\tfrac{4}{3}A$, so that $D = \tfrac{4}{3}A$. Thus, the equation may b written

$$Ax - \tfrac{4}{3}Az + \tfrac{4}{3}A = 0,$$

or

$$3x - 4z + 4 = 0.$$

The reader should check that the required conditions are satisfied by both the plane $x = 0$ and $3x - 4z + 4 = 0$.

It is sometimes of interest to find an equation of the plane through three given points. Such an equation is easily written by making use of the triple scalar product. If $\mathbf{r}$ is the position vector to a point $(x, y, z)$ in the plane, and $\mathbf{a}$, $\mathbf{b}$, $\mathbf{c}$ are the position vectors to the three given points $A$, $B$, $C$, respectively, then

$$\mathbf{r} - \mathbf{a}, \quad \mathbf{b} - \mathbf{a}, \quad \text{and} \quad \mathbf{c} - \mathbf{a}$$

are three vectors in the plane. Consequently,

$$(\mathbf{r} - \mathbf{a}) \cdot (\mathbf{b} - \mathbf{a}) \times (\mathbf{c} - \mathbf{a}) = 0.$$

(Explain.) This result may be written in the determinant form

$$\begin{vmatrix} x - a_1 & y - a_2 & z - a_3 \\ b_1 - a_1 & b_2 - a_2 & b_3 - a_3 \\ c_1 - a_1 & c_2 - a_2 & c_3 - a_3 \end{vmatrix} = 0,$$

which may then be expanded to obtain the usual linear form.

---

*Example 14.7d.* Find the equation of the plane through the three points $(1, 1, 1)$, $(2, -3, 0)$, $(5, 0, 6)$.

The desired equation may be written

$$\begin{vmatrix} x - 1 & y - 1 & z - 1 \\ 1 & -4 & -1 \\ 4 & -1 & 5 \end{vmatrix} = 0,$$

which gives

$$-21(x - 1) - 9(y - 1) + 15(z - 1) = 0,$$

or

$$7x + 3y - 5z - 5 = 0.$$

---

If the three given points are the points where the plane intersects the coordinate axes, say $(a, 0, 0)$, $(0, b, 0)$ and $(0, 0, c)$, it is easy to show that the equation may be reduced to the so-called **intercept form**:

$$\frac{x}{a} + \frac{y}{b} + \frac{z}{c} = 1.$$

This is left as an exercise for the reader.

Just as the concept of a family of lines proved useful in solving certain of the problems of plane analytic geometry, so does the concept of a family of planes prove useful. For instance, we may regard

$$\frac{x}{2} + \frac{y}{3} + \frac{z}{c} = 1$$

as the equation of the family of planes that pass through the two points $(2, 0, 0)$ and $(0, 3, 0)$. The $z$-intercept, $c$, is the parameter in this family.

---

*Example 14.7e.* Find the equation of each plane that has $x$-intercept 2, $y$-intercept 3, and is at distance $\frac{6}{7}$ from the origin.

We use the equation of the preceding family, since these planes all satisfy the intercept conditions. Putting this equation into the normal form, we find

$$p = \pm\left(\frac{1}{4} + \frac{1}{9} + \frac{1}{c^2}\right)^{-1/2}$$

Since $|p| = \frac{6}{7}$, we have

$$\left(\frac{13}{36} + \frac{1}{c^2}\right)^{1/2} = \frac{7}{6},$$

or

$$\frac{1}{c^2} = \frac{49}{36} - \frac{13}{36} = 1,$$

so that

$$c = \pm 1.$$

The required equations are thus

$$3x + 2y \pm 6z = 6.$$

## Exercises 14.7

1. Find an equation of each of the two planes that are 2 units away from the origin and have a normal that makes angles of $60°$ with both the $x$- and the $y$-axes.
2. Write an equation of the plane that passes through the point $(2, -1, 5)$ and is perpendicular to a line with direction numbers $[3, 4, -2]$.
3. If the planes $2x + 3y + z = 1$ and $4x + By + Cz = 8$ are parallel, what must be the values of $B$ and $C$?
4. If the planes $2x + 3y + z = 1$ and $x - 4y + Cz = 20$ are perpendicular, what must be the value of $C$?
5. Write an equation of the plane that passes through $(-3, 2, 0)$ and is parallel to the plane $3x - 4y + z = 7$.
6. Write an equation of the plane that passes through the origin and is perpendicular to a line with direction numbers $[2, -1, -2]$.
7. Find the equations of the planes for which $\alpha = 45°$, $\beta = 60°$, and $p = 6$.
8. How far is the plane $3x + 4y - 2z = 5$ from the origin?
9. How far is it from the plane $3x + 4y - 2z = 5$ to the point $(-1, 3, 5)$?
10. Find an equation of the plane that passes through the origin and is perpendicular to the intersection of the two planes

$$2x + 4y - 6z + 7 = 0,$$
$$x - 2y + 5z - 3 = 0.$$

11. Find an equation of the plane that passes through the point $(-2, 3, 1)$ and is perpendicular to the two planes $3x + 2y - z = 1$ and $2x - 5y + 4z = 7$.
12. The $y$-intercept of a plane is one unit shorter than its $z$-intercept and two units longer than its $x$-intercept. If the volume enclosed by the plane and the three coordinate planes is 15 cubic units, find an equation of the plane.
13. Find an equation of the plane that passes through the three points $(2, 5, 6)$ $(-3, 4, 4)$, and $(3, -4, 0)$.
14. Find the distance between the parallel planes

$$2x + y + 2z = -9 \quad \text{and} \quad 2x + y + 2z = 27.$$

5. Find an equation of the plane that passes through the two points $(2, 0, -1)$ and $(0, 2, 5)$ and that is perpendicular to the plane

$$3x + y - z = 7.$$

6. Carry out the details of obtaining the intercept form of the equation of a plane.

7. Show how to use the normal form of the equation of a plane to find the distance from a point to a line in the $xy$-plane. *Hint*: Let the line be regarded as the intersection of the $xy$-plane and a plane perpendicular to the $xy$-plane.

## 4.8 INTERSECTIONS OF PLANES

Let us consider the equation of a plane in the general form

$$Ax + By + Cz + D = 0.$$

The intersections of this plane with the coordinate planes can be found by putting $z = 0$ for the $xy$-plane, $y = 0$ for the $xz$-plane, and $x = 0$ for the $yz$-plane. Thus,

$$z = 0, \quad Ax + By + D = 0$$

are two equations that describe the intersection of the given plane with the $xy$-plane. In the $xy$-plane, the equation $Ax + By + D = 0$ is clearly that of a straight line. This straight line is called the **trace** of the given plane on the $xy$-plane. In a similar fashion, the equations of the traces on the other two coordinate planes may be written as

$$y = 0, \quad Ax + Cz + D = 0,$$

and

$$x = 0, \quad By + Cz + D = 0.$$

The second equation in each case is that of a straight line in the coordinate plane of the two variables appearing in the equation. Notice, however, that it takes two equations, such as $z = 0$, $Ax + By + D = 0$, to describe one of the lines.

The traces of a plane are quite helpful in making a sketch of the plane, as illustrated in the following example.

---

*Example 14.8a.* Find the traces and sketch the plane

$$3x + 6y + 4z = 12.$$

The equations of the traces are easily written down as follows:

$$xy\text{-plane:} \quad z = 0, \quad x + 2y = 4;$$
$$xz\text{-plane:} \quad y = 0, \quad 3x + 4z = 12;$$
$$yz\text{-plane:} \quad x = 0, \quad 3y + 2z = 6.$$

The sketch of the portion of the plane that lies in the $(+, +, +)$ octant is shown in Figure 14.8a.

---

Suppose next that the equations of two planes are given in the form

$$A_1x + B_1y + C_1z + D_1 = 0,$$
$$A_2x + B_2y + C_2z + D_2 = 0.$$

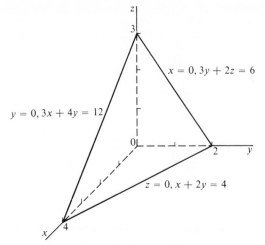

$$x = 0, 3y + 2z = 6$$

$$y = 0, 3x + 4y = 12$$

$$z = 0, x + 2y = 4$$

**FIGURE 14.8a**

Let us consider the following linear combination of these two equations:

(1)     $\lambda(A_1x + B_1y + C_1z + D_1) + \mu(A_2x + B_2y + C_2z + D_2) = 0,$

where $\lambda$ and $\mu$ are constants. This equation may be written as

(2)   $(\lambda A_1 + \mu A_2)x + (\lambda B_1 + \mu B_2)y + (\lambda C_1 + \mu C_2)z + \lambda D_1 + \mu D_2 = 0.$

Since all the coefficients are constants, it is evident that the last equation is also that of a plane. Furthermore, since every point whose coordinates satisfy both of the given equations will also lie on the plane given by (1) or (2), it is evident that (1) or (2) for fixed $\lambda$ and $\mu$ is always a plane that contains the intersection of the two given planes. For different values of $\lambda$ and $\mu$, the planes given by (2) will generally be different. We may regard Equation (1) or Equation (2) as being that of a family of planes through the intersection of the two given planes.

Since $\lambda$ and $\mu$ are at our disposal, let us investigate the results of certain special choices. Let us first choose $\lambda$ and $\mu$ so that $\lambda C_1 + \mu C_2 = 0$. This can always be done, for example, by taking $\lambda = C_2$ and $\mu = -C_1$. The resulting equation will be of the form

(3)                         $A_3x + B_3y + D_3 = 0.$

This single equation is that of a plane which must be perpendicular to the $xy$-plane (and thus parallel to the $z$-axis), since no matter what value is given to $z$, the relation between $x$ and $y$ is the same. In a similar manner, we may choose $\lambda$ and $\mu$ so that $\lambda B_1 + \mu B_2 = 0$ in order to obtain another equation, this time of the form

(4)                         $A_4x + C_4z + D_4 = 0,$

which is the equation of a plane perpendicular to the $xz$-plane (and hence parallel to the y-axis). Finally by choosing $\lambda$ and $\mu$ so that $\lambda A_1 + \mu A_2 = 0$, we obtain

(5) $$B_5 y + C_5 z + D_5 = 0,$$

the equation of a plane perpendicular to the yz-plane (and therefore parallel to the x-axis). All three of the planes given by (3), (4), and (5) pass through the intersection of the two given planes.

Suppose that none of the coefficients of $x$, $y$, $z$ in (4) and (5) is zero. Then, if we let $z = t$, we may solve for $x$ and $y$ to get the set of equations

$$x = -\frac{C_4}{A_4}t - \frac{D_4}{A_4}, \quad y = -\frac{C_5}{B_5}t - \frac{D_5}{B_5}, \quad z = t,$$

which are evidently parametric equations of a straight line.

Although we have made the special assumption that none of the coefficients is zero in order to arrive at the preceding parametric equations, it can be shown by considering the various possible cases that every pair of equations

$$A_1 x + B_1 y + C_1 z + D_1 = 0, \quad A_2 x + B_2 y + C_2 z + D_2 = 0$$

describes a pair of planes that either are parallel or else intersect in a straight line.

Equations (3), (4), and (5) are sometimes called the **projection forms** of the straight line equations. Of course, any two of these suffice to describe the line. A sketch of the line is usually easy to make when the projection forms of the equations are known.

---

*Example 14.8b.* Sketch the line given by

$$3x + 4y = 12, \quad 2x + z = 4.$$

The first plane is perpendicular to the xy-plane, cutting the x-axis at $(4, 0, 0)$ and the y-axis at $(0, 3, 0)$. The second plane is perpendicular to the xz-plane, cutting the -axis at $(2, 0, 0)$ and the z-axis at $(0, 0, 4)$. The sketch is given in Figure 14.8b. Notice

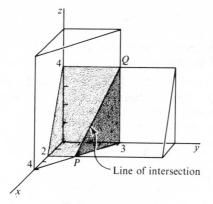

**FIGURE 14.8b**

that $P$ and $Q$ are the points where the line pierces the $xy$-plane and the $yz$-plane respectively. These two points are easily located, since $P$ is the intersection of the trace of the two projection planes on the $xy$-plane and $Q$ is the corresponding point in the $yz$-plane. The fact that the planes are projection planes means that each of these trace is parallel to one of the coordinate axes.

In order to summarize the work on the straight line in space, let us recal that in the early part of this chapter the line was given in vector form by

$$\mathbf{r} = \mathbf{a} + t\mathbf{c},$$

where $\mathbf{a}$ is a position vector to a point on the line and $\mathbf{c}$ is a vector along th line. If corresponding components in the preceding equation are equated, th result is the set of parametric equations

$$x = a_1 + tc_1,$$
$$y = a_2 + tc_2,$$
$$z = a_3 + tc_3.$$

If we rewrite the vector form of the equation by subtracting $\mathbf{a}$ from bot members and then cross multiplying by $\mathbf{c}$, we obtain

$$\mathbf{c} \times (\mathbf{r} - \mathbf{a}) = \mathbf{0}$$

since $\mathbf{c} \times \mathbf{c} = \mathbf{0}$. It is of interest to express this last equation in terms of th usual rectangular components. This gives

$$\begin{vmatrix} \mathbf{i} & \mathbf{j} & \mathbf{k} \\ c_1 & c_2 & c_3 \\ x - a_1 & y - a_2 & z - a_3 \end{vmatrix} = \mathbf{0},$$

which implies that the separate components must be zero. Hence, we find

$$c_2(z - a_3) - c_3(y - a_2) = 0,$$
$$c_3(x - a_1) - c_1(z - a_3) = 0,$$
$$c_1(y - a_2) - c_2(x - a_1) = 0,$$

which are exactly the projection forms of the straight line equation.

*Example 14.8c.* A line passes through the two points $(3, 1, 2)$ and $(1, 4, 3)$. In tw different ways find projection equations of the line.

(a) Let us choose to find the plane perpendicular to the $xy$-plane and the plane perpendicular to the $xz$-plane. The trace of the first of these must pass through th projections of the two given points on the $xy$-plane; that is, $(3, 1, 0)$ and $(1, 4, 0)$ Hence, the equations of this trace are

$$z = 0, \quad \frac{y - 1}{x - 3} = \frac{4 - 1}{1 - 3},$$

or

$$z = 0, \quad 3x + 2y = 11.$$

The second of the last two equations is the required projection equation. In a simila ashion, the trace of the second plane must pass through the points $(3, 0, 2)$ and $1, 0, 3)$. This leads to the equations

$$y = 0, \quad x + 2z = 7,$$

he second of these being the desired projection equation.

Thus, the straight line is given by the pair of projection equations:

$$3x + 2y = 11, \quad x + 2z = 7.$$

(b) We use the vector form

$$\mathbf{c} \times (\mathbf{r} - \mathbf{a}) = \mathbf{0},$$

where $\mathbf{a} = (3, 1, 2)$ and $\mathbf{c} = (3, 1, 2) - (1, 4, 3) = (2, -3, -1)$. Thus,

$$\begin{vmatrix} \mathbf{i} & \mathbf{j} & \mathbf{k} \\ 2 & -3 & -1 \\ x - 3 & y - 1 & z - 2 \end{vmatrix} = \mathbf{0},$$

or

$$\mathbf{i}(-3z + 6 + y - 1) - \mathbf{j}(2z - 4 + x - 3) + \mathbf{k}(2y - 2 + 3x - 9) = \mathbf{0}.$$

Since all three components must be zero, we have

$$\begin{aligned} y - 3z + 5 &= 0, \\ x + 2z - 7 &= 0, \\ 3x + 2y - 11 &= 0, \end{aligned}$$

which are all three of the projection equations.

---

*Example 14.8d.* Find the vector equation of the line of intersection of the planes $3x + y - 2z = 5$ and $x + 2y + z = 3$.

In order to write the required equation, we need a vector in the direction of the line and a point on the line. Since the line of intersection of the two planes lies in both planes, its direction must be perpendicular to the normals to the two planes. These normals have direction numbers $[3, 1, -2]$ and $\lceil 1, 2, 1 \rceil$, respectively, as indicated by the coefficients in the given equation. Consequently, a vector $\mathbf{c}$ perpendicular to these normals is given by

$$\mathbf{c} = (3, 1, -2) \times (1, 2, 1)$$

$$= \begin{vmatrix} \mathbf{i} & \mathbf{j} & \mathbf{k} \\ 3 & 1 & -2 \\ 1 & 2 & 1 \end{vmatrix}$$

$$= 5\mathbf{i} - 5\mathbf{j} + 5\mathbf{k}.$$

Any other vector in the direction of $\mathbf{c}$, such as

$$\mathbf{c}_1 = \mathbf{i} - \mathbf{j} + \mathbf{k},$$

would, of course, serve the same purpose.

A point on the line can be found by assigning a convenient value to one of $x$, $y$, $z$ in the given equations and then solving for the other two. For instance, putting $x = 0$, we have

$$y - 2z = 5, \quad 2y + z = 3,$$

which are satisfied by $y = \frac{11}{5}$, $z = -\frac{7}{5}$, so that $(0, \frac{11}{5}, -\frac{7}{5})$ is a point on the line.

Now, by using the vector form

$$\mathbf{r} = \mathbf{a} + t\mathbf{c}_1,$$

we have

$$\mathbf{r} = (0, \tfrac{11}{5}, -\tfrac{7}{5}) + t(1, -1, 1).$$

---

It is worth noting that symmetric equations of the line are fairly easy to find from the preceding equation. The parametric equations are

$$x = 0 + t, \quad y = \tfrac{11}{5} - t, \quad z = -\tfrac{7}{5} + t.$$

Upon solving these for $t$ and equating the results, we get

$$\frac{x}{1} = \frac{y - \tfrac{11}{5}}{-1} = \frac{z + \tfrac{7}{5}}{1}.$$

Direction cosines of the line are obtained by dividing each denominator by $\sqrt{3}$

## Exercises 14.8

In each of Numbers 1 to 4, find (a) the vector equation, (b) the projections of the line of intersection of the given planes.

1. $x + y + z = 1, \ 3x - y + 2z = 5.$    3. $8x - 9y + 3z = 2, \ y + z = 7.$
2. $2x + 3y - z = 5, \ x + y - 2z = 3.$    4. $3x - y + 7 = 0, \ 8x - 2y - z = 3.$

In each of Numbers 5 to 10, find (a) the vector equation, (b) the projection equations of the line through the given points.

5. $(1, 1, 5), (2, 3, 4).$    8. $(3, 3, 7), (3, 3, 12).$
6. $(1, 0, 2), (5, 2, 1).$    9. $(x_1, y_1, z_1), (x_2, y_2, z_2).$
7. $(-1, 3, 6), (-1, 2, 9).$    10. $(0, 0, 0), (a, b, c).$

11. Find the equation of the plane that passes through the line of intersection of the planes $3x - y + 2z = 5, \ 8x + 2y - z = 3$ and contains the origin.
12. Find the equation of the plane that passes through the line in Number 11 and contains the point $(1, 1, 1)$.
13. Find the angle between the line of intersection of $3x + y + 3z = 5$ with $x - y + z = 2$ and the line of intersection of $8x - y + 7z = 3$ with $x - y + z = 2$
14. What angle does the line of intersection of $3x + 4y = 12$ and $2x + z = 2$ make with the normal to the plane $x + y + 2z = 2$?
15. Find symmetric equations of the line that passes through the point $(5, -3, 4$ and is perpendicular to the plane $3x - y + 2z = 0$.
16. Find symmetric equations of the line that passes through the origin and is perpendicular to two lines with direction numbers $[3, -2, 4]$ and $[2, 3, -5]$, respectively.
17. Find the vector equation of the line whose projection on the $xy$-plane is given by $z = 0, \ x - 2y = 5$, and whose projection on the $yz$-plane is $x = 0, \ z = y + 2$
18. Write the vector equation of a line parallel to the $x$-axis. What would be projection equations of such a line?

19. Show that the line $5x - 2y + 3z = 5$, $x + 4y + 5z = -15$
    (a) lies in the plane $2x - 3y - z = 10$;
    (b) is parallel to the plane $x + y + 2z = 4$;
    (c) is perpendicular to the plane $x + y - z = 7$.

20. Let $A_1x + B_1y + C_1z + D_1 = 0$, $A_2x + B_2y + C_2z + D_2 = 0$, where

$$\frac{A_1}{A_2} = \frac{B_1}{B_2} \neq \frac{C_1}{C_2}, \quad C_1C_2 \neq 0,$$

be the equations of two planes. Show that these imply a corresponding set of parametric equations

$$x = x_0 + at, \quad y = y_0 + bt, \quad z = z_0.$$

Interpret geometrically.

21. Suppose that none of $x$, $y$, $z$ occurs in both the equations of two planes. What possible linear forms can be assumed by the parametric equations of the intersection of the two planes? Does this show that the intersection is always a straight line?

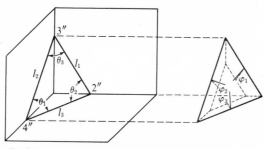

FIGURE 14.8c          FIGURE 14.8d

22. A man wishes to cut a triangular board to fit snugly in a corner, as shown in Figure 14.8c. Find the angles of the corners and the lengths of the edges on the outer face of the board. Find also the angles at which (Figure 14.8d) the saw blade must be set so that the cut edges will lie flat against the walls of the corner.

---

# Summary of Chapter 14

---

he use of vectors in analytic geometry is an extremely important and valuable syn-
esis of several mathematical ideas that were developed earlier. It is important
at the reader have a clear understanding of the related techniques as they are used
 this chapter in connection with

(1) the vector equation of a straight line (Section 14.1);
(2) the derivation of simple formulas, such as the point of division formula (Section 14.1);

(3) the location of points, distance between points, and direction numbers in three dimensions (Section 14.2);

(4) vector relationships in three dimensions, such as direction numbers and direction angles, and the equation of a line (Section 14.3);

(5) the dot product of two vectors and its geometric significance in connection with projections and orthogonality conditions (Section 14.4);

(6) the use of the dot product in describing geometric conditions vectorially (Section 14.4);

(7) the vector product of two vectors and its geometric significance (Section 14.5);

(8) the algebraic properties of the vector product as compared with algebraic properties of other types of products (Section 14.5);

(9) the geometric significance of the triple scalar product (Section 14.5);

(10) relationships involving multiple vector products and the reduction of such products to simpler forms (Section 14.6);

(11) the meaning of right-handed orthogonal sets of unit vectors (Section 14.6);

(12) the development of the equation of a plane, and the characterization of a plane by the direction numbers of a normal vector to the plane (Section 14.7);

(13) the intersections of planes (Section 14.8).

# Chapter 15     Matrices

## 15.1 SYSTEMS OF LINEAR EQUATIONS

From time to time, particularly in the two preceding chapters of this book, we have encountered problems that required the solution of a system of two equations in two unknowns. For example, it might be required to find the point of intersection of the two lines given by

$$2x - 3y = 6$$

and

$$x + 2y = 4.$$

In order to obtain the coordinates of the desired point, we may solve the second equation for $x$ and substitute the result in the first to get an equation in a single unknown. Thus,

$$x = 4 - 2y \quad \text{and} \quad 2(4 - 2y) - 3y = 6,$$

which imply that

$$y = \tfrac{2}{7} \quad \text{and} \quad x = \tfrac{24}{7}.$$

This purely mechanical process tends to obscure the real idea behind the determination of $x$ and $y$. For instance, what right do we have to replace the $x$ in one equation by the $x$ from the other equation? To answer this question, let us interpret each equation in terms of sets. If we let

$$S_1 .=. \ \{(x, y): 2x - 3y = 6\}$$

and

$$S_2 .=. \ \{(x, y): \ x + 2y = 4\},$$

then the problem of solving the system of equations becomes that of finding the intersection

$$S_1 \cap S_2$$

of the solution sets of the two equations. Geometrically speaking, this is equivalent to finding the point of intersection of two straight lines.

For any point common to both sets, the $x$-coordinates must be the same and the $y$-coordinates must be the same. The act of solving one equation for $x$ and substituting it in the other equation is based on this fact. Using this idea in a slightly different fashion, we may develop a formula for the solution of two equations in two unknowns in the general case. If

$$a_1 x + b_1 y = c_1$$

and

$$a_2 x + b_2 y = c_2,$$

then by multiplying the first equation by $b_2$ and the second by $b_1$, we get

$$a_1 b_2 x + b_1 b_2 y = c_1 b_2$$

and

$$a_2 b_1 x + b_1 b_2 y = c_2 b_1.$$

Subtraction of the second equation from the first now gives,

$$(a_1 b_2 - a_2 b_1) x = c_1 b_2 - c_2 b_1,$$

or, if $a_1 b_2 - a_2 b_1 \neq 0$,

$$x = \frac{c_1 b_2 - c_2 b_1}{a_1 b_2 - a_2 b_1}.$$

Similarly,

$$y = \frac{a_1 c_2 - a_2 c_1}{a_1 b_2 - a_2 b_1}.$$

If $a_1 b_2 - a_2 b_1 = 0$, so that the lines have the same direction numbers, and $c_1 b_2 - c_2 b_1 \neq 0$; then the solution sets have an empty intersection. (The line are parallel.) If both $a_1 b_2 - a_2 b_1 = 0$ and $c_1 b_2 - c_2 b_1 = 0$, then the solutio sets are identical and the two equations represent the same line.

In a similar way we may solve a system of three equations in three unknown or four equations in four unknowns, and so on. In the general problem, th number of equations and the number of unknowns need not be the same. Re gardless of the number of equations and the number of unknowns in a system the system does *not* depend upon the letters used to represent the unknown but rather depends only upon the *coefficients* of the unknowns.

For example, the system

$$\begin{aligned} 2x + y - z &= 0, \\ -x - 3y + z &= 4, \\ 3x - 2y - 3z &= -1 \end{aligned}$$

is essentially the same as the system

$$\begin{aligned} 2r + s - t &= 0, \\ -r - 3s + t &= 4, \\ 3r - 2s - 3t &= -1. \end{aligned}$$

Apparently, a system of equations of this type is characterized by the coefficien alone. For example, the numbers

$$\begin{bmatrix} 2 & 1 & -1 & 0 \\ -1 & -3 & 1 & 4 \\ 3 & -2 & -3 & -1 \end{bmatrix}$$

can be used to characterize the preceding system of equations, provided th relative positions of the numbers are not changed.

Let us solve this system by eliminating unknowns in the usual way, but at the same time, let us retain the characterization of the system, in terms of the coefficients alone. Thus, from

$$2r + s - t = 0, \qquad \begin{bmatrix} 2 & 1 & -1 & 0 \\ -1 & -3 & 1 & 4 \\ 3 & -2 & -3 & -1 \end{bmatrix},$$
$$-r - 3s + t = 4, \quad \text{or}$$
$$3r - 2s - 3t = -1,$$

after adding three times the second equation to the third, we get

$$2r + s - t = 0, \qquad \begin{bmatrix} 2 & 1 & -1 & 0 \\ -1 & -3 & 1 & 4 \\ 0 & -11 & 0 & 11 \end{bmatrix}.$$
$$-r - 3s + t = 4, \quad \text{or}$$
$$0 - 11s + 0 = 11,$$

Next, after adding the second equation to the first and interchanging the last two equations, we obtain

$$r - 2s + 0 = 4, \qquad \begin{bmatrix} 1 & -2 & 0 & 4 \\ 0 & -11 & 0 & 11 \\ -1 & -3 & 1 & 4 \end{bmatrix}.$$
$$0 - 11s + 0 = 11, \quad \text{or}$$
$$-r - 3s + t = 4,$$

The interchange of equations is made purely as a matter of convenience.

We continue by adding the first equation to the third and dividing the second equation by $-11$ to get

$$r - 2s + 0 = 4, \qquad \begin{bmatrix} 1 & -2 & 0 & 4 \\ 0 & 1 & 0 & -1 \\ 0 & -5 & 1 & 8 \end{bmatrix}.$$
$$0 + s + 0 = -1, \quad \text{or}$$
$$0 - 5s + t = 8,$$

Finally, upon multiplying the second equation by 2 and adding the result to the first, and also upon multiplying the second equation by 5 and adding the result to the last equation, we get

$$r + 0 + 0 = 2, \qquad \begin{bmatrix} 1 & 0 & 0 & 2 \\ 0 & 1 & 0 & -1 \\ 0 & 0 & 1 & 3 \end{bmatrix}.$$
$$0 + s + 0 = -1, \quad \text{or}$$
$$0 + 0 + t = 3,$$

It is now obvious that the desired solution is

$$r = 2, \quad s = -1, \quad t = 3.$$

Each time that a manipulation on an equation is made, an identical manipulation is made on the corresponding row of the array of numbers. Hence, the array of numbers also indicates the solution of the system of equations. In fact, the simplicity of manipulating rows in the array of numbers suggests that it might be easier to solve a system of equations by using the array of coefficients rather than by working directly with the equations themselves. With this possibility in mind, we shall study rectangular arrays of numbers in some detail.

We shall call a rectangular array of numbers a **matrix**. Examples of matrices are the arrays of numbers that accompanied the system of equations in the preceding discussion. A matrix having three rows and four columns, as occurred for this system, is called a "three by four" or a "3 × 4" matrix, the number of rows always being given first. If we wish to discuss a general $3 \times 4$ matrix, we write

$$\begin{bmatrix} a_{11} & a_{12} & a_{13} & a_{14} \\ a_{21} & a_{22} & a_{23} & a_{24} \\ a_{31} & a_{32} & a_{33} & a_{34} \end{bmatrix},$$

where the $a_{11}$, $a_{12}$ (read "a-one-one," "a-one-two") and so on represent real numbers. The double subscript notation is convenient to identify the location of an element in the matrix. For example, $a_{32}$ represents the element in the third row and the second column of a matrix. The first subscript always identifies the row to which the element belongs and the second identifies the column to which it belongs. Thus, in the matrix

$$\begin{bmatrix} 2 & 6 & 0 & 4 \\ 0 & 2 & -1 & 1 \\ 3 & 5 & -3 & -2 \end{bmatrix},$$

the element $a_{23}$ is $-1$, the element $a_{34}$ is $-2$, and the element $a_{13}$ is 0.

To save space in writing, it is especially convenient to represent a matrix $A$ in an abbreviated form such as

$$A = [a_{ij}]_{mn},$$

or simply as

$$A = [a_{ij}],$$

where $a_{ij}$ is a typical element in the matrix. The subscripts on the brackets indicate the number of rows, $m$, and columns, $n$, in the matrix, and are called the **dimensions** of the matrix.

## Exercises 15.1

1. What matrix characterizes each of the following systems of equations?

(a) $2x - y = 3,$
$\quad x \quad = 1.$

(b) $-x + 2y - 1 = 0,$
$\quad 2x - y + 2 = 0,$
$\quad 3x + y - 4 = 0.$

(c) $3x - y + 2z = 4,$
$\quad x - 2y - z = 1,$
$\quad 2x + y - 3z = 7.$

(d) $w + x - y + 2z = 1,$
$\quad w + 2x + y \quad = 3,$
$\quad\quad\quad y + z = 2.$

2. What system of equations could be represented by each of the following matrices?

(a) $\begin{bmatrix} 2 & 0 & 1 & 3 \\ -1 & 2 & 3 & 0 \\ 0 & 0 & 1 & 1 \end{bmatrix},$ (b) $\begin{bmatrix} 1 & 2 & 3 \\ 3 & 2 & 1 \\ 1 & 0 & 1 \\ 3 & 0 & 2 \end{bmatrix},$ (c) $\begin{bmatrix} 0 & 1 & 0 & 2 & 0 & 3 \\ -1 & 1 & 0 & 1 & 2 & 3 \\ 2 & -2 & 0 & 2 & 1 & 3 \\ 3 & -1 & 0 & -1 & 2 & 0 \end{bmatrix}.$

3. Given the matrix

$$A = \begin{bmatrix} 1 & 0 & 3 & 1 & 4 & -2 \\ 2 & -1 & 3 & 7 & 4 & -3 \\ 0 & 2 & 9 & -6 & 1 & 4 \\ 3 & 2 & 5 & 0 & 1 & 0 \\ 0 & 0 & 1 & -4 & 4 & 0 \end{bmatrix}.$$

(a) What is the element $a_{24}$? the element $a_{54}$? the element $a_{43}$? the element $a_{26}$?

(b) Which elements are equal to 2? to 3? to 5?

4. Is it possible for two distinct systems of linear equations to have the same matrix representation?

5. Solve the system $2x - 3y = 6$, $x + 2y = 4$ by operating on the rows of the matrix

$$\begin{bmatrix} 2 & -3 & 6 \\ 1 & 2 & 4 \end{bmatrix}.$$

6. Solve the system $2x - y = 10$, $3x + 2y = 1$ by operating on the rows of the matrix

$$\begin{bmatrix} 2 & -1 & 10 \\ 3 & 2 & 1 \end{bmatrix}.$$

7. Solve the system

$$\begin{aligned} 2x + y + z &= -6, \\ x - 2y - 3z &= 7, \\ -3x + 2y + 2z &= 2, \end{aligned}$$

by operating on the rows of the matrix

$$\begin{bmatrix} 2 & 1 & 1 & -6 \\ 1 & -2 & -3 & 7 \\ -3 & 2 & 2 & 2 \end{bmatrix}.$$

8. Solve the system

$$\begin{aligned} 2x + 4y - z &= 1, \\ -x - 2y + z &= -3, \\ 3x + 2y + 3z &= -5, \end{aligned}$$

by operating on the rows of the matrix

$$\begin{bmatrix} 2 & 4 & -1 & 1 \\ -1 & -2 & 1 & -3 \\ 3 & 2 & 3 & -5 \end{bmatrix}.$$

## 15.2 OPERATIONS ON MATRICES

A matrix represents a kind of algebraic element unlike any of the elements we have encountered up to this point, although in special cases a matrix may resemble a vector. For example, a vector was denoted by an ordered triple

$$\mathbf{a} = (a_1, a_2, a_3).$$

A $1 \times 3$ matrix such as

$$\begin{bmatrix} a_1 & a_2 & a_3 \end{bmatrix},$$

or even a $3 \times 1$ matrix such as

$$\begin{bmatrix} a_1 \\ a_2 \\ a_3 \end{bmatrix},$$

would appear to be a suitable representation of a vector.

Later we shall find it extremely useful to represent vectors in one or the other of these two matrix forms. A matrix of the first form is called a **row matrix,** and a matrix of the second form is called a **column matrix.**

In any case, if we hope to make matrices an efficient tool, we shall certainly find it necessary to develop an algebra for them. The first step in this direction is to specify under what conditions two matrices $A$ and $B$ will be equal.

**Definition 15.2a.** $A_{mn} = B_{mn} \Leftrightarrow a_{ij} = b_{ij}; i = 1, 2, \ldots, m; j = 1, 2, \ldots, n$. That is, two matrices are equal if and only if they are of the same dimensions and have identical elements in identical positions.

Next, we need to define some algebraic operations such as "addition" and "multiplication" for matrices. Just how such operations should be defined is not obvious, since operations may be defined in many different ways. The definitions that we ultimately agree to use are those that provide us with useful applications.

For example, if matrices are used as vectors in some cases, then they must satisfy a rule of addition that is equivalent to the rule of addition for vectors. Since vectors are "added" element by element, that is, since

$$(a_1, a_2, a_3) + (b_1, b_2, b_3) = (a_1 + b_1, a_2 + b_2, a_3 + b_3),$$

it appears that the "addition" of matrices should be defined in a similar way.

**Definition 15.2b.** If $A .=. [a_{ij}]_{mn}$ and $B .=. [b_{ij}]_{mn}$, then

$$A + B .=. [a_{ij} + b_{ij}]_{mn}.$$

Thus, if

$$A .=. \begin{bmatrix} 2 & -1 & 2 \\ 0 & 2 & 3 \end{bmatrix} \text{ and } B .=. \begin{bmatrix} -2 & 3 & -1 \\ 1 & 4 & 3 \end{bmatrix},$$

then

$$A + B = \begin{bmatrix} 2 + (-2) & (-1) + 3 & 2 + (-1) \\ 0 + 1 & 2 + 4 & 3 + 3 \end{bmatrix} = \begin{bmatrix} 0 & 2 & 1 \\ 1 & 6 & 6 \end{bmatrix}.$$

Addition for matrices is not defined when the matrices are of different dimensions. Consequently, whenever an addition of matrices is indicated, it must be understood that the matrices have the same dimensions.

That matrix addition has both the associative and the commutative properties is stated in the next theorems.

**Theorem 15.2a.** $(A + B) + C = A + (B + C)$.

PROOF: Let $A = [a_{ij}]_{mn}$, $B = [b_{ij}]_{mn}$, $C = [c_{ij}]_{mn}$. Then, by Definition 15.2b,

$$A + B = [a_{ij} + b_{ij}]_{mn},$$

and

$$(A + B) + C = [(a_{ij} + b_{ij}) + c_{ij}]_{mn}.$$

Similarly,

$$B + C = [b_{ij} + c_{ij}]_{mn},$$

and

$$A + (B + C) = [a_{ij} + (b_{ij} + c_{ij})]_{mn}.$$

By the associative law of addition for numbers,

$$(a_{ij} + b_{ij}) + c_{ij} = a_{ij} + (b_{ij} + c_{ij}).$$

Hence
$$(A + B) + C = A + (B + C),$$
as was to be shown.

**Theorem 15.2b.** $A + B = B + A$.

PROOF: Left to the reader.

A matrix having all elements zero is called a 0-matrix (zero-matrix), and will be denoted by 0, or by $0_{mn}$ when the dimensions are to be specified. An $m \times n$ 0-matrix is the additive identity for general $m \times n$ matrices.

**Theorem 15.2c.** The set of all $m \times n$ matrices whose elements are taken from a specified field is a group with respect to matrix addition.

PROOF: Left for the reader.

Another concept that is suggested by operations on vectors is multiplication by a scalar, as in
$$k(a_1, a_2, a_3) = (ka_1, ka_2, ka_3).$$
This result has a natural extension to matrices.

**Definition 15.2c.** If $k$ is a real number and if $A .=. [a_{ij}]_{mn}$, then
$$kA .=. Ak .=. [ka_{ij}]_{mn}.$$

For example,
$$3 \begin{bmatrix} 2 & -1 & 3 \\ 4 & 2 & 0 \end{bmatrix} = \begin{bmatrix} 6 & -3 & 9 \\ 12 & 6 & 0 \end{bmatrix}.$$

The following distributive laws are consequences of this definition and may easily be verified by the reader.

**Theorem 15.2d.** $(k + m)A = kA + mA$.

**Theorem 15.2e.** $k(A + B) = kA + kB$.

Another useful operation on a matrix is one that interchanges rows and columns.

**Definition 15.2d.** If $A .=. [a_{ij}]_{mn}$, then the matrix
$$B .=. [b_{ij}]_{nm},$$
where
$$b_{ij} = a_{ji}$$
is called the **transpose** of $A$, and is denoted by $A^T$.

For example, if
$$A .=. \begin{bmatrix} 1 & 3 & 0 \\ -1 & 2 & 1 \end{bmatrix},$$
then
$$A^T = \begin{bmatrix} 1 & -1 \\ 3 & 2 \\ 0 & 1 \end{bmatrix}.$$

In particular, if $A$ is a row matrix, then $A^T$ is a column matrix.

Certain basic properties of the transpose of a matrix are given in the next two theorems.

**Theorem 15.2f.** $(A^T)^T = A$.

PROOF: Let

$$A = [a_{ij}]_{mn}.$$

Then

$$A^T = [b_{ij}]_{nm}, \qquad b_{ij} = a_{ji}.$$

We also have

$$(A^T)^T = [c_{ij}]_{mn}, \qquad c_{ij} = b_{ji}.$$

However, since $b_{ij} = a_{ji}$, then $b_{ji} = a_{ij}$. Hence, $c_{ij} = a_{ij}$, and

$$(A^T)^T = [a_{ij}]_{mn} = A.$$

**Theorem 15.2g.** $(A + C)^T = A^T + C^T$.

PROOF: Left to the reader.

There are several important special types of matrices that appear in practical considerations from time to time.

**Definition 15.2e.** A matrix $A_{mn}$ for which $m = n$ is called a **square matrix.**

**Definition 15.2f.** If $A = [a_{ij}]$ is a square matrix for which $A^T = A$, that is, $a_{ij} = a_{ji}$, then $A$ is called a **symmetric matrix.**

Thus

$$\begin{bmatrix} 1 & -1 & 2 \\ -1 & 2 & 3 \\ 2 & 3 & 0 \end{bmatrix}$$

is a symmetric matrix.

**Definition 15.2g.** A square matrix $A = [a_{ij}]$ for which $A^T = -A$, that is, $a_{ij} = -a_{ji}$, is called a **skew-symmetric matrix.**

The reader may verify that the matrix

$$A = \begin{bmatrix} 0 & -2 & 1 & -3 \\ 2 & 0 & -1 & 0 \\ -1 & 1 & 0 & 2 \\ 3 & 0 & -2 & 0 \end{bmatrix}$$

is skew-symmetric.

**Definition 15.2h.** A square matrix $A = [a_{ij}]$, for which $a_{ij} = 0$ for every $i > j$, is called a **triangular matrix.**

For example,

$$\begin{bmatrix} 1 & 4 & 1 & 6 \\ 0 & -2 & 5 & 2 \\ 0 & 0 & 3 & 3 \\ 0 & 0 & 0 & 1 \end{bmatrix}$$

is a triangular matrix.

In a square matrix, the elements in the diagonal from the extreme upper left to the extreme lower right constitute what is called the **main diagonal.** In a triangular matrix, all elements below the main diagonal have the value zero.

**Definition 15.2i.** A **diagonal matrix** is a square matrix for which $a_{ij} = 0$ for $i \neq j$; that is, for which all elements off the main diagonal are zero.

### Exercises 15.2

1. Prove Theorem 15.2b.
2. Prove Theorem 15.2c.
3. Prove Theorem 15.2d.

4. Prove Theorem 15.2e.
5. Prove Theorem 15.2g.

6. Show that every square matrix may be written as the sum of a symmetric and a skew-symmetric matrix by first showing that, for any $A$, $A + A^{\mathsf{T}}$ is symmetric and $A - A^{\mathsf{T}}$ is skew-symmetric.

7. Prove that $(kA)^{\mathsf{T}} = kA^{\mathsf{T}}$.

8. If

$$A .= . \begin{bmatrix} 2 & -1 \\ 3 & 2 \end{bmatrix}, \quad B .= . \begin{bmatrix} 4 & 2 \\ -3 & -1 \end{bmatrix}, \quad C .= . \begin{bmatrix} -2 & -3 \\ -1 & 1 \end{bmatrix},$$

find each of the following:

(a) $2A + 3B$;
(b) $A + B^{\mathsf{T}}$;

(c) $-2A + B + C^{\mathsf{T}}$;
(d) $A^{\mathsf{T}} - B + C^{\mathsf{T}}$.

9. If

$$A .= . \begin{bmatrix} 1 & 3 & 0 \\ -1 & 0 & 2 \\ -3 & 1 & -1 \end{bmatrix}, \quad B .= . \begin{bmatrix} 2 & -1 & 2 \\ -1 & 0 & 1 \\ 2 & 1 & 2 \end{bmatrix}, \quad C .= . \begin{bmatrix} -1 & 3 & 2 \\ -1 & 2 & 3 \\ -1 & 1 & -1 \end{bmatrix},$$

find

(a) $2A - 3B$;
(b) $A - 2B + 2C$;
(c) $2A^{\mathsf{T}} - B^{\mathsf{T}}$;

(d) $A^{\mathsf{T}} + B^{\mathsf{T}}$;
(e) $(A + B)^{\mathsf{T}}$.

10. With reference to the matrices in Number 8, find values of $k$ and $m$ (if they exist) such that $kA + mB = 0$.

11. With reference to the matrices in Number 8, find values of $k$, $m$, $n$ (if they exist) such that $kA + mB + nC = 0$.

12. Prove that in a skew-symmetric matrix the main diagonal elements must be zero.

13. Prove that $A + C = B + C \Leftrightarrow A = B$.

## 15.3 MATRIX MULTIPLICATION

As was indicated in the first section of this chapter, matrices are intimately associated with systems of linear equations such as

$$a_1 x + b_1 y = c_1,$$
$$a_2 x + b_2 y = c_2.$$

In 1843, the English mathematician, Cayley, discovered that a system of linear equations could be represented as a linear equation in matrix form provided the product of matrices is defined in an appropriate way. For example, by using the matrices.

$$A .=. \begin{bmatrix} a_1 & b_1 \\ a_2 & b_2 \end{bmatrix}, \quad X .=. \begin{bmatrix} x \\ y \end{bmatrix}, \quad C .=. \begin{bmatrix} c_1 \\ c_2 \end{bmatrix},$$

we may write the preceding system of equations as

$$AX = C,$$

where

$$AX = \begin{bmatrix} a_1 & b_1 \\ a_2 & b_2 \end{bmatrix} \begin{bmatrix} x \\ y \end{bmatrix}$$

represents the matrix

$$\begin{bmatrix} a_1x + b_1y \\ a_2x + b_2y \end{bmatrix}.$$

When this matrix is set equal to $C$, the equations of the system are obtained by equating corresponding elements of $AX$ and $C$. The matrix $AX$ is called the **product** of $A$ and $X$.

Although this method of defining a product of two matrices appears complicated, and is somewhat surprising, it is also suggested by other important considerations, as will be seen later. To see how the product is actually formed, we shall find it convenient to make use of the dot product of two vectors.

Let $\mathbf{a} = (a_1, a_2)$ and $\mathbf{b} = (b_1, b_2)$. Then the dot product of $\mathbf{a}$ and $\mathbf{b}$ is the scalar

$$\mathbf{a} \cdot \mathbf{b} .=. a_1b_1 + a_2b_2.$$

It was suggested in the second section of this chapter that a row or column matrix can be used to represent a vector. Thus, let

$$\mathbf{a} = A .=. \begin{bmatrix} a_1 & a_2 \end{bmatrix}$$

and

$$\mathbf{b} = B .=. \begin{bmatrix} b_1 \\ b_2 \end{bmatrix}.$$

Then the dot product of the two vectors may be written in matrix form as

$$AB = \begin{bmatrix} a_1 & a_2 \end{bmatrix} \begin{bmatrix} b_1 \\ b_2 \end{bmatrix} = \begin{bmatrix} a_1b_1 + a_2b_2 \end{bmatrix}.$$

The reason for writing the second vector as a column matrix instead of a row matrix is simply a matter of convenience in expressing products in general.

If we wish to form the product

$$AX = \begin{bmatrix} a_1 & b_1 \\ a_2 & b_2 \end{bmatrix} \begin{bmatrix} x \\ y \end{bmatrix},$$

then we regard the matrix $A$ as a matrix of two row vectors, $R_1$ and $R_2$, where each row vector is to be multiplied by the column vector

$$\begin{bmatrix} x \\ y \end{bmatrix}.$$

Then the matrix product may be written as

$$AX = \begin{bmatrix} R_1 \\ R_2 \end{bmatrix} X = \begin{bmatrix} R_1 X \\ R_2 X \end{bmatrix}$$
$$= \begin{bmatrix} a_1 x + b_1 y \\ a_2 x + b_2 y \end{bmatrix},$$

where it is to be understood that a product such as $R_1 X$ appearing in a matrix represents the scalar element of the one-by-one matrix $R_1 X$.

A matrix is said to be **partitioned** when its rows (or columns) are treated as individual matrices representing vectors. The partitioning of a matrix is often convenient in simplifying a discussion involving the rows or columns of a matrix.

The definition of the product of two matrices is motivated by a desire to systematize such a problem as the following. Let $x_1$ and $x_2$ be given in terms of $y_1$ and $y_2$ by a set of linear equations:

$$x_1 = a_{11} y_1 + a_{12} y_2,$$
$$x_2 = a_{21} y_1 + a_{22} y_2.$$

Furthermore, let $y_1$ and $y_2$ be given similarly in terms of $z_1$ and $z_2$ by

$$y_1 = b_{11} z_1 + b_{12} z_2,$$
$$y_2 = b_{21} z_1 + b_{22} z_2.$$

We want to express the $x$'s directly in terms of the $z$'s.

Direct substitution of the $y$'s from the second set of equations into the first yields

$$x_1 = (a_{11} b_{11} + a_{12} b_{21}) z_1 + (a_{11} b_{12} + a_{12} b_{22}) z_2,$$
$$x_2 = (a_{21} b_{11} + a_{22} b_{21}) z_1 + (a_{21} b_{12} + a_{22} b_{22}) z_2.$$

Using the matrix notation just introduced, we may write

$$X \doteq \begin{bmatrix} x_1 \\ x_2 \end{bmatrix}, \quad Y \doteq \begin{bmatrix} y_1 \\ y_2 \end{bmatrix}, \quad Z \doteq \begin{bmatrix} z_1 \\ z_2 \end{bmatrix},$$
$$A \doteq \begin{bmatrix} a_{11} & a_{12} \\ a_{21} & a_{22} \end{bmatrix}, \quad B \doteq \begin{bmatrix} b_{11} & b_{12} \\ b_{21} & b_{22} \end{bmatrix},$$
$$C \doteq \begin{bmatrix} a_{11} b_{11} + a_{12} b_{21} & a_{11} b_{12} + a_{12} b_{22} \\ a_{21} b_{11} + a_{22} b_{21} & a_{21} b_{12} + a_{22} b_{22} \end{bmatrix}.$$

Then the three sets of equations in matrix form appear thus:

$$X = AY, \quad Y = BZ, \quad X = CZ.$$

We can hardly resist the temptation to obtain the third equation from the first two by direct substitution for $Y$, which gives

$$X = ABZ.$$

If this is to be correct, then we must have

$$AB = C.$$

It is possible to state this result in terms of dot products of row and column vectors, as was previously done for the product $AX$. Let $A$ be partitioned into row vectors so that

$$A = \begin{bmatrix} R_1 \\ R_2 \end{bmatrix},$$

where $R_1 .=. [a_{11} \quad a_{12}]$ and $R_2 .=. [a_{21} \quad a_{22}]$. Similarly, let $B$ be partitioned into column vectors so that

$$B = [C_1 \quad C_2],$$

where

$$C_1 .=. \begin{bmatrix} b_{11} \\ b_{21} \end{bmatrix} \quad \text{and} \quad C_2 .=. \begin{bmatrix} b_{12} \\ b_{22} \end{bmatrix}.$$

Then

$$AB = \begin{bmatrix} R_1 \\ R_2 \end{bmatrix} [C_1 \quad C_2] .=. \begin{bmatrix} R_1C_1 & R_1C_2 \\ R_2C_1 & R_2C_2 \end{bmatrix},$$

which is exactly the matrix denoted by $C$, as the reader may easily verify.

This pattern can be extended to provide a general definition for the product of two matrices.

**Definition 15.3a.** Let

$$A .=. \begin{bmatrix} a_{11} & a_{12} & \cdots & a_{1n} \\ a_{21} & a_{22} & \cdots & a_{2n} \\ \vdots & \vdots & & \vdots \\ a_{m1} & a_{m2} & \cdots & a_{mn} \end{bmatrix} = \begin{bmatrix} R_1 \\ R_2 \\ \vdots \\ R_m \end{bmatrix},$$

and let

$$B .=. \begin{bmatrix} b_{11} & b_{12} & \cdots & b_{1p} \\ b_{21} & b_{22} & \cdots & b_{2p} \\ \vdots & \vdots & & \vdots \\ b_{n1} & b_{n2} & \cdots & b_{np} \end{bmatrix} = [C_1 \quad C_2 \quad \cdots \quad C_p].$$

Then

$$AB .=. [c_{ij}]_{mp},$$

where

$$c_{ij} = R_iC_j$$

$$= [a_{i1} \quad a_{i2} \quad \cdots \quad a_{in}] \begin{bmatrix} b_{1j} \\ b_{2j} \\ \vdots \\ b_{nj} \end{bmatrix}$$

$$= a_{i1}b_{1j} + a_{i2}b_{2j} + \cdots + a_{in}b_{nj}$$

$$= \sum_{\alpha=1}^{n} a_{i\alpha}b_{\alpha j}.$$

This definition means that the $ij$th element in the product $AB$ is formed from the dot product of the *i*th row vector of $A$ and the *j*th column vector of $B$. The reader should observe that the definition of multiplication applies only when the left-hand matrix has exactly as many columns as the right-hand matrix has rows. In this case the matrices are said to be **conformable.** Thus,

$$\begin{bmatrix} 1 & 2 & -1 \\ 3 & 0 & 1 \end{bmatrix} \begin{bmatrix} 2 & 1 & 0 \\ -1 & 2 & 3 \\ 0 & 1 & 2 \end{bmatrix}$$

$$= \begin{bmatrix} (1)(2)+(2)(-1)+(-1)(0) & (1)(1)+(2)(2)+(-1)(1) & (1)(0)+(2)(3)+(-1)(2) \\ (3)(2)+(0)(-1)+(1)(0) & (3)(1)+(0)(2)+(1)(1) & (3)(0)+(0)(3)+(1)(2) \end{bmatrix}$$

$$= \begin{bmatrix} 0 & 4 & 4 \\ 6 & 4 & 2 \end{bmatrix}.$$

In contrast to the preceding illustration, the product

$$\begin{bmatrix} 2 & 1 & 0 \\ -1 & 2 & 3 \\ 0 & 1 & 2 \end{bmatrix} \begin{bmatrix} 1 & 2 & -1 \\ 3 & 0 & 1 \end{bmatrix}$$

is not defined, since the two matrices are not conformable.

This result shows at once that matrix multiplication is *not* a commutative operation. That is, in general,

$$AB \neq BA.$$

This result was so startling to most mathematicians of the middle 1800's that they refused to give matrices serious consideration for several years.

In addition to the noncommutativity of matrix multiplication, another even more surprising result appears in the next example.

---

*Example 15.3a.* Find $AB$ if

$$A = \begin{bmatrix} 1 & -1 \\ 2 & -2 \end{bmatrix}, \quad B = \begin{bmatrix} 1 & 0 \\ 1 & 0 \end{bmatrix}.$$

By using Definition 15.3a, it is easy to verify that

$$AB = \begin{bmatrix} 0 & 0 \\ 0 & 0 \end{bmatrix}.$$

---

The result of Example 15.3a shows that the product of two nonzero matrices may be a zero-matrix. Such a result does not occur in the familiar algebraic systems of numbers. As the reader must surmise by now, the usual properties of the number system do not hold for matrices. Accordingly, it becomes necessary to investigate carefully the properties of matrix multiplication.

For example, can we be certain that matrix multiplication is associative? The next theorem provides the answer.

**Theorem 15.3a.** If $A$, $B$, $C$, are matrices, then

$$A(BC) = (AB)C$$

whenever the products are defined.

PROOF: This theorem can be proved most easily in the case when $A$, $B$, $C$ are each $2 \times 2$ matrices. The details of the argument are more difficult in the general case and will not be given here. The reader may show that the theorem is true in the $2 \times 2$ case, by considering

$$\begin{bmatrix} a_{11} & a_{12} \\ a_{21} & a_{22} \end{bmatrix} \left( \begin{bmatrix} b_{11} & b_{12} \\ b_{21} & b_{22} \end{bmatrix} \begin{bmatrix} c_{11} & c_{12} \\ c_{21} & c_{22} \end{bmatrix} \right)$$

and

$$\left( \begin{bmatrix} a_{11} & a_{12} \\ a_{21} & a_{22} \end{bmatrix} \begin{bmatrix} b_{11} & b_{12} \\ b_{21} & b_{22} \end{bmatrix} \right) \begin{bmatrix} c_{11} & c_{12} \\ c_{21} & c_{22} \end{bmatrix}.$$

The proof for the general case uses essentially the same idea, depending only on the basic laws of addition and multiplication of numbers.

We can also show that matrix multiplication is distributive with respect to addition, as indicated in

**Theorem 15.3b.** If $A$, $B$, $C$ are matrices, then

$$A(B + C) = AB + AC.$$

PROOF: Let

$$A = [a_{ij}]_{mn}, \quad B = [b_{ij}]_{np}, \quad C = [c_{ij}]_{np}.$$

Then

$$A(B + C) = [a_{ij}]_{mn}[b_{ij} + c_{ij}]_{np}$$

$$= \left[ \sum_{k=1}^{n} a_{ik}(b_{kj} + c_{kj}) \right]_{mp}$$

Similarly,

$$AB = \left[ \sum_{k=1}^{n} a_{ik} b_{kj} \right]_{mp}$$

and

$$AC = \left[ \sum_{k=1}^{n} d_{ik} c_{kj} \right]_{mp},$$

so that

$$AB + AC = \left[ \sum_{k=1}^{n} a_{ik} b_{kj} + \sum_{k=1}^{n} a_{ik} c_{kj} \right]_{mp}$$

$$= \left[ \sum_{k=1}^{n} (a_{ik} b_{kj} + a_{ik} c_{kj}) \right]_{mp}$$

$$= \left[ \sum_{k=1}^{n} a_{ik}(b_{kj} + c_{kj}) \right]_{mp}.$$

Therefore,

$$A(B + C) = AB + AC.$$

The reader is again cautioned that familiar algebraic rules do not always hold for matrices. Another example will illustrate this fact quite clearly. First we need to define the "power" of a matrix.

**Definition 15.3b.** Let $A^1 .=. A$, and for $k = 2, 3, 4, \ldots$, let

$$A^{k+1} .=. A^k A.$$

Thus, the power of a matrix is defined by induction for positive integral exponents.

---

*Example 15.3b.* Show that, in general, $(A + B)^2 \neq A^2 + 2AB + B^2$.

By the distributive law, we have

$$\begin{aligned}
(A + B)^2 &= (A + B)(A + B) \\
&= (A + B)A + (A + B)B \\
&= A^2 + BA + AB + B^2.
\end{aligned}$$

The last expression is *not* equal to $A^2 + 2AB + B^2$ unless $AB = BA$, which, as we have seen, is generally not true.

---

Another deviation from the familiar occurs in connection with the determination of a multiplicative identity.

**Definition 15.3c.** If a square matrix $S_{nn}$ has the property that

$$X_{mn} S_{nn} = X_{mn}$$

for every $m \times n$ matrix $X_{mn}$, then $S_{nn}$ is called a **right identity** for $m \times n$ matrices.

**Definition 15.3d.** If a square matrix $T_{mm}$ has the property that

$$T_{mm} X_{mn} = X_{mn}$$

for every $m \times n$ matrix $X_{mn}$, then $T_{mm}$ is called a **left identity** for $m \times n$ matrices.

If $A$ is not a square matrix, then it follows at once from the preceding two definitions that

$$T_{mm} \neq S_{nn},$$

since $m \neq n$.

To illustrate: observe that

$$\begin{bmatrix} a_1 & a_2 & a_3 \\ b_1 & b_2 & b_3 \end{bmatrix} \begin{bmatrix} 1 & 0 & 0 \\ 0 & 1 & 0 \\ 0 & 0 & 1 \end{bmatrix} = \begin{bmatrix} a_1 & a_2 & a_3 \\ b_1 & b_2 & b_3 \end{bmatrix},$$

so that

$$\begin{bmatrix} 1 & 0 & 0 \\ 0 & 1 & 0 \\ 0 & 0 & 1 \end{bmatrix}$$

is a right identity for $m \times 3$ matrices. Observe also that

$$\begin{bmatrix} 1 & 0 \\ 0 & 1 \end{bmatrix} \begin{bmatrix} a_1 & a_2 & a_3 \\ b_1 & b_2 & b_3 \end{bmatrix} = \begin{bmatrix} a_1 & a_2 & a_3 \\ b_1 & b_2 & b_3 \end{bmatrix},$$

so that

$$\begin{bmatrix} 1 & 0 \\ 0 & 1 \end{bmatrix}$$

is a left identity for $2 \times n$ matrices.

Since so many "unusual" results occur with matrix multiplication, we may well wonder if the right or left identities are unique. That is, if

$$XS_1 = X \quad \text{and} \quad XS_2 = X,$$

does it follow that $S_1 = S_2$? Since $XS_1$ and $XS_2$ are both equal to $X$, we have

$$XS_1 = XS_2.$$

However, may we conclude that $S_1 = S_2$? As yet, we have no cancellation law for matrices such as we have for numbers, so that another approach must be used. Although we may write

$$XS_1 - XS_2 = 0,$$

or

$$X(S_1 - S_2) = 0,$$

it does not follow from this alone that $S_1 = S_2$, since it is possible for the product of two matrices to be zero without either matrix being equal to zero. In this case, we must make use of the fact that the equation

$$X(S_1 - S_2) = 0$$

must hold for *every* matrix $X$ that can be multiplied by $S_1 - S_2$. For example, in the case in which $S_1$ and $S_2$ are $3 \times 3$ matrices, suppose that $X$ is a matrix with $a_{11} \neq 0$ and with all other elements zero. Then if

$$S_1 - S_2 = \begin{bmatrix} s_{11} & s_{12} & s_{13} \\ s_{21} & s_{22} & s_{23} \\ s_{31} & s_{32} & s_{33} \end{bmatrix},$$

we have

$$\begin{bmatrix} a_{11} & 0 & 0 \\ 0 & 0 & 0 \\ 0 & 0 & 0 \end{bmatrix} \begin{bmatrix} s_{11} & s_{12} & s_{13} \\ s_{21} & s_{22} & s_{23} \\ s_{31} & s_{32} & s_{33} \end{bmatrix} = \begin{bmatrix} a_{11}s_{11} & a_{11}s_{12} & a_{11}s_{13} \\ 0 & 0 & 0 \\ 0 & 0 & 0 \end{bmatrix},$$

which must equal the zero-matrix. Accordingly,

$$a_{11}s_{11} = 0, \quad a_{11}s_{12} = 0, \quad a_{11}s_{13} = 0,$$

and since $a_{11} \neq 0$, it follows that $s_{11} = 0$, $s_{12} = 0$, $s_{13} = 0$.

In a similar way, each $s_{ij}$ can be shown to be zero by means of special choice for $X$, so that we may properly conclude that $S_1 = S_2$. Furthermore, it is evident that the $n \times n$ matrix $I_{nn}$, with 1's on the main diagonal and zeros elsewhere, is a right identity for all $m \times n$ matrices, so that it must be the unique right identity for such matrices. In a similar way, it follows that the $m \times m$ matrix $I_{mm}$, with 1's on the main diagonal and zeros elsewhere, is the unique left identity for $m \times n$ matrices. As a consequence of these two facts, we have

**Theorem 15.3c.** The matrix $I_{nn}$ having 1's on the main diagonal and zeros everywhere else is both the right and the left multiplicative identity for $n \times n$ matrices.

If the order of a square matrix $A$ is understood, then the identity matrix is usually denoted by $I$ without subscripts. The preceding theorem may then be stated:

$$IA = AI = A.$$

## Exercises 15.3

1. If

$$A .=. \begin{bmatrix} 2 & -1 \\ 3 & 2 \end{bmatrix}, \quad B .=. \begin{bmatrix} 4 & 2 \\ -3 & -1 \end{bmatrix}, \quad C .=. \begin{bmatrix} -2 & -3 \\ 2 & -1 \\ -1 & 2 \end{bmatrix}, \quad D .=. \begin{bmatrix} 1 & 2 & 3 \\ 3 & 2 & 0 \end{bmatrix},$$

find each of the following:

(a) $AB$;

(b) $BA$;

(c) $CA$;

(d) $CD$;

(e) $DC + AB$;

(f) $(AB)D$ and $A(BD)$.

2. Find the following products:

(a) $\begin{bmatrix} 1 & -1 & 0 \\ 0 & 1 & -1 \\ 1 & 0 & -1 \end{bmatrix} \begin{bmatrix} 2 & 2 & 2 \\ 2 & 2 & 2 \\ 2 & 2 & 2 \end{bmatrix}$;

(b) $\begin{bmatrix} 1 & 2 \\ -1 & 2 \\ 0 & 3 \\ 1 & -1 \end{bmatrix} \begin{bmatrix} 0 & 2 & 3 \\ 1 & -1 & 1 \end{bmatrix}$;

(c) $\begin{bmatrix} 1 & 2 & -1 & 0 \\ 0 & -1 & 1 & 0 \end{bmatrix} \begin{bmatrix} 1 & 0 \\ -1 & 3 \\ 2 & -1 \\ 1 & 2 \end{bmatrix}$;

(d) $\begin{bmatrix} 1 & 2 & 1 & -1 \\ 0 & -1 & 3 & -2 \\ 2 & -1 & 0 & 1 \end{bmatrix} \begin{bmatrix} 1 \\ -1 \\ 1 \\ 0 \end{bmatrix}$.

3. Find $A^2$ if

$$A .= \begin{bmatrix} 0 & 2 & 0 \\ 2 & 3 & 1 \\ 0 & 1 & -1 \end{bmatrix}.$$

4. Find $A^3$ for the matrix of Number 3.

5. Find $A^2$ if

$$A = \begin{bmatrix} 2i & 3-i \\ 1 & 2+4i \end{bmatrix}.$$

6. Find $A^2$ if

$$A = \begin{bmatrix} i & 1-i & 0 \\ -i & 0 & -1 \\ 3 & 0 & 2 \end{bmatrix}.$$

7. Find $A^4$ if

$$A = \begin{bmatrix} 0 & 1 & 0 & 0 \\ 0 & 0 & 1 & 0 \\ 0 & 0 & 0 & 1 \\ 0 & 0 & 0 & 0 \end{bmatrix}.$$

8. Prove that $(AB)^T = B^T A^T$.
9. Prove that if $A$ is a square matrix, then $AA^T$ is symmetric.
10. Prove or disprove that $(AB)^2 = A^2 B^2$.
11. Prove or disprove that $A^2 - B^2 = (A - B)(A + B)$.
12. Show that $AA^k = A^k A$, $k \in \mathfrak{N}$. *Hint:* Use mathematical induction and the associative law of matrix multiplication.
13. Does the power of a matrix obey the law of exponents $A^m A^n = A^{m+n}$, $m, n \in \mathfrak{N}$? Explain.
14. A toy manufacturer uses screws, nails, braces, and clamps in assembling three models of toys. The following table shows the number required for each toy:

|                    | Toy A | Toy B | Toy C |
|--------------------|-------|-------|-------|
| Number of screws   | 6     | 3     | 4     |
| Number of nails    | 5     | 4     | 3     |
| Number of clamps   | 2     | 1     | 5     |
| Number of braces   | 2     | 0     | 1     |

The manufacturer's production schedule for the last six months of the year is as follows:

|       | July | Aug | Sept | Oct | Nov | Dec |
|-------|------|-----|------|-----|-----|-----|
| Toy A | 7    | 6   | 8    | 9   | 12  | 6   |
| Toy B | 4    | 3   | 5    | 7   | 8   | 2   |
| Toy C | 0    | 1   | 4    | 6   | 9   | 1   |

Use matrix multiplication to determine the inventory of parts needed each month for the assembly of the toys.

15. Observe that if

$$J = \begin{bmatrix} 1 & 0 & 0 \\ x & 0 & y \\ 0 & 0 & 1 \end{bmatrix} \quad \text{and} \quad A = \begin{bmatrix} 1 & 0 & 1 \\ 2 & 0 & 0 \end{bmatrix},$$

then

$$AJ = \begin{bmatrix} 1 & 0 & 1 \\ 2 & 0 & 0 \end{bmatrix} = A.$$

That is, $J$ is a right identity of $A$. Does this fact contradict the statement in the text that

$$I = \begin{bmatrix} 1 & 0 & 0 \\ 0 & 1 & 0 \\ 0 & 0 & 1 \end{bmatrix}$$

is a *unique* right identity for $2 \times 3$ matrices? Explain.

16. If

$$A = \begin{bmatrix} 2 & 2 & -1 \\ 2 & -1 & 3 \\ -3 & 2 & 1 \end{bmatrix} \quad \text{and} \quad B = \begin{bmatrix} -3 & 1 & -2 \\ 3 & 2 & 0 \\ 2 & -1 & 3 \end{bmatrix},$$

let $B_1, B_2, B_3$ denote the rows of $B$, and show that

$$AB = \begin{bmatrix} 2B_1 + 2B_2 - B_3 \\ 2B_1 - B_2 + 3B_3 \\ -3B_1 + 2B_2 + B_3 \end{bmatrix}.$$

## 15.4 EQUIVALENT MATRICES

The operations carried out on the system of equations in the first section of this chapter were all operations on the rows of the matrix of the system. These operations are of three basic types.

(1) The interchange of two rows.
(2) Multiplication of a row by a scalar.
(3) Addition of one row to another.

These three operations are called **elementary row operations** on a matrix.

It is possible to carry out elementary row operations on a matrix $A$ by multiplying $A$ on the left by an appropriate matrix. For example, if we wish to interchange the second and third rows of

$$A .=. \begin{bmatrix} a_{11} & a_{12} & a_{13} \\ a_{21} & a_{22} & a_{23} \\ a_{31} & a_{32} & a_{33} \end{bmatrix},$$

we can do so by multiplying $A$ on the left by the matrix

$$\begin{bmatrix} 1 & 0 & 0 \\ 0 & 0 & 1 \\ 0 & 1 & 0 \end{bmatrix}.$$

Thus

$$\begin{bmatrix} 1 & 0 & 0 \\ 0 & 0 & 1 \\ 0 & 1 & 0 \end{bmatrix} \begin{bmatrix} a_{11} & a_{12} & a_{13} \\ a_{21} & a_{22} & a_{23} \\ a_{31} & a_{32} & a_{33} \end{bmatrix} = \begin{bmatrix} a_{11} & a_{12} & a_{13} \\ a_{31} & a_{32} & a_{33} \\ a_{21} & a_{22} & a_{23} \end{bmatrix}.$$

Similarly, **premultiplication** (multiplication on the left) of $A$ by the matrix

$$\begin{bmatrix} 1 & 0 & 0 \\ 0 & k & 0 \\ 0 & 0 & 1 \end{bmatrix}$$

yields the matrix $A$ with its second row multiplied by $k$. Premultiplication of $A$ by

$$\begin{bmatrix} 1 & 0 & 1 \\ 0 & 1 & 0 \\ 0 & 0 & 1 \end{bmatrix}$$

gives a matrix in which the third row of $A$ is added to the first row of $A$. Thus

$$\begin{bmatrix} 1 & 0 & 1 \\ 0 & 1 & 0 \\ 0 & 0 & 1 \end{bmatrix} \begin{bmatrix} a_{11} & a_{12} & a_{13} \\ a_{21} & a_{22} & a_{23} \\ a_{31} & a_{32} & a_{33} \end{bmatrix} = \begin{bmatrix} a_{11} + a_{31} & a_{12} + a_{32} & a_{13} + a_{33} \\ a_{21} & a_{22} & a_{23} \\ a_{31} & a_{32} & a_{33} \end{bmatrix}.$$

In each case, the matrix used as the premultiplier is one obtained from the multiplicative identity matrix by carrying out on the identity the operation desired on the matrix $A$. For example, if we want to add the second row of $A$ to the third row of $A$, we premultiply $A$ by

$$\begin{bmatrix} 1 & 0 & 0 \\ 0 & 1 & 0 \\ 0 & 1 & 1 \end{bmatrix}.$$

If we want to multiply the first row of $A$ by 3, we premultiply $A$ by

$$\begin{bmatrix} 3 & 0 & 0 \\ 0 & 1 & 0 \\ 0 & 0 & 1 \end{bmatrix}.$$

**Definition 15.4a.** A square matrix $E$ that brings about an elementary row operation on a matrix $A$ by premultiplication is called an **elementary matrix.**

Since there are three distinct elementary operations possible, there are three types of elementary matrices:

(1) $E_{ij}$, which interchanges the $i$th and $j$th rows;
(2) $E_i(k)$, which multiplies the $i$th row by $k$, $k \neq 0$;
(3) $E_{i+j}$, which adds the $i$th row to the $j$th row.

Thus, for $3 \times 3$ matrices,

$$E_{12} = \begin{bmatrix} 0 & 1 & 0 \\ 1 & 0 & 0 \\ 0 & 0 & 1 \end{bmatrix}, \quad E_2(4) = \begin{bmatrix} 1 & 0 & 0 \\ 0 & 4 & 0 \\ 0 & 0 & 1 \end{bmatrix}, \quad E_{2+3} = \begin{bmatrix} 1 & 0 & 0 \\ 0 & 1 & 0 \\ 0 & 1 & 1 \end{bmatrix}.$$

The following example illustrates these concepts.

---

*Example 15.4a.* By elementary row operations, show that the matrix

$$A = \begin{bmatrix} 2 & 1 & -1 \\ 1 & 0 & 2 \\ -1 & 1 & 1 \end{bmatrix}$$

can be changed into the matrix

$$\begin{bmatrix} 1 & 0 & 0 \\ 0 & 1 & 0 \\ 0 & 0 & 1 \end{bmatrix}.$$

We have

$$E_{12}A = \begin{bmatrix} 0 & 1 & 0 \\ 1 & 0 & 0 \\ 0 & 0 & 1 \end{bmatrix}\begin{bmatrix} 2 & 1 & -1 \\ 1 & 0 & 2 \\ -1 & 1 & 1 \end{bmatrix} = \begin{bmatrix} 1 & 0 & 2 \\ 2 & 1 & -1 \\ -1 & 1 & 1 \end{bmatrix},$$

and

$$E_{1+3}E_{12}A = \begin{bmatrix} 1 & 0 & 0 \\ 0 & 1 & 0 \\ 1 & 0 & 1 \end{bmatrix}\begin{bmatrix} 1 & 0 & 2 \\ 2 & 1 & -1 \\ -1 & 1 & 1 \end{bmatrix} = \begin{bmatrix} 1 & 0 & 2 \\ 2 & 1 & -1 \\ 0 & 1 & 3 \end{bmatrix}.$$

In general, it is not really necessary to write out the elementary matrices, since the result of the multiplication can be done, in simple cases, by inspection. Thus, at the next stage we multiply the first row by $(-2)$ and add to the second row. This process is denoted by writing

$$E_1(-\tfrac{1}{2})E_{1+2}E_1(-2)E_{1+3}E_{12}A = \begin{bmatrix} 1 & 0 & 2 \\ 0 & 1 & -5 \\ 0 & 1 & 3 \end{bmatrix},$$

where $E_1(-\frac{1}{2})$ restores a 1 in the $a_{11}$ position after the first row is multiplied by $-2$. Continuing in this way, we obtain

$$E_2(-1)E_{2+3}E_2(-1)\begin{bmatrix} 1 & 0 & 2 \\ 0 & 1 & -5 \\ 0 & 1 & 3 \end{bmatrix} = \begin{bmatrix} 1 & 0 & 2 \\ 0 & 1 & -5 \\ 0 & 0 & 8 \end{bmatrix}$$

and

$$E_{3+2}E_3(\tfrac{5}{8})\begin{bmatrix} 1 & 0 & 2 \\ 0 & 1 & -5 \\ 0 & 0 & 8 \end{bmatrix} = \begin{bmatrix} 1 & 0 & 2 \\ 0 & 1 & 0 \\ 0 & 0 & 5 \end{bmatrix},$$

$$E_3(-\tfrac{1}{2})E_{3+1}E_3(-\tfrac{2}{5})\begin{bmatrix} 1 & 0 & 2 \\ 0 & 1 & 0 \\ 0 & 0 & 5 \end{bmatrix} = \begin{bmatrix} 1 & 0 & 0 \\ 0 & 1 & 0 \\ 0 & 0 & 1 \end{bmatrix}.$$

By combining these results, we get

$$E_3(-\tfrac{1}{2})E_{3+1}E_3(-\tfrac{2}{5})E_{3+2}E_3(\tfrac{5}{8})E_2(-1)E_{2+3}E_2(-1)E_1(-\tfrac{1}{2})E_{1+2}E_1(-2)E_{1+3}E_{12}A$$

$$= \begin{bmatrix} 1 & 0 & 0 \\ 0 & 1 & 0 \\ 0 & 0 & 1 \end{bmatrix}.$$

This example suggests a number of important ideas. For instance, since the final matrix is the multiplicative identity, the product

$$E_3(-\tfrac{1}{2})E_{3+1}E_3(-\tfrac{2}{5}) \cdots E_{1+3}E_{12}$$

must be a multiplicative inverse of $A$. This idea merits further investigation, but we must proceed with care. Therefore, let us consider some additional preliminary ideas.

**Definition 15.4b.** If there exists a sequence of elementary matrices $E_1, E_2, \ldots, E_n$ such that

$$E_n E_{n-1} \cdots E_1 A = B,$$

then $A$ is said to be **row equivalent** to $B$, and we write $A \sim_r B$.
In the preceding example, $A$ is row equivalent to $I_{33}$.

Although row operations on a matrix are suggested by operations on a system of linear equations, there are no operations on a system of equations that suggest operations on columns of a matrix. Nevertheless, it is possible to consider elementary operations on the columns of a matrix as well as on the rows. Such a discussion is not within the scope of our work here, but it proceeds in quite the same manner as that for row operations.

In general, by means of elementary row operations, we may obtain from any given matrix $A$ a matrix that is "almost triangular," where every element below the principal diagonal of the matrix is zero and certain other simple conditions are satisfied. Such matrices are described in

**Definition 15.4c.** A **modified triangular matrix** (MTM) is a matrix that satisfies the following four conditions.
   (1) The first nonzero element (if there is one) in each row is 1.

(2) Every other element in a column containing the first nonzero element of a row is zero.

(3) The first nonzero element of a given row is farther to the left than the first nonzero element in each following row.

(4) A row containing only zeros does not precede a row containing a nonzero element.

For example,

$$\begin{bmatrix} 1 & 0 & 2 \\ 0 & 1 & 3 \\ 0 & 0 & 0 \end{bmatrix}, \quad \begin{bmatrix} 0 & 1 & 2 \\ 0 & 0 & 0 \\ 0 & 0 & 0 \end{bmatrix}, \quad \begin{bmatrix} 1 & -2 & 0 & 0 \\ 0 & 0 & 1 & 0 \\ 0 & 0 & 0 & 1 \end{bmatrix}$$

are modified triangular matrices. The matrices

$$\begin{bmatrix} 1 & 0 & 0 & 2 \\ 0 & 0 & 1 & 1 \\ 0 & 1 & 0 & 2 \\ 0 & 0 & 0 & 0 \end{bmatrix} \quad \text{and} \quad \begin{bmatrix} 0 & 0 & 0 \\ 0 & 1 & 0 \\ 0 & 0 & 1 \end{bmatrix}$$

are *not* modified triangular matrices.

**Theorem 15.4a.** Every matrix $A$ is row equivalent to a modified triangular matrix.
PROOF: The proof consists in showing how to construct the MTM. Suppose the element $a_{11} \neq 0$. Divide the first row by $a_{11}$ to get a 1 in the upper left-hand corner. Then, if $a_{21} \neq 0$, the operations indicated by $E_1\left(-\dfrac{1}{a_{21}}\right) E_{1+2} E_1(-a_{21})$ will yield a zero in the $a_{21}$ position. In a similar fashion, a zero may be obtained in each first-column position where a nonzero element is present, except for the $a_{11}$ position, which now has the element 1. (If $a_{11} = 0$, then by interchange of rows a nonzero element can be placed in the $a_{11}$ position unless every element in the first column is zero. If the latter is the case, then begin with the first column that does contain a nonzero element.) Now proceed to the $a_{22}$ position and, if $a_{22} \neq 0$, divide the second row by $a_{22}$ to obtain a 1 there. Next, operate in the same manner as before to produce zeros everywhere in the second column, except in the $a_{22}$ position. (If $a_{22} = 0$, interchange the second row and any succeeding row that has a nonzero element in the second column. If all second-column elements are zero, proceed to the next column that does have a nonzero element in it, and operate as before.) Since the dimensions of the matrix are finite, this procedure may be continued until the end result is a modified triangular matrix.

It is instructive to find a procedure for determining if two matrices are equivalent. After consideration of the multiplicative inverse of a matrix in the next section, we shall prove

**Theorem 15.4b.** $A \sim_r C$ and $B \sim_r C \Rightarrow A \sim_r B$.

It is a direct consequence of this theorem that $A \sim_r B \Rightarrow B \sim_r A$, and thus two matrices $A$ and $B$ are row equivalent to each other if they are row equivalent to the same matrix. The next example illustrates this idea.

---

*Example 15.4b.* Are the matrices

$$A = \begin{bmatrix} 1 & 2 & 1 \\ 3 & 0 & 2 \\ -1 & 0 & 1 \end{bmatrix} \quad \text{and} \quad B = \begin{bmatrix} 2 & 0 & 1 \\ -1 & 1 & 1 \\ 1 & 2 & 1 \end{bmatrix}$$

row equivalent?

To answer the question, we first find a modified triangular matrix equivalent to each matrix.

$$A = \begin{bmatrix} 1 & 2 & 1 \\ 3 & 0 & 2 \\ -1 & 0 & 1 \end{bmatrix} \sim_r \begin{bmatrix} 1 & 2 & 1 \\ 0 & -6 & -1 \\ 0 & 2 & 2 \end{bmatrix} \sim_r \begin{bmatrix} 1 & 0 & \frac{2}{3} \\ 0 & 1 & -1 \\ 0 & 0 & \frac{5}{3} \end{bmatrix} \sim_r \begin{bmatrix} 1 & 0 & 0 \\ 0 & 1 & 0 \\ 0 & 0 & 1 \end{bmatrix},$$

$$B = \begin{bmatrix} 2 & 0 & 1 \\ -1 & 1 & 1 \\ 1 & 2 & 1 \end{bmatrix} \sim_r \begin{bmatrix} 2 & 0 & 1 \\ 0 & 1 & \frac{3}{2} \\ 0 & 2 & \frac{1}{2} \end{bmatrix} \sim_r \begin{bmatrix} 2 & 0 & 1 \\ 0 & 1 & 0 \\ 0 & 0 & -\frac{5}{2} \end{bmatrix} \sim_r \begin{bmatrix} 1 & 0 & 0 \\ 0 & 1 & 0 \\ 0 & 0 & 1 \end{bmatrix}.$$

Since $A$ and $B$ are both row equivalent to the same MTM, they must be row equivalent to each other.

## Exercises 15.4

1. For each of the following matrices, find a row equivalent MTM.

(a) $\begin{bmatrix} 2 & 2 \\ 3 & 3 \end{bmatrix}$.

(b) $\begin{bmatrix} -1 & 2 & 1 \\ 2 & 1 & 0 \\ 1 & 5 & 3 \end{bmatrix}$.

(c) $\begin{bmatrix} 1 & 1 & 2 \\ 1 & -1 & 1 \\ 0 & 1 & 2 \\ -2 & 2 & 0 \\ 1 & 2 & 2 \end{bmatrix}$.

(d) $\begin{bmatrix} 1 & 2 & 1 \\ 3 & 0 & -1 \\ 2 & 0 & 4 \\ 1 & -1 & 1 \end{bmatrix}$.

(e) $\begin{bmatrix} 1 & -1 & 2 & 0 \\ 5 & -5 & 10 & 0 \\ 6 & -6 & 12 & 3 \\ -1 & 1 & -2 & 1 \end{bmatrix}$.

(f) $\begin{bmatrix} a & a^2 & a^3 & a^4 \\ b & b^2 & b^3 & b^4 \\ c & c^2 & c^3 & c^4 \end{bmatrix}$.

2. Show that

$$A = \begin{bmatrix} 1 & 2 \\ 3 & -1 \end{bmatrix} \sim_r \begin{bmatrix} 1 & 0 \\ 0 & 1 \end{bmatrix}$$

by finding elementary matrices such that

$$E_n \dots E_1 A = \begin{bmatrix} 1 & 0 \\ 0 & 1 \end{bmatrix},$$

and then calculate the matrix $E_n \dots E_1 = B$.

3. In Example 15.4a, find the matrix that is the product of all the $E$'s used.

4. (a) Is it true that $E_{ij}^T = E_{ij}$?
   (b) Is it true that $E_i^T(k) = E_i(k)$?
   (c) Is it true that $E_{i+j}^T = E_{i+j}$?
5. Which of the following matrices are row equivalent?

$$A = \begin{bmatrix} 1 & 2 & -1 \\ 3 & -1 & 2 \\ 4 & -2 & 5 \end{bmatrix}, \quad B = \begin{bmatrix} 2 & -1 & 1 \\ -3 & 2 & 4 \\ 2 & 0 & 12 \end{bmatrix},$$

$$C = \begin{bmatrix} 1 & 2 & 0 \\ 3 & 6 & 0 \\ -2 & -4 & 0 \end{bmatrix}, \quad D = \begin{bmatrix} 2 & 1 & 3 \\ 1 & 3 & 2 \\ 3 & 2 & 1 \end{bmatrix}.$$

## 15.5 NONSINGULAR MATRICES

It has been shown that every matrix $A = [a_{ij}]$ has an additive inverse $[-a_{ij}] = -A$. Can the same statement be made about a multiplicative inverse? That is, for a given matrix $A$ is there a matrix, $A^{-1}$, such that $AA^{-1} = A^{-1}A = I$? If, for example, we can show that such a multiplicative inverse exists for a matrix $A$, then a system of equations such as

$$a_{11}x + a_{12}y + a_{13}z = c_1,$$
$$a_{21}x + a_{22}y + a_{23}z = c_2,$$
$$a_{31}x + a_{32}y + a_{33}z = c_3,$$

when written in the matrix form,

$$AX = C,$$

where

$$A \,.=.\, [a_{ij}], \quad X \,.=.\, \begin{bmatrix} x \\ y \\ z \end{bmatrix}, \quad C \,.=.\, \begin{bmatrix} c_1 \\ c_2 \\ c_3 \end{bmatrix},$$

can be solved very simply by writing

$$A^{-1}(AX) = A^{-1}C,$$

or

$$(A^{-1}A)X = A^{-1}C,$$

so that

$$IX = X = A^{-1}C.$$

However, as the next example shows, not every matrix has a multiplicative inverse.

---

*Example 15.5a.* Prove that the matrix

$$\begin{bmatrix} 0 & 1 \\ 0 & 0 \end{bmatrix}$$

has no multiplicative inverse.

Suppose that

$$\begin{bmatrix} x & y \\ u & v \end{bmatrix} \begin{bmatrix} 0 & 1 \\ 0 & 0 \end{bmatrix} = \begin{bmatrix} 1 & 0 \\ 0 & 1 \end{bmatrix}.$$

Then

$$\begin{bmatrix} 0 & x \\ 0 & u \end{bmatrix} = \begin{bmatrix} 1 & 0 \\ 0 & 1 \end{bmatrix},$$

which is not possible.

Consequently, before attempting to find an inverse for a given matrix $A$, it is desirable to determine conditions under which a matrix will have an inverse. The next theorem illustrates one reason why the concept of the elementary matrix is important.

**Theorem 15.5a.** If $E$ is an elementary matrix, then there is a matrix $S$ such that $SE = I$. That is, every elementary matrix has a multiplicative inverse.

PROOF: It is sufficient to exhibit the matrix $S$ for each type of elementary matrix.

(1) If $E = E_{ij}$, then $S = E_{ij}$. Since two successive interchanges of the $i$th and $j$th rows of $I$ restore the matrix $I$, we have

$$E_{ij}E_{ij} = I.$$

(2) If $E = E_i(c)$, then $S = E_i(1/c)$. This result is verified by the fact that

$$E_i(1/c)E_i(c) = I.$$

(3) If $E = E_{i+j}$, then $S = E_i(-1)E_{i+j}E_i(-1)$. The reader can verify this by showing that

$$\{E_i(-1)E_{i+j}E_i(-1)\}\, E_{i+j} = I.$$

If a matrix $A$ has a left inverse $S$ and a right inverse $T$, then we can prove

**Theorem 15.5b.** $SA = I$ and $AT = I \Rightarrow S = T$.

PROOF: The proof is a simple consequence of the associative law. We have

$$S_{nm}(A_{mn}T_{nm}) = S_{nm}I_{mm} = S_{mn}$$

and

$$(S_{nm}A_{mn})T_{nm} = I_{nn}T_{nm} = T_{nm}.$$

Therefore,

$$S_{nm} = T_{nm}.$$

This theorem strongly suggests that a nonsquare matrix cannot have both a right and a left inverse, but a proof of this result will be omitted here. Thus, the only matrices that can have both a right and a left inverse are square matrices, although not every square matrix has an inverse, as was shown in Example 15.5a.

**Definition 15.5a.** A square matrix $A$ is said to be a **nonsingular matrix** if there is a matrix $B$ such that $BA = I$. The matrix $B$ is called the **inverse** of $A$ and is customarily denoted by $A^{-1}$. A square matrix that is not nonsingular is called **singular**.

For example, in the proof of Theorem 15.5a, it was shown that the elementary matrices are all nonsingular and that

$$E_{ij}^{-1} = E_{ij}, \quad E_i^{-1}(c) = E_i\left(\frac{1}{c}\right), \quad E_{i+j}^{-1} = E_i(-1)E_{i+j}E_i(-1).$$

The reader may verify that these matrices are also right inverses.

It is now possible to give an easy proof of Theorem 15.4b. Thus, $A \sim_r C$ and $B \sim_r C$ implies that there are two sequences of elementary matrices $E_1, E_2, \ldots , E_n$ and $E_1', E_2', \ldots , E_m'$ such that

$$E_n \cdots E_2 E_1 B = C \quad \text{and} \quad E_m' \cdots E_2' E_1' A = C.$$

Hence

$$E_m' \cdots E_2' E_1' A = E_n \cdots E_2 E_1 B,$$

and thus

$$E_1^{-1} E_2^{-1} \cdots E_n^{-1} E_m' \cdots E_2' E_1' A = B.$$

We have just shown, however, that the inverses of the elementary matrices are, themselves, either elementary matrices or products of such matrices. Consequently, it follows that $A \sim_r B$, as Theorem 15.4b states.

The following sequence of theorems establishes the most important properties of nonsingular matrices.

**Theorem 15.5c.** If $A$ is a nonsingular matrix, and if $BA = I$, then $AB = I$.

PROOF: By Theorem 15.4a, the matrix $B$ is row equivalent to a modified triangular matrix $M$, and $M$ must have a row of zeros unless $M = I$. (Why?) Thus there are elementary matrices $E_1, E_2, \ldots , E_k$ such that

(1) $$E_k \cdots E_2 E_1 B = M.$$

Then, postmultiplying by $A$ on both sides and using $BA = I$, we get

$$E_k \cdots E_2 E_1 I = MA \Rightarrow E_k \cdots E_2 E_1 = MA.$$

Since the elementary matrices all have inverses, we may write

(2) $$MAE_1^{-1} E_2^{-2} \cdots E_k^{-1} = I.$$

Let $AE_1^{-1} E_2^{-1} \cdots E_k^{-1} = S$, so that $MS = I$. But, if $M$ has a row of zeros, then the product $MS$ must also have a row of zeros and therefore cannot equal $I$. Consequently, $M$ must be the identity matrix $I$, and it follows from (2) that

$$AE_1^{-1} E_2^{-1} \cdots E_k^{-1} = I.$$

Furthermore, since $M = I$, Equation (1) shows that

$$B = E_1^{-1} E_2^{-1} \cdots E_k^{-1},$$

and hence $AB = I$, as was to be proved.

*Note:* By Definition 15.5a, this theorem is equivalent to the statement that $A^{-1}A = AA^{-1}$.

That the inverse of a nonsingular matrix is unique is stated in

**Theorem 15.5d.** $AB = I$ and $AC = I \Rightarrow B = C$.

PROOF: Left for the reader (see Exercises 15.5, Number 10).

**Theorem 15.5e.** If $A$, $B$ are nonsingular, then $AB$ is nonsingular, and

$$(AB)^{-1} = B^{-1}A^{-1}.$$

PROOF: Consider the product $(AB)(B^{-1}A^{-1})$. The details are left for the reader.

**Theorem 15.5f.** $A \sim, I \Leftrightarrow A$ is nonsingular.

PROOF: Left for the reader (see Exercises 15.5, Number 11).

Theorem 15.5f suggests an easy way to find the inverse of a nonsingular matrix $A$. To find $A^{-1}$ in a practical fashion, we carry out elementary row operations on $A$ to reduce it to $I$, at the same time carrying out each row operation on $I$ to build up $A^{-1}$. The following example illustrates the method.

---

*Example 15.5b.* Find the inverse of

$$A = \begin{bmatrix} 1 & 0 & 1 \\ 2 & 2 & 0 \\ 0 & 1 & 3 \end{bmatrix}.$$

The work is arranged as follows.

If $S_1 = E_1(-\tfrac{1}{2})E_{1+2}E_1(-2)$, then

$$S_1A = \begin{bmatrix} 1 & 0 & 1 \\ 0 & 2 & -2 \\ 0 & 1 & 3 \end{bmatrix}, \quad S_1I = \begin{bmatrix} 1 & 0 & 0 \\ -2 & 1 & 0 \\ 0 & 0 & 1 \end{bmatrix},$$

and if $S_2 = E_2(-1)E_{2+3}E_2(-\tfrac{1}{2})$, then

$$S_2S_1A = \begin{bmatrix} 1 & 0 & 1 \\ 0 & 1 & -1 \\ 0 & 0 & 4 \end{bmatrix}, \quad S_2S_1I = \begin{bmatrix} 1 & 0 & 0 \\ -1 & \tfrac{1}{2} & 0 \\ 1 & -\tfrac{1}{2} & 1 \end{bmatrix}.$$

Finally, if $S_3 = E_3(-1)E_{3+1}E_3(-1)E_{3+2}E_3(\tfrac{1}{4})$, then

$$S_3S_2S_1A = \begin{bmatrix} 1 & 0 & 0 \\ 0 & 1 & 0 \\ 0 & 0 & 1 \end{bmatrix}, \quad S_3S_2S_1I = \begin{bmatrix} \tfrac{3}{4} & \tfrac{1}{8} & -\tfrac{1}{4} \\ -\tfrac{3}{4} & \tfrac{3}{8} & \tfrac{1}{4} \\ \tfrac{1}{4} & -\tfrac{1}{8} & \tfrac{1}{4} \end{bmatrix},$$

and the last matrix is $A^{-1}$.

The inverse of a matrix will prove to be of considerable value in problems that we shall discuss in the next chapter. As indicated in the next section, it is useful in solving a system of linear equations, but it is not necessarily the most practical means of obtaining a solution.

## Exercises 15.5

1. Find either a right or a left inverse for each of the following, and show that the other inverse does not exist:

(a) $[1 \quad 2]$; (b) $\begin{bmatrix} 3 \\ -1 \end{bmatrix}$; (c) $\begin{bmatrix} 1 & 2 & 0 \\ 0 & 2 & 1 \end{bmatrix}$.

In Numbers 2 to 7, find an inverse for the given matrix if an inverse exists.

2. $\begin{bmatrix} 2 & 3 \\ -1 & 2 \end{bmatrix}$.

3. $\begin{bmatrix} 1 & 2 \\ -2 & -4 \end{bmatrix}$.

4. $\begin{bmatrix} 1 & 3 & -1 \\ 0 & 2 & 1 \\ -1 & 1 & 2 \end{bmatrix}$.

5. $\begin{bmatrix} 2 & -1 & 0 \\ 1 & 2 & -1 \\ -1 & -1 & 2 \end{bmatrix}$.

6. $\begin{bmatrix} 1 & 2 & 1 \\ -1 & 0 & 1 \\ 1 & 4 & 3 \end{bmatrix}$.

7. $\begin{bmatrix} 1 & 2 & 0 & 2 \\ -1 & 2 & -2 & -2 \\ 1 & 3 & -1 & 2 \\ 0 & 1 & 2 & 1 \end{bmatrix}$.

8. Prove that if $A$ is a nonsingular matrix, then $A^T$ is nonsingular and
$$(A^T)^{-1} = (A^{-1})^T.$$

9. Show that if $A \sim_r B$, then there exists a nonsingular matrix $S$ such that $SA = B$.
10. Prove Theorem 15.5d. *Hint*: Use the associative property.
11. Prove Theorem 15.5f by using the results in the proof of Theorem 15.5c.

## 15.6 THE SOLUTION OF A SYSTEM OF LINEAR EQUATIONS

The discussion in the first part of Section 15.3 showed that a system of linear equations can be conveniently represented in matrix form. For instance, let us consider the system

$$(1) \qquad \begin{aligned} a_1x + b_1y + c_1z &= d_1, \\ a_2x + b_2y + c_2z &= d_2, \\ a_3x + b_3y + c_3z &= d_3, \end{aligned}$$

and let

$$A .=. \begin{bmatrix} a_1 & b_1 & c_1 \\ a_2 & b_2 & c_2 \\ a_3 & b_3 & c_3 \end{bmatrix}, \quad X .=. \begin{bmatrix} x \\ y \\ z \end{bmatrix}, \quad \text{and} \quad D .=. \begin{bmatrix} d_1 \\ d_2 \\ d_3 \end{bmatrix}.$$

Then the system (1) may be represented as

$$(2) \qquad AX = D.$$

The matrix $A$ is called the **coefficient matrix,** and $X$ may be regarded as a **vector of unknowns,** or an unknown vector whose components are to be determined. Thus, the problem of solving the system of equations may be interpreted as that of finding a vector $X$ that will satisfy (2).

From geometry we know that each equation in (1) represents a plane. Hence the solution set of (1) is the set of points common to all three planes. If the planes intersect at a point, we would expect to obtain a solution for $X$ in Equation (2). If, however, two of the planes are parallel, no solution exists.

*Example 15.6a.* Find the solution set of the system

$$\begin{aligned} 2x - y + z &= 2, \\ x + 2y - z &= 3, \\ 3x + y + 2z &= -1. \end{aligned}$$

In matrix form, the system is

$$\begin{bmatrix} 2 & -1 & 1 \\ 1 & 2 & -1 \\ 3 & 1 & 2 \end{bmatrix}\begin{bmatrix} x \\ y \\ z \end{bmatrix} = \begin{bmatrix} 2 \\ 3 \\ -1 \end{bmatrix}.$$

The solution can be obtained in either of two ways. Elementary row operations may be performed on the matrix equation, or the inverse of

$$A .=. \begin{bmatrix} 2 & -1 & 1 \\ 1 & 2 & -1 \\ 3 & 1 & 2 \end{bmatrix},$$

if it exists, may be calculated and used as a premultiplier on both sides of the matrix equation. However, since the work of calculating the inverse is the same as the work done in carrying out elementary row operations on $A$ to make it equivalent to $I$, it is more practical to carry out elementary row operations on the matrix equation directly. Following this procedure, we get, by interchanging the first and second rows on both sides,

$$\begin{bmatrix} 1 & 2 & -1 \\ 2 & -1 & 1 \\ 3 & 1 & 2 \end{bmatrix}\begin{bmatrix} x \\ y \\ z \end{bmatrix} = \begin{bmatrix} 3 \\ 2 \\ -1 \end{bmatrix}.$$

Then, by adding $-2$ times the first row to the second row and adding $-3$ times the first row to the third row of $A$, and doing the same on the right side of the equation, we find

$$\begin{bmatrix} 1 & 2 & -1 \\ 0 & -5 & 3 \\ 0 & -5 & 5 \end{bmatrix}\begin{bmatrix} x \\ y \\ z \end{bmatrix} = \begin{bmatrix} 3 \\ -4 \\ -10 \end{bmatrix}.$$

Subtracting the second row from the third, then dividing the third by 2, we get

$$\begin{bmatrix} 1 & 2 & -1 \\ 0 & -5 & 3 \\ 0 & 0 & 1 \end{bmatrix}\begin{bmatrix} x \\ y \\ z \end{bmatrix} = \begin{bmatrix} 3 \\ -4 \\ -3 \end{bmatrix}.$$

Now we may multiply the third row by $-3$ and add to the second row, and add the third row to the first to get

$$\begin{bmatrix} 1 & 2 & 0 \\ 0 & -5 & 0 \\ 0 & 0 & 1 \end{bmatrix}\begin{bmatrix} x \\ y \\ z \end{bmatrix} = \begin{bmatrix} 0 \\ 5 \\ -3 \end{bmatrix}.$$

Finally, upon dividing the second row by $-5$, then multiplying it by $-2$ and adding to the first row, we get

$$\begin{bmatrix} 1 & 0 & 0 \\ 0 & 1 & 0 \\ 0 & 0 & 1 \end{bmatrix}\begin{bmatrix} x \\ y \\ z \end{bmatrix} = \begin{bmatrix} 2 \\ -1 \\ -3 \end{bmatrix}.$$

Hence, the vector solution is

$$\begin{bmatrix} x \\ y \\ z \end{bmatrix} = \begin{bmatrix} 2 \\ -1 \\ -3 \end{bmatrix},$$

so that $x = 2$, $y = -1$, $z = -3$.

The reader should keep in mind that the row operations used to obtain this solution are actually effected by operating on both sides of the matrix equation with elementary matrices. These matrices were not written out in the preceding example because they are not explicitly needed.

As explained in Chapter 14, if

$$ax + by + cz = d$$

is the equation of a plane, then $a$, $b$, and $c$ are direction numbers of a normal to the plane. Hence, if two planes are parallel they must have proportional direction numbers. Conversely, an equation such as

$$kax + kby + kcz = e$$

represents a plane parallel to

$$ax + by + cz = d.$$

If a system of equations is of the form

$$
\begin{aligned}
ax + by + cz &= d, \\
px + qy + rz &= s, \\
kax + kby + kcz &= e,
\end{aligned}
$$

then the matrix of coefficients is

$$
\begin{bmatrix}
a & b & c \\
p & q & r \\
ka & kb & kc
\end{bmatrix}.
$$

By elementary row operations, it follows that this matrix is row equivalent to

$$
\begin{bmatrix}
a & b & c \\
p & q & r \\
0 & 0 & 0
\end{bmatrix},
$$

in which there is a row all of whose elements are zero. Consequently, if elementary row operations are used on this matrix to obtain from the equation

$$
\begin{bmatrix}
a & b & c \\
p & q & r \\
ka & kb & kc
\end{bmatrix}
\begin{bmatrix}
x \\ y \\ z
\end{bmatrix}
=
\begin{bmatrix}
d \\ s \\ e
\end{bmatrix}
$$

the form

$$
\begin{bmatrix}
1 & 0 & u \\
0 & 1 & v \\
0 & 0 & 0
\end{bmatrix}
\begin{bmatrix}
x \\ y \\ z
\end{bmatrix}
=
\begin{bmatrix}
c_1 \\ c_2 \\ c_3
\end{bmatrix},
$$

then the equation $AX = C$ cannot have a solution unless $c_3 = 0$, since the equations

$$
\begin{aligned}
x + uz &= c_1, \\
y + vz &= c_2, \\
0 &= c_3
\end{aligned}
$$

cannot be satisfied otherwise.

If, however, $c_3 = 0$, then the system of equations is equivalent to only two equations of the form

$$a_{11}x + a_{12}y + a_{13}z = d_1,$$
$$a_{21}x + a_{22}y + a_{23}z = d_2.$$

Geometrically, these two equations represent planes that have a *line of intersection*, if they are not parallel. Therefore, we can expect to obtain a solution set that includes all the points on the line of intersection. This solution set may be described in a number of ways (see Section 14.7), but one of the simplest is to obtain two unknowns in terms of the third as a parameter. Such a solution can be obtained in matrix form, as the next example illustrates.

---

*Example 15.6b.* Find a solution, if one exists, for the system

$$2x - y + 3z = 6,$$
$$x + 2y - z = 4.$$

In matrix form, we have

$$AX = \begin{bmatrix} 2 & -1 & 3 \\ 1 & 2 & -1 \end{bmatrix} \begin{bmatrix} x \\ y \\ z \end{bmatrix} = \begin{bmatrix} 6 \\ 4 \end{bmatrix}.$$

Although $A$ has no inverse, we may still carry out elementary row operations, as before, to obtain a modified triangular matrix that is row-equivalent to $A$. Thus, from

$$\begin{bmatrix} 1 & 2 & -1 \\ 0 & -5 & 5 \end{bmatrix} \begin{bmatrix} x \\ y \\ z \end{bmatrix} = \begin{bmatrix} 4 \\ -2 \end{bmatrix},$$

we get

$$\begin{bmatrix} 1 & 0 & 1 \\ 0 & 1 & -1 \end{bmatrix} \begin{bmatrix} x \\ y \\ z \end{bmatrix} = \begin{bmatrix} \frac{16}{5} \\ \frac{2}{5} \end{bmatrix}.$$

This matrix equation represents the system

$$x + z = \tfrac{16}{5}, \quad \text{or} \quad x = \tfrac{16}{5} - z,$$
$$y - z = \tfrac{2}{5}, \quad \text{or} \quad y = \tfrac{2}{5} + z.$$

These two equations are the projection equations of a line, so that upon making any arbitrary choice for $z$ we obtain the corresponding values for $x$ and $y$. Hence, the system has infinitely many solutions, and a general solution can be expressed in terms of one of the unknowns. This unknown then serves as a parameter to specify the set of all solutions—that is, the set of all points on the line.

---

The preceding discussion may be extended to include systems of $m$ equations in $n$ unknowns, where $n > m$, or where $n \leq m$ if the given system is equivalent to a system in which there are more unknowns than equations. In either case, a solution for the system is said to exist if some of the unknowns can be expressed in terms of the remaining unknowns, as in Example 15.6b.

Another situation may occur in which there are more equations than unknowns.

*Example 15.6c.* The equations

$$\begin{aligned}
x - y + z &= 3, \\
2x + y - z &= 6, \\
-x + 2y + 2z &= 1, \\
3x - 2y - 2z &= -1
\end{aligned}$$

represent four planes. We may expect a solution only if the four planes have a point in common. Examine this system for a solution.

Upon writing this system in matrix form, we have

$$\begin{bmatrix} 1 & -1 & 1 \\ 2 & 1 & -1 \\ -1 & 2 & 2 \\ 3 & -2 & -2 \end{bmatrix} \begin{bmatrix} x \\ y \\ z \end{bmatrix} = \begin{bmatrix} 3 \\ 6 \\ 1 \\ -1 \end{bmatrix}.$$

By elementary row operations on both members, we reduce the coefficient matrix to an equivalent MTM:

$$\begin{bmatrix} 1 & 0 & 0 \\ 2 & 1 & -1 \\ -1 & 2 & 2 \\ 2 & 0 & 0 \end{bmatrix} \begin{bmatrix} x \\ y \\ z \end{bmatrix} = \begin{bmatrix} 3 \\ 6 \\ 1 \\ 0 \end{bmatrix},$$

$$\begin{bmatrix} 1 & 0 & 0 \\ 0 & 1 & -1 \\ 0 & 2 & 2 \\ 0 & 0 & 0 \end{bmatrix} \begin{bmatrix} x \\ y \\ z \end{bmatrix} = \begin{bmatrix} 3 \\ 0 \\ 4 \\ -6 \end{bmatrix},$$

$$\begin{bmatrix} 1 & 0 & 0 \\ 0 & 1 & -1 \\ 0 & 0 & 1 \\ 0 & 0 & 0 \end{bmatrix} \begin{bmatrix} x \\ y \\ z \end{bmatrix} = \begin{bmatrix} 3 \\ 0 \\ 1 \\ -6 \end{bmatrix},$$

and

$$\begin{bmatrix} 1 & 0 & 0 \\ 0 & 1 & 0 \\ 0 & 0 & 1 \\ 0 & 0 & 0 \end{bmatrix} \begin{bmatrix} x \\ y \\ z \end{bmatrix} = \begin{bmatrix} 3 \\ 1 \\ 1 \\ -6 \end{bmatrix}.$$

This matrix equation represents the set of equations

$$x = 3, \quad y = 1, \quad z = 0, \quad 0 = -6,$$

the last of which is not true. Hence the system has no solution.

---

Matrix techniques can conveniently be used to determine the solutions (if there are any) of any system of linear equations, even if the number of unknowns differs from the number of equations. Suppose that elementary row operations have been carried out on the matrix equation

$$AX = C$$

to transform it into the equation

$$A_1 X = C_1.$$

where $A_1$ is a modified triangular matrix. Then, as the preceding examples suggest, the system has a solution if, and only if, the vector $C_1$ has a zero in every row in which only zeros appear in the matrix $A_1$. Clearly, these ideas may be applied to a general system independently of any geometric interpretation.

In discussing the general case, we shall find it convenient to introduce a new concept that will simplify the discussion considerably. It has been pointed out a number of times that a vector can be represented either by a row matrix or by a column matrix. Similarly, each row (and each column) of a given matrix may be regarded as a vector. For example, we may partition the matrix

$$\begin{bmatrix} 1 & 2 & 0 \\ 0 & -1 & 1 \\ 2 & 2 & 2 \end{bmatrix}$$

into the row vectors

$$\begin{aligned} R_1 &.=. \begin{bmatrix} 1 & 2 & 0 \end{bmatrix}, \\ R_2 &.=. \begin{bmatrix} 0 & -1 & 1 \end{bmatrix}, \\ R_3 &.=. \begin{bmatrix} 2 & 2 & 2 \end{bmatrix}. \end{aligned}$$

Whenever a matrix $A$ is premultiplied by another matrix, the result is a matrix whose rows are linear combinations of the rows of $A$. For instance, consider

$$\begin{bmatrix} 2 & 1 & 0 \\ -1 & 3 & 2 \\ 2 & 2 & -1 \end{bmatrix} \begin{bmatrix} 1 & 2 & 0 \\ 0 & -1 & 1 \\ 2 & 2 & 2 \end{bmatrix} = \begin{bmatrix} 2 & 1 & 0 \\ -1 & 3 & 2 \\ 2 & 2 & -1 \end{bmatrix} \begin{bmatrix} R_1 \\ R_2 \\ R_3 \end{bmatrix}$$

$$= \begin{bmatrix} 2R_1 + R_2 \\ -R_1 + 3R_2 + 2R_3 \\ 2R_1 + 2R_2 - R_3 \end{bmatrix} = \begin{bmatrix} 2[1 \ 2 \ 0] + [0 \ -1 \ 1] \\ -[1 \ 2 \ 0] + 3[0 \ -1 \ 1] + 2[2 \ 2 \ 2] \\ +2[1 \ 2 \ 0] + 2[0 \ -1 \ 1] - [2 \ 2 \ 2] \end{bmatrix}$$

$$= \begin{bmatrix} 2 & 3 & 1 \\ 3 & -1 & 7 \\ 0 & 0 & 0 \end{bmatrix}.$$

In this example, we have found that

$$2R_1 + 2R_2 - R_3 = 0,$$

which is a result of special significance.

**Definition 15.6a.** A set of vectors $R_1, R_2, \ldots, R_n$ is said to be **linearly dependent** if there are scalars $\alpha_1, \alpha_2, \ldots, \alpha_n$ *not all zero* such that

$$\alpha_1 R_1 + \alpha_2 R_2 + \ldots + \alpha_n R_n = 0.$$

If this relationship is true only when all the $\alpha$'s are zero, then the vectors are said to be **linearly independent.**

In the preceding illustration, $R_1, R_2, R_3$ are linearly dependent. This concept is further illustrated in the next example.

---

*Example 15.6d.* Are the following vectors linearly dependent or linearly independent?

$$R_1 .=. \begin{bmatrix} 0 & 1 & 3 \end{bmatrix}, \quad R_2 .=. \begin{bmatrix} 1 & -1 & -2 \end{bmatrix}, \quad R_3 .=. \begin{bmatrix} 2 & 0 & 1 \end{bmatrix}.$$

To answer this question, we try to find constants $\alpha_1$, $\alpha_2$, $\alpha_3$ such that

$$\alpha_1 R_1 + \alpha_2 R_2 + \alpha_3 R_3 = 0.$$

From

$$\alpha_1[0 \quad 1 \quad 3] + \alpha_2[1 \quad -1 \quad -2] + \alpha_3[2 \quad 0 \quad 1] = 0,$$

we get the system of equations

$$\begin{aligned}
\alpha_2 + 2\alpha_3 &= 0, \\
\alpha_1 - \alpha_2 &= 0, \\
3\alpha_1 - 2\alpha_2 + \alpha_3 &= 0,
\end{aligned}$$

or, in matrix form,

$$\begin{bmatrix} 0 & 1 & 2 \\ 1 & -1 & 0 \\ 3 & -2 & 1 \end{bmatrix} \begin{bmatrix} \alpha_1 \\ \alpha_2 \\ \alpha_3 \end{bmatrix} = \begin{bmatrix} 0 \\ 0 \\ 0 \end{bmatrix}.$$

By carrying out elementary row operations, we find

$$\begin{bmatrix} 1 & 0 & 0 \\ 0 & 1 & 0 \\ 0 & 0 & 1 \end{bmatrix} \begin{bmatrix} \alpha_1 \\ \alpha_2 \\ \alpha_3 \end{bmatrix} = \begin{bmatrix} 0 \\ 0 \\ 0 \end{bmatrix},$$

or $\alpha_1 = 0$, $\alpha_2 = 0$, $\alpha_3 = 0$. Since this is the only solution for the $\alpha$'s, the vectors are linearly independent.

---

The concept of linear independence is important in a number of respects, as will be shown from time to time. For the present, after we obtain some preliminary theorems, we can use this concept to sum up the preceding results on solving systems of equations.

**Definition 15.6b.** The number of linearly independent rows of a matrix $A$ is called the **rank** of $A$, and is denoted by $r(A)$.

We have already shown that if

$$A = \begin{bmatrix} 1 & 2 & 0 \\ 0 & -1 & 1 \\ 2 & 2 & 2 \end{bmatrix},$$

then $r(A) = 2$. This means that one row vector of $A$ is a linear combination of the other two. In the matrix $B$ of Example 15.6a,

$$\begin{bmatrix} 0 & 1 & 2 \\ 1 & -1 & 0 \\ 3 & 2 & 1 \end{bmatrix},$$

it is not possible for one row vector to be a linear combination of the other two since $r(B) = 3$.

**Theorem 15.6a.** The rank of a modified triangular matrix is exactly the number of rows that contain a nonzero element.

PROOF: This follows directly from the fact that the first nonzero element of any row is the only nonzero element in its column. Thus, if the first $p$ rows all contain a nonzero element, then

$$\alpha_1 R_1 + \alpha_2 R_2 + \cdots + \alpha_p R_p = 0 \Leftrightarrow \alpha_1 = \alpha_2 = \cdots = \alpha_p = 0.$$

(The reader may check this by noting that if the first nonzero element in $R_1$ is in the $j$th column, then for the elements in the $j$th column, it must follow that $\alpha_1 = 0$. The same argument applies for each of the first $p$ rows.) Hence these rows are linearly independent. If the remaining rows have only zero elements, then the equation

$$\alpha_1 R_1 + \alpha_2 R_2 + \cdots + \alpha_p R_p + \alpha_{p+1} R_{p+1} + \cdots + \alpha_n R_n = 0$$

is true for $\alpha_1 = \alpha_2 = \cdots = \alpha_p = 0$ and for any arbitrary nonzero values of the remaining $\alpha$'s. Thus, there are exactly $p$ linearly independent rows, and the rank is $p$.

The concept of rank turns out to be important, since according to the next theorem, the rank of a matrix is left unchanged by elementary row operations. Thus, using Theorem 15.6a, the rank of a matrix can be found by first obtaining an equivalent MTM and then counting the number of rows that contain a non-zero element.

**Theorem 15.6b.** If $E$ is an elementary matrix, and if $A$ is any matrix for which $EA$ is defined, then

$$r(EA) = r(A).$$

(That is, the matrix $EA$ has as many linearly independent rows as $A$.)
PROOF: If $E$ is $E_{ij}$, then the interchange of two rows cannot alter the number of independent rows, since the rows are unaltered except for the order of their appearance.

If $E$ is $E_i(k)$, $k \neq 0$, and if $A$ has $p$ independent rows, $EA$ still has $p$ independent rows, as the following argument shows. Suppose $R_1, \ldots, R_i, \ldots, R_p$ are the independent rows of $A$ (by row interchanges, the independent rows can be put in the first $p$ positions) and suppose that

$$\alpha_1 R_1 + \alpha_2 R_2 + \cdots + \alpha_i k R_i + \cdots + \alpha_p R_p = 0,$$

with the $\alpha$'s not all zero. It follows that

$$\beta_1 R_1 + \beta_2 R_2 + \cdots + \beta_i R_i + \cdots + \beta_p R_p = 0,$$

where $\beta_j = \alpha_j, j \neq i$, and $\beta_i = k\alpha_i$, so that the $\beta$'s are also not all zero. Thus, it would follow that $R_1, \ldots, R_p$ are linearly dependent, which is a contradiction. It is left to the reader to make the slight modification that is needed in the argument if $i > p$.

Finally, if $E = E_{i+j}$, $EA$ still has $p$ independent rows. The reader can supply the details by assuming that $R_1, R_2, \ldots, R_p$ are the independent rows of $A$, and by showing that if the rows of $E_{i+j}A$, $R_1, R_2, \ldots, R_i + R_j, \ldots, R_p$ are dependent, then there is again a contradiction.

The next theorem is the goal for which we have been striving.

**Theorem 15.6c.** A system of equations $AX = C$ has a solution $\Leftrightarrow r(A) = r([A, C])$, where $[A, C]$ is the matrix formed by appending to $A$ the column $C$.

That is, the system has a solution if, and only if, the number of independent rows of $A$ is the same as that of $[A, C]$.

PROOF: First, suppose that the system has a solution. Then the solution can be obtained from $AX = C$ by elementary row operations which reduce the equation to the form

$$A_1 X = C_1,$$

where $A_1$ is a modified triangular matrix. Since the equation is assumed to have a solution, it follows that for each row of zeros in $A_1$, there is a corresponding zero in $C_1$. Hence, if a row of $A$ is a linear combination of other rows of $A$, the same row of $[A, C]$ is a linear combination of the corresponding rows of $[A, C]$, so that the number of linearly independent rows of $A$ and of $[A, C]$ must be the same. Thus the existence of a solution implies $r(A) = r([A, C])$.

For the second part of the proof, we must show that $r(A) = r([A, C])$ implies that there is a solution. Again, let us use elementary row operations to reduce the equation to the form

$$A_1 X = C_1,$$

where $A_1$ is a modified triangular matrix. Then, by Theorem 15.6b,

$$r(A) = r(A_1) \quad \text{and} \quad r([A, C]) = r([A_1, C]).$$

Since $r(A) = r([A, C])$, it follows that $r(A_1) = r([A_1, C])$. Therefore, if $A_1$ has a row of zeros, then $C_1$ has a zero in the same row. In this case, the matrix equation $A_1 X = C_1$ represents a system of $m$ equations in $n$ unknowns where $m \leq n$, and these equations furnish a solution of the original system. If $m = n$, the values of the unknowns are found by equating corresponding elements of the two matrices $A_1$ and $C_1$. If $m < n$, then $m$ of the unknowns may be expressed in terms of the remaining $n - m$ unknowns by simply transferring the terms with the appropriate unknowns to the right side of each equation in the system symbolized by $A_1 X = C_1$. Thus, we conclude that there is a solution of the given system, and this completes the proof of the theorem.

The reader may verify a number of interesting observations that follow from this theorem. If $C = 0$, the system always has at least one solution, the zero solution (see Example 15.6d). If there are more unknowns than equations, and if $C = 0$, then there is always a nonzero solution. Finally, the reader should notice that, in practice, it is sufficient to work directly for a solution of the system in order to use Theorem 15.6c to advantage.

As an illustration of the preceding discussion, we may refer to Example 15.6c. In that example,

$$A = \begin{bmatrix} 1 & -1 & 1 \\ 2 & 1 & -1 \\ -1 & 2 & 2 \\ 3 & -2 & -2 \end{bmatrix} \sim_r \begin{bmatrix} 1 & 0 & 0 \\ 0 & 1 & 0 \\ 0 & 0 & 1 \\ 0 & 0 & 0 \end{bmatrix},$$

which shows that $r(A) = 3$. Similarly,

$$[A, C] = \begin{bmatrix} 1 & -1 & 1 & 3 \\ 1 & -1 & 1 & 3 \\ -1 & 2 & 2 & 1 \\ 3 & -2 & -2 & -1 \end{bmatrix} \sim_r \begin{bmatrix} 1 & 0 & 0 & 0 \\ 0 & 1 & 0 & 0 \\ 0 & 0 & 1 & 0 \\ 0 & 0 & 0 & 1 \end{bmatrix},$$

so that $r([A, C]) = 4$.

Thus, $r(A) \neq r([A, C])$, and the matrix equation

$$AX = C$$

has no solution, as was shown in Example 15.6c.

## Exercises 15.6

In Numbers 1 to 8, find the rank of each of the matrices by first reducing it to an equivalent MTM.

1. $\begin{bmatrix} 1 & 0 & 0 \\ 0 & 1 & 0 \\ 0 & 0 & 1 \end{bmatrix}$.

2. $\begin{bmatrix} 1 & 0 & 0 & 0 \\ 0 & 1 & 0 & 0 \\ 0 & 0 & 1 & a \end{bmatrix}$.

3. $\begin{bmatrix} 1 & 0 & 0 \\ 0 & 1 & 0 \\ 0 & 0 & 1 \\ x & y & z \end{bmatrix}$.

4. $\begin{bmatrix} 1 & 2 \\ 3 & 6 \\ -1 & -2 \end{bmatrix}$.

5. $\begin{bmatrix} 1 & 2 & 2 \\ -2 & 1 & -1 \\ -1 & 8 & 4 \end{bmatrix}$.

6. $\begin{bmatrix} 1 & 2 & 2 & 1 \\ -2 & 1 & -1 & 2 \\ -1 & 8 & 4 & 1 \end{bmatrix}$.

7. $\begin{bmatrix} 2 & 1 & 3 & 4 \\ 1 & -1 & 0 & 2 \\ 2 & -1 & 1 & 3 \\ 4 & 1 & 5 & -1 \end{bmatrix}$.

8. $\begin{bmatrix} 2 & -1 & 3 \\ 1 & -2 & 1 \\ 0 & 2 & 2 \\ -1 & 3 & 1 \\ 4 & 1 & 3 \end{bmatrix}$.

Find solutions, if any exist, for the following systems of equations. Give a geometric interpretation in Numbers 9 to 14, inclusive.

9. $x - y + z = 4,$
$2x + y - 3z = 0,$
$x + y + z = 2.$

10. $2x + 3y - z = 9,$
$3x + 4y + 2z = 5,$
$x - 6y - 5z = -9.$

11. $2u - 5v + 2w = -2,$
$4u + 6v - w = 23,$
$2u + 7v + 4w = 24.$

12. $x + 5y - 2z = 1,$
$2x + y - z = 2.$

13. $2r - 3s - 8t = 0,$
$5r - 2s - 3t = 0,$
$3r + 3s + 11t = 0.$

14. $8x + 4y = 1,$
$3x + 5y = 3,$
$5x + 3y = 1.$

15. $w + x + y + z = 2,$
$2w + x - y - 3z = 14,$
$w - 3x - 2y - z = -3,$
$3w - 5x + 2y + 2z = -15.$

16. $2u - v + 3w = a,$
$u + v - 2w = b,$
$-u + 2v + 2w = c.$

17. $3x + 2y + z = 5,$
$2x + y - 2z = 4,$
$x \qquad - 5z = 15.$

18. $3a + 2b - c = 1,$
$a + b + 2c = 2,$
$-a - 2b + 3c = -1,$
$a + b - c = 0.$

## 15.7 DETERMINANTS

Just as we associate a real number $(a^2 + b^2)^{1/2}$ with the vector $(a, b)$, we may associate a real number with a given square matrix. One way in which this can be done is suggested by the form of the solution of a general system of equations.
For the system

$$a_1x + b_1y = c_1,$$
$$a_2x + b_2y = c_2,$$

it has been shown that

$$x = \frac{c_1b_2 - c_2b_1}{a_1b_2 - a_2b_1}.$$

This result can be written in terms of determinants, which were introduced in Section 14.4, as

$$x = \frac{\begin{vmatrix} c_1 & b_1 \\ c_2 & b_2 \end{vmatrix}}{\begin{vmatrix} a_1 & b_1 \\ a_2 & b_2 \end{vmatrix}}.$$

Similarly, for the system

$$a_1x + b_1y + c_1z = d_1,$$
$$a_2x + b_2y + c_2z = d_2,$$
$$a_3x + b_3y + c_3z = d_3,$$

it can be shown that

(1) $$x = \frac{d_1b_2c_3 + d_3b_1c_2 + d_2b_3c_1 - d_1b_3c_2 - d_2b_1c_3 - d_3b_2c_1}{a_1b_2c_3 + a_3b_1c_2 + a_2b_3c_1 - a_1b_3c_2 - a_2b_1c_3 - a_3b_2c_1},$$

or in terms of third-order determinants, as introduced in Section 14.4,

$$x = \frac{\begin{vmatrix} d_1 & b_1 & c_1 \\ d_2 & b_2 & c_2 \\ d_3 & b_3 & c_3 \end{vmatrix}}{\begin{vmatrix} a_1 & b_1 & c_1 \\ a_2 & b_2 & c_2 \\ a_3 & b_3 & c_3 \end{vmatrix}}.$$

Evidently each determinant is a number that can be associated with a matrix of coefficients of the system of equations, such as

$$\begin{bmatrix} a_1 & b_1 \\ a_2 & b_2 \end{bmatrix} \quad \text{or} \quad \begin{bmatrix} a_1 & b_1 & c_1 \\ a_2 & b_2 & c_2 \\ a_3 & b_3 & c_3 \end{bmatrix}.$$

A study of the terms in the denominator of (1) shows that each term contains one $a$, one $b$, and one $c$, and each row index appears exactly once in each term. Thus, there is never a term of the form $a_1 b_1 c_3$ or $a_1 a_3 b_2$. Each term in the denominator is a product of three elements such that one and only one element is taken from each row and each column of the matrix of coefficients. In this particular case, such products can be formed in $(3)(2)(1) = 6$ ways. Hence, *every* possible combination of letters and row numbers, one and only one being taken from each column and row, is included in the terms of the denominator.

The combination of terms, each with an appropriate sign, constructed in an analogous way from the elements of any square matrix, is called the **determinant of the matrix**. Although the preceding discussion suggests the way in which the determinant of a general $n \times n$ matrix may be defined, we must find a scheme that can be used to designate the sign to be attached to each term. For this purpose it is convenient to use double subscript notation. If

$$A .=. \begin{bmatrix} a_{11} & a_{12} & a_{13} \\ a_{21} & a_{22} & a_{23} \\ a_{31} & a_{32} & a_{33} \end{bmatrix},$$

then each term of the determinant of $A$ is of the form

$$a_{1\alpha_1} a_{2\alpha_2} a_{3\alpha_3},$$

where $\alpha_1$, $\alpha_2$, $\alpha_3$ are the numbers 1, 2, and 3 in some order; that is, a typical term in the determinant of $A$ has factors with the numbers 1, 2, and 3 in that order as first subscripts, and 1, 2, and 3 *in some order* as second subscripts, such as

$$a_{12} a_{23} a_{31}.$$

As we shall soon see, the sign to be associated with a term of this kind depends on the order of the numbers in the second subscripts when the first subscripts are written in their natural order 1, 2, 3.

An arrangement of objects such as the numbers 1, 2, and 3 in some order is called a **permutation** of those objects. For example, the arrangement 2, 3, 1 is a permutation of the numbers 1, 2, 3. For three objects there are six possible permutations, since the first object may be chosen from among three, the second may be chosen from the remaining two, and the last object must be the one left. Hence, there are $(3)(2)(1) = 6$ permutations possible. By similar reasoning it can be shown that there are $4! = 24$ permutations possible with 4 objects, and that there are $n!$ permutations possible with $n$ objects.

An interchange of two of the objects in a given arrangement is called a **transposition**. For example, in the number 2134, the digits 4 and 1 are transposed from the 4 and 1 in the number 2431. A permutation is said to be **even** if the number of transpositions required to put the objects into their original order is even, and is said to be **odd** if the number of transpositions required is odd.

For example, the numbers in the permutation 3142 can be put into natural order by the following successive transpositions:

$$3142, \quad 1342, \quad 1243, \quad 1234.$$

Since three transpositions are needed to obtain the natural order, the permutation 3142 of the numbers 1, 2, 3, 4 is said to be odd.

Of course, it is conceivable that different transpositions can be used to obtain natural order, and that the number of transpositions needed will be different. For example, we have

$$3142, \quad 3412, \quad 1432, \quad 1423, \quad 1243, \quad 1234$$

as a possible way of obtaining 1234 from 3142. The number of transpositions involved is still odd, so that the permutation 3142 is odd. But can we be assured that no matter in what way transpositions are made, the number of transpositions will always be odd? We shall leave as an exercise for the reader to show that the answer to this question is *yes* (see Exercises 15.7, Number 7).

With the aid of this information, we can now prescribe a rule for determining a sign to be associated with each term in a determinant.

**Definition 15.7a.** Let $p$ denote a permutation of the numbers 1, 2, 3, . . . , $n$. Then

$$\operatorname{sgn}(p) .=. +1 \text{ if } p \text{ is even,}$$
$$\operatorname{sgn}(p) .=. -1 \text{ if } p \text{ is odd,}$$

where "sgn" is the abbreviation for the Latin *signum*, meaning sign.

For example, the preceding discussion shows that

$$\operatorname{sgn}(3142) = -1.$$

With the help of this definition, we can give a proper definition for the determinant of an $n \times n$ matrix $A$.

**Definition 15.7b.** The **determinant** of an $n \times n$ matrix $A$ is the number

$$\det A .=. \sum_p \operatorname{sgn}(p) a_{1\alpha_1} a_{2\alpha_2} \cdots a_{n\alpha_n},$$

where $p$ is a permutation $\alpha_1, \alpha_2, \ldots, \alpha_n$ of the numbers 1, 2, . . . , $n$, and the summation extends over all such permutations.

To illustrate, let $n = 3$. Then

$$\det A .=. \sum_p \operatorname{sgn}(p) a_{1\alpha_1} a_{2\alpha_2} a_{3\alpha_3}$$

$$= \operatorname{sgn}(123) a_{11}a_{22}a_{33} + \operatorname{sgn}(132) a_{11}a_{23}a_{32} + \operatorname{sgn}(213) a_{12}a_{21}a_{33}$$
$$+ \operatorname{sgn}(231) a_{12}a_{23}a_{31} + \operatorname{sgn}(312) a_{13}a_{21}a_{32} + \operatorname{sgn}(321) a_{13}a_{22}a_{31}$$
$$= a_{11}a_{22}a_{33} - a_{11}a_{23}a_{32} - a_{12}a_{21}a_{33} + a_{12}a_{23}a_{31} + a_{13}a_{21}a_{32} - a_{13}a_{22}a_{31}.$$

This expression is exactly that given at the beginning of this section if $a_1 = a_{11}$.

$a_2 = a_{21}$, $a_3 = a_{31}$, $b_1 = a_{12}$, and so on. If $n = 4$, then det $A$ has 24 terms, a typical one of which is

$$\text{sgn}\,(3241)a_{13}a_{22}a_{34}a_{41} = a_{13}a_{22}a_{34}a_{41}.$$

As we shall soon see, determinants are useful in a number of ways. However, before considering possible applications, let us obtain a number of fundamental properties that will simplify the evaluation of a determinant in special cases.

**Theorem 15.7a.** If the elements in a row of a matrix $B$ have a common factor $c$, and if $A$ is the matrix $B$ with the common factor removed from the appropriate row, then

$$\det B = c \det A.$$

PROOF: If $c$ is a common factor in the $i$th row, and if $A = [a_{ij}]$, then

$$\det B = \sum_p \text{sgn}\,(p)a_{1\alpha_1} \cdots ca_{i\alpha_i} \cdots a_{n\alpha_n}$$

by the definition of det $B$, so that

$$\det B = c \sum_p \text{sgn}\,(p)a_{1\alpha_1} \cdots a_{i\alpha_i} \cdots a_{n\alpha_n},$$

since every term in the sum contains one factor from the $i$th row of $B$, which includes the factor $c$. By the definition of det $A$, we get

$$\det B = c \det A.$$

To illustrate the theorem, we have, for example,

$$\begin{vmatrix} 2 & 2 & 4 \\ 3 & 3 & -6 \\ -1 & 4 & 3 \end{vmatrix} = 2 \begin{vmatrix} 1 & 1 & 2 \\ 3 & 3 & -6 \\ -1 & 4 & 3 \end{vmatrix} = 2 \cdot 3 \begin{vmatrix} 1 & 1 & 2 \\ 1 & 1 & -2 \\ -1 & 4 & 3 \end{vmatrix}.$$

The next theorem is also easily proved.

**Theorem 15.7b.** If two rows of a square matrix $A$ are interchanged to obtain a square matrix $B$, then det $B = -\det A$.

PROOF: To illustrate the method of proof let us prove the special case of the theorem for $3 \times 3$ matrices. In that case

$$\det A = \sum_p \text{sgn}\,(p)a_{1\alpha_1}a_{2\alpha_2}a_{3\alpha_3}.$$

Suppose the first and third rows are interchanged to obtain the matrix $B$. Then in each term of det $A$, the factors $a_{1\alpha_1}$ and $a_{3\alpha_3}$ are interchanged to form det $B$. But such an interchange imposes a single transposition on each permutation $p$. Hence, the sign of the new permutation, say $q$, is opposite that of the old, and we may write

$$\det A = \sum_p \text{sgn}\,(p)a_{1\alpha_1}a_{2\alpha_2}a_{3\alpha_3}$$

$$= -\sum_q \text{sgn}\,(q)a_{3\alpha_3}a_{2\alpha_2}a_{1\alpha_1}$$

$$= -\det B.$$

This argument applies to the interchange of any two rows, and thus the theorem is proved for $3 \times 3$ matrices.

The proof in the general case follows the same pattern. Suppose the $i$th and $j$th rows are interchanged in $A$ to obtain matrix $B$. Then

$$\det A = \sum_p \text{sgn}\,(p)a_{1\alpha_1} \cdots a_{i\alpha_i} \cdots a_{j\alpha_j} \cdots a_{n\alpha_n}$$

$$= -\sum_q \text{sgn}\,(q)a_{1\alpha_1} \cdots a_{j\alpha_j} \cdots a_{i\alpha_i} \ldots a_{n\alpha_n}$$

$$= -\det (B),$$

and the theorem follows.

The reader should show that

$$\begin{vmatrix} 1 & 2 & 1 \\ 0 & -1 & 2 \\ 1 & 1 & 0 \end{vmatrix} = 3,$$

and that

$$\begin{vmatrix} 0 & -1 & 2 \\ 1 & 2 & 1 \\ 1 & 1 & 0 \end{vmatrix} = -3.$$

An interesting, simple consequence of the last theorem is given in

**Theorem 15.7c.** If a square matrix $A$ has two identical rows, then

$$\det A = 0.$$

PROOF: If the identical rows are interchanged, then the sign of the determinant is changed, although the matrix $A$ is unchanged. Hence, we must have

$$\det A = -\det A,$$

so that

$$\det A = 0.$$

By making use of the following basic result, we can easily show that the preceding theorems remain valid if the word "row" is everywhere replaced by the word "column."

**Theorem 15.7d.** If $A$ is a square matrix, then

$$\det A^{\mathsf{T}} = \det A.$$

PROOF: Let $B = [b_{ij}] = A^{\mathsf{T}}$, so that $b_{ij} = a_{ji}$. Then

$$\det B = \sum_p \text{sgn}\,(p)b_{1\alpha_1}b_{2\alpha_2} \cdots b_{n\alpha_n}$$

$$= \sum_p \text{sgn}\,(p)a_{\alpha_1 1}a_{\alpha_2 2} \cdots a_{\alpha_n n}.$$

Now the permutation $\alpha_1\alpha_2 \ldots \alpha_n$ of the numbers $1, 2, \ldots, n$ must be changed to obtain natural order. This can be done by rearranging the $a$'s, but in the process, a permutation $q$ is induced upon the second subscripts. That is

$$\det B = \sum_q \text{sgn}\,(q)a_{1\beta_1}a_{2\beta_2}\cdots a_{n\beta_n}.$$

Every time an interchange is made on the first subscripts, a corresponding transposition is imposed upon the second subscripts. Hence, the sign of a term, as determined by the permutation of second subscripts with the first subscripts in natural order, is the same as that determined by the permutation of first subscripts with the second subscripts in natural order. Evidently,

$$\sum_q \text{sgn}\,(q)a_{1\beta_1}a_{2\beta_2}\cdots a_{n\beta_n} = \det A.$$

It follows immediately from this theorem that each of the preceding theorems remains valid if the word "row" is replaced by the word "column" throughout. This fact and the foregoing theorems are fundamental to the more important and practical properties of determinants that will be discussed in the next section.

## Exercises 15.7

1. Determine if the following permutations are even or odd:

(a) 3412;    (b) 4321;    (c) 35142;
(d) 623514;    (e) 25143;    (f) 536124.

2. If each of the following is a term in the determinant of a square matrix, determine if the term should be preceded by a $+$ or $-$ sign.

(a) $a_{31}a_{22}a_{13}$.

(b) $a_{41}a_{22}a_{13}a_{34}$.

(c) $a_{53}a_{21}a_{42}a_{15}a_{34}$.

(d) $a_{41}a_{32}a_{23}a_{14}a_{55}$.

(e) $a_{34}a_{56}a_{61}a_{13}a_{25}a_{42}$.

(f) $a_{21}a_{33}a_{62}a_{56}a_{15}a_{44}$.

In Numbers 3 to 5, inclusive, prove the statement by using only the definitions and theorems in this section rather than by direct evaluation.

3.
$$\begin{vmatrix} 2 & -2 & 6 \\ -1 & 1 & -3 \\ 5 & 4 & -3 \end{vmatrix} = 0.$$

4.
$$\begin{vmatrix} a_1 + \alpha_1 & b_1 & c_1 \\ a_2 + \alpha_2 & b_2 & c_2 \\ a_3 + \alpha_3 & b_3 & c_3 \end{vmatrix} = \begin{vmatrix} a_1 & b_1 & c_1 \\ a_2 & b_2 & c_2 \\ a_3 & b_3 & c_3 \end{vmatrix} + \begin{vmatrix} \alpha_1 & b_1 & c_1 \\ \alpha_2 & b_2 & c_2 \\ \alpha_3 & b_3 & c_3 \end{vmatrix}.$$

5.
$$\begin{vmatrix} 0 & b_{12} & b_{13} & b_{14} & b_{15} \\ -b_{12} & 0 & b_{23} & b_{24} & b_{25} \\ -b_{13} & -b_{23} & 0 & b_{34} & b_{35} \\ -b_{14} & -b_{24} & -b_{34} & 0 & b_{45} \\ -b_{15} & -b_{25} & -b_{35} & -b_{45} & 0 \end{vmatrix} = 0.$$

★6. The general theorem corresponding to the result of Number 5 states that the determinant of every skew-symmetric matrix of odd order is zero. Prove this theorem.

★7. Prove that if a permutation $p$ of the numbers $1, 2, \ldots, n$ can be put into natural order by $k$ transpositions in one way and by $m$ transpositions in another way, then $k - m$ is an even integer. *Hint*: Consider the expression

$$q(x_1, x_2, \ldots, x_n)$$
$$= (x_1 - x_2)(x_1 - x_3) \cdots (x_1 - x_n)(x_2 - x_3) \cdots (x_2 - x_n) \cdots (x_{n-1} - x_n).$$

When a transposition of the numbers $\alpha$, $\beta$ in $p$ is made, transpose $x_\alpha$ and $x_\beta$ in $q$, and show that one such transposition changes $q$ into $-q$. If the permutation $p$ is $\alpha_1, \alpha_2, \ldots, \alpha_n$, which represents $1, 2, \ldots, n$ in some order, then consider $q(x_{\alpha_1}, x_{\alpha_2}, \ldots, x_{\alpha_n})$ where the $x$'s have been rearranged so that the subscripts are in the order $p$. Now carry out the $k$ transpositions to obtain the $x$'s in proper order. This means that

$$q(x_{\alpha_1}, x_{\alpha_2}, \ldots, x_{\alpha_n}) = (-1)^k q(x_1, x_2, \ldots, x_n).$$

Similarly, by the other set of $m$ transpositions, we get

$$q(x_{\alpha_1}, x_{\alpha_2}, \ldots, x_{\alpha_n}) = (-1)^m q(x_1, x_2, \ldots, x_n).$$

These two expressions must be equal, and are equal only if $k - m$ is an even integer.

## 15.8 EXPANSION OF A DETERMINANT BY MINORS

Although the determinant of a square matrix can be evaluated directly from the definition of a determinant given in the preceding section, it is by no means a practical procedure when the order of the determinant is large. A determinant of order 5, for example, involves the sum of 120 terms. Consequently, there is considerable merit in seeking a procedure that will be useful in evaluating a determinant in a less painful manner. The first step in this direction consists merely in making an observation.

Suppose the terms of det $A$ are grouped in such a way that all those containing $a_{i1}$ as a factor are together, those containing $a_{i2}$ are together, and so on for each of the elements in the $i$th row of $A$. If $C_{i\alpha}$ denotes the coefficient of $a_{i\alpha}$, then we may write

$$\det A = a_{i1}C_{i1} + a_{i2}C_{i2} + \cdots + a_{in}C_{in}$$

$$= \sum_{\alpha=1}^{n} a_{i\alpha}C_{i\alpha}.$$

The quantity $C_{i\alpha}$ is called the **cofactor** of $a_{i\alpha}$.

The reader may verify that

$$\begin{vmatrix} a_{11} & a_{12} & a_{13} \\ a_{21} & a_{22} & a_{23} \\ a_{31} & a_{32} & a_{33} \end{vmatrix}$$

$$= a_{21}(a_{32}a_{13} - a_{12}a_{33}) + a_{22}(a_{11}a_{33} - a_{31}a_{13}) + a_{23}(a_{31}a_{12} - a_{11}a_{32}),$$

so that $a_{32}a_{13} - a_{12}a_{33}$ is the cofactor $C_{21}$ of $a_{21}$ for a third-order determinant. A cofactor may be written in a determinant form. For example,

$$C_{21} = a_{32}a_{13} - a_{12}a_{23} = \begin{vmatrix} a_{13} & a_{12} \\ a_{33} & a_{32} \end{vmatrix},$$

and

$$C_{22} = a_{11}a_{33} - a_{31}a_{13} = \begin{vmatrix} a_{11} & a_{13} \\ a_{31} & a_{33} \end{vmatrix}.$$

In the second case the elements of the determinant are in the same relative position as they were in the original determinant, whereas in the first case the columns are interchanged from their order in the original determinant.

By interchanging columns to restore their original order, we may write

$$(1) \quad \begin{vmatrix} a_{11} & a_{12} & a_{13} \\ a_{21} & a_{22} & a_{23} \\ a_{31} & a_{32} & a_{33} \end{vmatrix} = -a_{21} \begin{vmatrix} a_{12} & a_{13} \\ a_{32} & a_{33} \end{vmatrix} + a_{22} \begin{vmatrix} a_{11} & a_{13} \\ a_{31} & a_{33} \end{vmatrix} - a_{23} \begin{vmatrix} a_{11} & a_{12} \\ a_{31} & a_{32} \end{vmatrix}.$$

Each second-order determinant on the right side of this equation can be obtained from the original determinant by deleting in it the row and column containing the element that is the coefficient of this second-order determinant. Thus, the coefficient of $a_{23}$,

$$- \begin{vmatrix} a_{11} & a_{12} \\ a_{31} & a_{32} \end{vmatrix},$$

is obtained from

$$\cdots \begin{vmatrix} a_{11} & a_{12} & a_{13} \\ a_{21} \cdots a_{22} \cdots a_{23} \\ a_{31} & a_{32} & a_{33} \end{vmatrix} \cdots$$

by deleting the second row and third column, as is indicated.

These illustrations suggest the general discussion that follows.

**Definition 15.8a.** The matrix obtained by deleting the $i$th row and $j$th column of a matrix $A$ is called the $ij$th **submatrix** of $A$ and is denoted by $S_{ij}$.

For example, if

$$A .=. \begin{bmatrix} 1 & 2 & 1 & 0 \\ 3 & -1 & 2 & -3 \\ 1 & 0 & 4 & -2 \end{bmatrix},$$

then

$$S_{23} = \begin{bmatrix} 1 & 2 & 0 \\ 1 & 0 & -2 \end{bmatrix} \quad \text{and} \quad S_{12} = \begin{bmatrix} 3 & 2 & -3 \\ 1 & 4 & -2 \end{bmatrix}.$$

The expression for the third-order determinant in Equation (1) can be described more conveniently in terms of submatrices than in terms of cofactors, provided a rule can be formulated for finding the proper sign for each term. Thus, if $A$ is a $3 \times 3$ matrix, we may write

$$\det A = -a_{21} \det S_{21} + a_{22} \det S_{22} - a_{23} \det S_{23}$$

directly from $\det A$ once the appropriate signs are determined.

Let us introduce the abbreviation

$$M_{ij} .=. \det S_{ij}$$

whenever $A$ is a square matrix. The determinant $M_{ij}$ is called the **minor** of the element $a_{ij}$ in det $A$. Any desired minor may be constructed directly from det $A$ merely by deleting the appropriate row and column of $A$.

With the double-subscript notation, it is easy to find the proper sign for any term $a_{ij}M_{ij}$ in the expansion of det $A$. If we observe that the cofactor $C_{11}$ is identical with the minor $M_{11}$ for every square matrix, then we can prove

**Theorem 15.8a.** For any square matrix $A$,

$$C_{ij} = (-1)^{i+j}M_{ij}.$$

PROOF: We first interchange the $i$th row and the $(i - 1)$th row of the matrix $A$, then we interchange the new $(i - 1)$th row and the $(i - 2)$th row, and so on until the original $i$th row of $A$ is in the first-row position. The rows of $A$ are now in the order $R_i, R_1, R_2, \ldots, R_{i-1}, R_{i+1}, \ldots, R_n$. Since this arrangement is accomplished by $i - 1$ interchanges, the resulting matrix has a determinant equal to $(-1)^{i-1}$ det $A$. Similarly, the $j$th column of the rearranged matrix can be placed in the first-column position of $A$ by $j - 1$ interchanges. The resulting determinant is equal to $(-1)^{j-1}\{(-1)^{i-1}$ det $A\}$. Thus, if $B$ is the final arrangement of $A$, in which $a_{ij}$ is now in the $a_{11}$ position, then

$$\det B = (-1)^{i+j-2} \det A,$$

or

$$(-1)^{i+j} \det B = \det A.$$

Now the coefficient of $a_{ij}$ (in the $a_{11}$ position) in $B$ is $M_{ij}$, and the coefficient of $a_{ij}$ in det $A$ is $C_{ij}$. Hence, it follows that

$$(-1)^{i+j}M_{ij} = C_{ij}.$$

These results can be used to express any determinant of order $n$ as a sum of terms involving determinants of submatrices of a given row (or column). From the grouping

$$\det A = \sum_{\alpha=1}^{n} a_{i\alpha}C_{i\alpha},$$

we may write

(2)
$$\det A = \sum_{\alpha=1}^{n} (-1)^{i+\alpha}a_{i\alpha}M_{i\alpha}.$$

An expression of the type given in (2) is called an **expansion** of the determinant of $A$ by the minors of the $i$th row. A similar expansion may be written using elements of the $j$th column. Thus,

(3)
$$\det A = \sum_{\alpha=1}^{n} (-1)^{j+\alpha}a_{\alpha j}M_{\alpha j}.$$

---

*Example 15.8a.* Using minors of the second row, expand the determinant

$$\begin{vmatrix} 1 & 0 & 2 & -1 \\ 1 & -3 & 0 & 2 \\ -3 & 1 & 2 & 1 \\ 0 & 3 & 1 & 4 \end{vmatrix} = \det A.$$

We have

$$\det A = (-1)(1)\begin{vmatrix} 0 & 2 & -1 \\ 1 & 2 & 1 \\ 3 & 1 & 4 \end{vmatrix} + (+1)(-3)\begin{vmatrix} 1 & 2 & -1 \\ -3 & 2 & 1 \\ 0 & 1 & 4 \end{vmatrix}$$

$$+ (-1)(0)\begin{vmatrix} 1 & 0 & -1 \\ -3 & 1 & 1 \\ 0 & 3 & 4 \end{vmatrix} + (+1)(2)\begin{vmatrix} 1 & 0 & 2 \\ -3 & 1 & 2 \\ 0 & 3 & 1 \end{vmatrix}$$

$$= -\begin{vmatrix} 0 & 2 & -1 \\ 1 & 2 & 1 \\ 3 & 1 & 4 \end{vmatrix} - 3\begin{vmatrix} 1 & 2 & -1 \\ -3 & 2 & 1 \\ 0 & 1 & 4 \end{vmatrix} + 2\begin{vmatrix} 1 & 0 & 2 \\ -3 & 1 & 2 \\ 0 & 3 & 1 \end{vmatrix}.$$

The expansion of a determinant by minors can be useful as a means of evaluating a determinant of large order, since it reduces the evaluation of a determinant of order $n$ to the evaluation of determinants of order $n - 1$. Even this procedure may be lengthy unless the determinant has a row or a column containing several zeros, in which case the determinant may be conveniently expanded along this row or column, since the minor of a zero element need not be evaluated.

It is not too surprising that a method is available by means of which zeros can be obtained in at least all but one position in a given row or column. As a first step toward arriving at this method, we shall prove

**Theorem 15.8b.** $$\sum_{\alpha=1}^{n} a_{i\alpha}C_{k\alpha} = 0 \quad \text{if} \quad i \neq k.$$

PROOF: For every square matrix $A$, it has been shown that

$$\det A = \sum_{\alpha=1}^{n} a_{k\alpha}C_{k\alpha}$$

is the expansion of the determinant of $A$ along its $k$th row,

$$a_{k1} \, a_{k2} \cdots a_{kn}.$$

If the elements of the $k$th row of $A$ are replaced by the corresponding elements of another row of $A$—for instance, the $i$th row—then the preceding expansion becomes

$$\det B = \sum_{\alpha=1}^{n} a_{i\alpha}C_{k\alpha},$$

where $B$ is the matrix $A$ altered by having its $k$th row replaced by its $i$th row. Since the $i$th row of $A$ is unaltered, the $i$th and $k$th rows of $B$ are identical, and $\det B = 0$, as was to be shown.

As an illustration of Theorem 15.8b, note that, for a third-order determinant,

$$a_{11}C_{21} + a_{12}C_{22} + a_{13}C_{23} = -a_{11}(a_{12}a_{33} - a_{13}a_{32})$$
$$+ a_{12}(a_{11}a_{33} - a_{13}a_{31}) - a_{13}(a_{11}a_{32} - a_{12}a_{31}),$$

which is an expansion by minors along the first row of the determinant

$$\begin{vmatrix} a_{11} & a_{12} & a_{13} \\ a_{11} & a_{12} & a_{13} \\ a_{31} & a_{32} & a_{33} \end{vmatrix}.$$

By Theorem 15.7c, this determinant is zero.

The cofactor expansion of a determinant and Theorem 15.8b can be quite neatly combined into a single statement if we use the symbol described in

**Definition 15.8b.** The **Kronecker delta**:

$$\delta_{ij} .= . \begin{cases} 0 & \text{for } i \neq j, \\ 1 & \text{for } i = j. \end{cases}$$

In terms of the Kronecker delta, we may write

$$\sum_{\alpha=1}^{n} a_{i\alpha}C_{j\alpha} = \sum_{\alpha=1}^{n} a_{\alpha i}C_{\alpha j} = \delta_{ij} \det A.$$

Finally, we come to a major tool in the evaluation of a determinant.

**Theorem 15.8c.** Let

$$A = \begin{bmatrix} R_1 \\ \cdot \\ \cdot \\ \cdot \\ R_n \end{bmatrix},$$

and let

$$B = \begin{bmatrix} R_1 \\ \cdot \\ \cdot \\ \cdot \\ R_i + kR_j \\ \cdot \\ \cdot \\ \cdot \\ R_n \end{bmatrix},$$

where $A$ is a square matrix, and $R_i$ denotes the $i$th row of $A$. Then

$$\det B = \det A.$$

That is, if $k$ times a row of a matrix $A$ is added to another row of $A$, then the determinant of the resulting matrix is equal to the determinant of $A$.

PROOF: Expanding $\det B$ by minors of the $i$th row, we have

$$\det B = \sum_{\alpha=1}^{n} (a_{i\alpha} + ka_{j\alpha})C_{i\alpha}$$

$$= \sum_{\alpha=1}^{n} a_{i\alpha}C_{i\alpha} + \sum_{\alpha=1}^{n} ka_{j\alpha}C_{i\alpha}$$

$$= \sum_{\alpha=1}^{n} a_{i\alpha}C_{i\alpha} + 0 \quad \text{(by Theorem 15.8b)}$$

$$= \det A.$$

An example will serve to illustrate this important result.

*Example 15.8b.* Evaluate

$$\det A = \begin{vmatrix} 1 & 0 & 2 & -1 \\ 1 & -1 & 0 & 2 \\ -3 & 1 & 2 & 1 \\ 0 & 3 & 1 & 4 \end{vmatrix}.$$

If the first row is subtracted from the second row, and three times the first row is added to the third row, then we find that

$$\det A = \begin{vmatrix} 1 & 0 & 2 & -1 \\ 0 & -1 & -2 & 3 \\ 0 & 1 & 8 & -2 \\ 0 & 3 & 1 & 4 \end{vmatrix}.$$

Upon expanding this determinant by minors along the first column, we get

$$\det A = \begin{vmatrix} -1 & -2 & 3 \\ 1 & 8 & -2 \\ 3 & 1 & 4 \end{vmatrix}.$$

By a similar procedure, this determinant can be further reduced to obtain

$$\det A = \begin{vmatrix} -1 & -2 & 3 \\ 0 & 6 & 1 \\ 0 & -5 & 13 \end{vmatrix} = (-1)\begin{vmatrix} 6 & 1 \\ -5 & 13 \end{vmatrix}$$

$$= (-1)(78 + 5) = -83.$$

Determinants can be used to solve a system of equations when the number of unknowns is the same as the number of equations. In order to demonstrate how this can be done in the simplest way, let us make use of a special matrix.

**Definition 15.8c.** Let $A$ be a square $n \times n$ matrix, and let $C_{ij}$ be the cofactor of $a_{ij}$ in $\det A$. Then the matrix

$$A^a .=. [C_{ij}]^T$$

is called the **adjoint** of $A$.

That is, $A^a$ is the transpose of the matrix formed from $A$ by replacing each element $a_{ij}$ by its cofactor $C_{ij}$.

*Example 15.8c.* Find the adjoint of

$$A .=. \begin{bmatrix} 1 & 0 & 2 \\ 2 & -1 & 3 \\ 0 & 2 & 3 \end{bmatrix}.$$

Using $C_{ij} = (-1)^{i+j}M_{ij}$, we have

$$C_{11} = -3 - 6 = -9, \qquad C_{21} = (-1)(0 - 4) = 4, \qquad C_{31} = (0 + 2) = 2,$$
$$C_{12} = (-1)(6 - 0 = -6, \qquad C_{22} = (3 - 0) = 3, \qquad C_{32} = (-1)(3 - 4) = 1,$$
$$C_{13} = (4 + 0) = 4, \qquad C_{23} = (-1)(2 - 0) = -2, \qquad C_{33} = (-1 - 0) = -1.$$

Therefore,

$$A^a = [C_{ij}]^T = \begin{bmatrix} -9 & 4 & 2 \\ -6 & 3 & 1 \\ 4 & -2 & -1 \end{bmatrix}.$$

For the preceding example, let us investigate the product $AA^a$. We find

$$AA^a = \begin{bmatrix} 1 & 0 & 2 \\ 2 & -1 & 3 \\ 0 & 2 & 3 \end{bmatrix} \begin{bmatrix} -9 & 4 & 2 \\ -6 & 3 & 1 \\ 4 & -2 & -1 \end{bmatrix} = \begin{bmatrix} -1 & 0 & 0 \\ 0 & -1 & 0 \\ 0 & 0 & -1 \end{bmatrix}.$$

This is indeed a curious result. It is even more astonishing to observe that $\det A = -1$, so that we may write

$$AA^a = (\det A)I.$$

If, however, one investigates the product $AA^a$ in general, these results do not seem so astonishing after all. The following theorem results from such an investigation.

**Theorem 15.8d.** If $A$ is a square matrix, then

$$AA^a = (\det A)I.$$

PROOF: Let $A = [a_{ij}]$, so that $A^a = [C_{ji}]$. Then a typical term, $b_{ij}$, in the product $AA^a$ is given by

$$b_{ij} = \sum_{\alpha=1}^{n} a_{i\alpha} C_{j\alpha} = \delta_{ij} \det A.$$

Hence, the product $AA^a$ is always a matrix having zero elements in the off diagonal positions, and $\det A$ in each of the main diagonal positions. The theorem follows at once.

The result of Theorem 15.8d may be stated in another way.

**Theorem 15.8e.** If $\det A \neq 0$, then

$$A^{-1} = \frac{A^a}{\det A}.$$

PROOF: The proof follows immediately from Theorem 15.8d.

Now if we wish to solve the system

$$AX = Y,$$

where $A$ is an $n \times n$ matrix and $X$ and $Y$ are each vectors with $n$ components, we may write

$$A^{-1}AX = A^{-1}Y, \qquad \det A \neq 0,$$

or

$$X = \frac{1}{\det A} A^a Y.$$

Upon equating corresponding components of the vectors on both sides of this equation, we get

$$x_i = \frac{1}{\det A} \sum_{\alpha=1}^{n} C_{i\alpha} y_\alpha.$$

Let us denote by $A_i$ the matrix obtained from $A$ by replacing the $i$th column by the vector $Y$. Then, it is clear that

$$\det A_i = \sum_{\alpha=1}^{n} C_{i\alpha} y_\alpha,$$

since this summation is simply an expansion by minors along the $i$th column of $\det A_i$. Thus, we see that in order to calculate any unknown, say $x_i$, we divide $\det A_i$ by $\det A$. This rule is known as Cramer's Rule. The preceding derivation will be clarified if the reader will write it out in complete detail for the case in which $A$ is a $2 \times 2$ matrix.

The next example illustrates the use of Cramer's Rule.

*Example 15.8d.* Use determinants to find the solution of the system

$$\begin{aligned} 2x - y + z &= 3, \\ -x + 2y - z &= 1, \\ 3x + y + 2z &= -1. \end{aligned}$$

We have

$$x = \frac{\begin{vmatrix} 3 & -1 & 1 \\ 1 & 2 & -1 \\ -1 & 1 & 2 \end{vmatrix}}{\begin{vmatrix} 2 & -1 & 1 \\ -1 & 2 & -1 \\ 3 & 1 & 2 \end{vmatrix}} = \frac{\begin{vmatrix} 0 & 2 & 7 \\ 0 & 3 & 1 \\ -1 & 1 & 2 \end{vmatrix}}{\begin{vmatrix} 0 & 3 & -1 \\ -1 & 2 & -1 \\ 0 & 7 & -1 \end{vmatrix}} = \frac{(-1)(2 - 21)}{(1)(-3 + 7)} = \frac{19}{4},$$

$$y = \frac{\begin{vmatrix} 2 & 3 & 1 \\ -1 & 1 & -1 \\ 3 & -1 & 2 \end{vmatrix}}{4} = \frac{\begin{vmatrix} 0 & 5 & -1 \\ -1 & 1 & -1 \\ 0 & 2 & -1 \end{vmatrix}}{4} = \frac{-5 + 2}{4} = -\frac{3}{4},$$

$$z = \frac{\begin{vmatrix} 2 & -1 & 3 \\ -1 & 2 & 1 \\ 3 & 1 & -1 \end{vmatrix}}{4} = \frac{\begin{vmatrix} 0 & 3 & 5 \\ -1 & 2 & 1 \\ 0 & 7 & 2 \end{vmatrix}}{4} = \frac{6 - 35}{4} = -\frac{29}{4}.$$

## Exercises 15.8

In Numbers 1 to 6, evaluate the determinants by expanding by minors.

1. $\begin{vmatrix} 2 & 1 & 3 & 4 \\ -2 & 3 & 3 & 2 \\ 1 & 3 & 0 & -2 \\ 2 & -2 & 6 & 4 \end{vmatrix}.$

2. $\begin{vmatrix} 1 & 2 & 3 & 4 \\ 2 & 3 & 4 & 5 \\ 3 & 4 & 5 & 6 \\ -2 & 3 & 4 & -5 \end{vmatrix}.$

3. $\begin{vmatrix} 1 & a & 1 & b \\ a & 1 & b & 1 \\ 1 & b & 1 & a \\ b & 1 & a & 1 \end{vmatrix}.$

4. $\begin{vmatrix} a & b & b & b \\ a & b & a & a \\ a & a & b & a \\ b & b & b & a \end{vmatrix}.$

5. $\begin{vmatrix} 1 & 2 & -1 & 0 & 2 \\ 3 & -1 & 2 & 1 & 3 \\ -2 & 1 & 0 & 3 & 1 \\ 2 & -2 & 1 & 2 & -1 \\ -1 & 1 & 1 & 1 & -1 \end{vmatrix}.$

6. $\begin{vmatrix} 1 & x & x^2 & x^3 \\ 1 & y & y^2 & y^3 \\ 1 & z & z^2 & z^3 \\ 1 & w & w^2 & w^3 \end{vmatrix}.$

Use determinants to solve the systems of equations in Numbers 7 to 10.

7. $x - y + z = 3,$
   $2x + 3y - 2z = 5,$
   $3x + y - 4z = 12.$

8. $2x + y + 3z = 2,$
   $4x - 3y + 5z = 6,$
   $-3x + 2y + 4z = -4.$

9. $2u - 3v + 4w + 5x = 8,$
   $-u + 2v + w = -2,$
   $3u - v + 2w - x = -2,$
   $v + 2w + 3x = 6.$

10. $a + b - c - d = 6,$
    $a - b + c - d = 0,$
    $a - b - c + d = -2,$
    $a + b - c + d = 2.$

11. Show that the solution of the system

$$a_1x + b_1y + c_1z = 0,$$
$$a_2x + b_2y + c_2z = 0,$$

is given by

$$x = k \begin{vmatrix} b_1 & c_1 \\ b_2 & c_2 \end{vmatrix}, \quad y = k \begin{vmatrix} c_1 & a_1 \\ c_2 & a_2 \end{vmatrix}, \quad z = k \begin{vmatrix} a_1 & b_1 \\ a_2 & b_2 \end{vmatrix},$$

where $k$ is a parameter, and it is assumed that at least one of the second order determinants is different from zero.

12. Without expanding the determinant directly, show that

$$\begin{vmatrix} x^2 + y^2 & x & y & 1 \\ a^2 + b^2 & a & b & 1 \\ c^2 + d^2 & c & d & 1 \\ e^2 + f^2 & e & f & 1 \end{vmatrix} = 0$$

is the equation of a circle through the three points $(a, b)$, $(c, d)$, and $(e, f)$.

## 15.9 PRODUCTS OF DETERMINANTS

There is generally no simple expression for the sum of two determinants as a determinant with elements that are a combination of the elements of the two determinants. In certain special cases, however, such a result is possible. For instance, if all but one of the columns are common to both determinants, then the sum is a determinant with the same common columns and with the element of the remaining column as the sums of the corresponding elements of the two unlike columns. Thus it is easy to verify that

(1)
$$\begin{vmatrix} a_{11} & a_{12} & a_{13} \\ a_{21} & a_{22} & a_{23} \\ a_{31} & a_{32} & a_{33} \end{vmatrix} + \begin{vmatrix} b_{11} & a_{12} & a_{13} \\ b_{21} & a_{22} & a_{23} \\ b_{31} & a_{32} & a_{33} \end{vmatrix} = \begin{vmatrix} a_{11} + b_{11} & a_{12} & a_{13} \\ a_{21} + b_{21} & a_{22} & a_{23} \\ a_{31} + b_{31} & a_{32} & a_{33} \end{vmatrix}.$$

A similar result may be stated for the case in which all but one of the rows of two determinants are the same.

It is possible, however, to express the product of two determinants as the determinant of a combination of elements of the two determinants. To do this we need to make use of an interesting extension of Theorem 15.8c.

**Theorem 15.9a.** If det $A = 0$, and if $B$ is a square matrix whose rows (or columns) are linear combinations of the rows (or columns) of $A$, then det $B = 0$

PROOF: The proof for the $2 \times 2$ case can be constructed by a repeated use of 1). For example, if

$$B = \begin{bmatrix} a_{11}R_1 + a_{12}R_2 \\ a_{21}R_1 + a_{22}R_2 \end{bmatrix},$$

where $R_1$, $R_2$ are the rows of $A$, then

$$\det B = \det \begin{bmatrix} a_{11}R_1 \\ a_{21}R_1 + a_{22}R_2 \end{bmatrix} + \det \begin{bmatrix} a_{12}R_2 \\ a_{21}R_1 + a_{22}R_2 \end{bmatrix}$$

$$= \det \begin{bmatrix} a_{11}R_1 \\ a_{21}R_1 \end{bmatrix} + \det \begin{bmatrix} a_{11}R_1 \\ a_{22}R_2 \end{bmatrix} + \det \begin{bmatrix} a_{12}R_2 \\ a_{21}R_1 \end{bmatrix} + \det \begin{bmatrix} a_{12}R_2 \\ a_{22}R_2 \end{bmatrix}$$

$$= a_{11}a_{21} \det \begin{bmatrix} R_1 \\ R_1 \end{bmatrix} + a_{11}a_{22} \det \begin{bmatrix} R_1 \\ R_2 \end{bmatrix}$$

$$+ a_{12}a_{21} \det \begin{bmatrix} R_2 \\ R_1 \end{bmatrix} + a_{12}a_{22} \det \begin{bmatrix} R_2 \\ R_2 \end{bmatrix}.$$

The determinants having identical rows are, of course, zero. However,

$$\det A = \det \begin{bmatrix} R_1 \\ R_2 \end{bmatrix} = -\det \begin{bmatrix} R_2 \\ R_1 \end{bmatrix},$$

so that

$$\det A = 0 \Rightarrow \det B = 0.$$

This same idea can be applied no matter what the order of the determinant may be, there being $n^n$ terms involving determinants that contain only rows of $A$ when $A$ is of order $n$. As long as $\det A = 0$, every determinant in such an expression will be zero.

From the definition of a determinant it follows that if $E$ is one of the elementary matrices, then $\det E = +1$, $-1$, or $c$, as the reader may easily verify. This observation suggests

**Theorem 15.9b.** Let $A$ be any square matrix, and let $E$ be an elementary matrix. Then

$$\det (EA) = \det E \det A = \det (AE).$$

PROOF: The reader should find it easy to prove this statement for each of the three types of elementary matrices.

It was stated in Theorem 15.5f and in the note following the theorem that if $A$ is a nonsingular matrix, then $A \sim_r I$. That is, there exists a sequence of elementary matrices $E_1, \ldots, E_k$ such that

$$E_k \cdots E_1 A = I.$$

From this fact we obtain another important result.

**Theorem 15.9c.** A matrix $A$ is nonsingular $\Leftrightarrow$ there exists a sequence of elementary matrices $E_1, \ldots, E_k$ such that

$$A = E_1 \cdots E_n.$$

PROOF: If $A$ is nonsingular, then by Theorem 15.5f, there is a set of elementary matrices $\overline{E}_1, \overline{E}_2, \ldots, \overline{E}_n$ such that

$$\overline{E}_n \cdots \overline{E}_1 A = I,$$

or

$$A = \overline{E}_1^{-1} \overline{E}_2^{-1} \cdots \overline{E}_n^{-1}.$$

But the inverse of an elementary matrix is either an elementary matrix or a product of elementary matrices (see Section 15.5). Hence, the desired result follows.

If $A = E_1 \ldots E_k$, then

$$E_k^{-1} \cdots E_1^{-1} A = I$$

and $A$ is nonsingular. Hence, the proof is complete.

The reader may already have guessed the following theorem, which states an interesting relationship between a nonsingular matrix $A$ and its determinant.

**Theorem 15.9d.** A square matrix $A$ is nonsingular $\Leftrightarrow$ det $A \neq 0$.
PROOF: By the two previous theorems, $A$ is nonsingular if, and only if,

$$E_k \cdots E_1 A = I,$$

so that

$$\det (E_k \cdots E_1 A) = \det I = 1,$$

or

$$\det E_k \cdots \det E_1 \det A = 1,$$

from which it follows that det $A \neq 0 \Leftrightarrow A$ is nonsingular.

The next theorem provides a general rule for finding the product of two determinants.

**Theorem 15.9e.** If $A$ and $B$ are square $n \times n$ matrices, then

$$\det A \det B = \det (AB).$$

PROOF: There are two cases to consider.

(i) If $B$ is singular then det $B = 0$. By the definition of the product of two matrices, $AB$ is a matrix whose rows are linear combinations of the rows of $B$ (Why?) Hence, by Theorem 15.9a, det $(AB) = 0$, and the theorem is true in this case.

(ii) If $B$ is nonsingular, then $B = E_1 \cdots E_k$, and by repeated applications of Theorem 15.9b, it follows that

$$\begin{aligned}
\det (AB) &= \det (AE_1 \cdots E_k) \\
&= \det A \det (E_1 \cdots E_k) \\
&= \det A \det B.
\end{aligned}$$

This result will be of use in a later discussion of linear transformations using matrices.

*Example 15.9a.* Find the value of the product

$$\begin{vmatrix} 1 & 2 & -1 \\ 3 & 0 & 2 \\ 2 & -3 & 4 \end{vmatrix} \begin{vmatrix} 2 & -1 & -2 \\ 1 & 1 & 3 \\ 4 & 2 & 4 \end{vmatrix}$$

by means of Theorem 15.9e.

Let $A$ be the matrix of elements in the first determinant and $B$ be the matrix of elements in the second determinant. Then, by Theorem 15.9e,

$$\det A \det B = \det(AB) = \begin{vmatrix} 0 & -1 & 0 \\ 14 & 1 & 2 \\ 17 & 3 & 3 \end{vmatrix} = 8.$$

---

A system of equations in the matrix form $AX = 0$ is called homogeneous. Such systems are important in many applications and will be met often in the succeeding chapters. It is clear that every such system has the so-called **trivial** solution $(0, 0, \ldots, 0)$. Any solution (if there is one) having at least one nonzero component is said to be **nontrivial.** Perhaps the most important theorem concerned with linear homogeneous equations is

**Theorem 15.9f.** If $A$ is an $n \times n$ matrix, then the system $AX = 0$ has a nontrivial solution $\Leftrightarrow \det A = 0$.

PROOF: It follows from the discussion in Section 15.6 and from Theorems 15.9d and 15.9e, that if the rank of an $n \times n$ matrix is less than $n$, then the matrix is singular and its determinant is zero. Conversely, if the determinant of an $n \times n$ matrix is zero, the matrix is singular and its rank is less than $n$.

For the first part of the proof, suppose that $\det A = 0$. Since $\det A^T = \det A$, it follows that $\det A^T = 0$ and $A^T$ is singular and its rank is less than $n$. Consequently, the rows of $A^T$ (the columns of $A$) are linearly dependent. Thus, if $A$ is partitioned into column vectors $C_1, C_2, \ldots C_n$, then there exist scalars $\alpha_1, \alpha_2, \ldots, \alpha_n$ *not all zero* such that

$$\alpha_1 C_1 + \alpha_2 C_2 + \cdots + \alpha_n C_n = 0.$$

Now, by equating to zero the separate components of the vector on the left, we get

$$\alpha_1 a_{1i} + \alpha_2 a_{2i} + \cdots + \alpha_n a_{ni} = 0, \quad i = 1, 2, \ldots, n.$$

This means that $(\alpha_1, \alpha_2, \ldots, \alpha_n)$ is a nontrivial solution of the given matrix equation, and that $\det A = 0 \Rightarrow$ the existence of a nontrivial solution.

For the second part of the proof, suppose that there is a nontrivial solution. Then the preceding argument may be repeated in reverse order to complete the proof of the theorem.

---

*Example 15.9b.* Find the values of $k$ for which the following system has nontrivial solutions:

$$\begin{aligned} kx - 4y + \phantom{k}z &= 0, \\ 2x - 2y - kz &= 0, \\ x + 2y - 2z &= 0. \end{aligned}$$

According to the preceding theorem, the system has nontrivial solutions if, and only if, the determinant of the coefficients is zero. This determinant is

$$\begin{vmatrix} k & -4 & 1 \\ 2 & -2 & -k \\ 1 & 2 & -2 \end{vmatrix} = 2k^2 + 8k - 10 = 2(k-1)(k+5).$$

Therefore, the system has nontrivial solutions for $k = 1$ and for $k = -5$.

For $k = 1$, the reader may show that the nontrivial solutions are given by $(2t, t, 2t)$, where $t$ is an arbitrary parameter. Similarly, for $k = -5$, the solutions are given by $(2t, -3t, -2t)$.

## Exercises 15.9

In Numbers 1 to 3, inclusive, evaluate each product in two ways.

1. $\begin{vmatrix} 2 & 1 \\ -1 & 0 \end{vmatrix} \begin{vmatrix} 2 & 3 \\ -2 & 1 \end{vmatrix}.$

2. $\begin{vmatrix} 3 & 1 & 2 \\ 4 & 0 & 1 \\ -1 & 2 & 0 \end{vmatrix} \begin{vmatrix} -1 & 2 & 1 \\ 2 & -1 & 1 \\ 3 & -2 & -1 \end{vmatrix}.$

3. $\begin{vmatrix} 1 & 2 & 3 & 1 \\ 0 & -1 & 2 & 2 \\ 2 & 3 & 0 & 1 \\ 1 & 0 & -1 & 2 \end{vmatrix} \begin{vmatrix} 2 & 0 & 1 & 1 \\ -1 & 1 & 2 & -2 \\ 3 & 0 & 1 & 2 \\ -1 & 2 & 0 & 1 \end{vmatrix}.$

4. Prove that

$$\begin{vmatrix} a & b & c & d \\ e & f & g & h \\ 0 & 0 & j & k \\ 0 & 0 & l & m \end{vmatrix} = \begin{vmatrix} a & b \\ e & f \end{vmatrix} \begin{vmatrix} j & k \\ l & m \end{vmatrix}.$$

5. Prove that

$$\begin{vmatrix} a_1 & a_2 & a_3 & a_4 & a_5 \\ b_1 & b_2 & b_3 & b_4 & b_5 \\ 0 & 0 & c_3 & c_4 & c_5 \\ 0 & 0 & d_3 & d_4 & d_5 \\ 0 & 0 & e_3 & e_4 & e_5 \end{vmatrix} = \begin{vmatrix} a_1 & a_2 \\ b_1 & b_2 \end{vmatrix} \begin{vmatrix} c_3 & c_4 & c_5 \\ d_3 & d_4 & d_5 \\ e_3 & e_4 & e_5 \end{vmatrix}.$$

6. Replace the question marks by the proper numbers in the equation

$$\begin{vmatrix} 2 & 5 & -3 \\ 4 & -7 & 0 \\ 3 & 4 & 1 \end{vmatrix} = \begin{vmatrix} 2 & 5 & 1 \\ 4 & -7 & 2 \\ 3 & 4 & 3 \end{vmatrix} + \begin{vmatrix} 2 & 5 & ? \\ 4 & -7 & ? \\ 3 & 4 & ? \end{vmatrix}.$$

7. Show that

$$\begin{vmatrix} b_1 + c_1 & c_1 + a_1 & a_1 + b_1 \\ b_2 + c_2 & c_2 + a_2 & a_2 + b_2 \\ b_3 + c_3 & c_3 + a_3 & a_3 + b_3 \end{vmatrix} = 2 \begin{vmatrix} a_1 & b_1 & c_1 \\ a_2 & b_2 & c_2 \\ a_3 & b_3 & c_3 \end{vmatrix}.$$

In each of Numbers 8 and 9, find the value, or values, of $k$ (if there are any) for which the given system has nontrivial solutions, and find these solutions.

8. $2kx - 3y - 2z = 0,$
$\quad 3kx + y + 2z = 0,$
$\quad 3x + 7y + 6z = 0.$

9. $u - 4v + 13s = 0,$
$\quad ku + 2v - s = 0,$
$\quad 2u - v + 2ks = 0.$

10. (a) Show that if the system

$$a_1 x + b_1 y = c_1, \quad a_2 x + b_2 y = c_2, \quad a_3 x + b_3 y = c_3$$

has a solution, then

$$\begin{vmatrix} a_1 & b_1 & c_1 \\ a_2 & b_2 & c_2 \\ a_3 & b_3 & c_3 \end{vmatrix} = 0.$$

(b) Show, however, that if the determinant is zero, the system still might not have a solution. *Hint*: Construct a suitable example.

In each of Numbers 11 and 12, find the value, or values, of $k$ (if there are any) for which the given system has solutions and find these solutions. See Number 10.

11. $8x + 4y = 1$,
$3x + ky = 3$,
$kx + 3y = 1$.

12. $kx + 3y = 1$,
$2kx - y = -5$,
$4x + 5y = 4$.

13. If $A$ is nonsingular, is it true that $(\det A)^{-1} = \det (A^{-1})$?

◄14. Prove that $\det A^a = (\det A)^{n-1}$.

◄15. Is the inverse of a symmetric matrix a symmetric matrix?

---

# Summary of Chapter 15

---

The reader should regard this chapter not only as an introduction to a useful tool but also as an introduction to a significantly different type of algebraic structure. For these reasons, he must try to develop an awareness of the more abstract ideas that he encounters, as well as the use of these ideas in solving practical problems. It is important, therefore, that he follow closely the thread of thought that

(1) originates with the discussion of the solution of a system of equations and the characterization of systems by matrices (Section 15.1);

(2) leads to the algebraic properties of addition and multiplication by a scalar (Section 15.2);

(3) leads to the definition of matrix multiplication and the corresponding algebraic properties (Section 15.3).

Other concepts that are important include

(4) special types of matrices, such as the transpose of a matrix, symmetric matrices, skew-symmetric matrices, and diagonal matrices (Section 15.2);

(5) the concept of partitioning a matrix (Section 15.3);

(6) the meaning of identity for matrix multiplication (Section 15.3);

(7) the elementary row operations on a matrix, and elementary matrices (Section 15.4);

(8) the meaning of row equivalence between matrices (Section 15.4);

(9) the modified triangular matrix (Section 15.4);

(10) nonsingular matrices and the multiplicative inverse of a matrix (Section 15.5);

(11) the use of matrices in solving systems of equations (Section 15.6);

(12) the meaning of linear dependence and independence (Section 15.6);

(13) the meaning of rank of a matrix and its significance in connection with the solution of a system of equations (Section 15.6);

(14) the definition of the determinant of a square matrix, and the elementary properties of determinants (Section 15.7);

(15) the technique of expanding a determinant by minors or cofactors, and the technique of adding multiples of one row to another (Section 15.8);

(16) the Kronecker delta (Section 15.8);

(17) the use of determinants in solving systems of equations (Sections 15.8, 15.9);

(18) the formation of products of determinants (Section 15.9).

# Chapter 16     Linear Transformations

## 16.1 COORDINATE SYSTEMS

In Section 13.2 we discussed a translation of coordinates as a means of simplifying the equation of a curve. For example, the equation

(1) $$x^2 + 2x + 4y^2 - 24y = -1$$

can be transformed into a simpler form by completing the squares on $x$ and $y$ to obtain

$$(x + 1)^2 + 4(y - 3)^2 = 36.$$

If we let $u = x + 1$ and $v = y - 3$, then the equation may be written in the form

(2) $$u^2 + 4v^2 = 36.$$

This equation describes the same ellipse as does Equation (1), but is much easier to interpret geometrically (see Figure 16.1a).

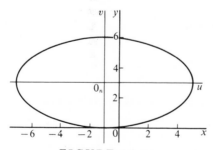

FIGURE 16.1a

Equation (2) gives coordinates of points on the curve relative to an origin $O_n$ at the point $(-1, 3)$ in the original coordinate system, whereas Equation (1) gives the coordinates of these points relative to the point $O$. Evidently the points on the curve may be specified relative to any convenient coordinate system, and a change of the coordinate system alone does not alter the curve. The advantage of making such a change lies in the fact that it is frequently easier to construct the graph of an equation by examining the corresponding equation relative to a new coordinate system rather than by trying to deal directly with the given equation.

The process of changing from one coordinate system to another is called a **transformation.** The translation of coordinates described earlier is a very special type of transformation. Although it is beyond the scope of this book to discuss transformations in any very general fashion, we are particularly interested in the transformations that correspond to a rigid rotation of the coordinate axes— that is, a rotation about the origin that maintains the orthogonality of the axes and their right-handed orientation and preserves the distance between every pair of points. As we shall see later, such rotations play an important role in the analysis of quadratic forms.

It is convenient to discuss these transformations in terms of vectors and to use matrices as the principal tool. In the earlier work with vectors, it was seen that in ordinary (euclidean) two-dimensional space, $\mathcal{V}_2$, each vector may be written in the form $x\mathbf{i} + y\mathbf{j}$; and in three-dimensional euclidean space, $\mathcal{V}_3$, each vector may be written in the form $x\mathbf{i} + y\mathbf{j} + z\mathbf{k}$. The vectors $\mathbf{i}$ and $\mathbf{j}$ are called **base vectors,** and the set $\{\mathbf{i}, \mathbf{j}\}$ is called a **basis** for the two-dimensional space. Similarly, $\mathbf{i}, \mathbf{j}, \mathbf{k}$ are base vectors, and the set $\{\mathbf{i}, \mathbf{j}, \mathbf{k}\}$ is a basis for the three-dimensional space. In each case, every vector in the space is a linear combination of the base vectors in that space.

It is easily made apparent by the next example that $\mathbf{i}$ and $\mathbf{j}$ are not the only base vectors possible in the space $\mathcal{V}_2$. This can be done in a similar way for the space $\mathcal{V}_3$. The reader should recall that $(x, y)$ may be regarded either as a point in $\mathcal{V}_2$ or as a vector with the rectangular components $x$ and $y$. To **represent** a vector relative to a given basis means to express the vector as a linear combination of the base vectors.

---

*Example 16.1a.* Represent the vector $\mathbf{a} .=. (3, 1)$ relative to the basis $\mathbf{e}_1 .=. (1, -1)$ $\mathbf{e}_2 .=. (1, 2)$.

To obtain the proper representation, we must write $\mathbf{a}$ as a linear combination of $\mathbf{e}$ and $\mathbf{e}_2$ in the form $\mathbf{a} = p\mathbf{e}_1 + q\mathbf{e}_2$, or

$$(3, 1) = p(1, -1) + q(1, 2).$$

This equation is satisfied if, and only if,

$$p + q = 3,$$

and

$$-p + 2q = 1.$$

It follows that $p = \frac{5}{3}, q = \frac{4}{3}$, so that

$$(3, 1) = \tfrac{5}{3}(1, -1) + \tfrac{4}{3}(1, 2),$$

or

$$\mathbf{a} = \tfrac{5}{3}\mathbf{e}_1 + \tfrac{4}{3}\mathbf{e}_2.$$

See Figure 16.1b.

---

Since $e_1$ and $e_2$ are linearly independent, any vector $\mathbf{b} = (x, y)$ can be repre-
sented just as $\mathbf{a}$ is represented relative to the basis $\{e_1, e_2\}$. The numbers $\frac{5}{3}$ and $\frac{4}{3}$
in the preceding example are called the **components** or **coordinates** of $\mathbf{a}$ relative
to the basis $\{e_1, e_2\}$. Evidently, $\mathbf{a}$ has different components relative to different
base systems, so that *each basis of a vector space determines a coordinate system.*

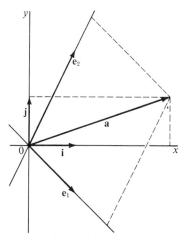

**FIGURE 16.1b**

These considerations suggest that any two nonparallel vectors may be used
as a basis for the space $\mathcal{V}_2$, an observation that is easily generalized as follows
to any number of dimensions.

**Definition 16.1a.** A set of vectors $\{e_1, e_2, e_3, \ldots, e_n\}$ is called a **basis** or a **base
set** for a vector space $\mathcal{V}$ if

    (a) every vector in $\mathcal{V}$ is a linear combination of $e_1, e_2, \ldots, e_n$, and
    (b) the vectors $e_1, e_2, \ldots, e_n$ are linearly independent.

The set $\{e_1, e_2, \ldots, e_n\}$ may be said to *generate* the space for which it is a basis.
If the e's are mutually orthogonal, the set is called an **orthogonal set.**

Now, suppose we wish to express any vector in $\mathcal{V}_2$ relative to a given basis.
How may this be done? For instance, in Example 16.1a, the base system is
$e_1 = (1, -1)$ and $e_2 = (1, 2)$. Let us find the coordinates, $u$ and $v$, of a general
vector $(x, y)$ relative to this basis. We must have

$$(x, y) = u(1, -1) + v(1, 2),$$

which implies that

(3) $$x = u + v, \quad y = -u + 2v,$$

and

(4) $$v = \tfrac{1}{3}(x + y), \quad u = \tfrac{2}{3}x - \tfrac{1}{3}y.$$

Equations (3) give the $xy$-coordinates relative to the $\mathbf{i}, \mathbf{j}$ basis in terms of the
$uv$-coordinates relative to the $e_1, e_2$ basis. Equations (4) express the inverse of

this relationship. We say that Equations (3) express the transformation from *xy*-coordinates to *uv*-coordinates, and Equations (4) express the transformation from *uv*-coordinates to *xy*-coordinates. One transformation is said to be the **inverse** of the other.

In the type of transformation discussed here, each coordinate of a point in one coordinate system is a **linear combination** of the coordinates of the point in the other coordinate system. Transformations of this type belong to a class of transformations called **linear transformations**. Evidently, a linear transformation from one coordinate system to another in $\mathcal{V}_2$ is determined by the base vectors chosen in each coordinate system, since once it is known how the base vectors transform, it follows that the transformation of any vector is determined.

**Theorem 16.1a.** Let

$$e_1 .=. e_{11}\mathbf{i} + e_{21}\mathbf{j},$$
$$e_2 .=. e_{12}\mathbf{i} + e_{22}\mathbf{j}$$

be a set of base vectors in the *xy*-plane. Then the components $(x, y)$ relative to the $\mathbf{i}$, $\mathbf{j}$ base vectors are given in terms of the components $(u, v)$ relative to the $e_1$, $e_2$ base vectors by the transformation equations

$$x = e_{11}u + e_{12}v,$$
$$y = e_{21}u + e_{22}v.$$

PROOF: Let $\mathbf{r}$ be any vector given relative to the $e_1$, $e_2$ basis by the equation

$$\mathbf{r} = u e_1 + v e_2.$$

Then

$$\mathbf{r} = u(e_{11}\mathbf{i} + e_{21}\mathbf{j}) + v(e_{12}\mathbf{i} + e_{22}\mathbf{j})$$
$$= (e_{11}u + e_{12}v)\mathbf{i} + (e_{21}u + e_{22}v)\mathbf{j}.$$

Hence, since $\mathbf{r} = x\mathbf{i} + y\mathbf{j}$ relative to the $\mathbf{i}$, $\mathbf{j}$ base vectors,

$$x = e_{11}u + e_{12}v,$$
$$y = e_{21}u + e_{22}v,$$

as the theorem states.

Notice that the matrix

$$\begin{bmatrix} e_{11} & e_{12} \\ e_{21} & e_{22} \end{bmatrix},$$

which gives $(x, y)$ in terms of $(u, v)$, is exactly the transpose of the matrix that gives the new basis $\{e_1, e_2\}$ in terms of the old $\{\mathbf{i}, \mathbf{j}\}$.

Results similar in every respect to these hold also for three dimensions and in fact, for *n* dimensions. The three-dimensional case is left as an exercise for the reader.

Since the equations involved are linear equations, the preceding ideas can be expressed in much neater form by the use of matrices. Thus, let the vector with rectangular components $(x, y)$ be written as a column matrix. We then have

$$\begin{bmatrix} x \\ y \end{bmatrix} . = . (x, y), \quad \begin{bmatrix} e_{11} \\ e_{21} \end{bmatrix} . = . \mathbf{e}_1, \quad \begin{bmatrix} e_{12} \\ e_{22} \end{bmatrix} . = . \mathbf{e}_2,$$

and hence

$$\begin{bmatrix} x \\ y \end{bmatrix} = u \begin{bmatrix} e_{11} \\ e_{21} \end{bmatrix} + v \begin{bmatrix} e_{12} \\ e_{22} \end{bmatrix} = \begin{bmatrix} e_{11} & e_{12} \\ e_{21} & e_{22} \end{bmatrix} \begin{bmatrix} u \\ v \end{bmatrix},$$

which describes the transformation of the components $(u, v)$ relative to the basis $\{\mathbf{e}_1, \mathbf{e}_2\}$ into the components $(x, y)$ relative to the basis $(\mathbf{i}, \mathbf{j})$.
If we use the notation

$$X . = . \begin{bmatrix} x \\ y \end{bmatrix}, \quad U . = . \begin{bmatrix} u \\ v \end{bmatrix}, \quad T . = . \begin{bmatrix} e_{11} & e_{12} \\ e_{21} & e_{22} \end{bmatrix},$$

then the transformation equations assume the matrix form

$$X = TU.$$

The inverse transformation—the transformation from the $(x, y)$ components to the $(u, v)$ components—may be represented by the matrix $T^{-1}$, so that

$$U = T^{-1}X.$$

As a further illustration, we return to the base vectors $\mathbf{e}_1 . = . (1, -1)$, $\mathbf{e}_2 . = . (1, 2)$ introduced in Example 16.1a. Writing these as column vectors,

$$\mathbf{e}_1 = \begin{bmatrix} 1 \\ -1 \end{bmatrix}, \quad \mathbf{e}_2 = \begin{bmatrix} 1 \\ 2 \end{bmatrix},$$

we see at once that the transformation matrix $T$ to be used in the equation $X = TU$ is

$$T = \begin{bmatrix} 1 & 1 \\ -1 & 2 \end{bmatrix}.$$

In other words, the columns of $T$ are exactly the vectors $\mathbf{e}_1$ and $\mathbf{e}_2$. Furthermore, the inverse of $T$ is given by

$$T^{-1} = \begin{bmatrix} 1 & 1 \\ -1 & 2 \end{bmatrix}^{-1} = \begin{bmatrix} \frac{2}{3} & -\frac{1}{3} \\ \frac{1}{3} & \frac{1}{3} \end{bmatrix},$$

so that the equation for the inverse transformation is

$$\begin{bmatrix} u \\ v \end{bmatrix} = \begin{bmatrix} \frac{2}{3} & -\frac{1}{3} \\ \frac{1}{3} & \frac{1}{3} \end{bmatrix} \begin{bmatrix} x \\ y \end{bmatrix}.$$

---

*Example 16.1b.* Suppose that $\mathbf{e}_1 . = . (1, -1)$, $\mathbf{e}_2 . = . (1, 1)$ is a basis in the $xy$-plane and that $\mathbf{f}_1 . = . (1, 2)$, $\mathbf{f}_2 . = . (2, -1)$ is a second basis in the $xy$-plane. If a vector has the representation $u_1\mathbf{e}_1 + u_2\mathbf{e}_2$ relative to the first basis and $w_1\mathbf{f}_1 + w_2\mathbf{f}_2$ relative to the second basis, find the matrix that will transform the $u$-components into the $w$-components.

It is convenient to denote the vector by $X$ relative to the $\{\mathbf{i}, \mathbf{j}\}$ basis, by $U$ relative to the $\{\mathbf{e}_1, \mathbf{e}_2\}$ basis, and by $W$ relative to the $\{\mathbf{f}_1, \mathbf{f}_2\}$ basis. Then, using the notation suggested by the preceding discussion, we may write

$$X = TU \quad \text{and} \quad X = SW,$$

where

$$T = \begin{bmatrix} 1 & 1 \\ -1 & 1 \end{bmatrix} \quad \text{and} \quad S = \begin{bmatrix} 1 & 2 \\ 2 & -1 \end{bmatrix}.$$

Notice that $T$ is formed by taking the components of $e_1$ as the first column and those of $e_2$ as the second column. The matrix $S$ is formed in the same manner from $f_1$ and $f_2$. By equating the two expressions for $X$, we obtain

$$SW = TU,$$

from which it follows that

$$W = S^{-1}TU.$$

The required matrix is therefore $S^{-1}T$, which we compute to be

$$\frac{1}{5} \begin{bmatrix} -1 & 3 \\ 3 & 1 \end{bmatrix}.$$

---

In order for a vector $(x, y)$ to have unique components $(u, v)$, and conversely, the determinant of the matrix $T$ must be different from zero. If $\det T = 0$, then the vectors $e_1$, $e_2$ are not linearly independent and therefore cannot serve as a basis for the entire space $\mathcal{V}_2$. This is the reason for

**Definition 16.1b.** A linear transformation represented by a matrix $T$ is said to be **singular** if $\det T = 0$. Otherwise, it is said to be **nonsingular.**

## Exercises 16.1

1. Find the components of the vector $(2, -2)$ relative to each of the following base systems.
   (a) $e_1 = (\frac{1}{2}\sqrt{2}, -\frac{1}{2}\sqrt{2})$, $e_2 = (\frac{1}{2}\sqrt{2}, \frac{1}{2}\sqrt{2})$.
   (b) $e_1 = (\frac{1}{2}\sqrt{3}, \frac{1}{2})$, $e_2 = (-\frac{1}{2}, \frac{1}{2}\sqrt{3})$.
   (c) $e_1 = (3, 4)$, $e_2 = (4, 3)$.
2. Find the components of the vector $(3, 1)$ relative to each of the following base systems.
   (a) $e_1 = (\frac{1}{2}, -\frac{1}{2}\sqrt{3})$, $e_2 = (\frac{1}{2}\sqrt{3}, \frac{1}{2})$.
   (b) $e_1 = (\frac{1}{2}\sqrt{2}, \frac{1}{2}\sqrt{2})$, $e_2 = (-\frac{1}{2}\sqrt{2}, \frac{1}{2}\sqrt{2})$.
   (c) $e_1 = (2, -1)$, $e_2 = (2, 3)$.
   (d) $e_1 = (3, 2)$, $e_2 = (2, 3)$.
3. In Section 14.6 it was shown that when $e_1$ and $e_2$ are orthogonal vectors in $\mathcal{V}_2$, the components $u$ and $v$ of $r$ relative to $e_1$ and $e_2$ are given by

$$u = \frac{e_1 \cdot r}{e_1 \cdot e_1}, \quad v = \frac{e_2 \cdot r}{e_2 \cdot e_2}.$$

   Is such a relation possible in general when $e_1$ and $e_2$ are not orthogonal? Explain.
4. Using the notation of Example 16.1b, determine the equations of the transformation from the first base system to the second, and find the equations of the inverse transformation. Find also the coordinates of the vector $(1, 1)$ in each system.
   (a) $(1, 2), (2, -3)$   to   $(-1, 1), (2, -1)$.
   (b) $(0, 2), (1, -1)$   to   $(2, -1), (3, 1)$.

(c) $(1, 0), (0, 1)$   to   $(0, 1), (1, 0)$.

(d) $(1, 0), (0, 1)$   to   $(\frac{1}{2}\sqrt{2}, \frac{1}{2}\sqrt{2}), (-\frac{1}{2}\sqrt{2}, \frac{1}{2}\sqrt{2})$.

5. Suppose that $e_1 .=. (3, -4)$, $e_2 .=. (4, 3)$ is a basis in the $xy$-plane, and that $f_1$, $f_2$ is another basis in the same plane. Let a vector have the representation $u_1 e_1 + u_2 e_2$ relative to the first basis and $w_1 f_1 + w_2 f_2$ relative to the second basis. If the matrix

$$\begin{bmatrix} -1 & 3 \\ 3 & 1 \end{bmatrix}$$

transforms the $u$-components of the vector into the $w$-components, find the vectors $f_1$ and $f_2$.

6. Suppose that a new base system in three dimensions is chosen as follows:

$$e_1 = (e_{11}, e_{21}, e_{31}), \quad e_2 = (e_{12}, e_{22}, e_{32}), \quad e_3 = (e_{13}, e_{23}, e_{33}).$$

Show that if the vector represented by $X .=. (x, y, z)$ is transformed into $U .=. (u, v, w)$, then the matrix $T$ in $X = TU$ is given in the same fashion as in the two-dimensional case; that is, the columns of $T$ are the vectors $e_1$, $e_2$, $e_3$ written in column vector form. Represent $X$ and $U$ by column matrices.

7. Find the components of the vector $(3, 1, 2)$ relative to each of the following base systems.

(a) $e_1 = (1, 0, 0)$, $e_2 = (1, 1, 0)$, $e_3 = (1, 1, 1)$.

(b) $e_1 = (1, 1, 0)$, $e_2 = (-1, 1, 0)$, $e_3 = (0, 0, 1)$.

(c) $e_1 = (3, -2, 1)$, $e_2 = (-2, 3, -1)$, $e_3 = (1, 1, -1)$.

8. Which of the following represent singular, and which nonsingular, transformations? In each of the singular cases, show that the last column is a linear combination of the other columns.

(a) $T = \begin{bmatrix} 1 & -2 \\ -3 & 6 \end{bmatrix}$.

(b) $T = \begin{bmatrix} 3 & 4 \\ -4 & 3 \end{bmatrix}$.

(c) $T = \begin{bmatrix} 0 & 1 & 2 \\ 2 & -1 & 1 \\ 4 & 1 & 8 \end{bmatrix}$.

(d) $T = \begin{bmatrix} 1 & -2 & 2 \\ -2 & 4 & -4 \\ -\frac{1}{2} & 1 & -1 \end{bmatrix}$.

# 16.2 ROTATION OF COORDINATES

We know that the magnitude of a vector $a = (a_1, a_2) = a_1 i + a_2 j$ in ordinary rectangular coordinates is given by

$$|a|^2 = a_1^2 + a_2^2.$$

If we express this same vector relative to some other base system $e_1$ and $e_2$, may we still say that the square of the magnitude of $a$ is merely the sum of the squares of the components of $a$ relative to the new base system?

Suppose that

$$a = A_1 e_1 + A_2 e_2.$$

Then

$$|a|^2 = a \cdot a = A_1^2 e_1 \cdot e_1 + 2A_1 A_2 e_1 \cdot e_2 + A_2^2 e_2 \cdot e_2.$$

This formula shows that in terms of the new components the expression for

$|\mathbf{a}|^2$ is considerably more complicated than in ordinary rectangular components. However, in the event that $\mathbf{e}_1 \cdot \mathbf{e}_2 = 0$, the formula simplifies to

$$|\mathbf{a}|^2 = A_1^2 \mathbf{e}_1 \cdot \mathbf{e}_1 + A_2^2 \mathbf{e}_2 \cdot \mathbf{e}_2,$$

which is more nearly like the original expression. If, in addition, $\mathbf{e}_1$ and $\mathbf{e}_2$ are unit vectors, then $\mathbf{e}_1 \cdot \mathbf{e}_1 = \mathbf{e}_2 \cdot \mathbf{e}_2 = 1$, and we get

$$\begin{aligned} |\mathbf{a}|^2 &= A_1^2 + A_2^2 \\ &= a_1^2 + a_2^2. \end{aligned}$$

That is, the expression for the magnitude of $\mathbf{a}$ is then of the same form in terms of the new coordinates $A_1$, $A_2$ as in terms of the old coordinates $a_1$, $a_2$.

When a form is left unchanged by a transformation $T$ in this way, we say that the transformation $T$ leaves the form **invariant**, or that the form is invariant under the transformation $T$.

A discussion of this type suggests a number of interesting problems, only one or two of which can be considered here. For example, we may ask what type of transformation leaves the scalar product invariant. That is, if

$$\mathbf{a} = a_1 \mathbf{i} + a_2 \mathbf{j} = A_1 \mathbf{e}_1 + A_2 \mathbf{e}_2$$

and

$$\mathbf{b} = b_1 \mathbf{i} + b_2 \mathbf{j} = B_1 \mathbf{e}_1 + B_2 \mathbf{e}_2,$$

then of what form is a transformation $T$ for which

$$\mathbf{a} \cdot \mathbf{b} = a_1 b_1 + a_2 b_2 = A_1 B_1 + A_2 B_2,$$

so that the scalar product is of the same form in both coordinate systems?

Since the transformation is characterized by the base vectors of the new system, we have

$$\begin{aligned} \mathbf{a} \cdot \mathbf{b} &= (a_1 \mathbf{i} + a_2 \mathbf{j}) \cdot (b_1 \mathbf{i} + b_2 \mathbf{j}) = (A_1 \mathbf{e}_1 + A_2 \mathbf{e}_2) \cdot (B_1 \mathbf{e}_1 + B_2 \mathbf{e}_2) \\ &= A_1 B_1 \mathbf{e}_1 \cdot \mathbf{e}_1 + A_2 B_1 \mathbf{e}_2 \cdot \mathbf{e}_1 + A_1 B_2 \mathbf{e}_1 \cdot \mathbf{e}_2 + A_2 B_2 \mathbf{e}_2 \cdot \mathbf{e}_2. \end{aligned}$$

Accordingly, we get

$$a_1 b_1 + a_2 b_2 = A_1 B_1 + A_2 B_2$$

if, and only if, $\mathbf{e}_1 \cdot \mathbf{e}_1 = \mathbf{e}_2 \cdot \mathbf{e}_2 = 1$ and $\mathbf{e}_1 \cdot \mathbf{e}_2 = 0$. In other words, the scalar product is invariant in form for all pairs of vectors if, and only if, the base vectors $\mathbf{e}_1$ and $\mathbf{e}_2$ form an orthogonal set of unit vectors. Such a set of base vectors is called an **orthonormal set** ("ortho" meaning orthogonal, and "normal" meaning normalized, or having a magnitude of one unit).

We have seen that when the base vectors of a new coordinate system are known, the transformation from the old system to the new is characterized by these base vectors. Consequently, any transformation from one set of orthonormal base vectors to another such set is called an **orthonormal transformation**.

Suppose that

$$T = \begin{bmatrix} e_{11} & e_{12} \\ e_{21} & e_{22} \end{bmatrix}$$

represents an orthonormal transformation, so that the vectors $\mathbf{e}_1 = e_{11}\mathbf{i} + e_{21}\mathbf{j}$ and $\mathbf{e}_2 = e_{12}\mathbf{i} + e_{22}\mathbf{j}$ are normalized orthogonal vectors. Then $T$ is called an **orthonormal matrix**, and

$$e_{11}^2 + e_{21}^2 = 1, \quad e_{12}^2 + e_{22}^2 = 1, \quad e_{11}e_{12} + e_{21}e_{22} = 0.$$

In view of these relationships, we may let $e_{11} = \cos \alpha$ and $e_{21} = \sin \alpha$. The reader may check that all three equations are then satisfied if $e_{12} = -\sin \alpha$ and $e_{22} = \cos \alpha$. (A complete solution is left for the exercises.) Thus, the equations of transformation are given by

(1)
$$\begin{bmatrix} x \\ y \end{bmatrix} = \begin{bmatrix} \cos \alpha & -\sin \alpha \\ \sin \alpha & \cos \alpha \end{bmatrix} \begin{bmatrix} u \\ v \end{bmatrix}.$$

Interpreted geometrically, this transformation represents a rigid rotation of the coordinate system in its own plane, since the base vectors

$$\begin{bmatrix} \cos \alpha \\ \sin \alpha \end{bmatrix}, \quad \begin{bmatrix} -\sin \alpha \\ \cos \alpha \end{bmatrix}$$

represent unit vectors in the positive direction of the new coordinate axes, which are thus shown to be rotated through the angle $\alpha$ with reference to the original axes (see Figure 16.2a).

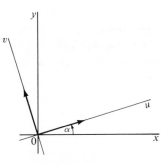

**FIGURE 16.2a**

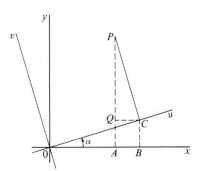

**FIGURE 16.2b**

Furthermore, we may verify by means of a geometric interpretation that a rigid rotation of coordinates results in an equation of the form of Equation (1). Let $P$ be a point having coordinates $(u, v)$ relative to an orthogonal set of axes rotated through an angle $\alpha$ with respect to the $xy$-coordinate system. From the geometry illustrated in Figure 16.2b, it follows that

$$x = OB - AB = OB - QC$$
$$= u \cos \alpha - v \sin \alpha,$$

and

$$y = QA + PQ = CB + PQ$$
$$= u \sin \alpha + v \cos \alpha.$$

In matrix form, these equations may be written as

$$\begin{bmatrix} x \\ y \end{bmatrix} = \begin{bmatrix} \cos\alpha & -\sin\alpha \\ \sin\alpha & \cos\alpha \end{bmatrix}\begin{bmatrix} u \\ v \end{bmatrix},$$

which agrees with the result obtained previously. We have already seen that such a rotation leaves the scalar product, and hence the expression for distance, invariant.

Rotations are a particularly important class of transformations, since they can be used to simplify such quadratic equations as

$$x^2 + 4xy - 2y^2 = 4,$$

so that it is easy to determine what curve the equation describes. In order to demonstrate how this may be accomplished, it is convenient to express the equation in matrix form. Such a form may be obtained by arranging the terms in the pattern

$$\begin{aligned} x^2 + 2xy \\ +2xy - 2y^2 = 4, \end{aligned}$$

so that

$$[x \ \ y]\begin{bmatrix} 1 & 2 \\ 2 & -2 \end{bmatrix}\begin{bmatrix} x \\ y \end{bmatrix} = 4.$$

The reader should verify that this expression is correct by multiplying it out.

The last equation is of the general form

$$X^\mathsf{T} A X = 4.$$

Hence, the question to be raised here is, can a transformation $X = TU$ be found that transforms the quadratic polynomial $X^\mathsf{T}AX$ into another such polynomial $U^\mathsf{T}BU$, in which the matrix $B$ is of a simpler form than $A$? Perhaps a diagonal form, such as

$$\begin{bmatrix} \alpha & 0 \\ 0 & \beta \end{bmatrix},$$

is about the simplest possible.

The next example will help to illustrate this idea.

---

*Example 16.2a.* Transform the equation $x^2 + 4xy - 2y^2 = 4$ by the transformation

$$T = \frac{1}{\sqrt{5}}\begin{bmatrix} 2 & -1 \\ 1 & 2 \end{bmatrix}.$$

Essentially, we want to introduce new coordinates, $u$ and $v$, by means of the equation $X = TU$; that is,

(2)
$$\begin{bmatrix} x \\ y \end{bmatrix} = \frac{1}{\sqrt{5}}\begin{bmatrix} 2 & -1 \\ 1 & 2 \end{bmatrix}\begin{bmatrix} u \\ v \end{bmatrix}.$$

By taking the transpose of both sides of Equation (2), we obtain

$$X^\mathsf{T} = (TU)^\mathsf{T} = U^\mathsf{T}T^\mathsf{T},$$

or, written out in full,

(3)
$$[x \ \ y] = \frac{1}{\sqrt{5}}[u \ \ v]\begin{bmatrix} 2 & 1 \\ -1 & 2 \end{bmatrix}.$$

If, in the matrix form of the given equation,

$$[x \ \ y]\begin{bmatrix} 1 & 2 \\ 2 & -2 \end{bmatrix}\begin{bmatrix} x \\ y \end{bmatrix} = 4,$$

we substitute for $\begin{bmatrix} x \\ y \end{bmatrix}$ and for $[x \ \ y]$ from Equations (2) and (3), we get

$$\left(\frac{1}{\sqrt{5}}\right)^2 [u \ \ v]\begin{bmatrix} 2 & 1 \\ -1 & 2 \end{bmatrix}\begin{bmatrix} 1 & 2 \\ 2 & -2 \end{bmatrix}\begin{bmatrix} 2 & -1 \\ 1 & 2 \end{bmatrix}\begin{bmatrix} u \\ v \end{bmatrix} = 4,$$

or

$$\frac{1}{5}[u \ \ v]\begin{bmatrix} 10 & 0 \\ 0 & -15 \end{bmatrix}\begin{bmatrix} u \\ v \end{bmatrix} = 4.$$

From this equation follows the simple form $2u^2 - 3v^2 = 4$. Thus, by means of the transformation, the equation

$$x^2 + 4xy - 2y^2 = 4$$

becomes, in the new coordinate system,

$$2u^2 - 3v^2 = 4.$$

Geometrically, the effect of the transformation $T$ is to rotate the axes by an amount that places them along the lines of symmetry of the curve described by $x^2 + 4xy - 2y^2 = 4$, as shown in Figure 16.2c.

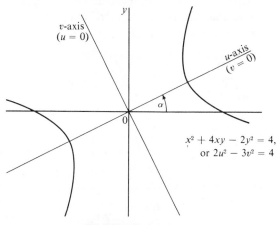

**FIGURE 16.2c**

The new coordinate axes can be found quite simply by means of the vector interpretation of the equation

$$\begin{bmatrix} x \\ y \end{bmatrix} = \frac{1}{\sqrt{5}}\begin{bmatrix} 2 & -1 \\ 1 & 2 \end{bmatrix}\begin{bmatrix} u \\ v \end{bmatrix}.$$

Since the vectors

$$\begin{bmatrix} \frac{2}{5}\sqrt{5} \\ \frac{1}{5}\sqrt{5} \end{bmatrix} \quad \text{and} \quad \begin{bmatrix} -\frac{1}{5}\sqrt{5} \\ \frac{2}{5}\sqrt{5} \end{bmatrix}$$

are the new base vectors expressed in terms of components relative to the original base system,

$$\mathbf{i} = \begin{bmatrix} 1 \\ 0 \end{bmatrix}, \quad \mathbf{j} = \begin{bmatrix} 0 \\ 1 \end{bmatrix},$$

these new base vectors locate the $u$- and $v$-coordinate axes and give their positive directions.

In order to determine the angle of rotation, we need only observe that in the equation $X = TU$, that is, in

$$\begin{bmatrix} x \\ y \end{bmatrix} = \frac{1}{\sqrt{5}} \begin{bmatrix} 2 & -1 \\ 1 & 2 \end{bmatrix} \begin{bmatrix} u \\ v \end{bmatrix} = \begin{bmatrix} \frac{2}{5}\sqrt{5} & -\frac{1}{5}\sqrt{5} \\ \frac{1}{5}\sqrt{5} & \frac{2}{5}\sqrt{5} \end{bmatrix} \begin{bmatrix} u \\ v \end{bmatrix},$$

$T$ is an orthonormal matrix. Thus we may let

$$\cos \alpha = \frac{2}{\sqrt{5}}, \quad \sin \alpha = \frac{1}{\sqrt{5}}$$

and write

$$\begin{bmatrix} x \\ y \end{bmatrix} = \begin{bmatrix} \cos \alpha & -\sin \alpha \\ \sin \alpha & \cos \alpha \end{bmatrix} \begin{bmatrix} u \\ v \end{bmatrix}.$$

The angle $\alpha$ can be found by means of tables.

It has been shown that a rotation of coordinates can be represented by an orthonormal matrix. Does every orthonormal matrix represent a rotation of coordinates? Observe that the determinant of the matrix $T$ in the preceding illustration is 1. Does this fact suggest a more general result?

**Theorem 16.2a.** If $T$ is an orthonormal matrix, then $T^\mathsf{T} = T^{-1}$, and $\det(T) = \pm 1$.
PROOF: Let

$$T = \begin{bmatrix} s_1 & t_1 \\ s_2 & t_2 \end{bmatrix}.$$

Then

$$T^\mathsf{T} T = \begin{bmatrix} s_1 & s_2 \\ t_1 & t_2 \end{bmatrix} \begin{bmatrix} s_1 & t_1 \\ s_2 & t_2 \end{bmatrix}$$

$$= \begin{bmatrix} s_1^2 + s_2^2 & s_1 t_1 + s_2 t_2 \\ s_1 t_1 + s_2 t_2 & t_1^2 + t_2^2 \end{bmatrix}$$

$$= \begin{bmatrix} 1 & 0 \\ 0 & 1 \end{bmatrix}. \quad \text{(Why?)}$$

Thus,

$$T^\mathsf{T} T = I$$

and hence

$$T^\mathsf{T} = T^{-1}.$$

Since $(T^\mathsf{T} T) = I$,

$$\det(T^\mathsf{T} T) = (\det T^\mathsf{T})(\det T)$$
$$= (\det T)^2$$
$$= 1.$$

Hence, $\det T = \pm 1$, and the proof of the theorem is complete.

In the particular case where

$$T = \begin{bmatrix} \frac{2}{5}\sqrt{5} & -\frac{1}{5}\sqrt{5} \\ \frac{1}{5}\sqrt{5} & \frac{2}{5}\sqrt{5} \end{bmatrix},$$

we found that det $T = 1$ and that the new coordinate system was indeed a rotation of the old. Let us consider another transformation that is a slight modification of $T$:

$$S.=. \begin{bmatrix} -\frac{1}{5}\sqrt{5} & \frac{2}{5}\sqrt{5} \\ \frac{2}{5}\sqrt{5} & \frac{1}{5}\sqrt{5} \end{bmatrix}.$$

This transformation is nothing more than $T$ with its columns interchanged, so that det $S = -1$. From the form

$$\begin{bmatrix} x \\ y \end{bmatrix} = \begin{bmatrix} -\frac{1}{5}\sqrt{5} & \frac{2}{5}\sqrt{5} \\ \frac{2}{5}\sqrt{5} & \frac{1}{5}\sqrt{5} \end{bmatrix} \begin{bmatrix} u \\ v \end{bmatrix}$$

it follows that

$$\begin{bmatrix} -\frac{1}{5}\sqrt{5} \\ \frac{2}{5}\sqrt{5} \end{bmatrix} \quad \text{and} \quad \begin{bmatrix} \frac{2}{5}\sqrt{5} \\ \frac{1}{5}\sqrt{5} \end{bmatrix}$$

are unit vectors in the positive $u$- and $v$-directions, respectively. These vectors are shown in Figure 16.2d. It is apparent that the $u$- and $v$-axes here are obtain-

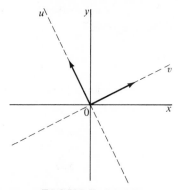

**FIGURE 16.2d**

able by interchanging those associated with the transformation $T$. It is also clear that there is no rotation in the plane that carries the $x$-axis into the $u$-axis, and the $y$-axis into the $v$-axis, as was the case with the $T$ transformation. Essentially, then, the transformation $S$ represents a rotation *and a reflection*.

These observations lead to

**Theorem 16.2b.** A transformation $T$ represents a *rotation* of coordinates in $\mathcal{V}_2 \Leftrightarrow T$ is an orthonormal matrix and det $T = 1$.

PROOF: Consider a rotation of coordinates through an angle $\alpha$, and let $e_1$, $e_2$ be unit vectors in the positive directions of the new coordinate axes. The vector $e_1$ may be represented as

$$e_1 = i \cos \alpha + j \sin \alpha.$$

Since $e_2$ makes an angle $\alpha + \pi/2$ with the $x$-axis (see Figure 16.2e), it may be written as

$$e_2 = -i \sin \alpha + j \cos \alpha.$$

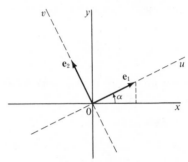

**FIGURE 16.2e**

Hence, the transformation is determined by the matrix

$$T = \begin{bmatrix} \cos \alpha & -\sin \alpha \\ \sin \alpha & \cos \alpha \end{bmatrix},$$

which has the desired properties. A reversal of this argument, using the matrix $T$, is sufficient to prove the converse.

## Exercises 16.2

In Numbers 1 to 6, determine if the transformations represent pure rotations. For each one that does, locate the new coordinate axes, and determine the angle of rotation.

1. $T = \dfrac{1}{2} \begin{bmatrix} 1 & -\sqrt{3} \\ \sqrt{3} & 1 \end{bmatrix}$.

2. $T = \dfrac{1}{5} \begin{bmatrix} -3 & 4 \\ 4 & 3 \end{bmatrix}$.

3. $T = \dfrac{1}{\sqrt{2}} \begin{bmatrix} 1 & 1 \\ -1 & 1 \end{bmatrix}$.

4. $T = \begin{bmatrix} -1 & -1 \\ 1 & -1 \end{bmatrix}$.

5. $T = \dfrac{1}{\sqrt{5}} \begin{bmatrix} -2 & 1 \\ -1 & -2 \end{bmatrix}$.

6. $T = \dfrac{1}{10} \begin{bmatrix} 3 & -4 \\ 4 & 3 \end{bmatrix}$.

In Numbers 7 to 10, transform each of the equations by the indicated transformation, where $X = TU$, and make a sketch showing the original axes, the new axes, and the curve.

7. $9x^2 - 24xy + 16y^2 = 4,\ T = \dfrac{1}{5} \begin{bmatrix} 4 & -3 \\ 3 & 4 \end{bmatrix}$.

8. $2xy = 1,\ T = \dfrac{1}{\sqrt{2}} \begin{bmatrix} 1 & -1 \\ 1 & 1 \end{bmatrix}$.

9. $5x^2 + 12xy = 4,\ T = \dfrac{1}{\sqrt{13}} \begin{bmatrix} 3 & -2 \\ 2 & 3 \end{bmatrix}$.

10. $2x^2 - 4xy - y^2 = 6$, $T = \dfrac{1}{\sqrt{5}} \begin{bmatrix} -1 & 2 \\ -2 & -1 \end{bmatrix}$.

11. Show that if $ax^2 + 2bxy + cy^2$ is transformed into $Au^2 + 2Buv + Cv^2$ by a rotation of coordinates, then $b^2 - ac = B^2 - AC$. (In other words, show that the quantity $b^2 - ac$ is invariant with respect to rotations.) *Hint:* $ac - b^2$ is the determinant of the matrix of the given quadratic form.

12. Show that the product of two orthonormal matrices is an orthonormal matrix, and hence two successive rotations lead to an equivalent single rotation of coordinates. Does the set of all orthonormal matrices form a group with respect to matrix multiplication? Explain.

13. Consider the equations $e_{11}^2 + e_{21}^2 = 1$, $e_{12}^2 + e_{22}^2 = 1$, $e_{11}e_{12} + e_{21}e_{22} = 0$, which were found (p. 635) for an orthonormal transformation. Evidently, we may take $e_{11} = \cos\alpha$, $e_{21} = \sin\alpha$ as the general form of the solution of the first equation. Substitution into the third equation gives

$$e_{12}\cos\alpha + e_{22}\sin\alpha = 0 \implies e_{12} = -m\sin\alpha, \quad e_{22} = m\cos\alpha.$$

The second equation implies $m = \pm 1$. (Why?) There are therefore two possibilities:

$$e_{12} = -\sin\alpha, \quad e_{22} = \cos\alpha,$$

and

$$e_{12} = \sin\alpha, \quad e_{22} = -\cos\alpha.$$

The first case has been discussed in the text. Show that the second case corresponds to a rotation in the plane plus a reflection.

# 16.3 EIGENVALUES AND EIGENVECTORS

We have shown that a rotation of coordinates can be used to simplify certain expressions when the new reference system is chosen in an appropriate way. Although we gave an example to show how an expression can be simplified, we did not indicate how to determine the appropriate rotation.

To deal with this problem, let us review in a general way the procedure discussed in the preceding section. A given quadratic form

$$p(x, y) = ax^2 + 2bxy + cy^2$$

may be written in matrix form as

$$p(x, y) = \begin{bmatrix} x & y \end{bmatrix} \begin{bmatrix} a & b \\ b & c \end{bmatrix} \begin{bmatrix} x \\ y \end{bmatrix}.$$

Notice that no matter what quadratic form is given, the matrix of coefficients

$$\begin{bmatrix} a & b \\ b & c \end{bmatrix}$$

will always be a symmetric matrix—an important fact that will prove to be useful. Next, we make the transformation

$$\begin{bmatrix} x \\ y \end{bmatrix} = \begin{bmatrix} s_1 & t_1 \\ s_2 & t_2 \end{bmatrix} \begin{bmatrix} u \\ v \end{bmatrix},$$

or

$$X = TU,$$

so that $p(x, y)$ becomes

$$q(u, v) = [u \quad v] \begin{bmatrix} s_1 & s_2 \\ t_1 & t_2 \end{bmatrix} \begin{bmatrix} a & b \\ b & c \end{bmatrix} \begin{bmatrix} s_1 & t_1 \\ s_2 & t_2 \end{bmatrix} \begin{bmatrix} u \\ v \end{bmatrix}.$$

The last equation may be written more conveniently as

$$q(u, v) = U^\mathsf{T} T^\mathsf{T} A T U.$$

The object of introducing the transformation $T$ is to change $A$ into a diagonal matrix; that is, we would like the result to be

(1)
$$T^\mathsf{T} A T = \begin{bmatrix} \lambda_1 & 0 \\ 0 & \lambda_2 \end{bmatrix},$$

for then we have

$$q(u, v) = U^\mathsf{T}(T^\mathsf{T} A T)U$$

$$= [u \quad v] \begin{bmatrix} \lambda_1 & 0 \\ 0 & \lambda_2 \end{bmatrix} \begin{bmatrix} u \\ v \end{bmatrix}$$

$$= \lambda_1 u^2 + \lambda_2 v^2.$$

Of course, we do not yet have any assurance that such a transformation exists. Thus, part of the problem with which we are faced is to determine under what conditions the desired transformation $T$ exists, and once this transformation is known to exist, the remainder of the problem is to find it.

Since we wish to determine a rotation of the coordinate system, we want to find an orthonormal matrix $T$ that will represent the rotation. We may therefore simplify the ensuing argument by making use of the important fundamental property of orthonormal matrices that was obtained in Theorem 16.2a—that is, if $T$ is an orthonormal matrix, then

$$T^{-1} = T^\mathsf{T}.$$

Using this result in Equation (1), and premultiplying each side by $T$, we get

$$T(T^\mathsf{T} A T) = A T = T \begin{bmatrix} \lambda_1 & 0 \\ 0 & \lambda_2 \end{bmatrix}.$$

If $T$ is written in terms of column vectors, then the last equation becomes

$$A[T_1 \quad T_2] = [T_1 \quad T_2] \begin{bmatrix} \lambda_1 & 0 \\ 0 & \lambda_2 \end{bmatrix}.$$

To show that $A[T_1 \quad T_2] = [AT_1 \quad AT_2]$ in partitioned form, let the matrix $A$ be partitioned into row vectors so that

$$AT = \begin{bmatrix} R_1 \\ R_2 \end{bmatrix} [T_1 \quad T_2] = \begin{bmatrix} R_1 T_1 & R_1 T_2 \\ R_2 T_1 & R_2 T_2 \end{bmatrix}.$$

Since

$$AT_1 = \begin{bmatrix} R_1 T_1 \\ R_2 T_1 \end{bmatrix} \quad \text{and} \quad AT_2 = \begin{bmatrix} R_1 T_2 \\ R_2 T_2 \end{bmatrix},$$

the product $AT$ may be written in partitioned form as

$$AT = [AT_1 \quad AT_2].$$

Furthermore, we may write

$$[T_1 \quad T_2]\begin{bmatrix} \lambda_1 & 0 \\ 0 & \lambda_2 \end{bmatrix} = [\lambda_1 T_1 \quad \lambda_2 T_2].$$

Consequently, we have the result

$$[AT_1 \quad AT_2] = [\lambda_1 T_1 \quad \lambda_2 T_2].$$

In order that these two matrices be equal, we must have

$$AT_1 = \lambda_1 T_1 \quad \text{and} \quad AT_2 = \lambda_2 T_2.$$

Each of these matrix equations represents a system of equations of the form

$$(A - \lambda I)T = 0,$$

which has a nontrivial solution for $T$ if, and only if,

(2)  $\qquad \det(A - \lambda I) = 0 \qquad$ (Theorem 15.9f),

that is, if, and only if,

$$\begin{vmatrix} a - \lambda & b \\ b & c - \lambda \end{vmatrix} = 0.$$

This equation is a quadratic equation in $\lambda$:

(3)  $\qquad \lambda^2 - (a + c)\lambda + ac - b^2 = 0.$

Apparently, the solutions of this equation are the values of $\lambda$ required for the diagonal matrix in Equation (1). Equation (2) and its solutions are important enough to be given special names.

**Definition 16.3a.** Let $A$ be any square matrix, and let $\lambda$ be an unknown scalar. Then the expression

$$\det(A - \lambda I)$$

is called the **characteristic polynomial** of $A$.

Thus, the characteristic polynomial of the matrix

$$A = \begin{bmatrix} 1 & 3 \\ 3 & 1 \end{bmatrix}$$

is

$$\det \begin{bmatrix} 1 - \lambda & 3 \\ 3 & 1 - \lambda \end{bmatrix} = \lambda^2 - 2\lambda - 8.$$

**Definition 16.3b.** The zeros of the characteristic polynomial of a matrix $A$ are called the **eigenvalues** of $A$.

The word *eigen* is a German word meaning "characteristic." In the preceding example, the eigenvalues of $A$ are the roots of

$$\lambda^2 - 2\lambda - 8 = 0,$$

or

$$\lambda = 4 \quad \text{and} \quad \lambda = -2.$$

As the foregoing discussion shows, to each eigenvalue, $\lambda_i$, there is associated a vector $T_i$ such that $AT_i = \lambda_i T_i$.

**Definition 16.3c.** The nonzero vectors $T_i$, for which $AT_i = \lambda_i T_i$, where $\lambda_i$ is an eigenvalue of $A$, are called **eigenvectors** of $A$.

---

*Example 16.3a.* Find the eigenvectors of the preceding matrix

$$A = \begin{bmatrix} 1 & 3 \\ 3 & 1 \end{bmatrix}.$$

To find the required vectors, we must solve the equations

$$\begin{bmatrix} 1 & 3 \\ 3 & 1 \end{bmatrix} \begin{bmatrix} s_1 \\ s_2 \end{bmatrix} = 4 \begin{bmatrix} s_1 \\ s_2 \end{bmatrix} \quad \text{and} \quad \begin{bmatrix} 1 & 3 \\ 3 & 1 \end{bmatrix} \begin{bmatrix} t_1 \\ t_2 \end{bmatrix} = -2 \begin{bmatrix} t_1 \\ t_2 \end{bmatrix},$$

or

$$\begin{bmatrix} -3 & 3 \\ 3 & -3 \end{bmatrix} \begin{bmatrix} s_1 \\ s_2 \end{bmatrix} = 0 \quad \text{and} \quad \begin{bmatrix} 3 & 3 \\ 3 & 3 \end{bmatrix} \begin{bmatrix} t_1 \\ t_2 \end{bmatrix} = 0.$$

A nontrivial solution for the first is given by

$$\begin{bmatrix} k \\ k \end{bmatrix},$$

and for the second by

$$\begin{bmatrix} m \\ -m \end{bmatrix},$$

where $k$ and $m$ are arbitrary nonzero real numbers. Since we are interested in unit vectors, we may choose $k$ and $m$ accordingly to get

$$T_1 = \begin{bmatrix} \frac{1}{2}\sqrt{2} \\ \frac{1}{2}\sqrt{2} \end{bmatrix} \quad \text{and} \quad T_2 = \begin{bmatrix} -\frac{1}{2}\sqrt{2} \\ \frac{1}{2}\sqrt{2} \end{bmatrix}.$$

---

It is easily verified that the matrix

$$T = \begin{bmatrix} \frac{1}{2}\sqrt{2} & -\frac{1}{2}\sqrt{2} \\ \frac{1}{2}\sqrt{2} & \frac{1}{2}\sqrt{2} \end{bmatrix},$$

formed from the eigenvectors of Example 16.3a, has the property that $T^T A T$ is a diagonal matrix. Notice that it was possible to normalize the two eigenvectors in such a manner that $\det T = +1$. Furthermore, these eigenvectors are orthogonal. Is this only accidental good fortune, or is there more to our investigation than first meets the eye? The next theorem provides a pleasing answer to this question for an $n \times n$ matrix.

**Theorem 16.3a.** If $\lambda_1$ and $\lambda_2$ are distinct eigenvalues of a symmetric matrix $A$, and if $T_1$ and $T_2$ are eigenvectors associated with $\lambda_1$ and $\lambda_2$, respectively, then $T_1$ and $T_2$ are orthogonal.

PROOF: Let

$$AT_1 = \lambda_1 T_1.$$

Then

$$T_2^\mathsf{T} A T_1 = \lambda_1 T_2^\mathsf{T} T_1,$$

and

$$(T_2^\mathsf{T} A T_1)^\mathsf{T} = \lambda_1 (T_2^\mathsf{T} T_1)^\mathsf{T},$$

or

$$T_1^\mathsf{T} A^\mathsf{T} T_2 = \lambda_1 T_1^\mathsf{T} T_2.$$

Since $A$ is symmetric, $A^\mathsf{T} = A$; therefore,

$$T_1^\mathsf{T} A T_2 = \lambda_1 T_1^\mathsf{T} T_2.$$

Furthermore, since $AT_2 = \lambda_2 T_2$, we get, by substitution into the preceding equation,

$$T_1^\mathsf{T} \lambda_2 T_2 = \lambda_1 T_1^\mathsf{T} T_2,$$

or

$$(\lambda_2 - \lambda_1) T_1^\mathsf{T} T_2 = 0.$$

Since $\lambda_2 \neq \lambda_1$, then $T_1^\mathsf{T} T_2 = 0$; that is, $T_1$, $T_2$ are orthogonal.

The work done so far has been based on the assumption that the eigenvalues of the matrix $A$ are real. In order to show that this assumption is justified, we must extend our discussion to include matrices with complex numbers for elements.

**Definition 16.3d.** If $A$ is a matrix that has complex elements, then $\overline{A}$ denotes the matrix whose elements are the conjugates of the elements of $A$. The matrix $\overline{A}$ is called the **conjugate** of $A$.

For example, if

$$A = \begin{bmatrix} 2 + i & i \\ 3 & -2 + 3i \end{bmatrix},$$

then

$$\overline{A} = \begin{bmatrix} 2 - i & -i \\ 3 & -2 - 3i \end{bmatrix}.$$

Similarly, if

$$A = \begin{bmatrix} a + bi \\ c + di \end{bmatrix},$$

then

$$\overline{A} = \begin{bmatrix} a - bi \\ c - di \end{bmatrix}.$$

Note that if the elements of $A$ are all real, then $A = \overline{A}$, since a real number is its own conjugate.

**Definition 16.3e.** The matrix $A^* .=. (\overline{A})^\mathsf{T}$ is called the **transposed conjugate** of $A$.

**Theorem 16.3b.** $(AB)^* = B^* A^*$.

PROOF: Left for the reader.

With the aid of this last result, we can prove a more fundamental result.

**Theorem 16.3c.** The eigenvalues of a real symmetric matrix are real.

PROOF: Suppose $\lambda$ is a complex eigenvalue of $A$, and let $X$ be a corresponding eigenvector, so that

$$AX = \lambda X.$$

If $\lambda$ is imaginary, then the elements of $X$ are, in general, also imaginary. In any case, we may premultiply both sides by the row matrix $X^*$ to get

(4) $$X^*AX = \lambda X^*X.$$

The reason for this step is that $X^*X$ is a real number, say $k$, so that

(5) $$X^*AX = \lambda k.$$

From this equation we then obtain

$$(X^*AX)^* = (\lambda k)^*,$$

or

$$X^*A^*(X^*)^* = \lambda^*k.$$

Now $\lambda$ is a complex number $\Rightarrow \lambda^* = \bar{\lambda}$, the conjugate of $\lambda$. Furthermore,

$$(X^*)^* = X,$$

and since $A$ is real and symmetric,

$$A^* = A.$$

It therefore follows that

$$X^*AX = \bar{\lambda}k,$$

which, by comparison with Equation (5), gives

$$\bar{\lambda}k = \lambda k.$$

In general, $k \neq 0$, so that $\bar{\lambda} = \lambda$, which is possible only if $\lambda$ is real.

Thus, it appears that if a matrix $A$ has distinct eigenvalues, corresponding eigenvectors can be found that form an orthonormal basis. The desired transformation may then be constructed from these eigenvectors.

**Theorem 16.3d.** For every symmetric $2 \times 2$ matrix $A$ that has distinct eigenvalues, $\lambda_i$, there is an orthonormal transformation $T$ such that

$$T^{-1}AT = \begin{bmatrix} \lambda_1 & 0 \\ 0 & \lambda_2 \end{bmatrix}.$$

PROOF: Let $T = [T_1 \quad T_2]$, where $T_1, T_2$ are the eigenvectors of $A$. Then

$$AT = A[T_1 \quad T_2] = [AT_1 \quad AT_2]$$
$$= [\lambda_1 T_1 \quad \lambda_2 T_2]$$
$$= [T_1 \quad T_2]\begin{bmatrix} \lambda_1 & 0 \\ 0 & \lambda_2 \end{bmatrix}$$
$$= T\begin{bmatrix} \lambda_1 & 0 \\ 0 & \lambda_2 \end{bmatrix}.$$

It follows that

$$T^{-1}AT = \begin{bmatrix} \lambda_1 & 0 \\ 0 & \lambda_2 \end{bmatrix}.$$

The preceding discussion leaves open the question of what happens if $A$ does not have distinct eigenvalues. It is interesting, however, to note

**Theorem 16.3e.** A nondiagonal $2 \times 2$ real symmetric matrix $S$ has distinct eigenvalues.

PROOF: Suppose

$$S = \begin{bmatrix} a & b \\ b & c \end{bmatrix}.$$

Then

$$\det \begin{bmatrix} a - \lambda & b \\ b & c - \lambda \end{bmatrix} = \lambda^2 - (a + c)\lambda + ac - b^2.$$

In order that this quadratic polynomial have a repeated zero, the discriminant, $B^2 - 4AC$, must be zero. But

$$B^2 - 4AC = (a + c)^2 - 4(ac - b^2) = (a - c)^2 + 4b^2,$$

which cannot be zero unless $b = 0$ and $a = c$, in which case $S$ would be diagonal, contrary to the hypothesis.

Let us summarize the results in this section with an example that will illustrate the various theorems.

---

*Example 16.3b.* Determine a rotation of coordinates that will eliminate the product term (the $xy$ term) in

$$2x^2 + 3xy - 2y^2 = 10,$$

and sketch the curve described by the equation.

Since we may write the equation as

$$[x \ y] \begin{bmatrix} 2 & \frac{3}{2} \\ \frac{3}{2} & -2 \end{bmatrix} \begin{bmatrix} x \\ y \end{bmatrix} = 10,$$

it follows that the characteristic polynomial is

$$\lambda^2 - \frac{25}{4}$$

and that the eigenvalues are $\frac{5}{2}$, and $-\frac{5}{2}$. To find the eigenvectors, we solve the equations

$$\begin{bmatrix} 2 & \frac{3}{2} \\ \frac{3}{2} & -2 \end{bmatrix} \begin{bmatrix} t_1 \\ t_2 \end{bmatrix} = \frac{5}{2} \begin{bmatrix} t_1 \\ t_2 \end{bmatrix} \quad \text{and} \quad \begin{bmatrix} 2 & \frac{3}{2} \\ \frac{3}{2} & -2 \end{bmatrix} \begin{bmatrix} s_1 \\ s_2 \end{bmatrix} = -\frac{5}{2} \begin{bmatrix} s_1 \\ s_2 \end{bmatrix},$$

or

$$-\tfrac{1}{2}t_1 + \tfrac{3}{2}t_2 = 0 \quad \text{and} \quad \tfrac{9}{2}s_1 + \tfrac{3}{2}s_2 = 0,$$

from which we get

$$t_1 = 3, \quad t_2 = 1 \quad \text{and} \quad s_1 = -1, \quad s_2 = 3.$$

Hence, the normalized eigenvectors are

$$T_1 = \begin{bmatrix} \frac{3}{10}\sqrt{10} \\ \frac{1}{10}\sqrt{10} \end{bmatrix} \quad \text{and} \quad T_2 = \begin{bmatrix} -\frac{1}{10}\sqrt{10} \\ \frac{3}{10}\sqrt{10} \end{bmatrix},$$

so that the transformation is given by

$$T = \begin{bmatrix} \frac{3}{10}\sqrt{10} & -\frac{1}{10}\sqrt{10} \\ \frac{1}{10}\sqrt{10} & \frac{3}{10}\sqrt{10} \end{bmatrix}.$$

Thus, if

$$\begin{bmatrix} x \\ y \end{bmatrix} = T \begin{bmatrix} u \\ v \end{bmatrix},$$

then the original equation is transformed into

$$\tfrac{5}{2}u^2 - \tfrac{5}{2}v^2 = 10,$$

or

$$u^2 - v^2 = 4.$$

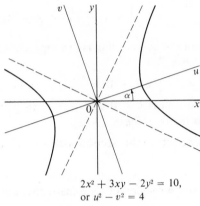

$$2x^2 + 3xy - 2y^2 = 10,$$
or $u^2 - v^2 = 4$

**FIGURE 16.3a**

A sketch of this curve is shown in Figure 16.3a. The angle of rotation is, of course, determined by the equations

$$\cos \alpha = 3/\sqrt{10}, \quad \sin \alpha = 1/\sqrt{10}.$$

---

It is worth mentioning that the order in which the eigenvectors are taken in the transformation matrix $T$ determines the order in which the eigenvalues appear in the matrix

$$\begin{bmatrix} \lambda_1 & 0 \\ 0 & \lambda_2 \end{bmatrix}.$$

The proof of Theorem 16.3d illustrates this fact. Note, however, that the eigenvectors in the transformation matrix must be in an order that makes $\det T = +1$. Another interesting observation follows from the fact that the expression $ac - b^2$, where

$$p(x, y) = ax^2 + 2bxy + cy^2,$$

is invariant with respect to rotations (see Exercises 16.2, Number 11). Consequently, since the polynomial

$$p(x, y) = ax^2 + 2bxy + cy^2$$

is transformed into

$$q(u, v) = \lambda_1 u^2 + \lambda_2 v^2$$

by an orthonormal transformation $T$, and since the signs of $\lambda_1$ and $\lambda_2$ determine whether the curve is an ellipse or a hyperbola, we can obtain information about the curve by comparing the determinants of the coefficient matrices.

Thus, from

$$\lambda_1 \lambda_2 = ac - b^2,$$

it follows that if $ac - b^2 < 0$, then $\lambda_1$, $\lambda_2$ are of opposite signs, and the curve is a hyperbola (or a degenerate hyperbola). If $ac - b^2 > 0$, then $\lambda_1$ and $\lambda_2$ are of the same sign and the curve is an ellipse, a circle, or a degenerate case of these curves. If $ac - b^2 = 0$, what is the curve?

For example, for the equation

$$2x^2 - 6xy + 3y^2 = 12,$$

we get

$$ac - b^2 = 6 - 9 = -3.$$

Hence, the graph of the equation is either a hyperbola or two intersecting straight lines.

## Exercises 16.3

In Numbers 1 to 6 determine a rotation that will eliminate the product term in each equation, and sketch the graph.

1. $x^2 - 4xy + y^2 = -9$.
2. $5x^2 - 8xy + 5y^2 = 9$.
3. $8x^2 - 12xy + 17y^2 = 80$.
4. $x^2 - 4xy - 2y^2 = 6$.
5. $17x^2 + 18xy - 7y^2 = 80$.
6. $3x^2 + 2xy + 3y^2 = 4$.

For each of the equations in Numbers 7 to 12, find a rotation that will remove the $xy$ term, and then find a translation (if necessary) that will reduce the equation to simplest standard form.

7. $16x^2 - 24xy + 9y^2 = 30x + 40y$.
8. $11x^2 - 24xy + 4y^2 + 6x + 8y = -15$.
9. $3x^2 + 2\sqrt{3}xy + y^2 = 12x - 12\sqrt{3}y + 24$.
10. $x^2 + 2xy + y^2 + \sqrt{2}x + 2\sqrt{2}y = 0$.
11. $2x^2 - 8xy - 4y^2 = 12\sqrt{5}x + 6\sqrt{5}y + 9$.
12. $x^2 + 4xy + 4y^2 = 8\sqrt{5}x + 6\sqrt{5}y + 10$.

13. Prove Theorem 16.3b.
14. Show that for any vector $X$ ($X$ is a column matrix) having complex components, $X^*X$ is a real number.
15. Prove that $(A^*)^* = A$.
16. Prove that $(\overline{A})^\mathsf{T} = \overline{(A^\mathsf{T})}$.
17. In Theorem 16.3e, it was required that the matrix $S$ be nondiagonal. Suppose that $S$ is diagonal; for instance,

$$S = \begin{bmatrix} a & 0 \\ 0 & c \end{bmatrix}.$$

Discuss the eigenvalues and eigenvectors. In particular, what is the geometric significance of two equal eigenvalues?

18. Find the set of points such that the sum of the distances of each point from the points $(c, c)$ and $(-c, -c)$ is a constant, $2a$. By rotation of axes reduce the equation to a simple standard form.

## *16.4 TRANSFORMATIONS IN THREE DIMENSIONS

Although nearly all of the work in Section 16.3 was done for $2 \times 2$ matrices, there is no theoretical reason for this restriction. Each theorem, except Theorem 16.3e, can be extended to general $n \times n$ matrices.

**Definition 16.4a.** If an $n \times n$ matrix $T = [t_{ij}]$ can be partitioned into $n$ column vectors that constitute an orthonormal basis, then $T$ is called an **orthonormal matrix.**

In an orthonormal matrix each column is a unit vector and the columns are mutually orthogonal. Thus, an orthonormal matrix is characterized by the fact that

$$\sum_{\alpha=1}^{n} t_{\alpha i} t_{\alpha j} = \delta_{ij} \quad \text{(the Kronecker delta)}.$$

The following theorem and its proof illustrate the extension of Theorem 16.2a to the $n \times n$ case. It is left to the reader to provide the more general proofs for the other theorems.

**Theorem 4.4a.** If $T$ is an orthonormal matrix, then

$$T^\mathsf{T} = T^{-1} \quad \text{and} \quad \det T = \pm 1.$$

PROOF: $T^\mathsf{T} = [s_{ij}]$, where $s_{ij} = t_{ji}$.
Therefore, $T^\mathsf{T} T = [p_{ij}]$, where

$$p_{ij} = \sum_{\alpha=1}^{n} s_{i\alpha} t_{\alpha j} = \sum_{\alpha=1}^{n} t_{\alpha i} t_{\alpha j} = \delta_{ij}.$$

Thus, $T^\mathsf{T} T = I$.
The remainder of the proof proceeds just as in Theorem 16.2a; the details are left to the reader.

The problem of finding a rotation of coordinates that will simplify a quadratic form represented by a symmetric matrix $A$ may be summarized by asking if there exists an orthonormal matrix $T$ such that

$$T^{-1} A T = D,$$

where $D$ is a diagonal matrix. If the matrix $T$ exists, then $A$ is said to be **similar to** $D$.
The next example illustrates the application of the theorems of Section 16. to a $3 \times 3$ matrix.

*Example 16.4a.* Determine a transformation $T$ such that $T^{-1} AT$ is a diagonal matrix if

$$A = \begin{bmatrix} 0 & 3 & 4 \\ 3 & 0 & 0 \\ 4 & 0 & 0 \end{bmatrix}.$$

The characteristic polynomial of $A$ is

$$\begin{vmatrix} -\lambda & 3 & 4 \\ 3 & -\lambda & 0 \\ 4 & 0 & -\lambda \end{vmatrix} = -\lambda^3 + 25\lambda.$$

The eigenvalues of the matrix are therefore 0, 5, $-5$. An eigenvector associated with the eigenvalue 0 can be found by solving

$$\begin{bmatrix} 0 & 3 & 4 \\ 3 & 0 & 0 \\ 4 & 0 & 0 \end{bmatrix}\begin{bmatrix} x \\ y \\ z \end{bmatrix} = 0\begin{bmatrix} x \\ y \\ z \end{bmatrix},$$

or

$$3y + 4z = 0,$$
$$3x = 0,$$
$$4x = 0.$$

A nontrivial solution is

$$\begin{bmatrix} 0 \\ 4 \\ -3 \end{bmatrix},$$

and the corresponding normalized solution is

$$T_1 = \begin{bmatrix} 0 \\ \frac{4}{5} \\ -\frac{3}{5} \end{bmatrix}.$$

The eigenvector associated with 5 can be found by solving

$$\begin{bmatrix} 0 & 3 & 4 \\ 3 & 0 & 0 \\ 4 & 0 & 0 \end{bmatrix}\begin{bmatrix} x \\ y \\ z \end{bmatrix} = 5\begin{bmatrix} x \\ y \\ z \end{bmatrix},$$

or

$$\begin{bmatrix} -5 & 3 & 4 \\ 3 & -5 & 0 \\ 4 & 0 & -5 \end{bmatrix}\begin{bmatrix} x \\ y \\ z \end{bmatrix} = 0,$$

or

$$-5x + 3y + 4z = 0,$$
$$3x - 5y = 0,$$
$$4x - 5z = 0.$$

A nontrivial normalized solution of these equations is

$$T_2 = \begin{bmatrix} \frac{1}{2}\sqrt{2} \\ \frac{3}{10}\sqrt{2} \\ \frac{4}{10}\sqrt{2} \end{bmatrix}.$$

Similarly, the eigenvector associated with $-5$ can be found by solving

$$\begin{bmatrix} 5 & 3 & 4 \\ 3 & 5 & 0 \\ 4 & 0 & 5 \end{bmatrix} \begin{bmatrix} x \\ y \\ z \end{bmatrix} = 0.$$

A nontrivial normalized solution is

$$T_3 = \begin{bmatrix} \tfrac{1}{2}\sqrt{2} \\ -\tfrac{3}{10}\sqrt{2} \\ -\tfrac{4}{10}\sqrt{2} \end{bmatrix}.$$

From these eigenvectors a transformation matrix $T$ is constructed by using the eigenvectors as the column vectors of $T$. The matrix $T$ can be constructed by putting the eigenvectors in any order, provided that det $T = 1$, since in that case the transformation may be interpreted geometrically as a rigid rotation of coordinates. The order of the eigenvectors in $T$ merely determines the order of the eigenvalues in the diagonal matrix

$$\begin{bmatrix} \lambda_1 & 0 & 0 \\ 0 & \lambda_2 & 0 \\ 0 & 0 & \lambda_3 \end{bmatrix}.$$

Thus, if we write $T = [T_1 \ \ T_2 \ \ T_3]$, or

$$T = \begin{bmatrix} 0 & \tfrac{1}{2}\sqrt{2} & \tfrac{1}{2}\sqrt{2} \\ \tfrac{4}{5} & \tfrac{3}{10}\sqrt{2} & -\tfrac{3}{10}\sqrt{2} \\ -\tfrac{3}{5} & \tfrac{4}{10}\sqrt{2} & -\tfrac{4}{10}\sqrt{2} \end{bmatrix},$$

then,

$$T^{-1}AT = \begin{bmatrix} 0 & 0 & 0 \\ 0 & 5 & 0 \\ 0 & 0 & -5 \end{bmatrix}.$$

If the order of the columns of the matrix $T$ is changed, the eigenvalues in the diagonal matrix will appear in a different order. For instance, the reader may verify in the preceding example that if

$$T = \begin{bmatrix} \tfrac{1}{2}\sqrt{2} & 0 & \tfrac{1}{2}\sqrt{2} \\ -\tfrac{3}{10}\sqrt{2} & \tfrac{4}{5} & \tfrac{3}{10}\sqrt{2} \\ -\tfrac{4}{10}\sqrt{2} & -\tfrac{3}{5} & \tfrac{4}{10}\sqrt{2} \end{bmatrix},$$

then

$$T^{-1}AT = \begin{bmatrix} -5 & 0 & 0 \\ 0 & 0 & 0 \\ 0 & 0 & 5 \end{bmatrix}.$$

In case we should wish to show that $T^{-1}AT$ actually is a diagonal matrix, we are faced with the prospect of making a straightforward evaluation of

$$\begin{bmatrix} 0 & \tfrac{1}{2}\sqrt{2} & \tfrac{1}{2}\sqrt{2} \\ \tfrac{4}{5} & \tfrac{3}{10}\sqrt{2} & -\tfrac{3}{10}\sqrt{2} \\ -\tfrac{3}{5} & \tfrac{4}{10}\sqrt{2} & -\tfrac{4}{10}\sqrt{2} \end{bmatrix}^{-1} \begin{bmatrix} 0 & 3 & 4 \\ 3 & 0 & 0 \\ 4 & 0 & 0 \end{bmatrix} \begin{bmatrix} 0 & \tfrac{1}{2}\sqrt{2} & \tfrac{1}{2}\sqrt{2} \\ \tfrac{4}{5} & \tfrac{3}{10}\sqrt{2} & -\tfrac{3}{10}\sqrt{2} \\ -\tfrac{3}{5} & \tfrac{4}{10}\sqrt{2} & -\tfrac{4}{10}\sqrt{2} \end{bmatrix},$$

which is somewhat discouraging. The procedure can, however, be simplified greatly by the use of some of the theorems in the preceding section.

For example, since $T$ is an orthonormal matrix, we know that $T^{-1} = T^{T}$, so that it is unnecessary to perform any computation to find $T^{-1}$. Moreover, Theorem 16.3d extended to $3 \times 3$ matrices assures us that if $A$ is a real symmetric matrix and if $T$ is an orthonormal transformation, such that

$$T^{-1}AT = D,$$

where $D$ is a diagonal matrix, then the diagonal elements of $D$ are the eigenvalues of $A$.

Therefore, we know *theoretically* that

$$T^{-1}AT = \begin{bmatrix} 0 & 0 & 0 \\ 0 & 5 & 0 \\ 0 & 0 & -5 \end{bmatrix}$$

without having to perform any computation at all. Perhaps the only reason for carrying out the computation would be to obtain a numerical check on the values of the elements in $T$.

As was indicated earlier, if the matrix $T$ transforms a symmetric matrix $A$ into a diagonal matrix $D$, that is, if

$$T^{-1}AT = D,$$

then $T$ may be interpreted geometrically as representing a rigid rotation of coordinates in three dimensions, provided $\det T = 1$. As an illustration, let us consider the matrix $T$ in the preceding example. Its eigenvectors are

$$T_1 = \begin{bmatrix} 0 \\ \frac{4}{5} \\ -\frac{3}{5} \end{bmatrix}, \quad T_2 = \begin{bmatrix} \frac{1}{2}\sqrt{2} \\ \frac{3}{10}\sqrt{2} \\ \frac{4}{10}\sqrt{2} \end{bmatrix}, \quad T_3 = \begin{bmatrix} \frac{1}{2}\sqrt{2} \\ -\frac{3}{10}\sqrt{2} \\ -\frac{4}{10}\sqrt{2} \end{bmatrix},$$

which may be interpreted as unit vectors in the direction of three new coordinate axes. The components of each of these vectors represent the cosines of the angles made by the vector with the $x$-, $y$-, and $z$-coordinate axes, respectively. These vectors are illustrated in Figure 16.4a.

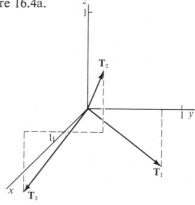

**FIGURE 16.4a**

In Section 16.3 we showed that a nondiagonal, symmetric $2 \times 2$ matrix always has distinct eigenvalues. This result does not hold for matrices of greater dimensions.

---

*Example 16.4b.* Determine eigenvalues and eigenvectors for the matrix

$$A = \begin{bmatrix} 0 & 1 & 1 \\ 1 & 0 & 1 \\ 1 & 1 & 0 \end{bmatrix}.$$

The characteristic polynomial of $A$ is

$$\begin{vmatrix} -\lambda & 1 & 1 \\ 1 & -\lambda & 1 \\ 1 & 1 & -\lambda \end{vmatrix} = -\lambda^3 + 3\lambda + 2,$$

and the zeros of this polynomial are $-1, -1, 2$. Thus, the matrix has a repeated eigenvalue, $-1$. This seemingly innocuous result is a source of some difficulty when we attempt to determine a transformation $T$ (if there is one) such that $T^{-1}AT$ is a diagonal matrix, since there are only two distinct eigenvalues and we need three distinct eigenvectors.

In this problem, an eigenvector associated with 2 is easily found to be

$$T_1 = \begin{bmatrix} 1 \\ 1 \\ 1 \end{bmatrix}.$$

To find an eigenvector associated with $-1$, we must solve the system

$$\begin{bmatrix} 0 & 1 & 1 \\ 1 & 0 & 1 \\ 1 & 1 & 0 \end{bmatrix} \begin{bmatrix} x \\ y \\ z \end{bmatrix} = -1 \begin{bmatrix} x \\ y \\ z \end{bmatrix},$$

which leads to the one equation

$$x + y + z = 0$$

three times. That is, the components of the vector

$$\begin{bmatrix} x \\ y \\ z \end{bmatrix}$$

need satisfy only the one condition $x + y + z = 0$. Therefore, we are free to choose a value for one of the components in any convenient fashion. For example, if we choose $z = 0$, then $x = 1$ and $y = -1$ satisfy the equation, and the eigenvector so determined is

$$T_2 = \begin{bmatrix} 1 \\ -1 \\ 0 \end{bmatrix}.$$

Since we may make an arbitrary choice for one of the components, it is reasonable to ask if we can make this choice in such a way that the resulting eigenvector is orthogonal to the eigenvector just obtained. In other words, we want to determine

$$\begin{bmatrix} x \\ y \\ z \end{bmatrix}$$

so that

$$x + y + z = 0,$$

and so that the orthogonality condition

$$[1 \quad -1 \quad 0] \begin{bmatrix} x \\ y \\ z \end{bmatrix} = 0, \quad \text{or} \quad x - y = 0,$$

is satisfied. In this case, we get $x = y$, and if $x = y = 1$, then $z = -2$. Hence, a *second* eigenvector

$$T_3 = \begin{bmatrix} 1 \\ 1 \\ -2 \end{bmatrix}$$

associated with $-1$ can be found. The first eigenvector is known by Theorem 16.3a to be orthogonal to both of the last two. Thus, we have again been able to determine an orthonormal transformation such that

$$T^{-1}AT = D.$$

---

The results in this example suggest that orthogonal eigenvectors can always be found for multiple eigenvalues. That such eigenvectors can be constructed for real symmetric matrices is a valid statement, but we shall not attempt to prove it here.

By this time the reader's curiosity may have led him to ask if it is necessary to restrict $A$ to being a symmetric matrix in order that there exist a diagonalizing transformation $T$. The answer is, in general, that for a nonsymmetric matrix $A$ no diagonalizing transformation exists, although it is possible to achieve an "almost diagonal" form. This subject is studied in matrix algebra under the title of the Jordan canonical form.

It is possible here to do no more than describe very briefly only one of the many important physical applications of matrices. In the analysis of the forces exerted at an interior point of a body under stress, it has been found necessary to consider the so-called **stress matrix.** This is a $3 \times 3$ matrix whose elements represent the forces at the point.

There are essentially two forces associated with each plane through the point in question. One of these forces is normal to the plane and tends to compress or extend the body in the direction perpendicular to the plane. The other force is in the plane and tends to shear the body along the plane. The second force is usually "decomposed" into a pair of orthogonal components in the plane, so that three forces are given for each plane.

If, at the point $P$, we set up a coordinate system with three orthogonal axes (see Figure 16.4b) and label these $x_1$, $x_2$, $x_3$, then we may associate three forces with each of the coordinate planes. The forces associated with the $x_2x_3$-plane are as shown in the figure. The normal force, $s_{11}$, acts along the $x_1$-axis, and the shear force components are $s_{12}$ and $s_{13}$ in the $x_2$- and $x_3$-directions, respectively. Such a decomposition may also be made for each of the other two coordinate planes, giving three forces associated with the $x_1x_2$-plane and three forces with the $x_1x_3$-plane. The force normal to the $x_1x_3$-plane acts along the $x_2$-axis and is denoted by $s_{22}$. The shearing forces in the $x_1x_3$-plane act in the $x_1$ and $x_3$ directions and are denoted by $s_{21}$ and $s_{23}$, respectively. Similar statements may be made for the $x_1x_2$-plane.

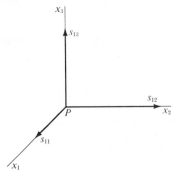

**FIGURE 16.4b**

The nine forces so described characterize completely the state of stress at the point $P$. These forces are conveniently displayed as the elements of a matrix

$$S . =. \begin{bmatrix} s_{11} & s_{12} & s_{13} \\ s_{21} & s_{22} & s_{23} \\ s_{31} & s_{32} & s_{33} \end{bmatrix}.$$

If the body is in equilibrium under all the forces acting on it, then it can be shown that $S$ is a symmetric matrix. Under these conditions, all the theory developed here applies at once. For instance, the matrix $S$ is reducible to diagonal form by means of an orthonormal transformation $T$, so that

$$T^T S T = \begin{bmatrix} f_{11} & 0 & 0 \\ 0 & f_{22} & 0 \\ 0 & 0 & f_{33} \end{bmatrix}.$$

The forces $f_{11}, f_{22}, f_{33}$ are called the **principal normal stresses,** and their directions are given by the eigenvectors of the matrix $S$. The reader will find further information on this and other applications of matrices in L. A. Pipes, *Matrix Methods for Engineering*, Prentice-Hall, Inc., Englewood Cliffs, New Jersey, 1963.

## Exercises 16.4

In Numbers 1 to 6, find the eigenvalues, the eigenvectors, and the corresponding orthonormal transformation matrix $T$ for diagonalizing the given matrix.

1. $\begin{bmatrix} 2 & 0 & 0 \\ 0 & 0 & -3 \\ 0 & -3 & 0 \end{bmatrix}.$
   
2. $\begin{bmatrix} 3 & 2 & 2 \\ 2 & 4 & 0 \\ 2 & 0 & 2 \end{bmatrix}.$

3. $\begin{bmatrix} 0 & 0 & -2 \\ 0 & 2 & -2 \\ -2 & -2 & 1 \end{bmatrix}.$

5. $\begin{bmatrix} 2 & -1 & 1 \\ -1 & 2 & -1 \\ 1 & -1 & 2 \end{bmatrix}.$

4. $\begin{bmatrix} 0 & 1 & 0 \\ 1 & 0 & 1 \\ 0 & 1 & 0 \end{bmatrix}.$

6. $\begin{bmatrix} 5 & -4 & -2 \\ -4 & 5 & -2 \\ -2 & -2 & 8 \end{bmatrix}.$

7. Show that an orthonormal transformation matrix (corresponding to a rotation of coordinates in three dimensions) leaves all the points on a certain straight line through the origin invariant, and show how to find this line for the rotation represented by the matrix

$$\frac{1}{3}\begin{bmatrix} 2 & 2 & 1 \\ -2 & 1 & 2 \\ 1 & -2 & 2 \end{bmatrix}.$$

8. Prove that if a linear transformation $T$ leaves some vector invariant, then $T$ has 1 as an eigenvalue.

9. Prove that the matrix

$$\begin{bmatrix} 1 & 2 \\ 0 & 1 \end{bmatrix}$$

is not similar to a diagonal matrix.

10. Prove that

$$\begin{bmatrix} 1 & 2 & -4 \\ 0 & -1 & 6 \\ 0 & -1 & 4 \end{bmatrix}$$

is not similar to a diagonal matrix.

11. Show that if $A$ is nonsingular, then the eigenvalues of $A^{-1}$ are the reciprocals of the eigenvalues of $A$.

12. If there is a positive integer $k$ such that $A^k = 0$, then $A$ is said to be **nilpotent**.
    (a) Show that

$$\begin{bmatrix} 0 & 1 & k \\ 0 & 0 & 1 \\ 0 & 0 & 0 \end{bmatrix}$$

is nilpotent.

(b) Prove that if a matrix is nilpotent, then all the eigenvalues of the matrix are zero.

13. The stress matrix at a point $P$ of a body is

$$\begin{bmatrix} 1 & -4 & 2 \\ -4 & 1 & -2 \\ 2 & -2 & -2 \end{bmatrix}.$$

Find the direction and magnitude of each of the principal normal stresses.

14. (a) Find the eigenvalues and the eigenvectors of the matrix

$$A = \begin{bmatrix} 0 & -1 & -3 \\ 2 & 3 & 3 \\ -2 & 1 & 1 \end{bmatrix}.$$

(b) Do the eigenvectors of $A$ form an orthogonal set?

(c) If the eigenvectors of $A$ are $T_1$, $T_2$, and $T_3$, and $T .=. [T_1 \ \ T_2 \ \ T_3]$, is $T^{-1}AT$ a diagonal matrix?

(d) Can the procedure employed here be used to diagonalize every matrix? *Hint:* Find the eigenvalues and the eigenvectors for the matrix

$$\begin{bmatrix} 0 & 5 & -3 \\ 1 & 0 & 1 \\ 2 & -4 & 4 \end{bmatrix}.$$

# Summary of Chapter 16

Some of the concepts introduced in Chapters 14 and 15 are employed in this chapter as a means of simplifying the analysis of certain kinds of equations. For this purpose the concepts to be recalled, developed further, and used include

(1) the transformation of a coordinate system (Section 16.1);

(2) sets of base vectors (Section 16.1);

(3) change of base and linear transformations (Section 16.1).

Significant consequences of these concepts include

(4) the matrix representation of a linear transformation (Section 16.1);

(5) orthonormal transformations, and rotations of the coordinate system (Section 16.2);

(6) the matrix representation of a quadratic form (Section 16.2);

(7) the characteristic polynomial of a matrix (Section 16.3);

(8) eigenvalues and eigenvectors of a matrix (Section 16.3);

(9) the determination of the matrix transformation that diagonalizes a given symmetric matrix (Section 16.3);

★(10) the extension of the preceding ideas to rotation of coordinates in three dimensions (Section 16.4).

# Chapter 17   Surfaces and Curves in Three Dimensions

The study of surfaces and curves in three dimensions is of interest not only to mathematicians but to people in other fields. For instance, the architect frequently uses the geometrical properties of surfaces to attain an artistic and practical design for the roof of a building. The engineer makes similar use of the properties of surfaces in designing the shape of an airplane wing or the shape of the nose cone of a rocket to obtain proper re-entry behavior. On a more sophisticated level, a generalization of the study of surfaces and curves is at the basis of much of Einstein's theory of relativity. Many other illustrations of the importance of this study could be cited.

## 17.1 SURFACES

In Section 14.6, we discussed the problem of representing a simple surface, a plane, by means of an equation. We found there that a linear equation

$$Ax + By + Cz + D = 0$$

always represents a plane if not all of $A$, $B$, $C$ are zero.

In general, a surface in three-dimensional space is described by an equation of the form

$$F(x, y, z) = 0,$$

where the solution set of the equation consists of the points on the surface. (A precise definition of surface must be postponed until Chapter 20.)

There will, of course, be exceptional cases, where the set of points is not a surface or where there are no real points whose coordinates satisfy the given equation. For example, the equation

$$x^2 + y^2 + z^2 = 0$$

is satisfied by only one real point $(0, 0, 0)$; the equation

$$x^2 + y^2 = 0$$

is satisfied only by the points on the $z$-axis; and the equation

$$x^2 + y^2 + z^2 + 1 = 0$$

is satisfied by no real points. We shall describe certain of the simpler surfaces in the sections that follow.

The intersection of a plane and a surface is called a **trace** of the surface in the plane. The reader will understand that the intersection of two surfaces is the set of points corresponding to the intersection of the solution sets of the corresponding two equations; that is, it is the set of points whose coordinates satisfy both equations. For the purpose of visualizing a given surface, it is often useful to have a clear mental picture of the traces in planes parallel to the coordinate planes. These traces are obtained by putting $x = c$, $y = c$, or $z = c$, respectively, in the equation of the surface.

*Example 17.1a.* Discuss the traces parallel to the coordinate planes for the surface $x^2 + y^2 = 4z$.

The planes parallel to the $xy$-plane are given by equations of the form $z = c$. The trace in such a plane has the equations

$$z = c, \quad x^2 + y^2 = 4c.$$

The trace is thus a circle with center on the $z$-axis and radius $2\sqrt{c}$ if $c > 0$; it is a point circle if $c = 0$, and there is no intersection if $c < 0$.

The traces parallel to the $xz$-plane are found by putting $y = c$ into the given equation. We have

$$y = c, \quad x^2 + c^2 = 4z.$$

This equation may be rewritten in the form

$$x^2 = 4(z - c^2/4),$$

showing that it is the equation of a parabola opening in the positive $z$-direction and with its vertex at $(0, c, c^2/4)$.

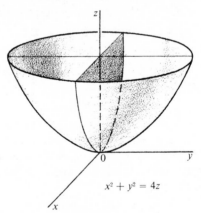

$$x^2 + y^2 = 4z$$

**FIGURE 17.1a**

The student should check to see that the traces parallel to the $yz$-plane are also parabolas exactly like those just obtained. A sketch of the surface appears in Figure 17.1a.

*Example 17.1b.* Sketch the first octant portion of the surface $xyz = 8$.

The trace of this surface in the plane $x = c$ is

$$x = c, \quad yz = 8/c, \quad c \neq 0.$$

his curve is a rectangular hyperbola with its asymptotes parallel to the $y$- and $z$-axes
see Figure 17.1b). The symmetry of the equation with respect to the variables $x$, $y$, $z$
nakes it unnecessary to discuss the traces in any other of the planes parallel to the
coordinate planes.

---

**Definition 17.1a.** The set of points each of which is at distance $a$ from a given
point $C(x_0, y_0, z_0)$ constitutes a surface called a *sphere*. The point $C$ is the
*center*, and the distance $a$ is the *radius* of the sphere (Figure 17.1c).

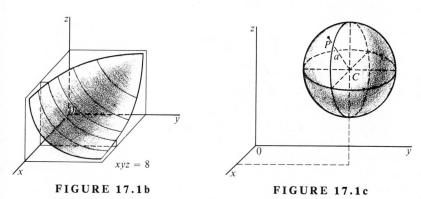

**FIGURE 17.1b**          **FIGURE 17.1c**

The distance formula immediately yields

$$(x - x_0)^2 + (y - y_0)^2 + (z - z_0)^2 = a^2$$

s the equation of the sphere. One particularly simple case occurs when the
center is at the origin; then the equation is

$$x^2 + y^2 + z^2 = a^2.$$

the binomials in Equation (1) are expanded and the terms collected, we obtain
n equation of the form

$$x^2 + y^2 + z^2 + Dx + Ey + Fz + G = 0.$$

onversely, if an equation of this type is given, it can always be put into the
orm of (1) by completing the squares in $x$, $y$, and $z$. The student should verify
that in the final equation

$$a^2 = \tfrac{1}{4}(D^2 + E^2 + F^2) - G.$$

$a^2 > 0$, the equation is that of a sphere of radius $a$; if $a^2 = 0$, the only real
oint that satisfies the equation is the center, and the surface is the degenerate
ne called a **point sphere**; if $a^2 < 0$, no real points satisfy the equation.

*Example 17.1c.* Find the center and radius of the sphere

$$4(x^2 + y^2 + z^2) + 8x - 12y + 10z - 1 = 0.$$

We divide both sides of the equation by 4 and complete the squares to get

$$(x^2 + 2x + 1) + (y^2 - 3y + \tfrac{9}{4}) + (z^2 + \tfrac{5}{2}z + \tfrac{25}{16}) = \tfrac{1}{4} + 1 + \tfrac{9}{4} + \tfrac{25}{16},$$

or

$$(x + 1)^2 + (y - \tfrac{3}{2})^2 + (z + \tfrac{5}{4})^2 = \tfrac{81}{16}.$$

From this equation, we read off the coordinates of the center $(-1, \tfrac{3}{2}, \tfrac{5}{4})$ and the radius $\tfrac{9}{4}$.

## Exercises 17.1

In each of Numbers 1 to 4, find the center and radius of the given sphere.

1. $x^2 + y^2 + z^2 + 4x + 6y = 3$.
2. $4x^2 + 4y^2 + 4z^2 - 4x - 12z = 15$.
3. $2x^2 + 2y^2 + 2z^2 + 4x - 8y - 16z + 41 = 0$.
4. $x^2 + y^2 + z^2 + 3x - 2y + z = 0$.

5. Show that a sphere is described by the equation $\mathbf{r} \cdot (\mathbf{r} - 2\mathbf{a}) = 0$, where $\mathbf{r}$ is the usual position vector from the origin and $\mathbf{a}$ is a vector from the origin to the point $(a_1, a_2, a_3)$. Find the center and radius of the sphere.
6. Find the equation of the plane that is tangent to the sphere $x^2 + y^2 + z^2 = 9$ a the point $(2, -1, 2)$.
7. Find the equation of the plane that is tangent to the sphere

$$x^2 + y^2 + z^2 - 2x + 2y - 4z = 3$$

at the point $(2, 1, 4)$.
8. Write symmetric equations for the radius that is perpendicular to the tangent plane in Number 7.
9. Show that the set of points each of which is twice as far from $(2, 2, 0)$ as from the origin is a sphere. Find the center and radius of this sphere.
10. Does the plane $x + 2y + 2z = 12$ cut the sphere $x^2 + y^2 + z^2 = 16$ in a circle in one point, or not at all?
11. Show that the spheres $x^2 + y^2 + z^2 - 2x + 2y - 4z = 3$ and

$$x^2 + y^2 + z^2 + 6x - 4y + 2z + 6\sqrt{34} = 29$$

are tangent to each other.

For each of the following surfaces discuss the traces in planes parallel to the coordinate planes and sketch the surface:

12. $y^2 + z^2 = -4x$.
13. $z = \ln x + \ln y$.
14. $z = \sin x$.
15. $z = xy$.

16. $z^2 = x^2 + 2xy + y^2$.
17. $x = 2z^2$.
18. $z = e^{-y^2}$.
19. $z = e^{-(x^2+y^2)}$.

## 17.2 CYLINDERS AND SURFACES OF REVOLUTION

In his previous experience in mathematics, the reader may have formed a rather restricted concept of the kind of surface that is termed *cylindrical*. He has probably been accustomed to visualizing such a surface to be that of a right circular cylinder. We shall now consider a more general type of cylindrical surface.

**Definition 17.2a.** A **cylinder** is a surface that is formed by the set of all straight lines that intersect a given plane curve $C$ and are parallel to a fixed line not in the plane of the curve. The curve $C$ is called a **directrix,** and each one of the set of lines is called an **element** of the cylinder.

For example, the set of all straight lines that intersect the parabola $y^2 = 4x$ in the $xy$-plane and are parallel to the $z$-axis constitutes a cylindrical surface called a **parabolic cylinder** (Figure 17.2a). The parabola is the directrix of the cylinder.

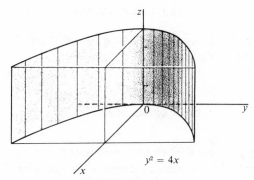

$$y^2 = 4x$$

**FIGURE 17.2a**

The analytic description of a cylinder can be given most simply by choosing the directrix curve in one of the coordinate planes and by taking the elements parallel to the coordinate axis that is perpendicular to this plane. This procedure will lead to an equation involving only two of $x$, $y$, $z$. There is actually no loss in generality here, since for a given cylinder, the directrix may be taken to be the trace of the surface in a plane perpendicular to the elements of the cylinder. Conversely, the geometric representation in three dimensions of an equation that involves only two of the variables $x$, $y$, $z$ is generally a cylindrical surface perpendicular to the plane of those two variables. For instance, an equation of the form $F(y, z) = 0$ describes a cylindrical surface perpendicular to the $yz$-plane, because the traces of the surface in the planes $x = c$, parallel to the $yz$-plane, are all curves with the same equation, $F(y, z) = 0$. Each element of the cylinder is a line given by the equations $y = y_1$, $z = z_1$, where $F(y_1, z_1) = 0$.

One of the simplest cylindrical surfaces is the familiar right circular cylinder such as that given by the equation

$$x^2 + y^2 = a^2.$$

The trace of this surface in each plane parallel to the $xy$-plane is a circle o
radius $a$ with its center on the $z$-axis (Figure 17.2b). We may regard this cylinde

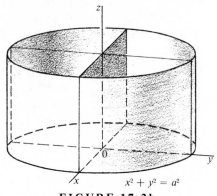

$$x^2 + y^2 = a^2$$

**FIGURE 17.2b**

as being formed by revolving the line $y = a$, $x = 0$ about the $z$-axis so that th
line remains always at distance $a$ from the $z$-axis.

We consider next another simple kind of surface, described as follows.

**Definition 17.2b.** A surface that is formed by revolving a given plane curve abou
an axis in its plane is called a **surface of revolution.** The curve is said to **gener**
**ate** the surface.

It thus appears that the right circular cylinder is an example of a surface o
revolution in which the generating curve is a straight line. We shall conside
here only the special cases in which the generating curve is given in one of th
coordinate planes and the axis of revolution is one of the coordinate axes i
the same plane.

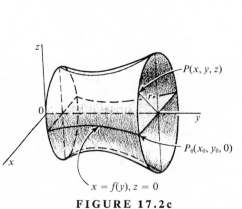

$$x = f(y), z = 0$$

**FIGURE 17.2c**

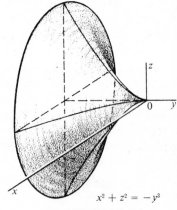

$$x^2 + z^2 = -y^3$$

**FIGURE 17.2d**

Let it be required to find the equation of the surface generated by revolving a curve $x = f(y)$ in the $xy$-plane about the $y$-axis (Figure 17.2c). Suppose $P_0(x_0, y_0, 0)$ is a point on the curve that rotates into the point $P(x, y, z)$ on the surface. Then $P$ is in the plane that passes through $P_0$ and is perpendicular to the $y$-axis. From the geometry of the figure, it follows that

$$r^2 = x^2 + z^2, \quad r = x_0, \quad y = y_0.$$

Since $x_0 = f(y_0)$, we have

$$x_0^2 = [f(y_0)]^2,$$

and, by substitution, we get the required equation:

$$x^2 + z^2 = [f(y)]^2.$$

It is left for the reader to show in a similar fashion that the equation

$$y^2 + z^2 = [g(x)]^2$$

describes the surface generated by revolving the curve

$$y = g(x), \quad z = 0$$

about the $x$-axis. What would be the equation of the surface generated by revolving the curve

$$x = h(z), \quad y = 0$$

about the $z$-axis?

In order that a surface be one of revolution about a coordinate axis, the traces of the surface in planes perpendicular to this axis must be circles with centers on the axis, and conversely. For example, if the equation is of the form

$$f(x^2 + y^2, z) = 0,$$

that is, if $x$ and $y$ occur only in the combination $x^2 + y^2$, we may immediately conclude that the surface is one of revolution about the $z$-axis.

---

*Example 17.2a.* Sketch the surface $x^2 + z^2 = -y^3$.

The trace of this surface in the plane $y = c$ is a circle with its center on the $y$-axis for $c < 0$ and a point circle for $c = 0$; there are no points of the surface for $c > 0$. Consequently, the surface is one of revolution about the $y$-axis. This surface can be generated by revolving the curve

$$x^2 = -y^3, \quad z = 0$$

about the $y$-axis. The sketch appears in Figure 17.2d.

---

*Example 17.2b.* Find the equation of the surface generated by revolving the curve

$$x^2 + 2y = 0, \quad z = 0$$

about the $x$-axis.

Since the surface must have an equation of the form $F(x, y^2 + z^2) = 0$ (why?), we must replace $y$ by $-\sqrt{y^2 + z^2}$ in the given equation to get the desired equation:

$$x^2 - 2\sqrt{y^2 + z^2} = 0.$$

## Exercises 17.2

For each of Numbers 1 to 12, sketch the surface described by the given equation.

1. $y^2 + z^2 = 4$.
2. $y^2 - z^2 = 4$.
3. $x^2 = z + 2$.
4. $x^2 = 4y$.
5. $y = e^{-z^2}$.
6. $z^2 = 4(1 - y)$.

7. $x^2 + y^2 = 4z$.
8. $x^2 + y^2 = 4z^2$.
9. $y^2 + z^2 + 4x = 0$.
10. $y^2 - 2\sqrt{x^2 + z^2} = 0$.
11. $x^2 + z^2 = -2y$.
12. $x^2 + z^2 = y^2$.

In each of Numbers 13 to 18, find the equation of the surface that is generated by revolving the given curve about the designated coordinate axis. Sketch each surface.

13. $y = x^2$, $z = 0$; $y$-axis.
14. $x = 0$, $y = 3$; $z$-axis.
15. $x^2 + z^2 = 16$, $y = 0$; $x$-axis.

16. $y = 2x$, $z = 0$; $x$-axis.
17. $9z^2 + 4y^2 = 36$, $x = 0$; $y$-axis.
18. $y^2 - z^2 = 1$, $x = 0$; $z$-axis.

★19. The quadratic polynomial $2xy + 2yz$ may be represented in matrix form by

$$[x \quad y \quad z] \begin{bmatrix} 0 & 1 & 0 \\ 1 & 0 & 1 \\ 0 & 1 & 0 \end{bmatrix} \begin{bmatrix} x \\ y \\ z \end{bmatrix}.$$

Diagonalize this matrix and use the result to show that the equation

$$2xy + 2yz = 9\sqrt{2}$$

describes a hyperbolic cylinder.

★20. Use the method of Number 19 to show that the equation

$$(x + y + z)^2 = 4y$$

describes a parabolic cylinder.

★21. Use the method of Number 19 to show that the equation

$$9x^2 - 7y^2 + 7z^2 + 8\sqrt{2}yz = 0$$

describes a right circular cone.

## 17.3 QUADRIC SURFACES

We learned in Section 16.3 that a quadratic equation in two variables, $x$ and $y$, always represents a conic section—an ellipse, a hyperbola, a parabola, or one of the degenerate forms consisting of two straight lines, a point, or no real points at all. Similarly, a quadratic equation in $x$, $y$, $z$ always represents in $\mathcal{U}_3$ one of the surfaces known as a **quadric surface.** Certain standard forms appear in the following illustrations, where the axes have been chosen in such a manner that the equations appear in as simple a form as possible. The student's visualization of each surface will be greatly aided if he forms a clear mental image of the traces in planes parallel to the coordinate planes.

(1) *The ellipsoid:*

$$\frac{x^2}{a^2} + \frac{y^2}{b^2} + \frac{z^2}{c^2} = 1.$$

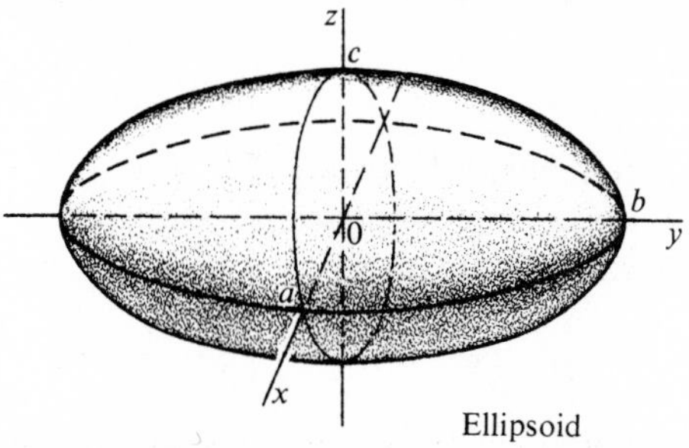

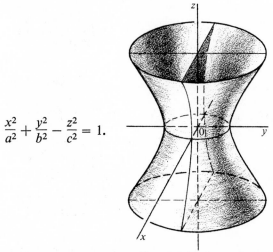

Ellipsoid

**FIGURE 17.3a**

The traces in the planes $z = k$ are the ellipses

$$\frac{x^2}{a^2} + \frac{y^2}{b^2} = 1 - \frac{k^2}{c^2}.$$

These will be real as long as $|k| \leqq c$, and imaginary when $|k| > c$. The surface may be regarded as generated by a variable ellipse that moves parallel to the $xy$-plane. The ends of one axis of the variable ellipse are always on the ellipse

$$\frac{x^2}{a^2} + \frac{z^2}{c^2} = 1, \quad y = 0,$$

and the ends of the other axis are on the ellipse

$$\frac{y^2}{b^2} + \frac{z^2}{c^2} = 1, \quad x = 0.$$

The reader should note that the traces in planes parallel to either the $xz$-plane or the $yz$-plane are also ellipses (see Figure 17.3a).

(2) *The hyperboloid of one sheet:*

$$\frac{x^2}{a^2} + \frac{y^2}{b^2} - \frac{z^2}{c^2} = 1.$$

Hyperboloid of one sheet

**FIGURE 17.3b**

The traces in the planes $z = k$ are the ellipses

$$\frac{x^2}{a^2} + \frac{y^2}{b^2} = 1 + \frac{k^2}{c^2}.$$

These are real for all values of $k$. The smallest of the ellipses occurs for $k = 0$, the axes becoming longer as $|k|$ increases.

The traces in the planes $y = k$ are the hyperbolas

$$\frac{x^2}{a^2} - \frac{z^2}{c^2} = 1 - \frac{k^2}{b^2}.$$

These hyperbolas have transverse axes in the $x$-direction for $|k| < b$ and in the $z$-direction for $|k| > b$. (Why?) For $|k| = b$, the hyperbola degenerates into the pair of straight lines

$$\frac{x}{a} - \frac{z}{c} = 0 \quad \text{and} \quad \frac{x}{a} + \frac{z}{c} = 0.$$

The reader should describe the traces in the planes $x = k$. This surface may be visualized as being generated by a variable ellipse moving parallel to the $xy$-plane (see Figure 17.3b). The ends of one axis of the ellipse are always on the hyperbola

$$\frac{x^2}{a^2} - \frac{z^2}{c^2} = 1, \quad y = 0,$$

and the ends of the other axis are on the hyperbola

$$\frac{y^2}{b^2} - \frac{z^2}{c^2} = 1, \quad x = 0.$$

(3) *The hyperboloid of two sheets:*

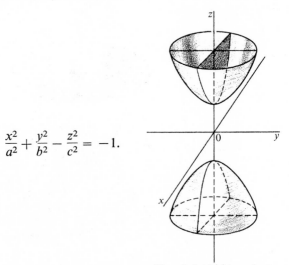

$$\frac{x^2}{a^2} + \frac{y^2}{b^2} - \frac{z^2}{c^2} = -1.$$

Hyperboloid of two sheets

**FIGURE 17.3c**

he traces in the planes $z = k$ are the ellipses

$$\frac{x^2}{a^2} + \frac{y^2}{b^2} = \frac{k^2}{c^2} - 1.$$

hese traces are imaginary unless $|k| > c$, showing that the surface does not
xtend between the planes $z = -c$ and $z = c$. An ellipse is obtained for each
alue of $k$, where $|k| > c$, and the larger the value of $|k|$, the larger is the ellipse.
s $k \to \pm c$, the ellipses shrink to points (see Figure 17.3c).

The traces in the planes $y = k$ are the hyperbolas

$$\frac{z^2}{c^2} - \frac{x^2}{a^2} = 1 + \frac{k^2}{b^2}.$$

hese all have transverse axes extending in the $z$-direction. Similarly, the traces
the planes $x = k$ are the hyperbolas

$$\frac{z^2}{c^2} - \frac{y^2}{b^2} = 1 + \frac{k^2}{a^2},$$

hich also have their transverse axes in the $z$-direction. The reader should
escribe how this surface could be generated by a moving variable ellipse.

(4) *The elliptic paraboloid:*

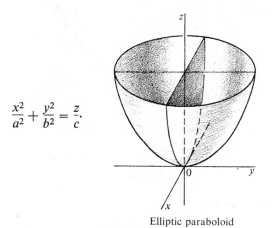

$$\frac{x^2}{a^2} + \frac{y^2}{b^2} = \frac{z}{c}.$$

Elliptic paraboloid

**FIGURE 17.3d**

gure 17.3d is drawn for $c > 0$. The reader may verify that the traces in the
anes $z = k > 0$ are ellipses, as indicated in the figure. The traces in planes
rallel to the $xz$-plane or to the $yz$-plane are parabolas. If $a = b$, the surface
a paraboloid of revolution.

(5) *The hyperbolic paraboloid:*

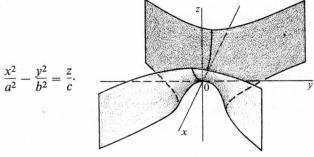

$$\frac{x^2}{a^2} - \frac{y^2}{b^2} = \frac{z}{c}.$$

Hyperbolic paraboloid

**FIGURE 17.3e**

Figure 17.3e is drawn for $c > 0$. Discussion of the traces is again left for the reader.

(6) *The quadric cone:*

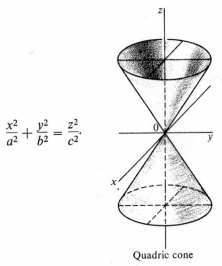

$$\frac{x^2}{a^2} + \frac{y^2}{b^2} = \frac{z^2}{c^2}.$$

Quadric cone

**FIGURE 17.3f**

(7) *The quadric cylinders:*

$$\frac{x^2}{a^2} + \frac{y^2}{b^2} = 1,$$

$$\frac{x^2}{a^2} - \frac{y^2}{b^2} = 1,$$

$$y^2 = 4ax.$$

These are all cylindrical surfaces perpendicular to the $xy$-plane. Construction of the surfaces is left as an exercise.

(8) *The degenerate quadric surfaces* include two planes, a line, a point, and even the cases in which the equation is satisfied by no real points. Examples of some of these have already been given in Section 17.1. The only requirement for an equation to describe a quadric surface or a degenerate quadric surface is that it be a polynomial equation of the second degree.

## Exercises 17.3

In Numbers 1 to 20, identify each of the surfaces, and sketch the surface if it is real.

1. $36x^2 + 9y^2 - 4z^2 = 36$.
2. $4x^2 + y^2 + z^2 = 4$.
3. $4y^2 - x^2 - 16z^2 = 16$.
4. $x^2 + y^2 = z^2$.
5. $x^2 + y^2 + z^2 = 36$.
6. $z^2 - 4y^2 = 0$.
7. $z^2 - 4y^2 = 4x$.
8. $x^2 + 4y^2 + 4z^2 = 0$.
9. $9y^2 + z^2 - x^2 = 0$.
10. $4x^2 + y^2 + z^2 + 4 = 0$.

11. $y^2 + z^2 = 16$.
12. $y^2 - 9x^2 = 9z$.
13. $9x^2 + 4y^2 = 36z$.
14. $16y^2 + 4z^2 - x^2 = 16$.
15. $9x^2 + z^2 = 9y$.
16. $4x^2 + z^2 = 9$.
17. $4x^2 - z^2 = 9$.
18. $9x^2 + 36y^2 + 4z^2 = 36$.
19. $4x^2 + 4y^2 + 4z^2 = 9$.
20. $z^2 - x^2 - 9y^2 = 9$.

1. Let $\mathbf{a}$ be the position vector to the fixed point $(a_1, a_2, a_3)$ in three-dimensional space, $\mathcal{U}_3$, and let $\mathbf{r}$ be a position vector to an arbitrary point $(x, y, z)$. Describe in words and sketch each of the following sets of points:

   (a) $\mathbf{r} \cdot \mathbf{a} = 0$;
   (b) $\mathbf{r} \cdot \mathbf{a} = \mathbf{r} \cdot \mathbf{r}$;
   (c) $|\mathbf{r} \times \mathbf{a}| = |\mathbf{a}|$;
   (d) $\mathbf{r} \cdot \mathbf{a} = \frac{1}{2}|\mathbf{r} \times \mathbf{a}|$.

2. Suppose $(x_0, y_0, 0)$ is a point on the surface

$$x^2 + \frac{y^2}{4} - \frac{z^2}{9} = 1.$$

   (a) Show that

$$\mathbf{r} = (x_0 + y_0 t)\mathbf{i} + (y_0 + 4x_0 t)\mathbf{j} + 6t\mathbf{k}$$

   describes a straight line that lies on the surface and passes through $(x_0, y_0, 0)$.
   (b) Let $(x, y, z)$ be any point on the surface. Show that a point $P(x_0, y_0, 0)$ and a value of $t$ can always be found such that the line described in (a) passes through $(x, y, z)$.

3. For a fixed value of $t$, say $t_0$, show that the points belonging to

$$S\left[\frac{x}{a} + \frac{z}{c} = t\left(1 + \frac{y}{b}\right)\right] \cap S\left[\frac{x}{a} - \frac{z}{c} = \frac{1}{t}\left(1 - \frac{y}{b}\right)\right]$$

   lie on a hyperboloid of one sheet. Show also that the two equations represent planes whose line of intersection is on the hyperboloid.

4. The vertex of a right circular cone is located at $(h, 0, 0)$; its axis is parallel to the vector $\mathbf{i} + \mathbf{j} + \mathbf{k}$, and its elements make an angle of $30°$ with its axis. Find its equation.

25. Show that if a liquid is rotated about a vertical axis, then its surface is a paraboloid of revolution. Assume that the angular speed $\omega$ is constant, and use the fact that the resultant of the gravitational and centrifugal forces acting on a particle on the surface is normal to the surface. *Hint:* The centrifugal force is $mgr\omega^2$ for a particle of mass $m$ at a distance $r$ from the axis.

## 17.4 CURVES IN THREE-DIMENSIONAL SPACE, $\mathcal{V}_3$

In two dimensions, a curve is a set of points that is generally associated with a continuous function. For example, an equation $y = f(x)$, where $f$ is a continuous function, describes a curve. In particular, if $y = mx + p$, the corresponding curve is a straight line. A straight line has also been described by parametric equations, $x = at + b$, $y = ct + d$, where the variable $t$ is called a parameter. In these equations, $x$ and $y$ exhibit a symmetry of form that is often useful in some types of problems.

We have used the parametric form to represent other curves in two dimensional space. Consider the two continuous functions $f$ and $g$ defined on a common domain, where

(1) $$x = f(t), \quad y = g(t)$$

such that one, say $f$, has an inverse. If $t = f^{-1}(x)$, then the composite function $y = g[f^{-1}(x)]$ describes a curve. Equations (1) are called parametric equations of this curve. For example, if

$$x = t, \quad y = \sqrt{a^2 - t^2},$$

then these are parametric equations of the curve described by

$$y = \sqrt{a^2 - x^2}.$$

It is clear that the parametric equations of a curve are not unique. The equations

$$x = a \cos \theta, \quad y = a \sin \theta, \quad 0 \leq \theta \leq \pi, \quad a > 0,$$

also represent the curve described by $y = \sqrt{a^2 - x^2}$. A set of parametric equations for a curve $y = f(x)$ can always be obtained by letting $x = t$, so that $y = f(t)$, although this form is not always the most desirable in some problems.

The preceding ideas on parametric equations are easily extended to three dimensions, where they are especially useful in certain types of problems.

$$x = f(t), \quad y = g(t), \quad z = h(t), \quad a \leq t \leq b,$$

where $f$, $g$, and $h$ are continuous functions on a common domain and $f$ has an inverse, then the set of points

$$\{(x, y, z): x = f(t), \quad y = g(t), \quad z = h(t), \quad a \leq t \leq b\}$$

is called a **curve in three-dimensional space**. If $t = f^{-1}(x)$, then the equations

$$y = g[f^{-1}(x)], \quad z = h[f^{-1}(x)]$$

must describe the same curve. Each of these equations may be considered separately as the equation of a cylinder. Hence, the curve is specified geometrically as the intersection of these two cylinders.

In more general terms, a curve in three-dimensional space, $\mathcal{V}_3$, is given as the intersection of two surfaces each of which is described by an equation of the form $F(x, y, z) = 0$; that is, two distinct equations of this form are required to describe a curve. Moreover, since any number of surfaces may be passed through a given curve, the representation of the curve by means of equations representing surfaces is not unique. The equations of *any* two distinct surfaces passing through the curve may be used to represent the curve. For example, the intersection of the plane $z = 0$ with the sphere $x^2 + y^2 + z^2 = a^2$ is the same as the intersection of the plane with the cylinder $x^2 + y^2 = a^2$.

When the equations of a curve are given in the form

$$F(x, y, z) = 0, \quad G(x, y, z) = 0,$$

it is sometimes possible to combine the equations into a single equation in which one of the variables is missing. As was shown earlier, such an equation represents a cylinder that is perpendicular to one of the coordinate planes. Since the cylinder must pass through the given curve, it is called a **projecting cylinder** of the curve. Generally, projecting cylinders can be used to simplify the sketching of a curve. The next example illustrates the procedure.

---

*Example 17.4a.* Sketch the first octant portion of the curve of intersection of

$$x^2 + y^2 = 2x \quad \text{and} \quad x^2 + y^2 + z^2 = 4.$$

Since the first equation describes a cylinder perpendicular to the $xy$-coordinate plane, it is one of the projecting cylinders of the curve. Another projecting cylinder can be found by eliminating $y$ between the two equations. By subtracting corresponding members, we get

$$z^2 = 4 - 2x,$$

which is the equation of a parabolic cylinder perpendicular to the $xz$-plane. Since the elements of both cylinders are perpendicular to the $x$-axis, each point on the required curve is an intersection of the traces of the two cylinders in a plane perpendicular to the $x$-axis. In Figure 17.4a, the point $P$ is located as follows: Choose a point $R$ on the

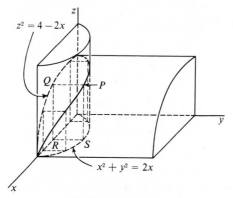

**FIGURE 17.4a**

*x*-axis. Draw a line parallel to the *z*-axis from *R* to the point *Q* on the parabola $z^2 = 4 - 2x$ in the *xz*-plane. Draw a second line parallel to the *y*-axis from *R* to the point *S* on the circle $x^2 + y^2 = 2x$ in the *xy*-plane. Complete the parallelogram on *QRS*. The vertex diagonally opposite *R* is the required point *P*. This construction can be repeated for as many points as desired.

The next example illustrates the sketching of a curve whose equations are given in parametric form.

*Example 17.4b.* Sketch the curve

$$x = a \cos t, \quad y = a \cos 2t, \quad z = a \sin t, \quad a > 0, \quad \text{for} \quad 0 \leqq t \leqq \pi/2.$$

Here it is probably simplest to obtain equations of the curve of the form $F(x, y, z) = 0$ and $G(x, y, z) = 0$ rather than to work directly with the parametric form, since the best we can do with the parametric form is to determine points for different values of *t*. However, we can get at once

$$x^2 + z^2 = a^2,$$

and since

$$\cos 2t = 1 - 2 \sin^2 t,$$

we have

$$y = a(1 - 2 \sin^2 t)$$
$$= a[1 - 2(z/a)^2],$$

or

$$z^2 = \frac{a}{2}(a - y), \quad -a \leqq y \leqq a.$$

Consequently, the curve is the intersection of the two cylinders

$$x^2 + z^2 = a^2 \quad \text{and} \quad z^2 = \frac{a}{2}(a - y), \quad -a \leqq y \leqq a.$$

The procedure illustrated in the preceding example may now be used to obtain a sketch of the curve, which is shown in Figure 17.4b. Notice that the curve is not defined

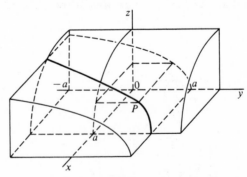

**FIGURE 17.4b**

for $|x| > a$, $|y| > a$, or $|z| > a$, even though the surfaces extend beyond these values. Why?

## Exercises 17.4

Sketch the first-octant portion of each of the curves in Numbers 1 to 13.

1. $x^2 + y^2 = 0$, $x = z$.
2. $x^2 + y^2 = 2z$, $x^2 + y^2 + z^2 = 8$.
3. $x^2 + y^2 + z^2 = 4$, $x^2 + y^2 = 1$.
4. $x^2 + y^2 + z^2 = 4$, $x^2 + z^2 = 4x$.
5. $x^2 + z^2 = 4$, $y^2 + z^2 = 4$.

6. $x^2 = 4y$, $y^2 = 4z$.
7. $y^2 - x^2 = 4$, $x = z$.
8. $x + 2y + z = 6$, $x^2 + y^2 = 1$.
9. $x = t$, $y = t^2$, $z = t^3$.
10. $x = 4 - t^2$, $y = t$, $z = t^3$.

11. $x = 2 \cos t$, $y = 2 \sin t$, $z = 3t$, $0 \leq t \leq \pi/2$.
12. $x = 2 \sin t$, $y = 4 \sin t$, $z = 4 \cos t$.
13. $x = e^{-t}$, $y = t$, $z = e^t$.
14. Find vectorially the equations of the circle through the points
$$(1, 0, 2), \quad (2, 1, 3), \quad (-1, -1, 1).$$
15. A curve of the form
$$x = a \sin \omega t, \quad y = a \cos \omega t, \quad z = bt$$
is called a **helix**. Can this curve be described as the intersection of two surfaces? Explain.
16. Show that the curve
$$x = 4 \cos t, \quad y = 4 \sin t, \quad z = 4 \cos t$$
is an ellipse, and find an equation for the plane in which the ellipse lies.

## *17.5 TRANSFORMATIONS IN THREE-DIMENSIONAL SPACE

Equations of the form
$$ax^2 + by^2 + cx + dy + e = 0$$
can be transformed into the form
$$au^2 + bv^2 = f$$
by translating coordinates. This same process can be used to simplify similar forms in three dimensions.

---

*Example 17.5a.* Simplify the equation
$$4x^2 + 9y^2 - z^2 + 8x - 36y + 2z = -3$$
by means of a translation of coordinates, and identify the surface that it represents.

Upon completing the squares on $x$, $y$, and $z$, we get
$$4(x + 1)^2 + 9(y - 2)^2 - (z - 1)^2 = 36.$$

The surface is clearly an elliptic hyperboloid of one sheet, and we may write the equation in the form
$$4u^2 + 9v^2 - w^2 = 36,$$

where the new origin of coordinates is at the point $(-1, 2, 1)$ and the equations

$$u = x + 1, \quad v = y - 2, \quad w = z - 1$$

are the translation equations.

---

The technique of finding a rotation of coordinates in two dimensions that permits the transformation of a quadratic form

$$ax^2 + 2bxy + cy^2$$

into the form

$$\lambda_1 u^2 + \lambda_2 v^2$$

can be used to simplify quadratic forms in three variables. The procedure to be followed is exactly the same as for quadratic forms in two variables.

---

*Example 17.5b.* Determine a rotation of coordinates that will simplify the quadratic form

$$p(x, y, z) = 2x^2 - 4y^2 + 2z^2 - 2xy - 5xz - 2yz,$$

and then identify the surface $p(x, y, z) = 18$.

The expression

$$\begin{aligned}
p(x, y, z) = 2x^2 &- xy - \tfrac{5}{2}xz \\
&- xy - 4y^2 - yz \\
&- \tfrac{5}{2}xz - yz + 2z^2
\end{aligned}$$

has the matrix form

$$X^\mathsf{T} A X = [x \quad y \quad z] \begin{bmatrix} 2 & -1 & -\tfrac{5}{2} \\ -1 & 4 & -1 \\ -\tfrac{5}{2} & -1 & 2 \end{bmatrix} \begin{bmatrix} x \\ y \\ z \end{bmatrix}.$$

The problem is therefore one of finding a transformation $T$ such that $X = TU$ and $T^\mathsf{T} A T$ is a diagonal matrix.

Hence, we first find the eigenvalues of $A$. We have

$$\det (A - \lambda I) = \begin{vmatrix} 2 - \lambda & -1 & -\tfrac{5}{2} \\ -1 & -4 - \lambda & -1 \\ -\tfrac{5}{2} & -1 & 2 - \lambda \end{vmatrix}$$

$$= \frac{81}{4} \lambda - \lambda^3.$$

The zeros of this polynomial are 0 and $\pm\tfrac{9}{2}$, and these are the eigenvalues of the matrix. Now the eigenvectors must be found. For the eigenvalue $\tfrac{9}{2}$ we solve

$$\begin{bmatrix} 2 - \tfrac{9}{2} & -1 & -\tfrac{5}{2} \\ -1 & -4 - \tfrac{9}{2} & -1 \\ -\tfrac{5}{2} & -1 & 2 - \tfrac{9}{2} \end{bmatrix} \begin{bmatrix} x \\ y \\ z \end{bmatrix} = 0,$$

or

$$\begin{aligned}
-\tfrac{5}{2}x - \quad y - \tfrac{5}{2}z &= 0, \\
-x - \tfrac{17}{2}y - \quad z &= 0, \\
-\tfrac{5}{2}x - \quad y - \tfrac{5}{2}z &= 0.
\end{aligned}$$

A solution of this system is $x = 1, y = 0, z = -1$. Hence a normalized eigenvector associated with the eigenvalue $\tfrac{9}{2}$ is

$$T_1 = [1/\sqrt{2} \quad 0 \quad -1/\sqrt{2}]^\mathsf{T}.$$

By a similar process an eigenvector associated with the eigenvalue $-\frac{9}{2}$ is found to be $[1 \quad 4 \quad 1]^\mathsf{T}$. The normalized eigenvector is $T_2 = [\frac{1}{6}\sqrt{2} \quad \frac{2}{3}\sqrt{2} \quad \frac{1}{6}\sqrt{2}]^\mathsf{T}$. Corresponding to the eigenvalue 0 is the normalized eigenvector $T_3 = [\frac{2}{3} \quad -\frac{1}{3} \quad \frac{2}{3}]^\mathsf{T}$. A transformation matrix $T$ representing a rotation of coordinates is constructed from the eigenvectors by letting

$$T = [T_1 \quad T_2 \quad T_3] = \begin{bmatrix} \dfrac{1}{\sqrt{2}} & \dfrac{1}{3\sqrt{2}} & \dfrac{2}{3} \\ 0 & \dfrac{4}{3\sqrt{2}} & -\dfrac{1}{3} \\ -\dfrac{1}{\sqrt{2}} & \dfrac{1}{3\sqrt{2}} & \dfrac{2}{3} \end{bmatrix}.$$

A check shows that $T$ is indeed an orthonormal matrix.

From the discussion in Section 16.4, we know that

$$T^\mathsf{T}AT = \begin{bmatrix} \frac{9}{2} & 0 & 0 \\ 0 & -\frac{9}{2} & 0 \\ 0 & 0 & 0 \end{bmatrix}.$$

Therefore,

$$p(x, y, z) = X^\mathsf{T}AX = U^\mathsf{T}(T^\mathsf{T}AT)U = q(u, v, w),$$

or

$$q(u, v, w) = [u \quad v \quad w] \begin{bmatrix} \frac{9}{2} & 0 & 0 \\ 0 & -\frac{9}{2} & 0 \\ 0 & 0 & 0 \end{bmatrix} \begin{bmatrix} u \\ v \\ w \end{bmatrix}$$

$$= \tfrac{9}{2}u^2 - \tfrac{9}{2}v^2$$
$$= \tfrac{9}{2}(u^2 - v^2).$$

It follows that the equation of the surface, $p(x, y, z) = 18$, is reduced to $q(u, v, w) = 18$, or

$$u^2 - v^2 = 4.$$

This shows that the surface is a hyperbolic cylinder with elements parallel to the $w$-axis.

## Exercises 17.5

In each of Numbers 1 to 4, identify the surface, and simplify the form of the equation by means of a translation.

1. $x^2 + 4y^2 + 2z^2 - 2x - 4y + 4z = 12$.
2. $4x^2 - y^2 + 9z^2 - 6x + 12y + 36z = 0$.
3. $x^2 + y^2 - z^2 - x + y + z = 0$.
4. $4x^2 + y^2 - 4x + 2y - 2z = 12$.

In each of Numbers 5 to 10, find a rotation that will eliminate the product terms, and identify the surface represented by the equation.

5. $9x^2 + y^2 + z^2 - 6xy + 6xz - 2yz = 44$.
6. $x^2 + y^2 - 2z^2 - 2xy - 4xz - 4yz = 4$.
7. $5x^2 + 5y^2 + 8z^2 - 8xy - 4xz - 4yz = 36$.

8. $5x^2 + 2y^2 + 2z^2 - 4xy = 0.$
9. $x^2 - y^2 - z^2 - 2yz = 0.$
10. $xy + yz - xz = 1.$

In each of Numbers 11 to 13, find a rotation and then a translation to simplify the equation.

11. $x^2 + y^2 - 2z^2 - 2xy - 4xz - 4yz + 4x + 4y - 4z = 10.$
12. $x^2 - z^2 - 4xy - 4yz + 6x - 6y = 27.$
13. $\sqrt{2}xy - \sqrt{2}yz + 2x - 2\sqrt{2}y - 2z = 8.$

---

# Summary of Chapter 17

---

This chapter deals primarily with the techniques of visualizing and sketching surfaces and curves in three dimensions. In addition to being able to make a reasonably clear sketch of a curve or surface in three dimensions the student should have a clear understanding of the following ideas:

    (1) the trace of a surface in a plane (Section 17.1);
    (2) the form of an equation of a sphere (Section 17.1);
    (3) the form of an equation of a cylinder with its elements parallel to one of the coordinate axes (Section 17.2);
    (4) surfaces of revolution (Section 17.2);
    (5) quadric surfaces and their degenerate cases (Section 17.3);
    (6) parametric representation of a curve in space (Section 17.4);
    (7) a curve as the intersection of two surfaces (Section 17.4);
    ★(8) the simplification of a quadratic form in three variables by a rotation of coordinates using matrices (Section 17.5).

# Chapter 18     Vector Functions and Applications

## 18.1 VECTOR FUNCTIONS

We have seen that three equations of the form

$$x = f(t), \quad y = g(t), \quad z = h(t),$$

where $f$, $g$, $h$ are functions with a common domain, may be regarded as the parametric equations of a graph in three-dimensional space, and that each value of $t$ in the domain determines a point $(x, y, z)$ on the graph. Furthermore, since the triple of numbers $(x, y, z)$ may be interpreted as a vector, we may write

$$\mathbf{r} = x\mathbf{i} + y\mathbf{j} + z\mathbf{k},$$

or

$$\mathbf{r} = \mathbf{u}(t) = f(t)\mathbf{i} + g(t)\mathbf{j} + h(t)\mathbf{k}.$$

For instance, in Section 14.3 an equation of a straight line was given as $\mathbf{r} = \mathbf{a} + t\mathbf{c}$, which is equivalent to the form

$$\mathbf{r} = (c_1 t + a_1)\mathbf{i} + (c_2 t + a_2)\mathbf{j} + (c_3 t + a_3)\mathbf{k}.$$

The following definition is important in this connection.

**Definition 18.1a.** A set of pairs $\{(t, \mathbf{u})\}$ is a **vector-valued function** of the variable $t$ if with each given $t$ in the domain of the set there is associated a unique vector $\mathbf{u}$.

It is customary to call a vector-valued function a **vector function** and to denote its value at $t$ by $\mathbf{r} = \mathbf{u}(t)$.

---

*Example 18.1a.* Describe geometrically the vector function defined by

$$\mathbf{r} = \cos t \, \mathbf{i} + \sin t \, \mathbf{j} + t\mathbf{k}.$$

Since we may interpret $\mathbf{r}$ as the position vector $x\mathbf{i} + y\mathbf{j} + z\mathbf{k}$, we have

$$x = \cos t, \quad y = \sin t, \quad z = t.$$

From these equations, it is easy to show that the curve is a helix wound on a cylinder of unit radius with the $z$-axis as its axis (see Figure 18.1a).

---

This example illustrates that a vector function may be regarded as a function whose values are vectors starting at the origin and terminating on the curve described by the parametric equations obtained from the rectangular components of the function.

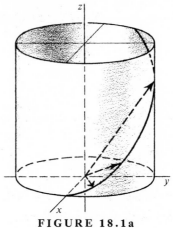

**FIGURE 18.1a**

In order to discuss the limit of a vector function, we need to extend the notion of a neighborhood that was used to develop the limit concept for ordinary (scalar) functions. For this purpose, let us recall that the distance between two points $P(x_1, y_1, z_1)$ and $Q(x_2, y_2, z_2)$ is given by

$$d(P, Q) = [(x_1 - x_2)^2 + (y_1 - y_2)^2 + (z_1 - z_2)^2]^{1/2}.$$

It is convenient to denote a point $(x, y, z)$ by a single letter, $X$.

**Definition 18.1b.** The set $\mathfrak{N}(P, \epsilon) .=. \{X: d(P, X) < \epsilon\}$ is called an **epsilon neighborhood,** or $\epsilon$-neighborhood, of $P$.

In geometric terms, a two-dimensional $\epsilon$-neighborhood of a point $P(x, y)$ is the set of points inside a circle of radius $\epsilon$ with its center at $P$ (see Figure 18.1b).

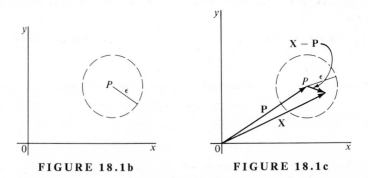

**FIGURE 18.1b**                **FIGURE 18.1c**

We say that a vector $X \in \mathfrak{N}(P, \epsilon)$ if $X$ terminates at a point in $\mathfrak{N}(P, \epsilon)$. This means that if the vector to $P$ is $P$, then $|X - P| < \epsilon$. The notation $\mathfrak{N}(P, \epsilon)$ denotes the same set of points as $\mathfrak{N}(P, \epsilon)$ (see Figure 18.1c).

In three dimensions, a neighborhood about a point $A$ is the interior of a sphere with its center at the point $A$. The statement $\mathbf{X} \in \mathfrak{N}(\mathbf{P}, \epsilon)$ means that the vector $\mathbf{X}$ terminates inside the sphere of radius $\epsilon$ with its center at the tip of $\mathbf{P}$. Generally, we shall illustrate most new concepts in two-dimensional cases, but the concepts themselves are not usually restricted to two dimensions.

A deleted neighborhood of a point $P$ is defined in the usual way.

**Definition 18.1c.** The set $\mathfrak{N}^*(P, \epsilon) .=. \mathfrak{N}(P, \epsilon) - \{P\}$ is called a **deleted neighborhood** of $P$.

**Definition 18.1d.** A vector function $\mathbf{u}$ is said to have a limit $\mathbf{A}$ as $t \to a$, if for each given $\mathfrak{N}(\mathbf{A}, \epsilon)$, there is a $\mathfrak{N}^*(a, \delta)$ such that

$$t \in \mathfrak{N}^*(a, \delta) \Rightarrow \mathbf{u} \in \mathfrak{N}(\mathbf{A}, \epsilon).$$

This somewhat elaborate language means simply that if $t$ is sufficiently near $a$, then $\mathbf{r} = \mathbf{u}(t)$ terminates within a distance $\epsilon$ from the tip of $\mathbf{A}$. The statement is illustrated in Figure 18.1d.

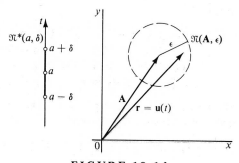

**FIGURE 18.1d**

The definition of the limit of a vector function is essentially equivalent to

**Theorem 18.1a.** Let

$$\mathbf{A} = A_1\mathbf{i} + A_2\mathbf{j} + A_3\mathbf{k},$$

and let

$$\mathbf{u}(t) = f(t)\mathbf{i} + g(t)\mathbf{j} + h(t)\mathbf{k}.$$

Then

$$\lim_{t \to a} \mathbf{u}(t) = \mathbf{A} \Leftrightarrow \lim_{t \to a} f(t) = A_1, \quad \lim_{t \to a} g(t) = A_2, \quad \lim_{t \to a} h(t) = A_3.$$

PROOF: Left for the reader. *Hint:*

$$\lim_{t \to a} \mathbf{u}(t) = \mathbf{A} \Leftrightarrow \lim_{t \to a} |\mathbf{u}(t) - \mathbf{A}| = 0.$$

The usual theorems (or their vector counterparts) on limits are valid.

**Theorem 18.1b.** Let

$$\lim_{t \to a} \mathbf{u}(t) = \mathbf{U} \quad \text{and} \quad \lim_{t \to a} \mathbf{v}(t) = \mathbf{V}.$$

Then

$$\text{(a) } \lim_{t \to a} [\mathbf{u}(t) + \mathbf{v}(t)] = \mathbf{U} + \mathbf{V},$$

$$\text{(b) } \lim_{t \to a} [\mathbf{u}(t) \cdot \mathbf{v}(t)] = \mathbf{U} \cdot \mathbf{V},$$

$$\text{(c) } \lim_{t \to a} [\mathbf{u}(t) \times \mathbf{v}(t)] = \mathbf{U} \times \mathbf{V}.$$

Furthermore, if $\varphi(t)$ is a scalar function, and if

$$\lim_{t \to a} \varphi(t) = \alpha,$$

then

$$\text{(d) } \lim_{t \to a} \varphi(t)\mathbf{u}(t) = \alpha\mathbf{U}.$$

PROOF: To illustrate the technique of constructing proofs for these results, we prove (c) and leave the remaining proofs for the reader. For convenience in writing, let

$$\mathbf{r} .=. \mathbf{u}(t) \quad \text{and} \quad \mathbf{p} .=. \mathbf{v}(t).$$

Consider the quantity

$$
\begin{aligned}
|\mathbf{r} \times \mathbf{p} - \mathbf{U} \times \mathbf{V}| &= |\mathbf{r} \times \mathbf{p} - \mathbf{U} \times \mathbf{p} + \mathbf{U} \times \mathbf{p} - \mathbf{U} \times \mathbf{V}| \\
&= |(\mathbf{r} - \mathbf{U}) \times \mathbf{p} + \mathbf{U} \times (\mathbf{p} - \mathbf{V})| \\
&\leq |(\mathbf{r} - \mathbf{U}) \times \mathbf{p}| + |\mathbf{U} \times (\mathbf{p} - \mathbf{V})| \\
&\leq |\mathbf{r} - \mathbf{U}||\mathbf{p}||\sin \theta| + |\mathbf{U}||\mathbf{p} - \mathbf{V}||\sin \varphi|,
\end{aligned}
$$

where $\theta$ is the angle between $\mathbf{r} - \mathbf{U}$ and $\mathbf{p}$, and $\varphi$ is the angle between $\mathbf{U}$ and $\mathbf{p} - \mathbf{V}$. Since $|\sin \theta| \leq 1$ and $|\sin \varphi| \leq 1$, then

$$|\mathbf{r} \times \mathbf{p} - \mathbf{U} \times \mathbf{V}| \leq |\mathbf{r} - \mathbf{U}||\mathbf{p}| + |\mathbf{U}||\mathbf{p} - \mathbf{V}|.$$

Since

$$\lim_{t \to a} \mathbf{p} = \mathbf{V},$$

then for $t \in \mathfrak{N}^*(a, \delta_1)$, where $\delta_1$ is sufficiently small, $|\mathbf{p}|$ is bounded; that is, there exists a number $B > 0$ such that $t \in \mathfrak{N}^*(a, \delta_1) \Rightarrow |\mathbf{p}| < B$. Also let $A$ be any positive number such that $|\mathbf{U}| < A$. (Recall that $\mathbf{U}$ is a constant vector.) We know that for $\delta_2$ sufficiently small,

$$t \in \mathfrak{N}^*(a, \delta_2) \Rightarrow |\mathbf{r} - \mathbf{U}| < \frac{\epsilon}{2B} \quad \text{and} \quad |\mathbf{p} - \mathbf{V}| < \frac{\epsilon}{2A}.$$

Therefore, for $\delta = \min(\delta_1, \delta_2)$,

$$t \in \mathfrak{N}^*(a, \delta) \Rightarrow |\mathbf{r} \times \mathbf{p} - \mathbf{U} \times \mathbf{V}| \leq |\mathbf{r} - \mathbf{U}|B + |\mathbf{p} - \mathbf{V}|A \leq \frac{\epsilon}{2} + \frac{\epsilon}{2} = \epsilon,$$

that is

$$\lim_{t \to a} \mathbf{r} \times \mathbf{p} = \mathbf{U} \times \mathbf{V},$$

as was to be proved.

Continuity for a vector function is defined in the usual way.

**Definition 18.1e.** A vector function $u$ is said to be continuous at $t = a$ if

$$\lim_{t \to a} \mathbf{u}(t) = \mathbf{u}(a).$$

It is easy to show that as a consequence of this definition and Theorem 18.1a, a vector function is continuous at $t = a$ if, and only if, each of its component functions is continuous at $t = a$. The details are left to the reader.

The discussion of a vector function **r** defined by the equation

$$\mathbf{r}(t) = f(t)\mathbf{i} + g(t)\mathbf{j} + h(t)\mathbf{k}$$

is equivalent to the discussion of the graph whose parametric equations are

$$x = f(t), \quad y = g(t), \quad z = h(t).$$

---

*Example 18.1b.* Discuss the vector function **u** defined by

$$\mathbf{u}(t) = (2 - \sin^2 t)\mathbf{i} + \cos t\,\mathbf{j}, \qquad -\pi \leqq t \leqq \pi.$$

If

$$x = 2 - \sin^2 t, \quad y = \cos t,$$

then an equation of a curve in rectangular coordinates that represents the vector function is

$$x = 1 + y^2, \qquad -1 \leqq y \leqq 1.$$

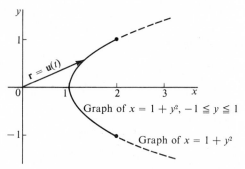

FIGURE 18.1e

The graph is shown in Figure 18.1e. The function is continuous for $-\pi \leqq t \leqq \pi$.

---

The reader may feel that some error has been made in calling **u** a vector function, since the graph in Figure 18.1e is not that of a function defined by an equation of the type $y = f(x)$, where $x$ and $y$ are rectangular coordinates. However, the graph is that of the given vector function, since with each value in the domain $-\pi \leqq t \leqq \pi$ there is associated a unique position vector to a point on the curve.

Note also that the entire graph of the equation $x = 1 + y^2$ does not coincide with the graph of the vector function. Evidently, some careful consideration of details is necessary here. Since $y = \cos t$, it is clear that $-1 \leqq y \leqq 1$. Similarly, $\leqq x \leqq 2$. Hence, in obtaining an equation in rectangular coordinates from parametric equations, we must take care to infer correctly the range of the variables $x$ and $y$ as functions of $t$.

It is instructive to consider vector functions in other coordinate systems, but for the time being we shall consider only polar coordinates. Suppose that

$$\mathbf{r} .=. \, x(t)\mathbf{i} + y(t)\mathbf{j}.$$

The equations relating rectangular coordinates with polar coordinates are

$$x = r \cos \theta, \quad y = r \sin \theta,$$

and if $x$ and $y$ are functions of a parameter $t$, it is implied that $r$ and $\theta$ are also functions of $t$. Hence,

$$\begin{aligned} \mathbf{r} &= r(t) \cos \theta(t)\, \mathbf{i} + r(t) \sin \theta(t)\, \mathbf{j} \\ &= r(t)[\cos \theta(t)\, \mathbf{i} + \sin \theta(t)\, \mathbf{j}]. \end{aligned}$$

The vector $\cos \theta\, \mathbf{i} + \sin \theta\, \mathbf{j}$ in the last expression is a unit vector in the radial direction and is denoted by $e_r$, so that

$$\mathbf{r} = r(t)e_r.$$

Note that $r(t)$ denotes the signed magnitude of the vector $\mathbf{r}$.

If both $\theta$ and $r$ are functions of $t$, and if it is possible to solve for $t$ in terms of $\theta$, say $t = g(\theta)$, then the vector function is given in a straightforward manner by

$$\mathbf{r} = f(\theta)e_r,$$

where $f(\theta) = r[g(\theta)]$ (see Figure 18.1f).

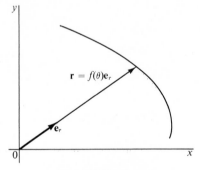

**FIGURE 18.1f**

The next example illustrates these comments.

---

*Example 18.1c.* Write the equation

$$\mathbf{r} = (a + a \cos t)\mathbf{i} + a \sin t\, \mathbf{j}$$

in polar coordinates.

We have given

$$x = a(1 + \cos t) = r \cos \theta,$$
$$y = a \sin t = r \sin \theta.$$

Accordingly,

$$\tan \theta = \frac{\sin t}{1 + \cos t} = \tan \frac{t}{2},$$

so that we may take

$$\frac{t}{2} = \theta,$$

or

$$t = 2\theta.$$

Moreover,

$$r = y \csc \theta = a \sin t \csc \theta$$
$$= a \sin 2\theta \csc \theta$$
$$= 2a \sin \theta \cos \theta \csc \theta = 2a \cos \theta.$$

Since $\mathbf{r} = r\mathbf{e}_r$, the required equation is

$$\mathbf{r} = 2a \cos \theta \, \mathbf{e}_r,$$

where $\theta = \frac{1}{2}t$. Note that $\mathbf{r}$ is the vector from the origin to a point $(r, \theta)$ on the curve $r = 2a \cos \theta$ in ordinary polar coordinates.

## Exercises 18.1

Sketch the curve described by the vector equation in each of Numbers 1 to 10, and give the points of continuity of the function defined in each case.

1. $\mathbf{r}(t) = \sin^2 t \, \mathbf{i} + \cos t \, \mathbf{j}.$
2. $\mathbf{r}(t) = \sin t \, \mathbf{i} + (1 - \cos 2t)\mathbf{j}.$
3. $\mathbf{r}(t) = \dfrac{t}{t^2 - 4}\mathbf{i} + \dfrac{t^2}{t^2 - 4}\mathbf{j}.$
4. $\mathbf{p}(t) = e^t\mathbf{i} + e^{-t}\mathbf{j}.$
5. $\mathbf{p}(s) = s^2\sqrt{1 + s^2}\,\mathbf{i} + 2s\mathbf{j}.$
6. $\mathbf{r}(s) = s^2\mathbf{i} + s^3\mathbf{j}.$
7. $\mathbf{r}(t) = \cos \omega t \, \mathbf{i} + \sin \omega t \, \mathbf{j} + \omega t \, \mathbf{k}.$
8. $\mathbf{p}(t) = t\mathbf{i} + 3t^2\mathbf{j} + 6t^3\mathbf{k}.$
9. $\mathbf{r}(t) = \sin t \, \mathbf{i} + t\mathbf{j} + (1 - \cos t)\mathbf{k}.$
10. $\mathbf{r}(t) = \frac{1}{2}\sqrt{2}\,\sin t \, \mathbf{i} + \frac{1}{2}\sqrt{2}\,\sin t \, \mathbf{j} + \cos t \, \mathbf{k}.$

11. Evaluate

$$\lim_{t \to 2} \left( t^2\mathbf{i} + \frac{t - 2}{t^2 - 4}\,\mathbf{j} \right).$$

12. Evaluate

$$\lim_{t \to 0} \left( e^{2t}\mathbf{i} + \frac{\sin 2t}{t}\,\mathbf{j} \right).$$

13. Prove Part (b) of Theorem 18.1b.

In Numbers 14 to 17, assume that $\mathbf{r} = x\mathbf{i} + y\mathbf{j}$, and write the vector equation in polar coordinates.

14. $\mathbf{r}(t) = 2t\mathbf{i} + t^2\mathbf{j}.$
15. $\mathbf{r}(t) = (t - 1)\mathbf{i} + 2t\mathbf{j}.$
16. $\mathbf{r}(t) = a \cos t \, \mathbf{i} + a(1 + \sin t)\mathbf{j}.$
17. $\mathbf{r}(t) = a(\cos t + \cos \alpha)\mathbf{i} + a(\sin t + \sin \alpha)\mathbf{j}.$

In each of Numbers 18 to 21, describe the curve given by the vector equation.

18. $\mathbf{r}(\theta) = \cos 2\theta \; \mathbf{e}_r, \; 0 \leq \theta \leq \pi.$

19. $\mathbf{r}(\theta) = \dfrac{2}{2 - \cos \theta} \, \mathbf{e}_r, \; 0 \leq \theta < 2\pi.$

20. $\mathbf{r}(\theta) = (2 - \cos \theta)\mathbf{e}_r, \; 0 \leq \theta < 2\pi.$
21. $\mathbf{r}(\theta) = (1 - 3 \sin \theta)\mathbf{e}_r, \; 0 \leq \theta < 2\pi.$

## 18.2 DERIVATIVE OF A VECTOR FUNCTION

If $\mathbf{r} = \mathbf{u}(t)$ describes a vector function, then as $t$ changes, the radius vector $\mathbf{r}$ changes in both magnitude and direction. These changes can be studied conveniently by means of the concept of the derivative.

**Definition 18.2a.** Let $\mathbf{u}$ be a vector function defined for $a \leq t \leq b$. If

$$\lim_{t \to 0} \frac{\mathbf{u}(t) - \mathbf{u}(t_0)}{t - t_0}, \qquad a < t_0 < b$$

exists, it is called the **derivative of the vector function u** at $t_0$, and is denoted by $\mathbf{u}'(t_0)$. The derivative at a general point is frequently written $D_t\mathbf{u}(t)$ or $\mathbf{u}'(t)$.

The next theorem is a simple consequence of this definition.

**Theorem 18.2a.** If $\mathbf{r}(t) = f(t)\mathbf{i} + g(t)\mathbf{j} + h(t)\mathbf{k}$, and if $D_t\mathbf{r}(t)$ exists, then

$$D_t\mathbf{r}(t) = D_t f(t)\mathbf{i} + D_t g(t)\mathbf{j} + D_t h(t)\mathbf{k}.$$

PROOF: Since

$$\frac{\mathbf{r}(t) - \mathbf{r}(t_0)}{t - t_0} = \frac{f(t) - f(t_0)}{t - t_0}\mathbf{i} + \frac{g(t) - g(t_0)}{t - t_0}\mathbf{j} + \frac{h(t) - h(t_0)}{t - t_0}\mathbf{k},$$

then by Theorem 18.1a and by virtue of the existence of

$$\lim_{t \to t_0} \frac{\mathbf{r}(t) - \mathbf{r}(t_0)}{t - t_0},$$

it follows that the limits of the individual components must exist. Hence applying the definition of the derivative to $f$, $g$, and $h$, we obtain the desired result.

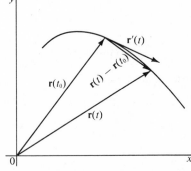

**FIGURE 18.2a**

Interpreted geometrically, the derivative of a vector is quite interesting. As illustrated in Figure 18.2a, the quantity $\mathbf{r}(t) - \mathbf{r}(t_0)$ is a vector subtending a portion of the curve associated with the function. As $t \to t_0$, the vector $\mathbf{r}(t) - \mathbf{r}(t_0)$ approaches a position of tangency to the curve at $\mathbf{r}(t_0)$. Thus, the vector $\mathbf{r}'(t_0)$ is a vector tangent to the curve at the point where $t = t_0$.

*Example 18.2a.* Let $\mathbf{r}(t) = 2t\mathbf{i} + 2(2t^2 - 1)\mathbf{j}$. Find the vector equation and an equation in rectangular coordinates of the tangent line to the curve described by $\mathbf{r}(t)$ at the point where $t = \frac{1}{2}$.

We have $\mathbf{r}(\frac{1}{2}) = \mathbf{i} - \mathbf{j}$, so that the point $(1, -1)$ corresponds to $t = \frac{1}{2}$. Since

$$\mathbf{r}'(t) = 2\mathbf{i} + 8t\mathbf{j},$$

a tangent vector is $\mathbf{r}'(\frac{1}{2}) = 2\mathbf{i} + 4\mathbf{j}$ (shown in Figure 18.2b). The equation of the tangent

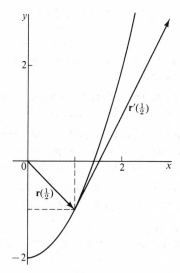

**FIGURE 18.2b**

line is then easily obtained. Since the vector $2\mathbf{i} + 4\mathbf{j}$ has direction numbers $[2, 4]$, and since the line passes through the point $(1, -1)$, the desired equation is

$$\mathbf{r} = (1, -1) + \sigma(2, 4),$$

where $\sigma$ is the parameter. The equation may also be written in rectangular coordinates:

$$\frac{y+1}{4} = \frac{x-1}{2} \quad \text{or} \quad y = 2x - 3.$$

The procedure used in Example 18.2a may also be employed if the vector function has three components.

*Example 18.2b.* Find symmetric equations of the line that is tangent to the curve $\mathbf{r}(t) = 2 \sin t\,\mathbf{i} + 2 \cos t\,\mathbf{j} + 2 \cos 2t\,\mathbf{k}$ at the point where $t = \pi/6$.

For $t = \pi/6$, we have $\mathbf{r}(\pi/6) = \mathbf{i} + \sqrt{3}\mathbf{j} + \mathbf{k}$, which corresponds to the point $(1, \sqrt{3}, 1)$ on the curve. We also have

$$\mathbf{r}'(t) = 2 \cos t\, \mathbf{i} - 2 \sin t\, \mathbf{j} - 4 \sin 2t\, \mathbf{k},$$

so that a tangent vector is given at this point by

$$\mathbf{r}'(\pi/6) = \sqrt{3}\mathbf{i} - \mathbf{j} - 2\sqrt{3}\mathbf{k}.$$

Thus, a vector equation of the tangent line may now be written

$$\mathbf{r} = (1, \sqrt{3}, 1) + \sigma(\sqrt{3}, -1, -2\sqrt{3}),$$

where $\sigma$ is a parameter. Parametric equations are then easily read off to be

$$x = 1 + \sqrt{3}\sigma, \quad y = \sqrt{3} - \sigma, \quad z = 1 - 2\sqrt{3}\sigma,$$

from which the following symmetric equations are obtained:

$$\frac{x-1}{\sqrt{3}} = \frac{y - \sqrt{3}}{-1} = \frac{z-1}{-2\sqrt{3}}.$$

---

The following results on derivatives are easily obtained from Theorem 18.1b and the definition of the derivative.

**Theorem 18.2b.** Let $\mathbf{r}(t)$ and $\mathbf{p}(t)$ be differentiable vector functions for $a \leqq t \leqq b$, and let $\varphi(t)$ be a differentiable scalar function. Then

(a) $D_t[\mathbf{r}(t)\cdot\mathbf{p}(t)] = [D_t\mathbf{r}(t)]\cdot\mathbf{p}(t) + \mathbf{r}(t)\cdot D_t\mathbf{p}(t),$

(b) $D_t[\mathbf{r}(t) \times \mathbf{p}(t)] = [D_t\mathbf{r}(t)] \times \mathbf{p}(t) + \mathbf{r}(t) \times D_t\mathbf{p}(t),$

(c) $D_t[\varphi(t)\mathbf{r}(t)] = [D_t\varphi(t)]\mathbf{r}(t) + \varphi(t)D_t\mathbf{r}(t).$

PROOF: (a) Consider the values of the vector functions at two points, $t$ and $t + h$, and let $\Delta\mathbf{r} = \mathbf{r}(t + h) - \mathbf{r}(t)$, $\Delta\mathbf{p} = \mathbf{p}(t + h) - \mathbf{p}(t)$. Then,

$$\mathbf{r}(t + h)\cdot\mathbf{p}(t + h) - \mathbf{r}(t)\cdot\mathbf{p}(t)$$
$$= \mathbf{r}(t + h)\cdot\mathbf{p}(t + h) - \mathbf{r}(t + h)\cdot\mathbf{p}(t) + \mathbf{r}(t + h)\cdot\mathbf{p}(t) - \mathbf{r}(t)\cdot\mathbf{p}(t),$$

or

$$\frac{\mathbf{r}(t + h)\cdot\mathbf{p}(t + h) - \mathbf{r}(t)\cdot\mathbf{p}(t)}{h}$$

$$= \mathbf{r}(t + h) \cdot \left[\frac{\mathbf{p}(t + h) - \mathbf{p}(t)}{h}\right] + \mathbf{p}(t) \cdot \left[\frac{\mathbf{r}(t + h) - \mathbf{r}(t)}{h}\right].$$

As $h \to 0$, the resulting limits yield the formula in (a). The proofs of (b) and (c) are left for the reader.

With the help of Theorem 18.2b, we can get several interesting results, one of which is obtained in the next example.

---

*Example 18.2c.* Let $\mathbf{r}(t)$ be a vector whose magnitude is constant for $a \leqq t \leqq b$. Describe the vector $D_t\mathbf{r}(t)$.

Since

$$\mathbf{r}(t)\cdot\mathbf{r}(t) = k^2,$$

where $k^2$ is a constant, we have

$$\mathbf{r}(t) \cdot D_t\mathbf{r}(t) + [D_t\mathbf{r}(t)] \cdot \mathbf{r}(t) = 0,$$

or

$$2\mathbf{r}(t) \cdot D_t\mathbf{r}(t) = 0.$$

Since the dot product is zero, either $D_t\mathbf{r}(t) = 0$ and $\mathbf{r}(t)$ is constant, or $\mathbf{r}(t)$ and $D_t\mathbf{r}(t)$ are perpendicular. In general, $\mathbf{r}(t)$ is not constant, since its direction may change, although its magnitude is fixed. Hence, $D_t\mathbf{r}(t)$ is a vector perpendicular to $\mathbf{r}(t)$.

The result of Example 18.2c is geometrically clear, for if $r(t)$ has a constant magnitude $k$, it must terminate on a circle of radius $k$. Since a tangent to the circle is perpendicular to a radius to the point of tangency (see Figure 18.2c), $D_t\mathbf{r}$

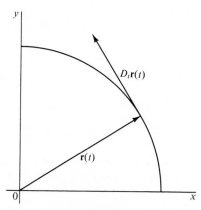

**FIGURE 18.2c**

must be perpendicular to $\mathbf{r}(t)$. This fact will prove to be valuable in some later developments.

If $\mathbf{r} = x(t)\mathbf{i} + y(t)\mathbf{j} + z(t)\mathbf{k}$ defines a differentiable vector function, so that

$$D_t\mathbf{r} = D_tx\mathbf{i} + D_ty\mathbf{j} + D_tz\mathbf{k},$$

then the magnitude of $D_t\mathbf{r}$ is

$$|D_t\mathbf{r}| = (D_t\mathbf{r} \cdot D_t\mathbf{r})^{1/2}$$
$$= [(D_tx)^2 + (D_ty)^2 + (D_tz)^2]^{1/2}.$$

The vector

$$\mathbf{T} = \frac{D_t\mathbf{r}}{|D_t\mathbf{r}|}$$

is a unit vector in the direction of a tangent line to the curve described by $\mathbf{r}$, so that we may write

$$D_t\mathbf{r} = |D_t\mathbf{r}|\mathbf{T}.$$

Differentiation of this equation leads to the following formula for the second derivative of $\mathbf{r}$:

$$D_t^2\mathbf{r} = (D_t|D_t\mathbf{r}|)\mathbf{T} + |D_t\mathbf{r}|D_t\mathbf{T}.$$

Since $\mathbf{T}$ is a **unit vector**, $D_t\mathbf{T}$ must be a vector perpendicular to $\mathbf{T}$, although it is not necessarily of unit length. If

$$\mathbf{N} .=. \frac{D_t\mathbf{T}}{|D_t\mathbf{T}|},$$

so that $\mathbf{N}$ is the unit vector in the direction of $D_t\mathbf{T}$, then

$$D_t^2\mathbf{r} = (D_t|D_t\mathbf{r}|)\mathbf{T} + |D_t\mathbf{r}||D_t\mathbf{T}|\mathbf{N}.$$

This equation expresses the vector $D_t^2\mathbf{r}$ in terms of two components, one in the

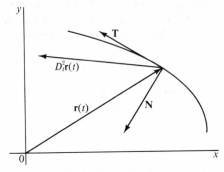

**FIGURE 18.2d**

tangential direction, and one in the normal direction (see Figure 18.2d). These results will be used in connection with velocities and accelerations in Section 18.4

---

*Example 18.2d.* Find $\mathbf{T}$ and $\mathbf{N}$ at the point where $t = \pi/6$ for the curve in Example 18.2b.

In Example 18.2b, we had

$$\mathbf{r} = 2\sin t\,\mathbf{i} + 2\cos t\,\mathbf{j} + 2\cos 2t\,\mathbf{k}$$

and

$$\mathbf{r}' = 2\cos t\,\mathbf{i} - 2\sin t\,\mathbf{j} - 4\sin 2t\,\mathbf{k}.$$

Hence,

$$|\mathbf{r}'| = (4\cos^2 t + 4\sin^2 t + 16\sin^2 2t)^{1/2} = 2(1 + 4\sin^2 2t)^{1/2},$$

and

$$\mathbf{T} = (\cos t\,\mathbf{i} - \sin t\,\mathbf{j} - 2\sin 2t\,\mathbf{k})(1 + 4\sin^2 2t)^{-1/2} = (1 + 4\sin^2 2t)^{-1/2}\mathbf{v},$$

where

$$\mathbf{v} = \cos t\,\mathbf{i} - \sin t\,\mathbf{j} - 2\sin 2t\,\mathbf{k}.$$

Thus,

$$D_t\mathbf{T} = (1 + 4\sin^2 2t)^{-1/2} D_t\mathbf{v} - 4\mathbf{v}(1 + 4\sin^2 2t)^{-3/2}\sin 4t,$$

and

$$D_t\mathbf{v} = -\sin t\,\mathbf{i} - \cos t\,\mathbf{j} - 4\cos 2t\,\mathbf{k}.$$

For $t = \pi/6$,

$$\mathbf{v} = \frac{\sqrt{3}}{2}\mathbf{i} - \frac{1}{2}\mathbf{j} - \sqrt{3}\mathbf{k},$$

$$D_t\mathbf{v} = -\frac{1}{2}\mathbf{i} - \frac{\sqrt{3}}{2}\mathbf{j} - 2\mathbf{k},$$

and
$$1 + 4 \sin^2 2t = 4.$$

Thus,
$$D_t\mathbf{T} = \frac{1}{2} D_t\mathbf{v} - \frac{\sqrt{3}}{4}\mathbf{v} = -\frac{5}{8}\mathbf{i} - \frac{\sqrt{3}}{8}\mathbf{j} - \frac{1}{4}\mathbf{k},$$

and
$$\mathbf{N} .=. \frac{D_t\mathbf{T}}{|D_t\mathbf{T}|} = \frac{-5\mathbf{i} - \sqrt{3}\mathbf{j} - 2\mathbf{k}}{\sqrt{25 + 3 + 4}} = \frac{-5\mathbf{i} - \sqrt{3}\mathbf{j} - 2\mathbf{k}}{4\sqrt{2}}.$$

If a vector is given in polar coordinates, then the same procedure leads to the following interesting results. Let
$$\mathbf{r} = r(\theta)\mathbf{e}_r,$$
so that

(1)
$$D_\theta\mathbf{r} = r'(\theta)\mathbf{e}_r + r(\theta) D_\theta\mathbf{e}_r.$$

Since $\mathbf{e}_r$ is a unit vector, $D_\theta\mathbf{e}_r$ is a vector perpendicular to $\mathbf{e}_r$. Let
$$\mathbf{e}_\theta .=. D_\theta\mathbf{e}_r,$$
so that

(2)
$$D_\theta\mathbf{r} = r'(\theta)\mathbf{e}_r + r(\theta)\mathbf{e}_\theta.$$

It is clear that $\mathbf{e}_\theta$ is a unit vector, since
$$\mathbf{e}_r = \cos\theta\,\mathbf{i} + \sin\theta\,\mathbf{j},$$
implies that
$$D_\theta\mathbf{e}_r = -\sin\theta\,\mathbf{i} + \cos\theta\,\mathbf{j},$$
and
$$|D_\theta\mathbf{e}_r| = 1.$$

Equation (2) states that in polar coordinates the vector $D_\theta\mathbf{r}$ tangent to the curve is given in terms of components relative to base vectors $\mathbf{e}_r$ and $\mathbf{e}_\theta$ at the point of tangency (see Figure 18.2e). The two components $r'(\theta)$ and $r(\theta)$ are called

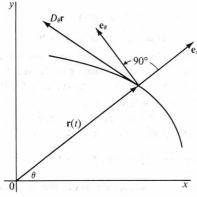

**FIGURE 18.2e**

the **radial** component and the **transverse** component, respectively. It appears that the vectors $\mathbf{e}_r$ and $\mathbf{e}_\theta$ are a natural set of base vectors for vectors in polar coordinates. As contrasted to the base vectors **i** and **j** in rectangular coordinates $e_r$ and $e_\theta$ are functions of the angle $\theta$, whereas **i** and **j** are constant vectors.

It is worth noting that the expression for $D_\theta e_r$, that is,

$$-\sin \theta \, \mathbf{i} + \cos \theta \, \mathbf{j},$$

shows that $D_\theta e_r$ is perpendicular to $e_r$. (How does it?) Furthermore,

$$D_\theta e_\theta = D_\theta(-\sin \theta \, \mathbf{i} + \cos \theta \, \mathbf{j})$$
$$= -\cos \theta \, \mathbf{i} - \sin \theta \, \mathbf{j} = -e_r,$$

a result that will be of some importance later in this chapter.

## Exercises 18.2

1. Find (i) $D_t\mathbf{r}$, (ii) the unit vector **T**, (iii) the unit vector **N**, for the curve described by each of the following vector equations.
   (a) $\mathbf{r}(t) = a \cos t \, \mathbf{i} + a \sin t \, \mathbf{j}$.
   (b) $\mathbf{r}(t) = \cos t^2 \, \mathbf{i} + \sin t^2 \, \mathbf{j}$.
   (c) $\mathbf{r}(t) = (t^3 - 3t)\mathbf{i} + 3t^2\mathbf{j}$.
   (d) $\mathbf{r}(t) = a \cos \omega t \, \mathbf{i} + a \sin \omega t \, \mathbf{j} + b\omega t\mathbf{k}$.
   (e) $\mathbf{r}(t) = a(3t - t^3)\mathbf{i} + 3at^2\mathbf{j} + a(3t + t^3)\mathbf{k}$.

   (f) $\mathbf{r}(w) = \ln \cos w \, \mathbf{i} + \ln \sin w \, \mathbf{j} + \sqrt{2}w\mathbf{k}, \ 0 < w < \dfrac{\pi}{2}.$

2. Prove parts (b) and (c) of Theorem 18.2b.
3. What conclusions may be drawn from the equation $\mathbf{r} \times D_t\mathbf{r} = 0$?
4. Evaluate $D_t(\mathbf{r} \cdot D_t\mathbf{r})$ if **r** is a vector function of $t$.
5. If $v .=. |\mathbf{v}|$, show that $\mathbf{v} \cdot D_t\mathbf{v} = v \, D_t v$.
6. If $\mathbf{r} = \mathbf{a} \cos \omega t + \mathbf{b} \sin \omega t$, where **a** and **b** are constant vectors, and $\omega$ is a constant, prove that
   (a) $\mathbf{r} \times D_t\mathbf{r} = \omega\mathbf{a} \times \mathbf{b}$;
   (b) $D_t^2\mathbf{r} + \omega^2\mathbf{r} = 0$.
7. If $D_t\mathbf{r} = \omega \times \mathbf{r}$, $D_t\mathbf{p} = \omega \times \mathbf{p}$, show that

   $$D_t(\mathbf{r} \times \mathbf{p}) = \omega \times (\mathbf{r} \times \mathbf{p}).$$

8. If $\mathbf{r} = \mathbf{a}e^{\omega t} + \mathbf{b}e^{-\omega t}$, and if **a**, **b**, $\omega$ are constants, show that $D_t^2\mathbf{r} - \omega^2\mathbf{r} = 0$.
9. For each of the following vector functions, find the vector equation of the tangent line at the indicated point on the curve described by the tip of the radius vector **r**
   (a) $\mathbf{r}(t) = \sqrt{t} \, \mathbf{i} + (t^2 - 1)\mathbf{j} + 2t\mathbf{k}; \ t = 1$.
   (b) $\mathbf{r}(t) = a \cos t \, \mathbf{i} + a \sin t \, \mathbf{j} + (b/\pi)t\mathbf{k}; \ t = \pi/6$.
   (c) $\mathbf{r}(t) = a(3t - t^3)\mathbf{i} + 3at^2\mathbf{j} + a(3t + t^3)\mathbf{k}; \ t = 1$.

   (d) $\mathbf{p}(t) = \dfrac{2t}{t^2 + 1}\mathbf{i} + \dfrac{t^2 - 1}{t^2 + 1}\mathbf{j} + 2t\mathbf{k}; \ t = -1.$

★10. If **a** and **b** are any two nonparallel vectors in the $xy$-plane, prove that

$$\mathbf{r} = \mathbf{a} \cos \omega t + \mathbf{b} \sin \omega t,$$

where $\omega$ is a constant, is a vector equation of an ellipse. *Hint*: Consider $\mathbf{r} \times \mathbf{a}$ and $\mathbf{r} \times \mathbf{b}$.

For each of Numbers 11 to 16, find $D_\theta \mathbf{r}$ in terms of $\mathbf{e}_r$ and $\mathbf{e}_\theta$ and sketch the curve, showing $\mathbf{e}_r$ and $\mathbf{e}_\theta$ at the given point. Note that $r$ and $\theta$ are polar coordinates.

11. $\mathbf{r}(\theta) = a \cos \theta\, \mathbf{i} + a \sin \theta\, \mathbf{j}; \theta = \pi/4$.
12. $\mathbf{r}(\theta) = \cos 2\theta\, \mathbf{e}_r; \theta = \pi/4$.
13. $\mathbf{r}(\theta) = (1 - \cos \theta)\mathbf{e}_r; \theta = \pi/3$.

14. $\mathbf{r}(\theta) = \dfrac{1}{1 - \cos \theta}\, \mathbf{e}_r; \theta = \pi/6$.

15. $\mathbf{r}(t) = 2t\mathbf{i} + t^2\mathbf{j}; t = 1$.
16. $\mathbf{r}(t) = a(1 + \cos t)\mathbf{i} + a \sin t\, \mathbf{j}; t = \pi/4$.

## 18.3 ARC LENGTH

Consider a curve $\mathcal{C}$ (see Section 17.4) described by a vector function with a continuous derivative and defined by

$$\mathbf{r}(t) = f(t)\mathbf{i} + g(t)\mathbf{j} + h(t)\mathbf{k}, \qquad a \le t \le b.$$

If all distinct values of $t$ in the open interval $a < t < b$ correspond to distinct points on $\mathcal{C}$, then $\mathcal{C}$ is called a **simple arc**. If the curve is a simple arc and $\mathbf{r}(a) = \mathbf{r}(b)$, then the arc is said to be a **simple closed arc**.

The curves with which the reader is most likely to be familiar, such as the conic sections, the polynomial curves, and practically all of the curves in the preceding sections of this book, are either simple arcs or else are easily partitioned into a finite set of simple arcs placed end to end. A polygon is a good example of the latter situation, since each side is clearly a simple arc.

Suppose that the curve $\mathcal{C}$ described by $\mathbf{r}(t)$ is a simple arc. On an intuitive basis, the "length of the arc $\mathcal{C}$" can be approximated by measuring the length of a broken line inscribed on $\mathcal{C}$. This idea is made more precise in the following discussion.

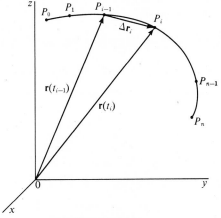

**FIGURE 18.3a**

Let $P_0, P_1, \ldots, P_n$ (Figure 18.3a) be a set of points corresponding to the vectors $\mathbf{r}(t_0), \mathbf{r}(t_1), \ldots, \mathbf{r}(t_n)$, where

$$a = t_0 < t_1 < t_2 < \cdots < t_n = b,$$

and let

$$\Delta \mathbf{r}_i = \mathbf{r}(t_i) - \mathbf{r}(t_{i-1}).$$

The quantity $|\Delta \mathbf{r}_i|$ is the length of a chord subtending that portion of the curve between $P_{i-1}$ and $P_i$. Therefore, we say that the sum

$$s_n = \sum_{i=1}^{n} |\Delta \mathbf{r}_i|$$

represents an approximation to what we intuitively call the "length of the curve" from $P_0$ to $P_n$.

**Definition 18.3a.** Let $\delta = \max |\Delta \mathbf{r}_i|$. Then if

$$\lim_{\delta \to 0} \sum_{i=1}^{n} |\Delta \mathbf{r}_i|$$

exists, it is called the length of the curve traced by the radius vector $\mathbf{r}(t)$ from $t = a$ to $t = b$, and the curve is said to be **rectifiable**.

As is often the case, this definition leaves us without an immediate, practical means for finding the length of a curve. However, since the definition involves the limit of a sum, it is reasonable to try to associate arc length with a definite integral. (Our success in this regard has been nothing short of astounding thus far.) In fact, we propose to prove

**Theorem 18.3a.** Let $\mathcal{C}$ be a simple arc defined by

$$\mathbf{r}(t) = x\mathbf{i} + y\mathbf{j} + z\mathbf{k},$$

where

$$x = f(t), \quad y = g(t), \quad z = h(t), \qquad a \leqq t \leqq b,$$

and $f$, $g$, and $h$ have continuous derivatives on the interval $a \leqq t \leqq b$. Then $\mathcal{C}$ is rectifiable and has arc length

$$s = \int_a^b [(D_t x)^2 + (D_t y)^2 + (D_t z)^2]^{1/2} \, dt = \int_a^b [D_t \mathbf{r} \cdot D_t \mathbf{r}]^{1/2} \, dt.$$

PROOF: From the Mean Value Theorem for derivatives, we may write for

$$\mathbf{r}(t_i) - \mathbf{r}(t_{i-1}) = [f(t_i) - f(t_{i-1})]\mathbf{i} + [g(t_i) - g(t_{i-1})]\mathbf{j} + [h(t_i) - h(t_{i-1})]\mathbf{k}$$

the expression

$$\mathbf{r}(t_i) - \mathbf{r}(t_{i-1}) = f'(u_i)(t_i - t_{i-1})\mathbf{i} + g'(v_i)(t_i - t_{i-1})\mathbf{j} + h'(w_i)(t_i - t_{i-1})\mathbf{k},$$

where $t_{i-1} \leqq u_i, v_i, w_i \leqq t_i$. If $\Delta t_i = t_i - t_{i-1}$, then

$$\mathbf{r}(t_i) - \mathbf{r}(t_{i-1}) = [f'(u_i)\mathbf{i} + g'(v_i)\mathbf{j} + h'(w_i)\mathbf{k}] \, \Delta t_i,$$

and

$$\lim_{\delta \to 0} \sum_{i=1}^{n} |\Delta \mathbf{r}_i| = \lim_{\delta \to 0} \sum_{i=1}^{n} [(f'(u_i))^2 + (g'(v_i))^2 + (h'(w_i))^2]^{1/2} \, \Delta t_i.$$

Although it is not possible to pass directly to the definite integral, since in each subinterval the $u_i$, $v_i$, $w_i$ are generally distinct, it is true, by a theorem known as *Duhamel's principle*, that the preceding limit is equal to the limit of the sum obtained by replacing $v_i$ and $w_i$ by $u_i$, $i = 1, 2, \ldots, n$. (Details are omitted here, but the reader may refer to such books as A. Taylor, *Advanced Calculus*, Ginn & Company, New York, 1955, pp. 515–520.)

Accordingly, by the definition of the definite integral, we obtain

$$\lim_{\delta \to 0} \sum_{i=1}^{n} |\Delta \mathbf{r}_i| = \lim_{\delta \to 0} \sum_{i=1}^{n} [(f'(u_i))^2 + (g'(u_i))^2 + (h'(u_i))^2]^{1/2} \Delta t_i$$

$$= \int_a^b [(D_t x)^2 + (D_t y)^2 + (D_t z)^2]^{1/2} dt$$

$$= \int_a^b [D_t \mathbf{r} \cdot D_t \mathbf{r}]^{1/2} dt.$$

If the upper limit of the integral in Theorem 18.3a is a variable, then the resulting indefinite integral defines the **arc length function**, $s$, associated with the curve given by $\mathbf{r}(t)$. That is,

$$s(t) = \int_a^t [(D_u x)^2 + (D_u y)^2 + (D_u z)^2]^{1/2} du$$

$$= \int_a^t [D_u \mathbf{r} \cdot D_u \mathbf{r}]^{1/2} du = \int_a^t [\mathbf{r}'(u) \cdot \mathbf{r}'(u)]^{1/2} du,$$

where the dummy variable $u$ is used to replace the $t$ in the integrand in order to avoid confusion with the upper limit of integration.

---

*Example 18.3a.* Find the length of the curve described by

$$\mathbf{r}(\theta) = a(\theta - \sin \theta)\mathbf{i} + a(1 - \cos \theta)\mathbf{j}$$

from $\theta = 0$ to $\theta = \pi$.

Since

$$D_\theta \mathbf{r} = a(1 - \cos \theta)\mathbf{i} + a \sin \theta \, \mathbf{j},$$

then

$$D_\theta \mathbf{r} \cdot D_\theta \mathbf{r} = a^2(1 - \cos \theta)^2 + a^2 \sin^2 \theta$$
$$= a^2[2 - 2 \cos \theta].$$

Hence, the length of the curve is

$$\int_0^\pi a\sqrt{2 - 2 \cos \theta} \, d\theta = 2a \int_0^\pi \sqrt{\frac{1 - \cos \theta}{2}} \, d\theta$$

$$= 2a \int_0^\pi \sin \frac{\theta}{2} \, d\theta$$

$$= 4a \left[ -\cos \frac{\theta}{2} \right]_0^\pi = 4a \text{ l.u.},$$

where l.u. stands for linear units.

---

From the equation

$$s(t) = \int_a^t [\mathbf{r}'(u) \cdot \mathbf{r}'(u)]^{1/2} \, du$$

we obtain, by means of the Fundamental Theorem of Integral Calculus, the equation

$$D_t s = [\mathbf{r}'(t) \cdot \mathbf{r}'(t)]^{1/2}.$$

The expression for $D_t s$ is precisely $|D_t \mathbf{r}|$, so that the tangent vector to a curve may now be written in the form

$$D_t \mathbf{r} = (D_t s)\mathbf{T},$$

where $\mathbf{T}$ is the unit tangent vector. If the parameter $t$ is the arc length $s$ itself then the preceding equation assumes the important form

$$D_s \mathbf{r} = \mathbf{T}.$$

In the two-dimensional case, the equation of a curve is often given in the form $y = f(x)$, rather than in parametric form. According to some earlier results $D_x y = D_t y / D_t x$, so that $D_t y = D_t x D_x y$ may be substituted into the formula

$$s = \int_a^b [(D_t x)^2 + (D_t y)^2]^{1/2} \, dt$$

to get

$$s = \int_a^b [(D_t x)^2 + (D_x y)^2 (D_t x)^2]^{1/2} \, dt$$

$$= \int_a^b [1 + (D_x y)^2]^{1/2} |D_t x| \, dt.$$

Since $|D_t x \, dt| = |dx|$, the integral may be written as

(1)
$$s = \int_\alpha^\beta [1 + (D_x y)^2]^{1/2} \, dx,$$

where the limits on $x$ cover the piece of curve corresponding to $a \leq t \leq b$. *These limits must be taken in the positive direction, since the integrand is positive throughout.*

---

*Example 18.3b.* Find the length of arc of the helix given by

$$\mathbf{r}(\theta) = a \cos \theta \, \mathbf{i} + a \sin \theta \, \mathbf{j} + a\theta \mathbf{k}$$

as a function of $\theta$.

Since

$$D_\theta \mathbf{r} = -a \sin \theta \, \mathbf{i} + a \cos \theta \, \mathbf{j} + a\mathbf{k},$$

we get

$$D_\theta \mathbf{r} \cdot D_\theta \mathbf{r} = 2a^2.$$

If the starting point is chosen at $\theta = 0$, then

$$s = \int_0^\theta \sqrt{2a^2} \, du,$$

or

$$s = \sqrt{2} a\theta.$$

This equation gives the length of arc of the curve from $\theta = 0$ to another specified value of $\theta$.

In the preceding example the simple relationship exhibited between the parameter $\theta$ and the arc length $s$ makes it possible to rewrite the vector function as a function of arc length. Thus, the equation

$$\mathbf{p}(s) = a \cos \frac{s}{a\sqrt{2}} \mathbf{i} + a \sin \frac{s}{a\sqrt{2}} \mathbf{j} + \frac{s}{\sqrt{2}} \mathbf{k}$$

describes the same curve as does the equation given for $\mathbf{r}(\theta)$ in the example. From

$$D_s\mathbf{p}(s) = -\frac{1}{\sqrt{2}} \sin \frac{s}{a\sqrt{2}} \mathbf{i} + \frac{1}{\sqrt{2}} \cos \frac{s}{a\sqrt{2}} \mathbf{j} + \frac{1}{\sqrt{2}} \mathbf{k},$$

it follows that

$$D_s\mathbf{p} \cdot D_s\mathbf{p} = 1,$$

which verifies, for this special case, that the derivative of the radius vector with respect to arc length yields the unit tangent vector $\mathbf{T}$.

The integral for the length of arc of a curve may be expressed in terms of other coordinate systems, of which one of the most usual is polar coordinates. In polar coordinates the vector equation of a curve is given in the form

$$\mathbf{r} = r(\theta)\mathbf{e}_r.$$

Thus,

$$D_\theta\mathbf{r} = (D_\theta r)\mathbf{e}_r + r D_\theta \mathbf{e}_r$$
$$= (D_\theta r)\mathbf{e}_r + r\mathbf{e}_\theta,$$

and

$$D_\theta\mathbf{r} \cdot D_\theta\mathbf{r} = (D_\theta r)^2 + r^2.$$

Hence,

$$s = \int_\alpha^\beta [(D_\theta r)^2 + r^2]^{1/2} \, d\theta.$$

*Example 18.3c.* Find the length of the curve $r = 1 + \cos \theta$ from $\theta = 0$ to $\theta = \pi/2$.

Using the preceding formula, we get

$$s = \int_0^{\pi/2} [(\sin \theta)^2 + (1 + \cos \theta)^2]^{1/2} \, d\theta$$

$$= \int_0^{\pi/2} [2 + 2 \cos \theta]^{1/2} \, d\theta$$

$$= 2 \int_0^{\pi/2} \left[\frac{1 + \cos \theta}{2}\right]^{1/2} \, d\theta$$

$$= 2 \int_0^{\pi/2} \cos \frac{\theta}{2} \, d\theta$$

$$= 4 \left[\sin \frac{\theta}{2}\right]_0^{\pi/2}$$

$$= 4 \frac{\sqrt{2}}{2} = 2\sqrt{2} \text{ l.u.}$$

From the indefinite integral for arc length in the two-dimensional case,

$$s = \int_a^t \{[x'(u)]^2 + [y'(u)]^2\}^{1/2}\, du,$$

we get

$$(D_t s)^2 = (D_t x)^2 + (D_t y)^2,$$

or

$$[(D_t s)\, dt]^2 = [D_t x\, dt]^2 + [D_t y\, dt]^2$$

so that, according to the definition of the differential,

$$ds^2 = dx^2 + dy^2,$$

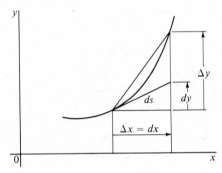

**FIGURE 18.3b**

where *ds* denotes the **differential of arc length**. Thus, *ds* is represented geometrically as the hypotenuse of a triangle having sides of length *dx* and *dy* (see Figure 18.3b).

## Exercises 18.3

In each of Numbers 1 to 18, find the length of the indicated curve.

1. $r(t) = (2t - 3)i + (2t)j$, $2 \leq t \leq 4$.
2. $r(t) = \cos^3 t\, i + \sin^3 t\, j$, for the entire curve.
3. $r(t) = e^t \cos t\, i + e^t \sin t\, j$, $0 \leq t \leq 1$.
4. $r(\theta) = a \cos \theta\, i + a \sin \theta\, j + b\theta k$, $0 \leq \theta \leq u$.
5. $y^2 = x^3$, from $(0, 0)$ to $(2, 2\sqrt{2})$.
6. $y = \ln \sin x$, from $x = \pi/4$ to $x = \pi/3$.
7. $x = \cosh y$, from $y = -2$ to $y = 2$.
8. One arch of the cycloid $x = 2(\theta - \sin \theta)$, $y = 2(1 - \cos \theta)$.
9. $(y - 2)^2 = x^3$, from $(0, 2)$ to $(4, 10)$.
10. $x^{2/3} + y^{2/3} = a^{2/3}$, the entire curve.
11. $x = a(\cos t + t \sin t)$, $y = a(\sin t - t \cos t)$, $-\pi/2 \leq t \leq \pi$.
12. $x = e^t + e^{-t}$, $y = 2t$, from $t = 0$ to $t = u$.
13. $x = \frac{1}{2}t^2 + t$, $y = \frac{1}{2}t^2 - t$, for $0 \leq t \leq 1$.
14. $r = \sin \theta$, the entire curve.
15. $r = 4 \sin \theta + 3 \cos \theta$, the entire curve.

16. $r = e^\theta$, from $\theta = 0$ to $\theta = 4\pi$.
17. $r = a(1 - \cos\theta)$, the entire curve.
18. $r = (1 - \sin\theta)^{-1}$, from $\theta = 0$ to $\theta = \alpha$.
19. Set up the integral for the entire length of the curve $r = a + b\cos\theta$, $a \neq b$. *Note*: The integral in this problem cannot be evaluated by inverse differentiation using any of the elementary functions that we have studied here. It can, however, be transformed into a standard form known as an elliptic integral, and can then be evaluated for given values of $a$ and $b$ from tables of such integrals.
20. Set up the integral for the entire length of the curve $r = \cos 2\theta$. Do not try to evaluate the integral, but see the note in Number 19.
21. Write the equations of the circle $x = a\cos\theta$, $y = a\sin\theta$ as functions of its arc length.
22. Obtain the arc length $s$ as a function of $\theta$ for the curve in Number 8.
23. Obtain the arc length $s$ as a function of $t$ for the curve in Number 12.
24. Obtain a formula similar to Equation (1) for the arc length of a curve in two dimensions in terms of an integration with respect to $y$.
25. What relationship, if any, exists between the arc lengths of the curve $y = e^x$, $0 \leq x \leq t$, and the curve $y = \ln x$, $1 \leq x \leq e^t$?

# 18.4 VELOCITY AND ACCELERATION

Suppose a particle moves through space along a path described by a vector $r(t)$, where the parameter $t$ may be taken as the time, so that the vector $r$ terminates at the position of the particle at the time $t$. The particle is said to have a *curvilinear motion*. Associated with any curvilinear motion are two quantities called *velocity* and *acceleration*. These quantities are represented conveniently in terms of derivatives by generalizing the concepts of velocity and acceleration in a straight-line motion.

**Definition 18.4a.** The **velocity** of a particle moving on a path given by $r(t)$ is the vector

$$v .=. D_t r.$$

That is, the velocity of the particle is defined as *the instantaneous time rate of change of its position vector*.

**Definition 18.4b.** The **acceleration** of a particle moving on a path $r(t)$ is the vector

$$a .=. D_t v = D_t^2 r.$$

That is, the acceleration of a particle is defined as the *instantaneous time rate of change of its velocity*.

Notice that velocity and acceleration are *vector quantities*. One important aspect of the definitions for these quantities is that, being given in vector form, velocity and acceleration are defined independently of any coordinate system. However, in order to compute with these quantities it is usually desirable to obtain representations for them in a suitable coordinate system.

Frequently, the simplest way to represent velocity and acceleration is in rectangular coordinates. Thus, if the position vector of the particle is

$$\mathbf{r} = x(t)\mathbf{i} + y(t)\mathbf{j} + z(t)\mathbf{k},$$

then

$$\mathbf{v} = D_t\mathbf{r} = D_tx\,\mathbf{i} + D_ty\,\mathbf{j} + D_tz\,\mathbf{k}.$$

Accordingly, the components of velocity in rectangular coordinates are

$$v_x .=. D_tx, \quad v_y .=. D_ty, \quad v_z .=. D_tz.$$

Similarly, the components of acceleration in rectangular coordinates are

$$a_x .=. D_t^2x, \quad a_y .=. D_t^2y, \quad a_z .=. D_t^2z.$$

The magnitude of the velocity, $|\mathbf{v}| = D_ts = v$, is called the **linear speed** of the particle. As the quantity $D_ts$ indicates, *speed is the instantaneous time rate of change of distance along the curve.* The direction angles of the velocity $\mathbf{v}$ are easily found from the relations

$$\cos \alpha = \frac{v_x}{v}, \quad \cos \beta = \frac{v_y}{v}, \quad \cos \gamma = \frac{v_z}{v}.$$

In a plane motion, the direction of $\mathbf{v}$ is usually given in terms of the angle $\theta$ between the x-axis and the vector $\mathbf{v}$. In that case

$$\cos \theta = \frac{v_x}{v}, \quad \sin \theta = \frac{v_y}{v}.$$

Similar expressions may be written to determine the direction of the acceleration $\mathbf{a}$.

---

*Example 18.4a.* A particle moves along the curve

$$\mathbf{r} = 4 \cos 3t\,\mathbf{i} + 5 \sin 3t\,\mathbf{j},$$

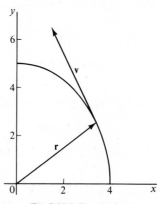

**FIGURE 18.4a**

where $t$ is time (see Figure 18.4a). Find the velocity and acceleration of the particle when $t = \pi/12$, and find the position of the particle when $|\mathbf{v}|$ is a minimum.

By differentiation with respect to $t$, we get

$$\mathbf{v} = -12 \sin 3t \, \mathbf{i} + 15 \cos 3t \, \mathbf{j},$$

and

$$\mathbf{a} = -36 \cos 3t \, \mathbf{i} - 45 \sin 3t \, \mathbf{j},$$

so that

$$\mathbf{a} = -9\mathbf{r}.$$

When $t = \pi/12$, then

$$\mathbf{v} = -6\sqrt{2}\mathbf{i} + (\tfrac{15}{2})\sqrt{2}\mathbf{j},$$
$$\mathbf{a} = -18\sqrt{2}\mathbf{i} - (\tfrac{45}{2})\sqrt{2}\mathbf{j}.$$

The fact that $\mathbf{a} = -9\mathbf{r}$ shows that the acceleration is always directed toward the origin $O$. (Why?)

Since

$$|\mathbf{v}| = (12^2 \sin^2 3t + 15^2 \cos^2 3t)^{1/2}$$
$$= (144 + 81 \cos^2 3t)^{1/2},$$

it follows that $|\mathbf{v}|$ has a minimum value when $\cos 3t = 0$, or when $3t = (2k + 1)\pi/2$, $k = 0, 1, 2, \ldots$ . Hence, $|\mathbf{v}|$ has a minimum value at $\mathbf{r} = 5\mathbf{j}$ or at $\mathbf{r} = -5\mathbf{j}$.

It is also of interest to note that the path of the motion is the ellipse

$$\frac{x^2}{16} + \frac{y^2}{25} = 1,$$

as may easily be seen by eliminating the parameter $t$ between the equations $x = 4 \cos 3t$, $y = 5 \sin 3t$. The points at which $|\mathbf{v}|$ is a minimum are the ends of the major axis.

---

There are many variations of the problems in curvilinear motion. The next example illustrates how the various quantities that we have considered can be used in order to obtain a solution.

---

*Example 18.4b.* A particle moves to the right along the curve $8y = x^2$ with a constant speed of 4 units per second. Find $\mathbf{a}$ and $\mathbf{v}$ at the point $(4, 2)$.

Since the path of the motion is given in rectangular coordinate form, it is implied that both $x$ and $y$ are functions of time. Hence, by differentiating both members of the equation $8y = x^2$ with respect to $t$, we get an equation relating $v_x$ and $v_y$:

$$8 \, D_t y = 2x \, D_t x \quad \text{or} \quad 4v_y = xv_x.$$

At $(4, 2)$ it follows that

$$v_y = v_x.$$

Since the speed is constant and equal to 4 units per second, we have

$$v_x^2 + v_y^2 = 16,$$

so that, at $(4, 2)$,

$$2v_x^2 = 16,$$

and

$$v_x = 2\sqrt{2} \text{ units per second.}$$

The positive square root is chosen to correspond to the statement that the motion is to the right. Consequently, at $(4, 2)$,

$$\mathbf{v} = 2\sqrt{2}\mathbf{i} + 2\sqrt{2}\mathbf{j}.$$

To find the components of acceleration, we must first differentiate both members of the equation $4v_y = xv_x$ with respect to $t$ to obtain

$$4a_y = v_x^2 + xa_x.$$

At (4, 2),

$$4a_y = 8 + 4a_x,$$

or

$$a_y = 2 + a_x.$$

In order to determine $a_x$ and $a_y$, we must have another relationship between them. It follows from

$$v^2 = v_x^2 + v_y^2,$$

by differentiation with respect to $t$, that

$$v \, D_t v = v_x a_x + v_y a_y.$$

Since $v$ is a constant, $D_t v = 0$, so that

$$0 = 2\sqrt{2}a_x + 2\sqrt{2}a_y$$

and

$$a_x = -a_y.$$

Consequently,

$$a_y = 1, \quad a_x = -1,$$

and at (4, 2)

$$\mathbf{a} = -\mathbf{i} + \mathbf{j}.$$

Notice particularly that the equation $4a_y = v_x^2 + xa_x$ must be obtained from the general equation relating the velocity components, and *not* from the equation $v_y = v_x$, which is true only at the point (4, 2).

---

In this example, we made use of the general scalar equation

(1) $$v \, D_t v = v_x a_x + v_y a_y.$$

This equation expresses a relationship between components of velocity and acceleration that must always hold for any object undergoing motion in a plane.

The preceding methods may be applied equally well to problems in three dimensions.

---

*Example 18.4c.* The position of a particle at time $t$ is given by

$$\mathbf{r}(t) = a \cos \omega t \, \mathbf{i} + a \sin \omega t \, \mathbf{j} + a\omega t \, \mathbf{k}.$$

Find the rate at which the particle turns about the $z$-axis, and the rate at which it turns about the $y$-axis.

The particle travels along a helical path, as shown in Figure 18.4b. If $\theta$ is the angle between the $xz$-plane and the plane determined by the $z$-axis and the vector $\mathbf{r}$, then the angular speed of the particle about the $z$-axis is given by $D_t \theta$. Since

$$x = a \cos \theta,$$

then

$$a \cos \omega t = a \cos \theta,$$

so that

$$\theta = \omega t$$

and

$$D_t \theta = \omega.$$

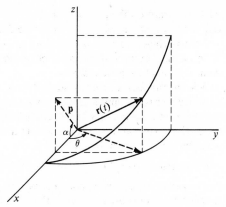

**FIGURE 18.4b**

The time rate of change of the angle $\alpha$ (see the figure) gives the angular speed with which the particle turns about the $y$-axis. Since

$$x = a \cos \omega t = p \cos \alpha = (x^2 + z^2)^{1/2} \cos \alpha,$$

then

$$\cos \alpha = (\omega^2 t^2 + \cos^2 \omega t)^{-1/2} \cos \omega t,$$

and, upon differentiating with respect to $t$, we get

$$-\sin \alpha \, D_t \alpha = \frac{-\omega^2 t(\omega t \sin \omega t + \cos \omega t)}{(\omega^2 t^2 + \cos^2 \omega t)^{3/2}}$$

after a small amount of simplification. We can easily obtain

$$\sin \alpha = \frac{\omega t}{(\omega^2 t^2 + \cos^2 \omega t)^{1/2}},$$

so that

$$D_t \alpha = \frac{\omega(\omega t \sin \omega t + \cos \omega t)}{\omega^2 t^2 + \cos^2 \omega t}.$$

## Exercises 18.4

In Numbers 1 to 12, the given vector describes the path of a particle in motion. Find $\mathbf{v}$, $\mathbf{a}$, and $D_t s$, and sketch the curve showing $\mathbf{v}$ and $\mathbf{a}$ at the point indicated.

1. $\mathbf{r}(t) = (t^2 + 4)\mathbf{i} + (t - 2)\mathbf{j}; t = 3.$
2. $\mathbf{r}(t) = \ln t \, \mathbf{i} + t^2\mathbf{j}; t = 1.$
3. $\mathbf{r}(t) = \cos 2t \, \mathbf{i} + \sin t \, \mathbf{j}; t = \pi/4.$
4. $\mathbf{r}(t) = e^{2t}\mathbf{i} + e^{3t}\mathbf{j}; t = 0.$
5. $\mathbf{r}(t) = \cos \omega t \, \mathbf{i} + \sin \omega t \, \mathbf{j} + \omega t \mathbf{k}; t = \pi/(4\omega).$
6. $\mathbf{r}(t) = 6t\mathbf{i} + 3t^2\mathbf{j} + 2t^3\mathbf{k}; t = 1.$
7. $\mathbf{r}(t) = 2 \sin \pi t \, \mathbf{i} + 2 \cos \pi t \, \mathbf{j} + 2 \sin \pi t \, \mathbf{k}; t = \frac{1}{3}.$
8. $\mathbf{r}(t) = \cos \omega t \, \mathbf{i} + 2 \sin \omega t \, \mathbf{j} + 2\omega t\mathbf{k}; t = \pi/(3\omega).$
9. $\mathbf{r}(t) = a \cos \pi t \, \mathbf{i} + a \sin \pi t \, \mathbf{j} + a \cos 4\pi t \, \mathbf{k}; t = \frac{1}{3}.$
10. $\mathbf{r}(t) = a(3t - t^3)\mathbf{i} + 3at^2\mathbf{j} + a(3t + t^3)\mathbf{k}; t = 1.$
11. $\mathbf{r}(t) = \ln \cos t \, \mathbf{i} + \ln \sin t \, \mathbf{j} + \sqrt{2}t\mathbf{k}; t = \pi/4.$
12. $\mathbf{r}(t) = a(t - \sin t)\mathbf{i} + a(1 - \cos t)\mathbf{j} + bt\mathbf{k}; t = \pi/2.$

13. A particle moves to the right on the path $x = 4y^2$, $y \geq 0$ with a constant speed of 2 units per second. Find $\mathbf{v}$ and $\mathbf{a}$ at $(4, 1)$. At what rate does the angle between the position vector of the particle and the $x$-axis change at $(4, 1)$?

14. A particle moves on a path at a constant speed. Show that its acceleration vector is always perpendicular to its tangent vector.

15. Suppose the particle in Number 13 moves so that $v_x$ is always equal to 2 units per second. Find $\mathbf{v}$ and $\mathbf{a}$ at $(4, 1)$, and find the rate at which the angle between the position vector of the particle and the $x$-axis is changing at $(4, 1)$.

16. When a wheel of radius $a$ rolls at a constant speed in a straight line without slipping, a particle on the rim moves in the path

$$x = a(\omega t - \sin \omega t), \quad y = a(1 - \cos \omega t),$$

where $\omega$ is in radians per second. Find $|\mathbf{v}|$ and $|\mathbf{a}|$, and find where $|\mathbf{v}|$ is a maximum

17. In Number 7, at what rate is the angle between the position vector and the $x$-axis changing at the time given?

18. In Number 9, find the rate at which the angle between the position vector and the $x$-axis changes as a function of time $t$.

## 18.5 CURVATURE

Since problems pertaining to velocities and accelerations are associated with first and second derivatives of vector functions, there is some merit in examining these derivatives in a general way. For example, we have shown that if $\mathbf{r}$ is a vector function, then $D_t \mathbf{r}(t)$ is a vector in the tangential direction of the curve described by the vector $\mathbf{r}$, and

$$D_t \mathbf{r}(t) = (D_t s)\mathbf{T},$$

where $\mathbf{T}$ is a unit tangent vector pointing in the direction of motion. For the second derivative, we have

$$D_t^2 \mathbf{r}(t) = (D_t^2 s)\mathbf{T} + (D_t s)\, D_t \mathbf{T}.$$

Since $\mathbf{T}$ is a unit vector, $D_t \mathbf{T}$ is a vector perpendicular to $\mathbf{T}$. It is reasonable to hope that a simple form for $D_t \mathbf{T}$ can be obtained.

We shall restrict the detailed discussion of this possibility to the two-dimensional case, and we shall consider the unit vector $\mathbf{T}$ as a new vector function. Let $\theta$ be the counterclockwise angle from the positive $x$-direction to the direction of $\mathbf{T}$. Then,

$$\mathbf{T} = \cos \theta \, \mathbf{i} + \sin \theta \, \mathbf{j}$$

and

$$D_\theta \mathbf{T} = -\sin \theta \, \mathbf{i} + \cos \theta \, \mathbf{j}.$$

It follows immediately that $D_\theta \mathbf{T}$ is a unit vector perpendicular to $\mathbf{T}$. (Why?) Furthermore, since

$$D_\theta \mathbf{T} = \cos (\pi/2 + \theta) \, \mathbf{i} + \sin (\pi/2 + \theta) \, \mathbf{j},$$

this vector is always 90° counterclockwise from the direction of $\mathbf{T}$ (see Figure 18.5a).

By the chain rule, we have

$$D_tT = D_t\theta\ D_\theta T = D_ts\ D_s\theta\ D_\theta T.$$

Since $D_ts = |\mathbf{v}|$, we see that $D_ts$ is an essentially nonnegative quantity—the speed along the curve. Thus,

$$|D_t\theta| = D_ts\ |D_s\theta|.$$

If we let **N** be a unit normal vector at the point of tangency and pointed toward the concave side of the curve (Figure 18.5b), then, $D_\theta T = \mathbf{N}$ or $-\mathbf{N}$,

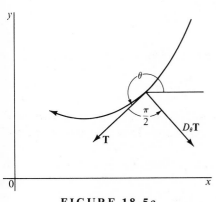

**FIGURE 18.5a**

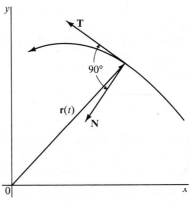

**FIGURE 18.5b**

depending on the sign of $D_t\theta$. If $D_t\theta > 0$, so that the tangent vector **T** turns counterclockwise as $t$ increases, then both **N** and $D_\theta T$ are 90° counterclockwise from **T** and

$$D_\theta T = \mathbf{N},$$

but if $D_t\theta < 0$, so that **T** turns clockwise, then **N** is 90° clockwise from the direction of **T**, and

$$D_\theta T = -\mathbf{N}.$$

In either case, we have

$$D_tT = D_ts\ |D_s\theta|\ \mathbf{N}.$$

The factor $|D_s\theta|$ on the right is worthy of more attention, since it occurs in many applications to problems in curvilinear motion.

**Definition 18.5a.** The **curvature** $K$ of a curve at a point $P$ is defined to be the absolute value of the rate of change of the inclination of the tangent vector **T** with respect to arc length $s$ along the curve; that is

$$K .=. |D_s\theta|$$

when the derivative exists.

This definition, dealing as it does with an intrinsic property of the curve, is, of course, independent of any coordinate system. (Note that $\theta$ could be measured from any fixed direction without changing the definition of the curvature $K$.) For actual computation of the curvature, it is desirable to have formulas in terms of the coordinate system that is being used. These formulas will be obtained as by-products of a further investigation of curvilinear motion.

At any point $P$ on a curve where $K$ exists, we may construct a circle of radius $R := 1/K$, tangent to the curve at $P$ and having its center on the normal drawn toward the concave side of the curve. This circle can be shown to fit the curve more closely than any other circle through the point $P$. For this reason, the circle is called the **circle of curvature** and its radius, the **radius of curvature**.

In terms of the curvature or the radius of curvature, we have

$$D_t\mathbf{T} = K D_t s \, \mathbf{N} = \frac{D_t s}{R} \mathbf{N}.$$

Consequently, the formula for the acceleration,

$$D_t^2\mathbf{r} = (D_t^2 s)\mathbf{T} + (D_t s)D_t\mathbf{T},$$

becomes

(1) $$D_t^2\mathbf{r} = (D_t^2 s)\mathbf{T} + \frac{(D_t s)^2}{R} \mathbf{N}.$$

The coefficients $D_t^2 s$ and $(D_t s)^2/R$ are called, respectively, the **tangential component** and the **normal component** of the acceleration. They are usually denoted by

(2) $$a_T := D_t^2 s \quad \text{and} \quad a_N := (D_t s)^2/R,$$

so that Formula (1) assumes the form

(3) $$D_t^2\mathbf{r} = a_T\mathbf{T} + a_N\mathbf{N}.$$

Although we shall not attempt to prove so, Formula (1) holds equally well for the three-dimensional case. The details of setting up the vector $\mathbf{N}$ are considerably more complicated than in the two-dimensional case, and it is beyond the scope of our discussion to include them here.

Equation (1) shows that if the speed $v = D_t s$ is constant for a particle, then the tangential component of acceleration is zero; but if the path of motion is curved, there is a nonzero normal component of acceleration. Anyone who has whirled a small weight tied to the end of a string has had physical experience of this normal acceleration.

It is possible to find the curvature or the radius of curvature at a given point on a curve by first calculating $D_t^2\mathbf{r}$ and then dot multiplying it by $\mathbf{N}$ to get

$$\mathbf{N} \cdot D_t^2\mathbf{r} = K(D_t s)^2,$$

or

$$K = \frac{\mathbf{N} \cdot D_t^2\mathbf{r}}{(D_t s)^2}.$$

For a curve in the $xy$-plane, we have

$$\begin{aligned}
\mathbf{T} = D_s\mathbf{r} &= D_s x \, \mathbf{i} + D_s y \, \mathbf{j} \\
&= (D_t x \, \mathbf{i} + D_t y \, \mathbf{j}) \, D_s t \\
&= \frac{D_t x}{D_t s}\mathbf{i} + \frac{D_t y}{D_t s}\mathbf{j} \\
&= \cos\theta \, \mathbf{i} + \sin\theta \, \mathbf{j},
\end{aligned}$$

where $\theta$ is the angle between the positive $x$-direction and the direction of **T**. Thus, as has been shown, **N** is either $D_\theta\mathbf{T}$ or $-D_\theta\mathbf{T}$; that is,

$$\mathbf{N} = \pm(-\sin\theta\,\mathbf{i} + \cos\theta\,\mathbf{j}),$$

or

$$\mathbf{N} = \pm\left(-\frac{D_t y}{D_t s}\mathbf{i} + \frac{D_t x}{D_t s}\mathbf{j}\right),$$

where the appropriate sign would have to be determined. (Recall that **N** points toward the concave side of the curve.)

Since

$$D_t^2\mathbf{r} = D_t^2 x\,\mathbf{i} + D_t^2 y\,\mathbf{j},$$

then

$$K = \frac{|\mathbf{N}\cdot D_t^2\mathbf{r}|}{(D_t s)^2} = \left|\frac{-\dfrac{D_t y}{D_t s}D_t^2 x + \dfrac{D_t x}{D_t s}D_t^2 y}{(D_t s)^2}\right|,$$

or

(4) $$K = \left|\frac{D_t y\,D_t^2 x - D_t x\,D_t^2 y}{(D_t s)^3}\right|.$$

The use of Formula (4) is illustrated in the next example.

---

*Example 18.5a.* Find the curvature at the point $(1, \frac{1}{6})$, on the curve described by

$$\mathbf{r} = t\mathbf{i} + \tfrac{1}{6}t^3\mathbf{j}.$$

Since

$$x = t, \quad y = \tfrac{1}{6}t^3,$$

it follows that

$$D_t x = 1, \quad D_t^2 x = 0, \quad D_t y = \tfrac{1}{2}t^2, \quad D_t^2 y = t$$

and

$$D_t s = [(D_t x)^2 + (D_t y)^2]^{1/2}$$
$$= \left(1 + \frac{t^4}{4}\right)^{1/2}$$

At $(1, \frac{1}{6})$, we have $t = 1$, so that

$$K = \frac{1}{(5/4)^{3/2}} = \frac{5\sqrt{5}}{8}.$$

---

If the equation of a curve is given in rectangular coordinates, Equation (4) may be used if the curve can be described in parametric form easily. Otherwise, another formula can be derived. It is left as an exercise (see Exercises 18.5, Number 11) for the reader to show that if $y = f(x)$, then

(5) $$K = \frac{|D_x^2 y|}{[1 + (D_x y)^2]^{3/2}}.$$

In three dimensions, the curvature can be found by a more direct approach. To find the curvature of the curve described by $\mathbf{r}(t)$, we may write

$$D_s\mathbf{r} = D_t\mathbf{r}\,D_s t,$$

where $s$ is arc length. Since $D_s\mathbf{r} = \mathbf{T}$, we have

$$\mathbf{T} = D_t\mathbf{r}\, D_s t.$$

By forming the dot product of each member of the preceding equation with itself, we find

$$1 = (D_t\mathbf{r} \cdot D_t\mathbf{r})(D_s t)^2,$$

so that

$$D_s t = \frac{1}{(D_t\mathbf{r} \cdot D_t\mathbf{r})^{1/2}}.$$

We have previously found that $D_t\mathbf{T} = K(D_t s)\mathbf{N}$. Consequently, if $s$ rather than $t$ is the parameter, we find

$$D_s\mathbf{T} = K\mathbf{N},$$

where $K$ is the curvature. Hence,

$$K^2 = D_s\mathbf{T} \cdot D_s\mathbf{T},$$

where, since $\mathbf{T} = D_t\mathbf{r}\, D_s t,$

$$\begin{aligned} D_s\mathbf{T} &= D_s(D_t\mathbf{r}\, D_s t) \\ &= [D_s(D_t\mathbf{r})]\, D_s t + D_t\mathbf{r}\, D_s^2 t \\ &= D_t^2\mathbf{r}(D_s t)^2 + D_t\mathbf{r}\, D_s^2 t. \end{aligned}$$

Since it is not promising to write a formula for $K$, it is better simply to use the procedure just outlined.

---

*Example 18.5b.* Find the curvature of the curve described by

$$\mathbf{r}(t) = \ln \cos t\, \mathbf{i} + \ln \sin t\, \mathbf{j} - \sqrt{2}t\mathbf{k}, \qquad 0 < t < \pi/2.$$

First, we find $\mathbf{T}$.

(6)
$$\mathbf{T} = D_s\mathbf{r} = \left(-\frac{\sin t}{\cos t}\mathbf{i} + \frac{\cos t}{\sin t}\mathbf{j} - \sqrt{2}\mathbf{k}\right) D_s t.$$

Hence,

$$\mathbf{T} \cdot \mathbf{T} = 1 = \left(\frac{\sin^2 t}{\cos^2 t} + \frac{\cos^2 t}{\sin^2 t} + 2\right)(D_s t)^2,$$

and

$$D_s t = \left(\frac{\cos^2 t \sin^2 t}{\sin^4 t + 2\sin^2 t \cos^2 t + \cos^4 t}\right)^{1/2} = \cos t \sin t,$$

which is positive, since $0 < t < \pi/2$. Thus, using this expression in Equation (6), we obtain

$$\mathbf{T} = -\sin^2 t\, \mathbf{i} + \cos^2 t\, \mathbf{j} - \sqrt{2} \cos t \sin t\, \mathbf{k}.$$

Then, differentiating with respect to $s$, we get

$$\begin{aligned} D_s\mathbf{T} = K\mathbf{N} &= [-2\sin t \cos t\, \mathbf{i} - 2\cos t \sin t\, \mathbf{j} - \sqrt{2}(\cos^2 t - \sin^2 t)\mathbf{k}]\, D_s t \\ &= (-\sin 2t\, \mathbf{i} - \sin 2t\, \mathbf{j} - \sqrt{2}\cos 2t\, \mathbf{k})\sin t \cos t. \end{aligned}$$

It follows that

$$\begin{aligned} K\mathbf{N} \cdot K\mathbf{N} = K^2 &= (2\sin^2 2t + 2\cos^2 2t)\sin^2 t \cos^2 t \\ &= 2\sin^2 t \cos^2 t, \end{aligned}$$

or

$$K^2 = \tfrac{1}{2} \sin^2 2t, \quad \text{and} \quad K = \frac{1}{\sqrt{2}} |\sin 2t|.$$

## Exercises 18.5

In each of Numbers 1 to 10, find the radius of curvature at the given point.

1. $4x = y^2$; $(0, 0)$.
2. $y = e^{2x}$; $(\ln 2, 4)$.
3. $4x^2 + 9y^2 = 36$; $(0, 2)$.
4. $x = \frac{1}{2}t^2 + t$, $y = \frac{1}{2}t^2 - t$; $t = 2$.
5. $x = 3 \cos \theta$, $y = 4 \sin \theta$; $\theta = \pi/4$.
6. $x = 2(\theta - \sin \theta)$, $y = 2(1 - \cos \theta)$; $\theta = \pi/3$.
7. $\mathbf{r}(t) = a \cos^3 t \, \mathbf{i} + a \sin^3 t \, \mathbf{j}$; $t = \pi/4$.
8. $\mathbf{r}(t) = 3t\mathbf{i} + 3 \ln t \, \mathbf{j}$; $t = 3$.
9. $y = \mathrm{Sin}^{-1} x$; $(\frac{1}{2}, \pi/6)$.

10. $\mathbf{r}(t) = 2 \tan t \, \mathbf{i} + 2 \cot t \, \mathbf{j}$; $t = \pi/4$.
11. Derive Equation (5). *Hint*: Write $x = t$, so that $y = f(t)$.
12. Show that the curvature of the curve described by
$$\mathbf{r}(t) = a(3t - t^3)\mathbf{i} + 3at^2\mathbf{j} + a(3t + t^3)\mathbf{k}$$
is
$$K = \frac{1}{3a(1 + t^2)^2}.$$

13. Find the curvature of the curve described by
$$\mathbf{r}(t) = a \cos \omega t \, \mathbf{i} + a \sin \omega t \, \mathbf{j} + b\omega t \mathbf{k}.$$

14. Find the curvature of the curve described by
$$\mathbf{r}(u) = a(u - \sin u)\mathbf{i} + a(1 - \cos u)\mathbf{j} + au\mathbf{k}$$
at the point where $u = \pi/2$.

In each of Numbers 15 to 17, find the tangential and normal components of $\mathbf{a}$ at the given points for a particle moving on the given curve. Assume the units are feet and seconds.

15. $\mathbf{r}(t) = (t^2 - 1)\mathbf{i} + (\frac{1}{3}t^3 - t)\mathbf{j}$; $t = 1$.
16. $\mathbf{r}(t) = 3 \cos t \, \mathbf{i} + 4 \sin t \, \mathbf{j}$; $t = \pi/4$.
17. $\mathbf{r}(t) = a \cos t^2 \, \mathbf{i} + a \sin t^2 \, \mathbf{j}$; $t = \sqrt{\pi}/2$.
18. A particle moves on the upper portion of the curve $y^2 = 4x$ with a constant horizontal speed of 4 units per second to the right. Find $a_T$ and $a_N$ at the point $(4, 4)$.
★19. For a curve given in polar coordinates, show that the curvature $K$ is given by
$$K = \frac{|r^2 + 2(D_\theta r)^2 - r D_\theta^2 r|}{[r^2 + (D_\theta r)^2]^{3/2}}.$$

*Hint*: Find $\mathbf{T}$ in terms of $\mathbf{e}_r$ and $\mathbf{e}_\theta$, and then find $D_s\mathbf{T}$.

In each of Numbers 20 to 23, find the radius of curvature at the indicated point by using the result of Number 19.

20. $r = 1 - \cos \theta$, $\theta = \pi/2$.
21. $r = 3 \cos \theta + 4 \sin \theta$, $\theta = \theta_0$.
22. $r = \sin 2\theta$, $\theta = \pi/6$.
23. $r^2 = a^2 \cos 2\theta$, $\theta = \pi/6$.

## 18.6 DERIVATIVES IN POLAR COORDINATES

A vector function in polar coordinates is given by an equation of the form

$$\mathbf{r} = r(\theta)\mathbf{e}_r,$$

where $\mathbf{e}_r$ is a unit vector making an angle $\theta$ with the $x$-axis. It has been shown in Section 18.2 that

(1)
$$D_\theta\mathbf{r} = D_\theta r \, \mathbf{e}_r + r\mathbf{e}_\theta,$$

where $\mathbf{e}_\theta$ is a unit vector perpendicular to $\mathbf{e}_r$.

In rectangular coordinates, $D_x y$ represents the slope of the curve $y = f(x)$ at a given point. We have seen (Section 13.4) that in polar coordinates, $D_\theta r$ is not the slope of the curve for a given value of $\theta$. To obtain a geometric interpretation for $D_\theta r$, we form the scalar product on both sides of Equation (1) with $\mathbf{e}_r$ to get

$$\mathbf{e}_r \cdot D_\theta\mathbf{r} = D_\theta r \Rightarrow |D_\theta\mathbf{r}| \cos\psi = D_\theta r,$$

and then form the vector product to get

$$\mathbf{e}_r \times D_\theta\mathbf{r} = r\mathbf{e}_r \times \mathbf{e}_\theta \Rightarrow |D_\theta\mathbf{r}| \sin\psi = r,$$

where $\psi$ is the angle between $D_\theta\mathbf{r}$ and $\mathbf{e}_r$. These two results show that

$$D_\theta r \neq 0 \Rightarrow \tan\psi = \frac{r}{D_\theta r}.$$

Thus, $r/D_\theta r$ is the tangent of the angle between the radial direction and the tangent line to the curve (see Figure 18.6a).

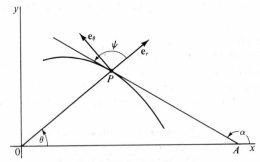

**FIGURE 18.6a**

The velocity of a particle moving on a path $\mathbf{r} = r(\theta)\mathbf{e}_r$ is given in terms of radial and transverse components by

$$\mathbf{v} = D_t\mathbf{r} = (D_t r)\mathbf{e}_r + rD_t\mathbf{e}_r$$
$$= (D_t r)\mathbf{e}_r + r(D_\theta\mathbf{e}_r)D_t\theta$$
$$= (D_t r)\mathbf{e}_r + (rD_t\theta)\mathbf{e}_\theta.$$

The quantity $D_t\theta$ is called the **angular speed** of the particle. From the equation for the velocity, we obtain the acceleration in terms of its radial and transverse components. That is,

$$\mathbf{a} .=. D_t^2\mathbf{r} = D_t^2r\, \mathbf{e}_r + D_tr\, D_t\mathbf{e}_r + D_tr\, D_t\theta\, \mathbf{e}_\theta + r\, D_t^2\theta\, \mathbf{e}_\theta + r\, D_t\theta\, D_t\mathbf{e}_\theta$$
$$= D_t^2r\, \mathbf{e}_r + 2D_tr\, D_t\theta\, \mathbf{e}_\theta + r\, D_t^2\theta\, \mathbf{e}_\theta + r\, D_t\theta\, D_t\theta(-\mathbf{e}_r)$$
$$= [D_t^2r - r(D_t\theta)^2]\mathbf{e}_r + [2D_tr\, D_t\theta + r\, D_t^2\theta]\mathbf{e}_\theta.$$

It is interesting to note the meanings of the individual terms of the two components of the acceleration. The term $D_t^2r$ is the acceleration that the particle would attain if it were simply receding from the origin along the radius vector fixed at angle $\theta$. The term $r(D_t\theta)^2$ is the normal acceleration that the particle would attain if it were moving in a circular path of radius $r$ with angular speed $D_t\theta$. This acceleration is directed toward the center of the circle (the origin). Thus, the difference of these two terms is a plausible result for the radial acceleration. The term $r\, D_t^2\theta$ is the tangential acceleration of a particle moving on a circle of radius $r$, since the angular acceleration is $D_t^2\theta$. The term $2(D_tr)(D_t\theta)$ is not so easy to explain. It is the so-called Coriolis acceleration that one finds in investigating the motion of a body whose position is referred to moving axes such as the unit vectors $\mathbf{e}_r$ and $\mathbf{e}_\theta$.

---

*Example 18.6a.* A particle moves with a constant angular speed of $\omega_0$ radians per second on the curve $r = a(1 - \cos\theta)$. Find the acceleration of the particle when $\theta = \pi/2$.

If

$$\mathbf{r} = a(1 - \cos\theta)\mathbf{e}_r,$$

then

$$\mathbf{v} = a\sin\theta\, D_t\theta\, \mathbf{e}_r + a(1 - \cos\theta)\, D_t\theta\, \mathbf{e}_\theta.$$

Since $D_t\theta = \omega_0$, a constant, it follows that

$$\mathbf{v} = a\omega_0\sin\theta\, \mathbf{e}_r + a\omega_0(1 - \cos\theta)\mathbf{e}_\theta,$$

and

$$\mathbf{a} = D_t\mathbf{v} = a\omega_0^2\cos\theta\, \mathbf{e}_r + 2a\omega_0^2\sin\theta\, \mathbf{e}_\theta - a\omega_0^2(1 - \cos\theta)\mathbf{e}_r$$
$$= a\omega_0^2(2\cos\theta - 1)\mathbf{e}_r + 2a\omega_0^2\sin\theta\, \mathbf{e}_\theta.$$

At $\theta = \pi/2$, $\mathbf{a} = -a\omega_0^2\mathbf{e}_r + 2a\omega_0^2\mathbf{e}_\theta$.

---

Suppose a particle revolves about a fixed axis, $L$, with an angular speed $\omega = D_t\theta$ radians per second. Let $O$ be an origin on $L$, and let $\mathbf{r}$ be the position vector of the particle relative to $O$. We found in Section 14.5 that the linear velocity $\mathbf{v}$ of the particle is given by

$$\mathbf{v} = \omega \times \mathbf{r},$$

where the angular velocity $\omega$ of the particle, has a magnitude equal to the angular speed $\omega$ and points in the direction along $L$, from which the rotation appears to be counterclockwise. Thus, since $\mathbf{v} = D_t\mathbf{r}$, we may write

$$D_t\mathbf{r} = \omega \times \mathbf{r}.$$

Note that this formula has been obtained only for rotation about a fixed axis.

*Example 18.6b.* Find the angular velocity vector of a particle moving on the path

$$\mathbf{r} = a \cos t^2 \, \mathbf{i} + a \sin t^2 \, \mathbf{j}.$$

Since

$$\mathbf{v} = D_t \mathbf{r} = -2ta \sin t^2 \, \mathbf{i} + 2ta \cos t^2 \, \mathbf{j},$$

and the motion is in the $xy$-plane, the angular velocity vector must be in the $z$-direction. We also have

$$\mathbf{i} = -\mathbf{k} \times \mathbf{j} \quad \text{and} \quad \mathbf{j} = \mathbf{k} \times \mathbf{i},$$

so that we may write

$$\begin{aligned}
\mathbf{v} &= 2ta \sin t^2 \, \mathbf{k} \times \mathbf{j} + 2ta \cos t^2 \, \mathbf{k} \times \mathbf{i} \\
&= 2t\mathbf{k} \times (a \cos t^2 \, \mathbf{i} + a \sin t^2 \, \mathbf{j}) \\
&= 2t\mathbf{k} \times \mathbf{r}.
\end{aligned}$$

Hence,

$$\boldsymbol{\omega} = 2t\mathbf{k}.$$

## Exercises 18.6

1. The angle of intersection, $\varphi$, of two curves is defined as the angle between their tangent lines at the point of intersection. If $\mathbf{r}_1 = r_1(\theta)\mathbf{e}_r$ and $\mathbf{r}_2 = r_2(\theta)\mathbf{e}_r$ are the vector equations of the two curves, and $\psi_1$ and $\psi_2$ are, respectively, the angles between $D_\theta\mathbf{r}$ and $\mathbf{e}_r$, show that $\varphi = |\psi_2 - \psi_1|$.

In Numbers 2, 3, and 4, use the result of Number 1 to find the angle of intersection between the curves.

2. $1 = 4r(1 + \cos\theta)$ and $r = 1 + \cos\theta$.
3. $r = 3a \cos\theta$ and $r = a(1 + \cos\theta)$.
4. $r = 2 \sin\theta$ and $r^2 = 2 \cos 2\theta$.

In Numbers 5 to 9, assume that a particle is moving on the given curve with a constant angular speed of $\omega_0$ radians per second. Find the acceleration of the particle at the given point. Make an appropriate sketch in each case.

5. $r = \dfrac{2}{1 + \cos\theta}$, $\theta = \pi/2$.

6. $r = 2 \sin\theta$, $\theta = \pi/6$.
7. $r = \sin 2\theta$, $\theta = \pi/6$.
8. $r = 2 - \cos\theta$, $\theta = \pi/3$.
9. $r^2 = a^2 \cos 2\theta$, $\theta = \pi/8$.

10. A particle moving in space has a velocity $\mathbf{v} = \omega\mathbf{k} \times \mathbf{r}$, where $\omega$ is constant. Prove that the particle moves along a circle and has a constant angular speed of $\omega$ radians per second. *Hint:* Show first that the motion must be in a plane parallel to the $xy$-plane, and then use the fact that $\mathbf{v} \cdot \mathbf{r} = 0$.

11. Suppose a particle moves on the curve

$$\mathbf{r} = a \sin \omega t \, \mathbf{i} + a \cos \omega t \, \mathbf{j} + b\omega t\mathbf{k}.$$

Show that the velocity of the particle is the sum of a translational velocity and a rotational velocity and find each. *Hint:* Consider $\mathbf{v} - b\omega\mathbf{k}$.

12. If $\alpha(t) = D_t\omega(t)$, where $\omega(t)$ is the angular velocity of a particle revolving about a fixed axis $L$, then $\alpha(t)$ is called the angular acceleration of the particle. Show that the linear acceleration $\mathbf{a}$ is given by

$$\mathbf{a} = (\boldsymbol{\omega}\cdot\mathbf{r})\boldsymbol{\omega} - \omega^2\mathbf{r} + \boldsymbol{\alpha} \times \mathbf{r}.$$

13. For the motion described in Example 18.6b, find $\mathbf{a}$ by direct use of the expression given for $\mathbf{r}$ and the definition $\mathbf{a} .=. D_t^2\mathbf{r}$. Show that your result is the same as that obtained by use of the formula in Number 12.

14. A thin disk of radius $b$ in the $xy$-plane rolls without slipping along the $x$-axis in the positive $x$-direction. Show that the linear velocity of any point $P$ on the disk is given by

$$\mathbf{v} = \mathbf{v}_c + \boldsymbol{\omega} \times \boldsymbol{\rho},$$

where $\mathbf{v}_c$ is the velocity of the center of the disk, $\boldsymbol{\rho}$ is a vector from the center of the disk to $P$, and $\boldsymbol{\omega}$ is the vector

$$-\frac{|\mathbf{v}_c|}{2\pi b}\,\mathbf{k}.$$

*Hint:* Let $\mathbf{r}$ be the vector from the origin to $P$. Then $\mathbf{r} = \mathbf{r}_c + \boldsymbol{\rho}$ and $\mathbf{v} = D_t\mathbf{r}$.

---

# Summary of Chapter 18

---

Many of the concepts introduced in this chapter will appear in later chapters. It is therefore very important to the reader that the following ideas be clearly understood:

(1) the definition of a vector function (Section 18.1);

(2) the neighborhood concept as used in connection with vector functions (Section 18.1);

(3) the limit of a vector function and related properties (Section 18.1);

(4) the continuity of a vector function (Section 18.1);

(5) the derivative of a vector function and related properties (Section 18.2);

(6) the equation of a tangent line and normal plane to a curve (Section 18.2);

(7) the geometric character of the derivative of a unit vector (Section 18.2);

(8) the definition of the length of arc of a curve (Section 18.3);

(9) the arc length function (Section 18.3);

(10) the differential of arc length and its relationship to the differentials of $x$ and $y$ in rectangular coordinates (Section 18.3);

(11) the definitions of velocity and acceleration (Section 18.4);

(12) the curvature of a curve (Section 18.5);

(13) the tangential and normal components of acceleration (Section 18.5);

(14) the derivative of a vector function in polar coordinates and the geometric meaning of $r/D_\theta r$ (Section 18.6);

(15) the angular velocity and angular speed of a particle (Section 18.6);

(16) velocity and acceleration in polar coordinates (Section 18.6).

# Chapter 19    Partial Differentiation I

## 19.1 FUNCTIONS OF SEVERAL VARIABLES

The representation of curves and surfaces in three dimensions by means of equations of the form $F(x, y, z) = 0$ suggests that the function concept can easily be extended so that it is not restricted to any particular number of dimensions. Just as we denote a point in a two-dimensional space by an ordered pair of real numbers, or denote a point in a three-dimensional space by an ordered triple of real numbers, we use an ordered $n$-tuple of real numbers $(x_1, x_2, \ldots, x_n)$ to denote what is called a *point in an n-dimensional space*. Thus, a point in an $n$-dimensional space is simply a definite, ordered arrangement of $n$ real numbers.

Let $\mho_n$ be the set of all ordered $n$-tuples of real numbers; that is, the set of all points in an $n$-dimensional space. We shall frequently find it convenient to represent a point in $\mho_n$ by a single letter such as $X$. Thus, the statement that $X$ is a point in $\mho_n$ means that $X$ is an ordered $n$-tuple of real numbers. For instance, $X \in \mho_2$ means that $X$ is an ordered pair $(x, y)$ of real numbers, a point in a two-dimensional space, and $X \in \mho_3$ means that $X$ is an ordered triple $(x, y, z)$ of real numbers, a point in a three-dimensional space.

**Definition 19.1a.** A set of ordered pairs $F = \{(X, u)\}$, where $X \in \mho_n$, and for which $(X_1, u_1) \in F$ and $(X_1, u_2) \in F \Rightarrow u_1 = u_2$, is called a *function of variables*.

This definition is simply a repetition of the definition of a function of one variable with a suitable alteration in the domain. In this case, the **domain** of the function is the set of points $\{X\}$ in the space $\mho_n$, and the **range** is the set of values $\{u\}$ appearing in the set of pairs in $F$.

As in the case of a function of one variable, it is convenient to describe function by means of an equation that expresses a relationship between the *coordinates* of the point $X$ and the functional value $u$. For example, in two dimensions, where $X .=. (x, y)$, the conditions $x^2 + y^2 = u^2$, $u \geq 0$ describe a function $\{(X, u)\}$.

It is easy to interpret such a function geometrically. The pair $(X, u)$ is essentially an ordered triple $(x, y, u)$, which may be interpreted as a point in three-dimensional space. From the discussion in Chapter 17, we know that the function

$$F .=. \{(X, u): X = (x, y), x^2 + y^2 = u^2, u \geq 0\}$$

is represented geometrically as a part of the surface of a cone, the first quadrant portion of which is shown in Figure 19.1a.

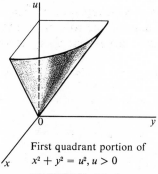

First quadrant portion of
$x^2 + y^2 = u^2, u > 0$

**FIGURE 19.1a**

The preceding discussion applies equally well to functions defined on $\mathcal{V}_3$ or $\mathcal{V}_k, k > 3$, although a similar geometric representation is not available. Furthermore, the functional notation introduced for functions $f$, where $y = f(x)$, can be extended to apply to functions defined on $\mathcal{V}_n$. If

$$F .=. \{(X, u)\},$$

where $X \in \mathcal{V}_n$, then we shall write

$$u = F(X)$$

and say that $F$ is a function of $n$ variables. For example, if the domain is in $\mathcal{V}_2$, we write

$$u = F(x, y) \quad \text{or} \quad u = F(X)$$

and say that $u$ is a function of two variables. The coordinates of the general point $X$ are called **independent variables,** and $u$ is called a **dependent variable.**

*Example19 .1a.* Find the domain and range of the function described by

$$u = \sqrt{4 - x^2 - y^2}.$$

Since we are concerned only with values of $x$ and $y$ for which $u$ is a real number, the domain is the set of points $\{(x, y): 4 - x^2 - y^2 \geq 0\}$, that is, the set of points that are interior to or that are on the circle $x^2 + y^2 = 4$. The range is seen, by inspection, to be the set $\{u: 0 \leq u \leq 2\}$.

In general, equations such as

$$x^2 + y^2 + z^2 = 4,$$

or

$$xyz = 1,$$

may be regarded as describing functions implicitly. Equations of this type are often represented by the general form

$$F(x, y, z) = C.$$

When such an equation is given, it is usually understood to imply one or more functions, and one variable may be regarded as dependent upon the other two variables, which therefore assume the role of independent variables. For example, if we wish to consider $z$ dependent upon the values of $x$ and $y$, we may write

$$F(x, y, z) = C \Rightarrow z = f(x, y).$$

Thus, if

$$F(x, y, z) .=. x^2 + y^2 + z^2 = 4,$$

then we may write

$$f_1(x, y) .=. z = \sqrt{4 - x^2 - y^2},$$

or

$$f_2(x, y) .=. z = -\sqrt{4 - x^2 - y^2}.$$

Although in this illustration the equation $F(x, y, z) = C$ can actually be solved for $z$ in terms of $x$ and $y$, there is no guarantee that such a form for $z$ can always be obtained in a practical sense. On occasion we must be content to know that such a relationship exists *theoretically*, even though we cannot find it explicitly. Thus, the equation

$$x^5y + x^3yz + y^2z^4 - 2y^5z^2 + 6z^5 = 12$$

cannot be solved conveniently for $x$, $y$, or $z$ in terms of the other two variables. Nevertheless, for each given point, for instance $(x, y) = (1, 2)$, we obtain an equation such as

$$-10 + 2z + 4z^4 - 64z^2 + 6z^5 = 0,$$

which actually has at least one real solution for $z$.

In much of the work that follows in the remainder of this chapter, we shall give proofs and illustrations for functions of two variables. However, the reader should keep in mind that corresponding results apply equally well to functions of more than two variables.

## Exercises 19.1

In each of Numbers 1 to 8, describe the domain of the given function, provided the function is to be real-valued.

1. $f(x, y) .=. \ln (1 + xy).$

2. $g(x, y) .=. \dfrac{xy}{\sqrt{1 - x^2 - y^2}}.$

3. $h(x, y) .=. \mathrm{Tan}^{-1} \sqrt{4 - x^2 - y^2}.$

4. $f(x, y) .=. \sqrt{\dfrac{x + y}{x - y}}.$

5. $f(x, y) .=. \sin \sqrt{x^2 + y^2 - 1}.$

6. $g(x, y) .=. \ln \sqrt{\dfrac{x^2 - y^2}{x^2 + y^2}}.$

7. $g(x, y) .=. \dfrac{x + y - 1}{x^2 + y^2 - 1}.$

8. $h(x, v) .=. xe^{x/y}.$

## 19.2 SETS OF POINTS

In order to discuss functions of two or more variables simply and concisely, we must make use of several concepts associated with sets of points in two or more dimensions. We shall assume that the space is euclidean—that is, that the distance between two points in $\mathcal{V}_n$,

$$X = (x_1, x_2, \ldots, x_n) \quad \text{and} \quad P = (p_1, p_2, \ldots, p_n),$$

is given by

$$d(P, X) = [(p_1 - x_1)^2 + (p_2 - x_2)^2 + \cdots + (p_n - x_n)^2]^{1/2}.$$

The reader should notice that this is a direct generalization of the definition of distance in the two- and three-dimensional cases. Definitions 18.1b and 18.1c, respectively, describe a neighborhood of $P$ and a deleted neighborhood of $P$. The reader should recall that

$$\mathfrak{N}(P, \epsilon) .=. \{X: d(P, X) < \epsilon\}$$

and

$$\mathfrak{N}^*(P, \epsilon) .=. \mathfrak{N}(P, \epsilon) - \{P\}.$$

In the discussion that follows, we shall usually be concerned with a subset $\mathcal{S} = \{(x, y)\}$ of points of the plane $\mathcal{V}_2$. Such a set partitions the plane into two parts, the set $\mathcal{S}$ and the remaining points of the plane that constitute the complement of $\mathcal{S}$.

**Definition 19.2a.** A point $P$ of a set $\mathcal{S}$ is called an **interior point** of $\mathcal{S}$ if there exists a neighborhood $\mathfrak{N}(P, \epsilon)$ that is contained entirely in $\mathcal{S}$. That is, if $P$ is an interior point of $\mathcal{S}$, then there must be a $\mathfrak{N}(P, \epsilon) \subset \mathcal{S}$.

For example, if $\mathcal{S} .=. \{(x, y): x^2 + y^2 \le 4\}$, then the point $P(1, 1)$ is an interior point of $\mathcal{S}$ because there is *some* neighborhood of $P$, such as $\mathfrak{N}(P, \frac{1}{10})$, that is contained entirely within $\mathcal{S}$. By contrast, the point $Q(2, 0)$ is not an interior point because every neighborhood of $Q$ contains points that are not in $\mathcal{S}$ (see Figure 19.2a).

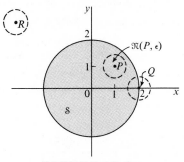

**FIGURE 19.2a**

The classification of certain points as interior points of a set $\mathcal{S}$ immediately suggests that other points in the space also deserve a special classification.

**Definition 19.2b.** A point $Q$ is called a **boundary point** of $S$ if *every* neighborhood of $Q$ contains both points of $S$ and points not in $S$.

In Figure 19.2b, the point $Q$ is a boundary point of $S$. Evidently, a boundary point of a set need not be in the set, as will be illustrated after

**Definition 19.2c.** A point $R$ that is an interior point of the complement of a set $S$ is called an **exterior point** of $S$.

The point $R$ in Figure 19.2a is an exterior point of $S$.

---

*Example 19.2a.* Describe the interior, exterior, and boundary points of the set

$$S \, . = . \, \{(x, y): x^2 + y^2 < 1, \, y \geq 0\}.$$

The set $S$ is shown graphically in Figure 19.2b. The boundary points of $S$ are those points on the semicircle and on the $x$-axis between $-1$ and $+1$.

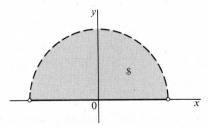

**FIGURE 19.2b**

If the set of boundary points is denoted by $S^b$, then

$$S^b = \{(x, y): y = \sqrt{1 - x^2}\} \cup \{(x, y): y = 0, \, -1 \leq x \leq 1\}.$$

The set of interior points of $S$, denoted by $S^i$, is the set

$$S^i = \{(x, y): 0 < y < \sqrt{1 - x^2}\}.$$

The set of exterior points of $S$, denoted by $S^e$, is the set

$$S^e = (S^i \cup S^b)';$$

that is, the set of all points that are neither in the shaded region nor on its boundary.

---

In general, for any subset of $S$ of $\mathcal{V}_2$, we may write $\mathcal{V}_2 = S^b \cup S^e \cup S^i$, where the sets $S^b$, $S^e$, and $S^i$ are **mutually disjoint**—that is, each pair has an empty intersection.

As the preceding example illustrates, not all the boundary points of a set need be in $S$. However, sets that contain none of their boundary points and sets that contain all of their boundary points are particularly important in many mathematical discussions.

**Definition 19.2d.** If all the points of a set $S$ are interior points then $S$ is called an **open set.**

The set of points $S . = . \{(x, y): x^2 + y^2 < 1\}$ is an example of an open set. Every point in $S$ is an interior point of $S$, since if any point $P$ in $S$ is selected, then some neighborhood of $P$ that is contained entirely in $S$ can be found.

**Definition 19.2e.** If a set $S$ contains all its boundary points, it is said to be a **closed set.**

The definition can be stated more precisely by saying that $S$ is closed if $S^b \subset S$. For example, the set $S . = . \{(x, y): x^2 + y^2 \leq 1\}$ is a closed set. The student should be warned that sets are not like doors which are either open or closed. Example 19.2a illustrates a set $S$ that is neither open nor closed, since it contains some, but not all, of its boundary points. (In Example 19.2a, what are the boundary points of the set $S$ that are in $S$?)

It may happen that a set consists of the union of two or more disjoint subsets, as, for example, in Figure 19.2c, where $S = \alpha \cup \beta$. If each of $\alpha$ and $\beta$ is an

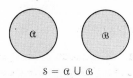

$$S = \alpha \cup \beta$$

**FIGURE 19.2c**

open set, then $S$ is an open set; and if each is closed, then $S$ is a closed set. In general, sets of this type are distinguished from other types of sets according to

**Definition 19.2f.** A set of points $S$ is said to be **connected** if any two points $P$, $Q$ in $S$ can be connected by a continuous curve that lies entirely in $S$. Otherwise, a set is *not connected.*

The set $S$ illustrated in Figure 19.2c is not connected. The set illustrated in Figure 19.2b is connected. The kind of connected set that we wish to make use of in much of the work that follows is described in

**Definition 19.2g.** A **region** is a **connected open set** plus none, some, or all of the boundary points of the set. A region consisting of an open set alone is called an **open region.** A region that is a closed set is called a **closed region.**

The sets of points shown in Figures 19.2a and 19.2b are both regions. The set in Figure 19.2c is not connected; hence, it is not a region. In Figure 19.2d are

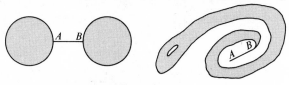

**FIGURE 19.2d**

illustrated two sets of points that are not regions. The reader should decide for himself why these sets are not regions. *Hint:* Are the points on the line segments marked *AB* interior points or boundary points of any open set?

## Exercises 19.2

In each of the following, determine $S^e$, $S^i$, $S^b$, and state whether the given set $S$ is a region.

1. $S .=. \{(x, y): 0 \leq x < 2, 0 \leq y < 1\}$.
2. $S .=. \{(x, y): x^2 + y^2 < 4, x^2 + y^2 > 1\}$.
3. $S .=. \{(x, y): x^2 + y^2 > 4\} \cup \{(x, y): x^2 + y^2 < 1\}$.
4. $S .=. \{(x, y): x^2 + y^2 \geq 1, \text{ or } y = 0 \text{ when } -1 < x < 1\}$.
5. $S .=. \{(x, y): x + 2y < 4 \text{ and } x + 2y > 2\}$.
6. $S .=. \{(x, y): x \geq 0 \text{ and } y \geq 0\}$.
7. $S .=. \{(x, y): x + 2y < 4\} \cap \{(x, y): x > y\}$.
$\star$8. $S .=. \{(x, y): 0 < y < 1, x = 1/n, \text{ for each } n \in \mathfrak{N}\}$.
$\star$9. $S .=. \{(x, y): 0 < x < 2, y = 1 - (1/n), \text{ for each } n \in \mathfrak{N}\}$.
$\star$10. $S .=. \{(x, y): x, y \in \mathfrak{F}\}$.

## 19.3 LIMITS AND CONTINUITY

It is reasonable to try to extend the notions of limit and continuity to functions defined in the space $\mathcal{V}_n$. The reader should notice the similarity between the ideas presented here and those in Section 18.1, which were concerned with vector functions of a single variable.

**Definition 19.3a.** Let $A$ be a given point in the domain of a function $F$. Then

$$\lim_{X \to A} F(X) = m$$

means that for a given $\mathfrak{N}(m, \epsilon)$ there is some $\mathfrak{N}^*(A, \delta)$ such that

$$X \in \mathfrak{N}^*(A, \delta) \Rightarrow F(X) \in \mathfrak{N}(m, \epsilon).$$

The reader should bear in mind that $X$ may represent a point in two- or three-dimensional space, $\mathcal{V}_2$ or $\mathcal{V}_3$, or in $n$-dimensional space, $\mathcal{V}_n$, and that $m$ is just a real number. The concept is illustrated geometrically in Figure 19.3a for

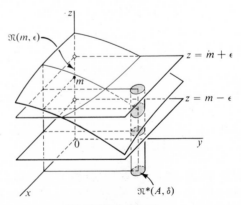

**FIGURE 19.3a**

$X \in \mathcal{V}_2$. In this case, we may give a graphical interpretation to the statement $\lim_{X \to A} F(X) = m$ by saying that as $\mathcal{N}^*(A, \delta)$ shrinks toward the point $A$, the corresponding set of points in the graph of $F$ must shrink toward a unique point $(A, m)$.

The statement in Definition 19.3a appears to be exactly like the one in Definition 4.4a for a function of one variable, but it will soon be clear that there are certain subtleties here that are not immediately apparent. As in the case of one variable, the proof that a limit exists and the evaluation of the limit may be somewhat involved. Although we shall not be greatly concerned with this kind of problem, it is appropriate to demonstrate the required technique.

---

*Example 19.3a.* Show that

$$\lim_{X \to (0,\, 0)} \frac{x^2 y^2}{x^2 + y^2} = 0.$$

Since we are interested in points in a $\mathcal{N}^*[(0, 0), \delta]$, we may represent the neighborhood as the set of points

$$\{(x, y): 0 < x^2 + y^2 < \delta^2\}.$$

This means that $\delta$ is the radius of the neighborhood. For points $(x, y)$ in this set, we want to have

$$\frac{x^2 y^2}{x^2 + y^2} \in \mathcal{N}(0, \epsilon).$$

To find what the $\delta$ should be, we may let

$$x = r \cos \theta, \quad y = r \sin \theta,$$

so that

$$r^2 = x^2 + y^2,$$

and write

$$f(x, y) = \frac{x^2 y^2}{x^2 + y^2} = \frac{r^4 \sin^2 \theta \cos^2 \theta}{r^2}$$

$$= r^2 \sin^2 \theta \cos^2 \theta \le r^2.$$

It follows that if $r^2 < \epsilon$, that is, if $0 < x^2 + y^2 < \epsilon$, then

$$|f(x, y)| < \epsilon.$$

Thus, with $\delta = \sqrt{\epsilon}$, we have shown that

$$(x, y) \in \mathcal{N}^*[(0, 0), \sqrt{\epsilon}] \Rightarrow f(x, y) \in \mathcal{N}(0, \epsilon),$$

or in other words, that

$$\lim_{(x,\, y) \to (0,\, 0)} f(x, y) = 0.$$

*Note:* It is left for the reader (see Exercises 19.3, Number 5) to show, for the preceding example, that a less restrictive value of $\delta$ is $2\sqrt{\epsilon}$.

---

It is to be particularly emphasized that the existence of $\lim_{X \to A} F(X)$ does not depend on the idea of a point $X$ approaching a point $A$ along some path. Instead, we should think of the effect of allowing $\mathcal{N}^*(A, \delta)$ to shrink toward the point $A$. As this happens, the corresponding set of values of $F(X)$ must shrink toward the point $m = \lim_{X \to A} F(X)$. Thus, if we should allow $X$ to approach $A$ in some special way, such as along some path, then we must obtain the value $m$ as the limit of $F(X)$ as $X \to A$ along that path. Consequently, the failure of the limit to exist can often be demonstrated by considering a special "path of approach."

---

*Example 19.3b.* Find

$$\lim_{X \to (0,\, 0)} \frac{x^2 - y^2}{x^2 + y^2}$$

if it exists.

One may be tempted to follow a procedure such as that used for a function of one variable. For example, we might wish to write

$$\lim_{y \to 0} \frac{x^2 - y^2}{x^2 + y^2} = \frac{x^2}{x^2}.$$

As $x \to 0$, $x^2/x^2 \to 1$, and it might appear that the required limit is 1. However, let us consider

$$\lim_{x \to 0} \frac{x^2 - y^2}{x^2 + y^2} = -\frac{y^2}{y^2}.$$

As $y \to 0$, $-y^2/y^2 \to -1$, which is an entirely different result from the preceding one. Evidently,

$$\lim_{(x,\, y) \to (0,\, 0)} \frac{x^2 - y^2}{x^2 + y^2}$$

does not exist.

---

Each of the two procedures used in the preceding example involves a process of finding two successive limits. Successive limits of this type are called **iterated limits**. In order to state more precisely what actually was done, we should write

$$\lim_{y \to 0} \left[ \lim_{x \to 0} \frac{x^2 - y^2}{x^2 + y^2} \right] = -1,$$

and

$$\lim_{x \to 0} \left[ \lim_{y \to 0} \frac{x^2 - y^2}{x^2 + y^2} \right] = 1.$$

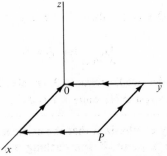

**FIGURE 19.3b**

Neither of these limits is the same as

$$\lim_{X \to (0,\,0)} \frac{x^2 - y^2}{x^2 + y^2},$$

since the iterated limits involve special ways of allowing $X$ to "approach" $(0, 0)$, as is illustrated in Figure 19.3b.

As Example 19.3b shows, the iterated limits may sometimes be used to show that a limit does not exist. However, it is even possible that the iterated limits exist and are equal, and yet that the limit itself does not exist. (See the next example.) Thus, evaluation of the iterated limits alone may *not* be used to show the existence of the unrestricted limit.

---

*Example 19.3c.* Discuss

$$\lim_{X \to (0,\,0)} \frac{x^2 y^2}{x^4 + y^4}.$$

The given expression is not defined at $(0, 0)$, but

$$\lim_{y \to 0} \left[ \lim_{x \to 0} \frac{x^2 y^2}{x^4 + y^4} \right] = \lim_{x \to 0} \left[ \lim_{y \to 0} \frac{x^2 y^2}{x^4 + y^4} \right] = 0.$$

Nevertheless, if $(x, y) \to (0, 0)$ along the line $y = mx$, we have

$$y = mx \Rightarrow \frac{x^2 y^2}{x^4 + y^4} = \frac{m^2 x^4}{(1 + m^4)x^4}$$

and

$$\lim_{x \to 0} \frac{m^2 x^4}{(1 + m^4)x^4} = \frac{m^2}{1 + m^4}.$$

Hence, the value of this limit taken along a line through the origin depends upon the slope of the line. Consequently, the unrestricted limit as given does not exist.

---

Although it was shown in Example 19.3c that the limit does not exist, by demonstrating that different limits are obtained for different lines $y = mx$, the reader must not conclude that the limit exists if all such lines give the same limit. A counter-example for such a conjecture is given in Exercises 19.3, Number 10.

By procedures quite similar to those used in Section 18.1a, it is possible to show that the fundamental limit theorems that were developed in Chapter 4 apply, with suitable modifications, to functions of more than one variable. These theorems frequently enable us to handle limits of sums, products, and quotients of simple functions, as well as limits of composite functions. For instance, on the basis of these theorems, we may write that

$$\lim_{(x,\,y) \to (2,\,-3)} (x^3 - 2xy + y^2 - 1) = 2^3 - (2)(2)(-3) + (-3)^2 - 1 = 28,$$

by arguing that the limit of the sum of the four terms is the sum of their respective limits, the limit of $x^3$ is the cube of the limit of $x$, and so on.

Once the limit concept for functions of several variables is clearly in mind, is easy to define continuity for such functions.

**Definition 19.3b.** A function $f$ is said to be continuous at a point $A$ if

$$\lim_{X \to A} f(X) = f(A).$$

As in the case of a function of one variable, this definition implies that if $f$ is continuous at $A$, then

        (a) $f(A)$ is defined,
        (b) $\lim_{X \to A} f(X)$ exists, and
        (c) the quantities in (a) and (b) are equal.

A function will fail to be continuous at $A$ if any one of these three statements fails to hold.

**Definition 19.3c.** A function $f$ is said to be continuous over an open region $\mathcal{R}$ if it is continuous at each point of $\mathcal{R}$.

The definition of continuity may be extended so that a function may be regarded as continuous at a boundary point of its domain if it is understood that the deleted neighborhoods involved in the consideration of $\lim_{X \to A} f(X)$ are to consist entirely of interior points of the domain of $f$. The details, however, are beyond the scope of our work here, and we shall be concerned mainly with continuity at interior points of the domain.

It is clear that the theorems about continuity developed for functions of one variable can be extended to functions of several variables. One of the most useful of these theorems states that a continuous function of a continuous function is continuous. The next three examples illustrate the use of such theorems.

*Example 19.3d.* Discuss the continuity of the function $f$ if

$$f(x, y) = \ln (1 + xy).$$

Since the logarithm function is continuous on its entire domain, $f(x, y)$ is continuous at points where $1 + xy$ is continuous and positive. Since $1 + xy$ is continuous for all

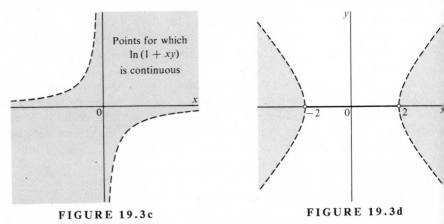

Points for which
ln (1 + xy)
is continuous

**FIGURE 19.3c**
                  **FIGURE 19.3d**

$x$ and $y$, it follows that $\ln (1 + xy)$ is continuous where $1 + xy > 0$ or $xy > -1$. This set of points is indicated by the shaded region in Figure 19.3c.

*Example 19.3e.* Discuss the continuity of the function $f$ where

$$f(x, y) .= . \begin{cases} \dfrac{\sin (x + y)}{x + y}, & x \neq -y, \\ 1, & x = -y, x > 0, \\ -1, & x = -y, x < 0. \end{cases}$$

For any point not on the line $x = -y$, the fraction $1/(x + y)$ defines a continuous function, and since the sine function is continuous on its entire domain, $f(x, y)$ is continuous at every point $(a, b)$, $a \neq -b$. For points on the line $x = -y$, we may let $x + y = v$, and consider

$$\lim_{v \to 0} \frac{\sin v}{v} = 1.$$

Since 1 is by definition the value of the function for $x > 0$ along the line $x = -y$, it follows that $f$ is continuous at each point $(a, -a)$, $a > 0$. Also by definition, the value of the function is $-1$ along $x = -y$ when $x < 0$, so that $f$ cannot be continuous at any point $(a, -a)$, $a < 0$, because

$$\lim_{X \to A} f(x, y) \neq f(a, -a).$$

At $(0, 0)$ the function is undefined and therefore is not continuous there.

---

*Example 19.3f.* What is the domain of the function $f$, where

$$f(x, y) .= . \frac{y}{\sqrt{x^2 - y^2 - 4}},$$

and at what points is $f$ continuous?

The value of $f(x, y)$ is real if

$$x^2 - y^2 - 4 > 0$$

or if $y = 0$, $x \neq \pm 2$. It follows that the domain of $f$ consists of the regions or portions of the plane on the concave sides of the hyperbola

$$x^2 - y^2 = 4,$$

and the portion of the $x$-axis for which $-2 < x < 2$. No points on the hyperbola are part of the domain (see Figure 19.3d). The function is continuous only in the shaded regions, excluding the boundary points.

## Exercises 19.3

1. Find $\displaystyle \lim_{X \to (0, 0)} \frac{x^3 y}{x^4 + y^4}$, if it exists.

2. Find $\displaystyle \lim_{X \to (0, 0)} \frac{x^3 y^2}{x^4 + y^4}$, if it exists.

3. Does $\displaystyle \lim_{X \to (0, 0)} \frac{xy}{x^2 + y^2}$ exist?

4. Find $\displaystyle \lim_{X \to (0, 0)} \frac{x^2 - y^2}{x^2 + y^2}$ if $X$ is confined to points on the line $y = mx$.

5. In Example 19.3a, show that the value $2\sqrt{\epsilon}$ can be used for $\delta$. *Hint:* Use the formula $\sin 2\theta = 2 \sin \theta \cos \theta$.

6. Does the function $f$, where $f(x, y) .=. (x^2y)/(x^2 + y^2)$, $(x, y) \neq (0, 0)$ and $f(0, 0) .=. 0$, have any points of discontinuity? Explain.

7. Let $f(x, y) .=. x^3y^3/(x^2 + y^2)$ for $(x, y) \neq (0, 0)$. Can $f(0, 0)$ be so defined that will be continuous at $(0, 0)$? Explain.

8. At what points is each of the following functions continuous?

   (a) $f(x, y) .=. \ln xy$.
   (b) $f(x, y) .=. (x^2 + y^2)/(4 - x^2 - y^2)^{1/2}$.
   (c) $f(x, y) .=. \sin xy$.
   (d) $f(x, y) .=. \text{Tan}^{-1} (y/x)$.
   (e) $f(x, y) .=. \ln (4 - x^2 - y^2) - \ln (x^2 + y^2 - 1)$.

9. Determine the domain and region of continuity of the function $f$ if

   (a) $f(x, y) .=. x\sqrt{y^2 - 4x^2 - 4}$;
   (b) $f(x, y) .=. y\sqrt{x^2 + y^2 - 1}$.

10. Consider $\lim_{X \to (0, 0)} f(x, y)$, where $f(x, y) = \dfrac{x^4y^4}{(x^2 + y^4)^3}$. Show that approach along a straight line through the origin always gives a zero limit. Examine what occur for approach along the parabola $y^2 = x$.

## 19.4 PARTIAL DERIVATIVES

The derivative of a function of one variable may be described as the rate o change of the functional value with respect to the independent variable. In a similar way, if $z = f(x, y)$ we often have occasion to consider the rate of change of $z$ associated with changes in the independent variables $x$ and $y$. In the case of functions of more than one variable, the function value is usually altered by a change in the value of any one or several of the independent variables. The most general way of designating a change in the functional value of $z = f(x, y)$ for instance, is

$$\Delta z = f(x + \Delta x, y + \Delta y) - f(x, y).$$

This formula takes account of the increments in both the independent variable $x$ and $y$.

Suppose that we wish to consider a rate of change of $z$. Then, since there are two independent variables, it seems reasonable to discuss the rate of change o $z$ with respect to each variable separately.

**Definition 19.4a.** Let $z = f(x, y)$. Then if

$$\lim_{\Delta x \to 0} \frac{f(x + \Delta x, y) - f(x, y)}{\Delta x}$$

exists, it is called the **partial derivative** of $z$ (or $f$) with respect to $x$ at th point $(x, y)$, and is denoted by any one of the symbols

$$\frac{\partial f(x, y)}{\partial x}, \quad \frac{\partial z(x, y)}{\partial x}, \quad f_x(x, y), \quad z_x(x, y).$$

The process of finding a partial derivative is called **partial differentiation.** The function associated with the partial derivative $f_x(x, y)$ is denoted by $f_x$. Hence, there are two distinct concepts associated with partial derivatives: the partial derivative function, $f_x$, and the value, $f_x(x, y)$, of the partial derivative at the point $(x, y)$. In order to avoid too cumbersome a notation, however, we shall allow the use of $f_x$ in place of $f_x(x, y)$ whenever the context makes clear what is intended.

As indicated in Definition 19.4a, a number of different symbols are commonly used to designate partial derivatives. The most frequently used of these symbols is of the form $\partial f/\partial x$, which in some respects is rather objectionable. It is not only clumsy to write, but it gives the *false* impression that a partial derivative is the ratio of $\partial f$ and $\partial x$, neither of which is separately meaningful. The subscript notation, $f_x$ or $z_x$, is probably the simplest notation for partial derivatives, and we shall use it in preference to other symbols. However, since the reader should be familiar with the other widely used notations, these will also occur in the following pages.

The partial derivative of a function of several variables with respect to any one of these variables is defined in a manner similar to that for functions of two variables. Thus, if $u = g(x, y, z, w)$, then

$$u_z .=. \lim_{\Delta z \to 0} \frac{g(x, y, z + \Delta z, w) - g(x, y, z, w)}{\Delta z}.$$

The important aspect of partial differentiation is that all but one of the independent variables are treated as if they were constants for the purpose of finding the partial derivative with respect to the remaining independent variable.

---

*Example 19.4a.* Find $f_x$ and $f_y$ if $f(x, y) .=. x^2y + y^2$.

To find $f_x$, we may proceed as follows:

$$f(x + \Delta x, y) - f(x, y) = (x + \Delta x)^2y + y^2 - x^2y - y^2$$
$$= 2xy \, \Delta x + y(\Delta x)^2,$$

and

$$f_x = \lim_{\Delta x \to 0} \frac{f(x + \Delta x, y) - f(x, y)}{\Delta x} = 2xy.$$

Similarly, to obtain $f_y$, we have

$$f(x, y + \Delta y) - f(x, y) = x^2(y + \Delta y) + (y + \Delta y)^2 - x^2y - y^2$$
$$= x^2 \, \Delta y + 2y \, \Delta y + (\Delta y)^2,$$

and

$$f_y = \lim_{\Delta y \to 0} \frac{f(x, y + \Delta y) - f(x, y)}{\Delta y} = x^2 + 2y.$$

---

In each case, the result in Example 19.4a can be obtained by simple differentiation with respect to the indicated variable, provided the other variable is treated as if it were constant. This is further illustrated in the next example. Moreover, an inspection of the definition shows that this is a generally valid procedure.

---

*Example 19.4b.* If $z = x^3 + xy^2 - 2xy^3$, find $z_x$ and $z_y$.

Regarding $y$ as constant, we get, by differentiation with respect to $x$,

$$z_x = 3x^2 + y^2 - 2y^3,$$

and regarding $x$ as constant, we get, by differentiation with respect to $y$,

$$z_y = 2xy - 6xy^2.$$

---

It is instructive to interpret geometrically the partial derivative $f_x(x_0, y_0)$ of a function $f$. Since $y$ is held fixed at the value $y_0$, we consider the equations

$$y = y_0, \quad z = f(x, y_0),$$

which describe a curve formed by the intersection of the plane $y = y_0$ and the surface $z = f(x, y)$. Hence, $f_x(x_0, y_0)$ may be interpreted as the slope of the curve at the point $(x_0, y_0)$ in the plane $y = y_0$ (see Figure 19.4a). Similarly, $f_y(x_0, y_0)$

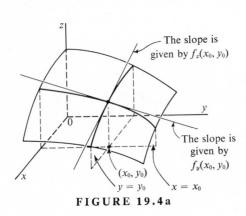

The slope is given by $f_z(x_0, y_0)$

The slope is given by $f_y(x_0, y_0)$

$(x_0, y_0)$

$y = y_0$    $x = x_0$

**FIGURE 19.4a**

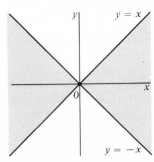

$y = x$

$y = -x$

$\mathcal{D}_f$ includes the boundaries
$\mathcal{D}_{f_z}$ does not include the boundaries

**FIGURE 19.4b**

represents the slope of the curve $x = x_0$, $z = f(x, y)$ at the point $(x_0, y_0)$ in the plane $x = x_0$.

The reader should keep in mind that, as in the case of functions of one variable, it is possible for a partial derivative function to have a domain that is a proper subset of the domain of the original function.

---

*Example 19.4c.* Compare the domains of the function $f$ and $f_x$ if

$$f(x, y) = \sqrt{x^2 - y^2}.$$

The domain of $f$, say $\mathcal{D}_f$, is the set $\{(x, y)\}$ of points for which $x^2 - y^2 \geq 0$. Since $f_x = x(x^2 - y^2)^{-1/2}$, the domain of $f_x$, say $\mathcal{D}_{f_x}$, is the set $\{(x, y)\}$ of points for which $x^2 - y^2 > 0$. Hence, in this example, $\mathcal{D}_{f_x}$ is a proper subset of $\mathcal{D}_f$, as illustrated in Figure 19.4b.

---

The mean value theorem for a function of one variable applies to a function of more than one variable, as stated in

**Theorem 19.4a.** If $z = f(x, y)$ is defined for $a \leq x \leq b$ and $c \leq y \leq d$, and if $f_x$ exists for $y = y_0$ and all $x$ for which $a \leq x \leq b$, then there exists a real number $x_1$, such that $a < x_1 < b$ and

$$f(b, y_0) - f(a, y_0) = (b - a)f_x(x_1, y_0).$$

PROOF: Let $g(x) . = . f(x, y_0)$. Then, $f_x(x, y_0) = D_x g(x)$. Since, by hypothesis, $f_x(x, y_0)$ exists on the closed interval $a \leq x \leq b$, it follows that $f(x, y_0)$ is a continuous function of $x$ on this interval. Hence, the mean value theorem for ordinary derivatives may be applied to show that there exists a point $x_1$ in the interval $a < x < b$ such that

$$g(b) - g(a) = (b - a)g'(x_1),$$

or

$$f(b, y_0) - f(a, y_0) = (b - a)f_x(x_1, y_0).$$

Note that the theorem is also useful in the form

$$f(x_0 + h, y_0) - f(x_0, y_0) = hf_x(x_1, y_0),$$

where $x_1$ is between $x_0$ and $x_0 + h$. Clearly, a similar statement may be made for the partial derivative with respect to any independent variable, provided the conditions of the theorem are satisfied for that variable.

## Exercises 19.4

In each of Numbers 1 to 9, find the indicated partial derivatives.

1. $u = xy - \ln xy$; $u_x, u_y$.
2. $z = ye^{x/y}$; $z_x, z_y$.
3. $z = \ln \dfrac{x^2 - y^2}{x^2 + y^2}$; $z_x, z_y$.
4. $z = \dfrac{x - y}{x + y}$; $z_x, z_y$.
5. $u = \sin xy$; $u_x, u_y$.
6. $z = \sqrt{st}$; $z_s, z_t$.
7. $z = \text{Tan}^{-1}(u/v)$; $z_u, z_v$.
8. $z = \exp(au + bv + cw)$; $z_u, z_w$.
9. $z = \cos xu \sin yu$; $z_x, z_u$.

10. If $z = \frac{1}{2} \ln (x^2 + y^2) + \text{Tan}^{-1}(y/x)$, find $z_x^2 + z_y^2$.
11. If $z = x^2 \sin (y/x) + y^2 \cos (y/x)$, find $xz_x + yz_y$.
12. If $u = x^2y + y^2z + z^2x$, show that $u_x + u_y + u_z = (x + y + z)^2$.
13. If $z = \text{Sin}^{-1}[(x - y)/(x + y)]$, find $xz_x + yz_y$.
14. If $z = \ln (e^x + e^y)$, find $z_x + z_y$.

In Numbers 15 to 18, use partial differentiation to find equations of the line tangent to the designated curve at the given point.

15. $y = x^2 + z^2$, $x = 3$; $(3, 10, 1)$.
16. $z = \sin xy$, $y = 2$; $(\pi/4, 2, 1)$.
17. $z = \exp(x^2y)$, $x = 1$; $(1, 1, e)$.
18. $z = \sqrt{x^2 + y^2}$, $y = 4$; $(3, 4, 5)$.

In Numbers 19 and 20, use partial differentiation to find the $y_1$ required by the mean value theorem (Theorem 19.4a) written with $x$ held constant.

19. $f(x, y) = x^2 + y^3$; $1 \leq y \leq 4$, $x = 5$.

20. $f(x, y) = \dfrac{xy}{y - 1}$; $2 \leq y \leq 4$, $x = 1$.

## 19.5 PARTIAL DERIVATIVES OF HIGHER ORDER

Since a partial derivative of a function of more than one variable is a new function of more than one variable, it is frequently possible to apply the differentiation process repeatedly. The result is that new functions, called partial derivatives of higher order, are obtained. For example, from $f_x(x, y)$ we obtain

$$f_{xx}(x, y) .=. \lim_{h \to 0} \frac{f_x(x + h, y) - f_x(x, y)}{h},$$

which is called the *second partial derivative of f with respect to x.*

Evidently, from a function $f$ of two variables there are four possible second partial derivatives,

$$f_{xx}, \quad f_{xy}, \quad f_{yx}, \quad f_{yy},$$

where the notation $f_{xy}$ denotes the partial derivative of $f_x$ with respect to $y$ and $f_{yx}$ denotes the partial derivative of $f_y$ with respect to $x$. Partial derivatives of the type $f_{xy}$ and $f_{yx}$ are called **mixed partial derivatives.** The second-order partial derivatives are also frequently written

$$\frac{\partial}{\partial x}\left(\frac{\partial f}{\partial x}\right) = \frac{\partial^2 f}{\partial x^2}, \quad \frac{\partial}{\partial y}\left(\frac{\partial f}{\partial x}\right) = \frac{\partial^2 f}{\partial y\,\partial x},$$

$$\frac{\partial}{\partial x}\left(\frac{\partial f}{\partial y}\right) = \frac{\partial^2 f}{\partial x\,\partial y}, \quad \frac{\partial}{\partial y}\left(\frac{\partial f}{\partial y}\right) = \frac{\partial^2 f}{\partial y^2}.$$

*Example 19.5a.* Find all the second partial derivatives of

$$z = 3x^2y + y^3 + x^2y^2.$$

From $z_x = 6xy + 2xy^2$ and $z_y = 3x^2 + 3y^2 + 2x^2y$, it follows that

$$z_{xx} = 6y + 2y^2,$$
$$z_{xy} = 6x + 4xy,$$
$$z_{yx} = 6x + 4xy,$$
$$z_{yy} = 6y + 2x^2.$$

*Example 19.5b.* If $z = x^2y - x \sin xy$, find all the second partial derivatives.

We find

$$z_x = 2xy - \sin xy - xy \cos xy,$$
$$z_y = x^2 - x^2 \cos xy,$$
$$z_{xx} = 2y - 2y \cos xy + xy^2 \sin xy,$$
$$z_{xy} = 2x - 2x \cos xy + x^2y \sin xy,$$
$$z_{yx} = 2x - 2x \cos xy + x^2y \sin xy,$$
$$z_{yy} = x^3 \sin xy.$$

Notice in these two examples that $z_{xy} = z_{yx}$. Is this result merely an unusual coincidence or dare we conjecture that this equality will always hold? Further light might be shed on the matter by examining some third partial derivatives. For this purpose, let us refer to Example 19.5a, where we obtained

$$z_{xx} = 6y + 2y^2,$$
$$z_{xy} = 6x + 4xy,$$
$$z_{yx} = 6x + 4xy,$$
$$z_{yy} = 6y + 2x^2.$$

By differentiating again with respect to $x$ and $y$, we find the third partial derivatives:

$$z_{xxx} = 0, \qquad z_{yxx} = 6 + 4y,$$
$$z_{xxy} = 6 + 4y, \qquad z_{yxy} = 4x,$$
$$z_{xyx} = 6 + 4y, \qquad z_{yyx} = 4x,$$
$$z_{xyy} = 4x, \qquad z_{yyy} = 6.$$

Upon comparing these expressions, we see that

$$z_{xxy} = z_{xyx} = z_{yxx},$$

and that

$$z_{yyx} = z_{yxy} = z_{xyy}.$$

These results are indeed encouraging support for the conjecture that the order in which partial derivatives are formed is immaterial to the end result, as long as the number of differentiations with respect to each of the independent variables is the same.

Unfortunately, it is possible to construct a counterexample for this simple conjecture and thus to show that unless some restrictions are placed on the derivatives, it is *not* always true that $z_{xy} = z_{yx}$. The basic difficulty stems from the fact that the mixed second derivatives are essentially iterated limits, and, as we have seen, the value of an iterated limit may depend on the order in which the limits are taken. The reader who wishes to pursue this matter further should refer to Exercises 19.5, Number 17.

The following theorem, which is stated here without proof, gives rather mild restrictions under which it is true that the second-order mixed partial derivatives are equal. These restrictions are usually satisfied in the applications of partial differentiation.

**Theorem 19.5a.** If
  (a) $f(x, y)$ is defined in some neighborhood of $(a, b)$,
  (b) $f_x(x, y), f_y(x, y), f_{xy}(x, y), f_{yx}(x, y)$ all exist in that neighborhood, and
  (c) $f_{yx}(x, y)$ is continuous at $(a, b)$,
  then

$$f_{xy}(a, b) = f_{yx}(a, b).$$

This theorem makes it clear that *for functions with continuous second-order partial derivatives* it is indeed true that

$$f_{xy}(x, y) = f_{yx}(x, y),$$

and we are justified in using these mixed partial derivatives interchangeably at points where the continuity conditions hold.

## Exercises 19.5

In each of Numbers 1 to 8, find all the second-order partial derivatives.

1. $f(x, y) = (x/y) - (y/x)$.
2. $f(x, y) = e^{2x} \sin y$.
3. $z = e^{xy}$.
4. $z = \text{Sin}^{-1}(y/x)$.

5. $u = \sin xyz$.
6. $u = e^x \sin yz + e^y \sin xz$.
7. $u = \text{Tan}^{-1}(y/x)$.
8. $z = \ln(x + \sqrt{x^2 + y^2})$.

In each of Numbers 9 to 12, show that the given function satisfies the equation

$$\frac{\partial^2 z}{\partial x^2} + \frac{\partial^2 z}{\partial y^2} = 0.$$

(This equation is called *Laplace's equation* in two dimensions.)

9. $z = \ln(x^2 + y^2)$.
10. $z = \text{Tan}^{-1}(y/x)$.

11. $z = \text{Tan}^{-1}[2xy/(x^2 - y^2)]$.
12. $z = e^x \sin y + e^y \sin x$.

13. Show that $w = (x^2 + y^2 + z^2)^{-1/2}$ satisfies Laplace's equation in three dimensions,

$$\frac{\partial^2 w}{\partial x^2} + \frac{\partial^2 w}{\partial y^2} + \frac{\partial^2 w}{\partial z^2} = 0.$$

14. Show that if $z = xy + y \ln xy$, then

$$x z_{xx} + y z_{xy} = y^2 z_{yy}.$$

15. Let $f(x, y) .=. \dfrac{2xy}{x^2 + y^2}$, $(x, y) \neq (0, 0)$ and $f(0, 0) .=. 0$.

   (a) Do $f_x(0, 0)$, $f_y(0, 0)$ exist?
   (b) Are $f_x(x, y)$, $f_y(x, y)$ continuous at $(0, 0)$?
   (c) Does $f_{xy}(0, 0) = f_{yx}(0, 0)$?

16. Under what conditions on $a$ and $b$ is Laplace's equation,

$$z_{xx} + z_{yy} = 0,$$

satisfied by $z = e^{ax+by}$?

★17. Find $f_{xy}(0, 0)$ and $f_{yx}(0, 0)$ for the function described by

$$f(x, y) .=. xy \frac{x^2 - y^2}{x^2 + y^2}, \qquad x^2 + y^2 \neq 0, \quad \text{and} \quad f(0, 0) .=. 0.$$

## 19.6 DIFFERENTIALS

A number of properties associated with a function of one variable and its derivatives do not generalize directly to a function of several variables and its partial derivatives. For example, we have seen that if a function of one variable has a derivative at a point $x = a$, then the function is continuous there. May we make a similar statement about a function of two variables if its partial derivatives exist at a point $(a, b)$?

To answer this question, we shall find it convenient first to prove an extension of Theorem 19.4a.

**Theorem 19.6a.** Let $f$ be a function defined over a closed region $\mathcal{R}$, and suppose $f_x$ and $f_y$ are continuous on $\mathcal{R}^i$, the interior of $\mathcal{R}$. If $\mathfrak{N}(P)$ is some neighborhood of a point $P(a, b)$ in $\mathcal{R}^i$, where $\mathfrak{N}(P) \subset \mathcal{R}^i$, and if $(a + h, b + k) \in \mathfrak{N}(P)$, then

$$f(a + h, b + k) - f(a, b) = hf_x(a, b) + kf_y(a, b) + h\epsilon_1 + k\epsilon_2,$$

where $\epsilon_1, \epsilon_2 \to 0$ as $(h, k) \to (0, 0)$.

PROOF: Upon adding and subtracting $f(a + h, b)$, we may write

$$f(a + h, b + k) - f(a, b)$$
$$= [f(a + h, b + k) - f(a + h, b)] + [f(a + h, b) - f(a, b)].$$

Since $f$ is defined everywhere on $\mathfrak{N}(P)$, and since $f_x$ and $f_y$ are continuous everywhere on $\mathfrak{N}(P)$, it follows, by Theorem 19.4a, that

$$f(a + h, b + k) - f(a + h, b) = kf_y(a + h, y_1), \qquad y_1 \text{ between } b \text{ and } b + k$$

and that

$$f(a + h, b) - f(a, b) = hf_x(x_1, b), \qquad x_1 \text{ between } a \text{ and } a + h.$$

Now let

$$\epsilon_1(h, k) .=. f_x(x_1, b) - f_x(a, b)$$

and

$$\epsilon_2(h, k) .=. f_y(a + h, y_1) - f_y(a, b).$$

Then, since $f_x$ and $f_y$ are continuous on $\mathfrak{N}(P)$,

$$f_x(x_1, b) \to f_x(a, b) \quad \text{as} \quad (h, k) \to (0, 0),$$

and

$$f_y(a + h, y_1) \to f_y(a, b) \quad \text{as} \quad (h, k) \to (0, 0).$$

Thus, it follows that $\epsilon_1, \epsilon_2 \to 0$ as $(h, k) \to (0, 0)$. Hence,

$$f(a + h, b + k) - f(a, b) = hf_x(x_1, b) + kf_y(a + h, y_1)$$
$$= h[f_x(a, b) + \epsilon_1] + k[f_y(a, b) + \epsilon_2]$$
$$= hf_x(a, b) + kf_y(a, b) + h\epsilon_1 + k\epsilon_2.$$

From Theorem 19.6a we may easily obtain a condition that is sufficient to guarantee the continuity of the given function $f$.

**Theorem 19.6b.** If $f$ is defined over a region $\mathcal{R}$, and $f_x$, $f_y$ are continuous over $\mathcal{R}^i$, then $f$ is continuous over $\mathcal{R}^i$.

PROOF: According to Theorem 19.6a, if $P(a, b) \in \mathcal{R}^i$, then for points

$$(a + h, b + k) \in \mathfrak{N}(P),$$

where $\mathfrak{N}(P) \subset \mathcal{R}^i$, we may write

$$f(a + h, b + k) = f(a, b) + hf_x(a, b) + kf_y(a, b) + h\epsilon_1 + k\epsilon_2.$$

Upon finding the limit as $(h, k) \to (0, 0)$, we have

$$\lim_{(h,\, k) \to (0,\, 0)} f(a + h, b + k) = f(a, b),$$

which shows that $f$ is continuous at $(a, b)$.

The mere existence of $f_x(a, b)$ and $f_y(a, b)$ is not sufficient to guarantee that $f$ is continuous at $(a, b)$, as the following example illustrates.

---

*Example 19.6a.* Find $f_x(0, 0)$ and $f_y(0, 0)$ if

$$f(x, y) \,.=. \frac{x^2 y^2}{x^4 + y^4}, \qquad (x, y) \neq (0, 0),$$

$$f(0, 0) \,.=. 0.$$

From the definition of the partial derivative, we find that

$$f_x(0, 0) = \lim_{h \to 0} \left[ \frac{1}{h} \left( \frac{0}{h^4 + 0} - 0 \right) \right] = 0,$$

and similarly that $f_y(0, 0) = 0$. Although the partial derivatives exist at $(0, 0)$, $f$ is not continuous there, as was shown in Example 19.3c.

---

If in $f(x, y)$ the variables $x$ and $y$ are changed by amounts $\Delta x$ and $\Delta y$, respectively, then Theorem 19.6a provides a useful means of representing the change in the value of $f$ in terms of the partial derivatives $f_x$ and $f_y$. Let the change in the value of $f$ be denoted by $\Delta f(x, y)$, so that

$$\Delta f(x, y) \,.=. f(x + \Delta x, y + \Delta y) - f(x, y).$$

Then, by Theorem 19.6a, we have

$$\Delta f(x, y) = f_x(x, y)\, \Delta x + f_y(x, y)\, \Delta y + \epsilon_1\, \Delta x + \epsilon_2\, \Delta y,$$

where $\epsilon_1, \epsilon_2 \to 0$ as $(\Delta x, \Delta y) \to (0, 0)$.

By analogy with functions of one variable, the expression

$$f_x(x, y)\, \Delta x + f_y(x, y)\, \Delta y$$

is called the **differential** of $f(x, y)$ and is denoted by $df(x, y)$. This designation assigns no meaning to the differentials of the independent variables, and it turns out that the most convenient choice to make is $dx \,.=. \Delta x$ and $dy \,.=. \Delta y$. We may summarize this discussion as follows.

**Definition 19.6a.** Let $f$ be a function having continuous first partial derivatives $f_x$ and $f_y$ over some closed region $\mathcal{R}$. Then over $\mathcal{R}^i$, the interior of this region,

(a) $df(x, y) \,.=. f_x(x, y)\, dx + f_y(x, y)\, dy,$

(b) $dx \,.=. \Delta x, \; dy \,.=. \Delta y$, *if $x$ and $y$ are the independent variables.*

We shall see later that (a) is universal whether $x$ and $y$ are the final independent variables or are dependent on still other variables, but (b) applies only to the independent variables themselves.

The results of Theorems 19.6a and 19.6b, and the concept of the differential, may easily be extended to functions of more than two variables. For example, with appropriate conditions on $f$, we may write

$$f(x + \Delta x, y + \Delta y, z + \Delta z) - f(x, y, z)$$
$$= f_x(x, y, z)\,\Delta x + f_y(x, y, z)\,\Delta y + f_z(x, y, z)\,\Delta z + \epsilon_1\,\Delta x + \epsilon_2\,\Delta y + \epsilon_3\,\Delta z,$$

where $\epsilon_1, \epsilon_2, \epsilon_3 \to 0$ as $(\Delta x, \Delta y, \Delta z) \to (0, 0, 0)$. The differential is then

$$df(x, y, z) = f_x(x, y, z)\,dx + f_y(x, y, z)\,dy + f_z(x, y, z)\,dz.$$

As in the case of functions of one variable, the differential $df$ is frequently useful as an approximation to $\Delta f(x, y, z)$, as is illustrated in the next examples.

---

*Example 19.6b.* How much error may be expected in the calculation of the volume of a rectangular solid having a square end of side 10.0 inches and a length of 20.0 inches, if the measurements are accurate to within 0.1 inch?

If $x$ represents the length of a side of the square end and $y$ represents the length of the box, then the volume $V$ is given by

$$V = x^2 y.$$

The actual amount of possible error in $V$ can be found directly by calculating

$$\Delta V = V(x \pm h, y \pm k) - V(x, y).$$

Thus,

$$\Delta V = (10.0 \pm 0.1)^2(20.0 \pm 0.1) - (10^2)(20).$$

The signs should be chosen in such a way as to give a maximum absolute value for $\Delta V$, since it is not known whether the errors in the measurements are positive or negative. We get

$$\Delta V = 50.401 \text{ cubic inches}$$

if the positive signs are chosen, and

$$\Delta V = 49.601 \text{ cubic inches}$$

if the negative signs are chosen. In this case, the error in $V$ is specified by writing

$$|\Delta V| \leq 50.401.$$

Satisfactory approximations to errors can be found by means of the differential when the increments of the independent variables are sufficiently small. In the preceding example,

$$dV = 2xy\,dx + x^2\,dy,$$

and if

$$x = 10.0, \quad dx = +0.1, \qquad y = 20, \quad dy = +0.1,$$

then

$$dV = (400)(0.1) + (100)(0.1)$$
$$= 50 \text{ cubic inches}.$$

---

*Example 19.6c.* What is the approximate percentage change in the volume of a right circular cone if the radius of the base is changed by 3% and the height is changed by 2%?

The volume of the cone is given by

$$V = \pi r^2 h/3,$$

so that

$$dV = \pi[2rh\,dr + r^2\,dh]/3.$$

The approximate *relative error* in $V$ is given by $(dV)/V$, so that

$$\frac{dV}{V} = \frac{[2rh\,dr + r^2\,dh]}{r^2 h}$$

$$= 2\frac{dr}{r} + \frac{dh}{h}.$$

The approximate percentage error is $100(dV)/V$, so that

$$100\,\frac{dV}{V} = 2 \times 100\,\frac{dr}{r} + 100\,\frac{dh}{h}$$

$$= 2 \times 3 + 2$$
$$= 8\%.$$

## Exercises 19.6

In Numbers 1 to 6 find the differential of the given function.

1. $z = x^3 + x^2 y - y^3$.
2. $z = \text{Tan}^{-1}(y/x)$.
3. $u = \ln(x^2 + y^2 + z^2)^{1/2}$.
4. $u = e^z \sin(x - y)z$
5. $u = e^{xyz}$.
6. $w = \text{Sin}^{-1}(y/x)$.

In Numbers 7 to 12, calculate the increment and the differential for the data given.

7. $z = x^3 y^2$, $x = y = 1$, $\Delta x = 0.01$, $\Delta y = -0.01$.
8. $z = 3x^2 + y^2$, $x = 2$, $y = 3$, $\Delta x = 0.01$, $\Delta y = 0.02$.
9. $z = x^2 + xy + y^2$, $x = 3$, $y = 2$, $\Delta x = 0.02$, $\Delta y = 0.03$.
10. $z = x\,\text{Tan}^{-1} xy$, $x = 0.5$, $y = 2$, $\Delta y = 0.01$, $\Delta x = -0.05$.
11. $z = x \ln y + y \ln x$, $x = y = 1$, $\Delta x = 0.01$, $\Delta y = 0.02$.
12. $z = x\sqrt{x - y}$, $x = 6$, $y = 2$, $\Delta x = \Delta y = 0.25$.

13. Use the differential to find an approximate value for

$$f(2.02, 1.01) \quad \text{if} \quad f(x, y) = x^2 + xy + y^2.$$

14. Use the differential to find an approximate value of

$$f(6.05, 2.01) \quad \text{if} \quad f(x, y) = x\sqrt{x - y}.$$

15. If the radius of a right circular cone is measured as 4.0 inches and the height is measured as 8.0 inches, what is the approximate maximum error made in calculating the volume of the cone if the measurements are subject to an error of 0.1 inch?

16. The period $T$ in seconds for a pendulum having small oscillations is given by

$$T = 2\pi\,\sqrt{\frac{L}{g}},$$

where $L$ is the length of the pendulum and $g$ is the acceleration due to gravity. What is the approximate error to be expected in $T$ when $L = 8$ feet and $g = 32$, if $L$ is accurate to within $\frac{1}{4}$ inch and the correct value of $g$ is 32.01 feet per second per second?

17. The area of a triangle can be calculated if the length of two sides and the included angle are known. What approximate error may be expected in the area if there is an error of 1% in the sides and an error of 2% in the angle, if the angle is acute?
18. If each of the dimensions of a rectangular box is measured with an error not exceeding 2%, what is the approximate greatest percentage error in the calculated value of the volume?
19. If two electrical resistances, $r_1$ and $r_2$, are connected in parallel, the circuit resistance $R$ is given by

$$\frac{1}{R} = \frac{1}{r_1} + \frac{1}{r_2}.$$

If the values $r_1$ and $r_2$ are subject to a percentage error $e$, what is the approximate maximum percentage error in $R$?

---

# Summary of Chapter 19

---

The chapter contains a discussion of a number of concepts that are fundamental to much of the work in succeeding chapters. They include:

(1) the definition of a function of several variables (Section 19.1);
(2) the domain and range of a function of several variables (Section 19.1);
(3) the generalized neighborhood concept (Section 19.2);
(4) interior points, exterior points and boundary points of a set $S$ (Section 19.2);
(5) open sets, closed sets, connected sets, and regions (Section 19.2);
(6) the limit of a function of several variables, and the distinction between the limit and iterated limits (Section 19.3);
(7) continuity of a function of several variables (Section 19.3);
(8) the definition of the partial derivatives of a function of two variables and their geometric interpretation (Section 19.4);
(9) partial derivatives of higher order and the related theorems (Section 19.5);
(10) the relationship between the continuity of a function $f$ and the partial derivatives of $f$ (Section 19.6);
(11) the differential of a function of several variables (Section 19.6);
(12) the use of differentials and partial derivatives in error analysis (Section 19.6).

# Chapter 20

# Partial Differentiation II

## 20.1 COMPOSITE FUNCTIONS

Just as we often encounter composite functions of one variable, such as is indicated by $y = f[g(x)]$, so we may expect to encounter composite functions of several variables. For example, a function $f$ defined over a region $\Re$ is described by

$$f(x, y) = x^2 + xy + y^2.$$

Suppose that $x$ and $y$ are each functions of two new variables $u$ and $v$, defined over a common region $\Re_1$, where

$$x = u \cos v = g(u, v), \quad (u, v) \in \Re_1,$$
$$y = u \sin v = h(u, v), \quad (u, v) \in \Re_1,$$

and that the pair $(x, y) \in \Re$ when $(u, v) \in \Re_1$. Then the expression

$$f[g(u, v), h(u, v)] = u^2 \cos^2 v + u^2 \cos v \sin v + u^2 \sin^2 v$$
$$= u^2(1 + \cos v \sin v)$$

represents a new function $F$, where

$$F(u, v) = f[g(u, v), h(u, v)].$$

It is *incorrect* to write $f(u, v)$ for the new function, since

$$f(u, v) = u^2 + uv + v^2,$$

an expression that is entirely different from $u^2(1 + \cos v \sin v)$.

Evidently, the function $F$ is determined by the three functions $f$, $g$, and $h$, and that being the case, we should be able to find the derivative functions associated with $F$, provided they exist, from $f$, $g$, and $h$. If $f_x$ and $f_y$ exist and are continuous on $\Re^i$, then by Theorem 19.6a, we may write, for points $(x, y) \in \Re^i$,

$$\Delta z = z_x \Delta x + z_y \Delta y + \epsilon_1 \Delta x + \epsilon_2 \Delta y$$

and

$$\frac{\Delta z}{\Delta u} = z_x \frac{\Delta x}{\Delta u} + z_y \frac{\Delta y}{\Delta u} + \epsilon_1 \frac{\Delta x}{\Delta u} + \epsilon_2 \frac{\Delta y}{\Delta u}.$$

If $x$ and $y$ are continuous functions of $u$ and $v$, and if the partial derivatives of $x$ and $y$ with respect to $u$ and $v$ exist at appropriate points, then, taking the limit as $\Delta u \to 0$, we get

(1)
$$z_u = z_x x_u + z_y y_u = \frac{\partial z}{\partial x}\frac{\partial x}{\partial u} + \frac{\partial z}{\partial y}\frac{\partial y}{\partial u}.$$

This result follows because $\Delta u \to 0 \Rightarrow \Delta x \to 0$ and $\Delta y \to 0$, and therefore $\Delta u \to 0 \Rightarrow \epsilon_1 \to 0$ and $\epsilon_2 \to 0$. By the same argument, we find

$$z_v = z_x x_v + z_y y_v = \frac{\partial z}{\partial x}\frac{\partial x}{\partial v} + \frac{\partial z}{\partial y}\frac{\partial y}{\partial v}.$$

The result expressed in Equation (1) may easily be generalized. Let

$$z = f(x_1, \ldots, x_n),$$

and let

$$x_i = g_i(u_1, u_2, \ldots, u_m), \qquad i = 1, 2, 3, \ldots, n.$$

Then, an argument like that which leads to Equation (1) yields

(2)
$$\frac{\partial z}{\partial u_i} = \sum_{\alpha=1}^{n} \frac{\partial z}{\partial x_\alpha}\frac{\partial x_\alpha}{\partial u_i}.$$

The reader is again cautioned that a symbol of the form $\partial z/\partial u_i$ is not to be construed as a fractional expression, and that such a mistaken notion can lead to serious errors. Even the notation $z_x$, $z_y$, and so on, for partial derivatives can sometimes be troublesome, since the letter $z$ is used to represent the value of two different functions, $f(x, y)$ and $F(u, v)$. That is,

$$z = f(x, y) = f[g(u, v), h(u, v)] = F(u, v).$$

We may avoid the ambiguity by writing out in full such an equation as

$$z_u = f_x(x, y)g_u(u, v) + f_y(x, y)h_u(u, v),$$

which seems to be unnecessarily involved, except where it is desirable to designate the values of the partial derivatives at particular points. Generally, the meaning of the notation will be clear from the context of the discussion in which it occurs; we shall most often use the notation in Equation (1). In any case, as the form of Equation (1) suggests, $z_u$ and $z_v$ may be treated as functions of four variables, $x$, $y$, $u$, and $v$, with only $u$ and $v$ as independent. It is always important in connection with partial derivatives to keep clearly in mind what variables are to be regarded as independent.

---

*Example 20.1a.* Find $z_u$ and $z_v$ if

$$z = x^2 + xy + y^2$$

and

$$x = u \cos v, \quad y = u \sin v.$$

Direct use of Equation (1) gives

$$z_u = (2x + y) \cos v + (x + 2y) \sin v$$

and, similarly,

$$z_v = (2x + y)(-u \sin v) + (x + 2y)(u \cos v).$$

It is evident that if left in this form, $z_u$ and $z_v$ actually are functions of four variables, although $x$ and $y$ depend on $u$ and $v$. Of course, the $x$ and $y$ may be eliminated by direct substitution when it is practical to do so.

---

This example and the preceding discussion raise the question: Why not substitute for $x$ and $y$ in $z = f(x, y)$ before carrying out the differentiation? For instance, in Example 20.1a, we might have written

$$z = u^2(1 + \cos v \sin v) = u^2(1 + \tfrac{1}{2} \sin 2v),$$

so that

$$z_u = 2u(1 + \tfrac{1}{2} \sin 2v)$$

and

$$z_v = u^2(1 + \cos 2v).$$

In this case it is clear that a direct substitution is simpler than the method used in the example. The next example, however, shows that such a substitution is not always practical.

---

*Example 20.1b.* Suppose that $u = f(x, y)$ and that new independent variables $r$ and $s$ are introduced by the equations

$$r = \tfrac{1}{2}(x^2 - y^2), \quad s = \tfrac{1}{2}(x^2 + y^2).$$

Find an expression in terms of $r$ and $s$ and partial derivatives of $u$ with respect to $r$ and $s$ that is equivalent to $u_x^2 + u_y^2$.

In this example, it would do no good to substitute for $x$ and $y$, since no explicit formula for $f(x, y)$ is given. Hence, we must make use of Equation (1), which gives

$$u_x = u_r r_x + u_s s_x \quad \text{and} \quad u_y = u_r r_y + u_s s_y.$$

From the equations relating $r$ and $s$ with $x$ and $y$, we get

$$r_x = x, \quad s_x = x, \quad r_y = -y, \quad s_y = y,$$

so that

$$u_x = x(u_r + u_s) \quad \text{and} \quad u_y = y(-u_r + u_s)$$

and

$$\begin{aligned}
u_x^2 + u_y^2 &= x^2(u_r + u_s)^2 + y^2(-u_r + u_s)^2 \\
&= (x^2 + y^2)(u_r^2 + u_s^2) + 2(x^2 - y^2)u_r u_s \\
&= 2s(u_r^2 + u_s^2) + 4r u_r u_s.
\end{aligned}$$

---

The general pattern of the development of rules for partial differentiation of composite functions follows easily from the procedure used in obtaining Equation (1). For example, if $x$ and $y$ are both functions of one variable $t$, say $x = g(t)$, $y = h(t)$, then $z$ may be represented as a composite function of the single variable $t$. In this case, it is *not* meaningful to speak of the *partial* derivative of $z$ with respect to $t$. Instead, the expression

$$\lim_{\Delta t \to 0} \frac{\Delta z}{\Delta t}$$

defines the ordinary derivative of $z$ with respect to $t$, and we have

(3) $$D_t z = z_x D_t x + z_y D_t y.$$

The expression in Equation (3) is called the **total derivative** of $z$ with respect to $t$. Another special situation arises when relationships of the form

$$u = f(x, y, z) \quad \text{and} \quad z = g(x, y)$$

are given. so that $u$ is a composite function of $x$ and $y$. Since

$$\Delta u = f_x(x, y, z)\, \Delta x + f_y(x, y, z)\, \Delta y + f_z(x, y, z)\, \Delta z + \epsilon_1\, \Delta x + \epsilon_2\, \Delta y + \epsilon_3\, \Delta z,$$

and since $x$ and $y$ are the independent variables, the partial derivatives of $u$ with respect to $x$ and $y$ may be found. Thus, if $y$ is held constant, so that $\Delta y = 0$, then

$$\frac{\Delta u}{\Delta x} = f_x(x, y, z) + f_z(x, y, z)\frac{\Delta z}{\Delta x} + \epsilon_1 + \epsilon_3 \frac{\Delta z}{\Delta x}.$$

Upon finding the limit, provided it exists, we get

(4) $$u_x = f_x(x, y, z) + f_z(x, y, z)z_x.$$

The reader may wonder why use was not made of the notation in Equation (1). Had this notation been used, we would have obtained a statement of the form

(5) $$u_x = u_x + u_z z_x,$$

a result that is indeed misleading. The difficulty here is that the symbol $u_x$ now represents two different quantities. On the left side of the equation, $u_x$ represents the rate of change with respect to $x$ of $u$ regarded as a function of the independent variables $x$ and $y$. On the right side $u_x$ represents the expression for the formal partial derivative with respect to $x$ of the function $f$ with all three of $x$, $y$, and $z$ regarded as independent. In circumstances such as this, the notation appearing in Equation (4) is to be preferred.

---

*Example 20.1c.* If $u = F(x, y, z) = x \sin x^2 y + 3xz^2 - y \ln z$ and $z = x^2 + xy$, find $u_x$.

According to Equation (4),

$$u_x = (\sin x^2 y + 2x^2 y \cos x^2 y + 3z^2) + \left(6xz - \frac{y}{z}\right)(2x + y).$$

The difference in the meaning of the $u_x$'s in Equation (5) should be apparent from this example.

---

We now return to the definition of the differential, Definition 19.6a, and consider the case where $x$ and $y$ are intermediate variables rather than independent variables. Suppose that

$$z = f(x, y), \quad x = g(u, v), \quad y = h(u, v),$$

where $u$ and $v$ are the final independent variables. Then

$$z = f[g(u, v), h(u, v)] = F(u, v),$$

and, by Definition 19.6a,

$$dz = dF(u, v) = F_u(u, v)\, du + F_v(u, v)\, dv.$$

By Equation (1), written out in full,

$$F_u(u, v) = f_x(x, y)g_u(u, v) + f_y(x, y)h_u(u, v),$$

and

$$F_v(u, v) = f_x(x, y)g_v(u, v) + f_y(x, y)h_v(u, v),$$

so that, upon substituting into the expression for $dz$ and rearranging terms, we get

$$dz = f_x(x, y)[g_u(u, v)\, du + g_v(u, v)\, dv] + f_y(x, y)[h_u(u, v)\, du + h_v(u, v)\, dv].$$

Again, by Definition 19.6a,

$$dx = g_u(u, v)\, du + g_v(u, v)\, dv,$$

and

$$dy = h_u(u, v)\, du + h_v(u, v)\, dv.$$

Accordingly,

$$dz = f_x(x, y)\, dx + f_y(x, y)\, dy,$$

as predicted in Section 19.6. Note, then, that in the more condensed notation, we may always write

$$dz = z_x\, dx + z_y\, dy,$$

where $z_x$ and $z_y$ are obtained as if $x$ and $y$ were independent variables (whether they are or not). This shows that the total differential is invariant in form whether $x$ and $y$ are the independent variables or are functions of two other independent variables.

The same procedure may be used to show that if $x$ and $y$ are both functions of a single independent variable $t$ or are both functions of several other independent variables, then the equation

$$dz = z_x\, dx + z_y\, dy$$

is still correct. This is a fact that can sometimes be used to advantage in obtaining desired derivative formulas.

---

*Example 20.1d.* Suppose that $u = f(x, y)$ and that $r$ and $\theta$ are the usual polar coordinates given by $x = r \cos \theta$ and $y = r \sin \theta$. Then $u = f(r \cos \theta, r \sin \theta) = F(r, \theta)$. Find $F_r$ and $F_\theta$ in terms of $f_x$ and $f_y$.

We may write

$$du = f_x\, dx + f_y\, dy,$$
$$dx = \cos \theta\, dr - r \sin \theta\, d\theta,$$
$$dy = \sin \theta\, dr + r \cos \theta\, d\theta.$$

Then, by substituting from the last two equations for $dx$ and $dy$ in the first equation, we get

$$du = (f_x \cos \theta + f_y \sin \theta)\, dr + (-f_x r \sin \theta + f_y r \cos \theta)\, d\theta.$$

Since this must be the same as

$$du = F_r\, dr + F_\theta\, d\theta,$$

we obtain the desired results:

$$F_r = f_x \cos \theta + f_y \sin \theta,$$
$$F_\theta = -f_x r \sin \theta + f_y r \cos \theta.$$

These results should, of course, check with those obtained by the direct use of Formula (1). This check is left to the reader.

## Exercises 20.1

In each of Numbers 1 to 9, find the indicated derivatives.

1. $u = x^3 - 3xy + y^3$; $x = r^2 + s$, $y = rs^2$; $u_r$.
2. $z = e^{xy}$; $x = \sqrt{u^2 + v^2}$, $y = \text{Tan}^{-1}(u/v)$; $z_u$, $z_v$.
3. $u = xy + yz$; $x = e^t/t$, $y = e^{-t}/t$, $z = t^2$; $D_t u$.
4. $z = x \ln y + y \ln x$; $x = e^{u+v}$, $y = e^{u-v}$; $z_u$, $z_v$.
5. $z = \ln(x^2 + y^2) + \sqrt{x^2 + y^2}$; $x = e^u \cos v$, $y = e^u \sin v$; $z_u$.
6. $z = e^x \cos y$; $x = \ln(u^2 + v^2)$, $y = \text{Tan}^{-1}(v/u)$; $z_u$.
7. $u = xy + yz + zx$; $x = r^s$, $y = sr$, $z = r + s$; $u_r$.
8. $u = \sqrt{x^2 + y^2 - z^2}$; $x = r \cos s \sin t$, $y = r \sin s \sin t$, $z = r \cos t$; $u_r$, $u_s$, $u_t$.
9. $u = xyz^2$; $x = re^s$, $y = re^{-s}$, $z = r/s$; $u_r$, $u_s$.

10. If $u = f(x, y, z)$, $z = g(x, y)$, $y = h(x)$, write an expression for $D_x u$.
11. If $u = f(x, y)$ and $x = r \cos \theta$, $y = r \sin \theta$, find an expression in terms of $x$ and $y$ equivalent to

$$u_r^2 + \frac{1}{r^2} u_\theta^2.$$

12. Suppose $u = f(x, y)$, $v = g(x, y)$ where $u_x = v_y$ and $u_y = -v_x$. If $x = r \cos \theta$, $y = r \sin \theta$, show that $u_r = (1/r)v_\theta$ and $v_r = -(1/r)u_\theta$.
13. If $z = xF(y/x)$, show that $xz_x + yz_y = z$.
14. If $u = f(x + az, y - az)$, show that $u_z = a(u_x - u_y)$.

## 20.2 IMPLICIT DIFFERENTIATION

It frequently happens that an expression of the form $F(x, y) = 0$ describes one or more functions implicitly. The concept of an implicit function was first introduced in Section 6.5. There we had to be content to assume that the function $F$ in the equation $F(x, y) = 0$ possessed the properties required to define $y$ as a function of $x$. With the tools now available we can specify more precisely the conditions under which an implicitly defined function actually exists. In addition, groundwork can be established from which a generalization of the implicit function concept can be formulated.

**Theorem 20.2a.** Let $F$ be a function of two variables defined on an open two-dimensional region $\Re$ having the point $P(a, b)$ in its interior. If
  (a) $F(a, b) = 0$,
  (b) $F_x(x, y)$ and $F_y(x, y)$ exist and are continuous on a neighborhood of $P$, where $\Re(P) \subset \Re^i$, and
  (c) $F_y(a, b) \neq 0$,
then in some $\Re(a, \delta)$ there exists a function $f$ such that
    (i) $b = f(a)$, and $y = f(x)$ satisfies the equation $F(x, y) = 0$ for all $x \in \Re(a, \delta)$,

(ii) $f$ is continuous on $\mathfrak{N}(a, \delta)$, and

(iii) $f'(a) = -\dfrac{F_x(a, b)}{F_y(a, b)}$.

★PROOF: The following argument is a good illustration of the way in which properties of continuous functions may be employed. First, by Theorem 19.6b, the continuity of $F_x$ and $F_y$ on a neighborhood of $P$ implies the continuity of $F$ itself on this neighborhood.

Since $F_y(a, b) \neq 0$, we may suppose $F_y(a, b) > 0$ without loss of generality, and since $F_y$ is continuous at $P(a, b)$, there is a neighborhood of $P$ on which $F_y(x, y) > 0$. For each $x$ in this neighborhood, $F$ is then an increasing function of $y$. Consequently, it follows from $F(a, b) = 0$ that $F(a, b + \epsilon) > 0$ and $F(a, b - \epsilon) < 0$ for a sufficiently small $\epsilon$ (see Figure 20.2a).

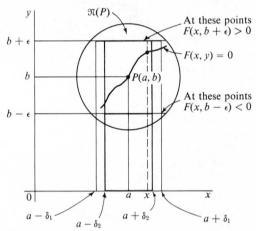

**FIGURE 20.2a**

Because $F$ is continuous at $(a, b)$, there is a $\delta_1$ such that $F(x, b + \epsilon) > 0$ for all $x \in \mathfrak{N}(a, \delta_1)$ and there is a $\delta_2$ such that $F(x, b - \epsilon) < 0$ for all $x \in \mathfrak{N}(a, \delta_2)$. Hence if $\delta = \min(\delta_1, \delta_2)$, then

$$x \in \mathfrak{N}(a, \delta) \Rightarrow F(x, b + \epsilon) > 0 \quad \text{and} \quad F(x, b - \epsilon) < 0.$$

The continuity of $F$ now insures that for each such $x$ there is a unique value of $y$ such that $F(x, y) = 0$. This means that on the interval $a - \delta < x < a + \delta$, $y$ is a function of $x$. Let this function be denoted by $f$ so that the value of $y$ corresponding to a given $x$ is $f(x)$. Then, in particular, $b = f(a)$.

The function $f$ is continuous because for every $x \in \mathfrak{N}(a, \delta)$, it follows that $y \in \mathfrak{N}(b, \epsilon)$. Furthermore, the preceding argument may be repeated at each point $x_1 \in \mathfrak{N}(a, \delta)$, where the point $(x_1, y_1)$ replaces $(a, b)$ in the argument.

Since, for points where $y = f(x)$, we have $F(x, y) = 0$, it follows that $\Delta F = 0$, and

$$0 = F_x(x, y) + F_y(x, y) \frac{\Delta y}{\Delta x} + \epsilon_1 + \epsilon_2 \frac{\Delta y}{\Delta x}.$$

If we let $\Delta x \to 0$, then we get

$$0 = F_x(x, y) + F_y(x, y)f'(x).$$

Hence, at $(a, b)$, since $F_y(a, b) \neq 0$,

$$f'(a) = -\frac{F_x(a, b)}{F_y(a, b)}.$$

If the conditions of Theorem 20.2a are satisfied, so that the function $f$ is determined, then we may write $y = f(x)$ and substitute $f(x)$ for $y$ in the equation $F(x, y) = 0$ to obtain the identity $F[x, f(x)] = 0$. This discussion shows that we may also calculate $D_x y$ directly from the equation $F(x, y) = 0$ by differentiating both members with respect to $x$, with the implied condition that $y = f(x)$.

The results of Theorem 20.2a may be extended to functions of more than two variables by an argument similar to the preceding one, but which will not be repeated here. We shall only state the theorem for functions of three variables.

**Theorem 20.2b.** Let $F$ be a function of the variables $x$, $y$, and $z$ defined on an open three-dimensional region $\mathfrak{R}$ having the point $P(a, b, c)$ in its interior. If
   (a) $F(a, b, c) = 0$,
   (b) $F_x(x, y, z)$, $F_y(x, y, z)$, and $F_z(x, y, z)$ exist and are continuous on some neighborhood of $P$, where $\mathfrak{N}(P) \subset \mathfrak{R}^i$, and
   (c) $F_z(a, b, c) \neq 0$,
then in some $\mathfrak{N}[(a, b), \delta]$ there exists a function $f$ such that
   (i) $c = f(a, b)$, and $z = f(x, y)$ satisfies the equation $F(x, y, z) = 0$ for all $(x, y) \in \mathfrak{N}[(a, b), \delta]$,
   (ii) $f$ is continuous on $\mathfrak{N}[(a, b), \delta]$, and

   (iii) $f_x(a, b) = -\dfrac{F_x(a, b, c)}{F_z(a, b, c)}$, $f_y(a, b) = -\dfrac{F_y(a, b, c)}{F_z(a, b, c)}$.

It should be clear that there is a need for Theorem 20.2b, since it is not immediately apparent that an equation such as

$$x^2 z^2 + y \sin zx = 2$$

determines a value of $z$ for a given value of $x$ and $y$ in such a way that a continuous function having partial derivatives is defined. This theorem stipulates certain conditions under which such a function exists; the theorem is thus an **existence theorem.**

---

*Example 20.2a.* Find $z_x$ if $x^2 z^2 + y \sin xz = 2$.

It is assumed that we shall be concerned with points at which the conditions of the theorem are satisfied. If $F(x, y, z) .=. x^2 z^2 + y \sin xz - 2 = 0$, then

$$F_x(x, y, z) = 2xz^2 + yz \cos xz,$$

and

$$F_z(x, y, z) = 2x^2 z + xy \cos xz,$$

so that

$$z_x = -\frac{2xz^2 + yz \cos xz}{2x^2z + xy \cos xz} = -\frac{z}{x}.$$

In this example, the equation $F(x, y, z) = 0$ is satisfied, for instance, by the point $(1, 0, \sqrt{2})$. In any neighborhood of this point, $F$ has continuous partial derivatives and $F_z(1, 0, \sqrt{2}) \neq 0$. Hence, the conditions of Theorem 20.2b are satisfied, so that there is a function $f$ such that $f(1, 0) = \sqrt{2}$ and $z_x = -\sqrt{2}/1 = -\sqrt{2}$ at $(1, 0)$. Furthermore, this function is such that $F[x, y, f(x, y)] = 0$ for all $(x, y)$ in some neighborhood of $(1, 0)$.

---

The results of Theorem 20.2b suggest that still further generalization is possible. To illustrate, suppose we are given two equations of the form

$$F(x, y, z) = 0,$$
$$G(x, y, z) = 0.$$

If we assume that the function $F$ satisfies the conditions of Theorem 20.2b, then we may state that

$$F(x, y, z) = 0 \Rightarrow z = f(x, y).$$

If this result is substituted in $G(x, y, z) = 0$, a new equation,

$$H(x, y) = 0,$$

is obtained that in turn implies the existence of a functional relationship of the form

$$y = h(x).$$

How may we determine, then, an expression for $D_x y$?

Although it is possible to state conditions under which $y$ may be regarded as a function of $x$ as a consequence of the equations $F(x, y, z) = 0$ and $G(x, y, z) = 0$, we shall not do so here, but instead shall be content to demonstrate the technique for finding derivatives under such conditions.

Since $y$ is considered a function of $x$, and $z$ a function of $x$ and $y$, we differentiate both of the given equations with respect to $x$ to obtain

$$F_x(x, y, z) + F_y(x, y, z)\, D_x y + F_z(x, y, z)\, D_x z = 0,$$

and

$$G_x(x, y, z) + G_y(x, y, z)\, D_x y + G_z(x, y, z)\, D_x z = 0.$$

From these two equations, we get, by means of determinants,

$$D_x y = -\frac{\begin{vmatrix} F_x(x, y, z) & F_z(x, y, z) \\ G_x(x, y, z) & G_z(x, y, z) \end{vmatrix}}{\begin{vmatrix} F_y(x, y, z) & F_z(x, y, z) \\ G_y(x, y, z) & G_z(x, y, z) \end{vmatrix}}.$$

Thus, $D_x y$ is expressed entirely in terms of the partial derivatives of the functions $F$ and $G$.

*Example 20.2b.* Find $D_x y$ if

$$xy + yz^2 + 3 = 0,$$
$$x^2 y + yz - z^2 + 1 = 0.$$

By differentiation with respect to $x$, we get

$$y + (x + z^2) D_x y + 2yz \, D_x z = 0,$$

and

$$2xy + (x^2 + z) D_x y + (y - 2z) D_x z = 0.$$

It follows that

$$D_x y = - \frac{\begin{vmatrix} y & 2yz \\ 2xy & y - 2z \end{vmatrix}}{\begin{vmatrix} x + z^2 & 2yz \\ x^2 + z & y - 2z \end{vmatrix}}$$

$$= - \frac{y^2 - 2yz - 4xy^2 z}{xy - yz^2 - 2xz - 2z^3 - 2x^2 yz}.$$

---

If two equations of the form

(1)
$$F(x, y, u, v) = 0,$$
$$G(x, y, u, v) = 0$$

are given, then under the appropriate conditions, we may say that

$$F(x, y, u, v) = 0 \Rightarrow v = f(x, y, u).$$

Upon substituting for $v$ in $G$, we get an expression of the form

$$H(x, y, u) = 0,$$

from which it follows that

$$u = h(x, y).$$

If this result is used in

$$v = f(x, y, u),$$

then

$$v = k(x, y).$$

Thus, the two equations in four variables imply that we may consider two of the variables as functions of the remaining two. It is necessary only to decide which of the variables shall be considered independent.

Accordingly, if $x$ and $y$ are taken as independent, we may differentiate the members of each of the original Equations (1) with respect to $x$, holding $y$ fixed, to obtain

$$F_x(x, y, u, v) + F_u(x, y, u, v)u_x + F_v(x, y, u, v)v_x = 0,$$
$$G_x(x, y, u, v) + G_u(x, y, u, v)u_x + G_v(x, y, u, v)v_x = 0.$$

In order to simplify the writing of the expressions for $u_x$ and $v_x$, we shall abandon the complete notation $F_x(x, y, u, v)$, and use $F_x$ with the understanding that we are referring to the partial derivative of $F(x, y, u, v)$ with respect to $x$, holding $y$, $u$, and $v$ all constant. Then,

$$(2) \qquad u_x = - \frac{\begin{vmatrix} F_x & F_v \\ G_x & G_v \end{vmatrix}}{\begin{vmatrix} F_u & F_v \\ G_u & G_v \end{vmatrix}}, \qquad v_x = - \frac{\begin{vmatrix} F_u & F_x \\ G_u & G_x \end{vmatrix}}{\begin{vmatrix} F_u & F_v \\ G_u & G_v \end{vmatrix}},$$

provided the denominator does not vanish at the point in question. Similar expressions may be found for $u_y$ and $v_y$.

The determinant appearing in the denominator of these expressions is so fundamental to many studies in calculus that it is given a special name. The expression

$$J\left(\frac{F, G}{u, v}\right) . = . \begin{vmatrix} F_u & F_v \\ G_u & G_v \end{vmatrix}$$

is called the **Jacobian** of the functions $F$ and $G$ with respect to $u$ and $v$. Similarly, the expression

$$J\left(\frac{F, G}{x, v}\right) . = . \begin{vmatrix} F_x & F_v \\ G_x & G_v \end{vmatrix}$$

is called the Jacobian of $F$ and $G$ with respect to $x$ and $v$. In terms of Jacobians, we may write

$$u_x = -J\left(\frac{F, G}{x, v}\right) \bigg/ J\left(\frac{F, G}{u, v}\right) \quad \text{and} \quad v_x = -J\left(\frac{F, G}{u, x}\right) \bigg/ J\left(\frac{F, G}{u, v}\right).$$

---

*Example 20.2c.* Find $u_x$ and $v_x$ if

$$u^2 - v^2 + 2x = 0,$$
$$uv - y = 0.$$

The desired expressions may be obtained by straightforward differentiation or by substitution in Equations (2). By differentiation with respect to $x$, we get

$$2uu_x - 2vv_x + 2 = 0,$$
$$vu_x + uv_x = 0,$$

so that

$$u_x = -\frac{u}{u^2 + v^2}, \qquad v_x = \frac{v}{u^2 + v^2}.$$

## Exercises 20.2

In each of Numbers 1 to 16, find the indicated derivatives.

1. $e^x \sin y + e^y \cos x = 1$; $D_x y$.
2. $x^3 + 3xy^2 + y^3 = a^3$; $D_x y$.
3. $\ln(x^2 + y^2) = 2 \operatorname{Tan}^{-1}(y/x)$; $D_x y$.
4. $x^y y^x = 1$; $D_x y$. (*Hint:* Use logarithms.)
5. $xy + yz + zx = 9xyz$; $z_x, z_y$.

6. $z = y \operatorname{Tan}^{-1}(z/x)$; $z_x, z_y$.
7. $xz = \cos yz + a$; $z_x, z_y$.
8. $e^x + e^y + e^z = 3xyz$; $y_x, y_z$.
9. $xyz = 1$, $xy + yz + xz = 3$; $D_x y$.
10. $x^2 + y^2 + z^2 = 9$, $xyz = 1$; $D_x y$.

11. $x \cos z + y \sin z = 2$, $x \sin z - y \cos z = 1$; $D_x y$.
12. $u^2 - v^2 + 2x = 0$, $uv - y = 0$; $u_y, v_y$.
13. $u^2 - v^2 - x^3 + 3y = 0$, $u + v - y^2 - 2x = 0$; $u_x, v_x$.
14. $xy + uv = 2$; $xu - yv = 1$; $u_x, u_y$.

15. $xyu = v + 2$; $y^2u + xv + y - v = 1$; $x_u$, $y_v$.

16. $x = ue^v$, $y = ue^{-v}$; $u_x$, $u_y$.

17. At what point, if any, on the curve $x^3 + y^3 - 8xy = 0$ is the slope zero?

18. If $F(x, y, z) = 0$, show that $x_y y_z z_x = -1$.

19. If $f(x, y) = 0$, show that

$$D_x^2 y = -(f_y^2 f_{xx} - 2f_x f_y f_{xy} + f_x^2 f_{yy})/f_y^3.$$

20. If $u = f(x, y)$ and $x = r\cos\theta$, $y = r\sin\theta$, write the equation $u_{xx} + u_{yy} = 0$ in terms of $r$ and $\theta$.

21. If $z = f(x, y)$, $x = g(u, v)$, $y = h(u, v)$, show that

$$z_{uu} = z_{xx}x_u^2 + 2z_{yx}x_u y_u + z_{yy}y_u^2 + z_x x_{uu} + z_y y_{uu}.$$

22. In Number 21, find an expression for $z_{uv}$.

23. If $F(x, y, z) = 0$, find an expression for $z_{xx}$.

## 20.3 THE TANGENT PLANE AND THE NORMAL LINE

We have called a function $f$ of a single variable differentiable at $x = a$ if $f'(a)$ exists. If the function is differentiable, then the graph of $f$ has a tangent line with slope $f'(a)$ at $x = a$. Is it possible to extend this geometric concept to functions of two variables? If $z = f(x, y)$, and if $f_x(a, b)$ and $f_y(a, b)$ both exist, is it true that the surface described by the equation has a "tangent plane" at $(a, b)$?

Although it appears intuitively evident that the answer to the first question is yes, a number of examples have already indicated that we must proceed with caution in answering the second. Indeed, before we can go further it is essential to give a precise meaning to the notions of surface and of a plane "tangent" to a surface at a given point.

**Definition 20.3a.** In ordinary three-dimensional euclidean space, a set of points described by a continuous function of two independent variables on a connected plane region $\mathcal{R}$ is called a **surface.**

Usually, the region $\mathcal{R}$ is in the $xy$-plane, and the function is defined by an equation of the form $z = f(x, y)$. We could, however, also have $x = g(y, z)$, with $\mathcal{R}$ in the $yz$-plane, or $y = h(x, z)$, with $\mathcal{R}$ in the $xz$-plane. Numerous examples of surfaces were given in Chapter 17.

The concept of a tangent plane to a surface is a generalization of the concept of a tangent line to a curve, as is indicated by

**Definition 20.3b.** At a point $P$ on a surface $S$, consider a plane determined by three noncollinear points, $P$ and two other points $Q_1$ and $Q_2$ on $S$. If for every choice of $Q_1$ and $Q_2$, the plane $PQ_1Q_2$ approaches the same plane, say $\mathcal{P}$, as $Q_1$ and $Q_2$ independently approach the point $P$ along the surface, then this limiting plane $\mathcal{P}$ is called the **tangent plane** to the surface $S$ at $P$.

Figure 20.3a shows a point $P$ on a surface $S$ with two other points $Q_1$ and $Q_2$. The curves $\mathcal{C}_1$ and $\mathcal{C}_2$ are two curves on the surface, with $\mathcal{C}_1$ joining $Q_1$ and $P$, and $\mathcal{C}_2$ joining $Q_2$ and $P$. Suppose that as $Q_1 \to P$ along $\mathcal{C}_1$ the line $PQ_1$ ap-

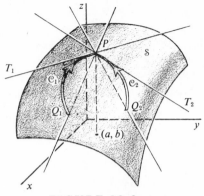

**FIGURE 20.3a**

proaches the line $PT_1$ as a limit, so that $PT_1$ is tangent to $e_1$ at $P$. Similarly, suppose that as $Q_2 \rightarrow P$ along $e_2$, the line $PQ_2$ approaches the line $PT_2$ as a limit; that is, $PT_2$ is the tangent to $e_2$ at $P$. Then the two lines $PT_1$ and $PT_2$ determine a plane, say $\mathcal{P}$. Suppose further that for every pair of arbitrary curves on $S$, one through $P$ and $Q_1$ and the other through $P$ and $Q_2$ and intersecting only at $P$, the plane $PQ_1Q_2$ has the same plane $\mathcal{P}$ as a limit as $Q_1 \rightarrow P$ and $Q_2 \rightarrow P$; then $\mathcal{P}$ is the tangent plane to $S$ at the point $P$.

The preceding discussion suggests that we examine the two curves that pass through the point $P$ and are cut from the surface by planes parallel to the $xz$-plane and the $yz$-plane, respectively. Let the equation of the surface be $z = f(x, y)$, and let $P(a, b, c)$ be the point on the surface corresponding to $x = a$, $y = b$. Suppose that $f_x(a, b)$ and $f_y(a, b)$ both exist. Then $f_x(a, b)$ is the slope at $P$ of the curve $e_1$ cut from the surface by the plane $y = b$. Similarly, $f_y(a, b)$ is the slope at $P$ of the curve $e_2$ cut from the surface by the plane $x = a$. Each of these curves thus has a tangent line at $P$ (see Figure 20.3b). Furthermore, by Definition 20.3b, it follows that *if there is a tangent plane to the surface at $P$*, then this tangent plane is the plane determined by these two tangent lines.

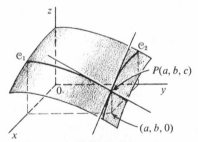

**FIGURE 20.3b**

Unfortunately, even though both $f_x(a, b)$ and $f_y(a, b)$ exist, it is possible for a surface to have no tangent plane at $P$. For example, consider a surface such as that illustrated in Figure 20.3c, where the surface is cut by the $xz$-plane in the curve $z = 1 - x^2$ and by the $yz$-plane in the curve $z = 1 - y^2$. Note that the surface has sharp edges, as indicated along both of these curves. At the point $P(0, 0, 1)$, $z_x = -2x = 0$ and $z_y = -2y = 0$, so that each of these curves has a tangent line at $P$. However, every plane, except the $xz$- and the $yz$-planes, through the point $P$ and perpendicular to the $xy$-plane, cuts from the surface a curve for which no slope is defined at $P$. Thus, the surface has no tangent plane (in the sense of Definition 20.3a) at $P$.

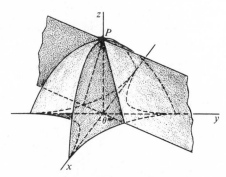

**FIGURE 20.3c**

If the surface $z = f(x, y)$ has a tangent plane at a point $P$, then the function $f$ is said to be **differentiable** at $P$. Hence, as the preceding illustrations show, the term "differentiable" connotes more than just the existence of the first partial derivatives at $P$. The rather difficult problem which arises here is beyond the scope of this book. The reader may refer to books in advanced calculus for a detailed discussion. We state, without proof, sufficient conditions for differentiability which are also sufficient conditions for the existence of a tangent plane to a surface.

**Theorem 20.3a.** If
    (a) $z = f(x, y)$ is defined on a neighborhood $\mathfrak{N}(P)$ of the point $P(a, b)$, and
    (b) $f_x(x, y)$ and $f_y(x, y)$ exist on $\mathfrak{N}(P)$, and
    (c) $f_x$ and $f_y$ are continuous at $P$,
  then $f$ is differentiable at $P$.

If a surface $S$ has a tangent plane at a point $P(a, b, c)$, then the line through $P$ perpendicular to the tangent plane is called the **normal** to the surface at $P$. The normal is useful in obtaining the equation of the tangent plane. Let the equation of the surface be $z = f(x, y)$, where $f$ has continuous first partial derivatives at the point in question. Then a set of direction numbers of the tangent line to the curve $\mathcal{C}_1$ cut from $S$ by the plane $x = a$ (see Figure 20.3b), is $[0, 1, z_y]$, evaluated at $P$. Similarly, for the curve $\mathcal{C}_2$ cut from $S$ by the plane $y = b$, a set of direction numbers is $[1, 0, z_y]$. Consequently,

$$t_1 = j + z_y k \quad \text{and} \quad t_2 = i + z_x k$$

are tangent vectors at $P$ to the curves $\mathcal{C}_1$ and $\mathcal{C}_2$, respectively. Hence, a **normal vector** to the surface at $P$ is given by

$$\mathbf{n} = \mathbf{t}_1 \times \mathbf{t}_2 = z_x\mathbf{i} + z_y\mathbf{j} - \mathbf{k}.$$

The equation of the tangent plane to a surface at a point $P(x_0, y_0, z_0)$ is easily obtained. If the surface is described by $z = f(x, y)$, then the equation of the tangent plane is given by

$$(1) \qquad f_x(P)(x - x_0) + f_y(P)(y - y_0) - (z - z_0) = 0,$$

since the normal vector $\mathbf{n} = (f_x(P), f_y(P), -1)$ must be orthogonal to every vector $\mathbf{r} - \mathbf{r}_0 = (x - x_0, y - y_0, z - z_0)$ in the plane. The equations of the **normal line** to the surface at $P$ are

$$(2) \qquad \frac{x - x_0}{f_x(P)} = \frac{y - y_0}{f_y(P)} = \frac{z - z_0}{-1}.$$

Frequently, the equation of a surface is given in the form $F(x, y, z) = 0$. Since, for $F_z(P) \neq 0$,

$$z_x = -\frac{F_x(P)}{F_z(P)}, \quad z_y = -\frac{F_y(P)}{F_z(P)},$$

the direction numbers of a normal to the surface at $P$ are given by

$$\left[ -\frac{F_x(P)}{F_z(P)}, -\frac{F_y(P)}{F_z(P)}, -1 \right],$$

or

$$[F_x(P), F_y(P), F_z(P)].$$

Hence, the equation of the tangent plane to the surface at $P(x_0, y_0, z_0)$ is given in *symmetric form* by

$$(3) \qquad F_x(P)(x - x_0) + F_y(P)(y - y_0) + F_z(P)(z - z_0) = 0.$$

Similarly, a symmetric form for the equations of the normal line is

$$(4) \qquad \frac{x - x_0}{F_x(P)} = \frac{y - y_0}{F_y(P)} = \frac{z - z_0}{F_z(P)}.$$

---

*Example 20.3a.* Find the tangent plane and the normal line to the surface

$$\frac{x^2}{4} + \frac{y^2}{9} + \frac{z^2}{16} = 1$$

at the point $P(2, 3, 4)$.

If $F(x, y, z) = x^2/4 + y^2/9 + z^2/16 - 1$, then

$$F_x(P) = \left[ \frac{2x}{4} \right]_{(2, 3, 4)}, \quad F_y(P) = \left[ \frac{2y}{9} \right]_{(2, 3, 4)}, \quad F_z(P) = \left[ \frac{2z}{16} \right]_{(2, 3, 4)},$$

or

$$F_x(P) = 1, \quad F_y(P) = \tfrac{2}{3}, \quad F_z(P) = \tfrac{1}{2}.$$

Hence, the equation of the tangent plane is

$$(x - 2) + \tfrac{2}{3}(y - 3) + \tfrac{1}{2}(z - 4) = 0$$

and the equations of the normal line are

$$\frac{x-2}{1} = \frac{y-3}{2/3} = \frac{z-4}{1/2}.$$

---

*Example 20.3b.* Two surfaces are **orthogonal** to each other at a point of intersection if their normals at the point are perpendicular to each other. Show that the sphere $(x-1)^2 + (y-1)^2 + z^2 = 66$ is orthogonal to the paraboloid $z = x^2 + y^2$ at the point (2, 2, 8).

We may write for the sphere

$$F(x, y, z) .=. (x-1)^2 + (y-1)^2 + z^2 - 66 = 0,$$

and for the paraboloid

$$G(x, y, z) .=. x^2 + y^2 - z = 0.$$

Then

$$F_x = 2(x-1), \quad F_y = 2(y-1), \quad F_z = 2z,$$

and

$$G_x = 2x, \quad G_y = 2y, \quad G_z = -1.$$

At the point (2, 2, 8), which the reader should verify is actually on the intersection of the two surfaces,

$$F_x = 2, \quad F_y = 2, \quad F_z = 16,$$
$$G_x = 4, \quad G_y = 4, \quad G_z = -1,$$

and

$$F_xG_x + F_yG_y + F_zG_z = 8 + 8 - 16 = 0.$$

Therefore, the normals are perpendicular to each other, and the surfaces are orthogonal, as was to be shown.

---

*Example 20.3c.* The surface of a cylindrical tank consists of a portion of the elliptic cylinder $x^2 + 2y^2 = 6$, the plane $z = 0$, and a portion of the paraboloid $x^2 + 2y^2 + z = 8$. Find a formula for the tangent of the angle at which the paraboloidal surface meets the elliptic cylinder.
*Note:* The angle of intersection of two surfaces at a point is the acute angle between their tangent planes at the point. The reader may verify that this angle is equal to the acute angle between the normals at the point.

From the equations of the surface, it is seen that the cylinder and the paraboloid intersect along the ellipse $x^2 + 2y^2 = 6$, $z = 8$. For the cylinder, we may write

$$F(x, y, z) .=. x^2 + 2y^2 - 6 = 0;$$

and for the paraboloid,

$$G(x, y, z) .=. x^2 + 2y^2 + z - 8 = 0.$$

Thus,

$$F_x = 2x, \quad F_y = 4y, \quad F_z = 0,$$

and

$$G_x = 2x, \quad G_y = 4y, \quad G_z = 1.$$

At each point on the cylinder, a normal vector is given by

$$\mathbf{n}_1 = 2x\mathbf{i} + 4y\mathbf{j},$$

and similarly for the paraboloid,

$$n_2 = 2xi + 4yj + k.$$

The angle $\varphi$ between $n_1$ and $n_2$ is given by

$$\cos \varphi = \frac{n_1 \cdot n_2}{|n_1||n_2|} = \frac{4x^2 + 16y^2}{\sqrt{4x^2 + 16y^2}\sqrt{4x^2 + 16y^2 + 1}}$$

$$= \sqrt{\frac{4x^2 + 16y^2}{4x^2 + 16y^2 + 1}}.$$

Accordingly, the acute angle of intersection of the surfaces at any point $(x, y, z)$ on the curve of intersection is

$$\varphi = \text{Tan}^{-1}(4x^2 + 16y^2)^{-1/2}.$$

## Exercises 20.3

1. Find a vector normal to the surface $x^2 + y^2 - z = 1$ at $(1, 1, 1)$.
2. Find a unit vector normal to the surface $x \ln z - y^2 = -4$ at $(-1, 2, 1)$.
3. Find the angle of intersection at $(-1, 2, 1)$ between the surfaces

$$x^2y + z = 3 \quad \text{and} \quad x \ln z - y^2 = -4.$$

4. Find direction numbers of the line tangent to the curve of intersection of the surface $z = x^2 + \frac{1}{4}y^2$ and the plane $y = x$ at $(2, 2, 5)$.
5. Find direction numbers of the line tangent to the curve of intersection of $z = x^2 + y^2$ and the plane $y = x + 1$ at $(1, 2, 5)$.

In each of Numbers 6 to 11, find the equation of the tangent plane and the normal line to the given surface at the indicated point.

6. $x^2 + 4y^2 = 2z$; $(2, 1, 4)$.        9. $z = x^2 - 4y^2$; $(3, 1, 5)$.
7. $z = x^2 + xy - 2y^2$; $(2, 2, 0)$.   10. $z = ye^{x/y}$; $(1, 1, e)$.
8. $xy - z^2 = 1$; $(2, 1, 1)$.        11. $x^2 + 4y^2 + z^2 - 2xy - 4yz = 25$; $(2, 1, -3)$.

12. Two surfaces are said to be tangent to each other at a point $P$ if they have the same tangent plane at $P$. Show that the surfaces described by $z^2 + 25 = 2x^2 + 2y^2$ and $5z = x^2 + y^2$ are tangent to each other at $(4, 3, 5)$.
13. Show that the surfaces described by $2z = -1 + x^2 + y^2$ and $2z = 1 - x^2 - y^2$ are orthogonal to each other at every point of intersection.
14. Find a value (if there is one) for the constant $k$ such that the two surfaces

$$(x - k)^2 + y^2 + z^2 = 4 \quad \text{and} \quad x^2 + (y - 1)^2 + z^2 = 1$$

are orthogonal to each other at every point of their intersection.
15. Suppose that $f(x, y) \geq 0$. Do the normals to the surfaces

$$z = \sqrt{f(x, y)} \quad \text{and} \quad z^2 = f(x, y), \quad z \geq 0$$

have the same direction at each point? Explain.

## 20.4 THE DIRECTIONAL DERIVATIVE AND THE GRADIENT

If $z = f(x, y)$, the two partial derivatives $z_x(a, b)$ and $z_y(a, b)$ give, respectively, the rate of change of $z$ at $(a, b)$ with respect to distance in the $x$-direction and in the *y*-direction. An important generalization of these partial derivatives may be employed to obtain the rate of change of *z* with respect to distance in any direction.

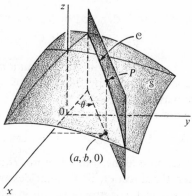

**FIGURE 20.4a**

Suppose $\mathcal{S}$ is the surface described by the equation $z = f(x, y)$. Let us study the curve $\mathcal{C}$ cut from this surface by a plane through the point $(a, b, 0)$ and perpendicular to the *xy*-plane (see Figure 20.4a). Parametric equations of such a plane may be given in the form

$$x = a + s \cos \theta, \quad y = b + s \sin \theta,$$

where $\theta$ is the angle from the positive *x*-direction to the plane. The parameter *s* is the directed distance from $(a, b, 0)$ to $(x, y, 0)$ along the straight line in which this plane cuts the *xy*-plane. This fact may be checked by noting from the parametric equations that $s^2 = (x - a)^2 + (y - b)^2$.

We assume that *f* has continuous first partial derivatives at $(a, b)$ and ask for the slope of the curve $\mathcal{C}$ at the point $P(a, b, c)$. Since *x* and *y* are functions of the parameter *s*, we may use Equation (3) of Section 20.1 to get

$$D_s z = z_x D_s x + z_y D_s y$$
$$= z_x \cos \theta + z_y \sin \theta.$$

This formula gives the rate of change of *z* with respect to distance in the *xy*-plane measured in the direction specified by the angle $\theta$. Accordingly, the expression

1) $$D_s z = z_x \cos \theta + z_y \sin \theta$$

is called the **directional derivative** of *z* in the direction of *s*.

It is instructive to write the directional derivative as a dot product of two vectors:

$$D_s z = (\cos \theta \, \mathbf{i} + \sin \theta \, \mathbf{j}) \cdot (z_x \mathbf{i} + z_y \mathbf{j}).$$

The first of these vectors, $\mathbf{U} . = . \cos \theta \, \mathbf{i} + \sin \theta \, \mathbf{j}$ is a unit vector in the direction of *s* as given by the angle $\theta$. The second vector, an especially important one, is the subject of

**Definition 20.4a.** If $z = f(x, y)$ has continuous first partial derivatives $z_x$ and $z_y$ at $(a, b)$, then the vector

$$z_x\mathbf{i} + z_y\mathbf{j}$$

is called the **gradient** of $z$ and is denoted by $\nabla z$ (read "del $z$"). Thus,

$$\nabla z .=. z_x\mathbf{i} + z_y\mathbf{j}.$$

It should be clear that, at each point in the common domain of $z_x$ and $z_y$, the vector $\nabla z$ is a vector determined by the values of $z_x$ and $z_y$ at that point. Suppose that the angle between the vector $\nabla z$ and the unit vector $\mathbf{U}$ is $\varphi$. Then by the definition of the dot product,

$$D_s z = \mathbf{U} \cdot \nabla z = (z_x{}^2 + z_y{}^2)^{1/2} \cos \varphi,$$

which, of course, depends on $\varphi$ alone. Furthermore, $D_s z$ has a maximum value for $\varphi = 0$, that is, when the direction of $\mathbf{U}$ coincides with that of $\nabla z$. Consequently, the vector $\nabla z$ is a vector in the direction in which the rate of change of $z$ is a maximum, and $|\nabla z|$ is the magnitude of this maximum rate of change.

To grasp the meaning of the gradient more clearly, let us use a kind of topographic representation of the function $z = f(x, y)$. In making a topographic map of a portion of the surface of the earth, we draw curves called **contour lines**. A contour line is a curve joining points all at the same elevation on this piece of the surface. Thus, if we regard $z = f(x, y)$ as being the equation of the surface, where $z$ is the elevation above some fixed base, the $xy$-plane, then a contour line is just a curve cut from the surface by a plane $z = c$ and then projected down onto the $xy$-plane. Sometimes the contour lines are called **level curves**. The family of these curves may be represented as in Figure 20.4b. Since

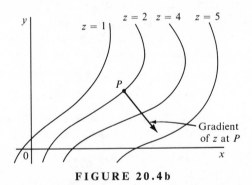

**FIGURE 20.4b**

the gradient of $z$ is in the direction in which the rate of change of $z$ is the greatest $\nabla z$ points in the direction of steepest ascent. (A mountain climber seldom ascends in the direction of the gradient of the surface, but he often descends in the direction of the negative gradient.)

The gradient furnishes us with a most efficient tool for handling the directional derivatives at a point. The gradient, in a manner of speaking, represents the entire packet of directional derivatives in one simple expression. We can pull out any specified one of these derivatives by dot multiplying the gradient by a unit vector in the desired direction.

---

*Example 20.4a.* Find the gradient of

$$z = \sqrt{\frac{x^2}{9} + \frac{y^2}{4}}$$

at the point (3, 2), and find the rate of change of $z$ in the direction [1, 1] at this point. The partial derivatives of $z$ are

$$z_x = \frac{x}{9z}, \quad z_y = \frac{y}{4z};$$

and at (3, 2), $z = \sqrt{2}$, so that

$$z_x = \frac{1}{3\sqrt{2}}, \quad z_y = \frac{1}{2\sqrt{2}}.$$

Hence,

$$\nabla z = \frac{1}{3\sqrt{2}} \mathbf{i} + \frac{1}{2\sqrt{2}} \mathbf{j}.$$

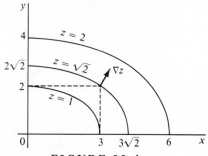

**FIGURE 20.4c**

This vector is shown in Figure 20.4c. The rate of change of $z$ in the direction [1, 1] at (3, 2) is obtained by dot multiplying the gradient by the unit vector $\frac{1}{\sqrt{2}} \mathbf{i} + \frac{1}{\sqrt{2}} \mathbf{j}$ in the direction [1, 1]. Thus,

$$\left(\frac{1}{3\sqrt{2}} \mathbf{i} + \frac{1}{2\sqrt{2}} \mathbf{j}\right) \cdot \left(\frac{1}{\sqrt{2}} \mathbf{i} + \frac{1}{\sqrt{2}} \mathbf{j}\right) = \frac{1}{6} + \frac{1}{4} = \frac{5}{12}.$$

---

The concept of the directional derivative is easily extended to functions of three variables. Suppose that

$$u = f(x, y, z)$$

and that $f_x, f_y, f_z$ are all continuous at a point $(a, b, c)$. The parametric equations of a line through $(a, b, c)$ with direction angles $\alpha, \beta, \gamma$ are

$$x = a + s \cos \alpha,$$
$$y = b + s \cos \beta,$$
$$z = c + s \cos \gamma.$$

Along this line, we may regard $u$ as a function of the distance $s$ from $(a, b, c)$. Hence, by using Equation (2) of Section 20.1, we obtain

$$D_s u = u_x \cos \alpha + u_y \cos \beta + u_z \cos \gamma,$$

which is the *directional derivative of u* in the direction of $s$. This derivative gives the rate of change of $u$ with respect to distance in the specified direction, and is frequently spoken of as the **space rate of change** of $u$ in the direction of $s$.

By proceeding in exactly the same manner as in the case of two variables, we may write $D_s u$ as the dot product of a unit vector

$$\mathbf{U} = \cos \alpha \, \mathbf{i} + \cos \beta \, \mathbf{j} + \cos \gamma \, \mathbf{k}$$

in the direction of $s$ and the vector

$$u_x \mathbf{i} + u_y \mathbf{j} + u_z \mathbf{k}.$$

On this account, we extend the concept of the gradient to functions of three variables.

**Definition 20.4b.** If $u = f(x, y, z)$ has continuous first partial derivatives at a point $P$, then the vector

$$u_x \mathbf{i} + u_y \mathbf{j} + u_z \mathbf{k}$$

is called the gradient of $u$ and is denoted by $\nabla u$, so that

$$\nabla u .=. u_x \mathbf{i} + u_y \mathbf{j} + u_z \mathbf{k}.$$

It follows from the preceding discussion that the directional derivative of $u$ in a specified direction is obtained by dot multiplying a unit vector, $\mathbf{U}$, in this direction by the gradient $\nabla u$. Thus,

$$D_s u = \mathbf{U} \cdot \nabla u.$$

This equation shows, just as in the case of two variables, that $\nabla u$ gives the magnitude and the direction of the greatest space rate of change of $u$.

For a function of three variables, given by $u = f(x, y, z)$, we may define a **contour surface** in a manner similar to that used for a contour line in the two-variable case. The contour surface (if there is one) through a point $P$ is the surface $f(x, y, z) = c$ that passes through $P$. A simple illustration is furnished by

$$u = x^2 + y^2 + z^2,$$

which leads to contour surfaces that are all spheres with centers at the origin. If $u = f(x, y, z)$, then

$$\nabla u = u_x \mathbf{i} + u_y \mathbf{j} + u_z \mathbf{k} = f_x \mathbf{i} + f_y \mathbf{j} + f_z \mathbf{k}$$

shows that the direction of $\nabla u$ at any point $P$ is given by the set of direction numbers $[f_x, f_y, f_z]$. Hence, the direction of $\nabla u$ is normal to the contour surface through $P$.

One of the important applications of the gradient is to problems in heat conduction. Imagine a uniform physical solid whose surface temperature is fixed in some specified fashion so that the temperature depends only on the coordinates of the point on the surface. After a time the temperature of the entire solid comes to an equilibrium state in which, at each point, there is no longer any sensible variation in temperature with time, although the temperature will generally be different from point to point. Suppose then that the temperature is given by $u = f(x, y, z)$ for all points of the solid. A contour surface $f(x, y, z) = c$ is one on which all points are at the same temperature $u = c$. Such a surface is called an **isothermal surface**. The vector $\nabla u$, calculated at a point $P$, is normal to the isothermal surface passing through $P$ and points in the direction of greatest rate of change of temperature. It is known that heat flows in the direction of the negative gradient (that is, in the direction of $-\nabla u$) and that the rate of flow of heat is proportional to the magnitude of this gradient.

*Example 20.4b.* Find the space rate of change of

$$u = 2x^2 + 3y^2 - z^2$$

in the direction of the outward-drawn normal to the sphere $x^2 + y^2 + z^2 = 14$ at the point $(-3, 2, 1)$.

We first find the gradient of $u$ at the point $(-3, 2, 1)$ to be

$$\nabla u = [4x\mathbf{i} + 6y\mathbf{j} - 2z\mathbf{k}]_{(-3,\,2,\,1)}$$
$$= -12\mathbf{i} + 12\mathbf{j} - 2\mathbf{k}.$$

An outward-drawn normal to the sphere at the same point is given by

$$\mathbf{n} = [\nabla(x^2 + y^2 + z^2)]_{(-3,\,2,\,1)} = [2x\mathbf{i} + 2y\mathbf{j} + 2z\mathbf{k}]_{(-3,\,2,\,1)}$$
$$= -6\mathbf{i} + 4\mathbf{j} + 2\mathbf{k}.$$

Consequently, a unit vector in the direction of this normal is

$$\mathbf{N} = \frac{\mathbf{n}}{|\mathbf{n}|} = \frac{-6\mathbf{i} + 4\mathbf{j} + 2\mathbf{k}}{\sqrt{56}} = \frac{-3\mathbf{i} + 2\mathbf{j} + \mathbf{k}}{\sqrt{14}}.$$

The required space rate of change is thus

$$D_s u = \mathbf{N} \cdot \nabla u = \frac{36 + 24 - 2}{\sqrt{14}} = \frac{58}{\sqrt{14}}.$$

# Exercises 20.4

In Numbers 1 to 8, find the rate of change of the given function in the indicated direction at the specified point or points.

1. $z = x^2 + y^2$; $\theta = \pi/4$; $(2, 1)$ and $(6, 3)$.
2. $z = x^2 y + y^3$; $\theta = \pi/6$; $(1, 1)$.
3. $z = \frac{1}{2} \ln(x^2 + y^2)$; $\theta = \pi/3$; $(1, 1)$.
4. $u = x^2 + y^2 + z^2$; $[1, 2, 2]$; $(2, 2, 1)$.
5. $u = xy - y^2 - zx$; $[2, 3, 6]$; $(3, 2, 1)$.
6. $u = 2x - 3y - z$ at $(1, 2, -2)$ in the direction of the outward normal to the sphere $x^2 + y^2 + z^2 = 9$.
7. $u = x^2 + y^2 - z^2$ at $(3, 4, 5)$ along the curve of intersection of the surfaces $2x^2 + 2y^2 - z^2 = 25$ and $x^2 + y^2 = z^2$.
8. $u = x^2 - y^2$ at a general point of the surface $x^2 + y^2 + z^2 = 9$ in the direction of the outward normal at that point.

9. Find the direction of the maximum rate of change of the function given by $z = x^2 + y^2$ at $(1, 2)$.

10. Find the direction of the maximum rate of change of the function given by $z = x^2y - x^3$ at $(1, 2)$.

11. Show that the curve $x = t^2$, $y = 3t$, $z = 2t^{1/2}$ pierces the surface $2x^2 + y^2 + 2z = 15$ at right angles at the point $(1, 3, 2)$.

12. Use the gradient to find the angle of intersection of the sphere $x^2 + y^2 + z^2 = b^2$ and the paraboloid $y^2 + z^2 = 2bx$.

13. Show that the curve $x = t^2 - 2t$, $y = t^3 - 6t$, $z = t^2$, pierces the sphere $x^2 + y^2 + z^2 = 32$ at a point on the curve where $t = 2$. At what angle does the curve pierce the surface?

14. The temperature at each point of a large, thin metal plate with insulated faces is given by

$$T = c \, \text{Tan}^{-1}\left(\frac{\cos \dfrac{\pi x}{2a}}{\sinh y}\right), \qquad -a \le x \le a, \quad y \ge 0,$$

where $c$ is a constant. Find the direction of heat flow at the point $(\tfrac{1}{2}a, 1)$.

## 20.5 TRANSFORMATIONS AND MAPPINGS

The partial derivative is an important tool in the study of transformations of coordinates and mappings. We have already discussed special kinds of transformations, including rotation of coordinates and transformation to polar coordinates, and we now propose to generalize some of the ideas introduced in connection with these special cases.

We have seen that a change of coordinates in two dimensions may be represented by equations of the form

(1) $$x = g(u, v), \quad y = h(u, v).$$

These equations also describe a transformation or mapping of the number-pair, or vector, $(u, v)$ to the number-pair $(x, y)$. We say that the point $(u, v)$ is mapped to the point $(x, y)$, because values for $x$ and $y$ are determined from given values of $u$ and $v$. If the equations associate a unique point $(x, y)$ to a given point $(u, v)$, and conversely, then the mapping is said to be *one-to-one* or to constitute a *one-to-one correspondence* between points.

Furthermore, if the expressions for $x$ and $y$ from Equations (1) are substituted into an equation $f(x, y) = 0$, a new equation

$$F(u, v) .=. f[g(u, v), h(u, v)] = 0$$

is obtained that describes in terms of the new $u$- and $v$-coordinates the same geometric curve as is described by $f(x, y) = 0$.

---

*Example 20.5a.* If $f(x, y) .=. 3x^2 + 2xy + y^2$, and if $x = u - v$, $y = u + 2v$, find $F(u, v) .=. f(u - v, u + 2v)$.

By direct substitution, we get

$$F(u, v) = 3(u - v)^2 + 2(u - v)(u + 2v) + (u + 2v)^2 = 6u^2 + 3v^2.$$

---

The result of the substitution in the preceding example is that an equation such as $F(u, v) = 3$ may be interpreted as the equation of the curve $f(x, y) = 3$ with respect to a new coordinate system—the $uv$-system. The reference axes of the new coordinate system are given by $u = 0$, $v = 0$. If $u = 0$, then $x = -v$, $y = 2v$ are the parametric equations, with $v$ as the parameter, of the $v$-axis: $y = -2x$. Similarly, $v = 0$ gives $x = u$, $y = u$ as the parametric equations of the $u$-axis: $x = y$.

As indicated in Section 13.3, for each different value of $u$, there is a corresponding curve called a $v$-curve. For example, if $u = 1$, then $x = 1 - v, y = 1 + 2v$, and $y = 1 + 2(1 - x) = -2x + 3$. There is a similar set of curves, the $u$-curves, associated with different values of $v$. The two sets of curves are the coordinate curves of the $uv$-coordinate system, and are analogous to the coordinate curves in the $xy$-coordinate system, which are the families of lines parallel to the $x$- and $y$-axes (see Figure 20.5a). For this reason, equations of the

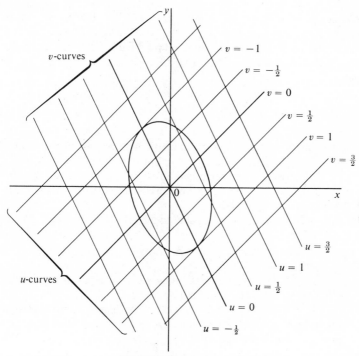

FIGURE 20.5a

form of Equations (1) are sometimes called equations of a **two-parameter family of curves.**

Although the coordinate curves in the preceding example are straight lines, there is no reason why we should be restricted to straight lines as coordinate curves, as is illustrated in part by the coordinate curves in polar coordinates, which we have already seen to be concentric circles about the origin and straight lines through the origin.

---

*Example 20.5b.* Sketch and discuss some of the coordinate curves of the two-parameter family

$$x = u^2 - v^2, \quad y = 2uv.$$

As before, by assigning specific values to one of the parameters and eliminating the other from the two equations, we obtain the equation of a coordinate curve in rectangular coordinates. For example,

$$v = 0 \Rightarrow x = u^2, \quad y = 0,$$

is a pair of equations which describe the nonnegative part of the $x$-axis. In a similar fashion,

$$v = 1 \Rightarrow x = u^2 - 1, \quad y = 2u$$

$$\Rightarrow x = \frac{y^2}{4} - 1, \quad \text{or} \quad 4x + 4 = y^2.$$

The equation $y = 2u$, however, requires that $y \geqq 0$ if $u \geqq 0$, and $y \leqq 0$ if $u \leqq 0$. Hence, the equations $x = u^2 - 1$, $y = 2u$ are parametric equations of a parabola symmetric with respect to the $x$-axis, the upper half of the curve corresponding to positive values of $u$; the lower half, to negative values of $u$.

In general,

$$v = v_0 \Rightarrow x = u^2 - v_0^2, \quad y = 2uv_0$$

$$\Rightarrow x = \frac{y^2}{4v_0^2} - v_0^2,$$

which is the equation of a parabola symmetric with respect to the $x$-axis. If $v_0 > 0$, then $u > 0 \Rightarrow y > 0$, and $u < 0 \Rightarrow y < 0$, but if $v_0 < 0$, then $u > 0 \Rightarrow y < 0$, and $u < 0 \Rightarrow y > 0$. However, the same parabola is obtained whether $v_0 < 0$ or $v_0 > 0$. The curves obtained by holding $v$ constant are called $u$-curves since these are the curves along which $u$ varies if $v$ is fixed.

A $v$-curve is obtained by taking $u$ equal to a constant, say $u = u_0$. This gives

$$x = u_0^2 - v^2, \quad y = 2u_0v, \quad \text{or} \quad x = u_0^2 - \frac{y^2}{4u_0^2}.$$

The $v$-curves are a family of parabolas symmetric with respect to the $x$-axis, but opening to the left, as shown in Figure 20.5b.

As suggested by the preceding discussion and by Figure 20.5b, corresponding to a pair of numbers $u = 1$, $v = 1$ there is a unique $(x, y)$, namely $(0, 2)$, but *not* conversely. Thus, $x = 0$, $y = 2$ give the equations

$$0 = u^2 - v^2, \quad 2 = 2uv,$$

which are satisfied by $u = 1$, $v = 1$ and also by $u = -1$, $v = -1$. This lack of uniqueness is often so troublesome that it is desirable to define a transformation in such a way, if possible, that there is a one-to-one correspondence between points in the $uv$-system and points in the $xy$-system.

To examine this problem in more detail, we need to obtain the equations for $u$ and $v$ in terms of $x$ and $y$. These equations are

$$u = \pm\sqrt{\frac{x + \sqrt{x^2 + y^2}}{2}},$$

(2)

$$v = \pm\sqrt{\frac{\sqrt{x^2 + y^2} - x}{2}},$$

which define the inverse transformation. In order to see how a one-to-one correspondence may be established, we must examine both the transformation and the inverse transformation.

The $\pm$ signs in Equations (2) show at once why ambiguities in the mappings arise. For example, as already noted, if $x = 0$, $y = 2$, then

$$u = \pm 1, \quad v = \pm 1.$$

It is for this reason that we do not have uniqueness. If we alter Equations (2) slightly, then uniqueness is obtained. Since the equations of the inverse transformation show that a choice of sign is available, let us impose the condition that $v$ is always nonnegative, and let $u$ be negative if $y$ is negative and positive if $y$ is positive. Then the lower half of each $v$-curve is no longer associated with a positive $u$, but instead is associated

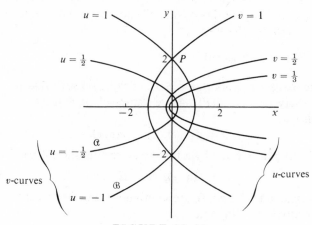

**FIGURE 20.5b**

with a negative $u$. Hence, in Figure 20.5b, the lower curve $\mathcal{C}$ is the $u = -\frac{1}{2}$ curve, and $\mathcal{B}$ is the $u = -1$ curve. Thus, we get the equations for the inverse transformation in the form

$$u = \pm\sqrt{\frac{x + \sqrt{x^2 + y^2}}{2}}, \qquad uy \geqq 0,$$

$$v = \sqrt{\frac{\sqrt{x^2 + y^2} - x}{2}}.$$

With these restrictions on $u$ and $v$, we have a one-to-one correspondence between the $xy$- and the $uv$-coordinates of points. For instance, the point $P$ in the figure now has the unique $uv$-coordinates $(1, 1)$. The reader is cautioned that such a resolution may not always be possible, as we shall see later. Furthermore, with this restriction, none of the points $(u, v)$, $v < 0$, has an image in the $xy$-plane.

It is possible to obtain some of the characteristics of transformations of the type considered in Example 20.5b directly from the equations of transformation with the aid of partial differentiation. If the equations of a transformation $T$ are given in the form

$$x = f(u, v), \quad y = g(u, v),$$

and if it is possible to obtain the variables $u$ and $v$ as explicit functions of $x$ and $y$ in the form

$$u = F(x, y), \quad v = G(x, y),$$

then these equations are called the equations of the inverse, $T^{-1}$, of the transformation $T$.

The important properties of a transformation and its inverse are given without proof in

**Theorem 20.5a.** Let

(a) $x = f(u, v)$, $y = g(u, v)$ describe a continuously differentiable transformation in a neighborhood $\mathfrak{N}(S)$ of a point $S(u_0, v_0)$, where $x_0 = f(u_0, v_0)$, $y_0 = g(u_0, v_0)$, and let

(b) $J\left(\dfrac{f, g}{u, v}\right) \neq 0$ at $(u_0, v_0)$.

Then there exists a neighborhood $\mathfrak{N}(P)$ of $P(x_0, y_0)$ such that

(i) for every $(x, y) \in \mathfrak{N}(P)$ unique values of $(u, v) \in \mathfrak{N}(S)$ can be found such that

$$x = f(u, v), \quad y = g(u, v),$$

and this pair is given by a functional relationship of the form

$$u = F(x, y), \quad v = G(x, y),$$

(ii) the functions $F$ and $G$ are continuous and have continuous partial derivatives in $\mathfrak{N}(P)$, and

$$F_x = \frac{g_v}{J}, \quad F_y = -\frac{f_v}{J}, \quad G_x = -\frac{g_u}{J}, \quad G_y = \frac{f_u}{J}.$$

Theorem 20.5a specifies the conditions under which a transformation describes a one-to-one mapping. If a continuously differentiable transformation does not give a one-to-one mapping at a point, then the Jacobian of the transformation is zero at that point. However, the Jacobian can be zero at a point where the mapping is one-to-one. A point where the Jacobian is zero is called a **singular point** of the transformation.

*Example 20.5c.* At what points does the transformation

$$x = r \cos \theta, \quad y = r \sin \theta$$

fail to be one-to-one?

The Jacobian of the transformation $T$ is

$$J\left(\frac{x, y}{r, \theta}\right) = \begin{vmatrix} \cos\theta & \sin\theta \\ -r\sin\theta & r\cos\theta \end{vmatrix} = r.$$

Hence, we examine the transformation for the value $r = 0$ and find that every pair $(r, \theta)$ for which $r = 0$ is mapped to the single pair $(0, 0)$ in the $xy$-coordinate system, so that the transformation $T$ fails to be one-to-one at the origin. At all other points, since $J \neq 0$, the transformation is unique, and an inverse transformation $T^{-1}$ exists such that there is a one-to-one correspondence between the $xy$-coordinates and the $r\theta$-coordinates of these points. In this example the equations of such an inverse transformation are easily obtained, and are given by

$$r = \sqrt{x^2 + y^2}, \quad r > 0,$$

$$\theta = \tan^{-1}(y/x) = \sin^{-1}\frac{y}{\sqrt{x^2 + y^2}}, \qquad 0 \leq \theta < 2\pi.$$

In the preceding discussion, it was indicated that a pair of equations such as

$$x = f(u, v), \quad y = g(u, v)$$

may be interpreted in two ways, as a *change of coordinates* from the $xy$-system to a new $uv$-system, or as a *mapping* of points $(u, v)$ to points $(x, y)$. A change of coordinates has been illustrated geometrically, but we have not yet considered a geometric interpretation for a mapping.

In this case it is convenient to regard both coordinate systems as rectangular coordinates in different planes, and to consider the way in which points in the $uv$-plane are mapped to points in the $xy$-plane, and conversely. This idea is illustrated in the next example.

*Example 20.5d.* Discuss the mapping described by

$$x = r\cos\theta, \quad y = r\sin\theta.$$

Two sets of planar coordinates are established side by side as shown in Figure 20.5c. It is evident that all points on the $\theta$-axis ($r = 0$) in the $r\theta$-plane map to the point $(0, 0)$

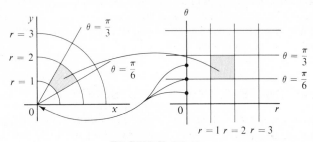

**FIGURE 20.5c**

in the $xy$-plane. Every other point in the $r\theta$-plane maps to a unique point in the $xy$-plane, but not conversely. For example, the point $r = 1$, $\theta = \pi/4$ in the $r\theta$-plane maps to the point $(\sqrt{2}, \sqrt{2})$ in the $xy$-plane. Moreover, all the points $r = 1$, $\theta = \pi/4 + 2n\pi$,

$n \in \mathfrak{N}$, map to the same point, $(\sqrt{2}, \sqrt{2})$, in the $xy$-plane. This lack of uniqueness shows that the mapping is not one-to-one. Although each point in the $r\theta$-plane maps to exactly one point in the $xy$-plane, each point in the $xy$-plane maps to infinitely many points in the $r\theta$-plane.

In order to make the mapping one-to-one, we must impose some restrictions on $r$ and $\theta$. If we use the inverse transformation with the restrictions found in Example 20.5c, where $r > 0$ and $0 \leq \theta < 2\pi$, then the only portion of the $r\theta$-plane used in the mapping is the first-quadrant strip bounded by the lines $r = 0$, $\theta = 0$, and $\theta = 2\pi$. Of the three boundary lines only $\theta = 0$ is to be included in the region. This strip maps to the entire $xy$-plane in a one-to-one manner.

It is of interest to see how a small region in the $r\theta$-plane maps into the $xy$-plane, and conversely. For this purpose, we shall use the one-to-one mapping described in the preceding paragraph, and we shall consider the region in the $r\theta$-plane bounded by the curves $r = 2$, $r = 3$, $\theta = \pi/6$, and $\theta = \pi/3$. The corresponding curves in the $xy$-plane have the equations $x^2 + y^2 = 4$, $x^2 + y^2 = 9$, $y = x/\sqrt{3}$, and $y = x\sqrt{3}$. Each point inside the region in the $r\theta$-plane is mapped to a point inside the corresponding region in the $xy$-plane, and conversely, as indicated in Figure 20.5c.

## Exercises 20.5

For the transformations given in Numbers 1 to 6, find and sketch the coordinate curves for the transformation. Calculate the Jacobian, and indicate points at which the transformation fails to be one-to-one. Find the inverse transformation.

1. $x = 2u + 3v$, $y = u + 2v$.
2. $x = uv$, $y = u^2 - v^2$.
3. $x = u \cosh v$, $y = u \sinh v$.
4. $2x - y + u = 0$, $x - 2y + 2v = 0$.
5. $x = u \cos \theta + v \sin \theta$, $y = -u \sin \theta + v \cos \theta$.
6. $x = e^u \cos v$, $y = e^u \sin v$.

7. If $x = au$, $y = bv$, find the curve in the $uv$-plane that corresponds to the curve in the $xy$-plane given by the equation $x^2/a^2 + y^2/b^2 = 1$.
8. Find the boundary of the region in the $uv$-plane corresponding to the region bounded by $x = 0$, $y = 0$, $x + y = 1$ in the $xy$-plane if $u = x + y$, $v = x - y$.
9. Find the point where the Jacobian of the transformation in Example 20.5b is zero. Is the transformation one-to-one there?

## 20.6 COORDINATE CURVES AND SURFACES

To inquire further into coordinate transformations and to extend the ideas of the preceding section to the three-dimensional case, we shall first look at the two-dimensional transformation in terms of vectors. Let the coordinate transformation be given by the equations

$$x = f(u, v), \quad y = g(u, v).$$

Then we may regard the position vector

$$\mathbf{r} = x\mathbf{i} + y\mathbf{j}$$

as a vector function of the two variables $u$ and $v$, where

$$\mathbf{r}(u, v) = f(u, v)\mathbf{i} + g(u, v)\mathbf{j}.$$

This function associates a vector $\mathbf{r}$ with each point in the space. Since $\mathbf{r}$ is a function of two variables, we may apply the definition of the partial derivative to $\mathbf{r}$ to obtain

$$\mathbf{r}_u(u, v) = f_u(u, v)\mathbf{i} + g_u(u, v)\mathbf{j}.$$

Suppose that $v$ is held fixed at $v_0$. Then $\mathbf{r}$ may be considered a function of $u$ alone, such that the end of the vector $\mathbf{r}$ traces the coordinate curve $v = v_0$ as $u$ varies. The vector $\mathbf{r}_u(u, v_0)$ must then represent a tangent vector to that curve. Similarly, if $u$ is held fixed at $u_0$, then

$$\mathbf{r}_v(u_0, v) = f_v(u_0, v)\mathbf{i} + g_v(u_0, v)\mathbf{j}$$

represents a vector tangent to the $v$-curve. These vectors at the point $(u_0, v_0)$ are illustrated in Figure 20.6a.

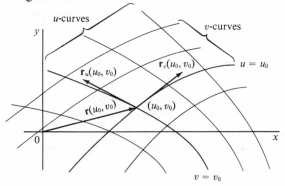

**FIGURE 20.6a**

The differential of a scalar function has already been defined. This definition is easily extended to vector functions and is useful in discussing arc length in a generalized coordinate system.

**Definition 20.6a.** The differential of the vector function

$$\mathbf{r} = f(u, v)\mathbf{i} + g(u, v)\mathbf{j}$$

is

$$d\mathbf{r} .=. \mathbf{r}_u \, du + \mathbf{r}_v \, dv.$$

Since the differential of arc length in the plane is given by

$$(ds)^2 .=. (dx)^2 + (dy)^2 = d\mathbf{r} \cdot d\mathbf{r},$$

then, in general,

$$ds^2 = (\mathbf{r}_u \, du + \mathbf{r}_v \, dv) \cdot (\mathbf{r}_u \, du + \mathbf{r}_v \, dv)$$
$$= \mathbf{r}_u \cdot \mathbf{r}_u \, du^2 + 2\mathbf{r}_v \cdot \mathbf{r}_u \, du \, dv + \mathbf{r}_v \cdot \mathbf{r}_v \, dv^2.$$

*Example 20.6a.* Find $ds^2$ in polar coordinates.

Since

$$\mathbf{r} = r\cos\theta\,\mathbf{i} + r\sin\theta\,\mathbf{j},$$

then

$$\mathbf{r}_r = \cos\theta\,\mathbf{i} + \sin\theta\,\mathbf{j},$$
$$\mathbf{r}_\theta = -r\sin\theta\,\mathbf{i} + r\cos\theta\,\mathbf{j},$$

and

$$\mathbf{r}_r\cdot\mathbf{r}_r = 1, \quad \mathbf{r}_r\cdot\mathbf{r}_\theta = 0, \quad \mathbf{r}_\theta\cdot\mathbf{r}_\theta = r^2,$$

so that

$$ds^2 = dr^2 + r^2\,d\theta^2.$$

---

In this example, the term $\mathbf{r}_r\cdot\mathbf{r}_\theta = 0$, so that the vectors $\mathbf{r}_r$ and $\mathbf{r}_\theta$ are perpendicular to each other, in which case we say that the coordinate system is **orthogonal**. Most coordinate systems that we shall encounter will be orthogonal systems, but nonorthogonal systems are also important in many physical problems.

The extension of the concepts introduced in Section 20.5 to three dimensions consists essentially of a repetition of the analytic argument used in two dimensions. There is, however, a change in the corresponding geometry. Three equations of the form

(1)
$$x = f(u, v, w),$$
$$y = g(u, v, w),$$
$$z = h(u, v, w)$$

are said to represent a **three-parameter family of surfaces.** For a fixed value of one of the variables, say $w_0$, the three equations describe a surface—a **coordinate surface**—in the $xyz$-coordinate system. This follows, since the variables $u$ and $v$ can (theoretically) be eliminated from the three equations, which implies a relationship of the form

$$F(x, y, z) = w_0.$$

We may illustrate the concept of coordinate surfaces by recalling that a point in three-dimensional rectangular coordinates is located at the intersection of three surfaces, which in this simple case are planes parallel to the coordinate planes (see Figure 20.6b). In general, coordinate surfaces are families of curved

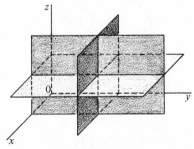

**FIGURE 20.6b**

surfaces. Two members of different families of coordinate surfaces intersect in a curve called a **coordinate curve**. The coordinate curves in three-dimensional rectangular coordinates are the straight lines in which the different sets of coordinate planes intersect.

The next example illustrates a new set of coordinate surfaces and curves.

---

*Example 20.6b.* Describe the coordinate surfaces and curves of the *uvw*-coordinate system if

$$x = u \cos v, \quad y = u \sin v, \quad z = w.$$

From these equations, we get

$$v = \tan^{-1}(y/x), \quad 0 \leq v < 2\pi,$$
$$u = \sqrt{x^2 + y^2}, \quad w = z.$$

For a fixed value of $w$, $w_0$, the equation $z = w_0$ describes a plane parallel to the $xy$-coordinate plane. For a fixed value of $u$, $u_0$, the equation $x^2 + y^2 = u_0^2$ describes a cylinder whose axis is the $z$-axis. The surface described by $v = v_0$ is a plane passing through the $z$-axis and making an angle of $v_0$ radians with the $x$-axis. These surfaces and their intersections (which are the coordinate curves) are shown in Figure 20.6c.

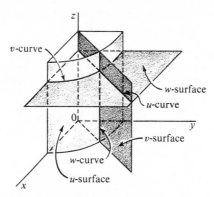

**FIGURE 20.6c**

---

The coordinate system illustrated there is called a **cylindrical coordinate system**. The surfaces obtained for a fixed value of $u$ (or $v$ or $w$) are called *u*-surfaces (or *v*- or *w*-surfaces). The curves obtained for fixed values of $v$ and $w$ and along which $u$ varies are called *u*-curves. The *v*- and *w*-curves may be described in a similar fashion.

---

As in the two-dimensional case, if we consider a coordinate transformation given by Equations (1), then the position vector

$$\mathbf{r} = x\mathbf{i} + y\mathbf{j} + z\mathbf{k}$$

may be interpreted as a vector function of three variables, where

$$\mathbf{r}(u, v, w) = f(u, v, w)\mathbf{i} + g(u, v, w)\mathbf{j} + h(u, v, w)\mathbf{k}.$$

If we hold $v$ and $w$ fixed and differentiate with respect to $u$, then the resulting vector,

$$\mathbf{r}_u = f_u(u, v, w)\mathbf{i} + g_u(u, v, w)\mathbf{j} + h_u(u, v, w)\mathbf{k},$$

must be a vector tangent to a $u$-curve. Similar interpretations apply to the vectors $\mathbf{r}_v$ and $\mathbf{r}_w$.

The differential of the vector function is

$$d\mathbf{r} = \mathbf{r}_u \, du + \mathbf{r}_v \, dv + \mathbf{r}_w \, dw,$$

and the differential of arc length $(ds)^2 .=. (dx)^2 + (dy)^2 + (dz)^2$ is given by

$$ds^2 = d\mathbf{r} \cdot d\mathbf{r} = \mathbf{r}_u \cdot \mathbf{r}_u \, du^2 + 2\mathbf{r}_u \cdot \mathbf{r}_v \, du \, dv + \mathbf{r}_v \cdot \mathbf{r}_v \, dv^2$$
$$+ 2\mathbf{r}_v \cdot \mathbf{r}_w \, dv \, dw + \mathbf{r}_w \cdot \mathbf{r}_w \, dw^2 + 2\mathbf{r}_u \cdot \mathbf{r}_w \, du \, dw.$$

For the same reason as in the two-dimensional case, the coordinate system is said to be *orthogonal* when the quantities $\mathbf{r}_u \cdot \mathbf{r}_v$, $\mathbf{r}_u \cdot \mathbf{r}_w$, and $\mathbf{r}_v \cdot \mathbf{r}_w$ are all zero.

---

*Example 20.6c.* Describe the coordinate surfaces for the $\rho\varphi\theta$-system if

$$x = \rho \sin \varphi \cos \theta,$$
$$y = \rho \sin \varphi \sin \theta,$$
$$z = \rho \cos \varphi.$$

By squaring both members of these equations and adding, we obtain

$$x^2 + y^2 + z^2 = \rho^2.$$

Since for each value of $\rho$ this is the equation of a sphere with its center at the origin, the $\rho$-surfaces are a family of concentric spheres centered at the origin. It is in view of this fact that the $\rho\varphi\theta$-coordinates are called **spherical coordinates**.

From the first pair of equations, we find that

$$x \sin \theta = \rho \sin \varphi \cos \theta \sin \theta,$$

and

$$y \cos \theta = \rho \sin \varphi \sin \theta \cos \theta,$$

so that

$$x \sin \theta = y \cos \theta.$$

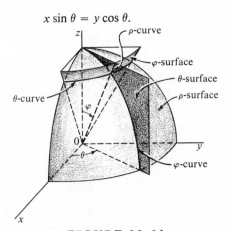

**FIGURE 20.6d**

For each fixed value of $\theta$, this is the equation of a plane containing the $z$-axis and making an angle $\theta$ with the positive $x$-axis.

By squaring both members of the first two of the given equations and adding, we get

$$x^2 + y^2 = \rho^2 \sin^2 \varphi.$$

Since

$$z^2 \sin^2 \varphi = \rho^2 \cos^2 \varphi \sin^2 \varphi$$

and

$$(x^2 + y^2) \cos^2 \varphi = \rho^2 \cos^2 \varphi \sin^2 \varphi,$$

we obtain

$$(x^2 + y^2) \cos^2 \varphi = z^2 \sin^2 \varphi,$$

which, for each fixed value of $\varphi$, is the equation of a right circular cone whose axis is the $z$-axis, whose vertex is at the origin, and whose vertex angle is $2\varphi$. The first-octant portions of these surfaces are shown in Figure 20.6d.

---

*Example 20.6d.* It is customary to use $r$, $\theta$, and $z$ in place of the $u$, $v$, and $w$ in the system of cylindrical coordinates of Example 20.6b. Write the equation of the surface described by

$$x^2 + y^2 = 2z$$

in the $r\theta z$-coordinates.

Since $x = r \cos \theta$, $y = r \sin \theta$, and $z = z$ in cylindrical coordinates, the equation becomes

$$r^2 \cos^2 \theta + r^2 \sin^2 \theta = 2z,$$

or

$$r^2 = 2z.$$

---

Thus, in the new coordinate system, the equation of the surface in Example 20.6d is considerably simplified, and it is this feature that makes the transformation to another coordinate system important in mathematical work. This fact will be brought out more clearly in the next chapter.

## Exercises 20.6

In each of Numbers 1 to 6, find the equation of the given surface in cylindrical coordinates, where $x = r \cos \theta$, $y = r \sin \theta$, $z = z$.

1. $x^2 + y^2 = z^2$.
2. $x^2 = z - y^2$.
3. $x^2 - y^2 = z^2$.

4. $x^2 + y^2 + z^2 = a^2$.
5. $x^2 - y^2 = 2xy + z^2$.
6. $x^2 + y^2 + z^2 = 2ax$.

In each of Numbers 7 to 12, find the equation of the given surface in spherical coordinates, where $x = \rho \sin \varphi \cos \theta$, $y = \rho \sin \varphi \sin \theta$, $z = \rho \cos \varphi$.

7. $x^2 + y^2 + z^2 = a^2$.
8. $x^2 + y^2 = z^2$.
9. $x^2 + y^2 = z$.

10. $x^2 - y^2 + z^2 = 1$.
11. $(x^2 + y^2 + z^2)^2 = az^3$.
12. $x^2 + y^2 + z^2 = 2az$.

13. Which of the following describes an orthogonal coordinate system?
    (a) $x = uv$, $y = u^2 - v^2$.
    (b) $x = e^u \cos v$, $y = e^u \sin v$.
    (c) $x = 2u + 3v$, $y = u + 2v$.
14. Describe the coordinate curves and surfaces for the transformation

$$x = u \cos v,$$
$$y = u \sin v,$$
$$z = u/w.$$

Find the Jacobian of the transformation. Is the transformation everywhere one-to-one? Is the new system orthogonal?

15. What is the Jacobian of the transformation from rectangular to cylindrical coordinates? Are there any points for which the transformation fails to be one-to-one?

16. Find the Jacobian of the transformation from rectangular to spherical coordinates. Are there any points for which this transformation fails to be one-to-one?

---

# Summary of Chapter 20

---

The fundamental concepts associated with partial differentiation are extended in this chapter and applied to a number of situations. The important results of this discussion include:

   (1) partial differentiation of a composite function (Section 20.1);
   (2) the total derivative of a composite function (Section 20.1);
   (3) partial differentiation of implicit functions (Section 20.2);
   (4) the Jacobian (Section 20.2);
   (5) the definition of surface (Section 20.3);
   (6) the tangent plane to a surface (Section 20.3);
   (7) the normal vector to a surface (Section 20.3);
   (8) the angle of intersection of two surfaces (Section 20.3);
   (9) the directional derivative of a function (Section 20.4);
  (10) the gradient of a function (Section 20.4);
  (11) contour lines and contour surfaces (Section 20.4);
  (12) the role of the Jacobian in transformations and mappings (Section 20.5);
  (13) coordinate curves and coordinate surfaces (Section 20.6);
  (14) cylindrical and spherical coordinates (Section 20.6).

# Chapter 21    Multiple Integrals

## 21.1 ITERATED INTEGRALS

Earlier we discussed the problem of finding a function of a single variable whose derivative was given. Now we can consider the problem of finding a function of several variables, one of whose partial derivatives is given.

---

*Example 21.1a.* Find $u(x, y)$ if $u_{xx} = x^2 + 2xy + y^2$.

Since $y$ is held constant in determining this partial derivative, $y$ is also regarded as constant in the integration. The first integration yields $u_x$, and the result is

$$u_x(x, y) = \frac{x^3}{3} + x^2y + xy^2 + C.$$

If the partial derivative with respect to $x$ of this expression is taken, we obtain the given second partial derivative. In fact, the same result would be obtained even if $C$ were a function of $y$, since its partial derivative with respect to $x$ would be zero. Consequently, the most general form for $u_x$ requires that $C$ be replaced by an arbitrary function of $y$, say $C = f(y)$. Thus,

$$u_x(x, y) = \frac{x^3}{3} + x^2y + xy^2 + f(y).$$

Integrating a second time while holding $y$ constant, we get

$$u(x, y) = \frac{x^4}{12} + \frac{x^3y}{3} + \frac{x^2y^2}{2} + xf(y) + g(y).$$

---

In many problems, additional conditions are given which enable one to find the arbitrary functions involved.

---

*Example 21.1b.* Find $u(x, y)$ if

$$u_{yx}(x, y) = y \cos xy,$$
$$u_y(0, y) = \cos y,$$
$$u(x, 0) = x^2.$$

The notation $u_y(0, y) = \cos y$ means that $u_y(x, y) = \cos y$ for all values of $y$ when $x = 0$; and the notation $u(x, 0) = x^2$ means that $u(x, y) = x^2$ for all values of $x$ when $y = 0$. If we hold $y$ constant and integrate $u_{yx}$ with respect to $x$, we get

$$u_y(x, y) = \sin xy + f(y).$$

Using the condition $u_y(0, y) = \cos y$, we find that

$$\cos y = f(y),$$

so that

$$u_y(x, y) = \sin xy + \cos y.$$

Integrating this result with respect to $y$, we obtain

$$u(x, y) = -\frac{1}{x} \cos xy + \sin y + g(x).$$

Then, applying the condition $u(x, 0) = x^2$, we get

$$x^2 = -\frac{1}{x} + g(x),$$

or

$$g(x) = x^2 + \frac{1}{x}.$$

Thus,

$$u(x, y) = -\frac{1}{x} \cos xy + \sin y + x^2 + \frac{1}{x}.$$

---

The two partial integrations that occur in the preceding example can be indicated by the notation

$$\iint y \cos xy \, dx \, dy.$$

This notation means that the first partial integration is with respect to $x$ ($y$ held constant), and that the second is with respect to $y$ ($x$ held constant).

Successive partial integrations frequently occur in connection with definite integrals rather than in connection with inverse differentiations as in the preceding examples. In such cases, we write

$$\int_a^b \left[ \int_{y_1}^{y_2} f(x, y) \, dy \right] dx,$$

or simply

$$\int_a^b \int_{y_1}^{y_2} f(x, y) \, dy \, dx.$$

Repeated definite or indefinite integrals of this form are called **iterated integrals**. The meaning of an iterated integral is illustrated in the next example.

---

*Example 21.1c.* Evaluate

$$\int_0^1 f(y) \, dy, \quad \text{where} \quad f(y) = \int_0^y y^2 \sin xy \, dx.$$

In evaluating the integral defining $f(y)$, it is necessary to keep in mind that the variable of integration is $x$ and that $y$ enters this integral in the role of a constant. Performing the integration, we get

$$f(y) = y^2 \int_0^y \sin xy \, dx$$
$$= [-y \cos xy]_{x=0}^{x=y}$$
$$= -y \cos y^2 + y.$$

Substituting this result in the first integral, we find

$$\int_0^1 f(y)\, dy = \int_0^1 (-y \cos y^2 + y)\, dy$$
$$= [-\tfrac{1}{2} \sin y^2 + \tfrac{1}{2} y^2]_0^1$$
$$= \tfrac{1}{2}(1 - \sin 1).$$

The expression for $f(y)$ in the preceding example may be substituted into the first integral before the integration is performed, so that we have

$$\int_0^1 \int_0^y y^2 \sin xy\, dx\, dy.$$

This notation will cause no confusion if it is noted that *the inside integral sign and inside differential go together*. Some authors use the notation

$$\int_0^1 dy \int_0^y y^2 \sin xy\, dx.$$

An iterated integral may involve any number of variables, the notation corresponding to that used for two variables.

*Example 21.1d.* Evaluate

$$\int_0^1 \int_x^{x^2} \int_{xy}^{x^2y^3} xy\, dz\, dy\, dx.$$

In evaluating the integral, we shall insert grouping symbols to indicate clearly the order of integration:

$$\int_0^1 \int_x^{x^2} \int_{xy}^{x^2y^3} xy\, dz\, dy\, dx = \int_0^1 \left\{ \int_x^{x^2} \left( \int_{xy}^{x^2y^3} xy\, dz \right) dy \right\} dx$$
$$= \int_0^1 \left\{ \int_x^{x^2} [xyz]_{z=xy}^{z=x^2y^3}\, dy \right\} dx$$
$$= \int_0^1 \left\{ \int_x^{x^2} (x^3y^4 - x^2y^2)\, dy \right\} dx$$
$$= \int_0^1 \left[ \frac{1}{5} x^3y^5 - \frac{1}{3} x^2y^3 \right]_{y=x}^{y=x^2} dx$$
$$= \int_0^1 \left( \frac{1}{5} x^{13} - \frac{1}{3} x^8 - \frac{1}{5} x^8 + \frac{1}{3} x^5 \right) dx$$
$$= \left[ \frac{1}{70} x^{14} - \frac{8}{135} x^9 + \frac{1}{18} x^6 \right]_0^1$$
$$= \frac{1}{70} - \frac{8}{135} + \frac{1}{18} = \frac{2}{189}.$$

## Exercises 21.1

Find $u(x, y)$ in each of Numbers 1 to 7.

1. $u_{yy}(x, y) = xy - y^2$.

2. $u_{xy}(x, y) = 4 - x$.

3. $u_{xx}(x, y) = y^2 + 1$.

4. $u_{xxy}(x, y) = 2$.

5. $u_{xy}(x, y) = \cos x \cos 2y$; $u_x(x, 0) = e^{2x}$; $u(0, y) = e^y$.

6. $u_{yy}(x, y) = x^2$; $u_y(x, 0) = 2$; $u(x, 0) = 3$.

7. $u_{yx}(x, y) = e^{2x} \cos 3y$; $u_y(0, y) = \sin 2y$; $u(x, 0) = 0$.

In each of Numbers 8 to 25, evaluate the integral.

8. $\displaystyle\int_1^2 \int_0^1 (x + y)\, dx\, dy$.

9. $\displaystyle\int_0^2 \int_0^1 xy\, dy\, dx$.

10. $\displaystyle\int_1^2 \int_0^y x^2\, dx\, dy$.

11. $\displaystyle\int_0^1 \int_1^\theta (1 - r^2)\, dr\, d\theta$.

12. $\displaystyle\int_0^1 \int_0^2 y e^{xy}\, dx\, dy$.

13. $\displaystyle\int_0^{\pi/2} \int_0^{2 \sin \theta} r \cos^2 \theta\, dr\, d\theta$.

14. $\displaystyle\int_0^2 \int_0^r r\, d\theta\, dr$.

15. $\displaystyle\int_0^1 \int_{2x}^{3x} e^{y-x}\, dy\, dx$.

16. $\displaystyle\int_1^2 \int_1^{\exp(y)} \frac{y}{x}\, dx\, dy$.

17. $\displaystyle\int_0^{\pi/2} \int_0^{x^2} \sin\left(\frac{y}{x}\right) dy\, dx$.

18. $\displaystyle\int_1^2 \int_1^{\tan y} (1 + x^2)^{-1}\, dx\, dy$.

19. $\displaystyle\int_0^1 \int_0^2 \int_0^1 yz\, dx\, dy\, dz$.

20. $\displaystyle\int_0^1 \int_0^y \int_0^{z+y} (z + y)\, dx\, dz\, dy$.

21. $\displaystyle\int_0^2 \int_0^{\pi/2} \int_0^{\sin \theta} r^2\, dr\, d\theta\, dz$.

22. $\displaystyle\int_0^{\pi/2} \int_0^{\pi/2} \int_0^1 r^2 \cos^2 \theta\, dr\, d\theta\, d\varphi$.

23. $\displaystyle\int_0^{\pi/2} \int_0^{\pi/2} \int_{\pi/2}^{z+y} \cos(x + y)\, dx\, dz\, dy$.

24. $\displaystyle\int_0^{\pi/2} \int_0^{2 \cos \theta} \int_r^{\cos \theta} rz \cos \theta\, dz\, dr\, d\theta$.

25. $\displaystyle\int_0^\pi \int_1^{\sin z} \int_0^{\ln y} y e^x\, dx\, dy\, dz$.

## 21.2 THE DOUBLE INTEGRAL

With the aid of the ideas that were introduced in the preceding section, it i
possible to extend the concept of the definite integral to functions of two or mor
variables. To do this, we must make use of certain geometric notions, whic
the following definitions help to make precise.

**Definition 21.2a.** A **simple arc** in the plane is a set of points that can, for som
orientation of the axes, be described by a continuous vector function,

$$\mathbf{r}(t) = f(t)\mathbf{i} + g(t)\mathbf{j}, \qquad a \le t \le b,$$

with a continuous derivative and such that every pair of distinct values of $t$
except possibly $t = a$ and $t = b$, corresponds to a distinct pair of points.

**Definition 21.2b.** A **simple curve** is either a simple arc or a succession of simpl
arcs joined together end to end so that if the curve is described by a vecto
function $\mathbf{r}(t)$, $a \le t \le b$, then, with the possible exception of $\mathbf{r}(a) = \mathbf{r}(b)$

$$\mathbf{r}(t_1) = \mathbf{r}(t_2) \iff t_1 = t_2.$$

If a simple curve is such that $\mathbf{r}(a) = \mathbf{r}(b)$, then it is called a **simple closed curve**

The reader should realize that these are mild restrictions, in the sense tha
they would be satisfied by almost all the curves with which he has had experience

Rectangles and triangles are examples of simple closed curves made up of simple arcs (in this case, straight-line segments). The circle and the ellipse are familiar examples of simple closed curves consisting of one simple arc. A semicircle and its diameter constitute a simple closed curve made up of two simple arcs. The reader may construct any number of other illustrations for himself.

Let us consider a lamina (that is, a thin sheet) of material covering a region $\mathcal{R}$ that is enclosed by a simple closed curve $\mathcal{C}$ in the $xy$-plane (Figure 21.2a), and

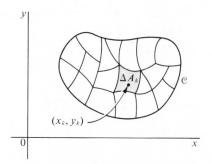

**FIGURE 21.2a**

suppose the density is a known function $\mu$ of the coordinates, so that at any point $(x, y)$ of $\mathcal{R}$, the mass per unit area is given by $\mu(x, y)$. Suppose further that we wish to find the total mass of the lamina. We may proceed in the following fashion: We first obtain an approximation for the mass by dividing the region $\mathcal{R}$ into subregions $\mathcal{R}_1, \mathcal{R}_2, \ldots, \mathcal{R}_n$ with simple arcs, numbering the subregions in any convenient order. We then let $\Delta A_k$ denote the area of the subregion $\mathcal{R}_k$, $k = 1, 2, \ldots, n$. Next, we choose a point $(x_k, y_k)$ inside or on the boundary of the subregion $\mathcal{R}_k$ and evaluate the density function there to find $\mu(x_k, y_k)$. The product $\mu(x_k, y_k) \Delta A_k$ is approximately the mass of that part of the lamina that covers the subregion $\mathcal{R}_k$. We may now construct the corresponding product for each of the other subregions and form the sum

$$\sum_{k=1}^{n} \mu(x_k, y_k) \Delta A_k.$$

This sum is an approximation to the mass of the entire lamina.

Clearly, the subdivision of $\mathcal{R}$ into subregions is a **partition** similar to that used in the definition of the ordinary definite integral, where we dealt with a line segment rather than a two-dimensional region. It now appears that better and better approximations to the desired mass can be obtained by properly refining the partition and by constructing the corresponding sums for the new partitions. The limit, if it exists, of the sequence of sums associated with a sequence of such refinements serves to define the desired mass.

In forming a sequence of refinements, we must be certain that the areas of all the subregions approach zero in such a way that no subregion has an arc as its limit. To enforce this restriction, we shall let $\delta_k$ be the maximum diameter (that is, the maximum distance between two points on the boundary) of the subregion $R_k$ in a given partition, and let $\delta$ be the maximum of all the $\delta_k$'s. Then the sequence of refinements is to be constructed so that $\delta \to 0$. (For any given partition, the number $\delta$ is called the **norm** of the partition.) Accordingly, we write

$$M .=. \lim_{\delta \to 0} \sum_{k=1}^{n} \mu(x_k, y_k) \, \Delta A_k.$$

The preceding limit, which is associated with the particular problem of finding a mass, suggests the following general statement.

**Definition 21.2c.** Let $z = f(x, y)$ define a function $f$ over a two-dimensional region $\mathcal{R}$. If, for every sequence of partitions of the region,

$$\lim_{\delta \to 0} \sum_{k=1}^{n} f(x_k, y_k) \, \Delta A_k$$

exists, it is called the **double integral** of $f$ over the region $\mathcal{R}$ and is denoted by

$$\int_{\mathcal{R}} f(x, y) \, dA.$$

In order to state a basic theorem that enables us to show in the next section how an iterated integral may be used to evaluate a double integral, we need one additional definition.

**Definition 21.2d.** A function $f$ of two variables is said to be **sectionally continuous** on a closed region $\mathcal{R}$, if it is possible by means of simple arcs to divide the region into a finite number of subregions such that $f$ is continuous on the interior of each subregion, and has a finite limit as any point on the boundary of a subregion is approached from within the subregion.

For instance, the function $f$, defined as follows over the rectangle $|x| \leq 1$ $|y| \leq 2$, is sectionally continuous on this rectangle:

$$f(x, y) = \begin{cases} x^2 - 2xy + 4 & \text{for} \quad x^2 + y^2 \leq 1, \\ 0 & \text{at all other points in the rectangle.} \end{cases}$$

The following theorem, which is proved in more advanced books, states sufficient conditions for the existence of the double integral and furnishes the basis for a practical means of evaluating double integrals.

**Theorem 21.2a.** Let $\mathcal{R}$ be a region in the $xy$-plane bounded by a simple closed curve. If $z = f(x, y)$ defines a sectionally continuous function $f$ on $\mathcal{R}$ and it boundary, then

$$\int_{\mathcal{R}} f(x, y) \, dA .=. \lim_{\delta \to 0} \sum_{k=1}^{n} f(x_k, y_k) \, \Delta A_k$$

exists.

Although the proof of this theorem is beyond the scope of this book, it fol lows from the proof that the value of the double integral depends only on the region $\mathcal{R}$ and on the integrand $f(x, y)$. It is independent of the way in which the partitions are made and of the way in which the point $(x_k, y_k)$ is chosen in the subregion $\mathcal{R}_k$ as long as the norm of the partition is made to approach zero. As we shall see in the next section, this important fact frequently allows us to use iterated integrals to evaluate double integrals.

Even though it is rarely practicable to evaluate a double integral by means of its definition, this should not detract from the reader's appreciation of the simplicity with which the double integral may be applied in many concrete cases. In each of the following applications, $f(x, y)$ is the integrand of the double integral of Theorem 21.2a.

*Area.* If $f(x, y) = 1$, then the double integral gives the area of the region $\mathcal{R}$; that is,

$$A = \int_{\mathcal{R}} dA.$$

*First Moment of Area.* If $f(x, y) = y$, the double integral gives the first moment of the area with respect to the x-axis. If $\bar{y}$ designates the y-coordinate of the centroid of the area, then the first moment is $A\bar{y}$, and

$$A\bar{y} = \int_{\mathcal{R}} y \, dA.$$

In a similar manner,

$$A\bar{x} = \int_{\mathcal{R}} x \, dA.$$

The representations of area and first moment of area given above can be shown to be consistent with the definitions previously given in terms of the simple integral.

*Second Moment of Area.* There are many instances in physics and in engineering where double integrals occur in which the integrand is the square of the distance of the "area element" from a given axis. Such an integral is called the *second moment of the area with respect to the axis.* It is customary to designate a second moment by the letter $I$ with a subscript to indicate the axis. Thus, the second moment of the area with respect to the x-axis is

$$I_x .= . \int_{\mathcal{R}} y^2 \, dA,$$

and with respect to the y-axis,

$$I_y .= . \int_{\mathcal{R}} x^2 \, dA.$$

*Mass.* It has already been shown that if $\mu(x, y)$ is a mass distribution (mass per unit area) over a plane lamina, then the mass $M$ is given by

$$M = \int_{\mathcal{R}} \mu(x, y) \, dA.$$

Using this, we can set up first and second moments of mass as follows:

$$M\bar{x} .= . \int_{\mathcal{R}} x\mu(x, y) \, dA,$$

$$M\bar{y} .=. \int_{\Re} y\mu(x, y)\, dA,$$

$$I_y .=. \int_{\Re} x^2\mu(x, y)\, dA,$$

$$I_x .=. \int_{\Re} y^2\mu(x, y)\, dA.$$

In the last five integrals the product $\mu(x, y)\, dA$ is often denoted by $dm$ and is called the **element of mass**. The last two integrals give the **moment of inertia** of the mass with respect to the $y$- and $x$-axes, respectively. Because of this fact, second moments are frequently (and mistakenly) called moments of inertia even when no mass is involved.

The moment of inertia is a fundamental notion in many physical problems dealing with rotational motion. Suppose a particle of mass $m$ is revolving about a fixed axis with an angular velocity of $\omega$ radians per second. If $v$ is the linear velocity of the particle, then the kinetic energy is given by

$$\text{K.E.} = \tfrac{1}{2}mv^2.$$

If the path of the particle is a circle of radius $r$, then the linear velocity of the particle is

$$v = r\omega.$$

Substituting this expression for $v$ in the formula for kinetic energy, we get

$$\text{K.E.} = \tfrac{1}{2}m(r\omega)^2 = \tfrac{1}{2}(r^2 m)\omega^2.$$

By definition, the quantity $r^2 m$ is the moment of inertia of the particle with respect to the axis of rotation. Thus, for the rotating particle one may write

$$\text{K.E.} = \tfrac{1}{2}I\omega^2,$$

which shows that the role of the moment of inertia $I$ in rotational motion is similar to that of the mass $m$ in translational motion. Furthermore, it is now evident that the integral

$$I = \int_{\Re} r^2\, dm$$

is the appropriate generalization from the moment of inertia of a mass particle to that of a finite mass.

*Volume Under a Surface.* Let us consider a surface $z = f(x, y)$ and a simple closed curve $\mathcal{C}$ lying below the surface, as shown in Figure 21.2b. Let $\Re$ be the plane region enclosed by the simple closed curve. Suppose we wish to define the volume of the cylindrical region lying above $\Re$ and below $z = f(x, y)$. Let us examine the product $f(x_k, y_k)\, \Delta A_k$, which appears in the definition of the double integral. Since $z_k = f(x_k, y_k)$ is the distance from the point $(x_k, y_k, 0)$ in the $xy$-plane to the point $(x_k, y_k, z_k)$ on the surface, it follows that $f(x_k, y_k)\Delta A_k$ is the volume of a cylinder with the element $\Delta A_k$ as base and with altitude

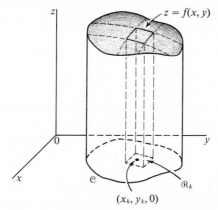

$(x_k, y_k, 0)$

**FIGURE 21.2b**

$(x_k, y_k)$. Accordingly, we define the volume below the surface and above the region ℜ to be the value of the double integral; that is,

$$V . = . \int_{\mathfrak{R}} f(x, y)\, dA.$$

The reader will realize that the assumption of an a priori notion of the volume below a surface immediately lends plausibility to the existence of the double integral of a continuous or a sectionally continuous function.

## Exercises 21.2

1. The *product of inertia* of a particle with respect to the axes in the $xy$-plane is defined to be the product of the directed distances of the particle from the axes and the mass of the particle. This is usually denoted by $H_{xy}$. What would you write for $H_{xy}$ for a mass distribution in the $xy$-plane?
2. Write a double integral corresponding to the so-called *polar moment of inertia*, which is the moment of inertia of a plane mass distribution with respect to an axis through the origin and perpendicular to the plane.

If ℜ is the region of the $xy$-plane bounded by the given curves, describe the volume defined by each of the following integrals.

3. $\int_{\mathfrak{R}} 4\, dA$; ℜ: $x^2 + y^2 = 1$.

4. $\int_{\mathfrak{R}} y\, dA$; ℜ: $x^2 + y^2 = 1, y \geq 0$.

5. $\int_{\mathfrak{R}} (2 - x - y)\, dA$; ℜ: $x = 0, y = 0, x + y = 2$.

6. $\int_{\mathfrak{R}} (4 - x^2)\, dA$; ℜ: $y = 0, y = x, x = 2$.

7. $\int_{\Re} (x^2 + y^2) \, dA$; $\Re: x^2 + 4y^2 = 4$.

8. $\int_{\Re} (x^2 + y^2) \, dA$; $\Re: y = 0, y = x, x = 2$.

9. $\int_{\Re} \sqrt{x^2 + y^2} \, dA$; $\Re: x^2 + y^2 = 9$.

10. $\int_{\Re} \sqrt{y} \, dA$; $\Re: x = \sqrt{y}, x = 0, y = 1$.

11. $\int_{\Re} 2 \, dA$; $\Re: y = \sqrt{x}, x = 0, y = 1$.

12. $\int_{\Re} \frac{4}{y^2 + 1} \, dA$; $\Re: y = x, y = 3, x = 0$.

## 21.3 EVALUATION OF THE DOUBLE INTEGRAL BY MEANS OF RECTANGULAR COORDINATES

As the discussion in Section 21.2 indicates, this section will be concerned with showing that the double integral can frequently be evaluated by the use of an iterated integral in ordinary rectangular coordinates. We shall give a detailed derivation for the special case in which the integrand function is continuous and the double integral is extended over a region $\Re$ that is bounded by a simple closed curve $\mathcal{C}$. We assume further that $\mathcal{C}$ is cut in not more than two points by any line parallel to one of the coordinate axes. These conditions mean that there are exactly two lines parallel to the $x$-axis and two lines parallel to the $y$-axis, each of which touches the curve $\mathcal{C}$ at exactly one point (see Figure 21.3a).

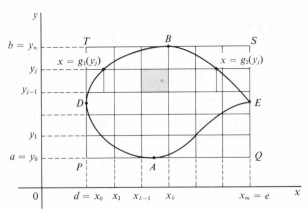

**FIGURE 21.3a**

The horizontal lines in the figure are $y = a$ and $y = b$, which touch the curve at $A$ and $B$, respectively, and the vertical lines are $x = d$ and $x = e$, which touch the curve at $D$ and $E$, respectively. The entire curve lies within the rectangle $PQST$.

Let the arc $ADB$, the left boundary of the region $\Re$, be given by $x = g_1(y)$; let the right boundary, arc $AEB$, be given by $x = g_2(y)$. Now define a function $F$ so that $F(x, y) = f(x, y)$ over the region $\Re$ and its boundary $\mathcal{C}$, and $F(x, y) = 0$ for all other points of the plane; that is,

$$F(x, y) .=. \begin{cases} f(x, y) & \text{for} \quad (x, y) \in \Re \cup \mathcal{C}, \\ 0 & \text{for} \quad (x, y) \notin \Re \cup \mathcal{C}. \end{cases}$$

With this definition it is clear that the double integral of $F$ taken over the region $\Re_1$ enclosed by the rectangle $PQST$ must be equivalent to the double integral of $f$ taken over the region $\Re$. In symbols,

$$\int_{\Re_1} F(x, y) \, dA = \int_{\Re} f(x, y) \, dA.$$

Since the double integral is independent of the mode of subdivision of the region $\Re_1$, we may subdivide the rectangle $PQST$ in any convenient fashion. Accordingly, we subdivide it into $mn$ rectangles by means of the $n$ horizontal lines, where $y$ has the values

$$a = y_0 < y_1 < \cdots < y_n = b,$$

and the $m$ vertical lines, where $x$ has the values

$$d = x_0 < x_1 < x_2 < \cdots < x_m = e.$$

Thus the lines $x = x_{k-1}$, $x = x_k$, $y = y_{j-1}$, $y = y_j$ enclose a small rectangular region whose area may be denoted by

$$\Delta A_{kj} = \Delta x_k \, \Delta y_j.$$

Consequently, a typical term in the formation of the double integral may be written

$$F(x_k, y_j) \Delta x_k \, \Delta y_j,$$

where we have chosen to evaluate $F$ at the corner $(x_k, y_j)$ of the rectangle, since the value of the double integral does not depend on this choice.

To form the double integral, we first form the sum

$$\sum_{j=1}^{n} \sum_{k=1}^{m} F(x_k, y_j) \Delta x_k \, \Delta y_j$$

and consider what happens to the limit of the sum as the norm, $\delta$, of the partition approaches zero. As previously defined, the norm of the partition is the maximum of the diameters of the subregions, which are now the small rectangles. Hence, the diameters are the diagonals of the rectangles. Consequently,

$$\delta \to 0 \iff \delta_1 .=. \max \Delta x_k \to 0 \quad \text{and} \quad \delta_2 .=. \max \Delta y_j \to 0.$$

Thus,

(1)
$$\int_{\Re_1} F(x, y) \, dA = \lim_{\delta \to 0} \sum_{j=1}^{n} \sum_{k=1}^{m} F(x_k, y_j) \Delta x_k \, \Delta y_j$$

$$= \lim_{\delta_2 \to 0} \sum_{j=1}^{n} \left[ \lim_{\delta_1 \to 0} \sum_{k=1}^{m} F(x_k, y_j) \Delta x_k \right] \Delta y_j.$$

In the last form of the limit we have taken advantage of the fact that the integral is independent of the manner in which $\delta \to 0$. Accordingly, we may choose to allow the $\Delta x$'s to approach zero first and then the $\Delta y$'s.

The inner sum is with respect to $x$ only, with $y_j$ held constant. By definition this limit is the definite integral

$$\int_d^e F(x, y_j)\, dx.$$

Along the line $y = y_j$, $F(x, y_j) = f(x, y_j)$ from $x = g_1(y_j)$ to $x = g_2(y_j)$; otherwise $F(x, y_j) = 0$. Therefore, we may write

(2)
$$\int_d^e F(x, y_j)\, dx = \int_{g_1(y_j)}^{g_2(y_j)} f(x, y_j)\, dx = \theta(y_j).$$

We use the notation $\theta(y_j)$ in Equation (2) to indicate that the integral defines a function of $y_j$ alone. If $\theta(y_j)$ is substituted for the inner limit in Equation (1) we have

(3)
$$\int_{\mathcal{R}_1} F(x, y)\, dA = \lim_{\delta_2 \to 0} \sum_{j=1}^n \theta(y_j)\, \Delta y_j$$
$$= \int_a^b \theta(y)\, dy,$$

by the definition of the definite integral. If the expression for $\theta(y)$ from Equation (2) is substituted into Equation (3), we obtain the desired iterated integral

$$\int_{\mathcal{R}} f(x, y)\, dA = \int_a^b \int_{g_1(y)}^{g_2(y)} f(x, y)\, dx\, dy.$$

It can be shown in a similar fashion that

$$\int_{\mathcal{R}} f(x, y)\, dA = \int_d^e \int_{h_1(x)}^{h_2(x)} f(x, y)\, dy\, dx,$$

where $y = h_1(x)$ is the lower boundary and $y = h_2(x)$ is the upper boundary of the region $\mathcal{R}_1$, and $d$ and $e$ are the left and right extreme values of $x$.

The preceding derivation constitutes the proof of the following two theorems.

**Theorem 21.3a.** Let a region $\mathcal{R}$ in the $xy$-plane be bounded by a simple closed curve $\mathcal{C}$, which is cut in not more than two points by any line parallel to the $y$-axis, and let the function $f$ be continuous on $\mathcal{R} \cup \mathcal{C}$. Then

$$\int_{\mathcal{R}} f(x, y)\, dA = \int_d^e \int_{h_1(x)}^{h_2(x)} f(x, y)\, dy\, dx,$$

where $y = h_1(x)$ and $y = h_2(x)$ describe the lower and upper portions of $\mathcal{C}$ respectively, and $d$ and $e$, $d < e$, are the extreme values of $x$.

**Theorem 21.3b.** Let a region $\mathcal{R}$ in the $xy$-plane be bounded by a simple closed curve $\mathcal{C}$, which is cut in not more than two points by any line parallel to the $x$-axis, and let the function $f$ be continuous on $\mathcal{R} \cup \mathcal{C}$. Then

$$\int_{\mathcal{R}} f(x, y)\, dA = \int_a^b \int_{g_1(y)}^{g_2(y)} f(x, y)\, dx\, dy,$$

where $x = g_1(y)$ and $x = g_2(y)$ describe the left and right portions of $e$, respectively, and $a$ and $b$, $a < b$, are the extreme values of $y$.

An examination of the foregoing discussion, in which we evaluated the double integral of $F(x, y)$ over a rectangular region, shows that no difficulty is caused if a portion of the boundary is parallel to one of the axes. A further and less trivial extension can be made to regions whose boundaries are simple closed curves cut in more than two points by lines parallel to the axes. This possibility occurs by virtue of the definition of the double integral, which shows that if a region $\mathcal{R}$ is cut into two subregions $\mathcal{R}_1$ and $\mathcal{R}_2$ by a simple arc, then

$$\int_{\mathcal{R}} f(x, y)\, dA = \int_{\mathcal{R}_1} f(x, y)\, dA + \int_{\mathcal{R}_2} f(x, y)\, dA.$$

Thus, any region that can be cut into subregions that satisfy the hypotheses of our derivation allows the double integral to be evaluated by iterated integrals taken over these subregions. Compare with the note at the end of the following example.

---

*Example 21.3a.* Find the centroid of the area of the region bounded by the line $y = x$ and the parabola $y = 4x - x^2$.

The points of intersection of the curves are $(0, 0)$ and $(3, 3)$ (see Figure 21.3b). It is apparent from the figure that if we integrate first with respect to $x$, then we must divide

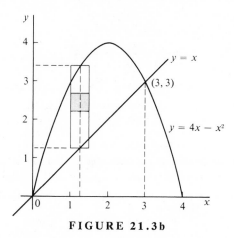

**FIGURE 21.3b**

the region into two parts and consider them separately (see the note at the end of this example). This is not necessary if we integrate first with respect to $y$. Since the lower boundary is given by $y = x$, the upper boundary by $y = 4x - x^2$, and the extreme values of $x$ are 0 and 3, we write

$$A = \int_0^3 \int_x^{4x-x^2} dy\, dx = \int_0^3 (4x - x^2 - x)\, dx = \frac{9}{2}.$$

For the first moment with respect to the y-axis, we have

$$A\bar{x} = \int_0^3 \int_x^{4x-x^2} x \, dy \, dx = \int_0^3 (3x^2 - x^3) \, dx = \frac{27}{4}.$$

Similarly, for the first moment with respect to the x-axis, we have

$$A\bar{y} = \int_0^3 \int_x^{4x-x^2} y \, dy \, dx$$

$$= \int_0^3 \frac{1}{2} [y^2]_x^{4x-x^2} \, dx$$

$$= \frac{1}{2} \int_0^3 (15x^2 - 8x^3 + x^4) \, dx = \frac{54}{5}.$$

Thus,

$$\bar{x} = \frac{A\bar{x}}{A} = \left(\frac{27}{4}\right)\left(\frac{2}{9}\right) = \frac{3}{2} \quad \text{and} \quad \bar{y} = \frac{A\bar{y}}{A} = \left(\frac{54}{5}\right)\left(\frac{2}{9}\right) = \frac{12}{5}.$$

*Note:* The student who insists on integrating first with respect to x will have to evaluate two iterated integrals, one taken over each of the subregions obtained by drawing a horizontal line through the point (3, 3). Thus,

$$A = \int_0^3 \int_{2-\sqrt{4-y}}^y dx \, dy + \int_3^4 \int_{2-\sqrt{4-y}}^{2+\sqrt{4-y}} dx \, dy.$$

*Example 21.3b.* Find the second moment with respect to the y-axis for the area of the preceding example.

By definition

$$I_y = \int_0^3 \int_x^{4x-x^2} x^2 \, dy \, dx$$

$$= \int_0^3 x^2 [y]_x^{4x-x^2} \, dx$$

$$= \int_0^3 (3x^3 - x^4) \, dx = \frac{243}{20}.$$

*Example 21.3c.* Find the volume of the solid in the first octant bounded by the cylinder $y = e^x$ and the planes $x = 0$, $x = 1$, $z = 0$, and $z = y$.

Figure 21.3c shows that $dy \, dx$ is the desirable order of integration. Thus, we write

$$V = \int_{\mathcal{R}} z \, dA$$

$$= \int_0^1 \int_0^{e^x} y \, dy \, dx$$

$$= \frac{1}{2} \int_0^1 e^{2x} \, dx = \frac{1}{4}(e^2 - 1).$$

*Example 21.3d.* A mass of density $\mu(x, y) = k(x + y)$ covers the first-quadrant region enclosed by the axes and the circle $x^2 + y^2 = a^2$. Find the moment of inertia of the

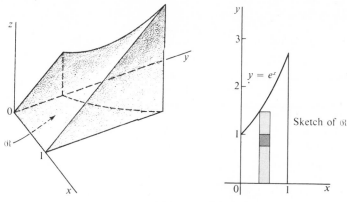

**FIGURE 21.3c**

mass with respect to the $y$-axis. Assume that $\mu$ is in slugs per square foot and that $a$ is in feet. *Note:* One slug is the mass to which a force of one pound gives an acceleration of one foot per second per second.

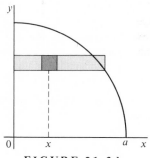

**FIGURE 21.3d**

Referring to Figure 21.3d, we find the required moment of inertia as follows:

$$I_y = \int_\Re x^2 \, dm = \int_0^a \int_0^{\sqrt{a^2-y^2}} x^2 k(x + y) \, dx \, dy$$

$$= k \int_0^a \left[ \frac{x^4}{4} + \frac{x^3 y}{3} \right]_{x=0}^{x=\sqrt{a^2-y^2}} dy$$

$$= k \int_0^a \left\{ \frac{(a^2 - y^2)^2}{4} + \frac{y(a^2 - y^2)^{3/2}}{3} \right\} dy$$

$$= \frac{ka^5}{5} \text{ (slugs)(feet}^2).$$

*Note:* The units of the answer are obtained by reasoning that since $\mu$ is dimensionally (slugs)(feet$^{-2}$), then $k$ is dimensionally (slugs)(feet$^{-3}$) because $x$ and $y$ must be in feet.

## Exercises 21.3

In Numbers 1 to 13, find the area of the region bounded by the given curves.

1. $x = y^2$, $x = y$.
2. $y = x^2$, $y = x^3$.
3. $y = \cos x$, $y = \cos 2x$, from $(0, 1)$ to the next point of intersection to the right.
4. $y = 4 - x^2$, $y = 3x$.
5. $x^2 + y^2 = 4$.
6. $y^2 = x^3$, $x^2 = y^3$.
7. $x^2 + y^2 = 64$, $x^{2/3} + y^{2/3} = 4$; first quadrant.
8. $x = y^2 - 2y$, $x = y$.
9. $2x = y^2 - 1$, $x = y + 1$.
10. $y = e^x$, $y = e^{-x}$, $x = 1$.
11. $y = (4 - x^2)^{-1/2}$, $y = (4 - x^2)^{1/2}$.
12. $y = \sin x$, $y = \cos x$, from $(\pi/4, \sqrt{2}/2)$ to the next point of intersection to the right.
13. $y = \ln x$, $y = e^x$, $x = 1$, $x = 3$.

In Numbers 14 to 22, find the centroid of the area of the region having the designated boundaries.

14. The region in Number 1.
15. The region in Number 2.
16. The circle $x^2 + y^2 = 4$; first quadrant.
17. $x^{1/2} + y^{1/2} = 2$, $x = 0$, $y = 0$.
18. $y = \ln x$, $y = 0$, $y = 1$, $x = 0$.
19. $y = x$, $y^3 = x^2$.
20. $x^2 + y^2 = 13$, $xy = 6$; first quadrant.
21. $x^{2/3} + y^{2/3} = 4$, $x = 0$, $y = 0$; first quadrant.
22. The region in Number 10.

In Numbers 23 to 27, find the designated second moment for the area of the region having the indicated boundaries.

23. The region of Number 1; $I_y$.
24. $x^{1/2} + y^{1/2} = 4$, $x = 0$, $y = 0$; $I_y$.
25. $xy = 6$, $x + y = 5$; $I_x$.
26. $y = e^x$, $x = 0$, $y = 2$; $I_x$.
27. $x^{2/3} + y^{2/3} = 4$; $I_x$.

In Numbers 28 to 32, find the volume of the region bounded by the specified surfaces.

28. $x = 0$, $y = 0$, $z = 0$, $x + y = 1$, $z = e^y$.
29. $x = 0$, $x = 1$, $y = 0$, $y = 1$, $z = 0$, $z = y$.
30. $y = 0$, $y = 3$, $z = 0$, $z = x$, $x = e^y$; first octant.
31. The first-octant region bounded by the planes $x = 0$, $y = 0$, $z = 0$, $z = y$, and the cylinder $x^2 + y^2 = 9$.
32. The cylinders $y^2 + z^2 = 9$ and $x^2 + z^2 = 9$.

In Numbers 33 to 38, find the indicated moment of inertia of the mass of a thin sheet that covers the region with the given boundaries and has density $\mu(x, y)$ as indicated.

33. $y = x$, $y = 2x - x^2$; $\mu(x, y) = kx$; $I_x$.
34. $xy = 6$, $x + 2y = 8$; $\mu(x, y) = kx$; $I_y$.
35. $x^2 + y^2 = 9$; $\mu(x, y) = k(x^2 + y^2)$; $I_y$.
36. $y = x^2$; $y = x + 2$; $\mu(x, y) = k(x + y)$; $I_y$.

37. $x = 0$, $y = 0$, $x^{2/3} + y^{2/3} = 4$, first quadrant; $\mu(x, y) = kx$; $I_y$.

38. $y = x + 1$, $y = \dfrac{2}{2 - x}$; $\mu(x, y) = kx$; $I_y$.

39. The product of inertia with respect to the axes of a particle of mass $m$ located at $P(x, y)$ is defined to be $H_{xy} = xym$. Find the product of inertia for the mass described in Example 21.3d.

## 21.4 EVALUATION OF THE DOUBLE INTEGRAL USING POLAR COORDINATES

Several instances have already occurred in which we have seen the advantage of a curvilinear system of coordinates in simplifying equations of curves and surfaces. It is thus not surprising that the use of such a system of coordinates can frequently simplify the evaluation of a double integral. As in ordinary rectangular coordinates, the procedure consists in expressing the double integral as an equivalent iterated integral in the curvilinear coordinate system. Moreover, as in rectangular coordinates, we use the coordinate curves to subdivide the given region into subregions.

The basic problem encountered in the use of a curvilinear coordinate system is that of obtaining the appropriate expression for the element of area that must be used in the iterated integral. We shall assume that the curvilinear coordinate system to be considered can be obtained from the usual cartesian coordinate system by means of a transformation,

$$x = f(u, v), \quad y = g(u, v),$$

which satisfies the hypotheses of Theorem 20.5a at every point of the region $\mathfrak{R}$ over which the integral is extended. This means that $f$ and $g$ are continuously

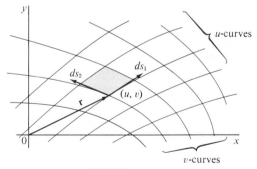

**FIGURE 21.4a**

differentiable and that the Jacobian of $x$ and $y$ with respect to $u$ and $v$ is different from zero throughout $\mathfrak{R}$.

In Figure 21.4a, the two sets of coordinate curves are shown: the $u$-curves along each of which $v$ is a constant, and the $v$-curves along each of which $u$ is a constant. The vector function

$$\mathbf{r} = f(u, v)\mathbf{i} + g(u, v)\mathbf{j}$$

describes the position vector from the origin to any point with curvilinear coordinates $(u, v)$. In the figure, $ds_1$ and $ds_2$ represent vectors tangent, respectively, to the $u$-curve and the $v$-curve through the point $(u, v)$, and having lengths equal to the differential element of arc along the appropriate coordinate curve. Thus $ds_1$ is obtained from Definition 20.6a by holding $v$ constant; and $ds_2$, by holding $u$ constant. This gives

(1) $$d\mathbf{s}_1 = \mathbf{r}_u \, du \quad \text{and} \quad d\mathbf{s}_2 = \mathbf{r}_v \, dv.$$

It appears plausible, and is actually proved in advanced work, that the element of area in the $uv$-coordinate system is the area of a parallelogram with $ds_1$ and $ds_2$ as adjacent sides. It is convenient for us to calculate this area by using the fact that the numerical measure of the area is the same as the numerical measure of the volume of a solid of unit height with this parallelogram as its base. Thus, for a right-handed coordinate system, we have

$$dA = \mathbf{k} \cdot d\mathbf{s}_1 \times d\mathbf{s}_2,$$

where $\mathbf{k}$ is the usual unit vector in the $z$-direction. Since

$$\mathbf{r}_u = f_u\mathbf{i} + g_u\mathbf{j} \quad \text{and} \quad \mathbf{r}_v = f_v\mathbf{i} + g_v\mathbf{j},$$

it follows from Equations (1) that

$$dA = \begin{vmatrix} 0 & 0 & 1 \\ f_u \, du & g_u \, du & 0 \\ f_v \, dv & g_v \, dv & 0 \end{vmatrix} = \begin{vmatrix} f_u & g_u \\ f_v & g_v \end{vmatrix} du \, dv$$

$$= J\left(\frac{x, y}{u, v}\right) du \, dv.$$

The preceding discussion makes plausible the following theorem, which is stated without proof.

**Theorem 21.4a.** Let the transformation $x = f(u, v)$, $y = g(u, v)$ be continuously differentiable and such that the Jacobian of $x$ and $y$ with respect to $u$ and $v$ is positive throughout the region $\Re$ and on its boundary $\mathcal{C}$. Then

$$\int_{\Re} F(x, y) \, dA = \int \int_{\Re} F[f(u, v), g(u, v)] \, J\left(\frac{x, y}{u, v}\right) du \, dv.$$

If we regard $u$ and $v$ as ordinary rectangular coordinates in a $uv$-plane, then the transformation is a mapping from the $xy$- to the $uv$-plane. The formula for $dA$ shows that the Jacobian plays the role of a "magnification factor" giving the ratio of the element of area $dx \, dy$ in the $xy$-plane to the element of area $du \, dv$ in the $uv$-plane.

One of the most commonly used systems of curvilinear coordinates in the plane is the system of polar coordinates given by

$$x = r \cos \theta, \quad y = r \sin \theta.$$

In Example 20.5c, the Jacobian of this transformation was found to be

$$J\left(\frac{x, y}{r, \theta}\right) = r.$$

Accordingly, we have for polar coordinates

$$dA = r \, dr \, d\theta,$$

and

$$\int_\mathbb{R} F(x, y) \, dA = \int \int_\mathbb{R} F(r \cos \theta, r \sin \theta) r \, dr \, d\theta.$$

A simple geometric procedure gives rise in a quite plausible fashion to the result just obtained. Let us consider the coordinate curves $r$ = constant and $\theta$ = constant. Then we may define an element of area as the area of the region that is bounded by the circular arcs $r = c_1$ and $r = c_2$, and the rays $\theta = k_1$ and $\theta = k_2$ (Figure 21.4b). If the radius $r$ is chosen to be the distance to the

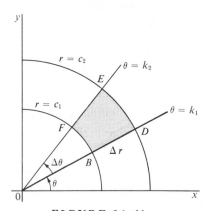

**FIGURE 21.4b**

circle that lies halfway between $r = c_1$ and $r = c_2$, then $c_1 = r - \frac{1}{2}\Delta r$ and $c_2 = r + \frac{1}{2}\Delta r$. The area $\Delta A$ of the element is the difference between the areas of sectors $OFB$ and $OED$; that is,

$$\Delta A = \frac{1}{2}(r + \frac{1}{2}\Delta r)^2 \, \Delta \theta - \frac{1}{2}(r - \frac{1}{2}\Delta r)^2 \, \Delta \theta$$
$$= r \, \Delta r \, \Delta \theta.$$

Hence the double integral is expressed as the limit of a double summation of terms of the type $F(r_i \cos \theta_j, r_i \sin \theta_j) r_i \, \Delta r_i \, \Delta \theta_j$, which leads to the given iterated integral in polar coordinates.

*Example 21.4a.* Find the area inside the cardioid $r = a(1 + \sin \theta)$ and outside the circle $r = a$.

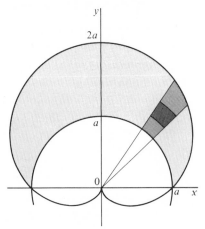

**FIGURE 21.4c**

A typical element of area is shown in Figure 21.4c. It is convenient in this problem to integrate first with respect to $r$. The lower limit on $r$ is the circle $r = a$ and the upper limit is the cardioid $r = a(1 + \sin \theta)$. The limits on $\theta$ are the $\theta$-coordinates of the points of intersection of the two curves, which in this example are on the rays $\theta = 0$ and $\theta = \pi$. Therefore, the desired area is given by

$$A = \int_0^\pi \int_a^{a(1+\sin\theta)} r \, dr \, d\theta$$

$$= \int_0^\pi \frac{a^2}{2} (2 \sin \theta + \sin^2 \theta) \, d\theta = \frac{a^2}{4} (8 + \pi)(\text{l.u.})^2.$$

*Note:* The second term in the last integral may be evaluated by Wallis' formula (Section 12.6).

---

*Example 21.4b.* Find the volume bounded by the cone $r = z$, the cylinder $r = a \cos \theta$, and the plane $z = 0$ (see Figure 21.4d).

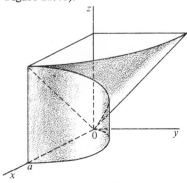

**FIGURE 21.4d**

If $\mathcal{R}$ is the region in the $xy$-plane bounded by $r = a \cos \theta$, then the volume $V$ is

$$V = \int_{\mathcal{R}} z \, dA.$$

The region is symmetric relative to the $xz$-plane, so that the required volume is twice the volume of the region in the first octant. Thus, using polar coordinates with $r \, dr \, d\theta$ for $dA$, and $z = r$, we have

$$V = 2 \int_0^{\pi/2} \int_0^{a \cos \theta} r(r \, dr \, d\theta)$$

$$= \tfrac{2}{3} \int_0^{\pi/2} [a \cos \theta]^3 \, d\theta$$

$$= \tfrac{2}{3} a^3 \int_0^{\pi/2} \cos^3 \theta \, d\theta = \tfrac{4}{9} a^3 \text{ (l.u.)}^3.$$

---

The alert reader will have noticed that the preceding example involved a region in the $xy$-plane having the origin on its boundary. At the origin the Jacobian is zero, so that Theorem 21.4a does not apply. It can be shown that if the integrand in the double integral is continuous, then no difficulty can occur if the origin is included in the region or on its boundary. This proof is accomplished by excising the origin by means of a small circle with center at the origin and considering the iterated integral that extends over the remaining region. The limit of this integral as the radius of the small circle approaches zero turns out to be the same as the integral taken over the entire region. The details of this are beyond the scope of our discussion.

## Exercises 21.4

In the following problems, unless it is otherwise directed, use polar coordinates and double integration to find the quantity indicated.

1. The area inside the circle $r = 2$ and outside the cardioid $r = 2(1 + \cos \theta)$.
2. The area common to the circles $r = 3$ and $r = 6 \cos \theta$.
3. The area inside the cardioid $r = 3(1 + \sin \theta)$ and outside the parabola $r(1 + \sin \theta) = 3$.
4. The area inside the circle $r = 3 \sin \theta$ and above the line $r \sin \theta = 2$.
5. The area inside the four-leaved rose $r = 4 \sin 2\theta$.
6. The area inside the inner loop of the limaçon $r = 1 - 2 \cos \theta$.
7. The area common to the circles $r = \sin \theta + \cos \theta$ and $r = 2 \sin \theta$.
8. The area in the first quadrant outside the circle $r = 3\sqrt{2} \sin \theta$ and inside the lemniscate $r^2 = 9 \sin 2\theta$.
9. The centroid of the area inside the circle $r = 4$ and to the right of the line $r = 2 \sec \theta$.
10. The centroid of the area inside the first-quadrant loop of the curve $r = 4 \sin 2\theta$.
11. The centroid of the area inside the cardioid $r = 3(1 + \cos \theta)$.
12. The centroid of the area inside the first-quadrant loop of the curve $r = 3 \sin 3\theta$.
13. The centroid of the area enclosed by the limaçon $r = 3 + \cos \theta$.

14. The second moment, with respect to the $x$-axis, of the area enclosed by the first-quadrant loop of the curve $r^2 = 4 \sin 2\theta$.

15. $I_x$ and $I_y$ for the area of the circle $r = 4 \sin \theta$.

16. The second moment of area with respect to an axis through the origin and perpendicular to the $xy$-plane is denoted by $I_0$ and is called the **polar second moment of area**. Find the polar second moment of the area enclosed by the cardioid $r = 3(1 - \sin \theta)$.

17. The mass of a thin sheet covering the region bounded by the cardioid $r = 2(1 - \sin \theta)$ if the density is $kr$.

18. The mass of a thin sheet covering the region bounded by the circle $r = 4 \cos \theta$ if the density is $kx$.

19. The volume inside the sphere $r^2 + z^2 = 16$ and also inside the cylinder $r = 2$.

20. The volume inside the sphere $r^2 + z^2 = 16$ and also inside the cylinder $r = 4 \cos \theta$.

Evaluate the integral in each of Numbers 21 to 24 by reversing the order of integration. *Hint:* Make a sketch of the region over which the integral is extended, and determine the new limits from your figure.

21. $\int_0^1 \int_y^1 \sin x^2 \, dx \, dy.$

22. $\int_0^1 \int_{\sqrt{w}}^1 \dfrac{dz \, dw}{1 + z^3}.$

23. $\int_0^1 \int_v^1 e^{u^2} \, du \, dv.$

24. $\int_0^{\pi/2} \int_y^{\pi/2} \dfrac{\cos x}{x} \, dx \, dy.$

Evaluate the integral in each of Numbers 25 to 28 by transforming to polar coordinates. (See the hint preceding Number 21.)

25. $\int_0^2 \int_0^x \dfrac{dy \, dx}{\sqrt{x^2 + y^2}}.$

26. $\int_0^a \int_0^{\sqrt{a^2 - y^2}} e^{-(x^2 + y^2)} \, dx \, dy.$

27. $\int_0^a \int_0^{\sqrt{a^2 - x^2}} \sqrt{x^2 + y^2} \, dy \, dx.$

28. $\int_0^a \int_0^{\sqrt{ax - x^2}} y^2 \, dy \, dx.$

★29. By considering the coordinate transformation

$$x + y = u, \quad y = v; \quad \text{that is,} \quad x = u - v, \quad y = v,$$

show that

$$\int_0^a \int_0^{a-y} e^{-(x+y)} F(x) G(y) \, dx \, dy = \int_0^a e^{-u} \int_0^u F(u - v) G(v) \, dv \, du.$$

*Hint:* Regard this as a mapping, and investigate the mapping on the $uv$-plane of the region over which the first integral is extended in the $xy$-plane.

★30. Find the area above the $x$-axis and bounded by the two parabolas $y^2 = 4(x + 1)$, $y^2 = -16(x - 4)$ by considering the mapping of Example 20.5b,

$$x = u^2 - v^2, \quad y = 2uv.$$

*Hint:* Take $u$ and $v$ as rectangular coordinates in a $uv$-plane, and show that the region of integration is mapped into the rectangle bounded by $u = 0$, $u = 2$, $v = 0$, $v = 1$. Notice that you need not bother to find the points of intersection of the parabolas.

## 21.5 AREA OF A SURFACE

There are a number of important physical problems that lead to a consideration of integrals extended over a curved surface. We shall see that such integrals, called **surface integrals,** can frequently be evaluated in terms of the double integral, which has occupied our attention thus far. However, before we consider surface integrals in general, we must define the area of a general curved surface.

Let the equation of the surface be in the form $F(x, y, z) = 0$, where the function $F$ is continuous and possesses continuous first partial derivatives with respect to $x$, $y$, and $z$. We assume further that this equation has a single-valued solution for $z$ as a function of $x$ and $y$, so that a line parallel to the $z$-axis pierces the surface not more than once. These assumptions mean that the graph of the equation consists of a single, smooth piece of surface with a well-defined tangent plane at each point.

Let us consider a portion of the surface that projects into a region $\mathcal{R}$ of the $xy$-plane that is bounded by a simple closed curve (Figure 21.5a). We subdivide

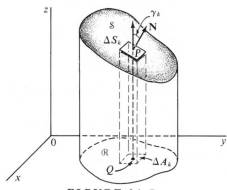

**FIGURE 21.5a**

the region $\mathcal{R}$ into $n$ subregions $\mathcal{R}_k$ with area $\Delta A_k$, as indicated in the figure. Let any point $Q(x_k, y_k, 0)$ be chosen in $\mathcal{R}_k$, and let $QP$ be a line that is perpendicular to the $xy$-plane and meets the surface at $P$. Construct at $P$ that piece of the tangent plane that projects into the region $\mathcal{R}_k$, and let the area of this piece of tangent plane be denoted by $\Delta S_k$.

Now carry out the same construction for each subregion $\mathcal{R}_k$, $k = 1, 2, \ldots, n$, in the region $\mathcal{R}$ of the $xy$-plane. In this way the surface will be covered with 'scales," each scale being a piece of a tangent plane. We shall obtain an approximate measure of the surface area by adding the areas of these "scales" to get

$$\sum_{k=1}^{n} \Delta S_k.$$

This approximation leads us to consider the following limiting process. Let $\delta$ be the maximum of the maximum diameters of the subregions $\mathfrak{R}_k$. Then we define the surface area $S$ as

$$S = \lim_{\delta \to 0} \sum_{k=1}^{n} \Delta S_k,$$

when this limit exists. Of course, as $\delta \to 0$ the partitioning of $\mathfrak{R}$ becomes finer and finer, and the number of subregions $\mathfrak{R}_k$ increases without limit.

We return to Figure 21.5a and consider the relation between $\Delta S_k$ and $\Delta A_k$. Since $\Delta A_k$ is the area in the $xy$-plane into which the area $\Delta S_k$ projects, then $\Delta A_k$ must be $\Delta S_k$ multiplied by the cosine of the angle between the $xy$-plane and the tangent plane. This angle, $\gamma_k$, is the same as the angle between the positive $z$-direction and the upward-drawn normal $\overrightarrow{PN}$ to the surface. Thus,

$$\Delta A_k = \Delta S_k \cos \gamma_k,$$

or

$$\Delta S_k = \Delta A_k \sec \gamma_k.$$

As we saw in Section 20.3, a set of direction numbers of the normal is given by $F_x$, $F_y$, $F_z$. From these, it follows that

$$\cos \gamma = \frac{|F_z|}{\sqrt{F_x^2 + F_y^2 + F_z^2}},$$

where the absolute-value bars on $F_z$ guarantee that the upward-drawn normal is used.

By substituting for $\sec \gamma_k$, we now have for the definition of $S$,

$$S = \lim_{\delta \to 0} \sum_{k=1}^{n} \left( \frac{\sqrt{F_x^2 + F_y^2 + F_z^2}}{|F_z|} \right)_k \Delta A_k,$$

where the subscript $k$ on the quantity in parentheses means that this quantity is to be evaluated at $P(x_k, y_k, z_k)$. Thus we are led to the formula

$$S = \int_{\mathfrak{R}} \frac{\sqrt{F_x^2 + F_y^2 + F_z^2}}{|F_z|} \, dA.$$

This double integral will surely exist if the integrand is continuous, and this can be assured by the further assumption that $F_z$ is different from zero everywhere on the surface.

We shall usually write the preceding integral in the form

$$S = \int_{\mathfrak{R}} \sec \gamma \, dA.$$

The foregoing discussion then constitutes the proof of

**Theorem 21.5a.** (a) Let a portion $\mathcal{S}$ of a surface project into a region $\mathfrak{R}$ in the $xy$-plane that is bounded by a simple closed curve.

(b) Let $\mathcal{S}$ be such that it is cut in exactly one point by every line perpendicular to the $xy$-plane at a point of $\mathfrak{R}$.

(c) Let the equation of $S$ be in the form $F(x, y, z) = 0$, where $F_x$, $F_y$, $F_z$ are all continuous on $S$ and $F_z \neq 0$ on $S$.

Then the surface area $S$ exists and is given by

$$S = \int_{\mathcal{R}} \sec \gamma \, dA,$$

where

$$\sec \gamma = \frac{\sqrt{F_x^2 + F_y^2 + F_z^2}}{|F_z|}.$$

It is easy to see that if it is convenient to project the surface onto the $yz$-plane or onto the $xz$-plane, then the following integrals may be used:

$$S = \int_{\mathcal{R}_{yz}} \sec \alpha \, dA, \quad S = \int_{\mathcal{R}_{xz}} \sec \beta \, dA.$$

These results are obtained by exactly the same procedure as that used to obtain Theorem 21.5a. The symbols $\mathcal{R}_{yz}$ and $\mathcal{R}_{xz}$ stand for the regions into which $S$ is projected on the $yz$-plane and on the $xz$-plane, respectively.

---

*Example 21.5a.* Find the area of the first-octant portion of the cylinder $x^2 + z^2 = a^2$ that is included between the planes $y = 0$ and $y = x$ (Figure 21.5b).

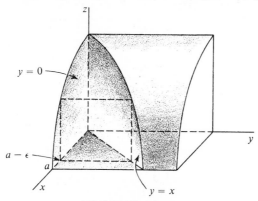

**FIGURE 21.5b**

Let $F(x, y, z) . = . x^2 + z^2 - a^2$. Then $F_x = 2x$, $F_y = 0$, $F_z = 2z$, and

$$\sec \gamma = \frac{\sqrt{4x^2 + 4z^2}}{2|z|} = \frac{2a}{2|z|} = \frac{a}{\sqrt{a^2 - x^2}}.$$

(It follows from the equation of the cylinder that $\sqrt{x^2 + z^2} = a$ and $|z| = \sqrt{a^2 - x^2}$.) Since the required surface projects into the triangle in the $xy$-plane bounded by $y = 0$, $y = x$, $x = a$, we have

$$S = \int_{\mathcal{R}} \frac{a}{\sqrt{a^2 - x^2}} \, dA = \int_0^a \int_0^x \frac{a \, dy \, dx}{\sqrt{a^2 - x^2}}$$

$$= \int_0^a \frac{ax}{\sqrt{a^2 - x^2}} \, dx = a^2 \text{ (l.u.)}^2.$$

---

The reader may have noticed in Example 21.5a that along the line $x = a$ in the $xy$-plane, $F_z = 0$, so that Theorem 21.5a does not apply directly. This means that the double integral used here is actually an improper integral. However, it is easy to show that the integral converges by integrating in the $x$-direction from $x = 0$ to $x = a - \epsilon$ and then taking the limit as $\epsilon \to 0^+$. The details are simple and are left to the reader. By making a proper excision of the discontinuities of the integrand and then taking a limit, it is possible in the problems that we consider to show that no actual difficulty arises. We shall leave such verification to the reader.

Suppose the curve $y = f(x)$, $z = 0$ is revolved about the $x$-axis to form the surface of revolution

$$y^2 + z^2 = [f(x)]^2.$$

The area of this surface between the planes $x = a$ and $x = b$ can be found by the preceding method, it being assumed that $f$ has a continuous derivative on the interval $a \le x \le b$. Thus, writing

$$F(x, y, z) .=. y^2 + z^2 - [f(x)]^2 = 0,$$

we have

$$F_x = -2f(x)f'(x), \quad F_y = 2y, \quad F_z = 2z,$$

$$\sec \gamma = \frac{\sqrt{[f(x)f'(x)]^2 + y^2 + z^2}}{|z|}$$

$$= \frac{\sqrt{[f(x)]^2[f'(x)]^2 + [f(x)]^2}}{\sqrt{[f(x)]^2 - y^2}}$$

$$= \frac{|f(x)|\sqrt{1 + [f'(x)]^2}}{\sqrt{[f(x)]^2 - y^2}}.$$

By making use of symmetry, we find that the desired area is

$$S = 4 \int_a^b \int_0^{|f(x)|} \frac{|f(x)|\sqrt{1 + [f'(x)]^2}}{\sqrt{[f(x)]^2 - y^2}} \, dy \, dx$$

$$= 4 \int_a^b |f(x)|\sqrt{1 + [f'(x)]^2} \left[ \mathrm{Sin}^{-1} \frac{y}{|f(x)|} \right]_0^{|f(x)|} dx$$

$$= 2\pi \int_a^b |f(x)|\sqrt{1 + [f'(x)]^2} \, dx.$$

Keeping in mind that $y = f(x)$ is the equation of the curve in the $xy$-plane and that

$$ds = \sqrt{1 + [f'(x)]^2} \, dx$$

is the element of arc for this curve, we may recast the preceding formula in the form

$$S = 2\pi \int_e |y| \, ds,$$

where the subscript $\mathcal{C}$ means that the integral is extended along the curve $\mathcal{C}$ with proper limits in the positive direction corresponding to the variable of integration used for the integral.

---

*Example 21.5b.* Find the area of the surface formed by revolving about the *x*-axis the parabola $y^2 = 2x - 1$ from $y = 0$ to $y = 1$ (See Figure 21.5c).

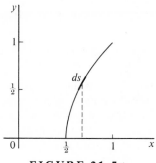

**FIGURE 21.5c**

Since $2y\,dy = 2\,dx$, the differential of arc length is given by

$$(ds)^2 .=. (dx)^2 + (dy)^2 = (1 + y^2)(dy)^2.$$

Furthermore, $y \geq 0$, so that $|y| = y$, and hence

$$S = 2\pi \int_0^1 y\sqrt{1 + y^2}\,dy$$

$$= \left[\frac{2\pi}{3}(1 + y^2)^{3/2}\right]_0^1$$

$$= \frac{2\pi}{3}(2\sqrt{2} - 1)(\text{l.u.})^2.$$

---

The reader should realize that a general formula for the area of a surface obtained by revolving a curve about a line is

$$S = \int_e 2\pi r\,ds,$$

where *r* is the radius from the axis of revolution to the element of arc *ds*.

## Examples 21.5

1. Find the area of the portion of the cone $x^2 + y^2 = z^2$ that lies above the square bounded by $x = 0$, $y = 0$, $x = 1$, $y = 1$ in the *xy*-plane.
2. Find the area of the portion of the surface of the sphere $x^2 + y^2 + z^2 = a^2$ that is inside the cylinder $x^2 + y^2 = ay$.
3. Find the area of the portion of the cylinder that lies inside the sphere in Number 2.
4. Find the area of the portion of the cylinder $x^2 + y^2 = a^2$ that lies above the *xy*-plane and is included between the two planes $z = y$ and $z = 2y$.

5. Find the area of the portion of the paraboloid $x^2 + y^2 = 2z$ that lies in the first octant and is cut off by the parabolic cylinder $x^2 = z$ and the planes $x = 0$, $z = 4$.
6. Find the area of the portion of the cylinder $x^2 + y^2 = a^2$ that lies inside the cylinder $x^2 + z^2 = a^2$.
7. Find the area of the portion of the cylinder $x^2 + z^2 = 4a^2$ that lies in the first octant and above the triangle bounded by the lines $x = 0$, $y = 0$, $x + y = a$ in the $xy$-plane.
8. Find the area of the first-octant portion of the surface $x = zy$ that lies inside the cylinder $y^2 + z^2 = 1$.

In Numbers 9 to 16, find the area of the surface that is formed by revolving the given curve as indicated.

9. The hypocycloid $x = a \cos^3 \psi$, $y = a \sin^3 \psi$ about the $x$-axis.
10. The circle $x^2 + y^2 = b^2$ about the line $x = a$, $a > b$.
11. The curve $3y = 2(x^2 + 1)^{3/2}$ from $x = 0$ to $x = 3$ about the $y$-axis.
12. The catenary $y = \cosh x$ from $x = 0$ to $x = 1$ about the $x$-axis.
13. The same curve as in Number 12 about the $y$-axis.
14. One arch of $y = \sin kx$ about the $x$-axis.
15. The cardioid $r = a(1 + \cos \theta)$ about the polar axis.
16. The lemniscate $r^2 = a^2 \cos 2\theta$ about the polar axis.

## 21.6 SURFACE INTEGRALS

We have already met a number of problems in which it was necessary to calculate moments of area, volume, or mass. Such moments serve to define the centroid of an area or a volume and the center of mass for a distributed mass. In the case of a piece of a curved surface, the definition of the moment with respect to a plane is arrived at in a similar fashion. If we let $z_k$ in Figure 21.5a be the distance of the element $\Delta S_k$ from the $xy$-plane, then the first moment of area of the surface $S$ with respect to the $xy$-plane is defined by

$$\lim_{\delta \to 0} \sum_{k=1}^{n} z_k \, \Delta S_k = \int_S z \, dS,$$

where the integral is to be regarded as a symbol for the limit of the sum. This integral may be evaluated as before by projecting the surface onto one of the coordinate planes. The $z$-coordinate, $\bar{z}$, of the centroid is then defined by the equation

$$\bar{z} S = \int_S z \, dS.$$

The $x$- and $y$-coordinates of the centroid are defined in a similar manner.

---

*Example 21.6a.* Find the coordinates of the centroid of the surface area described in Example 21.5a.

We shall use the same procedure as in Example 21.5a; that is, evaluation of the desired quantities by projection onto the $xy$-plane. Thus,

$$\bar{x}S = \int_S x \, dS = \int_0^a \int_0^x \frac{ax \, dy \, dx}{\sqrt{a^2 - x^2}}$$

$$= \int_0^a \frac{ax^2 \, dx}{\sqrt{a^2 - x^2}} = \frac{a^3 \pi}{4} \text{ (l.u.)}^3,$$

$$\bar{y}S = \int_S y \, dS = \int_0^a \int_0^x \frac{ay \, dy \, dx}{\sqrt{a^2 - x^2}}$$

$$= \int_0^a \frac{ax^2 \, dx}{2\sqrt{a^2 - x^2}} = \frac{a^3 \pi}{8} \text{ (l.u.)}^3,$$

$$\bar{z}S = \int_S z \, dS = \int_0^a \int_0^x \frac{az \, dy \, dx}{\sqrt{a^2 - x^2}},$$

where $z = \sqrt{a^2 - x^2}$ from the equation of the cylinder. Therefore,

$$\bar{z}S = \int_0^a \int_0^x a \, dy \, dx = \frac{a^3}{2} \text{ (l.u.)}^3.$$

Since $S = a^2$ (Example 21.5a), we have

$$\bar{x} = \frac{\pi a}{4}, \quad \bar{y} = \frac{\pi a}{8}, \quad \bar{z} = \frac{a}{2}.$$

The three integrals giving the first moments with respect to the coordinate planes in the preceding example are illustrations of the general type of integral called a **surface integral**. A physical example similar to the one with which we began the discussion of the double integral serves to introduce a more general surface integral.

Suppose that a mass is distributed over a curved surface $S$ and that the density at each point is given by $\mu(x, y, z)$ units of mass per unit of area. An analysis similar to those we have encountered before leads to the following definition for the total mass $M$:

$$M .=. \lim_{\delta \to 0} \sum_{k=1}^n \mu(x_k, y_k, z_k) \, \Delta S_k$$

$$.=. \int_S \mu(x, y, z) \, dS,$$

where again the integral stands for the limit of the preceding sum. The evaluation may be performed by projecting the surface onto one of the coordinate planes and making use of the equation of the surface.

Regardless of the interpretation of $f(x, y, z)$, we may look upon

$$\int_S f(x, y, z) \, dS .=. \lim_{\delta \to 0} \sum_{k=1}^n f(x_k, y_k, z_k) \, \Delta S_k$$

as a surface integral, provided, of course, that the limit exists.

*Example 21.6b.* Evaluate the integral $\int_S y^2 \, dS$, where $S$ is the first octant-portion of the sphere $x^2 + y^2 + z^2 = a^2$. (The integral here is the second moment of the area of this surface with respect to the $xz$-plane.)

From the equation of the sphere, we have

$$F(x, y, z) \,.=.\, x^2 + y^2 + z^2 - a^2 = 0.$$

Hence

$$F_x = 2x, \quad F_y = 2y, \quad F_z = 2z,$$

and

$$\sqrt{F_x^2 + F_y^2 + F_z^2} = 2a.$$

It follows that

$$\sec \alpha = \frac{a}{|x|}, \quad \sec \beta = \frac{a}{|y|}, \quad \sec \gamma = \frac{a}{|z|}.$$

Since only first-octant values of $x$, $y$, and $z$ will be used, the absolute-value bars may be dropped. Moreover, because of the factor $y^2$ in the integral, it appears that $\sec \beta = a/y$ will be the simplest of these to use. Thus,

$$dS = \sec \beta \, dx \, dz = (a/y) \, dx \, dz,$$

and

$$\int_S y^2 \, dS = \iint_{\Re_{xz}} ay \, dx \, dz$$

$$= \int_0^a \int_0^{\sqrt{a^2 - z^2}} a\sqrt{a^2 - x^2 - z^2} \, dx \, dz \qquad \text{(see Figure 21.6a)}$$

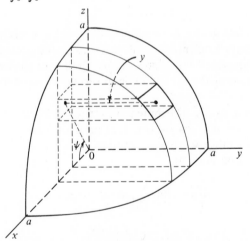

**FIGURE 21.6a**

This integral can be fairly easily evaluated by using a system of polar coordinates in the $xz$-plane with

$$x = \rho \cos \psi, \quad z = \rho \sin \psi.$$

Then

$$\int_S y^2 \, dS = \int_0^{\pi/2} \int_0^a a\sqrt{a^2 - \rho^2} \, \rho \, d\rho \, d\psi = \frac{\pi a^4}{6}.$$

We consider next an interesting and important physical application of the foregoing ideas. Let us imagine a fluid flowing through a region of space with the velocity at each point of the region being a vector function of the coordinates, say

$$U(x, y, z) = u(x, y, z)i + v(x, y, z)j + w(x, y, z)k.$$

Suppose we need to find the volume of fluid per unit time flowing through a specified surface in this region.

We look first at the simplest case, in which $U$ is a constant vector and the surface is planar (Figure 21.6b). The figure represents the volume of fluid that flows through the plane region of area $A$ in one unit of time. This volume is that of an oblique cylinder of base area $A$ and of altitude $U \cdot N$, where $N$ is the unit normal to the plane of $A$. Accordingly, the required result is

$$(U \cdot N)A.$$

This formula is the key to the solution of the problem in the case of the more general surface. Thus, consider a piece of surface $S$ with a specified direction for the unit normal $N$ at each point, and let $U(x, y, z)$ be the velocity of the fluid. Figure 21.6c shows an element of surface, a point $P_k$ at which $U$ is evaluated,

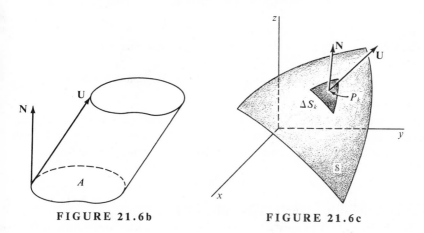

**FIGURE 21.6b**             **FIGURE 21.6c**

and the unit normal $N$ to the surface at $P_k$. An approximate expression for the volume of fluid per unit time flowing through this element of area $\Delta S_k$ is clearly

$$(U \cdot N)_k \, \Delta S_k.$$

By the usual limit-of-a-sum procedure, we now arrive at the following definition for the net volume $Q$ per unit time flowing through $S$:

$$Q .= . \lim_{\delta \to 0} \sum_{k=1}^{n} (U \cdot N)_k \, \Delta S_k = \int_S U \cdot N \, dS.$$

*Example 21.6c.* Let the velocity of a fluid be given by

$$U(x, y, z) = b(x\mathbf{i} + y\mathbf{j} + z\mathbf{k}),$$

where distances are in feet and the magnitude of the velocity is in feet per second. Find the volume of fluid per second flowing through the first-octant portion of the sphere $x^2 + y^2 + z^2 = a^2$ in the direction of the outward-drawn normal.

We write the equation of the sphere in the form

$$F(x, y, z) .=. x^2 + y^2 + z^2 - a^2 = 0.$$

Then $F_x = 2x$, $F_y = 2y$, $F_z = 2z$, so that the outward-drawn unit normal at each point is

$$\mathbf{N} = \frac{F_x\mathbf{i} + F_y\mathbf{j} + F_z\mathbf{k}}{\sqrt{F_x^2 + F_y^2 + F_z^2}}$$

$$= \frac{x\mathbf{i} + y\mathbf{j} + z\mathbf{k}}{\sqrt{x^2 + y^2 + z^2}} = \frac{x}{a}\mathbf{i} + \frac{y}{a}\mathbf{j} + \frac{z}{a}\mathbf{k}.$$

Thus

$$\mathbf{U}\cdot\mathbf{N} = b(x\mathbf{i} + y\mathbf{j} + z\mathbf{k}) \cdot \left(\frac{x}{a}\mathbf{i} + \frac{y}{a}\mathbf{j} + \frac{z}{a}\mathbf{k}\right)$$

$$= \frac{b}{a}(x^2 + y^2 + z^2) = ab,$$

since $x^2 + y^2 + z^2 = a^2$ at all points of the surface.

The volume of fluid per second flowing through the surface is then given by

$$Q = \int_S ab \, dS = ab \int_S dS = abS = \frac{\pi a^3 b}{2} \text{ cubic feet per second.}$$

---

If the surface $S$ is a closed surface bounding a three-dimensional region of space, it is customary to employ the *outward-drawn* unit normal $\mathbf{N}$. We shall later arrive at a most important result relating an integral of the form

$$\int_S \mathbf{U}\cdot\mathbf{N} \, dS$$

to an integral extended through the volume enclosed by $S$.

The reader should be aware that most of what we have dealt with in the last few pages has been discussed on an almost completely intuitive basis. We have assumed that the surfaces involved are all sufficiently "smooth" and that the functions are sufficiently well-behaved to guarantee the existence of the resulting integrals. It is shown in advanced studies of calculus that if the surface $S$ is of the type described in Theorem 21.5a and if $U(x, y, z)$ is continuous at all points of $S$, then

$$\int_S \mathbf{U}\cdot\mathbf{N} \, dS$$

does exist.

## Exercises 21.6

1. Find the coordinates of the centroid of the first-octant portion of the surface $x^2 + y^2 + z^2 = a^2$.
2. Find the centroid of the first-octant portion of the surface $x^2 + y^2 = z^2$ that lies between the planes $z = 0$ and $z = 1$.
3. Find the centroid of the first-octant portion of the surface of the paraboloid $z = x^2 + y^2$ that lies between the $xy$-plane and the plane $z = 2$.
4. Find the second moment with respect to the $z$-axis of the first-octant portion of the surface $x^2 + y^2 + z^2 = 1$.
5. If $S$ is given by an equation of the form $z = f(x, y)$, then the unit normal $N$ that points upward is given by

$$N = \frac{-f_x i - f_y j + k}{\sqrt{f_x^2 + f_y^2 + 1}}.$$

   If $U = u_1 i + u_2 j + u_3 k$, show that

$$\int_S U \cdot N \, dS = \int_{\mathcal{R}_{xy}} (-u_1 f_x - u_2 f_y + u_3) \, dA.$$

6. Use the result of Number 5 to evaluate $\int_S U \cdot N \, dS$, where

$$U = xi + yj + zk,$$

   and $S$ is the portion of the paraboloid $z = a^2 - x^2 - y^2$ that lies inside the cylinder $x^2 + y^2 = a^2$.

7. Use the result of Number 5 to evaluate $\int_S U \cdot N \, dS$, where $U = ai + bj + ck$

   ($a, b, c$ constant), and $S$ is the conical surface $z = \sqrt{x^2 + y^2}$ lying inside the cylinder $x^2 + y^2 = 1$.

8. Evaluate $\int_S U \cdot N \, dS$, where $U = xi + yj + zk$ and $S$ is the entire surface of the cube bounded by the coordinate planes and the planes $x = a, y = a, z = a$. Recall that in the case of a closed surface the *outward*-drawn normal is used.

9. Evaluate the same integral as in Number 8 for the entire surface of the sphere $x^2 + y^2 + z^2 = a^2$. *Hint:* The upper half of the surface is given by

$$z = \sqrt{a^2 - x^2 - y^2},$$

   and the upward-drawn normal is to be used. The lower half of the surface is given by $z = -\sqrt{a^2 - x^2 - y^2}$, and the downward-drawn normal is to be used.

10. Evaluate $\int_S U \cdot N \, dS$, where $U = yzi + xzj + xyk$ and $S$ is the entire surface of the hemispherical region bounded by $z = \sqrt{1 - x^2 - y^2}$ and the $xy$-plane.

## 21.7 THE TRIPLE INTEGRAL

Most three-dimensional regions that are of interest to us are bounded by what we have loosely called "smooth" surfaces. For purposes of further analysis, however, we must now give a precise meaning to the concept of "smooth" surface.

A surface will be called **smooth** if it is described by an equation of the form $F(x, y, z) = 0$, where $F_x$, $F_y$, $F_z$ exist and are continuous at each point of the surface, and if there is no point of the surface at which all three of these partial derivatives are zero. This means that at each point of the surface there is a well-defined unit-normal vector **N**, whose positive sense we may choose (as, for example, we have done in the preceding sections on surface integrals).

Once the positive sense of the unit normal is chosen, the side of the surface from which the positive end of the normal extends is called the "positive side" of the surface. It may appear that every surface is "two-sided," and that it would not be possible to move the unit normal continuously along a simple curve starting at a point $P$ and arriving again at $P$ with the sense of the normal reversed. That this is not true was shown by Möbius, a German mathematician. His surface, known as a Möbius strip, is an example of a "one-sided" surface. Such a surface can be formed by taking a long strip of paper (see Figure 21.7a),

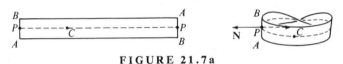

**FIGURE 21.7a**

giving it a half-twist, and pasting the ends together so that the vertices marked $A$ coincide and those marked $B$ coincide. In the figure, we have indicated a curve $\mathcal{C}$ along which the normal may be continuously displaced from a point $P$ to arrive at $P$ again with its sense reversed. It is interesting to construct such a surface and verify the foregoing discussion. What would be the result of cutting the surface along the curve $\mathcal{C}$?

We shall exclude from all further consideration these freak one-sided surfaces. They do not enter the simpler applications with which this book is concerned.

Let us consider a finite three-dimensional region $\mathcal{U}$ that is bounded by a smooth surface or by a finite number of smooth surfaces. The region inside a sphere or an ellipsoid is an example of a region bounded by a single smooth piece of surface. The region inside a cube is an example of a region bounded by a surface consisting of six smooth pieces.

We may now construct the following generalization of the double integral. Let $f$ be a continuous function of $x$, $y$, $z$ everywhere on $\mathcal{U}$ and its boundary. By means of simple smooth surfaces, the region $\mathcal{U}$ may be partitioned into $n$ subregions denoted by $\mathcal{U}_k$, $k = 1, 2, \ldots, n$ (Figure 21.7b). Let the volume of the subregion $\mathcal{U}_k$ be designated by $\Delta\tau_k$. Choose a point $P_k$, with coordinates $x_k, y_k, z_k$ inside $\mathcal{U}_k$ or on its surface. Evaluate $f$ at each point $P_k, k = 1, 2, \ldots, n$, and form the sum

$$\sum_{k=1}^{n} f(x_k, y_k, z_k) \, \Delta\tau_k.$$

The subregions $\mathcal{U}_k$ may be subdivided again and again, and the corresponding sums may be formed. For a given partition, let $\delta$ be the maximum of the set of largest diameters of the subregions, so that $\delta$ is the norm of the partition, and consider the sequence of sums as $\delta \to 0$.

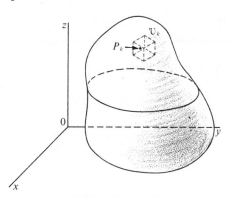

**FIGURE 21.7b**

**Definition 21.7a.** Let $u = f(x, y, z)$ define a function $f$ over a three-dimensional region $\mathcal{U}$. If, for every sequence of partitions of the region,

$$\lim_{\delta \to 0} \sum_{k=1}^{n} f(x_k, y_k, z_k)\, \Delta \tau_k$$

exists, it is called the triple integral of $f$ over the region $\mathcal{U}$ and is denoted by

$$\int_{\mathcal{U}} f(x, y, z)\, d\tau.$$

It can be shown, as in the case of the double integral, that if the function $f$ is continuous everywhere in $\mathcal{U}$ and on its boundary, then the triple integral of $f$ over the region $\mathcal{U}$ exists. Again, it is to be understood that the limit is independent of the mode of subdivision and of the point chosen at which to evaluate $f$ in each subregion.

As is true of the double integral, there are many useful applications of the triple integral.

(a) The volume $V$ itself is given by

$$V .=. \int_{\mathcal{U}} d\tau.$$

(b) By analogy with moments of area with respect to the axes, we can define moments of volume with respect to the coordinate planes. Thus,

$$V\bar{x} .=. \int_{\mathcal{U}} x\, d\tau, \quad V\bar{y} .=. \int_{\mathcal{U}} y\, d\tau, \quad V\bar{z} .=. \int_{\mathcal{U}} z\, d\tau.$$

These three integrals, along with that for $V$, serve to define the centroid $(\bar{x}, \bar{y}, \bar{z})$ of the volume.

(c) Let a mass $M$ be distributed throughout the region $\mathcal{V}$ so that the density (mass per unit volume) is given as a function $\mu(x, y, z)$ at each point. Then

$$M .=. \int_{\mathcal{V}} \mu(x, y, z) \, d\tau.$$

The product $\mu(x, y, z) \, d\tau$ is called the "element of mass," and is denoted by $dm$. The coordinates $(\bar{x}, \bar{y}, \bar{z})$ of the center of mass are given by

$$M\bar{x} .=. \int_{\mathcal{V}} x \, dm, \quad M\bar{y} .=. \int_{\mathcal{V}} y \, dm, \quad M\bar{z} .=. \int_{\mathcal{V}} z \, dm.$$

(d) The moments of inertia of a mass with respect to the coordinate axes are calculated by means of the formulas

$$I_x .=. \int_{\mathcal{V}} (y^2 + z^2) \, dm,$$

$$I_y .=. \int_{\mathcal{V}} (z^2 + x^2) \, dm,$$

$$I_z .=. \int_{\mathcal{V}} (x^2 + y^2) \, dm.$$

If $dm$ is replaced by $d\tau$ in these last three integrals, the results will be second moments of volume with respect to the axes.

The triple integral is most often evaluated by means of the threefold iterated integral. For ordinary rectangular coordinates, we subdivide the region $\mathcal{V}$ by means of planes parallel to the coordinate planes. This results in a number of rectangular subregions plus some irregular blocks next to the boundary surfaces. Thus, we may slice up the region by means of planes parallel to the $xy$-plane. Then we may cut the slices into columns by planes parallel to the $xz$-plane, and the columns into blocks by planes parallel to the $yz$-plane (see Figures 21.7c, d, and e).

We shall not attempt a detailed proof that the limit defining the triple integral may (under the assumptions we have made) be evaluated by means of an iterated limit. If, for example, the region $\mathcal{V}$ is bounded above and below by simple smooth surfaces that are each cut not more than once by a line parallel to the $z$-axis, and if the region projects into a region $\mathcal{R}$, in the $xy$-plane, of the type considered for the double integral, then

$$\int_{\mathcal{V}} f(x, y, z) \, d\tau = \int_{\mathcal{R}} \left[ \int_{F_1(x, y)}^{F_2(x, y)} f(x, y, z) \, dz \right] dA,$$

where $z = F_1(x, y)$ and $z = F_2(x, y)$ are the lower and upper bounding surfaces. The evaluation of the first integral leads at once to a double integral which may then be evaluated by the methods considered in preceding sections. The evaluation is thus reduced to

$$\int_{\mathcal{V}} f(x, y, z) \, d\tau = \int_a^b \int_{g_1(x)}^{g_2(x)} \int_{F_1(x, y)}^{F_2(x, y)} f(x, y, z) \, dz \, dy \, dx,$$

or to

$$\int_{\mathcal{V}} f(x, y, z)\, d\tau = \int_c^d \int_{h_1(y)}^{h_2(y)} \int_{F_1(x, y)}^{F_2(x, y)} f(x, y, z)\, dz\, dx\, dy.$$

The reader should realize that it is sometimes more convenient to project the region $\mathcal{V}$ onto the $yz$- or $xz$-plane rather than onto the $xy$-plane. Several different orders of integration are possible, and a figure is usually helpful in choosing a convenient one.

---

*Example 21.7a.* Find the $z$-coordinate of the centroid of the volume bounded by the planes $x + y + z = 4$, $x = 0$, $y = 0$, and $z = 0$ (see Figure 21.7c).

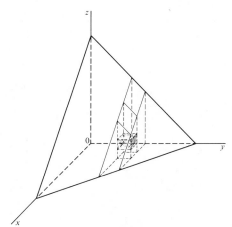

**FIGURE 21.7c**

If we regard the region as cut up by planes parallel to the coordinate planes, we may visualize the integration procedure as a reconstruction of the volume as follows: First we place the small blocks together in the $z$-direction to give a column extending from the $xy$-plane to the surface $x + y + z = 4$. Then we place the columns next to each other to form a slice parallel to the $xz$-plane, and finally we place the slices together to fill out the volume. These three steps correspond to summing the elements of volume first in the $z$-direction, then in the $x$-direction, and finally in the $y$-direction. The appropriate limiting procedures lead to the result

$$V .=. \int_{\mathcal{V}} d\tau = \int_0^4 \int_0^{4-y} \int_0^{4-x-y} dz\, dx\, dy$$

$$= \int_0^4 \int_0^{4-y} (4 - x - y)\, dx\, dy = \int_0^4 \frac{1}{2}(4 - y)^2\, dy = \frac{32}{3}\, \text{(l.u.)}^4.$$

Similarly,

$$V\bar{z} .=. \int_{\mathcal{V}} z\, d\tau = \int_0^4 \int_0^{4-y} \int_0^{4-x-y} z\, dz\, dx\, dy$$

$$= \int_0^4 \int_0^{4-y} \frac{1}{2}(4 - x - y)^2\, dx\, dy = \int_0^4 \frac{1}{6}(4 - y)^3\, dy = \frac{32}{3}\, \text{(l.u.)}^3,$$

and hence

$$\bar{z} = \left(\frac{32}{3}\right)\left(\frac{3}{32}\right) = 1.$$

*Example 21.7b.* Find the volume bounded by the cylinder $z = 4/(y^2 + 1)$ and the planes $y = x$, $y = 3$, $x = 0$, and $z = 0$ (see Figure 21.7d).

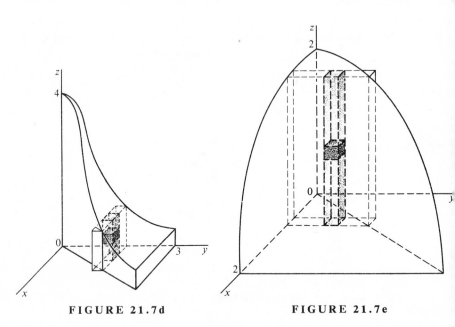

**FIGURE 21.7d**          **FIGURE 21.7e**

The figure indicates that the volume may be found by integrating first with respect to $z$ between 0 and $4/(y^2 + 1)$, then with respect to $x$ between 0 and $y$, and finally with respect to $y$, between 0 and 3. Thus we get

$$V = \int_0^3 \int_0^y \int_0^{4/(y^2+1)} dz\, dx\, dy$$

$$= \int_0^3 \int_0^y \frac{4}{y^2 + 1}\, dx\, dy$$

$$= \int_0^3 \frac{4y}{y^2 + 1}\, dy$$

$$= 2 \ln 10 \ (\text{l.u.})^3.$$

*Example 21.7c.* Find the moment of inertia with respect to the $z$-axis of the mass in the first octant bounded by the cylinder $x^2 + z^2 = 4$ and the planes $y = x$, $y = 0$ and $z = 0$, if the density is $\mu = kz$.

If the integration is taken first with respect to $z$ and then with respect to $y$, as indicated in Figure 21.7e, we have

$$I_z .=. \int_{\mathcal{V}} (x^2 + y^2)\, dm = \int_0^2 \int_0^x \int_0^{\sqrt{4-x^2}} (x^2 + y^2)\, kz\, dz\, dy\, dx$$

$$= \frac{k}{2} \int_0^2 \int_0^x (4 - x^2)(x^2 + y^2)\, dy\, dx$$

$$= k \int_0^2 (\tfrac{8}{3}x^3 - \tfrac{2}{3}x^5)\, dx = \frac{32k}{9}.$$

## Exercises 21.7

Use triple integration to find the indicated quantity.

1. The volume bounded by the planes $x + 2y + 3z = 6$, $x = 0$, $y = 0$, and $z = 0$.
2. The volume bounded by the cylinders $x^2 + z^2 = 4$ and $y^2 + z^2 = 4$.
3. The volume bounded by the cylinder $x^2 = y$ and the planes $z = y$, $y = 2$, $x = 0$, and $z = 0$.
4. The volume bounded by the planes $x + 2y + 3z = 6$, $y = z$, $x = 0$, and $y = 0$.
5. The volume bounded by the cylinder $x^2 = 4 - 4z$ and the planes $y = 0$ and $y = z$.
6. The volume in the first octant bounded by the paraboloid $z = x^2 + y^2$ and the planes $y = x$, $y = 0$, $x = 3$, and $z = 0$.
7. The volume in the first octant bounded by the cylinders $z = 9 - y^2$ and $z = 9 - x^2$ and the planes $x = 0$, $y = 0$, and $z = 0$.
8. The volume bounded by the cone $z^2 = x^2 + y^2$ and the plane $z = 1$.
9. The volume bounded by the paraboloid $z = x^2 + y^2$ and the plane $z = 4$.
10. The volume bounded by the paraboloids $z = 4x^2 + y^2$ and $z = 8 - 4x^2 - y^2$.
11. The centroid of the volume in Number 3.
12. The centroid of the volume in Number 8.
13. The second moment with respect to the $z$-axis for the volume in Number 3.
14. The mass of the solid bounded by the planes $y + z = 2$, $x + z = 2$, $x = 0$, $y = 0$, $z = 0$, if the density is $\mu(x, y, z) = kx$.
15. The mass in the first octant bounded by the cylinders $z^2 = y$ and $x^2 = y$ and the plane $y = 1$ if the density is $\mu(x, y, z) = kz$.
16. The mass in the first octant bounded by the parabolic cylinder $y^2 = x$ and the planes $x = 0$, $y = 1$, $z = 0$, and $z = y$ if the density is $\mu(x, y, z) = k(x + 2z)$.
17. The center of mass of the solid in Number 14.
18. The center of mass of the solid in Number 15.
19. The center of mass of the solid in Number 16.
20. The moment of inertia with respect to the $z$-axis for the mass of Number 14.
21. The moment of inertia with respect to the $x$-axis for the mass of Number 15.
22. The moment of inertia with respect to the $x$-axis for the mass of Number 16.
23. The moment of inertia $I_{xy}$ of a mass with respect to the $xy$-plane is defined by

$$I_{xy} = \int_{\mathcal{V}} z^2\, dm,$$

and similarly for the moments of inertia with respect to the $xz$- and $yz$-planes. Show that

$$I_z = I_{xz} + I_{yz}.$$

24. The "parallel axis" theorem for moments of inertia states that the moment of inertia of a mass with respect to any axis is equal to the moment of inertia with respect to a parallel axis through the center of mass plus the product of the mass

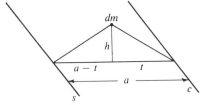

**FIGURE 21.7f**

and the square of the distance between the two axes. Use the concept of the triple integral to prove this theorem. *Hint:* See Figure 21.7f. Show that

$$I_s = I_c + a^2 M,$$

where $s$ stands for any axis and $c$ for the parallel axis through the center of mass

## 21.8 THE TRIPLE INTEGRAL; CURVILINEAR COORDINATES

To evaluate the triple integral by means of an iterated integral, using some convenient three-dimensional system of curvilinear coordinates, we shall follow the procedure that was used in Section 21.4 to obtain the element of area in a two-dimensional system of curvilinear coordinates. We shall denote the curvilinear coordinates by $u$, $v$, $w$ and regard them as given by the transformation equations

$$x = f(u, v, w),$$
$$y = g(u, v, w),$$
$$z = h(u, v, w).$$

The effectiveness of the iterated integral lies in the fact that integration is carried out with respect to one variable at a time, the other variables being held constant. This fact dictates that the element of volume be bounded by coordinate surfaces. Thus, the element is bounded by six surfaces:

$$u = a_1, \quad u = a_2, \quad v = b_1, \quad v = b_2, \quad w = c_1, \quad w = c_2,$$

as is indicated in Figure 21.8a.

The reader will recognize that the following procedure is the direct generalization of that used in Section 21.4. If the coordinate curves are called $u$-curves, $v$-curves, and $w$-curves, respectively, it is seen that a $u$-curve is always the intersection of two coordinate surfaces: $S_1$, on which $v$ is a constant, and $S_2$, on which $w$ is a constant. Similar statements hold for the $v$- and $w$-curves. Accordingly, at any point $P$, the vector $d\mathbf{s}_1$, tangent to the $u$-curve and having for magnitude the element of arc length along the $u$-curve through $P$, is given by

$$d\mathbf{s}_1 = \frac{\partial \mathbf{r}}{\partial u} du \quad \text{(See Definition 20.5a)},$$

where

$$\mathbf{r} = x\mathbf{i} + y\mathbf{j} + z\mathbf{k} \text{ as usual,}$$

and $x$, $y$, $z$ are functions of $u$, $v$, $w$.

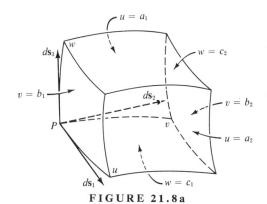

**FIGURE 21.8a**

In the same fashion, the corresponding vectors $d\mathbf{s}_2$ and $d\mathbf{s}_3$ along the $v$- and $w$-curves, respectively, are given by

$$d\mathbf{s}_2 = \frac{\partial \mathbf{r}}{\partial v} \, dv \quad \text{and} \quad d\mathbf{s}_3 = \frac{\partial \mathbf{r}}{\partial w} \, dw.$$

We shall accept here, without proof, that the proper formula for the element of volume is the formula for the volume of the parallelepiped having $d\mathbf{s}_1$, $d\mathbf{s}_2$, $d\mathbf{s}_3$ for adjacent edges. Thus, for a right-handed coordinate system,

$$d\tau = d\mathbf{s}_1 \cdot d\mathbf{s}_2 \times d\mathbf{s}_3$$

$$= \left( \frac{\partial \mathbf{r}}{\partial u} \cdot \frac{\partial \mathbf{r}}{\partial v} \times \frac{\partial \mathbf{r}}{\partial w} \right) du \, dv \, dw.$$

Since $\mathbf{r} = x\mathbf{i} + y\mathbf{j} + z\mathbf{k}$, the expression for $d\tau$ in more extended form is

$$\begin{vmatrix} \dfrac{\partial x}{\partial u} & \dfrac{\partial y}{\partial u} & \dfrac{\partial z}{\partial u} \\[2mm] \dfrac{\partial x}{\partial v} & \dfrac{\partial y}{\partial v} & \dfrac{\partial z}{\partial v} \\[2mm] \dfrac{\partial x}{\partial w} & \dfrac{\partial y}{\partial w} & \dfrac{\partial z}{\partial w} \end{vmatrix} du \, dv \, dw = J\left( \frac{x, y, z}{u, v, w} \right) du \, dv \, dw,$$

a result which, happily, is the exact three-dimensional analogue of that obtained for the twofold iterated integral.

As a result of the foregoing discussion, we have

**Theorem 21.8a.** Let $F(x, y, z)$ be continuous throughout a finite region $\mathcal{U}$ bounded by a finite number of smooth surfaces. Let a right-handed system of curvilinear coordinates $u$, $v$, $w$ be introduced by the transformation

$$x = f(u, v, w), \quad y = g(u, v, w), \quad z = h(u, v, w),$$

where $f$, $g$, and $h$ are continuously differentiable throughout $\mathcal{V}$. Suppose further that the Jacobian of $x$, $y$, and $z$ with respect to $u$, $v$, and $w$ is different from zero throughout $\mathcal{V}$ and its boundary. Then,

$$\int_{\mathcal{V}} F(x, y, z) \, d\tau = \iiint_{\mathcal{V}} F[f(u, v, w), g(u, v, w), h(u, v, w)] \, J\left(\frac{x, y, z}{u, v, w}\right) du \, dv \, dw.$$

*Note:* It can be shown that this theorem holds even if $J = 0$ on a set of points, provided the set of points has zero volume. This means that the Jacobian could be zero on a finite number of lines or surfaces, for example, without disturbing the result.

One of the more commonly employed systems of curvilinear coordinates is the system of cylindrical coordinates that was introduced in Example 20.6b. In terms of the letters $r$, $\theta$, and $z$, which are usually used in place of the $u$, $v$, and $w$ of that example, the transformation equations are

$$x = r \cos \theta, \quad y = r \sin \theta, \quad z = z,$$

as is indicated by Figure 21.8b. The $r$, $\theta$, $z$ coordinates are convenient in many problems involving cylinders.

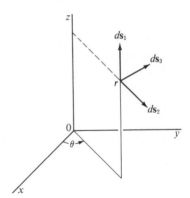

**FIGURE 21.8b**

In the figure, $ds_1$, $ds_2$, $ds_3$ are the three vectors pointing, respectively, in the directions in which $r$, $\theta$, and $z$ increase. The student should note that the order $r$, $\theta$, $z$ corresponds to a right-handed system of coordinates. The Jacobian of the transformation is

$$J\left(\frac{x, y, z}{r, \theta, z}\right) = \begin{vmatrix} \dfrac{\partial x}{\partial r} & \dfrac{\partial x}{\partial \theta} & \dfrac{\partial x}{\partial z} \\[2mm] \dfrac{\partial y}{\partial r} & \dfrac{\partial y}{\partial \theta} & \dfrac{\partial y}{\partial z} \\[2mm] \dfrac{\partial z}{\partial r} & \dfrac{\partial z}{\partial \theta} & \dfrac{\partial z}{\partial z} \end{vmatrix} = \begin{vmatrix} \cos \theta & -r \sin \theta & 0 \\ \sin \theta & r \cos \theta & 0 \\ 0 & 0 & 1 \end{vmatrix} = r.$$

The triple integral is thus given in terms of an iterated integral in cylindrical coordinates by the formula

$$\int_v f(x, y, z) \, d\tau = \iiint_v f[r \cos \theta, r \sin \theta, z] r \, dr \, d\theta \, dz.$$

It is not difficult to obtain the expression for the element of volume from direct geometric consideration of the system of cylindrical coordinates. As shown in Figure 21.8c, the element is bounded by two coordinate cylinders, two

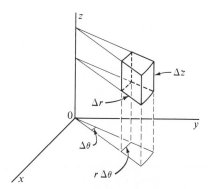

**FIGURE 21.8c**

coordinate planes passing through the $z$-axis and two coordinate planes parallel to the $xy$-plane. The base of the element of volume is the element of area in polar coordinates, which we showed in Section 21.4 to be $r \, dr \, d\theta$. Thus, for the volume element, we have

$$d\tau = (\text{height})(\text{area base})$$
$$= (dz)(r \, dr \, d\theta) = r \, dz \, dr \, d\theta.$$

*Example 21.8a.* Find the volume bounded by the plane $z = 1$ and the paraboloid $x^2 + y^2 = z$.

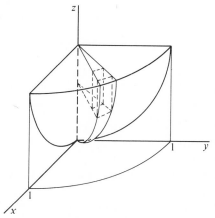

**FIGURE 21.8d**

From Figure 21.8d it can be seen that the lower limit on $z$ is the paraboloid $z = x^2 + y^2$ (or $z = r^2$ in cylindrical coordinates), and the upper limit is the plane $z = 1$. The limits on $r$ and $\theta$ will be determined by the projection of the region onto the $xy$-plane, as shown in the figure. Since, by symmetry, the total volume is four times the volume in the first octant, we have

$$V = 4 \int_0^{\pi/2} \int_0^1 \int_{r^2}^1 r \, dz \, dr \, d\theta$$

$$= 4 \int_0^{\pi/2} \int_0^1 [z]_{r^2}^1 r \, dr \, d\theta$$

$$= 4 \int_0^{\pi/2} \int_0^1 (r - r^3) \, dr \, d\theta$$

$$= 4 \int_0^{\pi/2} \left[ \frac{r^2}{2} - \frac{r^4}{4} \right]_0^1 d\theta$$

$$= \int_0^{\pi/2} d\theta = \frac{\pi}{2} \text{ (l.u.)}^3.$$

---

Cylindrical coordinates are extremely useful for many problems involving cylindrical surfaces, but are quite cumbersome in certain problems involving spheres. For many of the latter problems, spherical coordinates are most convenient. Spherical coordinates were introduced in Example 20.6c, and the reader may recall that if $\rho$ is the distance from the origin $O$ to the point $P(x, y, z)$, $\varphi$ the angle between the $z$-axis and the line segment $OP$, and $\theta$ the angle between the $x$-axis and the projection $ON$ of $OP$ in the $xy$-plane (as in polar coordinates), then the numbers $\rho$, $\varphi$, $\theta$ uniquely determine the point $P$ (see Figure 21.8e).

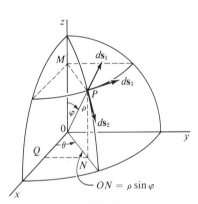

**FIGURE 21.8e**

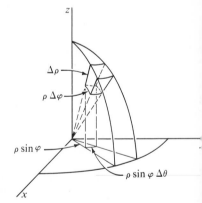

**FIGURE 21.8f**

The figure indicates that a right-handed system results if we take the coordinate in the order $\rho$, $\varphi$, $\theta$.

To obtain the relations between rectangular and spherical coordinates, we refer to Figure 21.8e again. Let $M$ be the foot of the perpendicular from $P$ to he z-axis, $N$ the foot of the perpendicular from $P$ to the $xy$-plane, and $Q$ the oot of the perpendicular from $N$ to the $x$-axis. Then,

$$ON = MP = \rho \sin \varphi.$$

since

$$x = OQ = ON \cos \theta \quad \text{and} \quad y = QN = ON \sin \theta,$$

t follows that

$$x = \rho \sin \varphi \cos \theta \quad \text{and} \quad y = \rho \sin \varphi \sin \theta.$$

Moreover,

$$z = OM = \rho \cos \varphi.$$

Hence, as given in Example 20.6c, the required transformation equations are

$$x = \rho \sin \varphi \cos \theta, \quad y = \rho \sin \varphi \sin \theta, \quad z = \rho \cos \varphi.$$

n order to give uniqueness to the spherical coordinates of a point, it is usually ssumed that

$$\rho > 0, \quad 0 < \varphi < \pi, \quad 0 \leq \theta < 2\pi.$$

At the origin, $\rho = 0$, and neither $\varphi$ nor $\theta$ is unique; for points on the z-axis, ther than the origin, $\theta$ is not unique, although $\varphi$ is. The Jacobian of this transformation is

$$J\left(\frac{x, y, z}{\rho, \varphi, \theta}\right) = \begin{vmatrix} \dfrac{\partial x}{\partial \rho} & \dfrac{\partial x}{\partial \varphi} & \dfrac{\partial x}{\partial \theta} \\[2mm] \dfrac{\partial y}{\partial \rho} & \dfrac{\partial y}{\partial \varphi} & \dfrac{\partial y}{\partial \theta} \\[2mm] \dfrac{\partial z}{\partial \rho} & \dfrac{\partial z}{\partial \varphi} & \dfrac{\partial z}{\partial \theta} \end{vmatrix}$$

$$= \begin{vmatrix} \sin \varphi \cos \theta & \rho \cos \varphi \cos \theta & -\rho \sin \varphi \sin \theta \\ \sin \varphi \sin \theta & \rho \cos \varphi \sin \theta & \rho \sin \varphi \cos \theta \\ \cos \varphi & -\rho \sin \varphi & 0 \end{vmatrix}.$$

t is left for the reader to show that this Jacobian has the value $\rho^2 \sin \varphi$ (see 'xercises 21.8, Number 29).

Accordingly, we may write

$$\int_{v} f(x, y, z) \, d\tau = \iiint_{v} f[\rho \sin \varphi \cos \theta, \rho \sin \varphi \sin \theta, \rho \cos \varphi] \rho^2 \sin \varphi \, d\rho \, d\varphi \, d\theta.$$

Let us consider the element of volume geometrically. The surfaces $\rho = $ con-
ant are spheres with centers at the origin. The surfaces $\varphi = $ constant are cones
'ith vertices at the origin and symmetric to the z-axis, and the surfaces $\theta = $ con-
ant are planes through the z-axis. Figure 21.8f shows that the element of vol-
me is bounded by two of the spheres, two of the cones, and two of the planes.
'rom the figure, we find that the dimensions of the element of volume are $\Delta\rho$,
$\Delta\varphi$, and $\rho \sin \varphi \, \Delta\theta$. Therefore, the volume, regarded as that of a rectangular
arallelepiped, is approximately $\rho^2 \sin \varphi \, \Delta\rho \, \Delta\varphi \, \Delta\theta$.

*Example 21.8b.* Suppose a homogeneous mass of density $k$ fills the spherical region $x^2 + y^2 + z^2 \leq a^2$. Find the moment of inertia of the mass with respect to the z-axis.

The square of the distance from the z-axis is $x^2 + y^2$, and in spherical coordinates, $x^2 + y^2 = \rho^2 \sin^2 \varphi$. We may consider the first-octant portion of the sphere and, using both the symmetry of the mass and the symmetry of the quantity $x^2 + y^2$, multiply by a factor of 8 to obtain the total required moment. Thus,

$$I_z = 8k \int_0^{\pi/2} \int_0^{\pi/2} \int_0^a (\rho^2 \sin^2 \varphi)\rho^2 \sin \varphi \, d\rho \, d\varphi \, d\theta$$

$$= \frac{8a^5k}{5} \int_0^{\pi/2} \int_0^{\pi/2} \sin^3 \varphi \, d\varphi \, d\theta = \frac{8\pi ka^5}{15}.$$

The reader should note carefully that it is only the symmetry or lack of symmetry of the *entire integrand* that determines whether or not a required quantity can be computed by integrating over only a portion of the region, as in Example 21.8b. To grasp this point, consider the difference between the center of mass of an empty homogeneous spherical shell and the center of mass of the shell plus contents if it is half full of mercury.

*Example 21.8c.* Find the second moment with respect to the z-axis for the volume above the xy-plane, below the cone $x^2 + y^2 = z^2$, and inside the cylinder $x^2 + y^2 - 2y = 0$ (see Figure 21.8g).

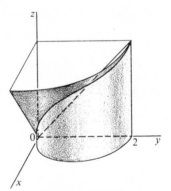

**FIGURE 21.8g**

We have for the required moment

$$I_z = \int_v (x^2 + y^2) \, d\tau = \int_v \rho^2 \sin^2 \varphi \, d\tau,$$

since in spherical coordinates, $x^2 + y^2 = \rho^2 \sin^2 \varphi$. We infer from the symmetry of the volume and of the distance that the moment of the entire volume is twice that of the volume in the first octant. The equation of the cone is $\varphi = \pi/4$, and of the cylinder $\rho = 2 \sin \theta \csc \varphi$. (Don't just read this! Verify it!!) Hence, the required moment is

$$I_z = 2 \int_0^{\pi/2} \int_{\pi/4}^{\pi/2} \int_0^{2 \sin \theta \csc \varphi} \rho^4 \sin^3 \varphi \, d\rho \, d\varphi \, d\theta$$

$$= \frac{64}{5} \int_0^{\pi/2} \int_{\pi/4}^{\pi/2} \sin^5 \theta \csc^2 \varphi \, d\varphi \, d\theta = \frac{512}{75} \, (\text{l.u.})^5.$$

*Example 21.8d.* Use spherical coordinates to evaluate the integral

$$\int_0^a \int_0^{\sqrt{a^2-z^2}} \int_0^{\sqrt{a^2-y^2-z^2}} \sqrt{x^2 + y^2 + z^2} \, dx \, dy \, dz.$$

From the limits on the integral, it is seen that the region of integration is the portion of the first octant that is bounded by the coordinate planes and the sphere $x^2 + y^2 + z^2 = a^2$. Since for spherical coordinates,

$$x^2 + y^2 + z^2 = \rho^2,$$

the given integral is equivalent to

$$\int_0^{\pi/2} \int_0^{\pi/2} \int_0^a \rho^3 \sin \varphi \, d\rho \, d\varphi \, d\theta = \frac{\pi a^4}{8}.$$

*Note:* If the reader has even the slightest doubt about the occasional usefulness of spherical coordinates, he should compare the work entailed in evaluating this integral with that required to evaluate the given integral directly.

## Exercises 21.8

Use cylindrical coordinates to find the indicated quantity in Numbers 1 to 10.

1. The centroid of the volume bounded by the cone $x^2 + y^2 = z^2$ and the plane $z = 4$.
2. The volume inside both the cylinder $x^2 + y^2 = 5$ and the sphere $x^2 + y^2 + z^2 = 9$.
3. The volume enclosed by the sphere $x^2 + y^2 + z^2 = 9$.
4. The volume inside the sphere $x^2 + y^2 + z^2 = 4$ and above the paraboloid $x^2 + y^2 = 3z$.
5. The volume above the paraboloid $x^2 + y^2 = z$ and below the plane $z = 4y$.
6. The volume bounded by the paraboloid $x^2 + y^2 = 4z$, the cylinder $x^2 + y^2 = 4y$, and the plane $z = 0$.
7. The centroid of the volume in Number 5.
8. The second moment with respect to the $z$-axis for the volume in Number 5.
9. The moment of inertia with respect to a diameter of a sphere of radius $a$ filled with a homogeneous mass ($\mu = k$).
10. The volume in the first octant inside the cylinder $r = \sin 2\theta$ and bounded by the planes $z = r \cos \theta$ and $z = 0$.

Use spherical coordinates to find the indicated quantity in Numbers 11 to 14.

11. The volume enclosed by the sphere $x^2 + y^2 + z^2 = 9$.
12. The volume inside the cylinder $x^2 + y^2 = 2x$, below the cone $x^2 + y^2 = 3z^2$, and above the $xy$-plane.
13. Find the centroid of the volume enclosed by the hemisphere $x^2 + y^2 + z^2 = 9$ $z \geq 0$, and the $xy$-plane.

14. The centroid of the volume bounded by the cone $x^2 + y^2 = z^2$ and the plane $z = 2$.

Find the indicated quantity in Numbers 15 to 18.

15. The centroid of the first-octant portion of the volume inside the sphere $x^2 + y^2 + z^2 = 9$.
16. The mass inside the sphere $x^2 + y^2 + z^2 = 9$, if the density is proportional to the distance from the $z$-axis.
17. The centroid of the volume in Number 12.
18. The second moment with respect to the $z$-axis for the volume in Number 12.
19. Locate the centroid of a spherical wedge of angle $2\beta$. *Hint:* Let the wedge be cut from the sphere $x^2 + y^2 + z^2 = a^2$ by the two planes $y = \pm x \tan \beta$.
20. Find the moment of inertia with respect to a tangent line of a solid sphere of radius $a$ and constant density $k$. *Hint:* Let the sphere be tangent to the $z$-axis.
21. Find the volume inside both of the spheres $x^2 + y^2 + z^2 = a^2$ and $x^2 + y^2 + z^2 = 2bz$, $b > a$.
22. Find the mass of a spherical shell of inside radius $a$ and outside radius $b$ if the density is proportional to the distance from the center.

Use cylindrical or spherical coordinates to evaluate the integral in each of Numbers 23 to 28.

23. $\int_0^h \int_0^b \int_0^{\sqrt{b^2-x^2}} \sqrt{x^2 + y^2} \, dy \, dx \, dz$.

24. $\int_0^a \int_0^{\sqrt{a^2-y^2}} \int_0^{\sqrt{a^2-x^2-y^2}} z(x^2 + y^2)^{-1/2} \, dz \, dx \, dy$.

25. $\int_0^a \int_0^{\sqrt{a^2-x^2}} \int_0^{\sqrt{a^2-x^2-y^2}} z\sqrt{a^2 - x^2 - y^2} \, dz \, dy \, dx$.

26. $\int_0^a \int_0^{\sqrt{a^2-z^2}} \int_0^{\sqrt{a^2-y^2-z^2}} (x^2 + y^2) \, dx \, dy \, dz$.

27. $\int_0^{1/\sqrt{2}} \int_0^x \int_0^{\sqrt{1-x^2-y^2}} z(x^2 + y^2)^{-1/2} \, dz \, dy \, dx$.

28. $\int_0^2 \int_0^{\sqrt{2z-z^2}} \int_0^{\sqrt{2z-z^2-y^2}} (x^2 + y^2 + z^2)^{-1/2} \, dx \, dy \, dz$.

29. For spherical coordinates, we found that

$$J\left(\frac{x, y, z}{\rho, \varphi, \theta}\right) = \begin{vmatrix} \sin\varphi\cos\theta & \sin\varphi\sin\theta & \cos\varphi \\ \rho\cos\varphi\cos\theta & \rho\cos\varphi\sin\theta & -\rho\sin\varphi \\ -\rho\sin\varphi\sin\theta & \rho\sin\varphi\cos\theta & 0 \end{vmatrix}.$$

By factoring out $\rho$ in the second row and $\rho \sin \varphi$ in the third row, we find

$$J\left(\frac{x, y, z}{\rho, \varphi, \theta}\right) = \rho^2 \sin\varphi \begin{vmatrix} \sin\varphi\cos\theta & \sin\varphi\sin\theta & \cos\varphi \\ \cos\varphi\cos\theta & \cos\varphi\sin\theta & -\sin\varphi \\ -\sin\theta & \cos\theta & 0 \end{vmatrix}.$$

Let $D$ stand for the last determinant. Show first that

$$(\sin\varphi\cos\varphi)D = \begin{vmatrix} \sin^2\varphi\cos\theta & \sin^2\varphi\sin\theta & \sin\varphi\cos\varphi \\ \cos^2\varphi\cos\theta & \cos^2\varphi\sin\theta & -\sin\varphi\cos\varphi \\ -\sin\theta & \cos\theta & 0 \end{vmatrix}.$$

Then, by adding the elements of the first row to the corresponding ones in the second row, show that

$$(\sin \varphi \cos \varphi)D = \sin \varphi \cos \varphi.$$

Thus,

$$D = 1 \quad \text{and} \quad J = \rho^2 \sin \varphi.$$

# ★21.9 THE DIVERGENCE THEOREM

In Section 20.4, we introduced the notion of the gradient, a vector

$$\nabla u .=. u_x\mathbf{i} + u_y\mathbf{j} + u_z\mathbf{k}.$$

Using an alternative notation for the partial derivatives and assuming that $f(x, y, z)$ possesses first partial derivatives with respect to $x$, $y$, and $z$, we may write

$$\nabla f = \frac{\partial f}{\partial x}\mathbf{i} + \frac{\partial f}{\partial y}\mathbf{j} + \frac{\partial f}{\partial z}\mathbf{k}.$$

It is the custom among physicists and engineers to rewrite the preceding equation in the form

$$\nabla f = \left(\mathbf{i}\frac{\partial}{\partial x} + \mathbf{j}\frac{\partial}{\partial y} + \mathbf{k}\frac{\partial}{\partial z}\right)f$$

and to regard the set of symbols inside the parentheses as an entity by itself, a "vector-differential operator" called the **del operator**. Thus we have

**Definition 21.9a.** 
$$\nabla .=. \mathbf{i}\frac{\partial}{\partial x} + \mathbf{j}\frac{\partial}{\partial y} + \mathbf{k}\frac{\partial}{\partial z}.$$

We see that this operator, acting on a scalar function $f$, produces the gradient of the function, that is, $\nabla f$. Notice that $\nabla$ does not commute with a scalar function. This means that

$$\nabla f \neq f\nabla,$$

since

$$\nabla f = \mathbf{i}f_x + \mathbf{j}f_y + \mathbf{k}f_z,$$

and

$$f\nabla = \mathbf{i}f\frac{\partial}{\partial x} + \mathbf{j}f\frac{\partial}{\partial y} + \mathbf{k}f\frac{\partial}{\partial z},$$

which is itself still an operator.

There is, however, an important advantage in considering the del operator as a vector operator, since it is possible to define operations other than that of producing the gradient of a scalar function. Two additional operations are usually defined for the del operator that make it possible to operate on vector functions.

Let **F** be a differentiable vector function defined by

$$\mathbf{F}(x, y, z) = u(x, y, z)\mathbf{i} + v(x, y, z)\mathbf{j} + w(x, y, z)\mathbf{k}.$$

**Definition 21.9b.** 
$$\nabla \cdot \mathbf{F} .=. \mathbf{i} \cdot \frac{\partial \mathbf{F}}{\partial x} + \mathbf{j} \cdot \frac{\partial \mathbf{F}}{\partial y} + \mathbf{k} \cdot \frac{\partial \mathbf{F}}{\partial z}.$$

For reasons that will appear shortly, $\nabla \cdot \mathbf{F}$ is called the **divergence** of $\mathbf{F}$; it is clearly a scalar function.

**Definition 21.9c.** $\quad \nabla \times \mathbf{F} .=. \mathbf{i} \times \dfrac{\partial \mathbf{F}}{\partial x} + \mathbf{j} \times \dfrac{\partial \mathbf{F}}{\partial y} + \mathbf{k} \times \dfrac{\partial \mathbf{F}}{\partial z}.$

This vector, which we only mention, is called the **curl** of $\mathbf{F}$, or the **rotation** of $\mathbf{F}$. It is useful in physical problems involving the analysis of general fluid flow.

The last two definitions give some indication of the two-sided character of the operator $\nabla$, as a vector operator capable of being employed in dot multiplication and cross multiplication, and as a differential operator producing the various derivatives in these definitions. In the following discussion we shall be concerned only with the **divergence operator** $\nabla \cdot$.

If we write out the vector $\mathbf{F}$ in terms of its components, it is easy to verify

**Theorem 21.9a.** $F(x, y, z) = u(x, y, z)\mathbf{i} + v(x, y, z)\mathbf{j} + w(x, y, z)\mathbf{k}$

$$\Rightarrow \nabla \cdot \mathbf{F} = \frac{\partial u}{\partial x} + \frac{\partial v}{\partial y} + \frac{\partial w}{\partial z}.$$

PROOF: The suggested details preceding the statement of the theorem should enable the reader to construct the proof.

---

*Example 21.9a.* Find $\nabla \cdot \mathbf{r}$ if $\mathbf{r}$ is the radial vector defined by

$$\mathbf{r} = x\mathbf{i} + y\mathbf{j} + z\mathbf{k}.$$

We have, by Theorem 21.9a,

$$\nabla \cdot \mathbf{r} = \frac{\partial x}{\partial x} + \frac{\partial y}{\partial y} + \frac{\partial z}{\partial z} = 3.$$

---

We learned in Section 21.6 that if the vector $\mathbf{U}$ is interpreted as the velocity of a fluid flowing in some region of space containing a surface $\mathbb{S}$, then the volume $Q$ of fluid flowing through the surface $\mathbb{S}$ per unit of time is given by

$$Q = \int_{\mathbb{S}} \mathbf{N} \cdot \mathbf{U} \, dS,$$

where $\mathbf{N}$ is the unit normal to $\mathbb{S}$. If the surface is closed, the integral is frequently written in the form

$$\oint_{\mathbb{S}} \mathbf{N} \cdot \mathbf{U} \, dS,$$

where $\oint$ denotes that $\mathbb{S}$ is a closed surface. The reader should recall that $\mathbf{N}$ is customarily the outward-drawn unit normal. We shall now obtain an important relation between the preceding integral and the integral of $\nabla \cdot \mathbf{U}$ taken over the enclosed volume.

**Theorem 21.9b.** The Divergence Theorem. Let

$$\mathbf{U} .=. u(x, y, z)\mathbf{i} + v(x, y, z)\mathbf{j} + w(x, y, z)\mathbf{k}$$

be continuously differentiable in some region $\mathcal{V}$ and on its boundary $\mathbb{S}$, where

S is a closed surface consisting of a finite number of smooth pieces. Then,

$$\oint_S \mathbf{N} \cdot \mathbf{U}\, dS = \int_v \mathbf{\nabla} \cdot \mathbf{U}\, d\tau.$$

PROOF: We shall prove this theorem for only one special case. We assume that the surface S is intersected at not more than two points by any line parallel to one of the coordinate axes. In this case, S may be pictured as in Figure 21.9a.

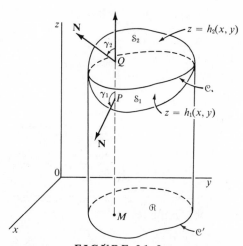

FIGURE 21.9a

On the surface, there is a curve $e$ that cuts the surface into two pieces, one piece entirely below $e$, denoted by $S_1$, and the second piece entirely above $e$, denoted by $S_2$. Both pieces project into the region $\mathcal{R}$ in the $xy$-plane, bounded by the curve $e'$, which is the projection of $e$ on this plane. A line drawn perpendicular to the $xy$-plane at a point $M \in \mathcal{R}$ pierces $S_1$ at a point, $P$, and $S_2$ at a point, $Q$. At $P$, the outward-drawn normal points in a downward direction, making an angle $\gamma_1 > 90°$ with the positive $z$-direction. At $Q$ the outward-drawn normal points in the upward direction, making an angle $\gamma_2 < 90°$ with the positive $z$-direction. Thus, $\cos \gamma_1 < 0$ and $\cos \gamma_2 > 0$. These facts will be of immediate importance to us.

In general, $\mathbf{N} = \mathbf{i} \cos \alpha + \mathbf{j} \cos \beta + \mathbf{k} \cos \gamma$, so that

$$\mathbf{N} \cdot \mathbf{U} = u \cos \alpha + v \cos \beta + w \cos \gamma.$$

Thus,

$$\oint_S \mathbf{N} \cdot \mathbf{U}\, ds = \oint_S u \cos \alpha\, dS + \oint_S v \cos \beta\, dS + \oint_S w \cos \gamma\, dS.$$

Let us next consider the last of the three integrals on the right. We have

$$\oint_S w \cos \gamma\, dS = \int_{S_1} w \cos \gamma_1\, dS + \int_{S_2} w \cos \gamma_2\, dS.$$

If the equation of $S_1$ is in the form $z = h_1(x, y)$ and that of $S_2$ is in the form

$z = h_2(x, y)$, then on $S_1$ the values of $w$ are given by $w[x, y, h_1(x, y)]$, and on $S_2$ by $w[x, y, h_2(x, y)]$. Furthermore, if $dA$ is the element of area for the double integral in the $xy$-plane, then for $S_1$ we have $\cos \gamma_1\, dS = -dA$, since $\cos \gamma$ is negative, and on $S_2$ we have $\cos \gamma_2\, dS = dA$, since $\cos \gamma_2$ is positive. Accordingly,

$$\oint_S w \cos \gamma\, dS = -\int_{\mathcal{R}} w[x, y, h_1(x, y)]\, dA + \int_{\mathcal{R}} w[x, y, h_2(x, y)]\, dA$$

$$= \int_{\mathcal{R}} [w(x, y, z)]_{z=h_1(x, y)}^{z=h_2(x, y)}\, dA.$$

Now, observe that

$$[w(x, y, z)]_{z=h_1(x, y)}^{z=h_2(x, y)} = \int_{h_1(x, y)}^{h_2(x, y)} \frac{\partial w(x, y, z)}{\partial z}\, dz.$$

Therefore,

$$\oint_S w \cos \gamma\, dS = \int_{\mathcal{R}} \int_{h_1(x, y)}^{h_2(x, y)} \frac{\partial w}{\partial z}\, dz\, dA$$

$$= \int_{\mathcal{V}} \frac{\partial w}{\partial z}\, d\tau.$$

By projection onto the $yz$- and $xz$-planes, respectively, and by the same type of argument, we obtain the results

$$\oint_S u \cos \alpha\, dS = \int_{\mathcal{V}} \frac{\partial u}{\partial x}\, d\tau \quad \text{and} \quad \oint_S u \cos \beta\, dS = \int_{\mathcal{V}} \frac{\partial v}{\partial y}\, d\tau.$$

Thus, by adding the three integrals, we have proved the required result:

$$\oint_S (u \cos \alpha + v \cos \beta + w \cos \gamma)\, dS = \int_{\mathcal{V}} \left( \frac{\partial u}{\partial x} + \frac{\partial v}{\partial y} + \frac{\partial w}{\partial z} \right) d\tau,$$

or, in the more handsome vector form,

$$\oint_S \mathbf{N} \cdot \mathbf{U}\, dS = \int_{\mathcal{V}} \nabla \cdot \mathbf{U}\, d\tau.$$

More complicated regions can frequently be handled by using smooth surfaces to partition them into pieces of the type considered in the foregoing proof. We shall not go into further detail but shall accept the theorem in the generality with which it is stated.

Note that if $\mathbf{U}$ is the velocity of a fluid, then the divergence theorem asserts that $Q$, the total volume of fluid issuing from the surface $S$ per unit of time, is equal to the integral of the divergence $\nabla \cdot \mathbf{U}$ over the total region $\mathcal{V}$ enclosed by $S$. This is an indication that the values of $\nabla \cdot \mathbf{U}$ on $\mathcal{V}$ constitute an important characteristic of the velocity, which we now investigate more closely.

Let $\mathbf{U}$ be the vector velocity of a fluid throughout some space region $\mathcal{W}$. Then, for *any* closed surface $S$ lying entirely within $\mathcal{W}$,

$$Q = \oint_S \mathbf{N} \cdot \mathbf{U}\, dS.$$

To normalize this quantity with respect to the volume $V$ enclosed by $S$, we may divide $Q$ by $V$ to get

$$\frac{1}{V} \oint_S \mathbf{N} \cdot \mathbf{U} \, dS.$$

This is then a formula for the quantity of fluid per unit time *per unit volume* flowing out of the region $\mathcal{V}$ enclosed by $S$. It is interesting to examine the limit of this ratio as the region $\mathcal{V}$ shrinks to a point. If we let $\delta$ be the maximum diameter of $\mathcal{V}$ and let $\mathcal{V}$ always enclose a fixed point $P$ as $\delta \to 0$, then the limit is denoted by

$$\lim_{\delta \to 0} \left[ \frac{1}{V} \oint_S \mathbf{N} \cdot \mathbf{U} \, dS \right].$$

By the divergence theorem, we may substitute for the preceding surface integral the triple integral of $\nabla \cdot \mathbf{U}$ taken over $\mathcal{V}$. Thus,

(1) $$\lim_{\delta \to 0} \left[ \frac{1}{V} \oint_S \mathbf{N} \cdot \mathbf{U} \, dS \right] = \lim_{\delta \to 0} \left[ \frac{1}{V} \int_{\mathcal{V}} \nabla \cdot \mathbf{U} \, d\tau \right].$$

Since we have assumed that $\mathbf{U}$ is continuously differentiable, $\nabla \cdot \mathbf{U}$ is a continuous scalar function on $\mathcal{V}$ and its boundary $S$.

We need next to use the Mean Value Theorem for a triple integral, which can be proved by a generalization of the ideas we used in proving this theorem for the simple integral. (See A. E. Taylor, *Advanced Calculus*, pp. 321–322.) This theorem states that, for a simple region of the type we have considered, if $f(x, y, z)$ is continuous on $\mathcal{V}$ and its boundary, then there is a point $(x_1, y_1, z_1) \in \mathcal{V}$ such that

$$\int_{\mathcal{V}} f(x, y, z) \, d\tau = f(x_1, y_1, z_1) \int_{\mathcal{V}} d\tau = f(x_1, y_1, z_1) V.$$

Applying this theorem to the left side of Equation (1), and denoting the value of $\nabla \cdot \mathbf{U}$ at $(x_1, y_1, z_1)$ by $(\nabla \cdot \mathbf{U})_1$, we get

$$\lim_{\delta \to 0} \frac{1}{V} \oint_S \mathbf{N} \cdot \mathbf{U} \, dS = \lim_{\delta \to 0} \frac{V(\nabla \cdot \mathbf{U})_1}{V} = \lim_{\delta \to 0} (\nabla \cdot \mathbf{U})_1.$$

Since the point $(x_1, y_1, z_1)$ is always inside $\mathcal{V}$, it follows that as $\delta \to 0$ this point must approach the point $P$ toward which the region $\mathcal{V}$ shrinks. Hence,

$$\lim_{\delta \to 0} \frac{1}{V} \int_S \mathbf{N} \cdot \mathbf{U} \, dS = (\nabla \cdot \mathbf{U})_P.$$

This result shows two things: (1) $\nabla \cdot \mathbf{U}$ is a function that does not depend on the coordinate system, since the limit on the left clearly is independent of any coordinate system; (2) $\nabla \cdot \mathbf{U}$ at a point is the limit of the quantity of fluid per unit time per unit volume flowing out of a region that always includes the point in its interior as the region shrinks into the point. (This last fact is the reason for the name "divergence.") If the fluid is incompressible and $\nabla \cdot \mathbf{U}$ is not zero at a point, then fluid is being created or destroyed there; that is, there is a "source" or a "sink" at the point, according as $\nabla \cdot \mathbf{U}$ is positive or negative. In a very rough manner of speaking, we may say that the integral of $\nabla \cdot \mathbf{U}$ over a region $\mathcal{V}$ sums all the "outputs" at the points of $\mathcal{V}$. If there are no sources or sinks, then $\nabla \cdot \mathbf{U} = 0$ everywhere in $\mathcal{V}$, and hence

$$[P \in \mathcal{V} \Rightarrow (\nabla \cdot \mathbf{U})_P = 0] \Rightarrow \oint_S \mathbf{N} \cdot \mathbf{U} \, dS = 0.$$

---

*Example 21.9b.* If the velocity $\mathbf{U}$ is $\mathbf{r}/r^3$, where $\mathbf{r} = \mathbf{i}x + \mathbf{j}y + \mathbf{k}z$ and

$$r = (x^2 + y^2 + z^2)^{1/2},$$

show that the flow through any simple closed surface that does not enclose the origin is zero.

In view of the preceding discussion, let us examine $\nabla \cdot \mathbf{U}$. We have, for $r \neq 0$,

$$\nabla \cdot (\mathbf{r}/r^3) = \frac{\partial(x/r^3)}{\partial x} + \frac{\partial(y/r^3)}{\partial y} + \frac{\partial(z/r^3)}{\partial z}$$

$$= \frac{1}{r^3} - \frac{3x^2}{r^5} + \frac{1}{r^3} - \frac{3y^2}{r^5} + \frac{1}{r^3} - \frac{3z^2}{r^5}$$

$$= \frac{3}{r^3} - \frac{3(x^2 + y^2 + z^2)}{r^5} = \frac{3}{r^3} - \frac{3}{r^3} = 0.$$

Therefore, if the origin is not included in $\mathcal{V}$,

$$\int_{\mathcal{V}} \nabla \cdot \mathbf{U} \, d\tau = 0,$$

and the required result follows from the divergence theorem.

## Exercises 21.9

1. If $\mathbf{U} = x\mathbf{i} + y\mathbf{j} + z\mathbf{k}$, show that $\oint_S \mathbf{N} \cdot \mathbf{U} \, dS = 3V$, where $V$ is the volume of the region enclosed by $S$.

2. If $\mathbf{U} = yz\mathbf{i} + zx\mathbf{j} + xy\mathbf{k}$, show that $\oint_S \mathbf{N} \cdot \mathbf{U} \, dS = 0$.

3. If $\mathbf{U} = u(y, z)\mathbf{i} + v(x, z)\mathbf{j} + w(x, y)\mathbf{k}$, show that $\oint_S \mathbf{N} \cdot \mathbf{U} \, dS = 0$.

4. Use the divergence theorem to evaluate $\oint_S \mathbf{N} \cdot \mathbf{U} \, dS$, where $S$ is the surface $x^2 + y^2 + z^2 = a^2$ and
   (a) $\mathbf{U} .=. \mathbf{i}x + \mathbf{j}y + \mathbf{k}z$;
   (b) $\mathbf{U} .=. \mathbf{i}xy + \mathbf{j}yz + \mathbf{k}zx$;
   (c) $\mathbf{U} .=. \mathbf{i}xy^2 + \mathbf{j}yz^2 + \mathbf{k}zx^2$.

5. Show that if $\mathbf{N}$ is the unit normal to a surface $S$ at a point $P$, then $\mathbf{N} \cdot \nabla g$ is the directional derivative of the function $g$ in the direction of the normal at $P$. This derivative is called the **normal derivative** of $g$ on the surface $S$, and is denoted by the symbol $\partial g / \partial n$.

6. Show that

$$\nabla^2 g .=. \nabla \cdot (\nabla g) = \frac{\partial^2 g}{\partial x^2} + \frac{\partial^2 g}{\partial y^2} + \frac{\partial^2 g}{\partial z^2}.$$

This expression is called the **Laplacian** of $g$.

7. Refer to Numbers 5 and 6 and show that the integral of the Laplacian of $g$ taken over a region $\mathcal{V}$ is equal to the integral of the normal derivative of $g$ taken over the surface $\mathcal{S}$ bounding $\mathcal{V}$.

8. Suppose that $g$ satisfies the equation $\nabla^2 g = 0$ everywhere on $\mathcal{V}$ and its boundary $\mathcal{S}$. Show that

$$\oint_\mathcal{S} g \frac{\partial g}{\partial n}\, dS = \int_\mathcal{V} (\nabla g)^2\, d\tau,$$

where $(\nabla g)^2 = (\nabla g) \cdot (\nabla g)$. (See Numbers 5 and 6.)

---

# Summary of Chapter 21

---

The student should be certain that he understands the following ideas:

  (1) partial integration (Section 21.1);
  (2) iterated integrals (Section 21.1);
  (3) a simple curve (Section 21.2);
  (4) the definition of the double integral (Section 21.2);
  (5) the definition of area, first and second moments of area, mass, and volume, by means of the double integral (Section 21.2);
  (6) the evaluation of the double integral by means of iterated integrals in rectangular coordinates (Section 21.3);
  (7) applications of the double integral (Section 21.3);
  (8) the transformation of a double integral from rectangular coordinates to a new set of coordinates, and the role of the Jacobian in such a transformation (Section 21.4);
  (9) the evaluation of the double integral using polar coordinates (Section 21.4);
(10) the area of a curved surface (Section 21.5);
(11) the area of a surface of revolution (Section 21.5);
(12) the definition of a surface integral (Section 21.6);
(13) the application of the surface integral in fluid flow (Section 21.6);
(14) the definition of a smooth surface (Section 21.7);
(15) the definition of the triple integral (Section 21.7);
(16) applications of the triple integral (Section 21.7);
(17) the triple integral in curvilinear coordinates, and the role of the Jacobian (Section 21.8);
(18) cylindrical coordinates and applications (Section 21.8);
(19) spherical coordinates and applications (Section 21.8);
★(20) the divergence of a vector function (Section 21.9);
★(21) the divergence theorem (Section 21.9).

# Chapter 22    Infinite Series

## 22.1 SEQUENCES REVISITED

In Section 9.2 it was stated that the number $e$ is given approximately by the expression

$$1 + \frac{1}{1!} + \frac{1}{2!} + \frac{1}{3!} + \cdots + \frac{1}{n!}$$

and that the larger the value of $n$, the more accurate this approximation for $e$. This suggests that

$$e = \lim_{n \to \infty} \left( 1 + \frac{1}{1!} + \frac{1}{2!} + \frac{1}{3!} + \cdots + \frac{1}{n!} \right)$$

and that we may write

$$e = 1 + \frac{1}{1!} + \frac{1}{2!} + \frac{1}{3!} + \cdots + \frac{1}{n!} + \cdots.$$

The set of symbols on the right of the last statement is an example of an infinite series. The final three dots indicate that more and more terms are to be appended without end, the $(n + 1)$th term being given by the formula $1/n!$. The equals sign in this equation is to be interpreted in terms of the preceding equation; that is, $e$ equals the infinite series in the sense that the sequence

$$1, 1 + \frac{1}{1!}, 1 + \frac{1}{1!} + \frac{1}{2!}, 1 + \frac{1}{1!} + \frac{1}{2!} + \frac{1}{3!}, \cdots,$$

$$1 + \frac{1}{1!} + \frac{1}{2!} + \frac{1}{3!} + \cdots + \frac{1}{n!}, \cdots$$

has a limit which is the number $e$. That the sequence has a limit will be proved in the following pages.

Infinite series, as we shall soon see, are essential in the calculation of values for many functions, and can frequently be used for the evaluation of definite integrals. They can also serve to define new and useful functions that are fundamental in many investigations in advanced mathematics and its applications. An understanding of infinite series is the key to many doors in scientific research.

As is indicated by our statements concerning the number $e$, the study of infinite series is based on the theory of sequences. Although the introduction to sequences set forth in Section 8.2 was adequate for the purpose of discussing the concept of the definite integral, it does not suffice as a basis for the discussion in the present chapter. Before proceeding to a more thorough investigation of sequences, we shall find it convenient to review the fundamental ideas introduced earlier.

Since a sequence is essentially a function whose domain is the set $\mathfrak{N}$ of positive integers, we may use, for the purpose of describing a sequence, almost any formula scheme that assigns a number to each value of $n \in \mathfrak{N}$. For example, if $a_n = n/(n + 3)$, for the sequence $\{a_n\}$, then the first four terms are $\frac{1}{4}, \frac{2}{5}, \frac{3}{6}, \frac{4}{7}$.

Another common method of specifying a sequence is by means of a **recursion formula,** in which the $(n + 1)$th term of the sequence is given in terms of the preceding term or terms of the sequence. For instance, if

$$a_1 .=. \frac{1}{2}, \quad a_{n+1} .=. \frac{1}{2a_n}, \quad n = 1, 2, 3, \ldots,$$

then a sequence is determined for which

$$a_1 = \frac{1}{2}, \quad a_2 = 1, \quad a_3 = \frac{1}{2}, \quad a_4 = 1,$$

or, in general,

$$a_{2k} = 1, \quad a_{2k+1} = \frac{1}{2},$$

as may be shown by mathematical induction. The formula

$$a_{n+1} .=. \frac{1}{2a_n}$$

is an example of a recursion formula.

Any function of a variable $x$ that is defined for all positive integral values of $x$ can be used to define a sequence. If $y = f(x)$ represents such a function, then we may let

$$a_n .=. f(n), \quad n \in \mathfrak{N}.$$

For example, if $f(x) = \sin(\pi x)/3$, then a sequence is defined by the expression

$$f(n) = \sin \frac{\pi n}{3}, \quad n \in \mathfrak{N}.$$

There are two problems of primary importance associated with sequences. The first is to determine if a limit for a given sequence exists. The second is to find the value of the limit of a sequence once it is known to exist. Before looking into these matters, however, it is necessary that we recall some of the terminology associated with sequences, and introduce some additional ideas.

The following definition is equivalent to Definition 8.2c.

**Definition 22.1a.** A sequence $\{a_n\}$ is said to **converge** to the value $A$ if for each given $\epsilon > 0$, there is an $N$ such that $a_n \in \mathfrak{N}(A, \epsilon)$ for every $n > N$, and we write

$$\lim_{n \to \infty} a_n = A.$$

The next definition extends the concept of the limit of a sequence.

**Definition 22.1b.** If $M$ is an arbitrarily chosen number, no matter how large, and if there is an $N$ such that $a_n > M$ for all $n > N$, then the limit of $\{a_n\}$ is said to be infinite, and we write

$$\lim_{n \to \infty} a_n = \infty.$$

The reader may provide a similar definition for $\lim_{n \to \infty} a_n = -\infty$.

**Definition 22.1c.** A number $A$ is said to be a **cluster point** of a sequence $\{a_n\}$ if every neighborhood of $A$, $\mathfrak{N}(A, \epsilon)$, contains infinitely many terms of the sequence.

For example, the sequence $\{0, \frac{1}{2}, \frac{2}{3}, \frac{1}{4}, \frac{4}{5}, \frac{1}{6}, \frac{6}{7}, \ldots\}$, where $a_{2n-1} = 1 - 1/(2n-1)$ and $a_{2n} = 1/(2n)$ has two cluster points, 0 and 1.

It follows immediately from Definition 22.1a that a sequence with more than one cluster point cannot converge.

**Definition 22.1d.** A sequence that does not converge is said to **diverge.**

Thus, a sequence is divergent if it has an infinite limit, if it has more than one cluster point, or if it has no cluster points. The following are illustrations of these cases.

(a) The sequence $\{a_n : a_n = 2n\}$ increases without bound as $n$ increases, and therefore is divergent.

(b) The sequence $\{a_n : a_n = (-1)^n[1 + (1/n)]\}$ has two cluster points, $+1$ and $-1$, and therefore diverges.

(c) The sequence $\{a_n : a_n = (-1)^n 2n\}$ has no cluster points, and therefore diverges.

In addition, a sequence may diverge because of a combination of the preceding cases. For example, if

$$a_n = \frac{1 - (-1)^n}{2} 3n + \frac{1}{n},$$

then the sequence $\{a_n\}$ has zero as a cluster point, and also has terms forming a sequence that increases without bound.

We may now turn to the important problem of discussing the limit of a sequence. One of the simplest theorems in this respect is

**Theorem 22.1a.** If $\{a_n\}$ is a sequence and if $f . = . \{(x, y): y = f(x)\}$ is a function for which $f(n) = a_n$, $n \in \mathfrak{N}$, for all $n$ greater than some positive integer $p$, then

$$\lim_{x \to \infty} f(x) = A \Rightarrow \lim_{n \to \infty} a_n = A.$$

PROOF: Left for the reader. *Hint:* Consider $\mathfrak{N}(A, \epsilon)$ and the definition of $\lim_{x \to \infty} f(x) = A$.

This theorem sometimes makes possible the use of L'Hôpital's Rule for the evaluation of the limit of a sequence, as in the next example.

*Example 22.1a.* Find $\lim_{n\to\infty} n(1 - a^{1/n})$.

Let $f(x) = x(1 - a^{1/x})$. Then $f(n) = n(1 - a^{1/n})$, and we need only to evaluate

$$\lim_{x\to\infty} x(1 - a^{1/x}).$$

By L'Hôpital's Rule, we have

$$\lim_{x\to\infty} x(1 - a^{1/x}) = \lim_{x\to\infty} \frac{D_x(1 - a^{1/x})}{D_x(1/x)}$$

$$= \lim_{x\to\infty} \frac{-a^{1/x}(\ln a)(-1/x^2)}{-1/x^2} = -\ln a.$$

Therefore, by Theorem 22.1a,

$$\lim_{n\to\infty} n(1 - a^{1/n}) = \ln \frac{1}{a}.$$

---

Certain types of sequences appear so frequently that they are given special names.

**Definition 22.1e.** A sequence $\{a_n\}$ for which $a_n \leq a_{n+1}$ (or $a_n \geq a_{n+1}$) for all $n \in \mathfrak{N}$, is called a **monotonic** sequence. If $a_n < a_{n+1}$, the sequence is said to be **monotonic increasing**, and if $a_n > a_{n+1}$, the sequence is said to be **monotonic decreasing**.

For example, if $a_n = 2n/(3n + 1)$, then $a_n < a_{n+1}$ and the sequence is monotonic increasing. If $a_n = e^{-n}$, the sequence $\{a_n\}$ is monotonic decreasing. This terminology is also used in a modified way when the sequence $\{a_n\}$ has the required property for all $n \geq p$, where $p$ is some positive integer. That is, the monotonic property may not appear until after the $p$th term. In that case we say that the sequence is **eventually monotonic**. For example, the sequence $\{a_n: a_n = \cos (8\pi)/n\}$ is eventually monotonic.

Monotonic sequences are frequently easy to deal with because of

**Theorem 22.1b.** A bounded monotonic sequence, $\{a_n\}$, converges.

PROOF: This is essentially a restatement of the content of Theorems 8.2b and 8.2c. The reader may refer to those theorems for the proof.

Theorem 22.1b is an existence theorem, since it states a condition under which the limit of a sequence exists without indicating how to find the limit.

---

*Example 22.1b.* Does the sequence $\{a_n\}$, where

$$a_n = 1 + \frac{1}{1!} + \frac{1}{2!} + \frac{1}{3!} + \cdots + \frac{1}{n!},$$

converge or diverge?

The reader is cautioned that the $n$th term of the sequence is given as the *sum* of $n + 1$ numbers and that $1/n!$ is *not* the $n$th term of the sequence. Let us attempt to apply Theorem 22.1b, by considering

$$a_{n+1} - a_n = \frac{1}{(n + 1)!}.$$

This expression is positive, so that $a_{n+1} > a_n$ and the sequence is monotonic increasing. Now we must attempt to show that the sequence is bounded. Since $n! \geq 2^{n-1}$,

$$\frac{1}{n!} \leq \frac{1}{2^{n-1}}.$$

Hence,

$$a_n - 1 \leq 1 + \frac{1}{2} + \frac{1}{2^2} + \cdots + \frac{1}{2^{n-1}},$$

or

$$a_n - 1 \leq \frac{\left(1 + \frac{1}{2} + \frac{1}{2^2} + \cdots + \frac{1}{2^{n-1}}\right)\left(1 - \frac{1}{2}\right)}{(1 - 1/2)},$$

or

$$a_n - 1 \leq \frac{1 - \frac{1}{2^n}}{1/2} < 2.$$

Thus, $a_n < 3$ for each value of $n$, which means that the sequence is bounded. Hence, the sequence converges, and we have established the existence of the limit that was given for the number $e$ at the beginning of this section.

---

Another useful result concerning infinite sequences is contained in

**Theorem 22.1c.** A bounded infinite sequence has at least one cluster point.

PROOF: Let all terms of the sequence satisfy the condition $a \leq a_n \leq b$. We may take $a \leq x \leq b$ as defining the segment of the $x$-axis from $x = a$ to $x = b$. Bisect this segment. Since the sequence is infinite, at least one of the two resulting segments contains infinitely many terms of the sequence. Bisect this segment (or one of the two if both contain infinitely many terms of the sequence). The same argument applies again and the bisection procedure may be continued indefinitely. This procedure defines a set of "nested" subintervals, each subinterval being contained within all the preceding ones and each containing infinitely many terms of the sequence. Since the length of the $n$th subinterval is $(b - a)/2^n$, this length approaches zero as $n \rightarrow \infty$. Consequently, there is a point $c$ contained in every subinterval such that every neighborhood of $c$ contains infinitely many points of the sequence. Hence, $c$ is a cluster point, and the theorem is proved.

The preceding theorem is vital to the proof of a well-known result that guarantees the existence of the limit of a sequence and that is due to the French mathematician A. Cauchy (pronounced kōshē).

**Theorem 22.1d. The Cauchy Criterion.** A sequence $\{a_n\}$ converges $\Leftrightarrow$ for any given $\epsilon$, there exists an integer $N$ such that $|a_n - a_m| < \epsilon$ for all $n, m > N$.

PROOF: Suppose $\{a_n\}$ converges to $A$. Then

$$|a_n - a_m| = |a_n - A + A - a_m|$$
$$\leq |a_n - A| + |A - a_m|.$$

According to the definition of convergence, an integer $N$ exists such that

$|a_k - A| < \epsilon/2$ for all $k > N$. Consequently, for $m, n > N$, it is true that $|a_n - A| < \epsilon/2$ and $|a_m - A| < \epsilon/2$, so that $|a_n - a_m| < \epsilon$. This shows that $\{a_n\}$ converges $\Rightarrow$ there is an integer $N$ such that $|a_n - a_m| < \epsilon$ for $m, n > N$.

For the second part of the theorem, suppose there is an integer $N$ such that $|a_n - a_m| < \epsilon$ for all $n, m > N$. In particular, if $\epsilon = 1$, there is a number $N$ such that

$$|a_n - a_m| < 1$$

for all $n, m > N$, and for $m = N + 1$, $|a_n - a_{N+1}| < 1$ for all $n > N$. Hence

$$-1 + a_{N+1} < a_n < 1 + a_{N+1} \qquad \text{for all } n > N.$$

This means that the terms of $\{a_n\}$ from $a_{N+1}$ on all lie in the interval from $-1 + a_{N+1}$ to $1 + a_{N+1}$. Since there are infinitely many terms in $\{a_n\}$, this sequence has, by Theorem 22.1c, at least one cluster point, say $A$. But there can be only one cluster point, since the condition $|a_n - a_m| < \epsilon$ for all $m, n > N$, requires that all $a_n \in \mathfrak{N}(A, \epsilon)$ for $n$ large enough, which means that $\lim_{n \to \infty} a_n = A$.

As in Theorem 22.1b, the Cauchy Criterion does not require any prior knowledge of the limit itself. The use of this criterion is illustrated in

---

*Example 22.1c.* Show that the sequence $\{x_n\}$, where

$$x_n = 1 - \frac{1}{2} + \frac{1}{3} - \frac{1}{4} + \cdots + \frac{(-1)^{n+1}}{n},$$

is convergent.

Consider the difference $|x_{n+p} - x_n|$, where $n + p$ replaces $m$ in Theorem 22.1d. Then

$$|x_{n+p} - x_n| = \left| \frac{(-1)^{n+2}}{n+1} + \frac{(-1)^{n+3}}{n+2} + \frac{(-1)^{n+4}}{n+3} + \cdots + \frac{(-1)^{n+p}}{n+p-1} + \frac{(-1)^{n+p+1}}{n+p} \right|$$

$$= |(-1)^{n+2}| \left| \frac{1}{n+1} - \frac{1}{n+2} + \frac{1}{n+3} - \cdots + \frac{(-1)^{p-2}}{n+p-1} + \frac{(-1)^{p-1}}{n+p} \right|.$$

Now the factor $|(-1)^{n+2}| = 1$, and the factor between the remaining absolute value bars is easily seen to be positive, since it can be grouped as

$$\left( \frac{1}{n+1} - \frac{1}{n+2} \right) + \left( \frac{1}{n+3} - \frac{1}{n+4} \right) + \cdots + P,$$

where

$$P = \begin{cases} \dfrac{1}{n+p-1} - \dfrac{1}{n+p} & \text{if } p \text{ is even,} \\[2ex] \dfrac{1}{n+p} & \text{if } p \text{ is odd.} \end{cases}$$

Furthermore, we may group the terms in another way:

$$\frac{1}{n+1} - \left( \frac{1}{n+2} - \frac{1}{n+3} \right) - \cdots - Q,$$

where

$$
Q = \begin{cases} \dfrac{1}{n+p-1} - \dfrac{1}{n+p} & \text{if } p \text{ is odd,} \\[2ex] \dfrac{1}{n+p} & \text{if } p \text{ is even.} \end{cases}
$$

In either case, this shows that

$$
|x_{n+p} - x_n| < \frac{1}{n+1}.
$$

Thus, if $1/(n+1) < \epsilon$, or $n > (1/\epsilon) - 1$, the Cauchy Criterion is satisfied and thus the sequence converges.

## Exercises 22.1

1. Use the definition of convergence to prove that $\left\{ \dfrac{2^n + 1}{2^{n+1}} \right\}$ converges to $\frac{1}{2}$.

In Numbers 2 to 11 determine whether the sequence $\{a_n\}$, with the indicated formula for $a_n$, converges.

2. $a_n = n^{(-1)^n}$.

3. $a_n = \dfrac{n}{n+1} - \dfrac{n+1}{n}$.

4. $a_n = \sqrt{n+1} - \sqrt{n}$.

5. $a_n = \dfrac{(-1)^n}{n} + \dfrac{1 + (-1)^n}{2}$.

6. $a_n = \dfrac{2^n + (-1)^n}{2^{n+1} + (-1)^{n+1}}$.

7. $a_n = \dfrac{\log_a n}{n}$.

8. $a_n = 1 + \dfrac{n}{n+1} \cos \dfrac{n\pi}{2}$.

9. $a_n = n(2/3)^n$.

10. $a_n = n^{1/n}$.

11. $a_n = \left(1 - \dfrac{1}{n}\right)^n$.

12. Prove that the sequence $\{a_n\}$, where

$$
a_1 .=. 1, \quad a_2 .=. \frac{1}{2}, \quad a_n .=. \frac{a_{n-1} + a_{n-2}}{2}, \quad n = 3, 4, \ldots,
$$

converges. *Hint:* Show that

$$
|a_{n-1} - a_{n-2}| = \frac{1}{2^{n-2}},
$$

and apply the Cauchy Criterion.

13. Let

$$
a_n = \frac{2 \cdot 4 \cdots 2n}{1 \cdot 3 \cdots (2n-1)} \cdot \frac{1}{n^2},
$$

and show that $a_n < 2/n$. What do you conclude about the sequence $\{a_n\}$ ?

14. Evaluate

$$
\lim_{n \to \infty} \left(\frac{1}{n^2} + \frac{2}{n^2} + \cdots \frac{n}{n^2}\right).
$$

15. We know that $\lim_{n \to \infty} (1 + 1/n)^n = e$. Use this fact to prove that

$$
\lim_{n \to \infty} (1 + a/n)^n = e^a.
$$

16. If $a_1 .=. \sqrt{2}$, $a_{n+1} .=. \sqrt{2a_n}$, $n = 1, 2, 3, \ldots$, find $\lim_{n\to\infty} a_n$.

17. If $x_n = \dfrac{1}{n} + \dfrac{1}{n+1} + \cdots + \dfrac{1}{2n}$, does $\{x_n\}$ converge or diverge?

★18. Use the Cauchy Criterion to show that the sequence $\{a_n\}$, where

$$a_n = 1 - \frac{1}{3} + \frac{1}{5} - \frac{1}{7} + \cdots + \frac{(-1)^{n-1}}{2n-1},$$

is convergent.

★19. If $\lim_{n\to\infty} a_n = 0$, and if $x_n .=. (1/n) \sum_{\alpha=1}^{n} a_\alpha$, show that $\lim_{n\to\infty} x_n = 0$.

## 22.2 INFINITE SERIES

When the concept of a sequence is associated with a physical event, some rather startling ideas result. For example, suppose a hiker travels from a point $A$ to a point $B$ two miles away by traveling in stages, where at each stage he travels one-half the remaining distance. Then, after the first stage, he has traveled one mile, after the second he has traveled $1 + \frac{1}{2} = \frac{3}{2}$ miles, and so on, so that after the $n$th stage he has traveled

$$1 + \frac{1}{2} + \frac{1}{2^2} + \cdots + \frac{1}{2^{n-1}}$$

miles. Does the hiker ever reach point $B$?

If we regard this process as continued indefinitely, then we may be tempted to write the expression

$$1 + \frac{1}{2} + \frac{1}{2^2} + \cdots + \frac{1}{2^{n-1}} + \cdots,$$

to indicate the total distance covered. Although such an expression may appear intuitively satisfying, there are serious questions about precisely what it means. In order to discuss these questions conveniently, we give such expressions a special name.

**Definition 22.2a.** An expression of the form

$$a_1 + a_2 + \cdots + a_n + \cdots = \sum_{n=1}^{\infty} a_n$$

is called an **infinite series.**

Although we now have given a name to such an endless summation, we still have not given it a meaning. To see how we might arrive at a reasonable meaning, let us consider another example, starting with the algebraic identity

(1) $$\frac{1}{1-x} = 1 + x + x^2 + x^3 + \cdots + \frac{x^n}{1-x},$$

which is obtained by the ordinary long division process. If we imagine the division process continued indefinitely, we obtain an infinite series

(2) $$\frac{1}{1-x} = 1 + x + x^2 + \cdots + x^n + \cdots = \sum_{n=0}^{\infty} x^n.$$

It is meaningful to replace $x$ in Equation (1) with a value of $x$ other than 1. For example, if $x = \frac{1}{2}$, then

$$\frac{1}{1-\frac{1}{2}} = 1 + \frac{1}{2} + \frac{1}{2^2} + \frac{1}{2^3} + \cdots + \frac{1}{2^{n-1}} + \frac{\frac{1}{2^n}}{1-\frac{1}{2}}$$

or

$$2 = 1 + \frac{1}{2} + \frac{1}{2^2} + \frac{1}{2^3} + \cdots + \frac{1}{2^{n-1}} + \frac{1}{2^{n-1}}.$$

Is it meaningful to replace $x$ by $\frac{1}{2}$ in Equation (2)? If so, we should have

(3)
$$2 = 1 + \frac{1}{2} + \frac{1}{2^2} + \frac{1}{2^3} + \cdots + \frac{1}{2^n} + \cdots,$$

which appears to be a reasonable statement.

Again, if $x = 2$ in Equation (1), then

$$-1 = 1 + 2 + 4 + 8 + \cdots + 2^{n-1} - 2^n,$$

which is a correct statement. But, if $x$ is replaced by 2 in Equation (2), then we have

$$-1 = 1 + 2 + 4 + 8 + 16 + \cdots + 2^n + \cdots,$$

which seems absurd.

As a result of these observations, it appears that a meaning can be given to an infinite series under certain conditions. For example, in the series

$$1 + \frac{1}{2} + \frac{1}{2^2} + \cdots + \frac{1}{2^n} + \cdots,$$

as a greater and greater number of terms are added together, the resulting sum gets closer and closer to the value 2. Thus, let us associate with the series a sequence $\{s_n\}$, where

$$s_1 = 1,$$

$$s_2 = 1 + \frac{1}{2},$$

$$s_3 = 1 + \frac{1}{2} + \frac{1}{2^2},$$

$$. \quad . \quad . \quad . \quad . \quad . \quad . \quad .$$

$$s_n = 1 + \frac{1}{2} + \frac{1}{2^2} + \cdots + \frac{1}{2^{n-1}}.$$

Then from Equation (1) it follows that

(4)
$$s_n = 2 - \frac{1}{2^{n-1}}.$$

Now, $\lim_{n \to \infty} s_n = 2$, which appears to be the sum of the series in Equation (3). This interesting result suggests

**Definition 22.2b.** For the series $\sum_{\alpha=1}^{\infty} a_\alpha$, let

$$s_n \,.=. \sum_{\alpha=1}^{n} a_\alpha.$$

If $\lim_{n \to \infty} s_n$ exists and is $S$, the series is said to **converge** to the value $S$, and we write

$$\sum_{\alpha=1}^{\infty} a_\alpha = S.$$

If $\lim_{n \to \infty} s_n$ does not exist, the series is said to **diverge**.

The terms of the sequence $\{s_n\}$ are called the **partial sums** for the series $\sum_{\alpha=1}^{\infty} a_\alpha$. Thus, to determine if a series $\sum_{\alpha=1}^{\infty} a_\alpha$ has a meaning, we must form the sequence of partial sums, and if this sequence has a limit $S$, then the series is meaningful within the scope of Definition 22.2b, and converges to the value $S$. Accordingly, by Equation (4), the series $\sum_{n=1}^{\infty} (1/2)^{n-1}$ converges to the value 2. This idea is illustrated further by means of series of the following type.

**Definition 22.2c.** A series of the form $\sum_{\alpha=0}^{\infty} ar^\alpha$ is called a **geometric series**.

The partial sums of a geometric series are called **geometric progressions**, and are of the form

$$s_n = a + ar + ar^2 + \cdots + ar^{n-1}.$$

Geometric series are easily handled because the partial sums can be greatly simplified. Thus, for $r \neq 1$,

$$s_n = \sum_{\alpha=0}^{n-1} ar^\alpha = \frac{\sum_{\alpha=0}^{n-1} ar^\alpha(1-r)}{(1-r)},$$

or

(5) $$s_n = \frac{a[(1-r) + (r-r^2) + \cdots + (r^{n-1} - r^n)]}{1-r} = \frac{a(1-r^n)}{1-r},$$

as the reader may easily verify. If

$$\lim_{n \to \infty} \frac{a(1-r^n)}{1-r}$$

exists, then the geometric series converges. Evidently the limit exists if $|r| < 1$, and we have

$$\lim_{n \to \infty} \frac{a(1-r^n)}{1-r} = \frac{a}{1-r}.$$

The limit does not exist if $|r| > 1$, and the series diverges in this case. Moreover, by direct substitution into $s_n$, it is seen that the series diverges for $r = \pm 1$. Thus, *the geometric series diverges if $|r| \geq 1$ and converges if $|r| < 1$.*

Unfortunately, other types of series cannot be handled so easily, because there is no general way of expressing the partial sums in a simplified form. Other techniques must be developed for handling such series. For example, consider the series $\sum_{\alpha=1}^{\infty} 1/\alpha^\alpha$. Does the series converge? The $n$th partial sum is of the form

$$s_n = 1 + \frac{1}{2^2} + \frac{1}{3^3} + \frac{1}{4^4} + \cdots + \frac{1}{n^n},$$

but there is no way of simplifying it. In this instance, however, we are able to obtain some results by means of the theorems on sequences. Since

$$s_{n+1} = s_n + \frac{1}{(n+1)^{n+1}},$$

it is clear that $s_{n+1} > s_n$. Furthermore, because

$$\frac{1}{\alpha^\alpha} < \frac{1}{2^\alpha} \qquad \text{for } \alpha > 2,$$

it is true that

$$s_n < 1 + \frac{1}{2^2} + \frac{1}{2^3} + \cdots + \frac{1}{2^n}, \qquad n > 2.$$

It follows, by Equation (5), that

$$s_n < 1 + \frac{1}{2^2}\left(1 + \frac{1}{2} + \cdots + \frac{1}{2^{n-2}}\right) = 1 + \frac{\frac{1}{2^2}\left(1 - \frac{1}{2^{n-1}}\right)}{1 - \frac{1}{2}},$$

or

$$s_n < 1 + \frac{1}{2} - \frac{1}{2^n} < \frac{3}{2}.$$

Hence, it has been shown that the sequence of partial sums is monotonic increasing and is bounded, so that it must have a limit. Therefore, the series $\sum_{\alpha=1}^{\infty} 1/\alpha^\alpha$ converges, although we do not know to what value.

By now it is becoming apparent that unless we develop more tools with which we can dissect series, we shall not learn much about them. Accordingly, let us examine some of the consequences of the definition of convergence. One of the simplest of these is contained in

**Theorem 22.2a.** $\qquad \displaystyle\sum_{n=1}^{\infty} a_n$ converges $\Rightarrow \displaystyle\lim_{n\to\infty} a_n = 0.$

PROOF: Since the series converges,

$$\lim_{n\to\infty} s_n = A,$$

where $s_n$ is the $n$th partial sum. Hence, by the Cauchy Criterion for sequences, we must have

$$|s_n - s_{n-1}| < \epsilon$$

for any given $\epsilon$ and for sufficiently large $n$. But $s_n - s_{n-1} = a_n$, so that $|a_n| < \epsilon$. That is, the general term of the series becomes arbitrarily small for $n$ sufficiently large and $\lim_{n\to\infty} a_n = 0$

The theorem states that in order for a series to converge, its $n$th term must approach zero as $n \to \infty$. It follows that if the limit of the $n$th term is not zero, then the series must diverge.

---

*Example 22.2a.* By examining the general term of

$$\sum_{n=1}^{\infty} \frac{n}{2n + 1},$$

show that the series diverges.

In this problem, we find that

$$\lim_{n \to \infty} \frac{n}{2n + 1} = \lim_{n \to \infty} \frac{1}{2 + \dfrac{1}{n}} = \frac{1}{2}.$$

Consequently, the series is divergent since the limit of the $n$th term is not zero.

---

It is important to realize that the converse of the preceding theorem is *not* true; that is, even if it is true for the series $\sum_{n=1}^{\infty} u_n$ that $u_n \to 0$ as $n \to \infty$, this is no guarantee that the series converges. The next example is an important illustration of this statement.

---

*Example 22.2b.* Prove that the series $\sum_{n=1}^{\infty} 1/n$ (the **harmonic series**) diverges.

Notice that the general term $1/n$ approaches zero as $n \to \infty$. However, since

$$s_n = 1 + \frac{1}{2} + \frac{1}{3} + \cdots + \frac{1}{n},$$

we may write

$$s_{2n} = s_n + \frac{1}{n + 1} + \frac{1}{n + 2} + \cdots + \frac{1}{2n}$$

$$\geqq s_n + \frac{1}{2n} + \frac{1}{2n} + \cdots + \frac{1}{2n}$$

$$\geqq s_n + \frac{1}{2}.$$

This statement implies that the partial sums are unbounded. For example,

$$s_2 = s_1 + \frac{1}{2} = \frac{3}{2},$$

$$s_4 > s_2 + \frac{1}{2} = 2,$$

$$s_8 > s_4 + \frac{1}{2} > 2 + \frac{1}{2} = \frac{5}{2},$$

$$s_{16} > \frac{5}{2} + \frac{1}{2} = 3,$$

and in general, for $m = 2^n$, $s_m \geqq (n + 2)/2$, so that $s_n \to \infty$ as $n \to \infty$. Thus, the harmonic series diverges even though $\lim_{n \to \infty} u_n = 0$.

## Exercises 22.2

In Numbers 1 to 12, determine whether the series is convergent or divergent.

1. $\displaystyle\sum_{n=1}^{\infty} \frac{2n}{n+1}$.

2. $\displaystyle\sum_{n=1}^{\infty} 3(\tfrac{1}{2})^n$.

3. $\displaystyle\sum_{n=1}^{\infty} \left(\frac{3}{2}\right)^n$.

4. $\displaystyle\sum_{n=1}^{\infty} (1)^n$.

5. $\displaystyle\sum_{n=1}^{\infty} \sin \frac{n\pi}{2}$.

6. $\displaystyle\sum_{n=1}^{\infty} \frac{5^n}{2^n+1}$.

7. $\displaystyle\sum_{n=2}^{\infty} \frac{1}{\ln n}$.

8. $\displaystyle\sum_{n=1}^{\infty} \frac{2^{n+1}}{3^n}$.

9. $\displaystyle\sum_{n=1}^{\infty} \int_{n-1}^{n} e^{-x^2}\, dx$. *Hint:* The $n$th partial sum is $\displaystyle\int_{0}^{n} e^{-x^2}\, dx$.

★10. $\displaystyle\sum_{n=1}^{\infty} \int_{n}^{n+1} e^{-\sqrt{x}}\, dx$. *Hint:* The $n$th partial sum is $\displaystyle\int_{1}^{n+1} e^{-\sqrt{x}}\, dx$.

11. $\displaystyle\sum_{n=1}^{\infty} \int_{n}^{n+1} \left|\frac{\sin \pi x/2}{x^2}\right| dx$. *Hint:* See Numbers 9 and 10.

12. $\displaystyle\sum_{n=0}^{\infty} \int_{n\pi}^{(n+1)\pi} \sin x\, dx$.

13. A series $\sum_{n=1}^{\infty} a_n$, where $a_n$ is given by a recursion relation of the form

$$a_n = b_n - b_{n+1}, \qquad n = 1, 2, 3, \ldots,$$

is called a *telescoping series*, because

$$S_n = \sum_{\alpha=1}^{n} a_\alpha = \sum_{\alpha=1}^{n} (b_\alpha - b_{\alpha+1})$$

$$= b_1 - b_{n+1}.$$

Hence, if $\lim_{n\to\infty} b_{n+1}$ exists, the series $\sum_{n=1}^{\infty} a_n$ converges. Use this method to dis cuss the convergence of

(a) $\displaystyle\sum_{n=1}^{\infty} \frac{1}{n(n+1)}$.

(b) $\displaystyle\sum_{n=1}^{\infty} \frac{2}{3n(n+2)}$.

14. Use the method of Number 13 to determine if the series

$$\sum_{n=1}^{\infty} \frac{\sqrt{n+1} - \sqrt{n}}{\sqrt{n^2 + n}}$$

is convergent or divergent.

# 22.3 THE CAUCHY CRITERION AND THE COMPARISON TEST

The use of the Cauchy Criterion for sequences in the proof of Theorem 22.2a suggests that we may formulate this criterion for series.

**Theorem 22.3a.** The Cauchy Criterion for Series. A series $\sum_{n=1}^{\infty} a_n$ converges $\Leftrightarrow$ there is a positive integer $N$ such that

$$\left| \sum_{\alpha=m}^{m+p} a_\alpha \right| = |a_m + a_{m+1} + \cdots + a_{m+p}| < \epsilon$$

for all $m \geq N$ and all $p \geq 0$.

PROOF: The proof follows from the Cauchy Criterion for sequences if we write

$$\left| \sum_{\alpha=m}^{m+p} a_\alpha \right| = \left| \sum_{\alpha=1}^{m+p} a_\alpha - \sum_{\alpha=1}^{m-1} a_\alpha \right| = |S_{m+F} - S_{m-1}|.$$

Two other simple properties of series are given in

**Theorem 22.3b.** If $\sum_{n=1}^{\infty} a_n = A$ and $\sum_{n=1}^{\infty} b_n = B$, and if $k$ is a constant, then

(a) $\sum_{n=1}^{\infty} (ka_n) = kA,$

(b) $\sum_{n=1}^{\infty} (a_n + b_n) = A + B.$

PROOF: Left for the reader.

Note carefully that the hypothesis of this theorem assumes convergence of the given series. It is not difficult, however, to see that if $k \neq 0$, then multiplication by $k$ as in (a) will not change the character of the series with respect to convergence or divergence. The reader should also observe that the convergence or divergence of a series does not depend on the first $m$ terms of the series; that is, if $\sum_{n=1}^{\infty} a_n$ converges, so does $\sum_{n=m}^{\infty} a_n$, and conversely. Of course, the values to which the two series converge will generally be different.

The fact that we have been examining series by comparing their partial sums with other expressions suggests that we might gain some knowledge about a series by comparing its terms with those of another series whose behavior is known. This kind of comparison is made in

**Theorem 22.3c.** The Comparison Test. Let $\sum_{n=1}^{\infty} a_n$ and $\sum_{n=1}^{\infty} b_n$ be two series of positive terms for which there is a positive integer $M$ such that

$$a_n \leq b_n \qquad \text{for all } n > M.$$

Then

$$\sum_{n=1}^{\infty} b_n \text{ converges} \Rightarrow \sum_{n=1}^{\infty} a_n \text{ converges},$$

and

$$\sum_{n=1}^{\infty} a_n \text{ diverges} \quad \Rightarrow \quad \sum_{n=1}^{\infty} b_n \text{ diverges.}$$

PROOF: Since $a_n \leqq b_n$ for all $n > M$, we have

$$\sum_{\alpha=1}^{p} a_{n+\alpha} \leqq \sum_{\alpha=1}^{p} b_{n+\alpha}$$

for every integer $n > M$. If

$$\sum_{n=1}^{\infty} b_n$$

converges, then for $n$ large enough, $\sum_{\alpha=1}^{\infty} b_{n+\alpha} < \epsilon$ by Theorem 22.3a. Hence, $\sum_{\alpha=1}^{\infty} a_{n+\alpha} < \epsilon$, so that $\sum_{n=1}^{\infty} a_n$ converges by Theorem 22.3a. But if $\sum_{\alpha=1}^{\infty} a_n$ *diverges*, then its partial sums increase without bound as $n \to \infty$. By virtue of the relationship $a_n \leqq b_n$, $n > M$, the partial sums for $\sum_{\alpha=1}^{\infty} b_\alpha$ must also increase without bound as $n \to \infty$.

---

*Example 22.3a.* Does the series $\sum_{n=1}^{\infty} 1/n!$ converge or diverge?

Since $1/n! < 1/2^n$ for $n > 4$ and since, $\sum_{n=1}^{\infty} 1/2^n$ is a convergent geometric series, it follows, by Theorem 22.3c, that the given series converges.

---

Another rather powerful result that is convenient for studying series is contained in the limit form of comparison test given by

**Theorem 22.3d.** Let $\sum_{n=1}^{\infty} a_n$ and $\sum_{n=1}^{\infty} b_n$ be two series of positive terms. Then

$$\lim_{n \to \infty} \frac{a_n}{b_n} = A, \qquad A \neq 0 \Rightarrow \text{the series converge or diverge together.}$$

PROOF: Since $a_n/b_n \to A$, then for $n$ sufficiently large, we may write

$$A - \epsilon < \frac{a_n}{b_n} < A + \epsilon.$$

In particular, if $\epsilon = \dfrac{A}{2}$, then

$$\frac{A}{2} < \frac{a_n}{b_n} < \frac{3A}{2}$$

or

$$b_n < \frac{2}{A} a_n \quad \text{and} \quad a_n < \frac{3A}{2} b_n.$$

Since the convergence or divergence of a series is not affected by multiplying each of its terms by a nonzero constant, we may quote Theorem 22.3c to complete the proof.

---

*Example 22.3b.* Does the series $\sum_{n=1}^{\infty} n^2/n!$ converge or diverge?

Since we are unable to compare this conveniently with a series whose behavior is known in order to apply Theorem 22.3c, let us try to use Theorem 22.3d with the known convergent series $\sum_{n=1}^{\infty} 1/n!$. We find first that

$$\frac{\dfrac{n^2}{n!}}{\dfrac{1}{n!}} = n^2,$$

which increases without bound as $n$ increases, and hence does not yield the information we are seeking. However, we may still use Theorem 22.3d by means of a small trick. Since the behavior of a series does not depend on the first two or three or four terms, we may consider the series

$$\sum_{n=3}^{\infty} \frac{n^2}{n!} = \sum_{n=1}^{\infty} \frac{(n+2)^2}{(n+2)!}$$

for the purpose of applying Theorem 22.3d. We now get

$$\frac{\dfrac{(n+2)^2}{(n+2)!}}{\dfrac{1}{n!}} = \frac{(n+2)^2}{(n+2)(n+1)},$$

and this ratio approaches 1 as $n \to \infty$. Hence, Theorem 22.3d does apply, and shows that the series $\sum_{n=3}^{\infty} n^2/n!$ converges, since $\sum_{n=1}^{\infty} 1/n!$ converges. Consequently, it is true that the given series also converges.

## Exercises 22.3

In Numbers 1 to 16, determine if the series is convergent or divergent.

1. $\displaystyle\sum_{n=1}^{\infty} \frac{n}{n^2 + 1}.$

2. $\displaystyle\sum_{n=1}^{\infty} \frac{n}{2^n}.$

3. $\displaystyle\sum_{n=1}^{\infty} \frac{2n - 1}{n^2 + n}.$

4. $\displaystyle\sum_{n=1}^{\infty} \frac{n}{n!}.$

5. $\displaystyle\sum_{n=1}^{\infty} \frac{1}{n^2 + 1}.$

6. $\displaystyle\sum_{n=1}^{\infty} \frac{1}{4n + 3}.$

7. $\displaystyle\sum_{n=1}^{\infty} \frac{2^n}{n!}.$

8. $\displaystyle\sum_{n=2}^{\infty} \frac{1}{\sqrt{n - 1}}.$

9. $\displaystyle\sum_{n=1}^{\infty} \frac{1}{(2n + 1)^2}.$

10. $\displaystyle\sum_{n=1}^{\infty} \frac{1}{8n}.$

11. $\displaystyle\sum_{n=1}^{\infty} \frac{n}{\sqrt{n^2 + 1}}.$

12. $\displaystyle\sum_{n=1}^{\infty} \frac{n^2}{n^3 + 1}.$

13. $\displaystyle\sum_{n=1}^{\infty} \frac{n}{e^n}.$

14. $\displaystyle\sum_{n=2}^{\infty} \frac{\ln n}{n}.$

15. $\displaystyle\sum_{n=1}^{\infty} \frac{2^n + 3^n}{6^n}.$

16. $\displaystyle\sum_{n=1}^{\infty} \frac{\sqrt{n + 1} - \sqrt{n}}{\sqrt{n^2 + 1}}.$

17. Prove that if $\sum_{n=1}^{\infty} a_n$ and $\sum_{n=1}^{\infty} b_n$ are series of positive terms, if $\sum_{n=1}^{\infty} b_n$ converges, and if $a_n/b_n \to 0$ as $n \to \infty$, then $\sum_{n=1}^{\infty} a_n$ converges.

18. Prove Theorem 22.3b.

## 22.4 THE INTEGRAL TEST

Although several techniques have been developed for determining the behavior of a series, there are always some series for which those techniques are not practical. For example, none of the methods developed so far are very efficient for examining a series of the form

$$\sum_{n=1}^{\infty} \frac{1}{n^p}, \qquad p \neq 1.$$

Consequently, it appears worthwhile to develop additional methods for studying the behavior of series.

One of the simplest tests was developed by Cauchy in 1837. It is an extension of the comparison test stated in Theorem 22.3c for a series of positive terms.

**Theorem 22.4a.** The Integral Test. Suppose $f$ is a function with the following properties.

(a) It is defined, continuous, and positive for $x \geq m$, where $m$ is some positive integer.

(b) $f(n) = u_n$ for $n \geq m$.

(c) $f$ is a decreasing function for all $x \geq m$.

Then

$$\int_m^{\infty} f(x)\, dx \text{ converges} \Longrightarrow \sum_{n=1}^{\infty} u_n \text{ converges},$$

and

$$\int_m^{\infty} f(x)\, dx \text{ diverges} \Longrightarrow \sum_{n=1}^{\infty} u_n \text{ diverges}.$$

PROOF: For $m \leq k \leq x \leq k + 1, f(k + 1) < f(x) < f(k)$, so that

$$\int_k^{k+1} f(k + 1)\, dx < \int_k^{k+1} f(x)\, dx < \int_k^{k+1} f(k)\, dx,$$

or

$$f(k + 1) < \int_k^{k+1} f(x)\, dx < f(k).$$

Summing for values of $k$ from $m$ to $m + n$, we get

$$\sum_{k=m}^{m+n} f(k + 1) < \int_m^{m+n} f(x)\, dx < \sum_{k=m}^{m+n} f(k),$$

or

(1)
$$\sum_{k=m+1}^{m+n} u_k < \int_m^{m+n} f(x)\, dx < \sum_{k=m}^{m+n-1} u_k.$$

This result is easily visualized geometrically in terms of areas, as is illustrated in Figure 22.4a. In this figure, the shaded areas $A_1$, $A_2$, $A_3$, ... correspond to rectangles inscribed between the curve and the $x$-axis. The respective

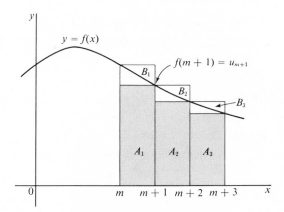

**FIGURE 22.4a**

rectangles have areas numerically equal to the terms $u_{m+1}$, $u_{m+2}$, $u_{m+3}$, ... of the series. The rectangles formed by combining the shaded and unshaded rectangles have areas numerically equal to $u_m$, $u_{m+1}$, $u_{m+2}$, ..., respectively. Thus,

$$A_1 = u_{m+1}, \quad A_2 = u_{m+2}, \quad \ldots, \quad A_n = u_{m+n},$$
$$A_1 + B_1 = u_m, \quad A_2 + B_2 = u_{m+1}, \quad \ldots, \quad A_n + B_n = u_{m+n-1}.$$

Since the sum of the areas $A_1$, $A_2$, ..., $A_n$ is less than the area under the curve from $x = m$ to $x = m + n$, it is true that

$$u_{m+1} + u_{m+2} + \cdots + u_{m+n} < \int_m^{m+n} f(x)\, dx,$$

which is the first part of Inequality (1). Similarly, the sum of the areas $A_1 + B_1$, $A_2 + B_2$, ..., $A_n + B_n$ is greater than the area under the curve, so that

$$\int_m^{m+n} f(x)\, dx < u_m + u_{m+1} + \cdots + u_{m+n-1},$$

which is the second part of (1).

From the Inequality (1), the relation

$$s_n = \sum_{k=m+1}^{m+n} f(k + 1) < \int_m^{m+n} f(x)\, dx$$

shows that the partial sums of the series $\sum_{k=m}^{\infty} u_{k+1}$ are bounded if $\int_m^{\infty} f(x)\, dx$ converges. Therefore, since $s_{n+1} > s_n$, the sequence $\{s_n\}$ converges. It follows that the series $\sum_{k=1}^{\infty} u_k$ converges.

Similarly, the relation

$$\int_m^{m+n} f(x)\,dx < \sum_{k=m}^{m+n-1} u_k = t_n$$

shows that the sequence $\{t_n\}$ increases without bound if $\int_m^\infty f(x)\,dx$ diverges. Therefore, the series $\sum_{k=1}^\infty u_k$ diverges if the integral does. This completes the proof.

With this result the investigation of series of the form $\sum_{n=1}^\infty 1/n^p$, $p \neq 1$ is easy. (It has already been shown that the series $\sum_{n=1}^\infty 1/n$ diverges.)

---

*Example 22.4a.* For what values of $p$ does the $p$-series $\sum_{n=1}^\infty 1/n^p$, $p \neq 1$ converge? If we let $f(x) = 1/x^p$, the Integral Test may be applied, and we find

$$\int_1^\infty \frac{1}{x^p}\,dx = \lim_{n \to \infty} \left[ -\frac{1}{x^{p-1}(p-1)} \right]_1^n$$

$$= \lim_{n \to \infty} \left[ \frac{1}{p-1} - \frac{1}{n^{p-1}(p-1)} \right].$$

If $p > 1$, the limit exists and is equal to $1/(p-1)$. Hence, if $p > 1$, the series converges. For example, $p = 2$ gives the convergent series $\sum_{n=1}^\infty 1/n^2$. If $p < 1$, the limit does not exist and the series diverges.

---

The $p$-series investigated in Example 22.4a is quite important as part of our stock of known series that can be used in the comparison tests.

The Integral Test is also useful in obtaining, to any desired degree of accuracy, estimates of the value to which a series converges. From Inequality (1),

$$\sum_{k=m+1}^{m+n} u_k < \int_m^{m+n} f(x)\,dx < \sum_{k=m}^{m+n-1} u_k,$$

it follows that

$$\sum_{k=m+1}^\infty u_k < \int_m^\infty f(x)\,dx < \sum_{k=m}^\infty u_k.$$

If we replace $m$ by $m + 1$ in these inequalities, then we have

$$\sum_{k=m+2}^\infty u_k < \int_{m+1}^\infty f(x)\,dx < \sum_{k=m+1}^\infty u_k.$$

Consequently, by combining the last two sets of inequalities, we see that

(2) $$\int_{m+1}^\infty f(x)\,dx < \sum_{k=m+1}^\infty u_k < \int_m^\infty f(x)\,dx.$$

The expression $\sum_{k=m+1}^\infty u_k$ is denoted by $R_m$ when the series is convergent to, say, $S$, and is called the **remainder** after $m$ terms, since $R_m = S - s_m$.

*Example 22.4b.* Find how much error is made in calculating the value of $\sum_{n=1}^{\infty} 1/n^2$ by adding only the first five terms and neglecting the remaining terms.

For $m = 5$ in Inequality (2), we have

$$\int_6^\infty \frac{1}{x^2}\, dx < \sum_{k=6}^\infty \frac{1}{k^2} < \int_5^\infty \frac{dx}{x^2},$$

or

$$\lim_{t \to \infty} \left[ -\frac{1}{x} \right]_6^t < \sum_{k=6}^\infty \frac{1}{k^2} < \lim_{t \to \infty} \left[ -\frac{1}{x} \right]_5^t,$$

and the remainder after 5 terms is bounded, as indicated by

$$\frac{1}{6} < \sum_{k=6}^\infty \frac{1}{k^2} < \frac{1}{5}.$$

Since

$$s_5 = \frac{5269}{3600},$$

it follows that

$$\frac{5269}{3600} + \frac{1}{6} < \sum_{k=1}^\infty \frac{1}{k^2} < \frac{5269}{3600} + \frac{1}{5},$$

or

$$\frac{5869}{3600} < \sum_{k=1}^\infty \frac{1}{k^2} < \frac{5989}{3600}.$$

A slightly better upper bound on the series may be obtained from the inequalities

(3)
$$\int_{m+1}^\infty f(x)\, dx < \sum_{k=m+1}^\infty u_k < \int_{m+1}^\infty f(x)\, dx + u_{m+1}.$$

From these, we can show that

$$\sum_{k=1}^\infty \frac{1}{k^2} < \frac{5969}{3600}.$$

It will be left as an exercise for the reader to verify Inequality (3).

## Exercises 22.4

In Numbers 1 to 14, test the series for convergence by using the Integral Test.

1. $\sum_{n=1}^\infty \dfrac{1}{2n - 1}.$

2. $\sum_{n=1}^\infty \dfrac{1}{1 + n^2}.$

3. $\sum_{n=2}^\infty \dfrac{\ln n}{n}.$

4. $\sum_{n=1}^\infty \dfrac{n}{e^{n^2}}.$

5. $\sum_{n=1}^\infty \dfrac{1}{e^n}.$

6. $\sum_{n=1}^\infty \dfrac{1}{\sqrt{2n + 1}}.$

7. $\displaystyle\sum_{n=1}^{\infty} \frac{n}{n^2 + 4}.$

8. $\displaystyle\sum_{n=1}^{\infty} \frac{1}{n^2} \cos \pi/n.$

9. $\displaystyle\sum_{n=2}^{\infty} \frac{1}{n \ln n}.$

10. $\displaystyle\sum_{n=1}^{\infty} \frac{1}{n\sqrt{n}}.$

11. $\displaystyle\sum_{n=1}^{\infty} \frac{n^2}{n^3 + 1}.$

12. $\displaystyle\sum_{n=4}^{\infty} \frac{1}{n^2 - 9}.$

13. $\displaystyle\sum_{n=2}^{\infty} \frac{1}{n \ln n[\ln (\ln n)]}.$

14. $\displaystyle\sum_{n=1}^{\infty} \frac{1}{n(n + 1)}.$

15. Use an integral to determine how many terms of the series

$$\sum_{n=1}^{\infty} \frac{1}{n^2}$$

must be used if $R_m < 0.001$.

16. Use an integral to determine how many terms of the series in Number 5 must be used if $R_m < 0.001$.

17. Prove that Inequality (3) is valid.

18. If $\sum_{n=1}^{\infty} u_n$ is a convergent series of positive terms, such that there is no $n$ for which $u_n = \pm 1$, prove that

(a) $\displaystyle\sum_{n=1}^{\infty} \frac{u_n}{1 + u_n},$

(b) $\displaystyle\sum_{n=1}^{\infty} \frac{u_n}{1 - u_n}$

are both convergent series. *Hint:* Apply Theorem 22.3d.

19. If $\sum_{n=1}^{\infty} u_n$ is a convergent series of positive terms, does it follow that (a) $\sum_{n=1}^{\infty} \sqrt{u_n}$ or (b) $\sum_{n=1}^{\infty} nu_n$ are convergent series?

★20. Show that

$$\sum_{k=n+1}^{\infty} \frac{1}{k(k + 1)} < \sum_{k=n+1}^{\infty} \frac{1}{k^2} < \sum_{k=n+1}^{\infty} \frac{1}{(k - 1)k}.$$

The two outside series can be "telescoped." Show that

$$\frac{1}{n + 1} + \sum_{k=1}^{n} \frac{1}{k^2} < \sum_{k=1}^{\infty} \frac{1}{k^2} < \frac{1}{n} + \sum_{k=1}^{n} \frac{1}{k^2}.$$

This shows that the sum of the first $n$ terms of $\sum_{k=1}^{\infty} 1/k^2$ differs from the sum of the infinite series by not more than $1/n(n + 1)$. Why?

## 22.5 THE CAUCHY RATIO TEST

Although the Integral Test is important in studying infinite series, its usefulness is limited by the difficulty frequently encountered in evaluating the integral. Consequently, other methods for studying series are needed. One of the most important techniques is associated with an extension of Theorem 22.3c, so that a given series is compared with the general geometric series.

**Theorem 22.5a.** The Cauchy Ratio Test. If $\sum_{n=1}^{\infty} u_n$ is a series of positive terms for which

$$\lim_{n \to \infty} \frac{u_{n+1}}{u_n} = R,$$

then

$$0 \leq R < 1 \Rightarrow \text{the series converges,}$$

and

$$R > 1 \Rightarrow \text{the series diverges.}$$

PROOF: Suppose first that $0 \leq R < 1$, and let $r$ be any number such that $R < r < 1$. Since

$$\lim_{n \to \infty} \frac{u_{n+1}}{u_n} = R,$$

it is possible to choose a positive integer $m$ so large that the difference between $R$ and $u_{n+1}/u_n$ is arbitrarily small and, in particular, is less than $r - R$ for all $n \geq m$. For all such values of $n$,

$$\frac{u_{n+1}}{u_n} < r.$$

Thus

$$\frac{u_{m+1}}{u_m} < r \Rightarrow u_{m+1} < r u_m,$$

$$\frac{u_{m+2}}{u_{m+1}} < r \Rightarrow u_{m+2} < r u_{m+1} < r^2 u_m,$$

$$\frac{u_{m+3}}{u_{m+2}} < r \Rightarrow u_{m+3} < r u_{m+2} < r^3 u_m,$$

$$\cdot \quad \cdot \quad \cdot \quad \cdot \quad \cdot \quad \cdot \quad \cdot \quad \cdot \quad \cdot \quad \cdot \quad \cdot \quad \cdot \quad \cdot$$

$$\frac{u_{m+k}}{u_{m+k-1}} < r \Rightarrow u_{m+k} < r u_{m+k-1} < r^k u_m,$$

$$\cdot \quad \cdot \quad \cdot \quad \cdot \quad \cdot \quad \cdot \quad \cdot \quad \cdot \quad \cdot \quad \cdot \quad \cdot \quad \cdot \quad \cdot$$

This shows that the series

$$(1) \qquad u_{m+1} + u_{m+2} + \cdots + u_{m+k} + \cdots$$

is term by term less than the series

$$(2) \qquad r u_m + r^2 u_m + \cdots + r^k u_m + \cdots.$$

Since (2) is a geometric series with ratio $r < 1$, it is convergent. Thus, by the comparison test (Theorem 22.3c), series (1) is convergent, and it follows that the given series is also convergent.

The second part of the theorem is quite easy to prove, since if $R > 1$ the terms of the series eventually must increase as $n$ increases, so that the $n$th term cannot have the limit zero as $n \to \infty$. Hence the series must be divergent.

*Example 22.5a.* Determine the behavior of the series

$$\sum_{n=1}^{\infty} \frac{1 \cdot 3 \cdot 5 \cdots (2n-1)}{2 \cdot 5 \cdot 8 \cdots (3n-1)}.$$

Here, the general term of the series is

$$u_n = \frac{1 \cdot 3 \cdot 5 \cdots (2n-1)}{2 \cdot 5 \cdot 8 \cdots (3n-1)},$$

so that

$$\frac{u_{n+1}}{u_n} = \frac{1 \cdot 3 \cdot 5 \cdots (2n-1)(2n+1)}{2 \cdot 5 \cdot 8 \cdots (3n-1)(3n+2)} \cdot \frac{2 \cdot 5 \cdot 8 \cdots (3n-1)}{1 \cdot 3 \cdot 5 \cdots (2n-1)} = \frac{2n+1}{3n+2}.$$

Hence,

$$\lim_{n \to \infty} \frac{u_{n+1}}{u_n} = \lim_{n \to \infty} \frac{2n+1}{3n+2} = \frac{2}{3}.$$

Since the limit exists and is less than unity, the series converges by the Cauchy Ratio Test.

---

*Example 22.5b.* Does the series $\sum_{n=1}^{\infty} n!/n^n$ converge or diverge?

Since

$$\frac{u_{n+1}}{u_n} = \frac{(n+1)!}{(n+1)^{n+1}} \cdot \frac{n^n}{n!} = \left(\frac{n}{n+1}\right)^n = \left[\left(1 + \frac{1}{n}\right)^n\right]^{-1},$$

it follows that

$$\lim_{n \to \infty} \frac{u_{n+1}}{u_n} = \frac{1}{e}.$$

Thus, by Theorem 22.5a, the series converges.

---

It is not difficult to show that if

$$\lim_{n \to \infty} \frac{u_{n+1}}{u_n} = 1,$$

then no information is obtained with regard to convergence or divergence. For this purpose, consider the *p*-series $\sum_{n=1}^{\infty} 1/n^p$, which have been shown to be convergent for $p > 1$ and divergent for $p \leq 1$. For such series,

$$\lim_{n \to \infty} \frac{u_{n+1}}{u_n} = \lim_{n \to \infty} \frac{n^p}{(n+1)^p} = \lim_{n \to \infty} \left(\frac{1}{1 + \frac{1}{n}}\right)^p = 1,$$

*regardless of the value of p.* Thus, it is evident that there are both convergent and divergent series for which the limit of the ratio of successive general terms is unity. This means that if the value 1 for the limit occurs in the investigation of a given series, then the Cauchy Ratio Test does *not* apply, and a different test must be used.

Another test developed by Cauchy is the so-called **root test**

**Theorem 22.5b.** If $\sum_{n=1}^{\infty} u_n$ is a series of positive terms such that

$$u_n^{1/n} \to R \quad \text{as} \quad n \to \infty,$$

then

$$R < 1 \Rightarrow \text{the series converges,}$$

and

$$R > 1 \Rightarrow \text{the series diverges.}$$

If $R = 1$, no conclusion may be drawn.

PROOF: The proof is similar to that of Theorem 22.5a, and is left for the reader.

---

*Example 22.5c.* Determine the convergence behavior of the series

$$\sum_{n=1}^{\infty} \left(\frac{n}{n+1}\right)^{n^2}.$$

Since the expression $u_n^{1/n} = [n/(n+1)]^n \to 1/e$ as $n \to \infty$, the series converges by the Cauchy Root Test (Theorem 22.5b).

# Exercises 22.5

Determine the behavior of the series in each of Numbers 1 to 18.

1. $\sum\limits_{n=1}^{\infty} n! \left(\frac{1}{3}\right)^n.$

2. $\sum\limits_{n=1}^{\infty} \frac{n+2}{n(3^n)}.$

3. $\sum\limits_{n=1}^{\infty} \frac{n^2}{2^n}.$

4. $\sum\limits_{n=1}^{\infty} \frac{5}{n^{0.7}}.$

5. $\sum\limits_{n=1}^{\infty} \frac{100^n}{n!}.$

6. $\sum\limits_{n=1}^{\infty} (\sqrt[n]{n} - 1)^n.$

7. $\sum\limits_{n=1}^{\infty} \frac{n+1}{(n+2)(n+3)(n+4)}.$

8. $\sum\limits_{n=1}^{\infty} \frac{(n!)^2}{(2n)!}.$

9. $\sum\limits_{n=1}^{\infty} \frac{1}{1 + \sqrt[n]{2}}.$

10. $\sum\limits_{n=1}^{\infty} \frac{n!}{n^2(n+1)^2}.$

11. $\sum\limits_{n=1}^{\infty} \frac{2^n n!}{n^n}.$

12. $\sum\limits_{n=6}^{\infty} \frac{1}{(n-3)(n-5)}.$

13. $\sum\limits_{n=1}^{\infty} \frac{1}{\left(n + \frac{1}{n}\right)^n}.$

14. $\sum\limits_{n=2}^{\infty} \frac{1}{(\ln n)^{1/n}}.$

15. $\sum\limits_{n=2}^{\infty} \frac{2^{n-1}}{(n-1)!}.$

16. $\sum\limits_{n=1}^{\infty} \frac{3^{3n}}{(3n)!}.$

17. $\sum\limits_{n=1}^{\infty} \frac{3n}{n^2+1}.$

18. $\sum\limits_{n=0}^{\infty} \frac{1}{1 + \sqrt{n}}.$

19. Suppose that the series $\sum_{n=1}^{\infty} u_n$ is shown to be convergent by the Cauchy Ratio Test. Show that $\sum_{n=1}^{\infty} n u_n$ is also convergent.

20. Suppose that the series $\sum_{n=1}^{\infty} u_n$ is shown to be convergent by the Cauchy Ratio Test. Show that $\sum_{n=1}^{\infty} u_n^2$ is also convergent.

21. Prove that in Theorem 22.5a, if $u_{n+1}/u_n \to \infty$, then the series is divergent.

★22. Prove Theorem 22.5b.

## 22.6 SERIES WITH MIXED SIGNS

The discussion of series has thus far been restricted to series of positive terms. It is not unusual, however, to encounter series in which some terms are positive and some are negative. (Series in which all terms are negative are easily handled by Theorem 22.3b, since the factor $-1$ may be removed without affecting the convergence.)

Series in which only a finite number of terms are negative (or positive) may still be handled by the preceding theorems on series, since from some point sufficiently far out, the remaining series is a series of positive or negative terms alone. With the exception of series for which the limit of the $n$th term is not zero, we are unable at this point to handle those series in which there are infinitely many terms having each sign. Series of this type are called **series with mixed signs.**

Some examples of series with mixed signs are

(a) $\displaystyle\sum_{n=1}^{\infty} \frac{(-1)^{n-1}}{n} = 1 - \frac{1}{2} + \frac{1}{3} - \frac{1}{4} + \cdots;$

(b) $\displaystyle\sum_{n=1}^{\infty} (-1)^{n-1} = 1 - 1 + 1 - 1 + \cdots;$

(c) $\displaystyle\sum_{n=1}^{\infty} \frac{k_n}{n} = 1 + \frac{1}{2} - \frac{1}{3} + \frac{1}{4} - \frac{1}{5} - \frac{1}{6} - \frac{1}{7} + \frac{1}{8} - \cdots,$

where $k_n = 1$ if $n$ is of the form $2^m$, and $k_n = -1$ otherwise;

(d) $\displaystyle\sum_{n=1}^{\infty} a_n = 1 - \frac{1}{\ln 2} - \frac{1}{2} + \frac{1}{3} - \frac{1}{\ln 3} - \frac{1}{4} + \cdots,$

where $a_{3m+1} = 1/(2m+1)$, $a_{3m+2} = -1/\ln(m+2)$, and $a_{3m+3} = -1/(2m+2)$, $m = 0, 1, 2, \ldots.$

In general, series with mixed signs are the most difficult to test, since there are few methods available for handling them. It is possible to obtain some information about a series with mixed signs, $\sum_{n=1}^{\infty} u_n$, by considering a related series of the form $\sum_{n=1}^{\infty} |u_n|$. One of the most basic results in this connection is given by

**Theorem 22.6a.** $\sum_{n=1}^{\infty} |u_n|$ is convergent $\Rightarrow \sum_{n=1}^{\infty} u_n$ is convergent.

PROOF: Since the series of absolute values is convergent, the Cauchy Criterion guarantees that there is an integer $M$ such that for each $\epsilon > 0$,

$$|u_n| + |u_{n+1}| + \cdots + |u_{n+p}| < \epsilon$$

for all $n \geq M$ and all $p \geq 0$.

However,

$$|u_n + u_{n+1} + \cdots + u_{n+p}| \leq |u_n| + |u_{n+1}| + \cdots + |u_{n+p}|,$$

so that the series $\sum_{n=1}^{\infty} u_n$ also satisfies the Cauchy Criterion and hence is convergent.

It follows from Theorem 22.6a that if a series of positive terms is convergent, then any series formed from it by altering the signs of the terms in an arbitrary fashion is also convergent. The sum of the new series is, of course, not the same as that of the original. These observations lead us to

**Definition 22.6a.** A series $\sum_{n=1}^{\infty} u_n$ is said to be **absolutely convergent** if the series $\sum_{n=1}^{\infty} |u_n|$ is convergent.

Note that by this definition every convergent series of positive terms is absolutely convergent.

Theorem 22.6a is frequently the key to testing a series with mixed signs for convergence. The corresponding series of absolute values is tested. If this series converges, then so does the given series; if it diverges, then the given series may still converge.

---

*Example 22.6a.* Test the series

$$\sum_{n=1}^{\infty} \frac{(-1)^{n-1}}{n^2}.$$

The corresponding series of absolute values is the $p$-series $\sum_{n=1}^{\infty} 1/n^2$. Since $p > 1$, this series converges. Therefore, the given series is absolutely convergent.

---

The reader should keep in mind that all the tests discussed in the preceding sections can be used to examine a given series for absolute convergence. As we shall see, the Cauchy Ratio Test is the most commonly used of these tests.

We now consider the case in which a given series is not absolutely convergent. (It is still possible for the series to be convergent.)

**Definition 22.6b.** If the series $\sum_{n=1}^{\infty} u_n$ is convergent and $\sum_{n=1}^{\infty} |u_n|$ is divergent, then the series $\sum_{n=1}^{\infty} u_n$ is said to be **conditionally convergent.**

Evidently, the signs of the terms play an essential role in the behavior of a conditionally convergent series.

---

*Example 22.6b.* Test the series

$$\sum_{n=1}^{\infty} \frac{(-1)^{n-1}}{n} = 1 - \frac{1}{2} + \frac{1}{3} - \cdots + \frac{(-1)^{n-1}}{n} + \cdots$$

for convergence.

It has been shown that

$$\sum_{n=1}^{\infty} \left| \frac{(-1)^{n-1}}{n} \right| = \sum_{n=1}^{\infty} \frac{1}{n}$$

is divergent. Hence, we know that the series with mixed signs cannot be absolutely convergent. To determine the behavior of the series, let us first examine the partial sums, $s_n$, for $n$ even, say $n = 2k$. It follows from the given series that

$$s_{2k} = 1 - \frac{1}{2} + \frac{1}{3} - \frac{1}{4} + \cdots + \frac{1}{2k-1} - \frac{1}{2k},$$

so that

$$s_{2k} = \left(1 - \frac{1}{2}\right) + \cdots + \left(\frac{1}{2k-1} - \frac{1}{2k}\right),$$

where every quantity in parentheses is positive, which implies that the sequence $\{s_{2k}\}$ is an increasing one.

Now consider these partial sums in the form

$$s_{2k} = 1 - \left(\frac{1}{2} - \frac{1}{3}\right) - \left(\frac{1}{4} - \frac{1}{5}\right) - \cdots - \left(\frac{1}{2k-2} - \frac{1}{2k-1}\right) - \frac{1}{2k},$$

which shows that $s_{2k} < 1$ for all values of $k$. Hence, by Theorem 22.1b, the sequence $\{s_{2k}\}$ must have a limit.

Furthermore,

$$\lim_{k \to \infty} (s_{2k+1} - s_{2k}) = \lim_{k \to \infty} \frac{1}{2k+1} = 0,$$

so that the sequence $\{s_{2k+1}\}$ of partial sums of odd index also converges, and to the same value as $\{s_{2k}\}$. The given series is therefore convergent. However, since the series of absolute values

$$\sum_{n=1}^{\infty} \left| \frac{(-1)^{n-1}}{n} \right|$$

diverges, the series with mixed signs is only *conditionally convergent*.

---

The series in Example 22.6b, in which the signs of the terms are alternately plus and minus, is a common type among series with mixed signs. Such a series is called an **alternating series** and can often be tested for convergence by means of

**Theorem 22.6b.** Leibniz's Test. If, for the series $\sum_{n=1}^{\infty} (-1)^{n-1} u_n$, where $u_n \geq 0$

> (a) $u_{n+1} \leq u_n$, and
> (b) $u_n \to 0$ as $n \to \infty$,

then the series converges.

PROOF: The proof of this theorem follows essentially the same line of reasoning as was used in Example 22.6b. Thus, consider the partial sums for even value of $n$, $s_{2k}$. We have

$$s_{2k} = u_1 - u_2 + u_3 - u_4 + \cdots + u_{2k-1} - u_{2k}$$
$$= (u_1 - u_2) + (u_3 - u_4) + \cdots + (u_{2k-1} - u_{2k}),$$

which shows, since the quantities in parentheses are all nonnegative, that the sequence $\{s_{2k}\}$ is monotonic increasing. Furthermore, since

$$s_{2k} = u_1 - (u_2 - u_3) - (u_4 - u_5) - \cdots - u_{2k},$$

it follows that $s_{2k} < u_1$ for all $k$, which shows $\{s_{2k}\}$ to be a bounded sequence. Hence, this sequence has a limit. Since

$$s_{2k+1} = s_{2k} + u_{2k+1},$$

and since $u_n \to 0$ as $n \to \infty$, it follows that the sequence $\{s_{2k+1}\}$ must have the same limit, which means that the original series converges.

---

*Example 22.6c.* Determine the behavior of the series

$$\sum_{n=1}^{\infty} \frac{(-1)^n}{\sqrt{n}}.$$

Since $1/\sqrt{n+1} < 1/\sqrt{n}$, and since $1/\sqrt{n} \to 0$ as $n \to \infty$, the series converges by virtue of Leibniz's Test.

---

*Example 22.6d.* Determine the behavior of the series

$$\sum_{n=1}^{\infty} \frac{(-1)^{n-1}n}{10n - 1}.$$

Again, it is true that

$$\frac{n+1}{10n + 9} < \frac{n}{10n - 1},$$

since

$$(n+1)(10n - 1) < n(10n + 9).$$

The series does not converge, however, because $u_n = n/(10n - 1)$ does not approach zero as $n \to \infty$. The condition that $u_n \to 0$ as $n \to \infty$ is *absolutely essential* for the convergence of any series.

---

*Example 22.6e.* Discuss the behavior of the series

$$\sum_{n=1}^{\infty} u_n = \frac{1}{1^2} - \frac{1}{6} + \frac{1}{3^2} - \frac{1}{12} + \frac{1}{5^2} - \frac{1}{20} + \cdots,$$

where the $n$th term is given by the formula

$$u_n = \frac{1 - (-1)^n}{2n^2} - \frac{2[1 - (-1)^{n+1}]}{(n+2)(n+4)}.$$

Although $u_n \to 0$ as $n \to \infty$, the condition that $u_{n+1} < u_n$ does not hold for all $n$. Hence, *Leibniz's Test does not apply*. In this instance, however, it is easy to show that the partial sums of even index are given by

$$s_{2k} = \sum_{n=1}^{k} \frac{1}{(2n - 1)^2} - \sum_{n=1}^{k} \frac{1}{(n+1)(n+2)}.$$

Since both of the series

$$\sum_{n=1}^{\infty} \frac{1}{(2n-1)^2} \quad \text{and} \quad \sum_{n=1}^{\infty} \frac{1}{(n+1)(n+2)}$$

converge, it follows that

$$\lim_{k \to \infty} s_{2k} = \sum_{n=1}^{\infty} \frac{1}{(2n-1)^2} - \sum_{n=1}^{\infty} \frac{1}{(n+1)(n+2)}.$$

The fact that $\lim_{n \to \infty} u_n = 0$ shows that the sequence $\{s_{2k+1}\}$ also converges to the same limit. Hence the given series converges even though Leibniz's Test does not apply.

---

The behavior of some series with alternating signs is extremely difficult to analyze, but since such series are rarely of interest in the elementary applications of infinite series, we shall not investigate them.

Series with mixed signs must be handled rather carefully. For example, it may appear that since the terms of the partial sums may be paired, the terms of the infinite series may also be paired. This is, of course, equivalent to the insertion of parentheses in the series. It is a remarkable fact, as the following illustration shows, that parentheses may *not* be inserted at will in an infinite series. Consider

$$\sum_{n=1}^{\infty} (-1)^{n-1} = 1 - 1 + 1 - 1 + \cdots + (-1)^n + \cdots.$$

If parentheses are inserted to obtain

$$(1-1) + (1-1) + \cdots + (1-1) + \cdots,$$

then the sum of each pair of terms is 0 and apparently the series converges to 0. But if we write

$$1 - (1-1) - (1-1) - \cdots,$$

then again the sum of pairs of terms in parentheses is 0 and apparently the series converges to 1. Actually, the partial sums have alternately the values 0 and 1, so that on the basis of the definition of convergence, the series does not converge.

Thus, this illustration shows that parentheses may not be inserted freely into a series, because such a grouping of terms can alter the character of the series. The following theorem, stated without proof, indicates the conditions under which parentheses may be inserted in a series.

**Theorem 22.6c.** If a series $\sum_{n=1}^{\infty} u_n$ is convergent, then parentheses may be inserted in the series without altering the convergence or the value to which the series converges.

Note that this theorem does *not* permit parentheses to be inserted in a series when the behavior of the series is unknown.

Let $\sum_{n=1}^{\infty} u_n$ be a series of mixed signs. Denote the positive terms in order by $a_k$ and the negative terms in order by $-b_k$, where $b_k > 0$. The series $\sum_{n=1}^{\infty} a_n$ and $\sum_{n=1}^{\infty} b_n$ will be called the **associated series** of $\sum_{n=1}^{\infty} u_n$. Again without proof, we state

**Theorem 22.6d.** If $\sum_{n=1}^{\infty} u_n$ is absolutely convergent, then the two associated series $\sum_{n=1}^{\infty} a_n$ and $\sum_{n=1}^{\infty} b_n$ both converge, and

$$\sum_{n=1}^{\infty} u_n = \sum_{n=1}^{\infty} a_n - \sum_{n=1}^{\infty} b_n.$$

That is, in an absolutely convergent series, the set of positive terms alone and the set of negative terms alone both form convergent series.

This theorem is sometimes useful in determining the value to which a series with mixed signs converges. For example,

$$1 - \frac{1}{2} + \frac{1}{3} - \frac{1}{2^2} + \frac{1}{3^2} - \frac{1}{2^3} + \cdots,$$

where $u_{2k} = -2^{-k}$ and $u_{2k-1} = 3^{1-k}$, $k = 1, 2, 3, \ldots$, converges to the value

$$\sum_{n=1}^{\infty} \frac{1}{3^{n-1}} - \sum_{n=1}^{\infty} \frac{1}{2^n} = \frac{3}{2} - 1 = \frac{1}{2}.$$

The notation of Theorem 22.6d is used in the following theorem, which is also stated without proof.

**Theorem 22.6e.** If the series $\sum_{n=1}^{\infty} u_n$ is conditionally convergent, then $\sum_{n=1}^{\infty} a_n$ and $\sum_{n=1}^{\infty} b_n$ both diverge.

A simple consequence of the two preceding theorems is

**Theorem 22.6f.** A series with mixed signs cannot converge if one of its associated series converges and the other diverges.

To illustrate, let us refer to the Series (c) given at the beginning of this section,

$$\sum_{n=1}^{\infty} \frac{k_n}{n} = 1 + \frac{1}{2} - \frac{1}{3} + \frac{1}{4} - \frac{1}{5} - \frac{1}{6} - \frac{1}{7} + \frac{1}{8} + \cdots,$$

where $k_n = 1$ if $n$ is of the form $2^m$ and $k_n = -1$ otherwise. The associated series are

$$\sum_{n=1}^{\infty} \frac{1}{2^{n-1}} \quad \text{and} \quad \frac{1}{3} + \frac{1}{5} + \frac{1}{6} + \frac{1}{7} + \frac{1}{9} + \cdots,$$

in which no term has a denominator that is a power of 2. The first of the associated series is a convergent geometric series, whereas the second can be shown to diverge (Exercises 22.6, Number 25). Hence the original series also diverges.

## Exercises 22.6

In Numbers 1 to 21, test the given series for convergence. If the series is convergent, find whether the convergence is conditional or absolute.

1. $\displaystyle\sum_{n=1}^{\infty} \frac{(-1)^{n+1}}{n}$.

2. $\displaystyle\sum_{n=1}^{\infty} \frac{(-1)^{n+1}}{\sqrt{2n-1}}$.

3. $\displaystyle\sum_{n=1}^{\infty} (-1)^{n+1} \frac{n}{e^n}$.

4. $\displaystyle\sum_{n=2}^{\infty} \frac{(-1)^n}{\ln n}$.

5. $\displaystyle\sum_{n=1}^{\infty} (-1)^{n+1} \frac{n+1}{3n}$.

6. $\displaystyle\sum_{n=1}^{\infty} (-1)^{n+1} \frac{n}{n^2+1}$.

7. $\displaystyle\sum_{n=2}^{\infty} (-1)^n \frac{\ln n}{n}$.

8. $\displaystyle\sum_{n=1}^{\infty} \frac{(-1)^n}{n!}$.

9. $\displaystyle\sum_{n=1}^{\infty} (-1)^{n+1} 2^{1/n}$.

10. $\displaystyle\sum_{n=1}^{\infty} \frac{(-1)^{n+1}}{\sqrt[3]{n}}$.

11. $\displaystyle\sum_{n=1}^{\infty} (-1)^n \left( \frac{1\cdot 3\cdot 5\cdots(2n-1)}{2\cdot 4\cdot 6\cdots 2n} \right)^2$.

12. $\displaystyle\sum_{n=1}^{\infty} \frac{(-1)^n}{\ln(e^n+e^{-n})}$.

13. $\displaystyle\sum_{n=1}^{\infty} \frac{(-1)^n}{\ln\left(1+\dfrac{1}{n}\right)}$.

14. $\displaystyle\sum_{n=1}^{\infty} (-1)^n \int_n^{n+1} \frac{e^{-x}}{x}\, dx$.

15. $\displaystyle\sum_{n=1}^{\infty} (-1)^{n-1} n \sin \frac{1}{n}$.

16. $\displaystyle\sum_{n=1}^{\infty} \frac{\sin(n\pi/4)}{n!}$.

17. $\displaystyle\sum_{n=1}^{\infty} (-1)^{n+1} \frac{2^n}{n!}$.

18. $\displaystyle\sum_{n=1}^{\infty} (-1)^{n+1} \frac{n^2}{2^n}$.

19. $\displaystyle\sum_{n=1}^{\infty} (-1)^{n+1} \frac{\sqrt{2n-1}}{n}$.

20. $\displaystyle\sum_{n=1}^{\infty} a_n$ where $a_n = \begin{cases} -\dfrac{1}{n}, & n \text{ is a square,} \\[2mm] \dfrac{1}{n^2} & \text{otherwise.} \end{cases}$

21. $\displaystyle\sum_{n=1}^{\infty} a_n$ where $a_n = \begin{cases} -\dfrac{1}{n}, & n \text{ a multiple of 3,} \\[2mm] \dfrac{1}{n^2} & \text{otherwise.} \end{cases}$

22. If $\sum |a_n|$ converges, prove that $\sum a_n^2$ converges. Find an example in which $\sum a_n^2$ converges but $\sum |a_n|$ diverges.

23. Is it true that $\sum a_n$ converges absolutely $\Rightarrow \sum a_n^2/(1+a_n^2)$ converges? Explain.

⋆24. Show that $\sum a_n$ converges absolutely $\Rightarrow \sum a_n/(1 + a_n)$ converges absolutely, provided no $a_n = -1$. Is this valid without "absolutely"?

25. Show that the harmonic series, with the terms of the form $1/2^n$ omitted,

$$\frac{1}{3} + \frac{1}{5} + \frac{1}{6} + \frac{1}{7} + \frac{1}{9} + \frac{1}{10} + \cdots,$$

is divergent. *Hint:* The sum of the first $2^n$ terms is

$$\left(1 + \frac{1}{2} + \frac{1}{3} + \cdots + \frac{1}{2^n}\right) - \left(1 + \frac{1}{2} + \frac{1}{4} + \cdots + \frac{1}{2^n}\right).$$

## 22.7 NUMERICAL APPROXIMATION OF A CONVERGENT SERIES

Since it is rarely practical to find a simple form for the numerical value to which a given series converges, it is often necessary to obtain an estimate or an approximation for this value by summing a finite number of terms of the series. Consequently, it is also desirable to indicate the amount of *break-off error* resulting from the fact that the terms of the series are not used after some point. An estimate for this break-off error was given in Section 22.4 by means of the Integral Test.

For certain alternating series we have a very simple method of estimating break-off error.

**Theorem 22.7a.** Let

$$\sum_{n=1}^{\infty} (-1)^{n-1} u_n, \qquad u_n > 0,$$

be an alternating series that converges by Leibniz's Test to a value $U$. Then

$$\left| U - \sum_{k=1}^{n} (-1)^{k-1} u_k \right| < u_{n+1}.$$

PROOF: To show this result we need only consider the value of the remaining series, $\sum_{k=n+1}^{\infty} (-1)^{k-1} u_k$. By the argument used in the proof of Theorem 22.6b, we know that the value of this series is no greater than $u_{n+1}$. The details are left for the reader.

According to Theorem 22.7a, the break-off error for a series that converges by Leibniz's Test is less in absolute value than the first term that is omitted. The use of this result is illustrated in the next example.

---

*Example 22.7a.* How many terms of the series

$$\sum_{n=1}^{\infty} (-1)^{n-1} \frac{1}{2^n}$$

must be used to find the value of the series correct to three decimal places?

Since we must have

$$\frac{1}{2^n} < 0.0005 = \frac{1}{2000},$$

it follows that $n = 11$ and that the sum of the first 10 terms will have the desired accuracy. (This result assumes that the terms will be left in exact form so that no round-off error occurs.)

---

The ratio test may frequently be used to obtain break-off error information.

**Theorem 22.7b.** Suppose the series $\sum_{n=1}^{\infty} u_n$ is absolutely convergent by the Ratio Test. If

$$\lim_{n \to \infty} \left| \frac{u_{n+1}}{u_n} \right| = r < R < 1,$$

then for $M$ sufficiently large,

$$\sum_{k=M+1}^{\infty} u_k < \frac{|u_{M+1}|}{1 - R}.$$

PROOF: Since $\lim_{n \to \infty} \left| \dfrac{u_{n+1}}{u_n} \right| = r < R$, then, for $M$ large enough, we have

$$|u_{M+2}| < R|u_{M+1}|,$$

and

$$|u_{M+p}| < R^{p-1}|u_{M+1}|.$$

Hence,

$$\sum_{k=M+1}^{\infty} |u_k| \leqq |u_{M+1}| + R|u_{M+1}| + \cdots + R^{p-1}|u_{M+1}| + \cdots,$$

or

$$\sum_{k=M+1}^{\infty} |u_k| < \frac{|u_{M+1}|}{1 - R}.$$

It follows that

$$\left| \sum_{k=M+1}^{\infty} u_k \right| < \frac{|u_{M+1}|}{1 - R},$$

since

$$\left| \sum_{k=M+1}^{\infty} u_k \right| \leqq \sum_{k=M+1}^{\infty} |u_k|.$$

Thus, the expression $|u_{M+1}|/(1 - R)$ may be used to determine an upper bound on the error incurred by neglecting the terms of the series after the $M$th term. Any value of $M$ may be used for which $|u_{M+2}| < R|u_{M+1}|$ once the $R$ is chosen, but the results are, of course, not valid for values of $M$ for which $|u_{M+2}| \geqq R|u_{M+1}|$. In case $|u_{n+1}/u_n| < r$ for all $n$, then $r$ itself may be used.

---

*Example 22.7b.* What error is made in the value of $\sum_{n=1}^{\infty} 1/(n5^n)$ by using the first six terms of the series?

Since

$$\frac{u_{n+1}}{u_n} = \frac{1}{(n+1)5^{n+1}} \cdot \frac{n5^n}{1} = \frac{1}{(1+1/n)5} < \frac{1}{5},$$

we may take $R = \frac{1}{5}$, which gives

$$\sum_{k=7}^{\infty} u_k < \frac{\dfrac{1}{7(5^7)}}{4/5} < 0.0000023,$$

which is an upper bound on the break-off error. A lower bound on the break-off error is easily obtained, since the error for the series in this example is certainly greater than the first term omitted. Thus,

$$\frac{1}{7(5^7)} < \sum_{k=7}^{\infty} u_k,$$

or

$$0.0000018 < \sum_{k=7}^{\infty} u_k.$$

---

Another interesting question is associated with the reordering or rearrangement of the terms of a given convergent series. It has been shown that the insertion of parentheses in an infinite series may cause drastic changes in the behavior of the series. In a similar way, rearranging the order of the terms of a series may cause a radical change in the behavior of the series.

**Definition 22.7a.** If two different series $\sum_{n=1}^{\infty} u_n$ and $\sum_{n=1}^{\infty} v_n$ are related so that every $u_n$ is some $v_k$ and every $v_n$ is some $u_k$, then one series is said to be a **rearrangement** of the other.

The following example illustrates this definition and the remarks made earlier.

---

*Example 22.7c.* Show that the series

$$1 + \frac{1}{3} - \frac{1}{2} + \frac{1}{5} + \frac{1}{7} - \frac{1}{4} + \frac{1}{9} + \frac{1}{11} - \frac{1}{6} + \cdots,$$

where $a_{3n-2} = 1/(4n-3)$, $a_{3n-1} = 1/(4n-1)$, $a_{3n} = -1/2n$, is a rearrangement of the series

$$1 - \frac{1}{2} + \frac{1}{3} - \frac{1}{4} + \frac{1}{5} - \cdots + (-1)^{n-1}\frac{1}{n} + \cdots,$$

and if

$$\ln 2 = \sum_{n=1}^{\infty} \frac{(-1)^{n+1}}{n},$$

find the value of the rearranged series.

To show that the first series is a rearrangement of the second, we need only observe that every term of one series occurs somewhere in the other series. To find the value of the rearranged series, observe that from the expression

$$\ln 2 = 1 - \frac{1}{2} + \frac{1}{3} - \frac{1}{4} + \frac{1}{5} - \frac{1}{6} + \cdots,$$

we get

$$\frac{1}{2} \ln 2 = \frac{1}{2} - \frac{1}{4} + \frac{1}{6} - \frac{1}{8} + \frac{1}{10} - \frac{1}{12} + \cdots,$$

which may be written as

$$\frac{1}{2} \ln 2 = 0 + \frac{1}{2} + 0 - \frac{1}{4} + 0 + \frac{1}{6} + 0 - \frac{1}{8} + \cdots$$

By adding

$$\ln 2 = 1 - \frac{1}{2} + \frac{1}{3} - \frac{1}{4} + \frac{1}{5} - \frac{1}{6} + \frac{1}{7} - \frac{1}{8} + \cdots$$

term by term to the preceding series, we get

$$\frac{3}{2} \ln 2 = 1 + 0 + \frac{1}{3} - \frac{1}{2} + \frac{1}{5} + 0 + \frac{1}{7} - \frac{1}{4} + \cdots$$

$$= 1 + \frac{1}{3} - \frac{1}{2} + \frac{1}{5} + \frac{1}{7} - \frac{1}{4} + \cdots$$

---

An **essential** rearrangement of the terms of a series occurs if there is no term beyond which the series assumes its original order. Example 22.7c shows that the value of the rearranged series may be different from the value of the original series. In this connection, we state without proof

**Theorem 22.7c.** The value of an absolutely convergent series is unaltered by any rearrangement of its terms. The value of a conditionally convergent series may be altered in an arbitrary manner, and the series may even be made divergent by a suitable rearrangement of the terms.

## Exercises 22.7

In each of Numbers 1 to 6, find upper and lower bounds on the break-off error if the value of the series is approximated by the first four terms.

1. $\sum_{n=1}^{\infty} \frac{1}{n!}$.

2. $\sum_{n=1}^{\infty} \frac{n}{10^n}$.

3. $\sum_{n=1}^{\infty} \frac{(-1)^{n-1}}{n \cdot 4^n}$.

4. $\sum_{n=1}^{\infty} \frac{(-1)^n}{2^n}$.

5. $\sum_{n=1}^{\infty} \frac{2^n}{n^n}$.

6. $\sum_{n=1}^{\infty} \frac{(-1)^{n-1}}{2n - 1}$.

In each of Numbers 7 to 10, find how many terms must be used so that the break-off error will not exceed 0.0005.

7. $\displaystyle\sum_{n=1}^{\infty} \frac{n}{10^n}.$

8. $\displaystyle\sum_{n=1}^{\infty} \frac{1}{2^n + 1}.$

9. $\displaystyle\sum_{n=1}^{\infty} e^{-n^2}.$

10. $\displaystyle\sum_{n=1}^{\infty} \frac{2^n}{n!}.$

In each of Numbers 11 to 16, calculate the value of the series correct to 4 decimal places.

11. $\displaystyle\sum_{n=1}^{\infty} \frac{n}{10^n}.$

12. $\displaystyle\sum_{n=1}^{\infty} \frac{(0.2)^n}{n!}.$

13. $\displaystyle\sum_{n=1}^{\infty} \frac{(-1)^{n-1}}{2^n}.$

14. $\displaystyle\sum_{n=1}^{\infty} \frac{(-1)^{n-1}}{n \cdot 5^n}.$

15. $\displaystyle\sum_{n=1}^{\infty} \frac{(-1)^{n-1}}{n!}.$

16. $\displaystyle\sum_{n=1}^{\infty} \frac{1}{n\,(n!)}.$

★17. Show that

$$1 + \frac{1}{3} + \frac{1}{5} - \frac{1}{2} - \frac{1}{4} - \frac{1}{6} + \cdots = \ln 2,$$

where the given series is a rearrangement of the series

$$\sum_{n=1}^{\infty} \frac{(-1)^{n-1}}{n} = \ln 2$$

obtained by taking alternately three positive and then three negative terms.

★18. Show that

$$1 - \frac{1}{2} - \frac{1}{4} + \frac{1}{3} - \frac{1}{6} - \frac{1}{8} + \cdots = \frac{1}{2}\ln 2,$$

where the given series is a rearrangement of the series

$$\sum_{n=1}^{\infty} \frac{(-1)^{n-1}}{n} = \ln 2$$

obtained by taking alternately one positive and then two negative terms.

# Summary of Chapter 22

The fundamental ideas presented in this chapter must be mastered before Chapter 23 is studied. These ideas include:

(1) the definition of convergent and divergent sequences (Section 22.1);
(2) the convergence of bounded monotonic sequences (Section 22.1);

(3) the Cauchy Convergence Criterion for infinite sequences (Section 22.1);

(4) the definition of an infinite series (as distinguished from that of an infinite sequence) (Section 22.2);

(5) the definition of convergence and divergence of an infinite series (Section 22.2);

(6) a necessary condition for the convergence of an infinite series (Section 22.2);

(7) the harmonic series (Section 22.2);

(8) the Cauchy Convergence Criterion for series (Section 22.3);

(9) the comparison tests for series (Section 22.3);

(10) the integral test (Section 22.4);

(11) the use of the integral test in obtaining bounds on convergent series (Section 22.4);

(12) the Cauchy Ratio Test (Section 22.5);

(13) the Cauchy root test (Section 22.5);

(14) absolute and conditional convergence (Section 22.6);

(15) the alternating series test (Leibniz's Test) (Section 22.6);

(16) numerical approximations for a convergent series and break-off error (Section 22.7).

# Chapter 23    Power Series and Expansion of Functions

## 23.1 SERIES OF VARIABLE TERMS

Whereas the preceding chapter dealt with series of constant terms, the present chapter will deal with series of variable terms. The following are examples of such series:

(a) $$\sum_{n=0}^{\infty} e^{nx} = 1 + e^x + e^{2x} + \cdots,$$

(b) $$\sum_{n=1}^{\infty} \frac{\cos nx}{n^2 + 1} = \frac{1}{2}\cos x + \frac{1}{5}\cos 2x + \frac{1}{10}\cos 3x + \cdots,$$

(c) $$\sum_{n=0}^{\infty} \frac{x^n}{(n+1)^2} = 1 + \frac{x}{4} + \frac{x^2}{9} + \cdots.$$

In these series, the terms are all functions of a single variable, and are thus examples of the general type of series symbolized by

$$\sum_{n=0}^{\infty} u_n(x) = u_0(x) + u_1(x) + u_2(x) + \cdots,$$

where it is assumed that there is some nonempty set common to the domains of $u_1, u_2, u_3, \ldots,$.

As we saw in the last chapter, an important question for a series of constant terms, $\sum a_n$, is: *Does the series converge?* The corresponding question for a series of variable terms, $\sum u_n(x)$, is: *For what real values of $x$, if any, does the series converge?* Since for each fixed $x$, in the domain on which all the $u_n$'s are defined, the series is one of constant terms, we shall expect to use the methods of Chapter 22 for most of our investigations. Evidently, the series "represents" a number, the number to which it converges, for each $x$ for which it converges. Hence, we may regard the series as defining a function whose domain consists of the values of $x$ for which the series converges.

It is not difficult to determine the values of $x$ for which each of the series in the preceding examples converges.

(a)
$$\sum_{n=0}^{\infty} e^{nx}.$$

Since $e^{(n+1)x}/e^{nx} = e^x$, the series is a geometric series with ratio $r = e^x$. We know that the geometric series converges if $|r| < 1$ and diverges if $|r| \geq 1$. Furthermore $e^x > 0$, so that the given series converges if $e^x < 1$, that is, if $x < 0$; and diverges if $e^x \geq 1$, that is, if $x \geq 0$. This series, being geometric, can actually be "summed" to the value $1/(1 - e^x)$, so that

$$\sum_{n=0}^{\infty} e^{nx} = \frac{1}{1 - e^x}, \qquad x < 0.$$

(b)
$$\sum_{n=1}^{\infty} \frac{\cos nx}{n^2 + 1}.$$

From the inequality $|\cos nx| \leq 1$, it follows that

$$\left| \frac{\cos nx}{n^2 + 1} \right| \leq \frac{1}{n^2 + 1}.$$

Moreover,

$$\frac{1}{n^2 + 1} < \frac{1}{n^2}.$$

Since $\sum_{n=1}^{\infty} 1/n^2$ is a convergent $p$-series, the Comparison Test shows that

$$\sum_{n=1}^{\infty} \left| \frac{\cos nx}{n^2 + 1} \right|$$

converges for each fixed value of $x$. Consequently, the given series converges absolutely for all real values of $x$.

(c)
$$\sum_{n=0}^{\infty} \frac{x^n}{(n + 1)^2}.$$

See Number 5 of the next set of exercises.

## Exercises 23.1

1. For what values of $x$ does the series $\sum_{n=0}^{\infty} e^{-nx^2}$ converge?
2. Show that $\sum_{n=1}^{\infty} (\sin nx)/n^2$ converges absolutely for all values of $x$.
3. Use the ratio test to show that the series $\sum_{n=1}^{\infty} e^{-nx}/n^2$ converges for $x > 0$. The series clearly diverges for $x < 0$. Why? What can you say for $x = 0$?
4. Are there any values of $x$ for which the series $\sum_{n=0}^{\infty} \cos nx$ converges? *Hint:* What can you say about $\lim_{n \to \infty} \cos nx$?
5. Show by means of the ratio test that the series in Example (c) on page 866 converges for $|x| < 1$ and diverges for $|x| > 1$. Observe the constant term series that results when you substitute $x = 1$ or $x = -1$ in the given series. Do these two series converge?
6. For what values of $x$ does the series $\sum_{n=1}^{\infty} n^{-x}$ converge? Explain.

7. Apply the Ratio Test to show that the series

$$\sum_{n=1}^{\infty} \frac{1}{n^2} \left( \frac{x}{1+x} \right)^n$$

converges for $x > -\frac{1}{2}$ and diverges for $x < -\frac{1}{2}$. What happens for $x = -\frac{1}{2}$?

8. For what values of $x$ does the geometric series

$$\sum_{n=1}^{\infty} \left( \frac{2x}{x-1} \right)^n$$

converge?

9. Show that the series

$$\sum_{n=1}^{\infty} \frac{1}{n^2} \left( \frac{x}{1+x^2} \right)^n$$

converges for all values of $x$. *Hint:* What is the maximum absolute value of $x/(1+x^2)$?

10. Show that the series

$$\sum_{n=1}^{\infty} \frac{\sec^2 nx}{n}$$

diverges for all values of $x$. *Hint:* What is the minimum value of $\sec^2 nx$?

11. Show that the series

$$\sum_{n=1}^{\infty} \frac{(-1)^{n-1}}{n-x}$$

converges for $x \notin \mathfrak{N}$. *Hint:* The series is eventually a simple alternating series.

12. Use the Ratio Test to show that the series $\sum_{n=1}^{\infty} n^2/x^n$ converges for $|x| > 1$ and diverges for $|x| < 1$. What can you say for $x = \pm 1$?

13. Two positive integers are said to be **relatively prime** if they have no common positive integral factors other than 1. Thus, 4 and 9 are relatively prime, as are 18 and 35. The Euler $\varphi$-function is defined on the set $\mathfrak{N}$ as follows: $\varphi(1) .=. 1$, and $\varphi(m) .=.$ the number of positive integers less than $m$ and relatively prime to $m$. For example, $\varphi(5) = 4$, since 1, 2, 3, 4 are all less than 5 and relatively prime to 5. Similarly, $\varphi(9) = 6$, since 1, 2, 4, 5, 7, 8 are all less than 9 and relatively prime to 9. Consider the infinite series

$$\sum_{m=1}^{\infty} \varphi(m)x^m = x + x^2 + 2x^3 + 2x^4 + 4x^5 + 2x^6 + \cdots.$$

Prove that this series is absolutely convergent for $|x| < 1$. *Hint:* $\varphi(m) \leq m$. You can't use the Ratio Test. Why?

14. A positive real number is defined to be an infinite decimal

$$a_0 . a_1 a_2 a_3 \ldots a_n \ldots,$$

where $a_0$ is a nonnegative integer and each of $a_1, a_2, a_3, \ldots$ is a digit. Show that this decimal can be written as an infinite series and that the series always converges. *Hint:* $0 \leq a_n \leq 9$, $n \geq 1$.

## 23.2 POWER SERIES

For the purposes of elementary calculus the most important series of variable terms are those of the form

$$\sum_{n=0}^{\infty} c_n(x - a)^n = c_0 + c_1(x - a) + c_2(x - a)^2 + \cdots,$$

where $a$ is a constant and the $c$'s are constant coefficients. This type of series is called a **power series** because its terms proceed in powers of the binomial $(x - a)$. Notice that for ease in including the first term $(n = 0)$ in the general formula, it is customary to define $(x - a)^0 = 1$ for $x = a$.

We shall pay special attention to the case for which $a = 0$ since the general power series $\sum_{n=0}^{\infty} c_n(x - a)^n$ may be regarded as arising from the more special type

$$\sum_{n=0}^{\infty} c_n x^n$$

by a shift of the origin, that is, by a replacement of $x$ by $x - a$. Consequently, the entire theory of power series may be obtained by consideration of this somewhat simpler special case.

The behavior of power series with respect to convergence can be illustrated by means of a few specific examples.

(a) The geometric series $\sum_{n=0}^{\infty} x^n$ converges absolutely to the sum $(1 - x)^{-1}$ for $|x| < 1$ and diverges for all other values of $x$.

(b) The Ratio Test shows that the series $\sum_{n=0}^{\infty} x^n/n!$ converges absolutely for all values of $x$, since for each fixed $x \neq 0$,

$$\lim_{n \to \infty} \left| \frac{u_{n+1}}{u_n} \right| = \lim_{n \to \infty} \left| \frac{x^{n+1}}{(n + 1)!} \frac{n!}{x^n} \right| = \lim_{n \to \infty} \left| \frac{x}{n + 1} \right| = 0.$$

(c) Consider the series $\sum_{n=0}^{\infty} n! x^n$. For $x = 0$, we have the series $1 + 0 + 0 + \cdots$, which clearly converges to the value 1. For $x \neq 0$, we may apply the Ratio Test to get

$$\lim_{n \to \infty} \left| \frac{u_{n+1}}{u_n} \right| = \lim_{n \to \infty} \left| \frac{(n + 1)! x^{n+1}}{n! x^n} \right| = \lim_{n \to \infty} |(n + 1)x| = \infty.$$

Thus the series diverges for all nonzero values of $x$.

These three simple examples illustrate the entire range of behavior that is possible for power series of the type $\sum_{n=0}^{\infty} c_n x^n$, as the following theorems show.

**Theorem 23.2a.** $\sum_{n=0}^{\infty} c_n x_1^n$ converges $\Rightarrow \sum_{n=0}^{\infty} c_n x^n$ converges absolutely for all $x$ such that $|x| < |x_1|$.

PROOF: $\sum_{n=0}^{\infty} c_n x_1^n$ converges $\Rightarrow |c_n x_1^n|$ is bounded (why?), say $|c_n x_1^n| < B$, where $B$ is a constant for all $n$. Hence,

$$|c_n x^n| = \left| c_n x_1^n \frac{x^n}{x_1^n} \right| = |c_n x_1^n| \left| \frac{x}{x_1} \right|^n < B \left| \frac{x}{x_1} \right|^n.$$

Since

$$|x| < |x_1| \Rightarrow \left|\frac{x}{x_1}\right| < 1,$$

it follows that $\sum_{n=0}^{\infty} B|x/x_1|^n$ is a convergent geometric series. Therefore, $\sum_{n=0}^{\infty} |c_n x^n|$ is convergent by the Comparison Test.

**Theorem 23.2b.** $\sum_{n=0}^{\infty} c_n x_2^n$ diverges $\Rightarrow \sum_{n=0}^{\infty} c_n x^n$ diverges for all $x$ such that $|x| > |x_2|$.

PROOF: Left for the reader. *Hint:* Suppose the theorem is false and the series converges for some $x$ such that $|x| > |x_2|$.

On the basis of these two theorems, we can prove

**Theorem 23.2c.** Every power series $\sum_{n=0}^{\infty} c_n x^n$ behaves in one of the following three ways.

(a) It converges only for the value $x = 0$.

(b) It converges absolutely for all values of $x$.

(c) There exists a positive number $R$ such that the series converges absolutely for $|x| < R$ and diverges for $|x| > R$.

PROOF: By direct substitution, we see that every power series $\sum_{n=0}^{\infty} c_n x^n$ converges for $x = 0$. If the series converges for no other values of $x$, then we have case (a).

If the series does converge for some $x_1 \neq 0$, then by Theorem 23.2a it converges absolutely for $|x| < |x_1|$. There still remain two possibilities: there is some $x_2$, $|x_2| > |x_1|$, for which the series diverges; or else there is no such $x_2$.

Suppose first that there is no such $x_2$, then we clearly must have a series that converges absolutely for all values of $x$. This is case (b).

Suppose next that this $x_2$ does exist. Then $|x_2|$ is an upper bound of the set of values of $|x|$ for which the series converges. Consequently, this set must have a least upper bound, which must be the $R$ of case (c). Thus, the proof is complete.

The number $R$ in Theorem 23.2c is called the **radius of convergence**, and the interval $-R < x < R$, the **interval of convergence** of the power series. In view of the manner in which $\sum_{n=0}^{\infty} c_n(x - a)^n$ can be obtained from $\sum_{n=0}^{\infty} c_n x^n$, it should be evident that each statement of the theorem applies to the more general type of series if $x$ is replaced everywhere by $x - a$ without any other alteration. The interval of convergence accordingly has its midpoint at $x = a$.

Probably the most useful elementary tool for finding the interval of convergence is the Ratio Test. This test will, of course, not tell us what happens at the end points of the interval, since at those points $\lim |u_{n+1}/u_n| = 1$, and the Ratio Test fails. By working out a few of the exercises at the end of this section, the reader will see that anything can happen at the end points. Quite often the end-point behavior of a power series is beyond the scope of our simple tests to determine. There is some consolation, however, in the fact that even if the series does converge at an end point, the convergence is so slow that the series is relatively impractical to use for direct computational purposes, although it may still be important and useful for other purposes.

---

*Example 23.2a.* Find the interval of convergence and test the end points for the series

$$\sum_{n=0}^{\infty} \frac{(-1)^n x^n}{(n+1)3^n}.$$

We apply the Ratio Test and find

$$\lim_{n\to\infty} \left| \frac{u_{n+1}}{u_n} \right| = \lim_{n\to\infty} \left| \frac{(-1)^{n+1} x^{n+1}}{(n+2)3^{n+1}} \frac{(n+1)3^n}{(-1)^n x^n} \right|$$

$$= \lim_{n\to\infty} \left| \frac{(n+1)x}{3(n+2)} \right| = \frac{|x|}{3}.$$

Hence, the series converges for

$$\frac{|x|}{3} < 1, \quad \text{or} \quad |x| < 3.$$

Thus, the radius of convergence is 3, and the interval of convergence is

$$-3 < x < 3.$$

The behavior at the end points is determined by replacing $x$ in the original series by the end point values. For $x = -3$, the series is

$$\sum_{n=0}^{\infty} \frac{(-1)^n (-3)^n}{(n+1)3^n} = \sum_{n=0}^{\infty} \frac{1}{n+1},$$

the harmonic series, which is divergent. For $x = 3$, the series is

$$\sum_{n=0}^{\infty} \frac{(-1)^n 3^n}{(n+1)3^n} = \sum_{n=0}^{\infty} \frac{(-1)^n}{n+1},$$

which is convergent by Leibniz's Test for alternating series.

To summarize, we have shown that the series converges for $-3 < x \leq 3$, and thus defines a function having this interval as its domain.

---

*Example 23.2b.* Determine the domain on which a function is defined by the series

$$\sum_{n=1}^{\infty} \frac{(x+4)^{2n-1}}{2n-1}.$$

By applying the Ratio Test, we find

$$\lim_{n\to\infty} \left| \frac{u_{n+1}}{u_n} \right| = \lim_{n\to\infty} \left| \frac{(x+4)^{2n+1}}{2n+1} \frac{2n-1}{(x+4)^{2n-1}} \right|$$

$$= \lim_{n\to\infty} \left| \frac{(x+4)^2(2n-1)}{2n+1} \right| = (x+4)^2.$$

The interval of convergence is thus found from

$$(x+4)^2 < 1 \implies -1 < x+4 < 1 \implies -5 < x < -3.$$

For $x = -5$, the given series becomes

$$\sum_{n=1}^{\infty} \frac{(-1)^{2n-1}}{2n-1} = -\sum_{n=1}^{\infty} \frac{1}{2n-1},$$

which is easily shown to be divergent by the Integral Test.
For $x = -3$, the series becomes $\sum_{n=1}^{\infty} 1/(2n-1)$, which is also divergent.
Thus, the given power series defines a function on the interval

$$-5 < x < -3.$$

---

*Example 23.2c.* Find the interval of convergence of the power series

$$\sum_{n=1}^{\infty} \frac{x^n \sin n}{n^2}.$$

In this problem, the Ratio Test is useless, since it would involve

$$\lim_{n \to \infty} \left| \frac{\sin (n+1)}{\sin n} \right|,$$

which does not exist. However, since $|\sin n| \leq 1$, we have

$$\left| \frac{x^n \sin n}{n^2} \right| \leq \left| \frac{x^n}{n^2} \right|.$$

It is easy to show that

$$\sum_{n=1}^{\infty} \left| \frac{x^n}{n^2} \right|$$

converges for the interval $-1 \leq x \leq 1$. Consequently, the given series is also convergent on this interval by the Comparison Test.
Furthermore, for $|x| > 1$, the given series diverges since, in this case,

$$\lim_{n \to \infty} u_n = \lim_{n \to \infty} \frac{x^n \sin n}{n^2}$$

does not exist. This follows because $\lim_{n \to \infty} |x^n/n^2| = \infty$ for $|x| > 1$ and $\lim_{n \to \infty} \sin n$
does not exist.

## Exercises 23.2

Find the interval of convergence and test the end points for the series in Numbers 1
to 20.

1. $\displaystyle\sum_{n=0}^{\infty} (-1)^n \frac{x^n}{n^2 + 1}.$

2. $\displaystyle\sum_{n=0}^{\infty} \frac{(n+1)x^n}{n!}.$

3. $\displaystyle\sum_{n=0}^{\infty} x^{2n}.$

4. $\displaystyle\sum_{n=0}^{\infty} \frac{(-1)^n x^{2n+1}}{2n+1}.$

5. $\displaystyle\sum_{n=0}^{\infty} \frac{x^{2n+1}}{(2n+1)!}.$

6. $\displaystyle\sum_{n=0}^{\infty} \frac{(x/2)^n}{(n!)^2}.$

7. $\sum_{n=0}^{\infty} (2n + 1)!x^{2n+1}$.

14. $\sum_{n=1}^{\infty} \frac{(-1)^{n-1}x^{n-1}}{2^{1/n}}$.

8. $\sum_{n=1}^{\infty} \frac{x^{n^2}}{n}$.

15. $\sum_{n=1}^{\infty} \frac{(-1)^{n-1}}{n^2} \left(\frac{x-5}{2}\right)^n$.

9. $\sum_{n=1}^{\infty} \frac{(-1)^{n-1}x^n}{2^n n}$.

16. $\sum_{n=0}^{\infty} \frac{1}{n!x^n}$.

10. $\sum_{n=1}^{\infty} n^2 x^n$.

17. $\sum_{n=1}^{\infty} \frac{(-1)^{n-1}n}{x^n}$.

11. $\sum_{n=0}^{\infty} \frac{n!(x+1)^n}{2n+1}$.

18. $\sum_{n=1}^{\infty} (n+1)^n(x-1)^n$.

12. $\sum_{n=1}^{\infty} \frac{(-1)^{n-1}(x-2)^n}{3^{n-1}(2n+1)}$.

19. $\sum_{n=1}^{\infty} \frac{(x+2)^n}{n^2}$.

13. $\sum_{n=1}^{\infty} \frac{x^n}{\sqrt{3n}}$.

20. $\sum_{n=1}^{\infty} \sqrt{n}x^{2n}$.

21. Suppose we play a game to construct an infinite series $\sum_{n=1}^{\infty} a_n x^n$ in the following fashion: To evaluate $a_n$, toss a fair coin $n$ times and let $a_n$ be the number of times the coin turns up heads. It is quite unlikely that two different people playing this game would come up with the same series. Regardless of this, show that the series must converge at least for $|x| < 1$.

22. Suppose $\sum_{n=0}^{\infty} a_n(t)x^n$ is a power series in $x$ with coefficients that are functions of another variable $t$, the domain of these coefficients being all real numbers. Suppose further that $|a_n(t)| \leq e^n$ for all real values of $t$. Based on this information, what is the least interval in which the power series must converge?

## 23.3 THE TAYLOR FORMULA

In this section we shall derive a basic formula that leads directly to the representation of the value of a function by means of a power series. We shall suppose that both the numbers $a$ and $x$ lie in an interval on which the function $f$ and its first $n$ derivatives are continuous, and we shall try to express the value $f(x)$ in terms of $x - a$ and the values of the function and its derivatives at $a$.

With the assumed continuity properties of $f$, we know that

$$f(x) - f(a) = \int_a^x f'(t) \, dt,$$

or

$$f(x) = f(a) + \int_a^x f'(t) \, dt.$$

In order to get the quantity $x - a$ into this formula, we make use of a small trick in conjunction with integration by parts. Let

$$u = f'(t) \quad \text{and} \quad dv = dt,$$

so that

$$du = f''(t) dt \quad \text{and} \quad v = t - x,$$

where $x$ is introduced as a constant of integration. This is permissible, since if $x$ plays the role of a constant, then $dv = d(t - x) = dt$. Thus,

$$f(x) = f(a) + [(t - x)f'(t)]_a^x - \int_a^x (t - x)f''(t) \, dt$$

$$= f(a) + (x - a)f'(a) + \int_a^x (x - t)f''(t) \, dt$$

Integrating by parts again with

$$u = f''(t) \quad \text{and} \quad dv = (x - t) \, dt,$$

so that

$$du = f'''(t) \, dt \quad \text{and} \quad v = -\frac{(x - t)^2}{2},$$

we get

$$f(x) = f(a) + (x - a)f'(a) + \frac{(x - a)^2}{2} f''(a) + \int_a^x \frac{(x - t)^2}{2} f'''(t) \, dt.$$

By repeated application of this integration by parts, we arrive at the result

$$f(x) = f(a) + \frac{f'(a)}{1!}(x - a) + \frac{f''(a)}{2!}(x - a)^2 + \frac{f'''(a)}{3!}(x - a)^3 + \cdots$$

$$+ \frac{f^{(n-1)}(a)}{(n - 1)!}(x - a)^{n-1} + R_n,$$

where

$$R_n = \int_a^x \frac{(x - t)^{n-1}}{(n - 1)!} f^{(n)}(t) \, dt.$$

The number $R_n$ in the preceding formula is called the **remainder after $n$ terms** of the series in powers of $x - a$. This remainder can be put into a somewhat more useful form for our purposes by noting that $x - t$ does not change sign on the interval of integration, so that

$$|R_n| \leq (\max |f^{(n)}(t)|) \left| \int_a^x \frac{(x - t)^{n-1}}{(n - 1)!} \, dt \right|,$$

where $\max |f^{(n)}(t)|$ stands for the maximum absolute value of $f^{(n)}(t)$ on the closed interval from $a$ to $x$. By performing the last integration, we obtain the inequality

$$|R_n| \leq (\max |f^{(n)}(t)|) \left| \frac{(x - a)^n}{n!} \right|.$$

The preceding derivation constitutes the proof of

**Theorem 23.3a.** Let a function $f$ and its first $n$ derivatives be continuous in some neighborhood of a fixed point $a$. Then, if $x$ is in this neighborhood,

$$f(x) = f(a) + \frac{f'(a)}{1!}(x-a) + \frac{f''(a)}{2!}(x-a)^2 + \cdots$$

$$+ \frac{f^{(n-1)}(a)}{(n-1)!}(x-a)^{n-1} + R_n$$

$$= \sum_{k=0}^{n-1} \frac{f^{(k)}(a)}{k!}(x-a)^k + R_n,$$

where

$$|R_n| \leq (\max |f^{(n)}(t)|)\left|\frac{(x-a)^n}{n!}\right|,$$

$t$ being in the closed interval from $a$ to $x$.

The formula given in Theorem 23.3a is known as *Taylor's formula with a remainder*, named after the English mathematician Brook Taylor (1685–1731). The special form of the formula in which $a = 0$ is called *Maclaurin's formula* in honor of the Scotch mathematician Colin Maclaurin (1698–1746), although the formula had been obtained earlier by Taylor and by another British mathematician, James Stirling (1692–1770). All three of these men were friends and admirers of Sir Isaac Newton.

If a function possesses derivatives of all orders at $x = a$, then the process used in arriving at Taylor's formula may be continued indefinitely to arrive at an infinite series, called a **Taylor's series,** that corresponds to the function. This series, of course, has the form

$$\sum_{k=0}^{\infty} \frac{f^{(k)}(a)}{k!}(x-a)^k.$$

The unwary beginner is apt to jump to the conclusion that the Taylor's series obtained from a given function must converge to the value of that function at each point of the interval of convergence. Unfortunately, this conclusion is not true, as is illustrated by Number 27, Exercises 23.3. However, it is easily seen from Theorem 23.3a that for each $x$ in the interval of convergence,

$$f(x) = \sum_{k=0}^{\infty} \frac{f^{(k)}(a)}{k!}(x-a)^k \Leftrightarrow \lim_{n \to \infty} R_n = 0.$$

That is, the series actually represents the function from which it came if, and only if, the limit of the remainder is zero.

---

*Example 23.3a.* Find the Maclaurin's series ($a = 0$) for the cosine function, and show that the series converges to the value of the function for all real $x$.

We may write

$$
\begin{array}{lllll}
f(x) & = & \cos x, & f(0) & = & 1, \\
f'(x) & = & -\sin x, & f'(0) & = & 0, \\
f''(x) & = & -\cos x, & f''(0) & = & -1, \\
f'''(x) & = & \sin x, & f'''(0) & = & 0, \\
f^{(4)}(x) & = & \cos x, & f^{(4)}(0) & = & 1,
\end{array}
$$

and so on. In general, $f^{(n)}(x) = \cos(x + n\pi/2)$ and $f^{(n)}(0) = \cos(n\pi/2)$. Hence, the Maclaurin's formula for $\cos x$ is

$$\cos x = 1 + 0 - \frac{x^2}{2!} + 0 + \frac{x^4}{4!} + 0 - \cdots + \frac{(-1)^n x^{2n-2}}{(2n-2)!} + 0 + R_{2n},$$

where

$$|R_{2n}| \leq \left|\frac{x^{2n}}{(2n)!}\right| \max |f^{(2n)}(t)| \leq \frac{x^{2n}}{(2n)!} \max \left|\cos\left(t + \frac{n\pi}{2}\right)\right|,$$

and $t$ is in the interval from 0 to $x$, inclusive. Notice that $2n$ terms, half of which are zeros, have been used. Since $|\cos\theta| \leq 1$, it follows that

$$|R_{2n}| \leq \frac{x^{2n}}{(2n)!}.$$

Moreover, $x^{2n}/(2n)!$ is the general term of an infinite series that converges for all values of $x$, so that

$$\lim_{n\to\infty} \frac{x^{2n}}{(2n)!} = 0.$$

Accordingly,

$$\lim_{n\to\infty} R_{2n} = 0,$$

and thus the Maclaurin's series

$$\sum_{n=0}^{\infty} \frac{(-1)^n x^{2n}}{(2n)!} = 1 - \frac{x^2}{2!} + \frac{x^4}{4!} + \cdots$$

converges to $\cos x$ for all real values of $x$.

---

It can be shown by the kind of analysis in Example 23.3a that each of the familiar elementary functions is actually represented by its Taylor's series in the interval of convergence. This means that for these functions, wherever the series converges, it converges to the correct value.

---

*Example 23.3b.* How accurately can $\ln 1.04$ be computed if the first three nonzero terms of the Maclaurin's series for $\ln(1 + x)$ are used?

We have

$$\begin{array}{llll}
f(x) & = & \ln(1 + x), & f(0) & = & 0, \\
f'(x) & = & (1 + x)^{-1}, & f'(0) & = & 1, \\
f''(x) & = & -(1 + x)^{-2}, & f''(0) & = & -1, \\
f'''(x) & = & 2(1 + x)^{-3}, & f'''(0) & = & 2, \\
f^{(4)}(x) & = & -6(1 + x)^{-4}, & f^{(4)}(t) & = & -6(1 + t)^{-4}.
\end{array}$$

Thus

$$\ln(1 + x) = 0 + x - \frac{x^2}{2} + \frac{x^3}{3} + R_4,$$

where

$$|R_4| \leq (\max |f^{(4)}(t)|)\left(\frac{x^4}{4!}\right).$$

For $x = 0.04$,

$$|R_4| \leq \left(\max \left|\frac{6}{(1+t)^4}\right|\right) \frac{(0.04)^4}{24}, \qquad 0 \leq t \leq 0.04.$$

Consequently,

$$|R_4| \leq \frac{(0.04)^2}{4} = 0.000\ 000\ 64,$$

and

$$\ln 1.04 = 0.04 - \frac{(0.04)^2}{2} + \frac{(0.04)^3}{3},$$

with an error not exceeding 0.000 000 64.

---

*Example 23.3c.* For what values of $x > -1$ is the approximate formula

$$\ln (1 + x) = x - \tfrac{1}{2}x^2 + \tfrac{1}{3}x^3$$

correct to two decimal places?

Writing $f(x) = \ln (1 + x)$, from the preceding example we have

$$\ln (1 + x) = x - \tfrac{1}{2}x^2 + \tfrac{1}{3}x^3 + R_4,$$

where

$$|R_4| \leq \frac{x^4}{4!} \max |f^{(4)}(t)|,$$

with $t$ between 0 and $x$. Since $f^{(4)}(x) = -6(1 + x)^{-4}$,

$$|R_4| \leq \frac{x^4}{4} \max |1 + t|^{-4}.$$

For $x \geq 0$ and $0 < t < x$, $\max |1 + t|^{-4} = 1$ and $|R_4| \leq \tfrac{1}{4}x^4$. In order to have $|R_4| < 0.005$, we must have

$$\frac{x^4}{4} < 0.005 \quad \text{or} \quad x < \sqrt[4]{0.02} = 0.376+.$$

Thus, for nonnegative values of $x$, the formula is correct to two decimal places for $0 \leq x < 0.376$.

For $-1 < x < 0$ and $x < t < 0$, $\max |1 + t|^{-4} = (1 + x)^{-4}$, so that

$$|R_4| \leq \frac{1}{4} \left(\frac{x}{1 + x}\right)^4.$$

If $x = -y$, then

$$-1 < x < 0 \implies 0 < y < 1,$$

and the inequality

$$\frac{1}{4} \frac{y^4}{(1 - y)^4} < 0.005$$

$$\implies \quad \frac{y}{1 - y} < \sqrt[4]{0.02} = 0.376+$$

$$\implies \quad y < 0.274$$

$$\implies \quad -0.274 < x < 0.$$

Consequently, the approximate formula has the desired accuracy for

$$-0.274 < x < 0.376.$$

*Example 23.3d.* Find the Taylor's series for $\sin x$ in powers of $(x - \pi/4)$.

We use Theorem 23.3a with $f(x) = \sin x$ and $a = \pi/4$ to get

$$
\begin{array}{llll}
f(x) & = & \sin x, & f(\pi/4) & = & 1/\sqrt{2}, \\
f'(x) & = & \cos x, & f'(\pi/4) & = & 1/\sqrt{2}, \\
f''(x) & = & -\sin x, & f''(\pi/4) & = & -1/\sqrt{2}, \\
f'''(x) & = & -\cos x, & f'''(\pi/4) & = & -1/\sqrt{2}, \\
f^{(4)}(x) & = & \sin x, & f^{(4)}(\pi/4) & = & 1/\sqrt{2},
\end{array}
$$

and so on. Thus,

$$
\sin x = \frac{1}{\sqrt{2}} + \frac{1/\sqrt{2}}{1!}\left(x - \frac{\pi}{4}\right) - \frac{1/\sqrt{2}}{2!}\left(x - \frac{\pi}{4}\right)^2 - \frac{1/\sqrt{2}}{3!}\left(x - \frac{\pi}{4}\right)^3 + \cdots.
$$

Since $|f^{(n)}(\pi/4)| = 1/\sqrt{2}$, it can be shown that this series converges for all values of $x$ to the value of the function from which it was generated.

---

*Example 23.3e.* Show how $\sin 46°$ may be computed accurately to five decimal places by using an infinite series.

Since, as the reader may verify, the Maclaurin's series for $\sin x$ is

$$
\sin x = \sum_{n=0}^{\infty} \frac{(-1)^n x^{2n+1}}{(2n+1)!},
$$

and since this series converges for all values of $x$, the value of $\sin 46°$ could be computed by replacing $x$ by $46\pi/180$ or $23\pi/90$ in the series. However, the number of terms needed to attain the required accuracy can be greatly reduced by the use of a different power series.

Thus, taking $x = 23\pi/90$ in the series obtained in the preceding example, we get

$$
\sin 46° = \frac{\sqrt{2}}{2} + \left(\frac{\sqrt{2}}{2}\right)\left(\frac{\pi}{180}\right) - \frac{\sqrt{2}}{2}\left(\frac{\pi}{180}\right)^2 - \frac{\sqrt{2}}{2(3!)}\left(\frac{\pi}{180}\right)^3 + \cdots.
$$

The rapidity with which the powers of $\pi/180$ decrease assures us of a fairly efficient calculation.

It is easy to show that the break-off error here is certainly less than the last term retained. Hence, the first four terms would yield a result with

$$
|\text{error}| < \frac{\sqrt{2}}{2(3!)}\left(\frac{\pi}{180}\right)^3 < 0.000\ 000\ 63,
$$

and the desired accuracy is obtained by using the first four terms of the series.

## Exercises 23.3

In each of Numbers 1 to 6, find the Maclaurin's series for the designated function and determine the values of $x$ for which the series converges.

1. $\sin 2x$.
2. $\cos 3x$.
3. $e^x$.
4. $\ln(1 - x)$.

5. $\dfrac{1}{2 + x}$.

6. $\dfrac{1}{(1 + x)^2}$.

In each of Numbers 7 to 12, find the Taylor's series for the given function about the designated point $a$.

7. $\cos x$; $a = \pi/4$.

8. $\sin x$; $a = \pi/6$.

9. $e^x$; $a = 2$.

10. $\tan x$; $a = \pi/4$.

11. $\sqrt{x}$; $a = 1$.

12. $\sec x$; $a = \pi/6$.

13. Show that in the Maclaurin's formula for $e^x$,

$$|R_n| \leq \frac{x^n e^x}{n!} \text{ for } x > 0 \quad \text{and} \quad |R_n| \leq \frac{|x^n|}{n!} \text{ for } x < 0.$$

14. Use the results of Number 13 to show that the Maclaurin's series for $e^x$ actually converges to $e^x$.

15. For what values of $x$ is the approximate formula $e^x = 1 + x$ correct to two decimal places?

16. Show that the Maclaurin's series for $\sin x$ converges to $\sin x$.

17. For what values of $x$ is the approximate formula $\sin x = x$ correct to two decimal places?

18. For what values of $x$ is the approximate formula $\cos x = 1 - \frac{1}{2}x^2$ correct to two decimal places?

In Numbers 19 to 22, use series to evaluate the given number correct to five decimal places.

19. $\cos 29°$.

20. $\ln 1.01$.

21. $\sin 61°$.

22. $\cos 44°$.

23. Use the equation

$$\text{Tan}^{-1} x = \int_0^x \frac{dt}{1 + t^2}$$

to show that the absolute value of the difference between $\text{Tan}^{-1} x$ and the first terms of its Maclaurin's series is less than the absolute value of the first term omitted for $-1 \leq x \leq 1$. This proves that the series actually converges to the proper functional value in this interval. *Hint:* Expand $(1 + t^2)^{-1}$ by long division and consider the remainder.

24. Calculate $\text{Tan}^{-1} 0.2$, using two terms of the Maclaurin's series for $\text{Tan}^{-1} x$. Estimate the accuracy of your answer. (See Number 23.)

25. Estimate for what values of $x$ the formula

$$\sqrt{1 - x} = 1 - \frac{1}{2}x$$

is correct to two decimal places.

26. Find the Maclaurin's series for $(1 + x)^k$. Show that the series converges for $|x| < 1$.

27. Let $f(x) . = . \exp(-1/x^2)$, $x \neq 0$ and $f(0) . = . 0$. Show that the Maclaurin's series for $f(x)$ is $0 + 0 + 0 + \cdots$, which surely converges everywhere but gives the correct functional value for $x = 0$ only.

## 23.4 ALGEBRAIC OPERATIONS WITH POWER SERIES

The following list of infinite series contains the relatively more important power series that occur in elementary applications of the calculus. In each case, the eries actually converges to the indicated function on the interval of convergence. The student is not expected to be able to verify this fact in all cases, nor is he expected to be able to verify the interval of convergence in Numbers 4, 5, 6, 7, and 15. He should, however, take it upon himself to obtain the coefficients as given in each case.

We shall use this set of infinite series as a stockpile from which to take most of the examples of this and the next section.

---

*Some Infinite Series for Reference*

1. $e^x = \displaystyle\sum_{n=0}^{\infty} \frac{x^n}{n!}, \ x \in \mathcal{R}.$

2. $\sin x = \displaystyle\sum_{n=0}^{\infty} \frac{(-1)^n x^{2n+1}}{(2n+1)!}, \ x \in \mathcal{R}.$

3. $\cos x = \displaystyle\sum_{n=0}^{\infty} \frac{(-1)^n x^{2n}}{(2n)!}, \ x \in \mathcal{R}.$

4. $\tan x = x + \dfrac{x^3}{3} + \dfrac{2x^5}{15} + \dfrac{17x^7}{315} + \cdots, \ |x| < \pi/2.$

5. $\cot x = \dfrac{1}{x} - \dfrac{x}{3} - \dfrac{x^3}{45} - \dfrac{2x^5}{945} - \cdots, \ 0 < |x| < \pi.$

6. $\sec x = 1 + \dfrac{x^2}{2} + \dfrac{5x^4}{24} + \dfrac{61x^6}{720} + \cdots, \ |x| < \pi/2.$

7. $\csc x = \dfrac{1}{x} + \dfrac{x}{6} + \dfrac{7x^3}{360} + \dfrac{31x^5}{15,120} + \cdots, \ 0 < |x| < \pi.$

8. $\ln(a + x) = \ln a + \displaystyle\sum_{n=1}^{\infty} \frac{(-1)^{n-1}}{n} \left(\frac{x}{a}\right)^n, \ a > 0, \ -a < x \leq a.$

9. $\ln \dfrac{a + x}{a - x} = 2 \displaystyle\sum_{n=1}^{\infty} \frac{(x/a)^{2n-1}}{2n - 1}, \ a > 0, \ |x| < a.$

10. $(a + x)^k = \displaystyle\sum_{n=0}^{\infty} \binom{k}{n} a^{k-n} x^n, \ |x| < |a|$ (The Binomial Series). This series reduces

to a polynomial valid for all values of $x$ if $k$ is a nonnegative integer.

11. $\text{Tan}^{-1} x = \displaystyle\sum_{n=1}^{\infty} \frac{(-1)^{n-1} x^{2n-1}}{2n - 1}, \ |x| \leq 1.$

12. $\text{Sin}^{-1} x = x + \displaystyle\sum_{n=2}^{\infty} \frac{(1)(3)\cdots(2n - 3)x^{2n-1}}{(2)(4)\cdots(2n - 2)(2n - 1)}, \ |x| \leq 1.$

13. $\sinh x = \displaystyle\sum_{n=0}^{\infty} \frac{x^{2n+1}}{(2n + 1)!}, \ x \in \mathcal{R}.$

14. $\cosh x = \sum_{n=0}^{\infty} \frac{x^{2n}}{(2n)!}$, $x \in \Re$.

15. $\tanh x = x - \frac{x^3}{3} + \frac{2x^5}{15} - \frac{17x^7}{315} + \cdots$, $|x| < \pi/2$.

16. $\tanh^{-1} x = \sum_{n=1}^{\infty} \frac{x^{2n-1}}{2n-1}$, $|x| < 1$.

17. $\sinh^{-1} x = x + \sum_{n=1}^{\infty} \frac{(-1)^n (1)(3) \cdots (2n-3) x^{2n-1}}{(2)(4) \cdots (2n-2)(2n-1)}$, $|x| \leqq 1$.

---

It has been shown in the work of Chapter 22 that convergent series of constants may be added term by term to obtain a convergent series with value equal to the sum of the values of the two series. A corresponding statement holds for subtraction. These results apply at once to convergent power series, since for each fixed value of $x$, a power series $\sum_{n=0}^{\infty} a_n x^n$ becomes a series of constants.

---

*Example 23.4a.* Show by adding the power series in $x$ for $\sinh x$ and $\cosh x$ that the series for $e^x$ is obtained. This is a verification of the formula

$$\cosh x + \sinh x = e^x.$$

We have, by adding corresponding terms,

$$\cosh x + \sinh x = \sum_{n=0}^{\infty} \frac{x^{2n}}{(2n)!} + \sum_{n=0}^{\infty} \frac{x^{2n+1}}{(2n+1)!}$$

$$= \sum_{k=0}^{\infty} \frac{x^k}{k!} = e^x, \qquad x \in \Re.$$

---

It is sometimes possible to find a series expansion for a given function by making an appropriate substitution in a known series representation. For instance, the series

$$\frac{1}{1-x} = \sum_{n=0}^{\infty} x^n, \qquad |x| < 1,$$

is easily remembered. To obtain a series for $1/(2+x)$, we may write

$$\frac{1}{2+x} = \frac{1}{2}\left(\frac{1}{1+x/2}\right) = \frac{1}{2}\sum_{n=0}^{\infty}\left(-\frac{x}{2}\right)^n, \qquad \left|\frac{x}{2}\right| < 1,$$

by replacing $x$ in the series for $1/(1-x)$ by $-x/2$. Thus,

$$\frac{1}{2+x} = \sum_{n=0}^{\infty} (-1)^n \frac{x^n}{2^{n+1}}, \qquad |x| < 2.$$

In a similar way, we may obtain an expansion for $1/(2+x)$ in powers of $x -$ by writing

$$\frac{1}{2+x} = \frac{1}{3+(x-1)} = \frac{1}{3}\left[\frac{1}{1+(x-1)/3}\right]$$

$$= \frac{1}{3}\sum_{n=0}^{\infty}(-1)^n\left(\frac{x-1}{3}\right)^n, \qquad \left|\frac{x-1}{3}\right| < 1,$$

or

$$\frac{1}{2+x} = \sum_{n=0}^{\infty}(-1)^n\frac{(x-1)^n}{3^{n+1}}, \qquad -2 < x < 4.$$

---

*Example 23.4b.* Find the power series in $x$ for the rational fraction

$$\frac{x}{(x-1)(x-2)}.$$

We decompose the given fraction into partial fractions to get

$$\frac{x}{(x-1)(x-2)} = \frac{2}{x-2} - \frac{1}{x-1}$$

$$= -\frac{1}{1-\dfrac{x}{2}} + \frac{1}{1-x}$$

$$= -\sum_{n=0}^{\infty}\left(\frac{x}{2}\right)^n + \sum_{n=0}^{\infty}x^n, \qquad |x| < 1$$

$$= \sum_{n=0}^{\infty}\left(1 - \frac{1}{2^n}\right)x^n, \qquad |x| < 1.$$

*Note:* The series for $2/(x-2)$ converges for $|x| < 2$, and that for $1/(1-x)$ converges for $|x| < 1$. Thus, the preceding series converges for $\{x : |x| < 2\} \cap \{x : |x| < 1\}$, which is the interval described by $|x| < 1$.

---

Suppose two functions, $f$ and $g$, are each represented by a Maclaurin's series, where

$$f(x) = \sum_{n=0}^{\infty}a_n x^n, \qquad |x| < R_1, \quad \text{and} \quad g(x) = \sum_{m=0}^{\infty}b_m x^m, \qquad |x| < R_2,$$

and we wish to find a series for the product

$$f(x)g(x) = \left(\sum_{n=0}^{\infty}a_n x^n\right)\left(\sum_{m=0}^{\infty}b_m x^m\right).$$

Since the distributive, associative, and commutative laws for ordinary algebraic quantities on the field of real numbers do not necessarily carry over to infinite series, we do not yet have a good basis for writing the product

$$\left(\sum_{n=0}^{\infty}a_n x^n\right)\left(\sum_{m=0}^{\infty}b_m x^m\right)$$

as a single series $\sum_{k=0}^{\infty}c_k x^k$. In fact, since we are dealing with a new type of expression, an infinite series, the problem is actually one of finding a suitable *definition* for the product.

Perhaps the most natural way of forming a product for two series is based on the assumption that the distributive law may be used term by term on the infinite series. In that case, we are led to an expression of the form

$$a_0 \left( \sum_{m=0}^{\infty} b_m x^m \right) + a_1 x \left( \sum_{m=0}^{\infty} b_m x^m \right) + \cdots + a_n x^n \left( \sum_{m=0}^{\infty} b_m x^m \right) + \cdots,$$

which may be written as the doubly infinite array

$$
\begin{array}{llll}
a_0 b_0 & + a_0 b_1 x & + a_0 b_2 x^2 + \cdots + a_0 b_m x^m & + \cdots \\
+ a_1 b_0 x & + a_1 b_1 x^2 & + a_1 b_2 x^3 + \cdots + a_1 b_m x^{m+1} & + \cdots \\
+ a_2 b_0 x^2 & + a_2 b_1 x^3 & + a_2 b_2 x^4 + \cdots + a_2 b_m x^{m+2} & + \cdots \\
+ \cdot & \cdot \quad \cdot \quad \cdot & \cdot \quad \cdot \quad \cdot \quad \cdot \quad \cdot \quad \cdot \quad \cdot \quad \cdot & \cdot \\
+ a_n b_0 x^n & + a_n b_1 x^{n+1} + & \cdots & + a_n b_m x^{m+n} + \cdots \\
+ \cdot & \cdot \quad \cdot \quad \cdot & \cdot \quad \cdot \quad \cdot \quad \cdot \quad \cdot \quad \cdot \quad \cdot \quad \cdot & \cdot.
\end{array}
$$

It is difficult, however, to interpret such an array without rearranging the terms a procedure that has been shown to be valid only under certain conditions ever for a single infinite series. Nevertheless, the natural arrangement we should hope to obtain appears to be

$$a_0 b_0 + (a_0 b_1 + a_1 b_0)x + (a_0 b_2 + a_1 b_1 + a_2 b_0)x^2 + \cdots$$

$$+ (a_0 b_n + a_1 b_{n-1} + \cdots + a_n b_0)x^n + \cdots = \sum_{0}^{\infty} c_n x^n$$

which is a simple power series in $x$.

Provided the series obtained in this way converges to the functional value $f(x)g(x)$, the preceding expression suggests a suitable definition of the product of two infinite series.

**Definition 23.4a.** The product

$$\left( \sum_{n=0}^{\infty} a_n \right) \left( \sum_{m=0}^{\infty} b_m \right) . = . \sum_{k=0}^{\infty} c_k,$$

where

$$c_k = a_0 b_k + a_1 b_{k-1} + a_2 b_{k-2} + \cdots + a_k b_0,$$

is called the **Cauchy product** of the two series

$$\sum_{n=0}^{\infty} a_n \quad \text{and} \quad \sum_{m=0}^{\infty} b_m.$$

That is, we write

$$\left( \sum_{n=0}^{\infty} a_n \right) \left( \sum_{m=0}^{\infty} b_m \right) = a_0 b_0 + (a_0 b_1 + a_1 b_0) + (a_0 b_2 + a_1 b_1 + a_2 b_0) + \cdots$$

$$+ (a_0 b_k + a_1 b_{k-1} + \cdots + a_k b_0) + \cdots$$

Notice that this grouping of terms is exactly the arrangement required for use with power series. Only one theorem on multiplication will be stated here; the proof will be omitted. (The student may refer to K. Knopp, *Theory and Application of Infinite Series*, New York, Hafner Publishing Company, 1948, for many of the details omitted in the present discussion.)

**Theorem 23.4a.** Let $A = \sum_{n=0}^{\infty} a_n$ and $B = \sum_{n=0}^{\infty} b_n$ be two absolutely convergent series, and let their Cauchy product be

$$\sum_{n=0}^{\infty} c_n,$$

where $c_n = \sum_{k=0}^{n} a_{n-k}b_k$. Then $\sum_{n=0}^{\infty} c_n$ is absolutely convergent to the value $C = AB$.

It is possible for the Cauchy product of two convergent series to be divergent! (See Exercises 23.4, Number 19.)

In what is for our purposes the most important case, that of two power series,

$$\sum_{n=0}^{\infty} c_n(x - a)^n \quad \text{and} \quad \sum_{n=0}^{\infty} d_n(x - a)^n,$$

the preceding theorem shows that the Cauchy product,

$$\sum_{n=0}^{\infty} \left( \sum_{k=0}^{n} c_{n-k}d_k \right)(x - a)^n,$$

converges in the interior of the intersection of the intervals of convergence of the given series.

---

*Example 23.4c.* Use multiplication of series to find the series in powers of $x$ for $(2 + x)^{-1} \ln (1 + x)$.

We have

$$\ln (1 + x) = \sum_{n=1}^{\infty} \frac{(-1)^{n-1}x^n}{n} = x \sum_{n=0}^{\infty} \frac{(-1)^n x^n}{n + 1}, \quad -1 < x \leq 1,$$

and

$$\frac{1}{2 + x} = \frac{1}{2(1 + x/2)} = \frac{1}{2} \sum_{n=0}^{\infty} \frac{(-1)^n x^n}{2^n}, \quad -2 < x < 2.$$

If only a few terms of the product are needed, they may be found by term-by-term multiplication, as for polynomials. Thus, from

$$\sum_{n=0}^{\infty} \frac{(-1)^n x^n}{n + 1} = 1 - \frac{x}{2} + \frac{x^2}{3} - \frac{x^3}{4} + \cdots,$$

and

$$\sum_{n=0}^{\infty} \frac{(-1)^n x^n}{2^n} = 1 - \frac{x}{2} + \frac{x^2}{4} - \frac{x^3}{8} + \cdots,$$

we get

$$1 - \frac{x}{2} + \frac{x^2}{3} - \frac{x^3}{4} + \cdots$$

$$- \frac{x}{2} + \frac{x^2}{4} - \frac{x^3}{6} + \cdots$$

$$+ \frac{x^2}{4} - \frac{x^3}{8} + \cdots$$

$$- \frac{x^3}{8} + \cdots$$

$$+ \cdots$$

$$= 1 - x + \tfrac{5}{6}x^2 - \tfrac{2}{3}x^3 + \cdots.$$

Therefore,

$$\frac{\ln(1+x)}{2+x} = \frac{1}{2}\left(x - x^2 + \frac{5}{6}x^3 - \frac{2}{3}x^4 + \cdots\right), \qquad |x| < 1.$$

In this example, we know the general terms of the two series, so that we can write the general term of the Cauchy product. We have

$$\frac{\ln(1+x)}{2+x} = \frac{x}{2}\left[\sum_{n=0}^{\infty} \frac{(-1)^n x^n}{n+1}\right]\left[\sum_{n=0}^{\infty} \frac{(-1)^n x^n}{2^n}\right]$$

$$= \frac{x}{2}\sum_{n=0}^{\infty}\left[\sum_{k=0}^{n} \frac{(-1)^{n-k}(-1)^k}{(n-k+1)2^k}\right] x^n$$

$$= \frac{1}{2}\sum_{n=0}^{\infty}(-1)^n\left[\sum_{k=0}^{n} \frac{1}{2^k(n-k+1)}\right] x^{n+1}, \qquad |x| < 1.$$

---

Since the operation of division rarely occurs except in connection with power series, the discussion will be restricted accordingly.

**Definition 23.4b.** The quotient of two power series

$$\frac{c_0 + c_1 x + c_2 x^2 + \cdots}{b_0 + b_1 x + b_2 x^2 + \cdots}, \qquad b_0 \neq 0,$$

is defined to be a power series

$$a_0 + a_1 x + a_2 x^2 + \cdots$$

(if there is one), such that the Cauchy product of the series $\sum_{n=0}^{\infty} a_n x^n$ and the series $\sum_{n=0}^{\infty} b_n x^n$ is the series $\sum_{n=0}^{\infty} c_n x^n$.

It can be shown that if $b_0 \neq 0$, and if the two given series converge in some neighborhood of $x = 0$, then the quotient series exists and converges in some neighborhood of $x = 0$. Unfortunately, there is no simple elementary rule for finding the interval of convergence of the quotient. We shall confine our attention here to methods of obtaining the coefficients.

*Example 23.4d.* Find the terms through the one involving $x^3$ of the Maclaurin's series for $e^x/(1 + e^x)$.

*First Method:* We may find the quotient series by direct use of Definition 23.4b and "undetermined coefficients." Since it is desired to obtain a Maclaurin's series for the result, we write

$$\frac{e^x}{1 + e^x} = \sum_{n=0}^{\infty} a_n x^n,$$

where the $a$'s in the last series are the unknown coefficients to be calculated. Multiplying both members by the denominator of the desired quotient, we get

$$e^x = (1 + e^x) \sum_{n=0}^{\infty} a_n x^n.$$

Then, substituting for $e^x$ its Maclaurin's series, we obtain the identity

$$\sum_{n=0}^{\infty} \frac{x^n}{n!} = \left( \sum_{n=0}^{\infty} a_n x^n \right) \left( \sum_{n=0}^{\infty} b_n x^n \right) = \sum_{n=0}^{\infty} \left( \sum_{k=0}^{n} a_{n-k} b_k \right) x^n,$$

where $b_0 = 2$, and $b_n = \dfrac{1}{n!}$, $n = 1, 2, 3, \ldots$.

Now, we make use of the fact (to be proved in Theorem 23.5e) that if a function has a Taylor's series expansion about a given point, then that series is unique; that is, only one set of values for the coefficients is possible. Therefore, since the left side of the preceding identity is the Maclaurin's series for $e^x$, the right side must be this same series. So we may equate coefficients of corresponding powers of $x$ to obtain the equations

$$\frac{1}{n!} = \sum_{k=0}^{n} a_{n-k} b_k, \qquad n = 0, 1, 2, \ldots,$$

from which the values of the $a$'s may be found. Thus,

$$\text{for } n = 0, \qquad 1 = 2a_0,$$
$$\text{for } n = 1, \qquad 1 = 2a_1 + a_0,$$

$$\text{for } n = 2, \qquad \frac{1}{2} = 2a_2 + a_1 + \frac{a_0}{2},$$

and, in general,

$$\frac{1}{n!} = 2a_n + \frac{a_{n-1}}{1!} + \frac{a_{n-2}}{2!} + \cdots + \frac{a_0}{n!}.$$

These equations may be solved in succession to get

$$a_0 = \frac{1}{2}, \quad a_1 = \frac{1}{4}, \quad a_2 = 0, \quad a_3 = -\frac{1}{48}, \cdots,$$

so that the desired quotient is

$$\frac{e^x}{1 + e^x} = \frac{1}{2} + \frac{x}{4} - \frac{x^3}{48} + \cdots.$$

*Second Method:* We write

$$\frac{e^x}{1 + e^x} = \frac{1 + x + \frac{x^2}{2!} + \frac{x^3}{3!} + \cdots}{2 + x + \frac{x^2}{2!} + \frac{x^3}{3!} + \cdots},$$

where the inclusion of all terms through those in $x^3$ will ensure our getting the required result. The quotient series may be found by ordinary long division of the polynomials formed from exactly the four terms written in numerator and denominator, respectively. The result is

$$\frac{e^x}{1 + e^x} = \frac{1}{2} + \frac{x}{4} - \frac{x^3}{48} + \cdots,$$

as before. It can be shown that the second method will always yield the same result as the first. An important advantage of the first method is the comparative ease with which additional coefficients can be found without having to start over from the beginning.

## Exercises 23.4

Use the methods of this section to verify the expansions in Numbers 1 to 7. Find the interval of convergence for each series.

1. $\cosh x = \dfrac{e^x + e^{-x}}{2} = \displaystyle\sum_{n=0}^{\infty} \dfrac{x^{2n}}{(2n)!}$.

2. $\cos x - \sin x = 1 - x - \dfrac{x^2}{2!} + \dfrac{x^3}{3!} + \dfrac{x^4}{4!} - \cdots$.

3. $\cos^2 2x = \dfrac{1}{2}(1 + \cos 4x) = 1 + \dfrac{1}{2}\displaystyle\sum_{n=1}^{\infty} \dfrac{(-1)^n (4x)^{2n}}{(2n)!}$.

4. $\sin^2 x = \dfrac{1}{2}(1 - \cos 2x) = \dfrac{1}{2}\displaystyle\sum_{n=1}^{\infty} \dfrac{(-1)^{n-1}(2x)^{2n}}{(2n)!}$.

5. $\ln\dfrac{a + x}{a - x} = \ln(a + x) - \ln(a - x) = 2\displaystyle\sum_{n=1}^{\infty} \dfrac{(x/a)^{2n-1}}{2n - 1}$.

6. $e^x \sin x = x + x^2 + \dfrac{x^3}{3} - \dfrac{x^5}{30} + \cdots$.

7. $e^{-x} \cos x = 1 - x + \dfrac{x^3}{3} - \dfrac{x^4}{6} + \dfrac{x^5}{30} + \cdots$.

Use the methods of this section to verify the expansions in Numbers 8 to 18.

8. $\tan x = \dfrac{\sin x}{\cos x} = x + \dfrac{x^3}{3} + \dfrac{2x^5}{15} + \dfrac{17x^7}{315} + \cdots$.

9. $\sec x = \dfrac{1}{\cos x} = 1 + \dfrac{x^2}{2} + \dfrac{5x^4}{24} + \dfrac{61x^6}{720} + \cdots$.

10. $\dfrac{x}{\sin x} = 1 + \dfrac{x^2}{6} + \dfrac{7x^4}{360} + \dfrac{31x^6}{15,120} + \cdots, \; x \neq 0$.

11. $\dfrac{\cosh x}{1 + x^2} = \displaystyle\sum_{n=0}^{\infty}\sum_{k=0}^{n} \dfrac{(-1)^{n-k}}{(2k)!} x^{2n} = 1 - \dfrac{x^2}{2!} + \dfrac{13x^4}{4!} - \dfrac{389x^6}{6!} + \cdots .$

12. $\dfrac{x}{e^x - 1} = 1 - \dfrac{x}{2} + \dfrac{x^2}{12} - \dfrac{x^4}{720} + \cdots (x \neq 0).$

13. $\dfrac{x^2}{\cos^2 x} = \dfrac{2x^2}{1 + \cos 2x} = x^2 + x^4 + \dfrac{2}{3} x^6 + \cdots .$

14. $\dfrac{1}{1 + \cos x} = \dfrac{1}{2} + \dfrac{x^2}{8} + \dfrac{x^4}{48} + \dfrac{17x^6}{5760} + \cdots .$

15. $\dfrac{\tan x}{1 + x} = x - x^2 + \dfrac{4}{3} x^3 - \dfrac{4}{3} x^4 + \dfrac{22}{15} x^5 - \dfrac{22}{15} x^6 + \cdots .$

16. $\operatorname{csch} x = \dfrac{2}{e^x - e^{-x}} = \dfrac{1}{x} - \dfrac{x}{6} + \dfrac{7x^3}{360} - \dfrac{31x^5}{15,120} - \cdots .$

17. $\cot x = \dfrac{1}{x} - \dfrac{x}{3} - \dfrac{x^3}{45} - \dfrac{2x^5}{945} - \cdots .$

18. $\csc x = \dfrac{1}{x} + \dfrac{x}{6} + \dfrac{7x^3}{360} + \cdots .$

★19. Verify that the Cauchy product for $\left( \displaystyle\sum_{n=0}^{\infty} \dfrac{(-1)^n}{\sqrt{n+1}} \right)^2$ is

$$\sum_{n=0}^{\infty} (-1)^n \sum_{k=0}^{n} \dfrac{1}{\sqrt{(n-k+1)(k+1)}}.$$

Show that this series diverges by showing that the general term

$$\sum_{k=0}^{n} \dfrac{1}{\sqrt{(n-k+1)(k+1)}}$$

does not have a zero limit as $n \to \infty$. This example shows that the Cauchy product of two conditionally convergent series may be divergent.

# 23.5 INTEGRATION AND DIFFERENTIATION OF POWER SERIES

The theorems of the preceding section indicate that, in the interior of the interval of convergence, power series behave essentially like polynomials with respect to the algebraic operations of addition and multiplication. In this section we shall show that a similarly pleasing behavior occurs with respect to the operations of calculus.

Attention here will be confined entirely to the interior of the interval of convergence, since the behavior at the end points of this interval is not only difficult to demonstrate, but also is of little use in the elementary applications. Although the discussion will deal with series of the type $\sum_{n=0}^{\infty} c_n x^n$, the reader should have no difficulty in perceiving the simple extension to the somewhat more general type of series $\sum_{n=0}^{\infty} c_n(x - a)^n$.

It is necessary first to obtain a preliminary result that is basic to the remainder of the discussion.

**Theorem 23.5a.** Let the interval of convergence of the series $\sum_{n=0}^{\infty} c_n x^n$ be $|x| < R, 0 < R \leq \infty$. Let $r$ be any number such that $0 < r < R$. Then corresponding to each $\epsilon > 0$, there is a positive integer $M$ such that $|\sum_{n=m}^{\infty} c_n x^n| < \epsilon$ for all $m \geq M$ and all $x$ such that $|x| \leq r$. ·

*Remark:* It is important to note that the number $M$ may depend on $r$ but does *not* depend on any particular value of $x$ for which $|x| < r$.

PROOF: Since $r$ is *inside* the interval of convergence, the series $\sum_{n=0}^{\infty} c_n r^n$ is absolutely convergent. Choose any $\epsilon_1$ such that $0 < \epsilon_1 < \epsilon$. By the Cauchy Criterion for series, $\sum_{n=0}^{\infty} |c_n| r^n$ is convergent $\Leftrightarrow$ there is a positive integer $M$ such that

$$\sum_{n=m}^{m+p} |c_n| r^n < \epsilon_1 \qquad \text{for } m \geq M \quad \text{and} \quad \text{all } p > 0.$$

Thus

$$|x| \leq r \Rightarrow |c_n x^n| \leq |c_n| r^n,$$

and

$$\left| \sum_{n=m}^{m+p} c_n x^n \right| \leq \sum_{n=m}^{m+p} |c_n x^n| \leq \sum_{n=m}^{m+p} |c_n| r^n < \epsilon_1.$$

Therefore,

$$\left| \sum_{n=m}^{\infty} c_n x^n \right| \leq \epsilon_1 < \epsilon,$$

and the proof is complete.

*Illustration:* In Example 22.7b it was shown that the error made in the value of $\sum_{n=1}^{\infty} 1/(n5^n)$ by using only the first six terms of the series is less than 0.000 002 7. Theorem 23.5a assures us that for *all* values of $x$, with $|x| \leq \frac{1}{5}$, the first six terms of $\sum_{n=1}^{\infty} x^n/n$ will give the value of the series with error in absolute value less than 0.000 002 7.

The notation in the remainder of this section is the same as that in Theorem 23.5a.

**Theorem 23.5b.** For a series $\sum_{n=0}^{\infty} c_n x^n$ having a radius of convergence $R$,

$$|a| < R \Rightarrow \lim_{x \to a} \sum_{n=0}^{\infty} c_n x^n = \sum_{n=0}^{\infty} c_n a^n.$$

That is, the series represents a *continuous* function at each point within its interval of convergence.

PROOF: For any fixed $m$, $\sum_{n=0}^{m-1} c_n x^n$ is a polynomial, so that

$$\lim_{x \to a} \sum_{n=0}^{m-1} c_n x^n = \sum_{n=0}^{m-1} c_n a^n.$$

This means that for each $\epsilon_1 > 0$, there is a $\delta > 0$ such that

$$\left| \sum_{n=0}^{m-1} c_n x^n - \sum_{n=0}^{m-1} c_n a^n \right| < \epsilon_1, \qquad 0 < |x - a| < \delta.$$

Therefore,

$$\left| \sum_{n=0}^{\infty} c_n x^n - \sum_{n=0}^{\infty} c_n a^n \right| = \left| \sum_{n=0}^{m-1} c_n x^n - \sum_{n=0}^{m-1} c_n a^n + \sum_{n=m}^{\infty} c_n x^n - \sum_{n=m}^{\infty} c_n a^n \right|$$

$$\leq \left| \sum_{n=0}^{m-1} c_n x^n - \sum_{n=0}^{m-1} c_n a^n \right| + \left| \sum_{n=m}^{\infty} c_n x^m \right| + \left| \sum_{n=m}^{\infty} c_n a^n \right|$$

By Theorem 23.5a, there is an $M$ such that

$$\sum_{n=m}^{\infty} c_n a^n < \epsilon_2, \qquad m \geq M,$$

and

$$\left| \sum_{n=m}^{\infty} c_n x^n \right| < \epsilon_3, \qquad m \geq M \text{ and all } x \text{ such that } |x| < r < R.$$

Thus, if $\epsilon_1 = \epsilon_2 = \epsilon_3 = \epsilon/3$, the preceding results show that

$$\left| \sum_{n=0}^{\infty} c_n x^n - \sum_{n=0}^{\infty} c_n a^n \right| < \epsilon \qquad \text{for } 0 < |x - a| < \delta_1.$$

That is,

$$\lim_{x \to a} \sum_{n=0}^{\infty} c_n x^n = \sum_{n=0}^{\infty} c_n a^n.$$

---

*Example 23.5a.* Evaluate

$$\lim_{x \to 0} \frac{1 - e^{x^2}}{1 - \cos x}.$$

The preceding theorems are the justification for the following procedure. We have

$$1 - e^{x^2} = 1 - \sum_{n=0}^{\infty} \frac{x^{2n}}{n!} = -\sum_{n=1}^{\infty} \frac{x^{2n}}{n!},$$

and

$$1 - \cos x = 1 - \sum_{n=0}^{\infty} \frac{(-1)^n x^{2n}}{(2n)!} = -\sum_{n=1}^{\infty} \frac{(-1)^n x^{2n}}{(2n)!}.$$

Thus

$$\lim_{x \to 0} \frac{1 - e^{x^2}}{1 - \cos x} = \lim_{x \to 0} \frac{-x^2 - \dfrac{x^4}{2!} - \dfrac{x^6}{3!} - \cdots}{\dfrac{x^2}{2!} - \dfrac{x^4}{4!} + \dfrac{x^6}{6!} + \cdots}$$

$$= \lim_{x \to 0} \frac{-1 - \dfrac{x^2}{2!} - \dfrac{x^4}{3!} - \cdots}{\dfrac{1}{2!} - \dfrac{x^2}{4!} + \dfrac{x^4}{6!} - \cdots} = -2.$$

**Theorem 23.5c.** If $a$ and $b$ are two numbers such that $-R < a < b < R$, then

$$\int_a^b \left( \sum_{n=0}^{\infty} c_n x^n \right) dx = \sum_{n=0}^{\infty} \int_a^b c_n x^n \, dx.$$

PROOF: We have

$$\int_a^b \left( \sum_{n=0}^{\infty} c_n x^n \right) dx = \int_a^b \left( \sum_{n=0}^{m-1} c_n x^n + \sum_{n=m}^{\infty} c_n x^n \right) dx$$

$$= \int_a^b \left( \sum_{n=0}^{m-1} c_n x^n \right) dx + \int_a^b \left( \sum_{n=m}^{\infty} c_n x^n \right) dx$$

$$= \sum_{n=0}^{m-1} \int_a^b c_n x^n \, dx + \int_a^b \left( \sum_{n=m}^{\infty} c_n x^n \right) dx,$$

since $\sum_{n=0}^{m-1} c_n x^n$ is only a polynomial.

By Theorem 23.5a, there is an $M$ such that for every $\epsilon_1 > 0$,

$$a \le x \le b \Rightarrow \left| \sum_{n=m}^{\infty} c_n x^n \right| < \epsilon_1, \qquad m \ge M,$$

so that

$$\left| \int_a^b \left( \sum_{n=m}^{\infty} c_n x^n \right) dx \right| \le \int_a^b \left| \sum_{n=m}^{\infty} c_n x^n \right| dx \le \int_a^b \epsilon_1 \, dx.$$

Moreover, $\int_a^b \epsilon_1 \, dx = (b - a)\epsilon_1$; consequently, the choice of $\epsilon_1 = \epsilon/(b - a)$ shows that

$$\left| \int_a^b \left( \sum_{n=m}^{\infty} c_n x^n \right) dx \right| < \epsilon \qquad \text{for } m \ge M.$$

That is, $|\int_a^b (\sum_{n=m}^{\infty} c_n x^n) \, dx|$ is arbitrarily small for all sufficiently large $m$. Therefore,

$$\int_a^b \left( \sum_{n=0}^{\infty} c_n x^n \right) dx = \sum_{n=0}^{\infty} \int_a^b c_n x^n \, dx,$$

as was to be shown.

---

*Example 23.5b.* Find the value of $\int_0^1 \sin x^2 \, dx$ correct to four decimal places.

We have, for all values of $x$,

$$\sin x^2 = \sum_{n=0}^{\infty} \frac{(-1)^n x^{4n+2}}{(2n + 1)!}.$$

Consequently, Theorem 23.5c allows us to write

$$\int_0^1 \sin x^2 \, dx = \sum_{n=0}^{\infty} \int_0^1 \frac{(-1)^n x^{4n+2}}{(2n + 1)!} \, dx$$

$$= \sum_{n=0}^{\infty} \left[ \frac{(-1)^n x^{4n+3}}{(2n + 1)! \, (4n + 3)} \right]_0^1$$

$$= \sum_{n=0}^{\infty} \frac{(-1)^n}{(2n+1)!\,(4n+3)}$$

$$= \frac{1}{(1!)(3)} - \frac{1}{(3!)(7)} + \frac{1}{(5!)(11)} - \frac{1}{(7!)(15)} + \cdots$$

$$= 0.333\,333 - 0.023\,810 + 0.000\,758 - 0.000\,013 + \cdots$$
$$= 0.3103 \quad \text{(correct to four decimal places).}$$

---

Suppose the power series $\sum_{n=0}^{\infty} c_n x^n$, with interval of convergence $|x| < R$, is differentiated term-by-term with respect to $x$ to give the series

$$\sum_{n=1}^{\infty} nc_n x^{n-1}.$$

We can show that the second series also has the interval of convergence $|x| < R$. For this purpose, let $x$ be any number in this interval, and let $r$ be a second number such that $|x| < r < R$. Then the series $\sum_{n=1}^{\infty} c_n r^n$ is absolutely convergent, and therefore $|c_n| r^n$ is bounded for all $n \in \mathfrak{N}$; that is, there is a number $A$ for which it is true that $|c_n| r^n < A$ for $n = 1, 2, 3, \ldots$. Hence, $|c_n| r^{n-1}$ is also bounded, and we may write

$$|c_n| r^{n-1} < B = \frac{A}{r}, \quad n \in \mathfrak{N},$$

so that

$$n|c_n x^{n-1}| = n|c_n| r^{n-1} \left|\frac{x}{r}\right|^{n-1} < nB \left|\frac{x}{r}\right|^{n-1}.$$

Since $|x/r| < 1$, it follows that the series $\sum_{n=1}^{\infty} nB|x/r|^{n-1}$ is convergent by the Cauchy Ratio Test. Consequently, the series $\sum_{n=1}^{\infty} nc_n x^{n-1}$ is absolutely convergent by the Comparison Test.

The preceding argument applies for each $x$ in the interval $|x| < R$, which shows that the series obtained by term-by-term differentiation has the same interval of convergence as the original series. (Note that no conclusions have been drawn about the behavior of the series at the end points of the interval.)

**Theorem 23.5d.** Let $R$ be the radius of convergence of the series $\sum_{n=0}^{\infty} c_n x^n$. Then, for every $x$ such that $|x| < R$,

$$D_x \sum_{n=0}^{\infty} c_n x^n = \sum_{n=1}^{\infty} nc_n x^{n-1}.$$

PROOF: The foregoing discussion shows that the series $\sum_{n=1}^{\infty} nc_n x^{n-1}$, obtained through term-by-term differentiation of the given series, is convergent inside the interval of convergence of the given series. Therefore, by Theorem 23.5c,

$$\int_0^x \left( \sum_{n=1}^{\infty} nc_n t^{n-1} \right) dt = \sum_{n=1}^{\infty} c_n x^n = \sum_{n=0}^{\infty} c_n x^n - c_0.$$

It follows, by the Fundamental Theorem of Calculus, that

$$D_x \sum_{n=0}^{\infty} c_n x^n = \sum_{n=1}^{\infty} n c_n x^{n-1}.$$

*Example 23.5c.* Obtain the Maclaurin's series for $1/(1 + x)^2$ by making use of the relation

$$D_x(1 + x)^{-1} = -(1 + x)^{-2}.$$

The power series in $x$ for $(1 + x)^{-1}$ is easily written down by long division or by using the binomial series. Thus,

$$(1 + x)^{-1} = 1 - x + x^2 - x^3 + \cdots = \sum_{n=0}^{\infty} (-1)^n x^n, \qquad |x| < 1.$$

By Theorem 23.5d, we may differentiate this series to obtain

$$(1 + x)^{-2} = -D_x(1 - x + x^2 - x^3 + \cdots) = -D_x \sum_{n=0}^{\infty} (-1)^n x^n$$

$$= 1 - 2x + 3x^2 - 4x^3 + \cdots \qquad = \sum_{n=1}^{\infty} (-1)^{n-1} n x^{n-1}, \qquad |x| < 1.$$

Note that the preceding theorems give no information regarding behavior at the end points, although the interval of convergence is not altered by term-by-term differentiation or integration. In the preceding example, it is evident that the original and the derived series both diverge for $x = \pm 1$.

The next theorem is an important consequence of the theorem on differentiation; it assures us of the uniqueness of the representation of a function by a power series.

**Theorem 23.5e.** $f(x) = \sum_{n=0}^{\infty} c_n(x - a)^n$ on any neighborhood of $a \Rightarrow c_n = f^{(n)}(a)/n!$, $n = 0, 1, 2, \ldots$, so that $\sum_{n=0}^{\infty} c_n(x - a)^n$ is the Taylor's series in powers of $x - a$ for $f(x)$.

PROOF: We are given

$$f(x) = c_0 + c_1(x - a) + c_2(x - a)^2 + \cdots + c_n(x - a)^n + \cdots$$

on some neighborhood of $a$. This means that for each value $x_1$ in this neighborhood, the series converges to the value $f(x_1)$. Thus, for $x = a$,

$$f(a) = c_0.$$

Next, we may differentiate the series term by term to get

$$f'(x) = c_1 + 2c_2(x - a) + \cdots + n c_n(x - a)^{n-1} + \cdots.$$

Again for $x = a$, we find $f'(a) = c_1$.

Theorem 23.5e permits successive term-by-term differentiation, so that we may continue this same procedure to arrive at the equation

$$f^{(n)}(x) = n! c_n + \sum_{m=n+1}^{\infty} D_x^n c_m(x - a)^m.$$

Since each term of the last series will still have $x - a$ as a factor after the differentiation is performed, the series converges to zero for $x = a$, so that $f^{(n)}(a) = n!c_n$. This completes the proof.

Theorem 23.5e gives the justification for the method of undetermined coefficients that was employed in the division of one power series by another. This theorem ensures that every method leading to a valid power-series representation of $f(x)$ about a point $a$ will give exactly the Taylor's series expansion for $f(x)$ in powers of $x - a$.

---

*Example 23.5d.* Obtain the Maclaurin's series for

$$f(x) = \int_0^x e^{-t^2} \, dt.$$

We have $e^x = \sum_{n=0}^\infty x^n/n!$ for all values of $x$, so that

$$e^{-t^2} = \sum_{n=0}^\infty \frac{(-1)^n t^{2n}}{n!}.$$

Therefore,

$$\int_0^x e^{-t^2} \, dt = \int_0^x \sum_{n=0}^\infty \frac{(-1)^n t^{2n}}{n!} \, dt = \sum_{n=0}^\infty \frac{(-1)^n x^{2n+1}}{n!(2n + 1)}.$$

Theorem 23.5e guarantees that this is a valid representation of the integral for all values of $x$.

## Exercises 23.5

In Numbers 1 to 6, evaluate the limit by using the appropriate power series.

1. $\lim_{x \to 0} \dfrac{1 - \cos x}{x \sin x}$.

2. $\lim_{\theta \to 0} \dfrac{\theta^2}{1 - \cos 3\theta}$.

3. $\lim_{t \to 0} \dfrac{t \ln (1 + t)}{\sin^2 t}$.

4. $\lim_{u \to 0} \dfrac{\sinh^2 u}{1 - \cosh u}$.

5. $\lim_{\varphi \to \pi/2} \dfrac{\cot \varphi}{\varphi - \pi/2}$.

6. $\lim_{x \to \pi} \dfrac{\sin 3x}{\sin 4x}$.

In Numbers 7 to 12, find the Maclaurin's series for the second expression by differentiating the series for the first.

7. $\cos x$; $\sin x$.
8. $\sinh x$; $\cosh x$.
9. $(1 - x^2)^{-1}$; $(1 - x^2)^{-2}$.

10. $(1 - s)^{1/2}$; $(1 - s)^{-1/2}$.
11. $\tanh x$; $\operatorname{sech}^2 x$.
12. $(1 - x^2)^{-1}$; $2x(1 - x^2)^{-2}$.

In Numbers 13 to 18, find the Maclaurin's series for the second expression by integrating the series for the first.

13. $\cos x$; $\sin x$.
14. $(1 - x)^{-1}$; $\ln (1 - x)$.
15. $(1 - x^2)^{-1/2}$; $\operatorname{Sin}^{-1} x$.
16. $(1 + x^2)^{-1}$; $\operatorname{Tan}^{-1} x$.

17. $(a^2 - x^2)^{-1}$; $\ln \dfrac{a + x}{a - x}$.

18. $\tan x$; $\ln \cos x$.

Evaluate each of the following integrals correct to four decimal places.

19. $\int_0^{0.2} \dfrac{\sin x}{1 - x^2} \, dx.$

22. $\int_0^{0.5} \sqrt{1 - t^3} \, dt.$

20. $\int_0^{1/2} e^{-x^2} \, dx.$

23. $\int_0^{0.1} \dfrac{\mathrm{Sin}^{-1} x}{x} \, dx.$

21. $\int_0^{1/2} \cos x^2 \, dx.$

24. $\int_0^{1/2} \dfrac{1 - e^{-x^2}}{x} \, dx.$

★25. The series $\sum_{n=1}^{\infty} n/(n+1)!$ can be "summed" in the following manner. If we write

$$f(x) = \sum_{n=1}^{\infty} \frac{nx^{n-1}}{(n+1)!},$$

then $f(1)$ is the desired "sum." We now have

$$f(x) = \sum_{n=1}^{\infty} \frac{nx^{n-1}}{(n+1)!} = D_x \sum_{n=1}^{\infty} \frac{x^n}{(n+1)!} = D_x \left[ \frac{1}{x} \sum_{n=1}^{\infty} \frac{x^{n+1}}{(n+1)!} \right]$$

$$= D_x \left[ \frac{1}{x} \left( \sum_{n=0}^{\infty} \frac{x^n}{n!} - 1 - x \right) \right] = D_x \left( \frac{e^x - 1 - x}{x} \right) = \frac{xe^x - e^x + 1}{x^2}.$$

Therefore,

$$\sum_{n=1}^{\infty} \frac{n}{(n+1)!} = \frac{1}{2!} + \frac{2}{3!} + \frac{3}{4!} + \cdots = 1.$$

Use a procedure like this to sum the series

$$\sum_{n=1}^{\infty} \frac{(-1)^{n-1} n}{(2n+1)!}.$$

## 23.6 TAYLOR'S SERIES FOR A FUNCTION OF TWO VARIABLES

Under proper conditions a function of more than one variable possesses a Taylor's series representation similar to that obtained in Section 23.3 for a function of one variable. In this section, we shall use a formal but plausible procedure to derive the Taylor's series for a function of two variables. For answers to questions of convergence and of properties of the series, the student should refer to more advanced books.

We assume that the function $f$, given by $z = f(x, y)$, possesses continuous partial derivatives of all orders on some neighborhood of the point $(a, b)$. We let $(a + h, b + k)$ be a point in this neighborhood and try to express $f(a + h, b + k)$ in terms of the values of $f$ and its derivatives at the point $(a, b)$.

In order to make use of the Taylor's series for a function of a single variable, we let

$$f(a + th, b + tk) = F(t),$$

so that

$$f(a + h, b + k) = F(1).$$

We assume that $F(t)$ can be represented by a Maclaurin's series that converges for $t = 1$, so that

(1) $$F(t) = F(0) + \frac{F'(0)}{1!} t + \frac{F''(0)}{2!} t^2 + \cdots + \frac{F^{(n)}(0)}{n!} t^n + \cdots.$$

This series requires the calculation of the derivatives of $F$ at $t = 0$.

Writing $x = a + th$, $y = b + tk$, we may use the usual chain-rule formula to find

$$F'(t) = f_x(x, y) D_t x + f_y(x, y) D_t y$$
$$= h f_x(x, y) + k f_y(x, y),$$

and

$$F'(0) = h f_x(a, b) + k f_y(a, b).$$

From $F'(t)$, we obtain

$$F''(t) = h[f_{xx}(x, y) D_t x + f_{xy}(x, y) D_t y] + k[f_{yx}(x, y) D_t x + f_{yy}(x, y) D_t y]$$
$$= h^2 f_{xx}(x, y) + 2hk f_{xy}(x, y) + k^2 f_{yy}(x, y),$$

and

$$F''(0) = h^2 f_{xx}(a, b) + 2hk f_{xy}(a, b) + k^2 f_{yy}(a, b).$$

The reader may show in a similar fashion that

$$F'''(0) = h^3 f_{xxx}(a, b) + 3h^2 k f_{xxy}(a, b) + 3hk^2 f_{xyy}(a, b) + k^3 f_{yyy}(a, b).$$

A symbolic form for these derivatives may be written as

(2) $$F^{(n)}(0) = \left[ \left( h \frac{\partial}{\partial x} + k \frac{\partial}{\partial y} \right)^n f(x, y) \right]_{(a, b)},$$

where the expression in parentheses is to be expanded in a formal fashion by the binomial theorem and then applied as an operator to $f(x, y)$. For instance, for $n = 2$,

$$\left( h \frac{\partial}{\partial x} + k \frac{\partial}{\partial y} \right)^2 = h^2 \frac{\partial^2}{\partial x^2} + 2hk \frac{\partial^2}{\partial x \, \partial y} + k^2 \frac{\partial^2}{\partial y^2}.$$

It is left to the reader to show by mathematical induction that Formula (2) is correct.

By substituting the expressions for $F(0)$, $F'(0)$, $F''(0)$, and so on, into the Maclaurin's series given by (1), we get

$$F(t) = f(a, b) + \frac{t}{1!} \left[ \left( h \frac{\partial}{\partial x} + k \frac{\partial}{\partial y} \right) f(x, y) \right]_{(a, b)}$$

$$+ \frac{t^2}{2!} \left[ \left( h \frac{\partial}{\partial x} + k \frac{\partial}{\partial y} \right)^2 f(x, y) \right]_{(a, b)} + \cdots$$

$$= \sum_{n=0}^{\infty} \frac{t^n}{n!} \left[ \left( h \frac{\partial}{\partial x} + k \frac{\partial}{\partial y} \right)^n f(x, y) \right]_{(a, b)}.$$

Then, putting $t = 1$, we obtain the series for $f(a + h, b + k)$ in powers of $h$ and $k$:

(3)  $f(a + h, b + k) = \displaystyle\sum_{n=0}^{\infty} \frac{1}{n!} \left[ \left( h \frac{\partial}{\partial x} + k \frac{\partial}{\partial y} \right)^n f(x, y) \right]_{(a, b)}$

$= f(a, b) + h f_x(a, b) + k f_y(a, b)$

$+ \dfrac{1}{2!} \left[ h^2 f_{xx}(a, b) + 2hk f_{xy}(a, b) + k^2 f_{yy}(a, b) \right] + \cdots.$

If in (3) we put $x = a + h$ and $y = b + k$, we get the Taylor's series for $f(x, y)$ in powers of $x - a$ and $y - b$. Thus,

(4)  $f(x, y) = f(a, b) + (x - a) f_x(a, b) + (y - b) f_y(a, b)$

$+ \dfrac{1}{2!} \left[ (x - a)^2 f_{xx}(a, b) + 2(x - a)(y - b) f_{xy}(a, b) + (y - b)^2 f_{yy}(a, b) \right] + \cdots.$

By putting $a = 0$, $b = 0$ into (4), we get the Maclaurin's series

(5)      $f(x, y) = f(0, 0) + x f_x(0, 0) + y f_y(0, 0)$

$+ \dfrac{1}{2!} \left[ x^2 f_{xx}(0, 0) + 2xy f_{xy}(0, 0) + y^2 f_{yy}(0, 0) \right] + \cdots.$

---

*Example 23.6a.* Expand $\sqrt{x + 2y}$ into a Taylor's series about the point $(2, 1)$. Write all the terms through those of second degree.

We may write

$$
\begin{array}{llll}
f(x, y) & = & (x + 2y)^{1/2}, & f(2, 1) = \sqrt{4} = 2, \\
f_x(x, y) & = & \tfrac{1}{2}(x + 2y)^{-1/2}, & f_x(2, 1) = \tfrac{1}{4}, \\
f_y(x, y) & = & (x + 2y)^{-1/2}, & f_y(2, 1) = \tfrac{1}{2}, \\
f_{xx}(x, y) & = & -\tfrac{1}{4}(x + 2y)^{-3/2}, & f_{xx}(2, 1) = -\tfrac{1}{32}, \\
f_{xy}(x, y) & = & -\tfrac{1}{2}(x + 2y)^{-3/2}, & f_{xy}(2, 1) = -\tfrac{1}{16}, \\
f_{yy}(x, y) & = & -(x + 2y)^{-3/2}, & f_{yy}(2, 1) = -\tfrac{1}{8}.
\end{array}
$$

Therefore

$\sqrt{x + 2y} = 2 + \dfrac{1}{4}(x - 2) + \dfrac{1}{2}(y - 1)$

$+ \dfrac{1}{2!} \left[ -\dfrac{1}{32}(x - 2)^2 - \dfrac{1}{8}(x - 2)(y - 1) - \dfrac{1}{8}(y - 1)^2 \right] + \cdots$

$= 2 + \dfrac{1}{4}(x - 2) + \dfrac{1}{2}(y - 1) - \dfrac{1}{64}(x - 2)^2$

$- \dfrac{1}{16}(x - 2)(y - 1) - \dfrac{1}{16}(y - 1)^2 + \cdots.$

## Exercises 23.6

1. Expand $x^2 - xy^2$ about the point $(1, -2)$.
2. Expand $x^3 + 2x^2y + y^2$ about the point $(2, 1)$.

3. Expand $\ln(x + y)$ in powers of $x - 1$ and $y - 2$. Write all the terms through those of the second degree.

4. Expand $\sqrt{3x + y}$ into a Taylor's series about the point $(2, 3)$. Write all the terms through those of the second degree.

5. Find the Taylor's series through the second-degree terms for $e^y \ln(2 + x)$ about $(0, 0)$.

6. Find the Taylor's series through the third-degree terms for $\cos(x^2 + y)$ about $(0, 0)$.

7. Find the Taylor's series through the second-degree terms for $e^x \cos y$ about $(0, 0)$.

8. Expand $\text{Tan}^{-1}(y/x)$ into a Taylor's series about $(1, 1)$. Write all the terms through those of the second degree.

9. Find the Taylor's series through the second-degree terms for $\sqrt{1 + x + y}$ about $(0, 0)$.

10. Expand $y \ln(y - x)$ into a Taylor's series about $(1, 2)$. Write all terms through those of the second degree.

## 23.7 EXTREMES OF FUNCTIONS OF MORE THAN ONE VARIABLE

In this section, we shall consider relative maxima and minima of functions of more than one variable, but shall be particularly concerned with functions of two variables. As for functions of one variable, a relative maximum (or minimum) point is simply a point $P$ at which the value of $f$ is the largest (or smallest) on a neighborhood of $P$. We shall assume that the functions to be considered possess continuous partial derivatives.

First, suppose that a function $f$ of two variables has an extreme at a point $(a, b)$. Then the function $g$, where $g(x) = f(x, b)$, must have an extreme for $x = a$. Hence, $g'(a) = 0$. But $g'(a) = f_x(a, b)$, so that $f_x(a, b) = 0$. Similarly, the function $h$, where $h(y) = f(a, y)$, has an extreme at $(a, b)$, and it follows that $h'(y) = 0 = f_y(a, b)$. Thus, we have proved

**Theorem 23.7a.** Let $f$ be a function of two variables with continuous derivatives in some neighborhood of a point $(a, b)$. Then

$$f(a, b) \text{ is an extreme} \Rightarrow f_x(a, b) = 0 \quad \text{and} \quad f_y(a, b) = 0.$$

Since the same argument applies to functions of several variables, it follows that a *necessary* condition for such a function to have an extreme at a point in the neighborhood of which all the first partial derivatives are continuous is that all these derivatives be zero at this point.

*Example 23.7a.* Examine the function $f$, where

$$f(x, y) = 6x - 4y - x^2 - 2y^2$$

for extremes.

Since $f$ is a continuous function with continuous partial derivatives, Theorem 23.7a applies. We differentiate to find

$$f_x(x, y) = 6 - 2x \quad \text{and} \quad f_y(x, y) = -4 - 4y.$$

Thus

$$f_x(x, y) = 0 = f_y(x, y) \Rightarrow x = 3, \quad y = -1.$$

The equation $z = 6x - 4y - x^2 - 2y^2$ describes a paraboloid having a vertical axis and opening in the negative $z$-direction. Hence, $f(3, -1) = 11$ is a maximum value.

---

It is customary in many applications to rely on physical or geometrical considerations to determine if an extreme exists and to distinguish between a maximum and a minimum. In some applications, however, it is essential to have an analytic criterion for a maximum or a minimum. We shall obtain such a test for a function of two variables under the assumption that the function can be represented by a convergent Taylor's series in some neighborhood of the point in question.

To be specific, we suppose $f$ to be a function of two variables with $f_x(a, b) = 0$ and $f_y(a, b) = 0$, so that $(a, b)$ is a critical point. Then,

$$f(a + h, b + k) = f(a, b) + \frac{1}{2!} [h^2 f_{xx}(a, b) + 2hk f_{xy}(a, b) + k^2 f_{yy}(a, b)] + \cdots,$$

or

$$(1) \qquad f(a + h, b + k) - f(a, b) = \frac{1}{2!} [Ah^2 + 2Bhk + Ck^2] + \cdots,$$

where

$$A .= . f_{xx}(a, b), \quad B .= . f_{xy}(a, b), \quad C .= . f_{yy}(a, b).$$

If, on a sufficiently small deleted neighborhood of $(a, b)$, the difference $f(a + h, b + k) - f(a, b)$ is

*negative*, then $f(a, b)$ is a relative *maximum;*
*positive*, then $f(a, b)$ is a relative *minimum;*
*variable in sign*, then $f(a, b)$ is *neither a maximum nor a minimum.*

Since the Taylor's series for $f(a + h, b + k)$ has been assumed to converge, then for all sufficiently small values of $h$ and $k$, the quadratic polynomial on the right of Equation (1) is greater in absolute value than the sum of the remaining series. Consequently, the sign of this polynomial determines the sign of the difference on the left side of the equation on a small neighborhood of $(a, b)$. Thus, we need to examine this second-degree polynomial in order to investigate the type of point that is present at $(a, b)$. If the discriminant $B^2 - AC$ of the polynomial is negative, the polynomial will have the same sign at all points of this neighborhood. Furthermore, $B^2 - AC < 0 \Rightarrow AC > 0$, so that $A$ and $C$ have the same sign. Hence, the polynomial is positive or negative according as $A$ is positive or negative. If $B^2 - AC > 0$, the polynomial will be variable in sign in every neighborhood of $(a, b)$. Thus, we get the following results for the critical point $(a, b)$.

(1) *If $B^2 - AC < 0$, then $f(a, b)$ is an extreme; $f(a, b)$ is a maximum if $A < 0$ and a minimum if $A > 0$.*

(2) *If $B^2 - AC > 0$, then $f(a, b)$ is neither a maximum nor a minimum.*

(3) *If $B^2 - AC = 0$, the test fails.*

The last statement can be shown by considering $f(x, y) = x^n + y^n$ at $(0, 0)$ for various integral values of $n > 2$. In every case the discriminant is zero, but even values of $n$ give a minimum value for $f(0, 0)$ and odd values of $n$ give no extreme.

---

*Example 23.7b.* Show that a closed cubical box has the smallest surface area of any rectangular box with a given volume.

Let the dimensions of the box be $x$, $y$, and $z$, respectively. Then the given volume is

$$xyz = V, \text{ a constant.}$$

The surface area is given by

$$S = 2xy + 2yz + 2zx,$$

and we can eliminate one of the variables, say $z$, by substitution from the volume equation. Thus,

$$S = 2xy + \frac{2V}{x} + \frac{2V}{y}.$$

We find

$$S_x = 2y - \frac{2V}{x^2}, \quad \text{and} \quad S_y = 2x - \frac{2V}{y^2},$$

$$S_{xx} = \frac{4V}{x^3}, \quad S_{xy} = 2, \quad S_{yy} = \frac{4V}{y^3}.$$

By putting $S_x = 0 = S_y$, we get $x = y = V^{1/3}$, and

$$S_{xx} = 4, \quad S_{xy} = 2, \quad S_{yy} = 4.$$

These are the respective coefficients $A$, $B$, $C$ of the polynomial in the preceding discussion. Hence, we find

$$B^2 - AC = 2^2 - (4)(4) = -12 < 0.$$

Since $A = 4 > 0$, it follows that $x = y = V^{1/3}$ gives a minimum value for $A$. The corresponding value of $z$ is also $V^{1/3}$, and therefore the box is a cube.

## Exercises 23.7

In each of Numbers 1 to 9, examine the function defined by the given equation for maximum and minimum values.

1. $f(x, y) = 4x^2 + 3y^2 - 8x$.
2. $f(x, y) = 2x^2 + 9y^2 + 6y$.
3. $f(x, y) = 6x - 3x^2 - y^2 + 2y$.
4. $f(x, y) = 2x^2 + xy - y^2 - 7x - 4y$.
5. $f(x, y) = x^2 + xy + y^2 - 2x - 6y$.
6. $f(x, y) = x^3 - 27xy + y^3$.
7. $f(x, y) = xy - x^2 - y^2 - 2x - 3y$.
8. $f(x, y) = x^4 + y^4 - 2x^2 - 2y^2$.
9. $f(x, y) = 9xy - x^3 - y^3$.

0. Find the point of the plane $x + 2y - z = 4$ that is nearest to the point $(1, 1, 2)$.
1. Find the point of the plane $2x - 3y + z = 1$ that is nearest to the point $(-2, 1, -1)$.

12. Find the points of the surface $xyz^2 = 16$ that are nearest to the origin.
13. Find the point for which the sum of the squares of the distances from the points $(x_1, y_1), (x_2, y_2), \ldots, (x_n, y_n)$ is a minimum.
14. A rectangular box without a top has a fixed surface area of $A$ square feet. If the length of the box is $x$ feet and the width is $y$ feet, show that the volume is greatest when the depth is $x/2$ feet and $x = y = \sqrt{A/3}$.

# Summary of Chapter 23

The ideas introduced in Chapter 22 are applied in a number of important ways in this chapter. The concepts of importance here include:

(1) series with variable terms (Section 23.1);
(2) power series and their behavior (Section 23.2);
(3) the radius of convergence of a power series (Section 23.2);
(4) functions defined by power series (Section 23.2);
(5) Taylor's formula with a remainder (Section 23.3);
(6) Taylor's series and Maclaurin's series corresponding to a given function (Section 23.3);
(7) the use of series to approximate the value of a function for a given value of $x$ and error estimates (Section 23.3);
(8) algebraic operations with series and the use of these operations in finding power series for functions (Section 23.4);
(9) the Cauchy product of infinite series (Section 23.4);
(10) the continuity of the function represented by a power series (Section 23.5);
(11) term-by-term integration of a power series (Section 23.5);
(12) term-by-term differentiation of a power series (Section 23.5);
(13) the use of series to evaluate definite integrals (Section 23.5);
(14) Taylor's series for functions of two variables (Section 23.6);
(15) relative maxima and minima of functions of more than one variable, and the related test (Section 23.7).

# Chapter 24 Differential Equations

## 24.1 WHAT IS A DIFFERENTIAL EQUATION?

Although pure mathematicians are generally interested in mathematics for its own sake as a system or structure, engineers, scientists, and applied mathematicians are usually interested in using mathematics to explain, describe, or help understand physical phenomena. The greatest breakthrough in the scientific and technological foundation of our present civilization occurred with the application of the calculus to physical problems. Indeed, much of the development of the calculus was a result of man's efforts to formulate physical problems in mathematical form so that related physical phenomena could be better described and understood.

Some of these efforts eventually led to the study of a new type of equation, now called a differential equation. For example, we know that $D_x y$ is the rate of change of $y$ with respect to $x$. Suppose that, by means of experiments and observations, we are able to discover an expression for this rate. Then we can set up an equation relating $x$, $y$, and $D_x y$, and we can study this equation to find, if possible, the direct relationship between $x$ and $y$.

To illustrate, suppose we observe the radioactive decay of radium into other substances. We might notice that the rate at which the decay takes place is proportional to the amount of radium instantaneously present. (This idea could be acquired from a graph of data taken over a long period of time.) If $x$ represents the amount of radium present at time $t$, then $D_t x$ represents the rate of change of $x$ with respect to time. Consequently, the experimental observation can be formulated mathematically in terms of the equation

$$D_t x = -kx,$$

where $k$ is a constant of proportionality, and where the negative sign indicates that the quantity $x$ is decreasing with respect to time.

An equation of this type involving an unknown function and its derivative is called a **differential equation**. A differential equation frequently is an expression of a physical problem in mathematical form. The problem of finding the unknown function, that is, of solving the differential equation, becomes one of mathematical technique.

Sir Isaac Newton and Gottfried Leibniz, both of whom independently developed the fundamental ideas of calculus, also were the first to consider differential equations. For example, Newton's well-known second law of mechanics can be expressed by means of a differential equation. This law states essentially that the mass of a moving particle times its acceleration is equal to the sum of the external forces acting on the particle, which may be expressed in mathematical form as

$$m\mathbf{a} = \sum_i \mathbf{F}_i.$$

If the particle moves so that some function $\mathbf{r}(t)$ specifies the position of the particle in space, then the acceleration is given by

$$\frac{d^2\mathbf{r}}{dt^2},$$

and Newton's law becomes

$$m\frac{d^2\mathbf{r}}{dt^2} = \sum_i \mathbf{F}_i.$$

This differential equation is said to be of **second order** because it involves the second derivative of the unknown function $\mathbf{r}(t)$. In general, the *order* of a differential equation is the order of its highest ordered derivative.

To illustrate Newton's second law in a specific case, let us consider a weight $W$ suspended by a spring from a rigid support (see Figure 24.1a). If the weight is

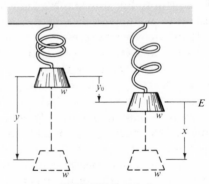

**FIGURE 24.1a**

displaced from its equilibrium position $E$ by an amount $x_0$ and released, the weight will move in a definite manner and will gradually settle to its equilibrium position. The entire phenomenon can be described mathematically by a differential equation.

If $y$ represents the distance of the weight below or above the end of the spring when it is unstretched, then the force acting on the weight due to the extension or compression of the spring is given by $-ky$, where $k$ is a constant. The minus sign is used because the direction of action of the force of the spring is opposite to the direction of the displacement of the weight. In a similar way, it has been found experimentally that the resistance to the motion is proportional to the velocity of the weight. Since this force acts in the direction opposite to that of the velocity, the expression representing it is given a negative sign, and is $-r(dy/dt)$, where $r$ is a positive constant. Hence, by Newton's law, we have as the differential equation of the motion of the weight

$$m\frac{d^2y}{dt^2} = -r\frac{dy}{dt} - ky + W,$$

where $m$ is the mass and $W$ is the gravitational force acting on the mass, or since $W = mg$,

$$m\frac{d^2y}{dt^2} + r\frac{dy}{dt} + ky = mg.$$

This equation can be somewhat simplified by choosing the point of equilibrium, where the spring force is exactly equal to the weight, as the origin. If $y = y_0$ is the distance the spring is stretched at the equilibrium position, then the spring force is $-ky_0$, so that

$$ky_0 = mg.$$

Now let $x$ be the distance below or above the position of equilibrium. Then

$$x = y - y_0$$

and

$$\frac{dy}{dt} = \frac{dx}{dt}, \qquad \frac{d^2y}{dt^2} = \frac{d^2x}{dt^2}.$$

Thus the differential equation becomes

$$m\frac{d^2x}{dt^2} + r\frac{dx}{dt} + k(x + y_0) = mg,$$

or, since $ky_0 = mg$,

$$m\frac{d^2x}{dt^2} + r\frac{dx}{dt} + kx = 0.$$

If the function $x$ satisfying the differential equation and the given starting conditions can be found, it will describe the position of the weight at any time $t$.

Another early important formulation of a physical problem leading to a study of differential equations occurred in connection with a problem in heat flow. This study was based on the experimental result that the rate of flow of heat across an area $A$ is proportional to the area and to the temperature gradient, which is the rate of change of the temperature $u$ with respect to distance $x$ in a direction normal to the area. If the heat flow is a constant $q$, independent of time, this result may be stated in the one dimensional case as

$$q = -kA\frac{du}{dx}.$$

These illustrations show how differential equations play an important role

in man's study of the physical world, and how a mathematical subject may b
suggested by a study of physical problems. Once the physical problem has bee
expressed in mathematical form, the problem becomes a purely mathematica
one. It is the latter aspect of differential equations that we shall consider nex

## 24.2 THE SOLUTION OF SIMPLE DIFFERENTIAL EQUATIONS

The simplest type of differential equation has been encountered frequently i
integration problems and is of the form

(1)
$$\frac{dy}{dx} = f(x).$$

In this case the unknown function $y$ can be found simply by finding an invers
derivative of $f(x)$, so that we may write

$$y = \int f(x)\, dx$$

as a "solution" of Equation (1), provided the inverse derivative exists.

The procedure discussed in the preceding paragraph suggests several impo
tant ideas. One is to explain more precisely what is *meant* by a solution of
differential equation. Another is to determine conditions under which a solutio
of a differential equation exists.

For example, the functions for which $y = e^x$ and $y = xe^x$ can both be show
to satisfy the equation

$$y'' - 2y' + y = 0.$$

This means that if $e^x$ or $xe^x$ is substituted for $y$ in the differential equatior
then an identity results. Thus, if $y = xe^x$, then

$$(xe^x + 2e^x) - 2(xe^x + e^x) + xe^x = 0.$$

In general, *a function is said to satisfy, or to be a solution of, a differenti
equation if, upon being substituted in the differential equation, it reduces th
equation to an identity.* However, as the preceding example illustrates, it ma
happen that more than one function satisfies the differential equation. Henc
it becomes important to specify clearly what is meant by a solution of a diffei
ential equation in a general sense. Furthermore, once it is determined what sha
be meant by a solution of a differential equation, it is necessary to determin
conditions under which a solution exists. It is evident, for instance, that a
equation such as

$$(y')^2 + x^2 + 1 = 0$$

is satisfied by no real function. In more complicated equations, it may not b
at all obvious that a solution does or does not exist.

The questions raised here are difficult to answer in the general case. Howeve
these points are easily clarified for the simplest types of differential equatior
by means of the next theorem, which is stated without proof.

**Theorem 24.2a.** If $f(x, y)$ and $f_y(x, y)$ are continuous functions of $x$ and $y$ in a region $\Re$, and if $P(x_0, y_0) \in \Re$, then there exists one and only one function $F$, $y = F(x)$, which in some neighborhood $\Re(P)$ satisfies the differential equation

$$y' = f(x, y),$$

and is such that $y_0 = F(x_0)$.

To illustrate the meaning of this theorem, let us consider a simple example.

---

*Example 24.2a.* Find a solution for the differential equation

$$y' = 2x$$

such that $y(1) = 2$.

Upon integrating, we get

$$y = x^2 + c,$$

and the arbitrary constant $c$ may be determined from the condition $y(1) = 2$. It follows that $c = 1$, and

$$y = x^2 + 1$$

is the required solution. Furthermore, Theorem 24.2a guarantees that this is the *only* solution.

---

Interpreted geometrically, the equation $y = x^2 + c$ of the preceding example describes a family of curves (often called **integral curves,** since they are obtained as solutions of a differential equation) and $y = x^2 + 1$ is that particular one of the curves which passes through the point $(1, 2)$. Theorem 24.2a guarantees that through any point at which the conditions of the theorem are satisfied, there is only one such curve, and that two curves of the family will not intersect except possibly at points where the conditions of the theorem are not satisfied (see Figure 24.2a).

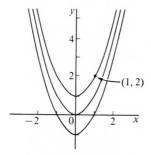

**FIGURE 24.2a**

Since every solution of $y' = 2x$ is of the form $y = x^2 + c$, this form is called **general solution** of the differential equation. A general solution always contains one or more arbitrary constants. In addition, the differential equation $y' = 2x$ called the differential equation of the family $y = x^2 + c$ because it is independent of the value of $c$ and consequently states a property that is common to all members of the family, namely, that the slope at each point is twice the $x$ coordinate of the point.

The next example illustrates this idea further.

---

*Example 24.2b.* Find the differential equation of the family

$$y = cx^2.$$

The desired result is to be a differential equation of **lowest possible order** in which the arbitrary constant $c$ does not appear. In order to eliminate $c$ we need a second equation involving $c$. Such an equation is obtained by differentiation. Thus, from the two equations

$$y = cx^2, \qquad y' = 2cx,$$

we get

$$\frac{y'}{y} = \frac{2cx}{cx^2} = \frac{2}{x},$$

or

$$y' = \frac{2y}{x}$$

as the differential equation of the family.

---

In the last differential equation, observe that $f(x, y) = 2y/x$ is discontinuous at points along the $y$-axis where $x = 0$. Hence, Theorem 24.2a does not guarantee anything about a solution passing through any point $(0, b)$. An examination of the graph in Figure 24.2b of members of the family shows that all curves

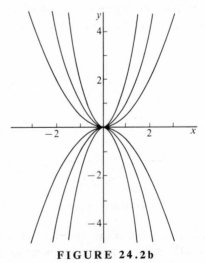

**FIGURE 24.2b**

pass through $(0, 0)$ so that there is no uniqueness of solution at that point. Furthermore, there is no solution at all passing through $(0, b)$, $b \neq 0$.

Suppose we wish to find the solution of the differential equation

$$y' = \frac{2y}{x}.$$

In this case, we may write

$$\frac{y'}{y} = \frac{2}{x},$$

and, even more conveniently, we may use differential notation so that the variables can be separated to obtain the equation

$$\frac{dy}{y} = 2\frac{dx}{x}.$$

If both $x$ and $y$ are positive, then, by straightforward integration, we get

$$\ln y = 2 \ln x + k,$$

where $k$ is an arbitrary constant. The solution may be rewritten as

$$y = e^k x^2.$$

If the arbitrary constant $k$ is introduced in the form $k = \ln c$, $c > 0$, then

$$y = cx^2.$$

If $x > 0$, $y < 0$, then the solution of the differential equation is

$$\ln(-y) = 2 \ln x + k,$$

and if $k = \ln(-c)$, $c < 0$, then

$$y = cx^2,$$

as before. The other cases, where $x < 0$, may be handled in a similar manner, and in each case the solution becomes

$$y = cx^2.$$

For this reason it is convenient to introduce logarithmic forms using absolute values, as

$$\ln|y| = 2 \ln|x| + \ln|c|,$$

which leads to the solution

$$y = cx^2,$$

regardless of the signs of the various quantities involved.

The preceding discussion also serves to illustrate the importance of introducing an arbitrary constant in a convenient form. The next example illustrates another important point.

---

*Example 24.2c.* Solve the differential equation

$$\sqrt{1 - x^2}\, dy + \sqrt{1 - y^2}\, dx = 0$$

with the condition that $y = 0$ if $x = \sqrt{3}/2$.

Separating the variables and integrating, we get successively

$$\frac{dy}{\sqrt{1 - y^2}} + \frac{dx}{\sqrt{1 - x^2}} = 0,$$

and

$$\text{Sin}^{-1} y + \text{Sin}^{-1} x = c.$$

When $x = \sqrt{3}/2$ and $y = 0$, then $c = \pi/3$, so that the desired solution is

$$\text{Sin}^{-1} y + \text{Sin}^{-1} x = \frac{\pi}{3}.$$

In the general form the equation may be expressed more conveniently without inverse trigonometric functions. From

$$\cos (\text{Sin}^{-1} y + \text{Sin}^{-1} x) = \cos c,$$

we get

$$\sqrt{1 - x^2} \sqrt{1 - y^2} - xy = \cos c,$$

or

$$x^2 + 2xy \cos c + y^2 = \sin^2 c.$$

For $c = \pi/3$, the equation becomes

$$x^2 + xy + y^2 = \frac{3}{4},$$

which represents an ellipse as shown in Figure 24.2c.

Observe that not all the points on the ellipse have coordinates satisfying

$$\text{Sin}^{-1} x + \text{Sin}^{-1} y = \frac{\pi}{3}.$$

Since $-\pi/2 \leqq \text{Sin}^{-1} x \leqq \pi/2$, it follows that

$$-\frac{\pi}{2} \leqq \frac{\pi}{3} - \text{Sin}^{-1} y \leqq \frac{\pi}{2},$$

which leads to the restrictions $-\frac{1}{2} \leqq y \leqq 1$ and $-\frac{1}{2} \leqq x \leqq 1$. These conditions, with the equation

$$\text{Sin}^{-1} x + \text{Sin}^{-1} y = \frac{\pi}{3},$$

describe a function that satisfies the differential equation and whose graph passes through $(\sqrt{3}/2, 0)$. The graph of this function is the portion of the ellipse indicated by the heavy curve in Figure 24.2c.

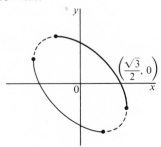

FIGURE 24.2c

Had the condition been $y = 0$, $x = -\sqrt{3}/2$ in place of $y = 0$, $x = \sqrt{3}/2$, the resulting equation would be

$$\text{Sin}^{-1} x + \text{Sin}^{-1} y = -\frac{\pi}{3},$$

implying the restrictions $-1 \leq x \leq \frac{1}{2}$, $-1 \leq y \leq \frac{1}{2}$, which pertain to the portion of the ellipse shown in Figure 24.2c by the light solid curve. At the points of the ellipse shown as a dotted curve the slope is positive, whereas the differential equation in the form

$$\frac{dy}{dx} = -\frac{\sqrt{1 - y^2}}{\sqrt{1 - x^2}}$$

describes a family of curves whose slopes are everywhere negative. Hence, these points are not associated with a solution of the given differential equation, even though they are part of the graph of

$$x^2 + xy + y^2 = \frac{3}{4}.$$

## Exercises 24.2

In each of Numbers 1 to 11, find the differential equation of the given family of curves. In Numbers 1 to 6, the constants to be eliminated are given following the equation.

1. $y = ax^2 + b$; $a$, $b$.
2. $y = A \sin x$; $A$.
3. $y = A \sin x + B \cos x$; $A$, $B$.
4. $b^2 x^2 + a^2 y^2 = a^2 b^2$; $a$, $b$.
5. $y = Ae^x + Be^{-x}$; $A$, $B$.
6. $y = C_1 x + C_2 e^x + C_3 e^{-x}$; $C_1$, $C_2$, $C_3$.

7. The family of circles with centers on the line $y = x$.
8. The family of all circles in the plane.
9. The family of parabolas with vertical axes, and passing through the point $(a, b)$.
10. The family of all hyperbolas having asymptotes parallel to the coordinate axes.
11. The family $y = Ax^n + Bx^{1-n}$
    (a) if $A$ and $B$ are arbitrary, and
    (b) if $A$, $B$, $n$ are arbitrary.

In each of Numbers 12 to 27, find a general solution of the given differential equation.

12. $dr + r \cos \theta \, d\theta = 0$.
13. $x^3 \, dx + y^3 \, dy = 0$.
14. $y \, dz + z \, dy = 0$.
15. $\frac{ds}{dt} = s$.
16. $(2x + 3)\frac{dy}{dx} = y^3$.
17. $\frac{dy}{dx} = x^2 y^3$.
18. $3\frac{ds}{dt} + 4s = 0$.
19. $r \, d\theta + \theta \, dr = 2 \, dr$.
20. $\frac{ds}{dt} = -\frac{s+1}{t+1}$.

21. $e^{3x}(y \, dx - dy) = 2 \, dy$.
22. $\frac{dv}{dx} = xe^{x+v}$.
23. $(4 + y^2)\frac{dx}{dy} = \sqrt{1 - x^2}$.
24. $\frac{dy}{dx} + x = \frac{x}{y}$.
25. $2 \cos x \frac{dy}{dx} = 1 + y^2$.
26. $e^x \frac{dy}{dx} = 1 - \tan x + \tan^2 x$.
27. $\frac{1}{\rho}\frac{d\rho}{d\theta} = \frac{\rho^2 - 1}{\rho^2 + 1} \tan \theta$.

In each of Numbers 28 to 33, find the particular solution satisfying the given conditions.

28. $dx + x^2y^2\,dy = 0$; when $x = 1$, $y = 2$.
29. $2u\,dv + 3v\,du = 0$; when $u = 2$, $v = 1$.
30. $e^s\,dt + e^t\,ds = 0$; when $s = 0$, $t = 0$.

31. $\dfrac{dx}{dy} = ye^xe^{y^2}$; when $x = 1$, $y = 1$.

32. $uv^3\,du + e^u\,dv = 0$; when $u \to \infty$, $v \to \frac{1}{4}$.
33. $e^{2y}\,dx + dy = 0$; when $y \to \infty$, $x \to 3$.

34. If $\csc \theta\,d\varphi - \sec \varphi\,d\theta = 0$, and $\varphi = 0$ for $\theta = 0$, find the smallest positive value of $\varphi$ for $\theta = \pi/2$.

35. If $dv = 2u(1 + v)\,du$, and $v = 0$ for $u = 1$, find the value of $v$ for $u = 3$.

## 24.3 SIMPLE APPLICATIONS

To illustrate the basic concepts in differential equations that we have encountered up to this point, let us consider some simple applications.

---

*Example 24.3a.* A car weighing 3200 pounds is being driven in a straight line by an engine exerting a driving force of 200 pounds. If the air resistance to the motion has a magnitude in pounds equal to two times the speed of the car in feet per second, and if the car starts from rest, find the speed and the distance traveled as functions of the time.

If the car travels $x$ feet in $t$ seconds, then the speed is $v = dx/dt$. Hence, using Newton's law, we get

$$\frac{3200}{g}\frac{dv}{dt} = 200 - 2v$$

as the differential equation of motion. If $g \approx 32$ feet per second per second, then

$$\frac{dv}{dt} = 2 - 0.02v.$$

In this equation the variables are separable, so that

$$\frac{dv}{2 - 0.02v} = dt$$

and

$$-\frac{1}{0.02}\ln (2 - 0.02v) = t - \frac{1}{0.02}\ln c_1.$$

Thus,

$$2 - 0.02v = c_1e^{-0.02t}.$$

Since the car starts from rest, $v = 0$ for $t = 0$, which gives $c_1 = 2$, and

$$2 - 0.02v = 2e^{-0.02t}.$$

Upon solving for $v$, we get

$$v = 100(1 - e^{-0.02t}).$$

This equation shows that, under the given conditions, since $v \to 100$ as $t \to \infty$, the car has a limiting velocity of 100 feet per second.

Since $v = dx/dt$, we may integrate to obtain

$$x = 100(t + 50e^{-0.02t}) + c_2.$$

Then, using the fact that $x = 0$ for $t = 0$, we find $c_2 = -5000$. Thus, the distance is given by

$$x = 100(t + 50e^{-0.02t}) - 5000.$$

---

*Example 24.3b.* In a chemical process, in which one molecule of a substance $C$ is formed by the combination of one molecule each of substances $A$ and $B$, the rate of formation of $C$ is proportional to the amounts of $A$ and $B$ present at time $t$. Obtain an expression for the amount of $C$ formed at time $t$ if when $t = 0$ there is no $C$ present.

Let $a$ and $b$ be the initial amounts of $A$ and $B$, respectively, and let $x$ be the amount of $C$ formed at time $t$. Then

$$\frac{dx}{dt} = k(a - x)(b - x)$$

and

$$\frac{dx}{(a - x)(b - x)} = k \, dt.$$

It is left for the reader to show that if $a \neq b$, then

$$\frac{b - x}{a - x} = \frac{b}{a} e^{(b-a)kt} \quad \text{or} \quad x = \frac{ab(1 - e^{(b-a)kt})}{a - be^{(b-a)kt}}.$$

What is the solution if $a = b$?

---

*Example 24.3c.* According to Newton's law of cooling, the temperature of a body changes at a rate that is proportional to the difference in temperature between the surrounding medium and the body itself. If a thermometer reading 65°F inside a room is taken outside, where the temperature is 45°F, and 2 minutes later the thermometer reads 55°F, express the thermometer reading as a function of time.

According to Newton's law, if $u$ is the thermometer reading at time $t$, then

$$\frac{du}{dt} = -k(u - 45),$$

and

$$\frac{du}{u - 45} = k \, dt,$$

or

$$u - 45 = ce^{-kt}.$$

When $t = 0$, $u = 65°F$, so that $c = 20$. Also, if $t = 2$, $u = 55$, so that

$$10 = 20e^{-2k}$$

and

$$-2k = \ln \tfrac{1}{2},$$

or

$$k = \tfrac{1}{2} \ln 2.$$

Thus, the equation for the thermometer reading is

$$u = 45 + 20 \exp\left(-\frac{t}{2}\ln 2\right),$$

or

$$u = 45 + 20(\tfrac{1}{2})^{t/2}.$$

---

The flow of heat through a homogeneous medium of cross-sectional area $A$ is found experimentally to be approximately proportional to the area and to the temperature gradient, which is the rate of change of the temperature $u$ with respect to distance $x$ measured normal to the area $A$. If the heat flow has reached a steady state, so that it is independent of the time, then we may formulate a simple differential equation for the case when the change in temperature depends upon only one variable $x$.

Suppose the rate of flow of heat through the surface of area $A$ is $q$ calories per second and depends only on the distance $x$ in centimeters measured in the direction of the flow. For example, $x$ may be the radius of a cylindrical surface of constant temperature, or the distance to a plane of constant temperature (Surfaces of constant temperature are called **isothermal surfaces**.) Then

$$q = -kA\frac{du}{dx},$$

where $k$, the constant of proportionality, is called the **thermal conductivity of the material**.

---

*Example 24.3d.* A pipe of radius 10 centimeters and carrying steam at 120°C is insulated with a material 4 centimeters thick having a thermal conductivity of $150 \times 10^{-6}$ calories per centimeter per degree per second. If the outer surface of the insulation is kept at 40°C, find the rate of heat loss per meter length of pipe. Also find the temperature halfway through the insulation.

We assume that the isothermal surfaces are cylinders coaxial with the pipe, and since the area $A$ of a meter length of such a surface of radius $x$ centimeters is $200\pi$ square centimeters, the differential equation is

$$q = -k(200\pi x)\frac{du}{dx}.$$

We may separate the variables and integrate between corresponding limits on $x$ and $u$ to obtain

$$q\int_{10}^{R}\frac{dx}{x} = -200\pi k\int_{120}^{U}du,$$

where $U$ is the temperature at radius $R$. The solution of the differential equation subject to the condition $U = 120$ for $x = 10$ is thus

$$q\ln\frac{R}{10} = -200\pi k(U - 120).$$

Using the given data that $U = 40$ when $R = 14$, and the value of $k$. we find

$$q \ln 1.4 = 2.4\pi,$$

so that the rate of heat loss is

$$q = \frac{2.4\pi}{\ln 1.4} \text{ calories per second.}$$

The temperature halfway through the insulation, where $R = 12$ centimeters, is obtained from

$$\frac{2.4\pi}{\ln 1.4} \ln 1.2 = -(200)(150 \times 10^{-6})\pi(U - 120),$$

which gives

$$U = 120 - 80 \frac{\ln 1.2}{\ln 1.4} = 76.7°C.$$

## Exercises 24.3

1. A 20-pound weight moves in a horizontal straight-line path under a constant force of 12 pounds, with a resisting force whose magnitude in pounds is four times the instantaneous velocity in feet per second. If the weight starts from rest at the origin, find its velocity and its distance from the origin at the end of 2 seconds.

2. At each point $(x, y)$ of a certain curve the slope is $y/(3x)$. Find the equation of the curve if it passes through the point $(8, 1)$.

3. A curve, whose slope at each of its points is given by $(x + 1)/(y + 1)$, passes through the point $(2, 3)$. Find an equation of the curve.

4. Suppose the slope formula in Number 3 is $(y + 1)/(x + 1)$. Find an equation of the curve.

5. If an amount $P$ dollars is invested at $r$ percent compounded continuously, then the accumulated amount $A$ dollars at the end of $t$ years satisfies the differential equation

$$100 \frac{dA}{dt} = rA.$$

How long would it take for a given amount of money to double itself at 5% compounded continuously?

6. A radioactive substance $S$ decays at a rate proportional to the amount of $S$ present. If the number $N$ of atoms of $S$ present at time $t = 0$ is $N_0$, find a formula for $N$ in terms of $t$.

7. The *half-life* of a radioactive substance is defined as the time required for half the atoms in a given sample to decay. If the isotope of uranium, $U^{238}$, has a half-life of $(4.5)(10^9)$ years, find a formula for the amount of $U^{238}$ left after $t$ years if the initial amount is one gram.

8. A mass $m$ falls from rest. If the resistance of the atmosphere is proportional to the velocity, and if the limiting velocity is 160 feet per second, find
   (a) the velocity at the end of 10 seconds, and
   (b) the time when the velocity is one-half the limiting velocity.

9. A car weighing 4800 pounds is driven by an engine that exerts a force of 900 pounds in driving it in a straight line. If the air resistance is numerically equal to one-sixteenth the square of the velocity, find the velocity as a function of time, if the car starts from rest. Is there a limiting velocity?

10. A chemical substance $A$ is changed into a substance $B$ at a rate proportional to the amount of $A$ present at time $t$. If, when $t = 0$, there is no $B$ present, find the time it takes for the amount of $B$ to equal the amount of $A$ remaining.

11. A certain chemical substance $C$ is formed from two substances $A$ and $B$ so that one unit of $C$ is obtained from 1 unit of $A$ and 2 units of $B$. The rate of formation of $C$ is proportional to the product of the number of units of $A$ and the number of units of $B$ present at time $t$. Suppose that at $t = 0$ there are 20 units of $A$ and 50 units of $B$ and none of $C$ present, and that at the end of 10 minutes one-half of $A$ is used up. Find an expression for the amount of $C$ in terms of $t$.

12. If a thermometer is moved from a room at 80°F to the outside, where the temperature is 20°F, and if the thermometer reads 60°F at the end of 30 seconds, find how long it will be before the thermometer reads 40°F.

13. A steam pipe having an inner radius $r_1$ and outer radius $r_2$ has a temperature $u_1$ at its inner surface and $u_2$ at its outer surface. Find an expression for the steady state temperature $u$ at the radial distance $r$, $r_1 < r < r_2$. Find the value of $u$ if $r_1 = 3$ centimeters, $r_2 = 4$ centimeters, $u_1 = 110°C$, $u_2 = 50°C$, and $r = 3.3$ centimeters.

14. A wall of thickness $t_1$ inches and conductivity $k_1$ in calories per inch per degree per second, having an area of $A$ square inches, is covered by an insulation of thickness $t_2$ inches and conductivity $k_2$ in calories per inch per degree per second. Find a expression for the heat loss in calories per second through the wall if the temperature at the inner surface is $u_1$ degrees and if at the outer surface of the insulation the temperature is $u_2$ degrees.

15. A colony of bacteria has a population growth that is jointly proportional to the number $x$ of bacteria present at time $t$ and the capability $u$ of the environment to support the number present at time $t$. If the capability $u$ of the environment is measured by the quantity $M - x$, where $M$ is the maximum number of bacteria that can be supported by the environment, find the growth formula for the colony.

16. Solve the differential equation in Example 24.3b to verify that the given solution is correct. Also, find the solution if $a = b$.

## 24.4 SUBSTITUTIONS

The illustrations in Examples 24.2b and 24.2c indicate that if a differential equation of the form $y' = f(x, y)$ has its variables separable, then it can be solved by direct integration procedures. It is frequently possible to change variables in a differential equation by means of a substitution in order to obtain an equation in which the new variables may be separated. Such a substitution is usually determined by inspection.

---

*Example 24.4a.* Find a solution for the equation

$$y' = (x - y)^2.$$

Since $(x - y)^2$ cannot be factored into a product of a factor depending only on $x$ and another factor depending only on $y$, the variables in this equation cannot be separated. However, if we let

$$u = x - y,$$

so that

$$y' = 1 - u',$$

then, by substitution into the given equation, we get

$$1 - u' = u^2,$$

or

$$\frac{du}{1 - u^2} = dx.$$

Hence, integration of both members gives

$$\frac{1}{2} \ln \left| \frac{1 + u}{1 - u} \right| = x + \frac{1}{2} \ln |c|,$$

or

$$1 + u = c(1 - u) \exp (2x).$$

Since $u = x - y$, we find that

$$1 + x - y = c(1 - x + y) \exp (2x)$$

is a general solution of the original differential equation. Notice that the arbitrary constant was introduced in the form $\frac{1}{2} \ln |c|$ as a matter of convenience.

---

*Example 24.4b.* Solve the equation

$$(x + y + 1)\frac{dy}{dx} = x + y - 2.$$

In this equation the double appearance of the quantity $x + y$ suggests that we let $u = x + y$, so that

$$y' = u' - 1.$$

Then

$$(u + 1)(u' - 1) = u - 2,$$

or

$$u' = \frac{2u - 1}{u + 1},$$

so that

$$\frac{u + 1}{2u - 1} du = dx.$$

Hence, a solution is given by

$$\int \frac{u + 1}{2u - 1} du = x + c,$$

or

$$\frac{u}{2} + \frac{3}{4} \ln |2u - 1| = x + c.$$

In terms of the original variables, and with $C = 4c$, this is

$$2y - 2x + 3 \ln |2x + 2y - 1| = C.$$

---

Of the many types of first-order equations that can be changed into equations having separable variables, there is one in which the coefficients have a certain common property. This property is described in

**Definition 24.4a.** An expression $f(x, y)$ for which

$$f(\lambda x, \lambda y) = \lambda^k f(x, y),$$

where $\lambda$ is an arbitrary multiplier, is said to be **homogeneous of degree** $k$. For instance, if $f(x, y) = x^3 - 2x^2y + y^3$, then

$$\begin{aligned}
f(\lambda x, \lambda y) &= \lambda^3 x^3 - 2\lambda^2 x^2 \lambda y + \lambda^3 y^3 \\
&= \lambda^3 [x^3 - 2x^2 y + y^3] \\
&= \lambda^3 f(x, y),
\end{aligned}$$

so that $f(x, y)$ is homogeneous of degree 3. Similarly, the expression $xy/(x^2 + 2y^2)$ is homogeneous of degree 0, and the expression $\sqrt{x + 3y}$ is homogeneous of degree $\frac{1}{2}$. (Why?)

The differential equation $y' = f(x, y)$ may be rewritten in the form

$$M(x, y)\, dx + N(x, y)\, dy = 0.$$

If the coefficients $M(x, y)$ and $N(x, y)$ are both homogeneous and of the same degree, then the equation may be changed into an equation having separable variables by means of the substitution $y = vx$ or $x = vy$.

Suppose $y = vx$ is substituted into

$$M(x, y)\, dy + N(x, y)\, dx = 0.$$

The result is

$$M(x, vx)(v\, dx + x\, dv) + N(x, vx)\, dx = 0.$$

Since $M(x, y)$ is homogeneous of degree $k$, $M(x, vx) = x^k M(1, v)$, and similarly $N(x, vx) = x^k N(1, v)$, so that

$$x^k M(1, v)(v\, dx + x\, dv) + x^k N(1, v)\, dx = 0.$$

It follows that

$$[N(1, v) + vM(1, v)]\, dx + M(1, v)x\, dv = 0,$$

or

$$\frac{M(1, v)\, dv}{N(1, v) + vM(1, v)} + \frac{dx}{x} = 0,$$

and the variables are separated.

---

*Example 24.4c.* Find a solution of $y^2\, dx - (xy + x^2)\, dy = 0$.

Since the coefficients are homogeneous of degree 2, we may let $x = vy$ (or $y = ux$). Then

$$y^2(v\, dy + y\, dv) - (vy^2 + v^2 y^2)\, dy = 0,$$

or

$$\frac{dy}{y} - \frac{dv}{v^2} = 0.$$

Hence,

$$\ln|y| + \frac{1}{v} = \ln|c|,$$

and a general solution may be written as

$$ye^{y/x} = c.$$

---

Occasionally it is possible to change variables in an equation in order to transform it into one with homogeneous coefficients. The new equation can then be handled by the preceding method.

---

*Example 24.4d.* Solve the equation

$$(-x + 2y - 7) \, dy - (2x + 2y - 4) \, dx = 0.$$

The coefficients are not homogeneous, but they are linear, a fact that can be used to eliminate the constant terms quite easily if we let

$$x = u + h, \quad y = v + k.$$

Then $(-u + 2v - h + 2k - 7) \, dv - (2u + 2v + 2h + 2k - 4) \, du = 0$, and we choose $h$ and $k$ so that

$$h - 2k + 7 = 0,$$
$$2h + 2k - 4 = 0.$$

It follows that $h = -1$ and $k = 3$, and the differential equation becomes

$$(-u + 2v) \, dv - (2u + 2v) \, du = 0.$$

This equation has homogeneous coefficients in $u$ and $v$, and may be solved by the method described previously.

Thus, we let $v = ru$ so that the equation becomes

$$(-u + 2ru)(r \, du + u \, dr) - (2u + 2ru) \, du = 0,$$

or

$$\frac{du}{u} + \frac{(2r - 1) \, dr}{2r^2 - 3r - 2} = 0.$$

Integrating and simplifying the result, we get

$$u^5(2r + 1)^2(r - 2)^3 = c,$$

and, by replacing $r$ by its equivalent $v/u$,

$$(2v + u)^2(v - 2u)^3 = c.$$

Finally, restoring the original variables by putting

$$u = x + 1, \quad v = y - 3,$$

we obtain

$$(2y + x - 5)^2(y - 2x - 5)^3 = c.$$

# Exercises 24.4

In Numbers 1 to 14, find a general solution for the given differential equation.

1. $\dfrac{dy}{dx} = 1 + \dfrac{y}{x}$.

2. $(x^2 + y^2) \, dx = 2xy \, dy$.
3. $x \, dy = (x^2 + y^2 + y) \, dx$.

4. $\dfrac{dy}{dx} = \dfrac{y}{x} + \dfrac{y^2}{x^2}$.

5. $\dfrac{dy}{dx} = \dfrac{x - y}{x + y}$.

6. $x(y + \sqrt{x^2 + y^2}) \, dy = y^2 \, dx$.
7. $(x^3 + y^3) \, dy = x^2 y \, dx$.

8. $y \, dx = x \left( \ln \dfrac{y}{x} - 2 \right) dy$.

9. $\left(y \cos \frac{y}{x} - 2x \sin \frac{y}{x}\right) dx + \left(y - x \cos \frac{y}{x}\right) dy = 0.$

10. $\dfrac{dy}{dx} = (x - y + 1)^2.$

11. $\dfrac{dy}{dx} = \dfrac{2 - 2x - y}{4 + x + 3y}.$

12. $(2x - y + 2)\dfrac{dy}{dx} + (4x - 2y + 1) = 0.$

13. $(x - y + 1)\dfrac{dy}{dx} + (2x - 2y - 3) = 0.$

14. $y(x^2 + y^2 + 1)\dfrac{dy}{dx} + x(x^2 + y^2 - 1) = 0.$

In Numbers 15 to 18, find a particular solution satisfying the given conditions.

15. $(x + 2y - 1) dx + (x + 2y + 4) dy = 0$; when $x = 1$, $y = 2$.
16. $(3 + 2 \sin y) dx + x \cos y \, dy = 0$; when $x = 2$, $y = \pi/2$.
17. $(x + 2y - 5) dx - (2x + y - 4) dy = 0$; when $x = 1$, $y = 3$.
18. $2y^2 \, dx + (3xy - x^2) \, dy = 0$; when $x = 4$, $y = 1$.

## 24.5 EXACT DIFFERENTIAL EQUATIONS

Sometimes the terms of a differential equation may be grouped so as to form exact differentials. In such a case, the equation can be solved quite simply by straightforward integration. For example, the equation

$$(y - x) \, dy - (2x + y) \, dx = 0$$

may be rewritten in the form

$$y \, dy - (x \, dy + y \, dx) - 2x \, dx = 0,$$

which can be integrated at once to give

$$\tfrac{1}{2}y^2 - xy - x^2 = \tfrac{1}{2}c,$$

or

$$y^2 - 2xy - 2x^2 = c.$$

This differential equation is an instance of a special type of equation, described by

**Definition 24.5a.** A differential equation of the form

(1) $$M(x, y) \, dx + N(x, y) \, dy = 0$$

is said to be an **exact** equation if there exists a function $F$ such that

$$dF = M(x, y) \, dx + N(x, y) \, dy,$$

so that the solution of Equation (1) is

$$F(x, y) = c.$$

The preceding definition requires that

$$F_x = M(x, y) \quad \text{and} \quad F_y = N(x, y).$$

If $F_{xy} = M_y(x, y)$ and $F_{yx} = N_x(x, y)$ are continuous, then it follows at once that

$$\text{Equation (1) is exact} \Rightarrow M_y = N_x.$$

(Why?) This result is incorporated into a more general statement in

**Theorem 24.5a.** If $M$, $N$, $M_y$, and $N_x$ in the differential equation

$$M(x, y)\, dx + N(x, y)\, dy = 0$$

are continuous over a closed region $\mathfrak{R}$, then the equation is exact $\Leftrightarrow M_y = N_x$.

PROOF: It remains to show that $M_y = N_x \Rightarrow$ there is a function $F$ such that $F(x, y) = c$ is a solution of Equation (1). This may be done in a number of ways, one of the simplest of which is given here. Let $(x_0, y_0)$ be a given point in $\mathfrak{R}^i$, and let $(x, y)$ be an arbitrary point in $\mathfrak{R}^i$. We may suppose that $F$ is a function for which

$$F_x(x, y) = M(x, y),$$

so that

$$F(x, y) = \int_{x_0}^{x} M(s, y)\, ds + \varphi(y),$$

where $\varphi$ is an arbitrary function of $y$ to be determined. Then

$$F_y = \frac{\partial}{\partial y} \int_{x_0}^{x} M(s, y)\, ds + \varphi'(y).$$

Since $M(s, y)$ and $M_y(s, y)$ are continuous, we may interchange the order of integration and differentiation to obtain

$$F_y = \int_{x_0}^{x} M_y(s, y)\, ds + \varphi'(y),$$

or, since $M_y = N_x$,

$$F_y = \int_{x_0}^{x} N_s(s, y)\, ds + \varphi'(y),$$

so that

$$F_y = N(x, y) - N(x_0, y) + \varphi'(y).$$

We already have $F_x(x, y) = M(x, y)$, and it now follows, if $\varphi'(y) = N(x_0, y)$, that $F_y(x, y) = N(x, y)$. Thus, if we write $\varphi(y) = \int_{y_0}^{y} N(x_0, t)\, dt$, then

$$(2) \qquad F(x, y) = \int_{x_0}^{x} M(s, y)\, ds + \int_{y_0}^{y} N(x_0, t)\, dt$$

is such that $dF = M(x, y)\, dx + N(x, y)\, dy$. The required solution is $F(x, y) = 0$.

The introduction of a particular point $(x_0, y_0)$ is equivalent to introducing an arbitrary constant $c$ and then finding the value of $c$ so that the solution passes through $(x_0, y_0)$.

*Example 24.5a.* Solve the equation

$$\frac{dy}{dx} = \frac{e^y}{2y - xe^y}.$$

If the equation is rewritten in the form

$$(2y - xe^y)\, dy - e^y\, dx = 0,$$

then

$$N_x = -e^y \quad \text{and} \quad M_y = -e^y.$$

Hence, $M_y = N_x$, and so the equation is exact. The solution of the differential equation may be written immediately from Equation (2) as

$$\int_{x_0}^{x} (-e^y)\, ds + \int_{y_0}^{y} (2t - x_0 e^t)\, dt = 0,$$

so that

$$(x_0 - x)e^y + y^2 - y_0^2 - x_0 e^y + x_0 e^{y_0} = 0,$$

or

$$y^2 - xe^y = y_0^2 - x_0 e^{y_0}.$$

Another approach, which is equivalent to the preceding one, can be used to obtain the solution. Since the solution is of the form $F(x, y) = c$, then

$$F_x(x, y) = -e^y,$$

so that

$$F(x, y) = -xe^y + \varphi(y)$$

and

$$F_y(x, y) = -xe^y + \varphi'(y).$$

This expression must equal $N(x, y)$; that is,

$$-xe^y + \varphi'(y) = 2y - xe^y.$$

Hence

$$\varphi'(y) = 2y$$

and

$$\varphi(y) = y^2.$$

Finally,

$$F(x, y) = y^2 - xe^y,$$

and a general solution to the differential equation is therefore

$$y^2 - xe^y = c.$$

In case we want the solution through the point $(x_0, y_0)$, we get

$$c = y_0^2 - x_0 e^{y_0},$$

or

$$y^2 - xe^y = y_0^2 - x_0 e^{y_0},$$

which agrees with the result obtained by means of Equation (2).

---

Now let us investigate an exact differential equation from a different point of view. Consider the differential equation of the family

$$e^x(\ln y + x) = c,$$

which is

$$e^x(\ln y + x + 1)\, dx + \frac{e^x}{y}\, dy = 0.$$

By multiplication of both sides by $e^{-x}y$, we may change this equation into the form

(3) $$y(\ln y + x + 1)\, dx + dy = 0.$$

The last equation is *not* exact, since

$$\frac{\partial}{\partial y}\left[y(\ln y + x + 1)\right] = 2 + x + \ln y$$

and

$$\frac{\partial}{\partial x}(1) = 0.$$

Yet we know that the equation can be made exact since it was obtained from $e^x(\ln y + x) = c$. The property of exactness was apparently lost when the original differential equation was multiplied by $e^{-x}y$. If the factor $e^x y^{-1}$ is re-introduced into Equation (3), it becomes exact, as the reader may verify. This observation leads to

**Definition 24.5b.** If a differential equation is multiplied by a quantity $\mu(x, y)$ and the new equation is exact, then the quantity $\mu(x, y)$ is called an **integrating factor** of the equation.

To illustrate the idea of the integrating factor further, consider the following example.

---

*Example 24.5b.* Solve $(2y^2 - 6xy)\, dx + (3xy - 4x^2)\, dy = 0$.

Since

$$\frac{\partial}{\partial y}(2y^2 - 6xy) = 4y - 6x$$

and

$$\frac{\partial}{\partial x}(3xy - 4x^2) = 3y - 8x,$$

the equation is not exact. However, it is known that the equation can be changed into an exact form if an integrating factor can be found. Since the coefficients are polynomials in $x$ and $y$, we try an integrating factor of the form $x^m y^n$. Hence we want to determine, if possible, a value for $m$ and $n$ so that

$$(2x^m y^{n+2} - 6x^{m+1}y^{n+1})\, dx + (3x^{m+1}y^{n+1} - 4x^{m+2}y^n)\, dy = 0$$

is exact. In that case we must have $M_y = N_x$; that is,

$$2(n + 2)x^m y^{n+1} - 6(n + 1)x^{m+1}y^n = 3(m + 1)x^m y^{n+1} - 4(m + 2)x^{m+1}y^n.$$

For this equation to be satisfied for all values of $x$ and $y$, we must have

$$2(n + 2) = 3(m + 1)$$

and

$$-6(n + 1) = -4(m + 2),$$

or

$$2n - 3m = -1, \quad 3n - 2m = 1.$$

It follows that $n = 1$, $m = 1$, and that an integrating factor is $xy$. Hence, we may solve $(2xy^3 - 6x^2y^2) \, dx + (3x^2y^2 - 4x^3y) \, dy = 0$ in the usual way to get

$$x^2y^3 - 2x^3y^2 = c$$

as the solution of the original differential equation. It is clear that if the equations involving $m$ and $n$ have no solution, then there is no integrating factor of the form $x^m y^n$.

## Exercises 24.5

In each of Numbers 1 to 15, find a general solution for the given differential equation.

1. $(3x^2 - 6xy) \, dx + (12y - 3x^2) \, dy = 0$.
2. $(2x + 3y) \, dx = (8y - 3x) \, dy$.
3. $\left(x + \dfrac{y}{x^2 + y^2}\right) dx + \left(y - \dfrac{x}{x^2 + y^2}\right) dy = 0$.
4. $(2x \cos y - e^x) \, dx - x^2 \sin y \, dy = 0$.
5. $\cos x \sec y \, dx + \sin x \sin y \sec^2 y \, dy = 0$.
6. $x \, dy - (y^2 + y + x^2) \, dx = 0$. *Hint:* Show that $(x^2 + y^2)^{-1}$ is an integrating factor.
7. $(3xy - 6y^3) \, dx = (12xy^2 - 2x^2) \, dy$.
8. $(3y^2 - 6x^2y) \, dx + (9xy - 4x^3) \, dy = 0$.
9. $(x^2y^5 - y) \, dx + (x + x^3y^4) \, dy = 0$.
10. $(2y - 3x^5 - 3xy^2) \, dx - x \, dy = 0$. Does the substitution $u = x^2/y$ yield an exact equation?
11. $(x^2y^2 - 1) \, dx - \dfrac{2x}{y} \, dy = 0$.
12. $(2 - 3xy^3) \, dx + 3\left(\dfrac{1}{xy} - \dfrac{x}{y}\right) dy = 0$.
13. $e^x(dx - dy) = e^y(x \, dy + y \, dx)$. Find an integrating factor of the form $\mu(y)$.
14. $dy + (2y - e^x) \, dx = 0$. Also find the integral curve through the point $(0, 1)$. *Hint:* Find an integrating factor of the form $\mu(x)$.
15. $(x + y + 1) \, dy + dx = 0$. Find an integrating factor of the form $\mu(y)$.

In each of Numbers 16 to 19, find a particular solution satisfying the given conditions.

16. $(4x^2 - 2xy) \, dx + (5y - x^2) \, dy = 0$; when $x = -1$, $y = 1$.
17. $(2x \sin y + 3y) \, dx + (3x + x^2 \cos y) \, dy = 0$; when $x = 2$, $y = \pi/6$.
18. $(e^{2x} - y^2) \, dx + (ye^{y^2} - 2xy) \, dy = 0$; when $x = 0$, $y = 0$.
19. $2xy \, dx + (y^5 - x^2) \, dy = 0$; when $x = 2$, $y = 2$.
20. Prove that if the coefficients $M(x, y)$ and $N(x, y)$ in $M(x, y) \, dx + N(x, y) \, dy =$ are homogeneous, then $[xM(x, y) + yN(x, y)]^{-1}$ is an integrating factor for th differential equation.
21. Prove that if $u(x, y) = C$ is a solution of $M(x, y) \, dx + N(x, y) \, dy = 0$, then

$$\dfrac{\dfrac{\partial u}{\partial x}}{M(x, y)} = \dfrac{\dfrac{\partial u}{\partial y}}{N(x, y)}.$$

# 24.6 THE LINEAR DIFFERENTIAL EQUATION OF ORDER 1

We are now in a position to begin an investigation of one of the most commonly occurring types of differential equations.

**Definition 24.6a.** Let $y$ be a function of $x$. A **linear differential expression** of the $n$th order in $y$ is a polynomial of the first degree in $y$, $y'$, $y''$, $\ldots$, $y^{(n)}$ with coefficients that are functions of $x$; that is,

$$L(y) .=. a_0(x)y^{(n)} + a_1(x)y^{(n-1)} + \cdots + a_n(x)y, \qquad a_0(x) \neq 0.$$

**Definition 24.6b.** A **linear differential equation** of the $n$th order is an equation of the form

$$L(y) = f(x),$$

or

$$a_0(x)y^{(n)} + a_1(x)y^{(n-1)} + \cdots + a_n(x)y = f(x).$$

Thus,

$$x^3 y''' - 2y' + (\sin x)y = 3xe^x$$

is a linear equation of order 3 in $y$, whereas

$$y''' - 2yy' + (\sin x)y = e^x$$

is *nonlinear* in $y$ because of the presence of the product $yy'$.

To begin an investigation of linear differential equations, we shall first examine in some detail the linear equation of order 1, the general form of which is

$$(1) \qquad a_0(x)y' + a_1(x)y = f(x).$$

In any neighborhood of a point $x$ where $a_0(x) \neq 0$, so that division by $a_0(x)$ is permissible, the equation may be rewritten in the standard form

$$(2) \qquad y' + p(x)y = q(x).$$

**Theorem 24.6a.** If $p$ and $q$ are continuous functions of $x$ over a common domain $\mathcal{D}$, then the equation

$$y' + p(x)y = q(x)$$

has the solution

$$y = e^{-\int p\,dx} \int e^{\int p\,dx} q\,dx + Ce^{-\int p\,dx}.$$

PROOF: To prove this theorem, we seek an integrating factor for the equation. Suppose $\mu(x, y)$ is such a factor. Then, in order that

$$\mu(x, y)\,dy + \mu(x, y)[p(x)y - q(x)]\,dx = 0$$

be exact, we must have

$$\mu_x = \mu_y(py - q) + \mu p.$$

This equation shows that if $\mu$ is independent of $y$, so that $\mu_y = 0$, then the resulting equation,

$$\mu_x = \mu p(x),$$

is one in $\mu$ and $x$ alone. Since the variables in the last equation are separable, it can be solved in an elementary fashion. We have

$$\frac{d\mu}{\mu} = p(x)\,dx$$

$$\Rightarrow \ln\mu = \int p(x)\,dx$$

$$\Rightarrow \quad \mu = e^{\int p(x)\,dx}.$$

A constant of integration is not introduced here because it can be divided out at a later stage, and does not assist in making the equation exact.

When $\mu$ is replaced by exp $[\int p(x)\,dx]$, the equation becomes

$$e^{\int p\,dx}y' + pe^{\int p\,dx}y = e^{\int p\,dx}q$$

or

$$\frac{d}{dx}(ye^{\int p\,dx}) = e^{\int p\,dx}q.$$

Therefore,

$$ye^{\int p\,dx} = \int e^{\int p\,dx}q\,dx + C.$$

A general solution may then be written as

$$y = e^{-\int p\,dx}\int e^{\int p\,dx}q\,dx + Ce^{-\int p\,dx},$$

and this completes the proof.

The term involving the arbitrary constant in the last result is called the **complementary part** of the solution, or simply the **complementary solution**. The other term is called the **particular part** of the solution, or the **particular solution**. The complementary solution, by itself, does not satisfy the differential equation

$$y' + py = q,$$

but actually is a solution of the equation

$$y' + py = 0,$$

which is called the **homogeneous associate** of the original equation. Observe that the equation $y' + py = 0$ has separable variables, so that its solution can be obtained by direct integration and is

$$y = Ce^{-\int p\,dx}.$$

It is instructive to solve the original differential equation by beginning with the solution of the homogeneous equation. To see how this may be accomplished, suppose we investigate the effect of a substitution of the form

$$y = u(x)v(x)$$

into the equation $y' + py = q$. We find the new equation to be

$$u'v + v'u + puv = a,$$

or

$$uv' + (u' + pu)v = q.$$

If $u$ is a function such that $u' + pu = 0$, then the preceding equation reduces to

$$uv' = q,$$

which can be solved for $v$ by simple integration. But $u' + pu = 0$ is the homogeneous associate of the original equation, and since $u = C \exp(-\int p\, dx)$, it follows that

$$v' = \frac{1}{C} e^{\int p\, dx} q,$$

and

$$v = \frac{1}{C} \int e^{\int p\, dx} q\, dx + C_1.$$

Hence,

$$y = C_2 e^{-\int p\, dx} + e^{-\int p\, dx} \int e^{\int p\, dx} q\, dx,$$

where $C_2 = CC_1$. This result is in agreement with the solution previously obtained.

The purpose of the preceding investigation is to illustrate an alternative approach to solving the differential equation, and to illustrate that the solution of the associated homogeneous differential equation can be used to generate the solution of the original equation. The importance of these ideas will become apparent when we consider the linear differential equation of order $n$.

The next example illustrates the process of obtaining a solution for a specific first-order linear differential equation.

---

*Example 24.6a.* Solve the differential equation

$$xy' - y = x^3\sqrt{1 - x^2}.$$

If the equation is rewritten in the standard form

$$y' - \frac{1}{x}y = x^2\sqrt{1 - x^2},$$

it is apparent from the preceding discussion that an integrating factor is

$$e^{\int -\frac{1}{x}\, dx} = e^{-\ln x} = \frac{1}{x}.$$

Hence,

$$\frac{1}{x}y' - \frac{1}{x^2} = x\sqrt{1 - x^2}$$

is exact, and may be written as

$$\frac{d}{dx}\left(\frac{y}{x}\right) = x\sqrt{1 - x^2}.$$

Upon integrating and multiplying by $x$, we find that

$$y = Cx - \frac{x}{3}(1 - x^2)^{3/2}$$

is a general solution.

---

The reader should keep in mind that the integrating factor is determined so as to make the differential equation exact. Consequently, after the integrating factor $e^{\int p\, dx}$ has been multiplied into the equation $y' + p(x)\, y = q$, the left side of the resulting equation is simply the derivative of the product of the integrating factor and the dependent variable $y$, as is illustrated by the preceding example.

---

*Example 24.6b.* Solve $y' - 2xy = x^2$.

An integrating factor of this equation is

$$e^{\int -2x\, dx} = e^{-x^2}.$$

Hence, upon multiplication by $\exp(-x^2)$, the equation may be written

$$\frac{d}{dx}(ye^{-x^2}) = x^2 e^{-x^2},$$

so that

$$ye^{-x^2} = \int x^2 e^{-x^2}\, dx = -\tfrac{1}{2}xe^{-x^2} + \tfrac{1}{2}\int e^{-x^2}\, dx.$$

Since no simpler form for the inverse derivative is available, we shall replace

$$\int e^{-x^2}\, dx \quad \text{by} \quad \int_a^x e^{-t^2}\, dt + 2C,$$

where $a$ is any convenient value of $x$ and $C$ is an arbitrary constant. Thus, we have

$$ye^{-x^2} = -\tfrac{1}{2}xe^{-x^2} + \tfrac{1}{2}\int_a^x e^{-t^2}\, dt + C,$$

or

$$y = -\tfrac{1}{2}x + \tfrac{1}{2}e^{x^2}\int_a^x e^{-t^2}\, dt + Ce^{x^2}.$$

---

To illustrate how the number $a$ in the preceding result may be chosen conveniently to suit the conditions of a problem, suppose it is required that $y = y_0$ for $x = x_0$. Then an excellent choice for $a$ is $x_0$, since the integral

$$\int_{x_0}^x e^{-t^2}\, dt$$

is zero for $x = x_0$. Thus,

$$y = -\tfrac{1}{2}x + \tfrac{1}{2}e^{x^2}\int_{x_0}^x e^{-t^2}\, dt + Ce^{x^2}$$
$$\Rightarrow y_0 = -\tfrac{1}{2}x_0 + 0 + C\exp(x_0^2)$$
$$\Rightarrow C = (y_0 + \tfrac{1}{2}x_0)\exp(-x_0^2).$$

Accordingly, the required solution takes the form

$$y = -\tfrac{1}{2}x + \tfrac{1}{2}e^{x^2}\int_{x_0}^x e^{-t^2}\, dt + (y_0 + \tfrac{1}{2}x_0)\exp(x^2 - x_0^2).$$

It is sometimes possible to obtain a linear equation from a nonlinear equation by means of a substitution. The **Bernoulli type** equation

$$y' + p(x)y = q(x)y^n, \qquad n \neq 1,$$

which is named after James Bernoulli (1654–1705), a member of a famous Swiss family of mathematicians, illustrates this point. If the equation is rewritten as

$$y^{-n}y' + py^{-n+1} = q(x)$$

and if the substitution $u = y^{-n+1}$ is made, then $u' = (-n + 1)y^{-n}y'$, so that the result is

$$\frac{u'}{1 - n} + pu = q(x).$$

This equation is readily seen to be linear in $u$. In a similar way, the equation

$$\frac{dx}{dy} + r(y)x = s(y)x^n, \qquad n \neq 1$$

is a Bernoulli type equation in $x$, and may be changed into a linear equation in $v$ by setting $v = x^{-n+1}$.

---

*Example 24.6c.* Solve the equation

$$3y^2 - (x^4 + 2xy)y' = 0.$$

If the equation is rewritten as

$$\frac{dx}{dy} - \frac{2}{3y}x = \frac{1}{3y^2}x^4,$$

it is easily seen to be a Bernoulli type equation in $x$. Hence, if we set $u = x^{-3}$, so that $du/dy = -3x^{-4}(dx/dy)$, the equation becomes

$$\frac{du}{dy} + \frac{2}{y}u = -\frac{1}{y^2}.$$

Thus, an integrating factor is

$$e^{\int 2/y \, dy} = e^{\ln y^2} = y^2.$$

The use of this factor yields

$$\frac{d}{dy}(y^2u) = -1$$

and

$$y^2u = -y + c,$$

or

$$y^2x^{-3} = c - y.$$

## Exercises 24.6

In Numbers 1 to 12, find a general solution for the given differential equation.

1. $y' - 2y = x.$
2. $xy' + y + 2x = e^x.$
3. $y' + ay = b$; $a, b$ are constants.

4. $y' + \dfrac{1}{x}y = e^{-x^2}.$

5. $y' + y \tan x = \sin 2x.$
6. $x(x + 1)y' + y = x(x + 1)^2e^{-x^2}.$

7. $y' \sin x + 2y \cos x = 1.$
8. $y' - 4y = 2e^xy^{1/2}.$
9. $dx - x \, dy = x^{1/2}y \, dy.$
10. $y \, dx + x \, dy = x^2y^2 \ln y \, dy.$
11. $y' + x \tan y = x^2 \sec y.$
12. $y' - y + y^2(x^2 + x + 1) = 0.$

In Numbers 13 to 15, find a particular solution satisfying the given conditions.

13. $\dfrac{dy}{dx} + 5y = e^{-3x}$; when $x = 0$, $y = 3$.

14. $(y - \sin^2 x)\, dx + \sin x\, dy = 0$; when $x = \pi/2$, $y = 1$.

15. $dy + y \sec x\, dx = x \cos x\, dx$; when $x = 0$, $y = 2$.

16. A tank contains 100 gallons of brine in which 50 pounds of salt is dissolved. Brine containing 2 pounds of salt per gallon runs into the tank at the rate of 6 gallons per minute. The mixture, kept uniform by stirring, runs out of the tank at the rate of 4 gallons per minute. Find the amount of salt in solution in the tank at the end of $t$ minutes.

17. A 1000-gallon tank contains 100 gallons of fresh water. Brine containing 1 pound of salt per gallon runs into the tank at a rate of 2 gallons per minute, and the mixture, kept uniform by stirring, runs out at a rate of 1 gallon per minute. Find (a) the amount of salt in the tank when the tank contains 400 gallons of brine, and (b) the concentration of salt in the tank at the end of 1 hour.

18. If $i$ is the current in amperes at time $t$ (seconds), the differential equation of a circuit containing a resistance $R$, inductance $L$, and electromotive force $E \sin \omega t$ is

$$L\frac{di}{dt} + Ri = E \sin \omega t.$$

Find the general solution.

19. If there is no electromotive force in the preceding problem, draw a graph of the current as a function of time. Assume the initial value of $i$ is $I_0$.

20. The slope at any point $(x, y)$ of a curve is $3x - 4y$. Find the equation of the curve if it passes through the origin.

21. Find the equation of a curve if its slope at any point $(x, y)$ is $(x^2 + 2y)$ and the curve passes through the point $(0, 2)$.

# Summary of Chapter 24

The subject of differential equations represents one of the most important applications of the calculus in providing a mathematical formulation of physical phenomena. An understanding of the following fundamental ideas is essential preparation for the further study and application of differential equations:

(1) the definition of and the terminology relating to differential equations (Section 24.1);

(2) the definition of a solution and a general solution of a differential equation (Section 24.2);

(3) the solution of differential equations by separation of variables (Section 24.2);

(4) the translation of simple physical problems into a mathematical form by means of differential equations (Section 24.3);

(5) the solution of differential equations by means of substitutions (Section 24.4).

(6) the solution of differential equations having homogeneous coefficients (Section 24.4);

(7) the solution of exact differential equations (Section 24.5);

(8) the determination of integrating factors (Section 24.5);

(9) the definition of a linear differential equation (Section 24.6);

(10) the solution of linear equations of order 1 (Section 24.6);

(11) the Bernoulli equation and other forms that can be made linear by means of a substitution (Section 24.6).

# Chapter 25    Linear Differential Equations

## 25.1 OPERATORS

The general form of a linear differential equation of order $n$ is

$$(1) \qquad a_0(x)y^{(n)} + a_1(x)y^{(n-1)} + \cdots + a_n(x)y = b(x),$$

where it is assumed that the functions $a_0, a_1, \ldots, a_n, b$ are all continuous over an open interval $\mathcal{J}$, $x_1 < x < x_2$. When $b(x) = 0$, the resulting equation is said to be **homogeneous.** Points at which $a_0(x) = 0$ are called **singular points,** since at such points complications which must be dealt with by special techniques often arise. In the work that follows we shall assume that $a_0(x)$ is never zero on the interval $\mathcal{J}$, and we shall understand that the symbol $\mathcal{J}$ stands for an open interval as indicated.

As was indicated earlier, Equation (1) may be written in an abbreviated form as

$$L(y) = b(x).$$

It is convenient to interpret $L$ as an "operator" that maps $y = f(x)$ to $b(x)$. Operators have already been encountered in the form $D$ or $\int$. The first maps a function $f$ to its derivative function, and the second maps a function $f$ to its inverse derivative function. The operator $L$ may be expressed as a polynomial in $D$, with coefficients that are functions of $x$, where $D^k$ denotes the $k$th derivative operator. That is,

$$L .=. a_0(x)D^n + a_1(x)D^{n-1} + \cdots + a_{n-1}(x)D + a_n(x).$$

To illustrate, consider the differential equation

$$y'' - y' - 6y = 0,$$

which, in operator form, is written

$$(D^2 - D - 6)y = 0.$$

Here

$$L = D^2 - D - 6.$$

An operator of the form of $L$ has an important fundamental property.

**Theorem 25.1a.** The operator $L$ is a linear operator; that is, if the $c$'s are constants, then

$$L(c_1 y_1 + c_2 y_2) = c_1 L(y_1) + c_2 L(y_2).$$

PROOF: Since the operator $D^k$ satisfies the condition that

$$D^k(c_1 y_1 + c_2 y_2) = c_1 D^k y_1 + c_2 D^k y_2,$$

the proof follows easily.

The reader may find it advantageous to illustrate the preceding result with a particular example. For instance, if

$$L = D^2 - 2D - 3,$$

then

$$(D^2 - 2D - 3)(3e^{3x} - \sin x)$$
$$= 3(D^2 - 2D - 3)e^{3x} + (-1)(D^2 - 2D - 3) \sin x,$$

as the reader may easily verify.

Theorem 25.1a indicates that if $y_1$ and $y_2$ are two distinct solutions of

$$L(y) = 0,$$

then the function defined by

$$y = c_1 y_1 + c_2 y_2,$$

where $c_1$ and $c_2$ are arbitrary constants, is also a solution of the differential equation. Consequently, if we are able to determine several particular functions that satisfy a given linear homogeneous differential equation, we may construct from them more elaborate solutions by forming linear combinations of the particular functions.

To see how these ideas are applied to a specific situation, let us make two simple observations. It has already been shown that a solution of $y' - py = 0$ is given by

$$y = ce^{px}.$$

Suppose we go a step further and find the differential equation of the family

$$y = c_1 e^{ax} + c_2 e^{bx},$$

where $c_1$ and $c_2$ are arbitrary constants and $a$ and $b$ denote specified numbers. The reader should find it easy to show that the required equation is

$$(2) \qquad y'' - (a + b)y' + aby = 0,$$

which is a linear homogeneous equation of order two with constant coefficients. Consequently, the original equation represents a solution of Equation (2).

These results suggest a method of attack that can be used for linear homogeneous differential equations having *constant* coefficients.

---

*Example 25.1a.* Find a solution of the equation

$$y'' - y' - 6y = 0.$$

On the basis of the preceding discussion, we may conjecture that the equation is satisfied by an expression of the form

$$y = e^{mx}.$$

In this case,
$$y' = me^{mx}, \quad y'' = m^2 e^{mx},$$
and
$$m^2 e^{mx} - m e^{mx} - 6 e^{mx} = 0.$$

Hence, $m$ must satisfy the equation
$$m^2 - m - 6 = 0,$$
which implies that
$$m = 3 \quad \text{or} \quad m = -2.$$

Apparently, then, there are two functions, represented by
$$y_1 = e^{3x} \quad \text{and} \quad y_2 = e^{-2x},$$
that satisfy the differential equation. According to Theorem 25.1a, the expression
$$y = c_1 e^{3x} + c_2 e^{-2x}$$
is also a solution of the differential equation.

---

May we be assured that no other functions satisfy the differential equation in Example 25.1a? No!! For example, the reader may show that
$$y = \sinh 3x + \cosh 3x$$
also satisfies the differential equation. Does it then become necessary to write
$$y = c_1 e^{3x} + c_2 e^{-2x} + c_3(\cosh 3x + \sinh 3x)$$
as a more general solution? If so, where does one stop? What shall we consider to be a satisfactory general solution of the differential equation?

To answer these questions, we are forced to turn to the "theory" of differential equations. It is only after we have developed some general results concerning linear differential equations that we can hope to achieve an organized systematic procedure for specifying the solution of such an equation.

## Exercises 25.1

1. Is it true that $xD = Dx$? Explain.

The "product" of two operators may be defined as follows: Let $(D - a)y = u$ and $(D - b)u = v$, where $a$ and $b$ are constants. By substitution, we get
$$(D - b)[(D - a)y] = v,$$
which describes a mapping of the function $y$ to the function $v$. The operator that maps $y$ to $v$ is denoted by
$$(D - b)(D - a).$$

Numbers 2 to 6 involve this notation.

2. Is it true that $(D - 3)(D - 2) = D^2 - 5D + 6$?
3. Is it true that $(D - b)(D - a) = (D - a)(D - b)$?
4. The operator $(D - 2)(D - x)$ is equivalent to an operator of the form $D^2 + \alpha D + \beta$. What are the expressions for $\alpha$ and $\beta$?
5. Is it true that $(D - 2)(D - x) = (D - x)(D - 2)$?

6. In general, under what circumstances do the linear operators $L_1$ and $L_2$ satisfy the relation $L_1L_2 = L_2L_1$?

In Numbers 7 to 15, use the method of Example 25.1a to find all possible solutions of the form $e^{mx}$.

7. $y'' + 5y' + 6y = 0.$
8. $4y'' + 4y' - 15y = 0.$
9. $y''' - 3y'' + 4y' - 2y = 0.$
10. $y'' - 6y' + 9y = 0.$
11. $y'' + 4y' + 4y = 0.$

12. $y''' - y'' - y' + y = 0.$
13. $y^{(4)} - 4y = 0.$
14. $y'' + 2y' - 2y = 0.$
15. $y'' + 4y = 0.$

16. Show that $y_1 = \cos ax$ and $y_2 = \sin ax$ are solutions of $(D^2 + a^2)y = 0$. Show also that each of these solutions is a linear combination of solutions of the form $e^{mx}$. (Note that $m$ is not restricted to real values.)

## 25.2 SOLUTIONS OF LINEAR DIFFERENTIAL EQUATIONS

In order to simplify matters, we shall restrict the present discussion to second-order equations. We shall first state without proof a fundamental theorem that indicates the conditions under which a solution to a given differential equation exists.

**Theorem 25.2a.** If in the expression

$$L(y) .=. a_0(x)y'' + a_1(x)y' + a_2(x)y,$$

$a_0$, $a_1$, and $a_2$ are continuous functions over an interval $\mathcal{I}$, and if $a_0(x) \neq 0$ at points in $\mathcal{I}$, then there exists a function $f$ that satisfies the differential equation

$$L(y) = 0$$

on $\mathcal{I}$, and that also satisfies the conditions

$$f(x_0) = b_0 \quad \text{and} \quad f'(x_0) = b_1,$$

where $x_0$ is a given point in $\mathcal{I}$, and $b_0$ and $b_1$ are given constants.

The conditions $f(x_0) = b_0, f'(x_0) = b_1$ are called **initial conditions**. The problem of finding a function that satisfies the differential equation and the initial conditions is called an **initial-value problem**. It is clear that a linear differential equation with constant coefficients satisfies the conditions of the theorem, so that there is always a solution to an initial-value problem in which the differential equation is of this simple type. The statement of the theorem may be extended easily to include linear differential equations of order $n$.

The next theorem, which concerns the uniqueness of the solution of a given second-order differential equation, is also stated without proof.

**Theorem 25.2b.** Let $f$ and $g$ be two functions that satisfy

$$L(y) .=. a_0(x)y'' + a_1(x)y' + a_2(x)y = 0$$

on an open interval $\mathcal{I}$ such that $a_0$, $a_1$, and $a_2$ are continuous on $\mathcal{I}$, $a_0(x) \neq 0$ on $\mathcal{I}$, and

$$f(x_0) = g(x_0) = b_0 \quad \text{and} \quad f'(x_0) = g'(x_0) = b_1.$$

Then $f(x) = g(x)$ for all $x \in \mathcal{I}$.

Theorem 25.2b appears to contradict the results obtained in Example 25.1a. However, initial conditions were not specified in that example, nor was the nature of the set of solutions of the differential equation specified. In order to clarify the situation, we must make use of the concepts of linear dependence and linear independence of the elements of a set of functions.

**Definition 25.2a.** A set of functions $\{u_1, u_2, \ldots, u_n\}$ is said to be a **linearly dependent** set on an interval $\mathcal{I}$ if there exist constants $c_1, c_2, \ldots, c_n$, not all zero, such that

$$c_1 u_1(x) + c_2 u_2(x) + \cdots + c_n u_n(x) = 0$$

for all $x \in \mathcal{I}$. If no such constants exist, then the set is said to be a **linearly independent** set on $\mathcal{I}$.

To illustrate, the functions described by

$$1, x, x^2, x^3, \ldots, x^n$$

are independent on every interval. The functions described by

$$1, \quad \sin^2 x, \quad \cos^2 x$$

are dependent on every interval, because

$$1 + (-1) \sin^2 x + (-1) \cos^2 x = 0$$

is an identity on $\mathcal{R}$. To say that the functions $u_1, u_2, \ldots, u_n$ are linearly dependent means simply that at least one of the expressions, say $u_1(x)$, may be written as a linear combination of the others. For example, $e^x$, $e^{-x}$, and $\cosh x$ are linearly dependent, since

$$e^x + e^{-x} - 2 \cosh x = 0,$$

or

$$\cosh x = \frac{e^x + e^{-x}}{2}.$$

Note that if one (or more) of the functions in Definition 25.2a is identically zero, then the set is always linearly dependent. For instance, if $u_1(x) = 0$, then the choice, $c_1 \neq 0$, $c_2 = c_3 = \cdots = c_n = 0$, satisfies the definition of linear dependence.

The next theorem will clarify the concept of the set of solutions of a linear differential equation of order two, and may be extended to linear differential equations of order $n$.

**Theorem 25.2c.** Let $u_1$ and $u_2$ be two linearly independent functions that satisfy the equation

$$L(y) .=. a_0(x)y'' + a_1(x)y' + a_2(x)y = 0$$

on an open interval $\mathscr{I}$, where $a_0$, $a_1$, and $a_2$ are all continuous on $\mathscr{I}$ and $a_0(x) \neq 0$ on $\mathscr{I}$. Then, if $f$ is a solution of $L(y) = 0$ on $\mathscr{I}$, there exist constants $\alpha$ and $\beta$ such that

$$f(x) = \alpha u_1(x) + \beta u_2(x).$$

PROOF: Let $x_0 \in \mathscr{I}$, and let us try to find a solution for the constants $c_1$ and $c_2$ in the equations

$$(1) \qquad \begin{aligned} c_1 u_1(x_0) + c_2 u_2(x_0) &= f(x_0), \\ c_1 u_1'(x_0) + c_2 u_2'(x_0) &= f'(x_0). \end{aligned}$$

If a solution for $c_1$ and $c_2$ exists at the point $x_0$, then

$$f(x) = c_1 u_1(x) + c_2 u_2(x)$$

for *all* values of $x \in \mathscr{I}$ by Theorem 25.2b. The set of equations (1) has a solution for $c_1$ and $c_2$ only if

$$\begin{vmatrix} u_1(x_0) & u_2(x_0) \\ u_1'(x_0) & u_2'(x_0) \end{vmatrix} \neq 0.$$

To show that this determinant is not zero, let us first consider the determinant

$$W(x) . =. \begin{vmatrix} u_1(x) & u_2(x) \\ u_1'(x) & u_2'(x) \end{vmatrix},$$

which is called the **Wronskian** of the functions $u_1$ and $u_2$. Since

$$W(x) = u_1(x)u_2'(x) - u_2(x)u_1'(x),$$

we may write

$$\frac{W}{u_1^2} = \frac{u_1 u_2' - u_2 u_1'}{u_1^2} = \frac{d}{dx}\left(\frac{u_2}{u_1}\right).$$

Now suppose $W(x) = 0$ for *all* $x \in \mathscr{I}$. Then,

$$\frac{d}{dx}\left(\frac{u_2}{u_1}\right) = 0 \quad \text{for all } x \in \mathscr{I},$$

and $u_2/u_1 = c$ or $u_2 - cu_1 = 0$. That is, $u_1$ and $u_2$ are linearly dependent, contrary to the hypothesis. Hence, $W(x) \neq 0$ at least at one point $x_1 \in \mathscr{I}$.
But, since

$$(2) \qquad \begin{aligned} W &= u_1 u_2' - u_2 u_1', \\ W' &= u_1 u_2'' - u_2 u_1''. \end{aligned}$$

Furthermore, $u_1$ and $u_2$ are solutions of the differential equation, so that

$$\begin{aligned} a_0 u_1'' + a_1 u_1' + a_2 u_1 &= 0, \\ a_0 u_2'' + a_1 u_2' + a_2 u_2 &= 0. \end{aligned}$$

Multiplying the first of these equations by $-u_2$ and the second by $u_1$, and adding the results, we get

$$a_0(u_1 u_2'' - u_2 u_1'') + a_1(u_1 u_2' - u_2 u_1') = 0.$$

Hence, by substitution from Equations (2),

$$a_0 W' + a_1 W = 0,$$

or

$$\frac{W'}{W} = -\frac{a_1}{a_0}.$$

Consequently,

(3) $$W(x) = W(x_1) \exp\left[-\int_{x_1}^{x} \frac{a_1(t)}{a_0(t)} dt\right].$$

(The reader may provide the details. See Exercises 25.2, Number 8.) Equation (3) shows that $W(x)$ is never zero on $\mathcal{J}$. Hence, the set of equations (1) always has a solution for $c_1$ and $c_2$ for any value of $x$ in $\mathcal{J}$.

The essence of the preceding theorem is that *every* solution of the differential equation may be expressed as a linear combination of two linearly independent solutions. It remains to be shown that there actually are two such solutions, and the existence of these is assured by

**Theorem 25.2d.** Let $L(y) . = . a_0(x)y'' + a_1(x)y' + a_2(x)y$, where $a_0$, $a_1$, $a_2$ are continuous on $\mathcal{J}$ and $a_0(x) \neq 0$ on $\mathcal{J}$. Let $u_1$ and $u_2$ be solutions of $L(y) = 0$ on $\mathcal{J}$ such that

$$u_1(x_0) = 1, \quad u_1'(x_0) = 0,$$
$$u_2(x_0) = 0, \quad u_2'(x_0) = 1,$$

where $x_0 \in \mathcal{J}$. Then $u_1$ and $u_2$ are linearly independent.

PROOF: The existence of the functions $u_1$ and $u_2$ satisfying the hypotheses of this theorem is guaranteed by Theorem 25.2b. To show that $u_1$ and $u_2$ are linearly independent, we must show that the only values of $c_1$ and $c_2$ for which

$$c_1 u_1(x) + c_2 u_2(x) = 0$$

for all $x \in \mathcal{J}$ are 0. Hence, we assume that there are constants, $c_1$ and $c_2$, for which

$$c_1 u_1(x) + c_2 u_2(x) = 0.$$

By differentiation, we get

$$c_1 u_1'(x) + c_2 u_2'(x) = 0.$$

At the point $x_0$, we have

$$c_1 u_1(x_0) + c_2 u_2(x_0) = 0,$$
$$c_1 u_1'(x_0) + c_2 u_2'(x_0) = 0,$$

which imply that

$$c_1 = 0 \quad \text{and} \quad c_2 = 0,$$

because of the given initial conditions. Hence, $u_1$ and $u_2$ are linearly independent.

The developments up to this point now assure us that a linear differential equation of the second order has two independent solutions, and that any other solution of the equation may be written as a linear combination of these two solutions. These results may be extended by similar arguments to include the linear equation of order $n$. In that case, we can prove that there are $n$ linearly independent solutions and that any other solution of the differential equation may be written as a linear combination of them.

## Exercises 25.2

In each of Numbers 1 to 6, determine if the given set of functions is linearly dependent or independent.

1. $e^x$, $xe^x$, $x^2e^x$.
2. $1$, $\sin x$, $\cos x$, $\sin^2 x$, $\cos^2 x$.
3. $x - 1$, $2x + 3$, $x + 4$.

4. $x^2 - x - 1$, $2x^2 + 1$, $3x - 2$.
5. $\sinh x$, $\cosh x$, $e^x$.
6. $e^x$, $e^{2x}$, $e^{3x}$.

7. Verify Equation (2).

8. Verify Equation (3).

9. Show that if $u_1$, $u_2$, $u_3$ are linearly dependent, twice differentiable functions on an interval $\mathcal{I}$, then their Wronskian

$$W(x) = \begin{vmatrix} u_1(x) & u_2(x) & u_3(x) \\ u_1'(x) & u_2'(x) & u_3'(x) \\ u_1''(x) & u_2''(x) & u_3''(x) \end{vmatrix}$$

is identically zero on $\mathcal{I}$.

10. The proof of Theorem 25.2c required the use of Theorem 25.2b, which was stated without proof. If Theorem 25.2c is assumed valid, it can be used to prove Theorem 25.2b. Show how this can be done by assuming that every solution of the differential equation is of the form

$$y = c_1u_1 + c_2u_2,$$

and obtaining the uniqueness theorem.

## 25.3 GENERAL SOLUTIONS OF LINEAR HOMOGENEOUS EQUATIONS WITH CONSTANT COEFFICIENTS

Although the development in the preceding section indicated how the solution of a linear differential equation may be set up, it did not provide a definite procedure for finding the independent solutions. It is time that we bring together the results of the first two sections into a workable procedure. For this purpose we shall consider only linear homogeneous differential equations with constant coefficients, such as

(1) $$a_0y^{(n)} + a_1y^{(n-1)} + \cdots + a_{n-1}y' + a_ny = 0.$$

It was suggested earlier that some solutions of this type of equation are of the form $e^{mx}$. If $e^{mx}$ is substituted for $y$ in Equation (1), the resulting equation,

(2) $$a_0m^n + a_1m^{n-1} + \cdots + a_{n-1}m + a_n = 0,$$

is a condition that must be satisfied by $m$ if $e^{mx}$ is a solution. This equation is called the **auxiliary equation** to Equation (1). In general, Equation (2) has $n$ roots,

$$m_1, \quad m_2, \quad \ldots, \quad m_n.$$

If these roots are all distinct, then the expressions

$$e^{m_1x}, \quad e^{m_2x}, \quad \ldots, \quad e^{m_nx}$$

describe $n$ independent functions in terms of which any solution of the differential equation may be expressed. Accordingly, we write

$$y = c_1e^{m_1x} + c_2e^{m_2x} + \cdots + c_ne^{m_nx}$$

as a *general solution* of the differential equation.

In case some of the roots of the auxiliary equation are repeated, there will *not* be $n$ independent solutions of the form $e^{mx}$, and in that event we must seek additional solutions of some other form. This problem will be discussed later. For the present let us illustrate these ideas with some examples.

---

*Example 25.3a.* Find the solution of the differential equation

$$y'' - y' - 6y = 0$$

that satisfies the conditions that when $x = 0$, $y = 3$, and as $x \to \infty$, $y \to 0$.

The auxiliary equation is

$$m^2 - m - 6 = 0,$$

so that

$$m = 3, \quad m = -2.$$

Hence, a general solution is of the form

$$y = c_1e^{3x} + c_2e^{-2x}.$$

As $x \to \infty$, we must have $y \to 0$. This can happen only if $c_1 = 0$. Furthermore, we want $y = 3$ when $x = 0$, so that $c_2 = 3$. Thus, the solution satisfying the given conditions is

$$y = 3e^{-2x}.$$

---

*Note:* As is often the case in practice, the conditions that the solutions of the differential equation in Example 25.3a is required to satisfy are not both given at the same point. To distinguish such conditions from initial conditions they are called **boundary conditions.** Example 25.3a illustrates that we can sometimes solve differential equations with boundary rather than initial conditions.

---

*Example 25.3b.* Find a general solution of

$$y''' + y'' - 3y' + y = 0.$$

The associated auxiliary equation is

$$m^3 + m^2 - 3m + 1 = 0,$$

or

$$(m - 1)(m^2 + 2m - 1) = 0,$$

which implies that

$$m = 1, \quad m = -1 \pm \sqrt{2}.$$

It follows that $e^x$, $e^{(-1+\sqrt{2})x}$, and $e^{(-1-\sqrt{2})x}$ describe independent functions that are solutions of the differential equation. Since there are three of these, and since the order of the differential equation is three, a general solution is given by

$$y = c_1e^x + e^{-x}(c_2e^{\sqrt{2}x} + c_3e^{-\sqrt{2}x}).$$

It is clear that an auxiliary equation may not always have real roots, but we need not be dismayed by such a turn of events, as the next example shows.

---

*Example 25.3c.* Find a general solution of

$$y'' - 2y' + 2y = 0.$$

The auxiliary equation is

$$m^2 - 2m + 2 = 0,$$

which implies $m = 1 \pm i$. Apparently, the independent solutions are described by

$$e^{(1+i)x} \quad \text{and} \quad e^{(1-i)x},$$

and a general solution is given by

$$y = e^x(c_1 e^{ix} + c_2 e^{-ix}).$$

Since we are usually interested in *real* solutions to the differential equation, and the solution as given is not in a form that we hoped to obtain, we try to modify it. Recall that

$$e^{ix} = \cos x + i \sin x$$

and

$$e^{-ix} = \cos x - i \sin x,$$

so that the general solution may be written in terms of the more familiar trigonometric functions, as

$$y = e^x[(c_1 + c_2) \cos x + i(c_1 - c_2) \sin x].$$

Since we have gone so far as to allow complex-valued functions as solutions of the differential equation, it may well be that with the proper choice of constants in imaginary form, we can obtain the general solution of the differential equation in a real form. In fact, if

$$c_1 = \frac{A - iB}{2}$$

and

$$c_2 = \frac{A + iB}{2},$$

where $A$, $B$ are real constants, then

$$c_1 + c_2 = A \quad \text{and} \quad i(c_1 - c_2) = B,$$

so that

$$y = e^x(A \cos x + B \sin x).$$

In other words, we actually do have a real general solution to the differential equation, a fact that was temporarily obscured by the form in which the solution was originally written.

---

In general, if the imaginary numbers $a + ib$ and $a - ib$ appear as roots of an auxiliary equation, then the corresponding functions that are solutions of the differential equation are described by

$$e^{ax} \cos bx \quad \text{and} \quad e^{ax} \sin bx,$$

a fact that the reader should verify (see Exercises 25.3, Number 23).

If there is a repeated root in the auxiliary equation, then it is not possible to determine an adequate number of functions described by the form $e^{mx}$ to construct a general solution as indicated in Theorem 25.2c. The next example illustrates the nature of this difficulty.

---

*Example 25.3d.* Find a general solution for the differential equation

$$y'' - 4y' + 4y = 0.$$

The auxiliary equation is

$$m^2 - 4m + 4 = 0,$$

which has the roots

$$m = 2, 2.$$

Hence, the only function of the form $e^{mx}$ that satisfies the differential equation is described by $e^{2x}$. Since Theorem 25.2c indicates that there are two independent solutions of the differential equation, the missing function is apparently *not* of the form $e^{mx}$.

Although it is possible to discover the other function by trial and error, it is more instructive to develop a systematic approach for dealing with problems of this type. Consequently, let us rewrite the differential equation in operator form as

$$(D^2 - 4D + 4)y = 0,$$

or

$$(D - 2)(D - 2)y = 0,$$

the operator always being factorable when it has constant coefficients.

Then let

$$u = (D - 2)y,$$

so that the differential equation becomes a linear first-order equation in $u$,

$$\frac{du}{dx} - 2u = 0.$$

It follows that

$$u = c_1 e^{2x}.$$

Upon replacing $u$ by $(D - 2)y$, we get

$$\frac{dy}{dx} - 2y = c_1 e^{2x},$$

which is a first-order linear equation in $y$. An integrating factor is $e^{-2x}$, so that

$$\frac{d}{dx}(e^{-2x}y) = c_1.$$

Then,

$$e^{-2x}y = c_1 x + c_2$$

and

$$y = c_1 x e^{2x} + c_2 e^{2x}.$$

The missing function has now appeared in the form $x e^{2x}$, and a general solution has been found.

---

The result of the preceding investigation suggests the general form for the additional functions associated with repeated roots of the auxiliary equation.

**Theorem 25.3a.** If a root, $r$, of an auxiliary equation occurs $p$ times, then the independent functions that satisfy the given differential equation and are associated with this root are of the form

$$e^{rx}, \; xe^{rx}, \; x^2e^{rx}, \; \ldots, \; x^{p-1}e^{rx}.$$

This statement applies even if $r$ is an imaginary root.

PROOF: If $r$ is a root of multiplicity $p$ in the auxiliary equation

$$a_0m^n + a_1m^{n-1} + \cdots + a_n = 0,$$

then the equation may be written in a factored form as

$$(m - r)^pQ(m) = 0.$$

This auxiliary equation is associated with an operator of the form

$$(D - r)^pQ(D),$$

where all the coefficients are constants. We need only show that if $k < p$, and $k$ and $p$ are nonnegative integers, then $y = x^ke^{rx}$ satisfies the differential equation $(D - r)^pQ(D)y = 0$, a task the reader may complete for himself (see Exercises 25.3, Number 24).

---

*Example 25.3e.* Find a general solution of the equation

$$y^{(4)} + 6y'' + 9y = 0.$$

The auxiliary equation

$$m^4 + 6m^2 + 9 = 0$$

has the roots

$$m = i\sqrt{3}, \; i\sqrt{3}, \; -i\sqrt{3}, \; -i\sqrt{3}.$$

The functions associated with these values are

$$e^{i\sqrt{3}x}, \; xe^{i\sqrt{3}x}, \; e^{-i\sqrt{3}x}, \; \text{and} \; xe^{-i\sqrt{3}x}.$$

We may replace these by the following linear combinations, which are real trigonometric functions:

$$\cos\sqrt{3}x = \frac{1}{2}e^{i\sqrt{3}x} + \frac{1}{2}e^{-i\sqrt{3}x},$$

$$\sin\sqrt{3}x = \frac{1}{2i}e^{i\sqrt{3}x} - \frac{1}{2i}e^{-i\sqrt{3}x},$$

$$x\cos\sqrt{3}x = \frac{1}{2}xe^{i\sqrt{3}x} + \frac{1}{2}xe^{-i\sqrt{3}x},$$

$$x\sin\sqrt{3}x = \frac{1}{2i}xe^{i\sqrt{3}x} - \frac{1}{2i}xe^{-i\sqrt{3}x}.$$

Hence, a general solution is given by

$$y = (c_1 + c_2x)\cos\sqrt{3}x + (c_3 + c_4x)\sin\sqrt{3}x.$$

## Exercises 25.3

In each of Numbers 1 to 20, find a general solution, or find a solution that satisfies the given conditions as indicated.

1. $y''' + 2y'' - 15y' = 0.$
2. $y'' + 3y' = 0.$
3. $y'' + 5y' + 4y = 0.$
4. $y''' + 3y'' - y' - 3y = 0.$

5. $(D^3 - 5D - 2)y = 0$.

6. $(D^4 - 2D^3 - 13D^2 + 38D - 24)y = 0$.

7. $y''' - 6y'' + 12y' - 8y = 0$.

8. $y''' - 4y'' + 4y' = 0$.

9. $y^{(5)} - 9y''' = 0$.

10. $(4D^4 + 4D^3 - 3D^2 - 2D + 1)y = 0$.

11. $(D^4 - 5D^2 - 6D - 2)y = 0$.

12. $(D^3 + D^2 - D - 1)y = 0$; when $x = 0$, $y = 1$; when $x = 1$, $y = 0$; and as $x \to \infty$, $y \to 0$.

13. $(D^3 + 5D^2 + 3D - 9)y = 0$; when $x = 0$, $y = 1$; when $x = 1$, $y = 1$; and as $x \to \infty$, $y \to 0$.

14. $y'' - 4y' + 7 = 0$.

15. $y'' + y = 0$; when $x = 0$, $y = A$, $y' = 0$.

16. $y^{(4)} + 2y''' + 10y'' = 0$.

17. $y^{(4)} + 18y'' + 81y = 0$.

18. $y^{(6)} + 9y^{(4)} + 24y'' + 16y = 0$.

19. $y'' + 2by' + k^2y = 0$, $k > b > 0$; when $x = 0$, $y = 0$, $y' = A$.

20. $(D^4 + 2D^2 + 1)y = 0$; when $x = \pi/2$, $y = 0$; when $x = 0$, $y = 0$; when $x = 0$, $y' = 1$; when $x = \pi$, $y = 0$.

21. $y^{(4)} + 4y''' + 4y'' = 0$; when $x = 0$, $y = 0$, $y' = 0$, $y'' = 4$, and as $x \to \infty$, $y' \to 1$. Find the value of $y$ when $x = 2$.

22. $y^{(4)} - y''' - 2y'' = 0$; when $x = 0$, $y = 0$, $y' = 0$, and as $x \to \infty$, $y' \to 2$. Find the value of $y$ when $x = 4$.

23. Show that if $a + ib$ and $a - ib$ are roots of the auxiliary equation of

$$y'' + \alpha y' + \beta y = 0,$$

then a general solution of the differential equation is given by

$$y = e^{ax}(c_1 \cos bx + c_2 \sin bx).$$

24. Show that $y = x^k e^{rx}$, with $k$ and $p$ nonnegative integers and $k < p$, satisfies any differential equation of the form

$$(D - r)^p Q(D)y = 0,$$

where $Q(D)$ is a linear operator with constant coefficients.

## 25.4 NONHOMOGENEOUS LINEAR EQUATIONS OF ORDER $N$

The nonhomogeneous linear equation occurs more frequently in practice than the homogeneous equation, but to find solutions for nonhomogeneous equations,

$$L(y) = f(x),$$

we must seek additional techniques.

It was suggested in Section 24.6 that a general solution of a nonhomogeneous equation is associated with a general solution of the corresponding homogeneous equation. This relationship is expressed more precisely in

**Theorem 25.4a.** Let $L$ denote a linear operator of order $n$ with coefficients that are continuous on an interval $\mathcal{I}$. Let $u_1, u_2, \ldots, u_n$ be $n$ independent solutions of $L(y) = 0$. Suppose also that $y_p$ is a solution of the equation $L(y) = f(x)$, where $f(x)$ is continuous on the interval $\mathcal{I}$. Then every solution of $L(y) = f(x)$ may be expressed in the form

$$y = y_p + \sum_{k=1}^{n} c_k u_k,$$

where $c_1, c_2, \ldots, c_n$ are constants.

PROOF: Observe first that if $y$ has the form given in the theorem, then

$$L\left(y_p + \sum_{k=1}^{n} c_k u_k\right) = L(y_p) + \sum_{k=1}^{n} c_k L(u_k) = f(x),$$

since $L(u_k) = 0$ and $L(y_p) = f(x)$ by hypothesis. Thus, $y$ is indeed a solution of the differential equation.

Suppose now that $y_2$ is another solution of $L(y) = f(x)$. Then

$$L(y_2 - y_p) = L(y_2) - L(y_p) = f(x) - f(x) = 0.$$

Hence, $y_2 - y_p$ is a solution of the homogeneous equation

$$L(y) = 0,$$

and therefore can be expressed as a linear combination of the $u_1, u_2, \ldots, u_n$. That is,

$$y_2 - y_p = \sum_{k=1}^{n} b_k u_k,$$

or

$$y_2 = y_p + \sum_{k=1}^{n} b_k u_k,$$

as was to be shown.

Theorem 25.4a shows that to determine the solution of a linear nonhomogeneous differential equation of order $n$, $L(y) = f(x)$, it is sufficient to determine (i) the general solution of the homogeneous equation $L(y) = 0$, and (ii) a function $y_p$, that satisfies $L(y) = f(x)$. A general solution of the nonhomogeneous equation then takes on the form

$$y = y_p + \sum_{k=1}^{n} c_k u_k.$$

It is customary to call $y_p$ a **particular solution** and $\sum_{k=1}^{n} c_k u_k$ the **complementary part** of the solution of $L(y) = f(x)$. Since we know how to construct the complementary part of the solution, which is usually denoted by $y_c$, we lack only a method for finding a particular solution $y_p$ of the nonhomogeneous equation.

One of the simplest procedures for finding a particular solution is the **method of undetermined coefficients.** Unfortunately, this method works only when $f(x)$ is of a rather restricted form. The procedure is based on the determination of a linear operator $L_1$, with real constant coefficients, such that $L_1(f) = 0$. The operator $L_1$ of lowest order with real constant coefficients, such that $L_1(f) = 0$, is called the **annihilator** of $f(x)$.

It follows from our study of the linear homogeneous equation that only special types of functions have such an annihilator. These are the functions defined by $x^n$ ($n$ a nonnegative integer), $e^{ax}$, $x^n e^{ax}$, $\cos bx$, $\sin bx$, $x^n e^{ax} \cos bx$, $x^n e^{ax} \sin bx$, or a linear combination of these forms. For any such function, we can construct the operator $L_1$ from our knowledge of the solutions of the linear homogeneous equation.

To illustrate: we know that the annihilator of $x^p$, where $p$ is a positive integer, is $D^{p+1}$. That is, $D^{p+1} x^p = 0$. Similarly, the annihilator of $e^{mx}$ is $D - m$, since

$$(D - m)e^{mx} = me^{mx} - me^{mx} = 0,$$

and the annihilator of $x^2 e^{mx}$ is $(D - m)^3$, as the reader may verify. The annihilators for $e^{ax} \sin bx$ and $e^{ax} \cos bx$ are the same, $D^2 - 2aD + a^2 + b^2$, as the reader may again verify. Annihilators of the type described here exist only for functions that are solutions of homogeneous linear equations with constant coefficients.

An example will illustrate how the annihilator can be used to obtain a particular solution.

---

*Example 25.4a.* Obtain a general solution for the equation

$$y'' - y' - 2y = x^2.$$

The equation may be written in operator form as

(1) $$(D^2 - D - 2)y = x^2.$$

A general solution of the homogeneous equation

$$(D^2 - D - 2)y = 0$$

is

$$y_c = c_1 e^{2x} + c_2 e^{-x},$$

which is the complementary part of the solution of Equation (1).

Operating on both sides of Equation (1) with the annihilator $D^3$ of $x^2$, we get

$$D^3(D^2 - D - 2)y = 0.$$

That is, we generate a new homogeneous differential equation from the original equation. A general solution for this new equation is

$$y = c_1 e^{2x} + c_2 e^{-x} + c_3 + c_4 x + c_5 x^2.$$

Since the first two terms of this expression constitute the complementary part of the solution of the original differential equation, the particular solution of the original equation must be of the form

$$y_p = c_3 + c_4 x + c_5 x^2,$$

since any solution of

$$(D^2 - D - 2)y = x^2$$

is also a solution of

$$D^3(D^2 - D - 2)y = 0.$$

Hence, we need only determine specific values for $c_3$, $c_4$, $c_5$. To do this, we substitute

$$y_p = c_3 + c_4 x + c_5 x^2$$

into the original differential equation to get

$$2c_5 - (c_4 + 2c_5 x) - 2(c_3 + c_4 x + c_5 x^2) = x^2.$$

In order that this equation be an identity in $x$, we must have

$$2c_5 - c_4 - 2c_3 = 0,$$
$$-2c_5 - 2c_4 = 0,$$
$$-2c_5 = 1.$$

Hence

$$c_5 = -\frac{1}{2}, \quad c_4 = +\frac{1}{2}, \quad c_3 = -\frac{3}{4}.$$

The general solution of the original equation is thus

$$y = c_1 e^{2x} + c_2 e^{-x} - \frac{3}{4} + \frac{1}{2} x - \frac{1}{2} x^2.$$

---

*Example 25.4b.* Obtain a general solution of

$$(D^2 - D - 2)y = e^{-x} + \sin x.$$

The complementary part of the solution is

$$y_c = c_1 e^{2x} + c_2 e^{-x},$$

as before. The annihilator for $e^{-x}$ is $D + 1$ and for $\sin x$ is $D^2 + 1$. Hence, we operate on both sides with the product of these two annihilators to get

$$(D^2 + 1)(D + 1)(D^2 - D - 2)y = 0,$$

or

$$(D^2 + 1)(D + 1)^2(D - 2)y = 0,$$

as the reader may verify.

A general solution for this equation is

$$y = c_1 e^{2x} + c_2 e^{-x} + c_3 x e^{-x} + c_4 \cos x + c_5 \sin x.$$

It follows that the desired particular solution, $y_p$, is of the form

$$y_p = c_3 x e^{-x} + c_4 \cos x + c_5 \sin x.$$

To determine the values of $c_3$, $c_4$, and $c_5$, we substitute $y_p$ into the original differential equation to get

$$c_3(-2e^{-x} + xe^{-x}) - c_4 \cos x - c_5 \sin x$$
$$-c_3(e^{-x} - xe^{-x}) + c_4 \sin x - c_5 \cos x$$
$$-2c_3 x e^{-x} - 2c_4 \cos x - 2c_5 \sin x = e^{-x} + \sin x.$$

Since $e^{-x}$, $\cos x$, and $\sin x$ are linearly independent, it follows that we may equate corresponding coefficients on both sides, thus obtaining

$$c_3 = -\frac{1}{3}, \quad c_4 = \frac{1}{10}, \quad c_5 = -\frac{3}{10}.$$

Consequently,

$$y_p = -\frac{1}{3} x e^{-x} + \frac{1}{10} \cos x - \frac{3}{10} \sin x,$$

and

$$y = c_1 e^{2x} + c_2 e^{-x} - \frac{1}{3} x e^{-x} + \frac{1}{10} \cos x - \frac{3}{10} \sin x.$$

---

The principal defect of the method of undetermined coefficients for calculating a particular solution of a nonhomogeneous differential equation is its lack of versatility. Unless the nonhomogeneous term is of the special form previously described, there is no annihilator of the type that has been discussed. A method that can be used when the method of undetermined coefficients is not available is described in the next section.

### Exercises 25.4

In Numbers 1 to 10, find annihilators for the given expressions.

1. $3x^2 + 2x$.
2. $xe^{2x}$.
3. $\cos 3x + \sin 3x$.
4. $e^x \sin 2x$.
5. $xe^x \cos x$.

6. $xe^{2x} + e^x \sin x$.
7. $x^3 - e^x \cos 2x$.
8. $e^x \cos 2x + e^{-x} \sin 2x$.
9. $x^2 + e^x + \sin x$.
10. $x \sin x + x^2 e^{-3x} + 1$.

In each of Numbers 11 to 23, find a general solution for the given differential equation.

11. $y'' - 2y' - 3y = e^x$.
12. $y'' + y' - 2y = 6e^{2x}$.
13. $y'' - y' - 2y = 6x + 6e^{-x}$.
14. $y'' - 4y' + 3y = 10 \sin x$.

15. $(D^4 - 1)y = x^2 - \cos x$.
16. $(D^3 - D^2 + D - 1)y = 4 \sin x$.
17. $(D^2 + 5)y = 12 \cos^2 x$.
18. $(D^2 - 2D + 1)y = 2xe^x$.

19. $(D^2 - 5D - 84)y = 120e^{-3x} - 210e^{-2x}$.
20. $(2D^2 + 5D - 3)y = \sqrt{e^x} + 1$.
21. $(D^2 + 2D + 4)y = 2 \sin x + \cos 2x$.
22. $(D^2 + 4D + 8)y = 34e^{-x} \sin 2x$.
23. $(D^3 + D^2 - D - 1)y = xe^x + e^{-x} \sin x$.

In each of Numbers 24 to 26, find a particular solution that satisfies the given conditions.

24. $y^{(4)} - y = 5x^2$; when $x = 0$, $y = 0$, $y' = 0$, $y'' = 2$, $y''' = 1$.
25. $y'' - y = 4xe^x$; when $x = 0$, $y = 0$ and $y' = 0$.
26. $y'' + y = \cos x$; when $x = 0$, $y = 2$ and $y' = 1$.
27. Find the value of $y$ that corresponds to $x = 2$ if

$$y'' + 2y' + y = e^{-x}, \text{ and } y = 3 \text{ and } y' = 5 \text{ when } x = 0.$$

28. Find the value of $y$ that corresponds to $x = \pi/6$ if

$$y'' + y = 8 \sin 3x, \ y = 2 \text{ when } x = 0, \text{ and } y = 0 \text{ when } x = \pi/2.$$

## 25.5 VARIATION OF PARAMETERS

It is easy to give an example for which the method of undetermined coefficients is useless, since we are unable to write down beforehand the form of a particular solution. Thus, consider the equation

$$y'' + y = \tan x.$$

The solution of the associated homogeneous equation is

$$y = c_1 \cos x + c_2 \sin x.$$

However, since there is no annihilator for $\tan x$ of the simple type discussed in the preceding section, we must seek another method for finding the particular solution. Such a method was first used by the Swiss mathematician Johann Bernoulli (1667–1748) and later by the French mathematician Joseph Lagrange (1736–1813), and is called the **method of variation of parameters.**

The method of variation of parameters is based on the assumption that the particular solution is obtainable from the complementary part of the solution by replacing the arbitrary constants by suitable functions of $x$. For the preceding equation, this is equivalent to assuming that

$$y_p = u(x) \cos x + v(x) \sin x.$$

If $y_p$ is substituted for $y$ in the original differential equation, the result may be computed as follows. We have

$$y_p' = -u \sin x + v \cos x + u' \cos x + v' \sin x$$

and

$$y_p'' = -u \cos x - v \sin x - u' \sin x + v' \cos x + \frac{d}{dx}(u' \cos x + v' \sin x).$$

Hence, the differential equation becomes

$$-u' \sin x + v' \cos x + \frac{d}{dx}(u' \cos x + v' \sin x) = \tan x.$$

Since we introduced two unknown functions $u$ and $v$ subject to only one condition, that they satisfy the differential equation, we are free to impose a second condition in any convenient fashion. Accordingly, we choose

$$u' \cos x + v' \sin x = 0,$$

since it apparently leads to the greatest amount of simplification. Thus, $u$ and $v$ are to satisfy the system

(1)
$$u' \cos x + v' \sin x = 0,$$
$$-u' \sin x + v' \cos x = \tan x.$$

Equations (1) may be solved for $u'$ and $v'$ by determinants to get

$$u' = \frac{\begin{vmatrix} 0 & \sin x \\ \tan x & \cos x \end{vmatrix}}{\begin{vmatrix} \cos x & \sin x \\ -\sin x & \cos x \end{vmatrix}}, \quad v' = \frac{\begin{vmatrix} \cos x & 0 \\ -\sin x & \tan x \end{vmatrix}}{\begin{vmatrix} \cos x & \sin x \\ -\sin x & \cos x \end{vmatrix}},$$

or

$$u' = -\frac{\sin^2 x}{\cos x}, \quad v' = \sin x.$$

Finally, $v = -\cos x$, $u = \sin x - \ln |\sec x + \tan x|$, where constants of integration have been omitted, since we are looking for a particular solution. The general solution of the differential equation is therefore

$$y = c_1 \cos x + c_2 \sin x - \cos x \ln |\sec x + \tan x|.$$

The reader should note that the chosen simplifying condition, the first of Equations (1), reduces $y_p'$ to the sum of terms that would have been obtained had the $u$ and $v$ been constant.

If the complementary part of the solution is known, the method of variation of parameters may always be used, although it is not always possible to find simple inverse derivatives for the expressions obtained for $u'$ and $v'$. The method can also be extended to equations of order higher than two by a similar procedure.

---

*Example 25.5a.* Find a formula for a particular solution of the equation

$$y'' + y' = r(x).$$

For this equation, the complementary part of the solution is

$$y = c_1 + c_2 e^{-x}.$$

Accordingly, we write

$$y_p = u(x) + v(x)e^{-x}.$$

Then

$$y_p' = u' + v'e^{-x} - ve^{-x},$$

and, choosing the simplifying condition,

$$u' + v'e^{-x} = 0,$$

we get

$$y_p'' = -v'e^{-x} + ve^{-x}.$$

Substitution into the given equation yields

$$-v'e^{-x} = r(x).$$

Thus, $u$ and $v$ are to satisfy the two equations

$$u' + v'e^{-x} = 0,$$
$$-v'e^{-x} = r(x).$$

These equations give

$$u' = r(x) \quad \text{and} \quad v' = -e^x r(x),$$

so that

$$u = \int r(x)\, dx \quad \text{and} \quad v = -\int e^x r(x)\, dx.$$

A better form for these results is obtained by writing

$$u = \int_a^x r(t)\, dt \quad \text{and} \quad v = -\int_a^x e^t r(t)\, dt,$$

where $a$ is any convenient value of $x$. Thus, we find

$$y_p = \int_a^x r(t)\, dt - e^{-x} \int_a^x e^t r(t)\, dt,$$

or

$$y_p = \int_a^x [1 - e^{-(x-t)}] r(t)\, dt.$$

## Exercises 25.5

In each of Numbers 1 to 14, find a general solution for the given differential equation.

1. $y'' + y = \sec x.$
2. $y'' + y = \sec^2 x.$
3. $y'' + y = \sec^4 x.$
4. $y'' + y = \tan x.$
5. $y'' + y = \cot x.$
6. $y'' + y = \csc x.$
7. $y'' + y = x \cos x.$

8. $y'' - y = \sin^2 x.$
9. $(D^2 - 2D + 2)y = 3x + e^x \tan x.$
10. $(D^2 + 3D + 2)y = \sin e^x.$
11. $y'' + 4y = 4 \cot 2x.$
12. $y'' + 2y' + 2y = e^{-x} \sec x.$
13. $y'' - y = e^x/x.$
14. $y'' - y = 1/x, \; x > 0.$

15. Show that $x$ and $e^x$ both satisfy the equation

$$(1 - x)y'' + xy' - y = 0.$$

Use this fact to solve the equation

$$(1 - x)y'' + xy' - y = (x - 1)^2.$$

16. Use the method of variation of parameters to show that the general solution of the equation $y'' + y = f(x), \; a \le x \le b$, is

$$y = C_1 \cos x + C_2 \sin x + \int_a^x f(t) \sin (x - t) \, dt.$$

★17. Suppose $u_1, u_2$ are solutions of the linear equation of order two

$$L(y) .=. \; y'' + p(x)y' + q(x)y = 0.$$

Use the method of variation of parameters to solve

$$y'' + p(x)y' + q(x)y = r(x)$$

by letting

$$y = v_1(x)u_1(x) + v_2(x)u_2(x).$$

Show that

$$v_1(x) = - \int u_2(x) \frac{r(x)}{W(x)} \, dx, \quad \text{and} \quad v_2(x) = \int u_1(x) \frac{r(x)}{W(x)} \, dx,$$

where $W(x)$ is the Wronskian of $u_1$ and $u_2$.

★18. If the equation in Number 17 has constant coefficients, then

$$u_1(x) = e^{m_1 x}, \quad u_2(x) = e^{m_2 x},$$

where $m_1, m_2$ are constants. Under these conditions show that the particular solution of

$$y'' + py' + qy = r(x)$$

may be written in the form

$$y_p(x) = \int_c^x f(x - t)r(t) \, dt,$$

where $c$ is any point in the interval $\mathcal{I}$ over which the differential equation has a solution, and where $f$ is a function determined by the left side of the differential equation.

## 25.6 MECHANICAL VIBRATION PROBLEMS

Linear differential equations with constant coefficients arise in many common physical problems. Several such problems will be considered here.

It was indicated in Section 24.1 that an object in motion obeys Newton' second law. In the case of a weight supported by a spring this law in mathematical form is

$$m \frac{d^2x}{dt^2} + r \frac{dx}{dt} + kx = 0,$$

where $m$ is the mass of the weight, $x$ is its displacement from its equilibrium position, and $r$ and $k$ are constants of proportionality. If frictional forces are neglected, then the differential equation of motion becomes

$$m \frac{d^2x}{dt^2} + kx = 0.$$

The motion described by this differential equation is called **simple harmonic motion.** The next example illustrates the character of such a motion. The spring mass problem is of importance not only of itself but also because many practical vibration problems are idealized in this form.

---

*Example 25.6a.* A spring is stretched 3 inches by a 6-pound weight. Suppose a 12-pound weight is attached to the spring and pulled down 6 inches below its equilibrium point. If the weight is then given an initial upward velocity of 2 feet per second describe the resulting motion of the weight. (Neglect resistive forces.)

The spring constant, $k$, is determined from the amount of stretch produced by a given weight. From Hooke's Law, $F = kx$, we get

$$6 = k(1/4),$$

or

$$k = 24 \text{ pounds per foot.}$$

Hence the differential equation of the motion is

$$\frac{12}{32} \frac{d^2x}{dt^2} + 24x = 0,$$

or

$$\frac{d^2x}{dt^2} + 64x = 0.$$

The initial conditions state that when $t = 0$, then

$$x = \tfrac{1}{2} \text{ foot,} \quad \text{and} \quad \frac{dx}{dt} = -2 \text{ feet per second.}$$

The velocity is given a negative sign, since it is in the direction of decreasing $x$. Note also that all dimensions must be consistent, preferably in feet and seconds, since the value of $g$ is taken as 32 feet per second per second.

A general solution of the differential equation is

$$x = c_1 \cos 8t + c_2 \sin 8t.$$

Then

$$\frac{dx}{dt} = -8c_1 \sin 8t + 8c_2 \cos 8t,$$

so that putting $t = 0$ and using the initial values of $x$ and $dx/dt$, we get

$$\frac{1}{2} = c_1,$$

and

$$-2 = +8c_2, \quad \text{or} \quad c_2 = -\frac{1}{4}.$$

Therefore, the position of the weight at time $t$ is given by

$$x = \frac{1}{2} \cos 8t - \frac{1}{4} \sin 8t.$$

By rewriting this equation in another form, we can get a better insight into the motion of the weight. If the right side of the equation is multiplied and divided by

$$\sqrt{(1/2)^2 + (1/4)^2} = \frac{1}{4} \sqrt{5},$$

then the formula for $x$ becomes

$$x = \frac{1}{4} \sqrt{5} \, (\cos \alpha \cos 8t - \sin \alpha \sin 8t)$$

$$= \frac{1}{4} \sqrt{5} \cos (8t + \alpha),$$

where

$$\cos \alpha = \frac{2}{5} \sqrt{5} \quad \text{and} \quad \sin \alpha = \frac{1}{5} \sqrt{5}.$$

This equation reveals that the weight oscillates with an amplitude of $\sqrt{5}/4$ feet and a

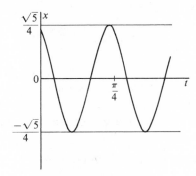

**FIGURE 25.6a**

period of $\pi/4$ seconds. The motion may be represented graphically, as shown in Figure 25.6a.

Now suppose that in addition to the forces described in Example 25.6a, the motion of the weight is subject to a damping force that is proportional to the velocity $dx/dt$. The differential equation of the motion is then

$$\frac{3}{8}\frac{d^2x}{dt^2} + r\frac{dx}{dt} + 24x = 0,$$

or

$$\frac{d^2x}{dt^2} + \frac{8r}{3}\frac{dx}{dt} + 64x = 0.$$

The roots of the auxiliary equation are

$$m = -\frac{4r}{3} \pm \sqrt{\frac{16r^2}{9} - 64} = -\frac{4r}{3} \pm \frac{4}{3}\sqrt{r^2 - 36}.$$

If $r > 6$, then the solution of the system is

$$x = c_1 \exp\left[\frac{1}{3}(-4r + 4\sqrt{r^2 - 36})t\right] + c_2 \exp\left[\frac{1}{3}(-4r - 4\sqrt{r^2 - 36})t\right]$$

$$= e^{-4rt/3}\left[c_1 \exp\left(\frac{4}{3}t\sqrt{r^2 - 36}\right) + c_2 \exp\left(-\frac{4}{3}t\sqrt{r^2 - 36}\right)\right].$$

As $t \to \infty$, $x \to 0$ because of the dominance of the factor $e^{-4rt/3}$, which is called the **damping factor.** In this case, where $r > 6$, the motion is said to be **over-damped,** and the weight does not oscillate, but simply settles slowly to rest. The motion is represented graphically in Figure 25.6b, the particular curve obtained depending on the magnitude and the direction of the initial velocity.

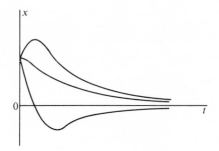

**FIGURE 25.6b**

If $0 < r < 6$, the roots of the auxiliary equation are imaginary, so that we have a solution in the form

(1) $$x = Ae^{-4rt/3}\cos(\omega t + \alpha),$$

where $\omega = \frac{4}{3}\sqrt{36 - r^2}$ (see Exercises 25.6, Number 11). The graph of this equation is shown in Figure 25.6c. Again, as $t \to \infty$, $x \to 0$ because of the damping factor $e^{-4rt/3}$.

In the event that there is an external applied force, represented by $f(t)$, the reader may verify that the differential equation for the motion of the weight is

$$m\frac{d^2x}{dt^2} + r\frac{dx}{dt} + kx = f(t).$$

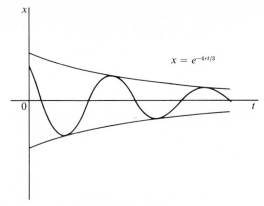

$$x = e^{-4rt/3}$$

**FIGURE 25.6c**

*Example 25.6b.* A weight of 32 pounds is attached to a spring for which the spring constant $k = 16$ pounds per foot, and the spring is attached to a fixed support. When the weight settles to its equilibrium position, a force $F = F_0 \sin \omega t$ is impressed on it. Neglect frictional forces, and find the equation of motion of the weight. Note that $\omega$ is a positive constant—the so-called **angular frequency** of the impressed force.

If $x$ is the downward displacement from the equilibrium position at time $t$, then the differential equation and the initial conditions are

$$\frac{d^2x}{dt^2} + 16x = F_0 \sin \omega t, \quad \text{and} \quad x = 0, v = 0 \text{ when } t = 0.$$

The complementary part of the solution of this equation is

$$x_c = c_1 \sin 4t + c_2 \cos 4t,$$

and the particular solution is of the form

$$x_p = A \sin \omega t + B \cos \omega t.$$

It is easy to see, however, that $B = 0$ for this differential equation. Why?

To determine the constant $A$, we have

$$-A\omega^2 \sin \omega t + 16A \sin \omega t = F_0 \sin \omega t,$$

so that

$$A = \frac{F_0}{16 - \omega^2}, \quad \omega \neq 4,$$

and a general solution in this case is

$$x = c_1 \sin 4t + c_2 \cos 4t + \frac{F_0}{16 - \omega^2} \sin \omega t, \quad \omega \neq 4.$$

Using the initial conditions, we find

$$c_2 = 0 \quad \text{and} \quad c_1 = -\frac{F_0\omega/4}{16 - \omega^2}.$$

The required equation of motion is therefore

$$x = \frac{F_0}{16 - \omega^2} \left( \sin \omega t - \frac{\omega}{4} \sin 4t \right).$$

If $\omega = 4$, then the particular solution is of the form

$$x_p = t(A \sin 4t + B \cos 4t).$$

By the usual procedure in the method of undetermined coefficients, we find

$$A = 0, \quad B = -\frac{F_0}{8},$$

and a general solution is

$$x = c_1 \sin 4t + c_2 \cos 4t - \frac{F_0}{8} t \cos 4t.$$

Again, applying the initial conditions, we get

$$c_2 = 0 \quad \text{and} \quad c_1 = \frac{F_0}{32},$$

so that the equation of motion is

$$x = \frac{F_0}{32} (\sin 4t - 4t \cos 4t).$$

---

Under the condition $\omega = 4$ in the preceding example, the system is said to be in **ideal resonance**, since, as $t$ increases, the amplitude of the oscillations increases indefinitely, as is shown by the $t \cos 4t$ term. Ideal resonance does not occur in an actual physical mass-spring system because of the presence of damping factors, which were assumed to be absent in this example. The present analysis is valuable, nevertheless, as it gives an approximation to the behavior of a system in which the damping effects are nearly negligible.

For a simple oscillating system of the preceding type with an impressed sinusoidal force and for which a damping force proportional to the velocity is assumed, the corresponding general solution, as the reader may verify, is of the form

$$x = e^{-at}g(t) + A(\omega) \cos (\omega t + \alpha).$$

Here, the term $e^{-at}g(t)$ approaches zero as $t \to \infty$, and the term $A(\omega) \cos (\omega t + \alpha)$ thus becomes the dominant term for large values of $t$. In this case, the system is said to be in **resonance** if the value of $\omega$ is such as to make the amplitude factor $A(\omega)$ a maximum.

## Exercises 25.6

1. A spring attached to a rigid support carries a weight of 10 pounds, which stretches the spring 6 inches. If the weight is pulled 3 inches below its equilibrium position and released, and if there is a resistance in pounds numerically equal to one-half the velocity in feet per second, find the period of the oscillation and the equation of motion of the weight.

2. A weight hung on a spring and vibrating in air has a period of one second with negligible damping. A damping vane of negligible mass is attached to the weight and causes a resistance proportional to the velocity. If the damping changes the period of oscillation of the weight to $3/2$ seconds, find the damping factor. Then write the differential equation of the motion, and obtain its solution.

3. A weight of 4 pounds is suspended on a spring, causing an elongation of 2 inches. When it is set in motion, its period is $\pi/6$ seconds. Find the time required for the damping factor to decrease to 25% of its initial value if the resistance is proportional to the velocity.

4. A 10-pound weight is hanging at rest on a spring that is stretched 6 inches by the weight. The upper end of the spring is attached to a moving support whose vertical displacement, $y$ feet, at time $t$ measured from its original position is given by $y = \sin 2\sqrt{g}t$. Find the equation of motion, and the position of the weight when $t = \pi\sqrt{g}$ seconds, if there is a resistance of $30/\sqrt{g}$ times the velocity.

5. A wooden cube 6 inches on a side and weighing 4 pounds floats in water (water weighs 62.4 pounds per cubic foot). If the cube is depressed slightly and then released, find its period of vibration, assuming that resistance is negligible and the top remains horizontal. If the initial depression is 1 inch below the equilibrium position, find the equation of motion for the block. *Hint:* The buoyant force exerted by the water is equal to the weight of the water that is displaced.

6. A cylindrical buoy 2 feet in diameter floats in water with its axis vertical. Upon being depressed slightly and released, it bobs with a period of 2 seconds. If the total frictional resisting force is numerically equal to one-half the velocity, find the weight of the buoy (see the hint in Number 5).

7. A wooden cube $\frac{1}{2}$ foot on an edge and weighing 3.2 pounds floats in water. The block is depressed slightly and released. What would be the period of vertical oscillation if there were no damping? (Use $g = 32$ feet per second per second.) If the period is actually observed to be $\pi/5$ second and a damping force $R$ times the velocity is assumed, find the value of $R$.

8. The motion of a weight suspended from a spring mounted on a moving support is described by

$$\frac{d^2x}{dt^2} + 2\alpha\frac{dx}{dt} + \beta^2 x = a \cos \omega t.$$

Determine the value of $\omega$ in terms of $\alpha$ and $\beta$ at which resonance occurs if $|\beta| > \alpha\sqrt{2}$.

9. Describe the motion in Number 8 if $\beta = \alpha$.

10. Show that the differential equation for the motion of a simple pendulum of weight $W$ and length $L$ is given by

$$\frac{d^2\theta}{dt^2} = -\frac{g}{L}\sin\theta,$$

where $\theta$ is the angular displacement of the pendulum from the vertical at time $t$.

11. Verify the solution given in Equation (1) for the case $0 < r < 6$. Obtain the solution for $r = 6$.

## 25.7 SIMPLE ELECTRIC CIRCUITS

Simple electric circuits are easily analyzed mathematically and are analogous to the mechanical systems discussed in the preceding section. The fundamental components of an electric circuit are

  (a) electromotive force, $E$, measured in volts,
  (b) resistance, $R$, measured in ohms,

(c) inductance, $L$, measured in henrys,
(d) capacitance, $C$, measured in farads,
(e) quantity of electricity, $q$, measured in coulombs,
(f) current, the time rate of flow of electricity, $i$, measured in amperes.

A consequence of the definitions of $q$ and $i$ is that

$$i = \frac{dq}{dt},$$

where $t$ is time in seconds. Other fundamental relationships between the components of a circuit are found experimentally. For example, the voltage drop across a resistance is given by

$$Ri,$$

the voltage drop across an inductance, by

$$L\frac{di}{dt},$$

and the voltage drop across a capacitor, by

$$\frac{1}{C}q.$$

There are two fundamental laws, known as **Kirchhoff's Laws,** that govern electric circuits.

I. *The Voltage Law. The sum of the voltage drops around any closed circuit in a specified direction is zero.*

II. *The Current Law. The sum of the currents flowing into or away from any point in a circuit is zero.*

The simplest circuit containing all the basic components is shown schematically in Figure 25.7a, where the source of the impressed voltage $E$ in the

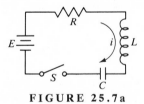

FIGURE 25.7a

circuit is a battery. If the switch $S$ is closed at time $t = 0$, then $i = 0$ and $q = 0$ if there is no initial charge on the capacitor. According to Kirchhoff's Voltage Law, we must have

$$Ri + L\frac{di}{dt} + \frac{1}{C}q - E = 0,$$

where $E$ represents a voltage *increase* in the clockwise direction, and is therefore opposite in sign to the voltage drops. Since $i = dq/dt$, the differential equation in terms of $q$ is

$$L \frac{d^2q}{dt^2} + R \frac{dq}{dt} + \frac{1}{C} q = E,$$

which is an ordinary linear equation with constant coefficients. If the impressed voltage is supplied by an alternating current generator, then $E$ is generally of the form

$$E = E_0 \sin \omega t.$$

---

*Example 25.7a.* An electric circuit has an impressed electromotive force given by $E_0 \sin 100t$, a resistance of 10 ohms, a capacitance of 0.002 farad, and an inductance of 0.1 henry. Determine the current in the circuit at time $t$, if $i = 0$ and $q = 0$ when $t = 0$.

The differential equation for the circuit is

$$0.1 \frac{d^2q}{dt^2} + 10 \frac{dq}{dt} + 500q = E_0 \sin 100t,$$

or

$$\frac{d^2q}{dt^2} + 100 \frac{dq}{dt} + 5000q = 10E_0 \sin 100t.$$

The roots of the auxiliary equation $m^2 + 100m + 5000 = 0$ are

$$m = -50 \pm 50j,$$

where $j = \sqrt{-1}$ has been written in order to avoid confusion with $i$ as the current. The complementary part of the solution is therefore

$$q_c = e^{-50t}(c_1 \sin 50t + c_2 \cos 50t).$$

The particular solution is of the form

$$q_p = A \cos 100t + B \sin 100t.$$

Hence, upon substituting $q_p$ in the differential equation, we find the conditions

$$-10^4 B - 10^4 A + 5 \times 10^3 B = 10E_0,$$
$$10^4 B - 10^4 A + 5 \times 10^3 A = 0.$$

Hence

$$B = \frac{1}{2} A,$$

and

$$A = -\frac{E_0}{1250}, \quad B = -\frac{E_0}{2500}.$$

Therefore,

$$q_p = -\frac{E_0}{2500} (2 \cos 100t + \sin 100t).$$

The constants $c_1$ and $c_2$ are determined from the initial conditions. By putting $t = 0$, $q = 0$ into

$$q = e^{-50t}(c_1 \sin 50t + c_2 \cos 50t) - \frac{E_0}{2500} (2 \cos 100t + \sin 100t),$$

we get

$$0 = c_2 - \frac{E_0}{1250}.$$

Moreover, with $t = 0$, $i = 0$ in

$$i = \frac{dq}{dt} = e^{-50t}(-50c_1 \sin 50t - 50c_2 \cos 50t + 50c_1 \cos 50t - 50c_2 \sin 50t)$$

$$- \frac{E_0}{2500}(-200 \sin 100t + 100 \cos 100t),$$

we find

$$0 = -50c_2 + 50c_1 - \frac{E_0}{25}.$$

These equations give

$$c_2 = \frac{E_0}{1250} \quad \text{and} \quad c_1 = \frac{E_0}{625}.$$

Hence,

$$i = \frac{E_0}{25}(2 \sin 100t - \cos 100t + e^{-50t} \cos 50t - 3e^{-50t} \sin 50t).$$

For large $t$, the terms having $e^{-50t}$ as a factor are negligible, so that

$$i \approx \frac{E_0}{25}(2 \sin 100t - \cos 100t).$$

That is, some time after $t = 0$ the current flow settles to a "steady state." Hence the particular solution of the differential equation is called the **steady-state solution.** The complementary part of the solution is, for obvious reasons, called the **transient solution.**

## Exercises 25.7

1. A circuit contains a resistance $R$, an inductance $L$, and a direct-current voltage source $E$ in series. If the current $i = 0$ when $t = 0$, find $i$ for $t > 0$.
2. Find the current $i$ in Number 1 if the voltage source is $E \sin \omega t$. Identify the steady-state solution and the transient solution.
3. A circuit contains a switch, a resistance $R$, a capacitance $C$, and a direct-current voltage source $E$ in series. When the switch is closed at $t = 0$, the charge on the capacitor is $q_0$. Find the initial current in the circuit and the current for $t > 0$.
4. For the circuit in Number 3, suppose that the voltage source is $E \sin \omega t$ and that when the switch is closed at $t = 0$, then $q = 0$ and $i = 0$. Find the current for $t > 0$.

Numbers 5 to 7 refer to a circuit containing a switch, an inductance $L$, a capacitance $C$, a resistance $R$, and a direct-current voltage source $E$ in series. Assume that when the switch is closed at $t = 0$ there is no charge on the capacitor and $i = 0$.

5. Assume that $\frac{R^2}{4L^2} - \frac{1}{LC} > 0$, let $a = \frac{R}{2L}$, $b = \sqrt{\frac{R^2}{4L^2} - \frac{1}{LC}}$, and find the current for $t > 0$.

6. Assume that $\frac{R^2}{4L^2} - \frac{1}{LC} = 0$, let $a = \frac{R}{2L}$ and find the current for $t > 0$.

7. Assume that $\frac{R^2}{4L^2} - \frac{1}{LC} < 0$, let $a = \frac{R}{2L}$, $b = \sqrt{\frac{1}{LC} - \frac{R^2}{4L^2}}$, and find the current for $t > 0$.

8. An inductance of 1 henry is connected in series with a capacitance of $10^{-4}$ farad and a voltage of $100 \sin 50t$ volts. If $q = i = 0$ when $t = 0$, find the current for $t > 0$, and find the maximum value of the current.

9. A series circuit contains a resistance of 10 ohms, an inductance of one henry, a capacitance of 0.02 farad, and a switch $S$. If the capacitor is charged initially with 90 coulombs, describe the current in the circuit for $t > 0$ if the switch $S$ is closed when $t = 0$ and $i = 0$.

10. A simple circuit contains inductance $L$, a capacitance $C$, a resistance $R$, and a voltage source $E_0 \sin \omega t$. If $R^2 < 16L/C$, find the value of $\omega$ in terms of $R$, $L$, and $C$ at which resonance in the circuit occurs.

## 25.8 SYSTEMS OF LINEAR DIFFERENTIAL EQUATIONS

In a number of practical situations such as in economic studies, biological problems, and certain chemical processes, it has been found that the state of a physical system at time $t$ is described by $n$ functions of $t$, such that the time rate of change of each function is a linear combination of the $n$ functions. An excellent illustration of this type of system occurs in the study of radioactive decay. For instance, a radioactive substance A decays to a second radioactive substance B, which decays to a third radioactive substance C, which in turn decays to a stable substance D. In each case, it is known from experiments and by observation that the rate of decay is proportional to the amount of parent substance present. Thus, if $x_1$, $x_2$, $x_3$, respectively, are the number of grams of A, B, C present at time $t$, then

$$\frac{dx_1}{dt} = -k_1 x_1,$$

$$\frac{dx_2}{dt} = k_1 x_1 - k_2 x_2,$$

$$\frac{dx_3}{dt} = k_2 x_2 - k_3 x_3,$$

where $k_1$, $k_2$, $k_3$ are the constants of proportionality.

In general, this kind of physical problem may be described by a system of differential equations such as

$$\frac{dx_1}{dt} = a_{11}(t)x_1 + a_{12}(t)x_2 + a_{13}(t)x_3,$$

(1)
$$\frac{dx_2}{dt} = a_{21}(t)x_1 + a_{22}(t)x_2 + a_{23}(t)x_3,$$

$$\frac{dx_3}{dt} = a_{31}(t)x_1 + a_{32}(t)x_2 + a_{33}(t)x_3.$$

In many cases the coefficients $a_{ij}$ are simply constants, so that the equations constitute a system of linear differential equations with constant coefficients. It is this particular type of system that we shall consider here.

It is interesting to note that a linear homogeneous equation of order $n$ with constant coefficients is equivalent to a system of linear equations with constant coefficients. For example, consider

$$y''' - y'' - y' + y = 0, \quad y' = \frac{dy}{dt}.$$

If we let

$$u_1 .=. y,$$
$$u_2 .=. y',$$
$$u_3 .=. y'',$$

then

$$u_3' = y''',$$

and we get the system

(2)
$$\begin{aligned} u_3' &= u_3 + u_2 - u_1, \\ u_2' &= u_3, \\ u_1' &= u_2. \end{aligned}$$

In order to discuss linear systems conveniently, we shall make use of matrices. Let $X$ be the column matrix (vector) of the variables

$$X .=. \begin{bmatrix} x_1 \\ x_2 \\ x_3 \end{bmatrix}.$$

Then, since the variables $x_1, x_2, x_3$ are functions of $t$, it is possible to define the derivative of $X$ with respect to $t$.

**Definition 25.8a.**

$$\frac{dX}{dt} .=. \begin{bmatrix} \dfrac{dx_1}{dt} \\ \dfrac{dx_2}{dt} \\ \dfrac{dx_3}{dt} \end{bmatrix}.$$

(This definition can be extended to apply to a general $m \times n$ matrix.)

With the aid of Definition 25.8a, the System (2) may be written as

$$\frac{dX}{dt} = AX,$$

where

$$A .=. \begin{bmatrix} 0 & 1 & 0 \\ 0 & 0 & 1 \\ -1 & 1 & 1 \end{bmatrix}.$$

More generally, the System (1) may also be written in the same form if

$$A .=. \begin{bmatrix} a_{11} & a_{12} & a_{13} \\ a_{21} & a_{22} & a_{23} \\ a_{31} & a_{32} & a_{33} \end{bmatrix}.$$

In the matrix form, $dX/dt = AX$, the system of differential equations appears to resemble the ordinary differential equation

$$\frac{dx}{dt} = ax,$$

whose solution is

$$x = ce^{at}.$$

A solution of the system represented by the matrix differential equation

(3)
$$\frac{dX}{dt} = AX$$

is a *vector* $X$ that satisfies the differential equation. Hence, since the solution of the equation $dx/dt = at$ is given in terms of an exponential function, it does not seem unreasonable to hope that a vector satisfying Equation (3) is of the form

$$X_1 = e^{\lambda t}T_1,$$

where $T_1$ is a constant vector to be determined. Let us investigate the consequences of assuming a solution of this kind.

If $X$ is replaced in Equation (3) by $e^{\lambda t}T_1$, the result is

$$\lambda e^{\lambda t}T_1 = Ae^{\lambda t}T_1,$$

or

$$e^{\lambda t}[A - \lambda I]T_1 = 0.$$

Since $e^{\lambda t}$ is never zero, we must have

$$[A - \lambda I]T_1 = 0.$$

This familiar equation indicates that there is indeed a solution of Equation (3) of the form $e^{\lambda t}T_1$, provided that $\lambda$ is an eigenvalue of $A$ and that $T_1$ is the associated eigenvector.

Furthermore, if $A$ is a $2 \times 2$ matrix having two distinct eigenvalues, $\lambda_1, \lambda_2$, then there are two distinct vector solutions of the differential equation, say

$$e^{\lambda_1 t}T_1 \quad \text{and} \quad e^{\lambda_2 t}T_2.$$

Since, in this case, Equation (3) is a linear equation having two distinct solutions, we may expect to form a more general solution by writing

$$X = c_1 e^{\lambda_1 t}T_1 + c_2 e^{\lambda_2 t}T_2,$$

provided $T_1$ and $T_2$ are linearly independent (as they must be if $\lambda_1$ and $\lambda_2$ are distinct, a fact that we shall prove later).

Let us illustrate the preceding discussion with an example.

---

*Example 25.8a.* Find a solution for the system

$$\frac{dx_1}{dt} = -3x_1 + 4x_2,$$

$$\frac{dx_2}{dt} = -2x_1 + 3x_2.$$

It is convenient to write the system in matrix form as

$$\frac{dX}{dt} = AX,$$

where

$$A = \begin{bmatrix} -3 & 4 \\ -2 & 3 \end{bmatrix} \quad \text{and} \quad X = \begin{bmatrix} x_1 \\ x_2 \end{bmatrix}.$$

In the preceding discussion it was indicated that we can find vector solutions of the equation by finding the eigenvalues and eigenvectors of $A$. Thus, we have

$$\det (A - \lambda I) = \begin{vmatrix} -3 - \lambda & 4 \\ -2 & 3 - \lambda \end{vmatrix} = \lambda^2 - 1,$$

which gives eigenvalues 1 and $-1$. For $\lambda = 1$, the corresponding eigenvector is determined from

$$\begin{bmatrix} -4 & 4 \\ -2 & 2 \end{bmatrix} \begin{bmatrix} x \\ y \end{bmatrix} = \begin{bmatrix} 0 \\ 0 \end{bmatrix},$$

which has the solution

$$T_1 = \begin{bmatrix} 1 \\ 1 \end{bmatrix}.$$

For $\lambda = -1$, we solve

$$\begin{bmatrix} -2 & 4 \\ -2 & 4 \end{bmatrix} \begin{bmatrix} x \\ y \end{bmatrix} = \begin{bmatrix} 0 \\ 0 \end{bmatrix},$$

to get

$$T_2 = \begin{bmatrix} 2 \\ 1 \end{bmatrix}.$$

Hence, a solution of the given differential equation is

$$X = \begin{bmatrix} x_1 \\ x_2 \end{bmatrix} = c_1 e^t \begin{bmatrix} 1 \\ 1 \end{bmatrix} + c_2 e^{-t} \begin{bmatrix} 2 \\ 1 \end{bmatrix},$$

or

$$x_1 = c_1 e^t + 2c_2 e^{-t},$$
$$x_2 = c_1 e^t + c_2 e^{-t}.$$

The reader may verify that these quantities do indeed satisfy the given differential equations.

---

In the preceding discussion, we made a number of assumptions about the solution of a matrix differential equation. The next theorem, stated without proof, indicates that these assumptions are justified.

**Theorem 25.8a.** If the elements $a_{ij}(t)$ of the $n \times n$ matrix $A$ are continuous functions of $t$ on the interval $t_1 < t < t_2$, then there exist $n$ linearly independent vectors $X_1, X_2, \ldots, X_n$ that satisfy the differential equation

$$\frac{dX}{dt} = AX$$

and any other solution $X$ of the equation may be expressed as a linear combination of $X_1, \ldots, X_n$.

That is, a general solution of the system is given by

$$X = c_1 X_1 + c_2 X_2 + \cdots + c_n X_n,$$

where $c_1, c_2, \ldots, c_n$ are constants. In particular, if the elements of $A$ are constants, the vector solutions $X_i$ generally take on the simpler form

$$X_i = e^{\lambda_i t} T_i,$$

where $T_i$ is an eigenvector of constants, associated with the eigenvalue $\lambda_i$, provided $\lambda_i$ is not an eigenvalue of multiplicity greater than 1. In fact, we can prove

**Theorem 25.8b.** If $A$ is an $n \times n$ matrix of constants having distinct eigenvalues, then the eigenvectors of $A$ are linearly independent.

PROOF: The proof will be given only for the case when $A$ is a $3 \times 3$ matrix. Let the eigenvectors of $A$ be $T_1, T_2, T_3$, and suppose that, contrary to the conclusion of the theorem, these vectors are linearly dependent so that

$$c_1 T_1 + c_2 T_2 + c_3 T_3 = 0,$$

where at least one of the $c$'s is different from zero. Premultiplying this equation by $A$, we get

$$c_1 A T_1 + c_2 A T_2 + c_3 A T_3 = 0.$$

Since $A T_i = \lambda_i T_i$, where $\lambda_i$ is the eigenvalue of $A$ associated with $T_i$, we have

$$c_1 \lambda_1 T_1 + c_2 \lambda_2 T_2 + c_3 \lambda_3 T_3 = 0.$$

Premultiplying by $A$ again, and replacing $A T_i$ by $\lambda_i T_i$, we obtain

$$c_1 \lambda_1^2 T_1 + c_2 \lambda_2^2 T_2 + c_3 \lambda_3^2 T_3 = 0.$$

In order that the three equations

$$\begin{aligned}
c_1 T_1 + c_2 T_2 + c_3 T_3 &= 0, \\
c_1 \lambda_1 T_1 + c_2 \lambda_2 T_2 + c_3 \lambda_3 T_3 &= 0, \\
c_1 \lambda_1^2 T_1 + c_2 \lambda_2^2 T_2 + c_3 \lambda_3^2 T_3 &= 0
\end{aligned}$$

have a nontrivial solution, it is necessary that

$$\begin{vmatrix} 1 & 1 & 1 \\ \lambda_1 & \lambda_2 & \lambda_3 \\ \lambda_1^2 & \lambda_2^2 & \lambda_3^2 \end{vmatrix} = 0.$$

This determinant is equivalent to

$$\begin{vmatrix} 1 & 0 & 0 \\ \lambda_1 & \lambda_2 - \lambda_1 & \lambda_3 - \lambda_1 \\ \lambda_1^2 & \lambda_2^2 - \lambda_1^2 & \lambda_3^2 - \lambda_1^2 \end{vmatrix} = (\lambda_2 - \lambda_1)(\lambda_3 - \lambda_1) \begin{vmatrix} 1 & 1 \\ \lambda_2 + \lambda_1 & \lambda_3 + \lambda_1 \end{vmatrix}$$

$$= (\lambda_2 - \lambda_1)(\lambda_3 - \lambda_1)(\lambda_2 - \lambda_3).$$

Since no two of the eigenvalues are equal, the determinant cannot be zero—a contradiction. Hence, the eigenvectors cannot be linearly dependent.

If the eigenvalues of $A_{nn}$ are not distinct, we may still find $n$ linearly independent vector solutions of the differential equation, but they are not necessarily of the form $e^{\lambda_i t} T_i$. Instead, as we shall see later, they are of the form $t^k e^{\lambda_i t} T_i$. The same technique applies even if the eigenvalues are imaginary.

---

*Example 25.8b.* Find a general solution for the system

$$\frac{dx_1}{dt} = 3x_1 + 2x_2,$$

$$\frac{dx_2}{dt} = -x_1 + x_2.$$

The eigenvalues of

$$A = \begin{bmatrix} 3 & 2 \\ -1 & 1 \end{bmatrix}$$

are obtained from

$$\begin{vmatrix} 3 - \lambda & 2 \\ -1 & 1 - \lambda \end{vmatrix} = 0,$$

or

$$\lambda^2 - 4\lambda + 5 = 0,$$

which implies that

$$\lambda = 2 \pm i.$$

For $\lambda = 2 + i$, we get

$$\begin{bmatrix} 1 - i & 2 \\ -1 & -1 - i \end{bmatrix} \begin{bmatrix} x \\ y \end{bmatrix} = \begin{bmatrix} 0 \\ 0 \end{bmatrix},$$

which has a solution

$$x = k, \quad y = -\frac{1 - i}{2} k.$$

Hence, an eigenvector is

$$\begin{bmatrix} 2 \\ -1 + i \end{bmatrix}.$$

For $\lambda = 2 - i$, a corresponding eigenvector is

$$\begin{bmatrix} 2 \\ -1 - i \end{bmatrix},$$

and a general solution for the matrix differential equation is

$$X = c_1 e^{(2+i)t} \begin{bmatrix} 2 \\ -1 + i \end{bmatrix} + c_2 e^{(2-i)t} \begin{bmatrix} 2 \\ -1 - i \end{bmatrix}.$$

---

Since it is preferable to have a solution of the differential equations in a real form, let us try to reduce a general form of the preceding type to a real form involving trigonometric functions. For this purpose, we consider an entirely general solution of the form

$$X = c_1 e^{(a+ib)t} \begin{bmatrix} m + in \\ p + iq \end{bmatrix} + c_2 e^{(a-ib)t} \begin{bmatrix} m - in \\ p - iq \end{bmatrix},$$

where the elements of the second vector are the conjugates of those in the first.

Since the complex numbers $m + in$ and $p + iq$ may be written in exponential form, let

$$m + in = r_1 e^{i\alpha} \quad \text{and} \quad p + iq = r_2 e^{i\beta},$$

where

$$r_1 = \sqrt{m^2 + n^2} \quad \text{and} \quad r_2 = \sqrt{p^2 + q^2}.$$

Then

$$X = e^{at} \left\{ c_1 e^{ibt} \begin{bmatrix} r_1 e^{i\alpha} \\ r_2 e^{i\beta} \end{bmatrix} + c_2 e^{-ibt} \begin{bmatrix} r_1 e^{-i\alpha} \\ r_2 e^{-i\beta} \end{bmatrix} \right\}$$

$$= e^{at} \begin{bmatrix} r_1 [ c_1 e^{i(bt+\alpha)} + c_2 e^{-i(bt+\alpha)} ] \\ r_2 [ c_1 e^{i(bt+\beta)} + c_2 e^{-i(bt+\beta)} ] \end{bmatrix},$$

or, by the use of Euler's formulas for $e^{i\theta}$ and $e^{-i\theta}$,

$$X = e^{at} \begin{bmatrix} r_1 [(c_1 + c_2) \cos(bt + \alpha) + i(c_1 - c_2) \sin(bt + \alpha)] \\ r_2 [(c_1 + c_2) \cos(bt + \beta) + i(c_1 - c_2) \sin(bt + \beta)] \end{bmatrix}.$$

Upon substitution of $C_1$ for $c_1 + c_2$ and $C_2$ for $i(c_1 - c_2)$, this matrix becomes

$$X = e^{at} \begin{bmatrix} r_1 [C_1 \cos(bt + \alpha) + C_2 \sin(bt + \alpha)] \\ r_2 [C_1 \cos(bt + \beta) + C_2 \sin(bt + \beta)] \end{bmatrix}.$$

Note that $c_1$ and $c_2$ must be conjugate imaginary numbers for $C_1$ and $C_2$ to be real.

In the preceding example, $m + in = 2$, $p + iq = -1 + i$, so that $r_1 = 2$, $r_2 = \sqrt{2}$, $\alpha = 0$, $\beta = 3\pi/4$, $a = 2$, $b = 1$. Therefore,

$$X = e^{2t} \begin{bmatrix} 2(C_1 \cos t + C_2 \sin t) \\ \sqrt{2}[C_1 \cos(t + 3\pi/4) + C_2 \sin(t + 3\pi/4)] \end{bmatrix}.$$

It is easy to show, if $A$ is a matrix of real elements with the eigenvalues $a \pm ib$, that the corresponding eigenvectors are also conjugates. Thus, if $\lambda$ is an eigenvalue, then

$$(A - \lambda I)T = 0,$$

where $T$ is the associated eigenvector. Taking conjugates everywhere, we have

$$\overline{(A - \lambda I)}\overline{T} = 0.$$

However, $A$ and $I$ are real, so that this equation is the same as

$$(A - \overline{\lambda} I)\overline{T} = 0,$$

which shows that if $T$ is the eigenvector corresponding to $\lambda$, then the conjugate of $T$ is the eigenvector corresponding to the conjugate of $\lambda$. The use of this relationship shortens the work considerably, since it is not necessary to calculate both eigenvectors independently.

In the event that there are repeated eigenvalues, we still may find solutions, provided the appropriate vectors $T_1$, $T_2$ can be found.

*Example 25.8c.* Obtain a general solution for the system

$$\frac{dx_1}{dt} = 3x_1 - x_2,$$

$$\frac{dx_2}{dt} = x_1 + x_2.$$

The eigenvalues of

$$A = \begin{bmatrix} 3 & -1 \\ 1 & 1 \end{bmatrix}$$

are obtained from

$$\begin{bmatrix} 3 - \lambda & -1 \\ 1 & 1 - \lambda \end{bmatrix} = 0,$$

or

$$\lambda^2 - 4\lambda + 4 = 0,$$

which implies that

$$\lambda = 2, 2.$$

An eigenvector associated with 2 is found by solving

$$\begin{bmatrix} 1 & -1 \\ 1 & -1 \end{bmatrix} \begin{bmatrix} x \\ y \end{bmatrix} = \begin{bmatrix} 0 \\ 0 \end{bmatrix},$$

which gives

$$x = k, \quad y = k.$$

Therefore, we may take

$$T_1 = \begin{bmatrix} 1 \\ 1 \end{bmatrix}.$$

It is apparent that there is no second eigenvector to be found. However, following the lead suggested by the case of a single differential equation, we may try a solution of the form

$$X_2 = e^{2t}(T_2 + tT_3).$$

Then, substituting into the equation $dX/dt = AX$, we get

$$2e^{2t}(T_2 + tT_3) + e^{2t}T_3 = e^{2t}A(T_2 + tT_3).$$

Since $e^{2t}$ and $te^{2t}$ are linearly independent, it follows that this equation is satisfied only if

$$2T_2 + T_3 = AT_2 \quad \text{and} \quad 2T_3 = AT_3.$$

The second of these equations shows that $T_3$ is the original eigenvector, $T_1$; the first equation shows that $T_2$ is determined from

$$[A - 2I]T_2 = T_3.$$

Hence, $T_2$ can be found by solving

$$\begin{bmatrix} 1 & -1 \\ 1 & -1 \end{bmatrix} \begin{bmatrix} x \\ y \end{bmatrix} = \begin{bmatrix} 1 \\ 1 \end{bmatrix},$$

or

$$x - y = 1.$$

A solution of this equation is $x = 1$, $y = 0$, so that

$$T_2 = \begin{bmatrix} 1 \\ 0 \end{bmatrix}.$$

Therefore,

$$X_2 = e^{2t}\left\{\begin{bmatrix}1\\0\end{bmatrix} + t\begin{bmatrix}1\\1\end{bmatrix}\right\} = e^{2t}\begin{bmatrix}1+t\\t\end{bmatrix},$$

and a general solution is

$$X = c_1 e^{2t}\begin{bmatrix}1\\1\end{bmatrix} + c_2 e^{2t}\begin{bmatrix}1+t\\t\end{bmatrix},$$

or

$$x_1 = [(c_1 + c_2) + c_2 t]e^{2t},$$
$$x_2 = [c_1 + c_2 t]e^{2t}.$$

---

The solution of a nonhomogeneous system of equations can frequently be obtained without much difficulty, once the solution of the associated homogeneous system is known. The method used in the next example is based on variation of parameters.

---

*Example 25.8d.* Find a general solution for the system

$$\frac{dx_1}{dt} = -3x_1 + 4x_2 + t,$$

$$\frac{dx_2}{dt} = -2x_1 + 3x_2 + e^{-t}.$$

In Example 25.8a, we found the solution of the associated homogeneous equation, and it is easy to verify that this solution may be put in the form

$$X = T\begin{bmatrix}c_1 e^t\\c_2 e^{-t}\end{bmatrix}, \qquad \text{where } T = \begin{bmatrix}1 & 2\\1 & 1\end{bmatrix}.$$

Accordingly, by substitution into the homogeneous equation $dX/dt = AX$, we obtain the equation

(4)
$$T\begin{bmatrix}c_1 e^t\\-c_2 e^{-t}\end{bmatrix} = AT\begin{bmatrix}c_1 e^t\\c_2 e^{-t}\end{bmatrix},$$

which is an *identity in the c's.*

Let us now assume that a particular solution of the given nonhomogeneous system is of the same form as the preceding vector $X$, where the $c$'s, however, are functions of $t$, say $c_1 = u(t)$ and $c_2 = v(t)$. Upon substituting for $X$ in the differential equation

$$\frac{dX}{dt} = AX + \begin{bmatrix}t\\e^{-t}\end{bmatrix}, \qquad \text{where } A = \begin{bmatrix}-3 & 4\\-2 & 3\end{bmatrix},$$

we obtain

$$T\begin{bmatrix}ue^t + u'e^t\\-ve^{-t} + v'e^{-t}\end{bmatrix} = AT\begin{bmatrix}ue^t\\ve^{-t}\end{bmatrix} + \begin{bmatrix}t\\e^{-t}\end{bmatrix},$$

or

$$T\begin{bmatrix}ue^t\\-ve^{-t}\end{bmatrix} + T\begin{bmatrix}u'e^t\\v'e^{-t}\end{bmatrix} = AT\begin{bmatrix}ue^t\\ve^{-t}\end{bmatrix} + \begin{bmatrix}t\\e^{-t}\end{bmatrix}.$$

But

$$T\begin{bmatrix}ue^t\\-ve^{-t}\end{bmatrix} = AT\begin{bmatrix}ue^t\\ve^{-t}\end{bmatrix},$$

since this is merely Equation (4) with $c_1$ and $c_2$ replaced by $u$ and $v$, respectively. Thus we are left with

$$T\begin{bmatrix} u'e^t \\ v'e^{-t} \end{bmatrix} = \begin{bmatrix} t \\ e^{-t} \end{bmatrix},$$

so that

$$\begin{bmatrix} u'e^t \\ v'e^{-t} \end{bmatrix} = T^{-1}\begin{bmatrix} t \\ e^{-t} \end{bmatrix} = \begin{bmatrix} -1 & 2 \\ 1 & -1 \end{bmatrix}\begin{bmatrix} t \\ e^{-t} \end{bmatrix}.$$

Consequently,

$$u'e^t = -t + 2e^{-t},$$

and

$$v'e^{-t} = t - e^{-t}.$$

It follows that

$$u = te^{-t} + e^{-t} - e^{-2t},$$
$$v = te^t - e^t - t,$$

and

$$X_p = T\begin{bmatrix} t + 1 - e^{-t} \\ t - 1 - te^{-t} \end{bmatrix}.$$

Hence, a general solution is

$$X = \begin{bmatrix} 1 & 2 \\ 1 & 1 \end{bmatrix}\begin{bmatrix} c_1e^t + t + 1 - e^{-t} \\ c_2e^{-t} + t - 1 - te^{-t} \end{bmatrix},$$

or

$$x_1 = c_1e^t + 2c_2e^{-t} + 3t - 1 - e^{-t} - 2te^{-t},$$
$$x_2 = c_1e^t + c_2e^{-t} + 2t - e^{-t} - te^{-t}.$$

## Exercises 25.8

In each of Numbers 1 to 10, find a general solution for the given system.

1. $\dfrac{dx_1}{dt} = 3x_1 - 4x_2, \dfrac{dx_2}{dt} = 2x_1 - 3x_2.$

2. $\dfrac{dx_1}{dt} = x_1 + x_2, \dfrac{dx_2}{dt} = 3x_1 - x_2.$

3. $\dfrac{dx_1}{dt} = 4x_1 - 4x_2, \dfrac{dx_2}{dt} = x_1.$

4. $\dfrac{dx_1}{dt} = 2x_1 + x_2, \dfrac{dx_2}{dt} = -4x_1.$

5. $\dfrac{dx_1}{dt} = x_1 - 2x_2, \dfrac{dx_2}{dt} = 4x_1 + 5x_2.$

6. $\dfrac{dx_1}{dt} = 2x_1 + x_2 + 2x_3, \dfrac{dx_2}{dt} = 3x_2 + 2x_3, \dfrac{dx_3}{dt} = -3x_1 - x_2 - 3x_3.$

7. $\dfrac{dx_1}{dt} = 4x_1 + x_2 + x_3, \dfrac{dx_2}{dt} = 4x_1 - x_2, \dfrac{dx_3}{dt} = 2x_1 - x_2 + x_3.$

8. $\dfrac{dx_1}{dt} = 3x_1 + x_2 - x_3, \dfrac{dx_2}{dt} = -x_1 + 2x_2 + x_3, \dfrac{dx_3}{dt} = x_1 + x_2 + x_3.$

9. $\dfrac{dx_1}{dt} = x_2, \dfrac{dx_2}{dt} = -\dfrac{3}{2}x_1 + 3x_2 - \dfrac{1}{2}x_3, \dfrac{dx_3}{dt} = -x_1 + x_2 + x_3.$

10. $\dfrac{dx_1}{dt} = x_1 + x_2, \dfrac{dx_2}{dt} = x_1 - x_3, \dfrac{dx_3}{dt} = 2x_2 + x_3.$

In Numbers 11 to 16, rewrite the given system as a system of first-order linear equations, and find a general solution. In each case $D = d/dt$.

11. $(D^2 - 2D)x - Dy = 0, 2x + Dy = 0.$
12. $(D^2 + 6)y + Dz = 0, (D + 2)y + (D - 2)z = 0.$
13. $(D + 2)x - y = t, (D - 1)x + (D - 1)y = 1.$
14. $(D - 1)x - y = 0, (D + 1)x + Dy = 2e^{-t}.$
15. $(D^2 - D)x + 2y = 4t, Dx + Dy = 2.$
16. $Dx + Dy + 3x = \sin t, Dx + y - x = \cos t.$

17. It is known that radioactive substances decay at a rate that is proportional to the amount of parent substance present. A radioactive substance A decays to a second radioactive substance B, which decays to a third radioactive substance C, which in turn decays into a stable substance D. If at $t = 0$ the number of grams of A, B, C present is $a, 0, 0$, respectively, find the number of grams of A, B, C present at time $t$.

# 25.9 APPLICATION OF SYSTEMS OF EQUATIONS

Systems of linear differential equations occur in many ways in connection with physical problems, and play an important part in the analysis of many complex problems in applied mathematics. Systems have acquired additional practical importance because modern computers have made it possible to obtain solutions in cases where, a few years ago, it was impractical to do the calculations. Here, little more can be done than to indicate in a very elementary fashion a few types of physical problems that lead to systems of differential equations.

*Example 25.9a.* A large tank, A, contains 100 gallons of brine in which is dissolved 50 pounds of salt. A second tank, B, contains 50 gallons of fresh water. Fresh water runs into tank A at the rate of 3 gallons per minute, and the uniformly mixed brine runs from A into B at the same rate. The uniformly mixed solution runs out of B at the same rate also. Find an expression for the amount of salt in B as a function of the time.

Let $x$ be the number of pounds of salt in A at time $t$ (minutes), and $y$ the number of pounds of salt in B at time $t$. Then the rate of outflow of salt from tank A is

$$\frac{3x}{100} \text{ pounds per minute,}$$

which is also the rate of inflow of salt into tank B. The rate of outflow of salt from tank B is

$$\frac{3y}{50} \text{ pounds per minute.}$$

Hence, the system of differential equations

$$\frac{dx}{dt} = -\frac{3x}{100},$$

$$\frac{dy}{dt} = \frac{3x}{100} - \frac{3y}{50},$$

along with the initial conditions $x = 50$, $y = 0$ when $t = 0$, describes the physical problem. In matrix form, the system of differential equations is

$$\frac{dX}{dt} = \begin{bmatrix} -0.03 & 0 \\ 0.03 & -0.06 \end{bmatrix} X = AX,$$

where

$$X = \begin{bmatrix} x \\ y \end{bmatrix}.$$

The eigenvalues of $A$ are $-0.03$ and $-0.06$, and the corresponding eigenvectors are

$$\begin{bmatrix} 1 \\ 1 \end{bmatrix}, \quad \begin{bmatrix} 0 \\ 1 \end{bmatrix},$$

respectively. Hence

$$X = c_1 e^{-0.03t} \begin{bmatrix} 1 \\ 1 \end{bmatrix} + c_2 e^{-0.06t} \begin{bmatrix} 0 \\ 1 \end{bmatrix},$$

or

$$x = c_1 e^{-0.03t},$$
$$y = c_1 e^{-0.03t} + c_2 e^{-0.06t}.$$

Using the initial conditions, $t = 0$, $x = 50$ and $y = 0$, we find

$$c_1 = 50,$$
$$0 = c_1 + c_2,$$

so that

$$c_2 = -50.$$

Hence, the final solution is

$$x = 50e^{-0.03t},$$
$$y = 50e^{-0.03t} - 50e^{-0.06t}.$$

---

Problems in mechanics and in electric circuits often lead to systems of differential equations of the second or higher order. Most of these problems are beyond the scope of our work here, except for the simplest special cases. The next example illustrates a simple mechanical problem and some of the associated mathematical complications.

---

*Example 25.9b.* Two springs, $S_1$ and $S_2$, having constants $k_1$ and $k_2$ (pounds per foot), are connected to masses $m_1$ and $m_2$, as shown in Figure 25.9a. If $E_1$ and $E_2$ are the equilibrium positions for masses $m_1$ and $m_2$, respectively, find the equation of motion for each of the masses if the upper spring is stretched downward a distance $x_0$ and released. Assume there are no resistive forces.

Let $x$ denote the downward displacement of $m_1$ from its equilibrium position and let $y$ denote the downward displacement of $m_2$ from its equilibrium position. The

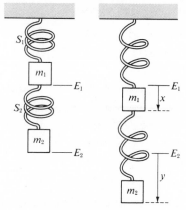

**FIGURE 25.9a**

forces acting on $m_1$ due to $S_1$ and $S_2$ are then $-k_1x$ and $k_2(y - x)$, respectively. The force acting on $m_2$ is $-k_2(y - x)$. Hence, we must have

$$m_1 \frac{d^2x}{dt^2} = -k_1x + k_2(y - x),$$

$$m_2 \frac{d^2y}{dt^2} = -k_2(y - x).$$

By putting

$$\omega_{11}^2 = k_1/m_1, \quad \omega_{12}^2 = k_2/m_1, \quad \omega_{22}^2 = k_2/m_2,$$

we get

$$\frac{d^2x}{dt^2} = -(\omega_{11}^2 + \omega_{12}^2)x + \omega_{12}^2y,$$

$$\frac{d^2y}{dt^2} = \omega_{22}^2x - \omega_{22}^2y.$$

This system of second-order equations may be converted into a system of first-order equations by letting

$$x = x_1, \quad y = x_2, \quad \frac{dx_1}{dt} = x_3, \quad \frac{dx_2}{dt} = x_4.$$

Then the system becomes

$$\frac{dx_1}{dt} = x_3, \quad \frac{dx_2}{dt} = x_4, \quad \frac{dx_3}{dt} = -(\omega_{11}^2 + \omega_{12}^2)x_1 + \omega_{12}^2x_2, \quad \frac{dx_4}{dt} = \omega_{22}^2x_1 - \omega_{22}^2x_2,$$

or

$$\frac{dX}{dt} = \begin{bmatrix} 0 & 0 & 1 & 0 \\ 0 & 0 & 0 & 1 \\ -(\omega_{11}^2 + \omega_{12}^2) & \omega_{12}^2 & 0 & 0 \\ \omega_{22}^2 & -\omega_{22}^2 & 0 & 0 \end{bmatrix} X = AX.$$

To use matrix methods in solving this differential equation, we must find the eigenvalues of the preceding $4 \times 4$ matrix. By expanding $\det(A - \lambda I) = 0$, we obtain the characteristic equation of $A$:

$$\lambda^4 + (\omega_{11}^2 + \omega_{12}^2 + \omega_{22}^2)\lambda^2 + \omega_{11}^2\omega_{22}^2 = 0.$$

Using the fact that this equation is of quadratic type, we find

$$2\lambda^2 = -(\omega_{11}^2 + \omega_{12}^2 + \omega_{22}^2) \pm \sqrt{(\omega_{11}^2 + \omega_{12}^2 + \omega_{22}^2)^2 - 4\omega_{11}^2\omega_{22}^2}.$$

The expression under the radical is less than $(\omega_{11}^2 + \omega_{12}^2 + \omega_{22}^2)^2$, and yet is positive, as is shown by the identity

$$(\omega_{11}^2 + \omega_{12}^2 + \omega_{22}^2)^2 - 4\omega_{11}^2\omega_{22}^2 = (\omega_{11}^2 - \omega_{22}^2)^2 + 2(\omega_{11}^2 + \omega_{22}^2)\omega_{12}^2 + \omega_{12}^4.$$

Accordingly, both values of $\lambda^2$ are real and negative, so that one of them may be denoted by $-\alpha^2$ and the other by $-\beta^2$, $\alpha > 0$, $\beta > 0$. Hence, $\lambda$ is of the form

$$\lambda = \pm i\alpha \quad \text{and} \quad \lambda = \pm i\beta,$$

and the solution is of the form

$$X = \cos \alpha t \, T_1 + \sin \alpha t \, T_2 + \cos \beta t \, T_3 + \sin \beta t \, T_4,$$

where $T_1, T_2, T_3, T_4$ are real vectors determined according to the discussion in Section 25.8 from the eigenvectors of $A$.

To see how the problem works out in a specific case, let us suppose that $k_1 = 4$ pounds per foot, $k_2 = 2$ pounds per foot, $m_1 = 2$ slugs, $m_2 = 1$ slug. Then, the characteristic equation becomes

$$\lambda^4 + 5\lambda^2 + 4 = 0,$$

so that

$$\lambda^2 = -4 \quad \text{or} \quad \lambda^2 = -1,$$

and

$$\lambda = \pm 2i \quad \text{or} \quad \pm i.$$

The reader may show that the eigenvectors corresponding to these eigenvalues are as follows:

$$\lambda = i, \quad T_1 = \begin{bmatrix} 1 \\ 2 \\ i \\ 2i \end{bmatrix}; \qquad \lambda = -i, \quad T_2 = \begin{bmatrix} 1 \\ 2 \\ -i \\ -2i \end{bmatrix};$$

$$\lambda = 2i, \quad T_3 = \begin{bmatrix} 1 \\ -1 \\ 2i \\ -2i \end{bmatrix}; \qquad \lambda = -2i, \quad T_4 = \begin{bmatrix} 1 \\ -1 \\ -2i \\ 2i \end{bmatrix}.$$

Thus, a solution of the system is

$$X = c_1 e^{it} T_1 + c_2 e^{-it} T_2 + c_2 e^{2it} T_3 + c_3 e^{-2it} T_4.$$

Since for $t = 0$ we have $x_1 = x_2 = x_0$ and $x_3 = x_4 = 0$, it follows that

$$\begin{bmatrix} x_0 \\ x_0 \\ 0 \\ 0 \end{bmatrix} = c_1 T_1 + c_2 T_2 + c_3 T_3 + c_4 T_4,$$

which implies the set of equations

$$\begin{aligned} x_0 &= c_1 + c_2 + c_3 + c_4, \\ x_0 &= 2c_1 + 2c_2 - c_3 - c_4, \\ 0 &= c_1 - c_2 + 2c_3 - 2c_4, \\ 0 &= 2c_1 - 2c_2 - 2c_3 + 2c_4. \end{aligned}$$

These equations are easily solved to obtain

$$c_1 = c_2 = \frac{1}{3} x_0 \quad \text{and} \quad c_3 = c_4 = \frac{1}{6} x_0,$$

so that

$$X = \frac{1}{3} x_0 (e^{it}T_1 + e^{-it}T_2) + \frac{1}{6} x_0 (e^{2it}T_3 + e^{-2it}T_4).$$

The method of Example 25.8b immediately yields

$$x = x_1 = \frac{2}{3} x_0 \cos t + \frac{1}{3} x_0 \cos 2t,$$

$$y = x_2 = \frac{4}{3} x_0 \cos t - \frac{1}{3} x_0 \cos 2t,$$

$$\frac{dx}{dt} = x_3 = -\frac{2}{3} x_0 \sin t - \frac{2}{3} x_0 \sin 2t,$$

$$\frac{dy}{dt} = x_4 = -\frac{4}{3} x_0 \sin t + \frac{2}{3} x_0 \sin 2t.$$

---

Electric networks generally lead to systems of differential equations similar to those obtained for a mechanical problem.

---

*Example 25.9c.* Find a system of linear first-order differential equations to describe the currents in the circuit shown in Figure 25.9b.

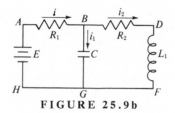

**FIGURE 25.9b**

According to Kirchhoff's Voltage Law, the sum of the voltage drops around a closed loop must be zero. In this network there are three possible closed paths, each of which leads to a separate equation. Around $ABGH$, we have

$$R_1 i + \frac{q_1}{C} = E.$$

Around $BDFG$, we have

$$R_2 i_2 + L \frac{di_2}{dt} - \frac{q_1}{C} = 0.$$

The equation for loop $ADFH$ is not needed, since it is simply a linear combination of the two equations already obtained. We also need the result of Kirchhoff's Current Law,

$$i = i_1 + i_2.$$

Thus, upon substitution for $i$, the equations become

$$R_1 i_1 + R_1 i_2 + \frac{1}{C} q_1 = E,$$

$$R_2 i_2 + L \frac{di_2}{dt} - \frac{1}{C} q_1 = 0,$$

or

(1) 
$$\begin{cases} R_1 \dfrac{dq_1}{dt} + \dfrac{1}{C} q_1 + R_1 i_2 = E, \\ L \dfrac{di_2}{dt} + R_2 i_2 - \dfrac{1}{C} q_1 = 0. \end{cases}$$

Writing $x_1 = q_1$ and $x_2 = i_2$, we obtain the form

$$\frac{dx_1}{dt} = -\frac{1}{R_1 C} x_1 - x_2 + \frac{E}{R_1},$$

$$\frac{dx_2}{dt} = \frac{1}{LC} x_1 - \frac{R_2}{L} x_2,$$

or, in matrix form,

$$\frac{dX}{dt} = \begin{bmatrix} -\dfrac{1}{R_1 C} & -1 \\ \dfrac{1}{LC} & -\dfrac{R_2}{L} \end{bmatrix} X + \begin{bmatrix} \dfrac{E}{R_1} \\ 0 \end{bmatrix}.$$

In this case the system is nonhomogeneous and can be handled by the method discussed in Example 25.8c.

---

In more complicated problems of this type, the matrix method may prove to be clumsy unless the problem can be programmed on a computer. It is possible, however, to solve the system by an elimination procedure in which a higher-order equation that contains only one unknown variable is obtained.

To see how this process may be used, observe that Equations (1) have constant coefficients and are of the general operator form

$$L_1(D)q_1 + L_2(D)i_2 = E_1(t),$$
$$L_3(D)q_1 + L_4(D)i_2 = E_2(t).$$

By operating on the first of these with $L_4(D)$ and on the second with $-L_2(D)$, and adding, we get

$$[L_4(D)L_1(D) - L_2(D)L_3(D)]q_1 = L_4(D)E_1(t) - L_2(D)E_2(t),$$

which is a linear equation that can be solved by the methods discussed earlier in this chapter.

To illustrate more explicitly: suppose that in Example 25.9c, $R_1 = 10$ ohms, $R_2 = 10$ ohms, $C = 5 \times 10^{-3}$ farad, $L = 0.1$ henry, and $E = 10$ volts. Then Equations (1) become

(2) 
$$\begin{cases} (D + 20)q_1 + \qquad\quad i_2 = 1, \\ \quad 2000q_1 - (D + 100)i_2 = 0. \end{cases}$$

Operating on the first equation with $(D + 100)$ and adding the corresponding members of the two equations, we get

$$(D^2 + 120D + 4000)q_1 = 100.$$

The solution of this equation is easily found to be

$$q_1 = c_1 e^{-60t} \cos 20t + c_2 e^{-60t} \sin 20t + \frac{1}{40},$$

and, from the first of Equations (2),

$$i_2 = 1 - (D + 20)q_1$$

$$= \frac{1}{2} + (40c_1 - 20c_2)e^{-60t} \cos 20t + 60c_2 e^{-60t} \sin 20t.$$

The constants $c_1$ and $c_2$ can be evaluated if initial conditions are given. If, for instance, $q_1 = 0$ and $i_2 = 0$ when $t = 0$, then we find $c_1 = c_2 = -1/40$, so that

$$q_1 = \frac{1}{40}(1 - e^{-60t} \cos 20t - e^{-60t} \sin 20t),$$

and

$$i_2 = \frac{1}{2}(1 - e^{-60t} \cos 20t - 3e^{-60t} \sin 20t).$$

## Exercises 25.9

1. A tank A initially contains 100 gallons of brine in which is dissolved 50 pounds of salt. Fresh water flows into the tank at the rate of two gallons per minute. The uniformly mixed solution flows from tank A to another tank B at the rate of two gallons per minute and another gallon per minute is drained out of A and discarded. The solution is uniformly mixed in tank B and fed back into tank A at the rate of one gallon per minute while one gallon per minute is drained out of tank B and discarded. If B is initially filled with 100 gallons of fresh water, find the amount of salt in each tank as a function of time $t$.

2. A substance X changes into a substance Y at a rate that is proportional to the amount of X present, while Y changes into X at a rate proportional to the amount of Y present. If $x$ is the amount of X and $y$ is the amount of Y at time $t$, find $x$ and $y$ as functions of time, if at $t = 0$, $x = A$, $y = B$.

3. A substance X changes into a substance Y at a rate proportional to the amount of X present. In turn, Y changes into another substance Z at a rate proportional to the amount of Y present, and Z changes back into X at a rate proportional to the amount of Z present. Set up the differential equations to describe the amounts of X, Y, Z present at time $t$. Let the second and third constants of proportionality each be $\frac{3}{16}$ of the first constant, and calculate the amounts of X, Y, and Z as functions of the time $t$. Assume that when $t = 0$, there are $x_0$ units of X and none of Y or Z present.

4. In Example 25.9b, for the same values of the masses and constants, suppose mass $m_2$ is driven by a force described by $4 \sin \omega t$. Determine the equations of motion for the system. For what value of $\omega$ does resonance occur? (Prove that your answer is correct.)

5. Set up a system of linear first-order differential equations for the problem in Example 25.9b if, in addition, there are damping forces given by $r_1(dx/dt)$ on mass $m_1$ and $r_2(dy/dt)$ on mass $m_2$.

6. Obtain the trigonometric form for the solution of the numerical illustration of the problem in Example 25.9b.

7. Find the loop currents $i_1$ and $i_2$ in the circuit shown in Figure 25.9c if, when $t = 0$, $q_1 = q_2 = 0$, and $R_{11} = 10$ ohms, $R_{22} = 5$ ohms, $C_{12} = 2 \times 10^{-3}$ farad, $C_{11} = 10^{-3}$ farad, $E = 10$ volts. Note that the current in the branch common to the two loops is $i_1 - i_2$ for loop 1 and $i_2 - i_1$ for loop 2.

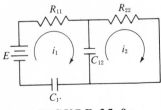

**FIGURE 25.9c**

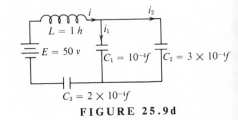

**FIGURE 25.9d**

8. Use matrix methods to work Example 25.9c with the numerical values given there.

9. Find the current $i_2$ as a function of time for the circuit in Figure 25.9d if at $t = 0$, $i = 0, q_1 = 0, q_2 = 0, q_3 = 0$.

---

# Summary of Chapter 25

---

Certain important types of differential equations, and some of their applications, are discussed in this chapter. The fundamental ideas include:

(1) the concept of a linear differential equation of order $n$ (Section 25.1);

(2) the operator notation, and the algebraic properties of operators (Section 25.1);

(3) the conditions under which a solution of a homogeneous linear differential equation of order $n$ exists (Section 25.2);

(4) the uniqueness of a solution satisfying given initial conditions (Section 25.2);

(5) linearly independent functions (Section 25.2);

(6) the significance of the Wronskian (Section 25.2);

(7) the form of a general solution of a linear homogeneous differential equation with constant coefficients (Section 25.3);

(8) the form of the solution when roots of the auxiliary equation are imaginary (Section 25.3);

(9) the form of the solution when roots of the auxiliary equation are repeated (Section 25.3);

(10) the form of the solution of a linear nonhomogeneous equation of order (Section 25.4);

(11) the method of annihilators and undetermined coefficients for finding a particular solution (Section 25.4);

(12) the method of variation of parameters for finding a particular solution (Section 25.5);

(13) the application of the linear differential equation to mechanical vibration problems (Section 25.6);

(14) the meaning of the terms frequency, damping factor, and resonance in connection with mechanical vibration problems (Section 25.6);

(15) the application of the linear differential equation to electrical circuits (Section 25.7);

(16) the meaning of steady-state and transient solutions (Section 25.7);

(17) matrix methods for solving systems of linear differential equations (Section 25.8);

(18) applications involving systems of differential equations (Section 25.9).

# APPENDIX A   List of Symbols

## Greek Alphabet

| | | | | | | | | | |
|---|---|---|---|---|---|---|---|---|---|
| Alpha | A | $\alpha$ | Iota | I | $\iota$ | Rho | P | $\rho$ |
| Beta | B | $\beta$ | Kappa | K | $\kappa$ | Sigma | $\Sigma$ | $\sigma$ |
| Gamma | $\Gamma$ | $\gamma$ | Lambda | $\Lambda$ | $\lambda$ | Tau | T | $\tau$ |
| Delta | $\Delta$ | $\delta$ | Mu | M | $\mu$ | Upsilon | $\Upsilon$ | $\upsilon$ |
| Epsilon | E | $\epsilon$ | Nu | N | $\nu$ | Phi | $\Phi$ | $\varphi$ |
| Zeta | Z | $\zeta$ | XI | $\Xi$ | $\xi$ | Chi | X | $\chi$ |
| Eta | H | $\eta$ | Omicron | O | $o$ | Psi | $\Psi$ | $\psi$ |
| Theta | $\Theta$ | $\theta$ | Pi | $\Pi$ | $\pi$ | Omega | $\Omega$ | $\omega$ |

## Special Symbols

| | | Page |
|---|---|---|
| $.=.$ | is defined to be | 2 |
| $[\![\ ]\!]$ | greatest integer in | 2 |
| $\Rightarrow$ | implies | 4 |
| $\Leftrightarrow$ | if and only if | 4 |
| $n!$ | factorial $n$ | 8 |
| $-p$ | negation of a proposition | 9 |
| $\{\ldots\}$ | set | 12 |
| $\{x:\ldots\}$ | set of objects $x$ such that | 12 |
| $\in$ | is an element of | 12 |
| $\notin$ | is not an element of | 12 |
| $\varnothing$ | empty set | 13 |
| $\subset$ | is a subset of | 14 |
| $\not\subset$ | is not a subset of | 14 |
| $\cup$ | set union | 17 |
| $\cap$ | set intersection | 17 |
| $\mathcal{A} - \mathcal{B}$ | set difference | 17 |
| $\mathcal{A}'$ | complement of a set | 19 |
| $\mathcal{R}$ | the set of real numbers | 20 |
| $\mathcal{N}$ | the set of natural numbers | 20 |
| $\mathcal{I}$ | the set of integers | 20 |
| $\mathcal{F}$ | the set of rational numbers | 20 |
| $\mathcal{C}$ | the set of complex numbers | 29 |
| $\mathcal{D}_f$ | domain of a function $f$ | 57 |
| $\mathcal{R}_f$ | range of a function $f$ | 57 |
| $|x|$ | absolute value of $x$ | 65 |
| $U(x)$ | unit step function | 67 |
| $f^{-1}$ | inverse function of $f$ | 70 |
| $g(f)$ | $g$ composite of $f$ | 72 |
| $[p, q]$ | direction numbers | 76 |
| $\mathcal{S}[\ldots]$ | solution set | 88 |

1. $1 + 2 + 3 + \cdots + n = \frac{1}{2}n(n + 1)$.
2. $1^2 + 2^2 + 3^2 + \cdots + n^2 = \frac{1}{6}n(n + 1)(2n + 1)$.
3. $1^3 + 2^3 + \cdots + n^3 = (1 + 2 + 3 + \cdots + n)^2 = \frac{1}{4}n^2(n + 1)^2$.

4. $1 + r + r^2 + \cdots + r^n = \dfrac{1 - r^{n+1}}{1 - r}$;

5. $a^{1/n} = \sqrt[n]{a} = $ principal $n$th root of $a$, $a > 0$.
6. $a^{m/n} = \sqrt[n]{a^m} = (\sqrt[n]{a})^m$, $a > 0$.
7. Theorem of Mathematical Induction.

Let $p(n)$ be a proposition associated with the natural number $n$. If $p(1)$ is true, and if $p(k) \Rightarrow p(k + 1)$ for an arbitrary natural number $k$, then $p(n)$ is true for every natural number $n$.

8. $\sin(-\theta) = -\sin\theta$.
9. $\cos(-\theta) = \cos\theta$.

10. $\tan\theta = \dfrac{\sin\theta}{\cos\theta}$.

11. $\cot\theta = \dfrac{\cos\theta}{\sin\theta}$.

12. $\sec\theta = \dfrac{1}{\cos\theta}$.

13. $\csc\theta = \dfrac{1}{\sin\theta}$.

14. Let $f$ denote one of the six fundamental trigonometric functions. Then, for each $n \in \mathcal{I}$,
$$f(\theta + n\pi) = \pm f(\theta)$$
and
$$f\left(\theta + n\pi + \frac{\pi}{2}\right) = \pm\text{co-}f(\theta)$$

where the appropriate sign must be chosen to correspond to the given function $f$ and the quadrant of the original angle, $\theta + n\pi$, or $\theta + n\pi + (\pi/2)$.

15. $\cos^2\theta + \sin^2\theta = 1$.
16. $\sec^2\theta = 1 + \tan^2\theta$.
17. $\csc^2\theta = 1 + \cot^2\theta$.
18. $\sin(\alpha + \beta) = \sin\alpha\cos\beta + \cos\alpha\sin\beta$.
19. $\sin(\alpha - \beta) = \sin\alpha\cos\beta - \cos\alpha\sin\beta$.
20. $\cos(\alpha + \beta) = \cos\alpha\cos\beta - \sin\alpha\sin\beta$.
21. $\cos(\alpha - \beta) = \cos\alpha\cos\beta + \sin\alpha\sin\beta$.

22. $\tan(\alpha + \beta) = \dfrac{\tan\alpha + \tan\beta}{1 - \tan\alpha\tan\beta}$.

23. $\tan (\alpha - \beta) = \dfrac{\tan \alpha - \tan \beta}{1 + \tan \alpha \tan \beta}$.

24. $\sin \alpha + \sin \beta = 2 \sin \frac{1}{2}(\alpha + \beta) \cos \frac{1}{2}(\alpha - \beta)$.

25. $\sin \alpha - \sin \beta = 2 \sin \frac{1}{2}(\alpha - \beta) \cos \frac{1}{2}(\alpha + \beta)$.

26. $\cos \alpha + \cos \beta = 2 \cos \frac{1}{2}(\alpha + \beta) \cos \frac{1}{2}(\alpha - \beta)$.

27. $\cos \alpha - \cos \beta = -2 \sin \frac{1}{2}(\alpha + \beta) \sin \frac{1}{2}(\alpha - \beta)$.

28. $\sin \alpha \cos \beta = \frac{1}{2}[\sin (\alpha + \beta) + \sin (\alpha - \beta)]$.

29. $\cos \alpha \cos \beta = \frac{1}{2}[\cos (\alpha + \beta) + \cos (\alpha - \beta)]$.

30. $\sin \alpha \sin \beta = \frac{1}{2}[\cos (\alpha - \beta) - \cos (\alpha + \beta)]$.

31. $\sin 2\alpha = 2 \sin \alpha \cos \alpha$.

32. $\cos 2\alpha = \cos^2 \alpha - \sin^2 \alpha$
$$= 2 \cos^2 \alpha - 1$$
$$= 1 - 2 \sin^2 \alpha.$$

33. $\sin \dfrac{\theta}{2} = \pm \sqrt{\dfrac{1 - \cos \theta}{2}}$.

34. $\cos \dfrac{\theta}{2} = \pm \sqrt{\dfrac{1 + \cos \theta}{2}}$.

35. $\tan \dfrac{\theta}{2} = \pm \sqrt{\dfrac{1 - \cos \theta}{1 + \cos \theta}} = \dfrac{\sin \theta}{1 + \cos \theta} = \dfrac{1 - \cos \theta}{\sin \theta}$.

36. *The Law of Sines.* In any triangle, the sides are proportional to the sines of the opposite angles.

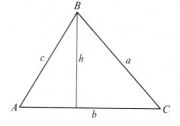

$$\frac{a}{\sin A} = \frac{b}{\sin B} = \frac{c}{\sin C}.$$

37. *The Law of Cosines.* The square of any side of a triangle is equal to the sum of the squares of the other two sides minus twice the product of these two sides multiplied by the cosine of the included angle.

$$c^2 = a^2 + b^2 - 2ab \cos C.$$

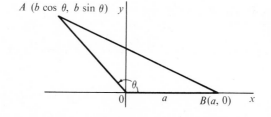

## APPENDIX C Table of Integrals.

In using this table the following items should be observed.

1. The standard formulas listed earlier, and some formulas easily reducible to the standard ones, are not listed.
2. A constant of integration should be supplied for each formula.
3. When the $\pm$ sign is used more than once in a formula, the formula is actually a composite of two formulas, one using the upper signs and another using the lower signs.
4. It is understood that the values of any letters used in the formulas are restricted so that the expressions are always real.
5. This is a brief table of integrals; any standard book of tables will have many times the number of integrals found here.

### Forms Containing $(a + bu)$

1. $\displaystyle \int u(a + bu)^m \, du = \frac{(a + bu)^{m+2}}{b^2(m + 2)} - \frac{a(a + bu)^{m+1}}{b^2(m + 1)},\ m \neq -1, -2.$

2. $\displaystyle \int \frac{u \, du}{(a + bu)^2} = \frac{1}{b^2}\left[\ln |a + bu| + \frac{a}{a + bu}\right].$

3. $\displaystyle \int \frac{u \, du}{(a + bu)^3} = \frac{1}{b^2}\left[-\frac{1}{a + bu} + \frac{a}{2(a + bu)^2}\right].$

4. $\displaystyle \int \frac{u^2 \, du}{(a + bu)^2} = \frac{1}{b^3}\left[a + bu - 2a \ln |a + bu| - \frac{a^2}{a + bu}\right].$

5. $\displaystyle \int \frac{du}{u(a + bu)} = \frac{1}{a}\ln \left|\frac{u}{a + bu}\right|.$

6. $\displaystyle \int \frac{du}{u(a + bu)^2} = \frac{1}{a(a + bu)} - \frac{1}{a^2}\ln \left|\frac{a + bu}{u}\right|.$

7. $\displaystyle \int \frac{du}{u^2(a + bu)} = -\frac{1}{au} + \frac{b}{a^2}\ln \left|\frac{a + bu}{u}\right|.$

8. $\displaystyle \int \frac{du}{u^2(a + bu)^2} = -\frac{a + 2bu}{a^2 u(a + bu)} + \frac{2b}{a^3}\ln \left|\frac{a + bu}{u}\right|.$

### Forms Containing $\sqrt{a + bu}$

9. $\displaystyle \int u\sqrt{a + bu} \, du = \frac{2(3bu - 2a)\sqrt{(a + bu)^3}}{15b^2}.$

10. $\displaystyle\int u^2\sqrt{a+bu}\,du = \frac{2(8a^2 - 12abu + 15b^2u^2)\sqrt{(a+bu)^3}}{105b^3}.$

11. $\displaystyle\int u^m\sqrt{a+bu}\,du = \frac{2}{b(2m+3)}\left[u^m\sqrt{(a+bu)^3} - ma\int u^{m-1}\sqrt{a+bu}\,du\right].$

12. $\displaystyle\int \frac{\sqrt{a+bu}}{u}\,du = 2\sqrt{a+bu} + \sqrt{a}\ln\left|\frac{\sqrt{a+bu} - \sqrt{a}}{\sqrt{a+bu} + \sqrt{a}}\right|.$

13. $\displaystyle\int \frac{\sqrt{a+bu}}{u^m}\,du = -\frac{1}{a(m-1)}\left[\frac{\sqrt{(a+bu)^3}}{u^{m-1}} + \frac{(2m-5)b}{2}\int \frac{\sqrt{a+bu}\,du}{u^{m-1}}\right],$
$m \neq 1.$

14. $\displaystyle\int \frac{du}{u\sqrt{a+bu}} = \frac{1}{\sqrt{a}}\ln\left|\frac{\sqrt{a+bu} - \sqrt{a}}{\sqrt{a+bu} + \sqrt{a}}\right|.$

15. $\displaystyle\int \frac{du}{u^m\sqrt{a+bu}} = -\frac{\sqrt{a+bu}}{(m-1)au^{m-1}} - \frac{(2m-3)b}{(2m-2)a}\int \frac{du}{u^{m-1}\sqrt{a+bu}}.$

16. $\displaystyle\int \frac{u\,du}{\sqrt{a+bu}} = \frac{2(bu - 2a)}{3b^2}\sqrt{a+bu}.$

17. $\displaystyle\int \frac{u^m\,du}{\sqrt{a+bu}} = \frac{2u^m\sqrt{a+bu}}{(2m+1)b} - \frac{2ma}{(2m+1)b}\int \frac{u^{m-1}\,du}{\sqrt{a+bu}}.$

**Forms Containing $u^2 + a^2$ or $u^2 - a^2$**

18. $\displaystyle\int \frac{du}{u^2 - a^2} = \frac{1}{2a}\ln\left|\frac{u-a}{u+a}\right|,$

19. $\displaystyle\int \frac{u^m\,du}{u^2 \pm a^2} = \frac{u^{m-1}}{m-1} \mp a^2\int \frac{u^{m-2}\,du}{u^2 \pm a^2}, \ m \neq 1.$

20. $\displaystyle\int \frac{du}{u(u^2 \pm a^2)} = \pm\frac{1}{2a^2}\ln\left|\frac{u^2}{u^2 \pm a^2}\right|.$

21. $\displaystyle\int \frac{du}{u^m(u^2 \pm a^2)} = \mp\frac{1}{a^2(m-1)u^{m-1}} \mp \frac{1}{a^2}\int \frac{du}{u^{m-2}(u^2 \pm a^2)}, \ m \neq 1.$

22. $\displaystyle\int \frac{du}{(u^2 \pm a^2)^m} = \pm\frac{u}{2a^2(m-1)(u^2 \pm a^2)^{m-1}} \pm \frac{2m-3}{2a^2(m-1)}\int \frac{du}{(u^2 \pm a^2)^{m-1}},$
$m \neq 1.$

23. $\displaystyle\int \frac{du}{u(u^2 \pm a^2)^m} = \pm\frac{1}{2a^2(m-1)(u^2 \pm a^2)^{m-1}} \pm \frac{1}{a^2}\int \frac{du}{u(u^2 \pm a^2)^{m-1}},$
$m \neq 1.$

24. $\displaystyle\int \frac{u^2\,du}{(u^2 \pm a^2)^m} = -\frac{u}{2(m-1)(u^2 \pm a^2)^{m-1}} + \frac{1}{2(m-1)}\int \frac{du}{(u^2 \pm a^2)^{m-1}},$
$m \neq 1.$

**Forms Containing** $\sqrt{u^2 \pm a^2}$

25. $\displaystyle \int \sqrt{u^2 \pm a^2} \, du = \frac{u}{2} \sqrt{u^2 \pm a^2} \pm \frac{a^2}{2} \ln |u + \sqrt{u^2 \pm a^2}|.$

26. $\displaystyle \int \frac{du}{\sqrt{u^2 \pm a^2}} = \ln |u + \sqrt{u^2 \pm a^2}|.$

27. $\displaystyle \int u^2 \sqrt{u^2 \pm a^2} \, du = \frac{u}{4} (u^2 \pm a^2)^{3/2} \mp \frac{a^2 u}{8} \sqrt{u^2 \pm a^2}$

$$- \frac{a^4}{8} \ln |u + \sqrt{u^2 \pm a^2}|.$$

28. $\displaystyle \int u^3 \sqrt{u^2 + a^2} \, du = \left( \frac{u^2}{5} - \frac{2a^2}{15} \right)(u^2 + a^2)^{3/2}.$

29. $\displaystyle \int u^3 \sqrt{u^2 - a^2} \, du = \frac{1}{5} (u^2 - a^2)^{5/2} + \frac{a^2}{3} (u^2 - a^2)^{3/2}.$

30. $\displaystyle \int \frac{\sqrt{u^2 + a^2}}{u} \, du = \sqrt{u^2 + a^2} - a \ln \left| \frac{a + \sqrt{u^2 + a^2}}{u} \right|.$

31. $\displaystyle \int \frac{\sqrt{u^2 - a^2}}{u} \, du = \sqrt{u^2 - a^2} - a \operatorname{Sec}^{-1} \frac{u}{a}.$

32. $\displaystyle \int \frac{\sqrt{u^2 \pm a^2}}{u^2} \, du = -\frac{\sqrt{u^2 \pm a^2}}{u} + \ln |u + \sqrt{u^2 \pm a^2}|.$

33. $\displaystyle \int \frac{\sqrt{u^2 + a^2}}{u^3} \, du = -\frac{\sqrt{u^2 + a^2}}{2u^2} - \frac{1}{2a} \ln \left| \frac{a + \sqrt{u^2 + a^2}}{u} \right|.$

34. $\displaystyle \int \frac{\sqrt{u^2 - a^2}}{u^3} \, du = -\frac{\sqrt{u^2 - a^2}}{2u^2} + \frac{1}{2a} \operatorname{Sec}^{-1} \frac{u}{a}.$

35. $\displaystyle \int \frac{du}{u\sqrt{u^2 + a^2}} = \frac{1}{a} \ln \left| \frac{u}{a + \sqrt{u^2 + a^2}} \right|.$

36. $\displaystyle \int \frac{du}{u\sqrt{u^2 - a^2}} = \frac{1}{a} \operatorname{Sec}^{-1} \frac{u}{a}.$

37. $\displaystyle \int \frac{u^2 \, du}{\sqrt{u^2 \pm a^2}} = \frac{u}{2} \sqrt{u^2 \pm a^2} \mp \frac{a^2}{2} \ln |u + \sqrt{u^2 \pm a^2}|.$

38. $\displaystyle \int \frac{du}{u^2 \sqrt{u^2 \pm a^2}} = \mp \frac{\sqrt{u^2 \pm a^2}}{a^2 u}.$

39. $\displaystyle \int \frac{du}{u^3 \sqrt{u^2 + a^2}} = -\frac{\sqrt{u^2 + a^2}}{2a^2 u^2} + \frac{1}{2a^3} \ln \left| \frac{a + \sqrt{u^2 + a^2}}{u} \right|.$

40. $\displaystyle \int \frac{du}{u^3 \sqrt{u^2 - a^2}} = \frac{\sqrt{u^2 - a^2}}{2a^2 u^2} + \frac{1}{2a^3} \operatorname{Sec}^{-1} \frac{u}{a}.$

41. $\int (u^2 \pm a^2)^{3/2}\, du = \frac{u}{4}(u^2 \pm a^2)^{3/2} \pm \frac{3a^2u}{8}\sqrt{u^2 \pm a^2}$

$$+ \frac{3a^4}{8}\ln|u + \sqrt{u^2 \pm a^2}|.$$

42. $\int \frac{du}{(u^2 \pm a^2)^{3/2}} = \pm\frac{u}{a^2\sqrt{u^2 \pm a^2}}.$

43. $\int u^2(u^2 \pm a^2)^{3/2}\, du = \frac{u}{6}(u^2 \pm a^2)^{5/2} \mp \frac{a^2u}{24}(u^2 \pm a^2)^{3/2} - \frac{a^4u}{16}\sqrt{u^2 \pm a^2}$

$$\mp \frac{a^6}{16}\ln|u + \sqrt{u^2 \pm a^2}|.$$

44. $\int u^3(u^2 \pm a^2)^{3/2}\, du = \frac{1}{7}(u^2 \pm a^2)^{7/2} \mp \frac{a^2}{5}(u^2 \pm a^2)^{5/2}.$

45. $\int \frac{(u^2 - a^2)^{3/2}}{u}\, du = \frac{(u^2 - a^2)^{3/2}}{3} - a^2\sqrt{u^2 - a^2} + a^3 \mathrm{Sec}^{-1}\frac{u}{a}.$

46. $\int \frac{(u^2 + a^2)^{3/2}}{u}\, du = \frac{(u^2 + a^2)^{3/2}}{3} + a^2\sqrt{u^2 + a^2} - a^3\ln\left|\frac{a + \sqrt{u^2 + a^2}}{u}\right|.$

47. $\int \frac{(u^2 \pm a^2)^{3/2}}{u^2}\, du = -\frac{(u^2 \pm a^2)^{3/2}}{u} + \frac{3u}{2}\sqrt{u^2 \pm a^2}$

$$\pm \frac{3a^2}{2}\ln|u + \sqrt{u^2 \pm a^2}|.$$

48. $\int \frac{u^2\, du}{(u^2 \pm a^2)^{3/2}}\, du = -\frac{u}{\sqrt{u^2 \pm a^2}} + \ln|u + \sqrt{u^2 \pm a^2}|.$

49. $\int \frac{du}{u(u^2 + a^2)^{3/2}} = \frac{1}{a^2\sqrt{u^2 + a^2}} - \frac{1}{a^3}\ln\left|\frac{a + \sqrt{u^2 + a^2}}{u}\right|.$

50. $\int \frac{du}{u(u^2 - a^2)^{3/2}} = -\frac{1}{a^2\sqrt{u^2 - a^2}} - \frac{1}{a^3}\mathrm{Sec}^{-1}\frac{u}{a}.$

51. $\int \frac{du}{u^2(u^2 \pm a^2)^{3/2}} = -\frac{1}{a^4}\left(\frac{\sqrt{u^2 \pm a^2}}{u} + \frac{u}{\sqrt{u^2 \pm a^2}}\right).$

52. $\int \frac{du}{u^3(u^2 + a^2)^{3/2}} = -\frac{1}{2a^2u^2\sqrt{u^2 + a^2}} - \frac{3}{2a^4\sqrt{u^2 + a^2}}$

$$+ \frac{3}{2a^5}\ln\left|\frac{a + \sqrt{u^2 + a^2}}{u}\right|.$$

53. $\int \frac{du}{u^3(u^2 - a^2)^{3/2}} = \frac{1}{2a^2u^2\sqrt{u^2 - a^2}} - \frac{3}{2a^4\sqrt{u^2 - a^2}} - \frac{3}{2a^5}\mathrm{Sec}^{-1}\frac{u}{a}.$

**Forms Containing $\sqrt{a^2 - u^2}$**

54. $\displaystyle\int \sqrt{a^2 - u^2}\, du = \frac{u}{2}\sqrt{a^2 - u^2} + \frac{a^2}{2}\,\text{Sin}^{-1}\frac{u}{a}.$

55. $\displaystyle\int u^2\sqrt{a^2 - u^2}\, du = -\frac{u}{4}(a^2 - u^2)^{3/2} + \frac{a^2 u}{8}\sqrt{a^2 - u^2} + \frac{a^4}{8}\,\text{Sin}^{-1}\frac{u}{a}.$

56. $\displaystyle\int u^3\sqrt{a^2 - u^2}\, du = \left(-\frac{u^2}{5} - \frac{2a^2}{15}\right)(a^2 - u^2)^{3/2}.$

57. $\displaystyle\int \frac{\sqrt{a^2 - u^2}}{u}\, du = \sqrt{a^2 - u^2} - a\ln\left|\frac{a + \sqrt{a^2 - u^2}}{u}\right|.$

58. $\displaystyle\int \frac{\sqrt{a^2 - u^2}}{u^2}\, du = -\frac{\sqrt{a^2 - u^2}}{u} - \text{Sin}^{-1}\frac{u}{a}.$

59. $\displaystyle\int \frac{\sqrt{a^2 - u^2}}{u^3}\, du = -\frac{\sqrt{a^2 - u^2}}{2u^2} + \frac{1}{2a}\ln\left|\frac{a + \sqrt{a^2 - u^2}}{u}\right|.$

60. $\displaystyle\int \frac{u^2\, du}{\sqrt{a^2 - u^2}} = -\frac{u}{2}\sqrt{a^2 - u^2} + \frac{a^2}{2}\,\text{Sin}^{-1}\frac{u}{a}.$

61. $\displaystyle\int \frac{u^3\, du}{\sqrt{a^2 - u^2}} = -\frac{2}{3}(a^2 - u^2)^{3/2} - u^2\sqrt{a^2 - u^2}.$

62. $\displaystyle\int \frac{du}{u\sqrt{a^2 - u^2}} = -\frac{1}{a}\ln\left|\frac{a + \sqrt{a^2 - u^2}}{u}\right|.$

63. $\displaystyle\int \frac{du}{u^2\sqrt{a^2 - u^2}} = -\frac{\sqrt{a^2 - u^2}}{a^2 u}.$

64. $\displaystyle\int \frac{du}{u^3\sqrt{a^2 - u^2}} = -\frac{\sqrt{a^2 - u^2}}{2a^2 u^2} - \frac{1}{2a^3}\ln\left|\frac{a + \sqrt{a^2 - u^2}}{u}\right|.$

65. $\displaystyle\int (a^2 - u^2)^{3/2}\, du = \frac{u}{4}(a^2 - u^2)^{3/2} + \frac{3a^2 u}{8}\sqrt{a^2 - u^2} + \frac{3a^4}{8}\,\text{Sin}^{-1}\frac{u}{a}.$

66. $\displaystyle\int \frac{du}{(a^2 - u^2)^{3/2}} = \frac{u}{a^2\sqrt{a^2 - u^2}}.$

67. $\displaystyle\int u^2(a^2 - u^2)^{3/2}\, du = -\frac{u}{6}(a^2 - u^2)^{5/2} + \frac{a^2 u}{24}(a^2 - u^2)^{3/2}$
$$+ \frac{a^2 u}{16}\sqrt{a^2 - u^2} + \frac{a^6}{16}\,\text{Sin}^{-1}\frac{u}{a}.$$

68. $\displaystyle\int u^3(a^2 - u^2)^{3/2}\, du = \frac{1}{7}(a^2 - u^2)^{7/2} - \frac{a^2}{5}(a^2 - u^2)^{5/2}.$

69. $\int \frac{(a^2 - u^2)^{3/2}}{u} du = \frac{1}{3}(a^2 - u^2)^{3/2} + a^2\sqrt{a^2 - u^2} - a^3 \ln\left|\frac{a + \sqrt{a^2 - u^2}}{u}\right|.$

70. $\int \frac{(a^2 - u^2)^{3/2}}{u^2} du = -\frac{(a^2 - u^2)^{3/2}}{u} - \frac{3u}{2}\sqrt{a^2 - u^2} - \frac{3a^2}{2}\text{Sin}^{-1}\frac{u}{a}.$

71. $\int \frac{u^2 du}{(a^2 - u^2)^{3/2}} = \frac{u}{\sqrt{a^2 - u^2}} - \text{Sin}^{-1}\frac{u}{a}.$

72. $\int \frac{u^3 du}{(a^2 - u^2)^{3/2}} = 2\sqrt{a^2 - u^2} + \frac{u^2}{\sqrt{a^2 - u^2}}.$

73. $\int \frac{du}{u(a^2 - u^2)^{3/2}} = \frac{1}{a^2\sqrt{a^2 - u^2}} + \frac{1}{a^3}\ln\left|\frac{a + \sqrt{a^2 - u^2}}{u}\right|.$

74. $\int \frac{du}{u^2(a^2 - u^2)^{3/2}} = \frac{1}{a^4}\left(\frac{u}{\sqrt{a^2 - u^2}} - \frac{\sqrt{a^2 - u^2}}{u}\right).$

75. $\int \frac{du}{u^3(a^2 - u^2)^{3/2}} = -\frac{1}{2a^2u^2\sqrt{a^2 - u^2}} + \frac{3}{2a^4\sqrt{a^2 - u^2}}$
$$- \frac{3}{2a^5}\ln\left|\frac{a + \sqrt{a^2 - u^2}}{u}\right|.$$

## Forms Containing Trigonometic Functions

76. $\int \sin^2 u\, du = \frac{u}{2} - \frac{1}{4}\sin 2u.$

77. $\int \sin^3 u\, du = \frac{\cos^3 u}{3} - \cos u.$

78. $\int \sin^m u\, du = -\frac{\sin^{m-1} u \cos u}{m} + \frac{m-1}{m}\int \sin^{m-2} u\, du.$

79. $\int \cos^2 u\, du = \frac{u}{2} + \frac{1}{4}\sin 2u.$

80. $\int \cos^3 u\, du = \sin u - \frac{1}{3}\sin^3 u.$

81. $\int \cos^m u\, du = \frac{\cos^{m-1} u \sin u}{m} + \frac{m-1}{m}\int \cos^{m-2} u\, du.$

82. $\int \frac{du}{a + b \sin u} = \frac{2}{\sqrt{a^2 - b^2}}\text{Tan}^{-1}\frac{a \tan\frac{u}{2} + b}{\sqrt{a^2 - b^2}}.$

83. $\int \frac{du}{a + b \cos u} = \frac{2}{\sqrt{a^2 - b^2}}\text{Tan}^{-1}\frac{\sqrt{a^2 - b^2}\tan\frac{u}{2}}{a + b}.$

84. $\int \sin mu \sin nu \, du = \dfrac{\sin (m - n)u}{2(m - n)} - \dfrac{\sin (m + n)u}{2(m + n)}, \; m^2 \neq n^2.$

85. $\int \cos mu \cos nu \, du = \dfrac{\sin (m - n)u}{2(m - n)} + \dfrac{\sin (m + n)u}{2(m + n)}, \; m^2 \neq n^2.$

86. $\int \sin mu \cos nu \, du = -\dfrac{\cos (m - n)u}{2(m - n)} - \dfrac{\cos (m + n)u}{2(m + n)}, \; m^2 \neq n^2.$

87. $\int \cos^m u \sin^n u \, du = \dfrac{\cos^{m-1} u \sin^{n+1} u}{m + n} + \dfrac{m - 1}{m + n} \int \cos^{m-2} u \sin^n u \, du.$

88. $\int \tan^2 u \, du = \tan u - u.$

89. $\int \tan^m u \, du = \dfrac{\tan^{m-1} u}{m - 1} - \int \tan^{m-2} u \, du, \; m \neq 1.$

90. $\int \cot^2 u \, du = -\cot u - u.$

91. $\int \cot^m u \, du = -\dfrac{\cot^{m-1} u}{m - 1} - \int \cot^{m-2} u \, du, \; m \neq 1.$

92. $\int \sec^m u \, du = \dfrac{\tan u \sec^{m-2} u}{m - 1} + \dfrac{m - 2}{m - 1} \int \sec^{m-2} u \, du, \; m \neq 1.$

93. $\int \csc^m u \, du = -\dfrac{\cot u \csc^{m-1} u}{m - 1} + \dfrac{m - 2}{m - 1} \int \csc^{m-2} u \, du, \; m \neq 1.$

**Other Forms**

94. $\int u \sin u \, du = \sin u - u \cos u.$

95. $\int u^2 \sin u \, du = 2u \sin u - (u^2 - 2) \cos u.$

96. $\int u^3 \sin u \, du = (3u^2 - 6) \sin u - (u^3 - 6u) \cos u.$

97. $\int u^m \sin u \, du = -u^m \cos u + m \int u^{m-1} \cos u \, du.$

98. $\int u \cos u \, du = \cos u + u \sin u.$

99. $\int u^2 \cos u \, du = 2u \cos u + (u^2 - 2) \sin u.$

100. $\int u^3 \cos u \, du = (3u^2 - 6) \cos u + (u^3 - 6u) \sin u.$

101. $\int u^m \cos u \, du = u^m \sin u - m \int u^{m-1} \sin u \, du.$

102. $\int \sin^{-1} u \, du = u \sin^{-1} u + \sqrt{1 - u^2}.$

103. $\displaystyle\int \operatorname{Sec}^{-1} u \, du = u \operatorname{Sec}^{-1} u - \ln \left| u + \sqrt{u^2 - 1} \right|.$

104. $\displaystyle\int \operatorname{Tan}^{-1} u \, du = u \operatorname{Tan}^{-1} u - \frac{1}{2} \ln (1 + u^2).$

105. $\displaystyle\int u \, e^{au} \, du = \frac{e^{au}}{a^2} (au - 1).$

106. $\displaystyle\int u^m e^{au} \, du = \frac{1}{a} u^m e^{au} - \frac{m}{a} \int u^{m-1} e^{au} \, du.$

107. $\displaystyle\int e^{au} \sin bu \, du = \frac{e^{au}}{a^2 + b^2} (a \sin bu - b \cos bu).$

108. $\displaystyle\int e^{au} \cos bu \, du = \frac{e^{au}}{a^2 + b^2} (a \cos bu + b \sin bu).$

109. $\displaystyle\int \ln u \, du = u(\ln u - 1).$

110. $\displaystyle\int (\ln u)^m \, du = u(\ln u)^m - m \int (\ln u)^{m-1} \, du.$

111. $\displaystyle\int u^m \ln u \, du = u^{m+1} \left[ \frac{\ln u}{m + 1} - \frac{1}{(m + 1)^2} \right], \quad m \neq -1.$

112. $\displaystyle\int u^m (\ln u)^n \, du = \frac{u^{m+1} (\ln u)^n}{m + 1} - \frac{n}{m + 1} \int u^m (\ln u)^{n-1} \, du, \quad m, n \neq -1.$

113. $\displaystyle\int \sinh u \, du = \cosh u.$

114. $\displaystyle\int \cosh u \, du = \sinh u.$

115. $\displaystyle\int \tanh u \, du = \ln \cosh u.$

116. $\displaystyle\int \coth u \, du = \ln |\sinh u|.$

117. $\displaystyle\int \operatorname{sech} u \, du = \operatorname{Tan}^{-1} (\sinh u).$

118. $\displaystyle\int \operatorname{csch} u \, du = \ln \left| \tanh \frac{u}{2} \right|.$

119. $\displaystyle\int \sinh^2 u \, du = \frac{1}{4} \sinh 2u - \frac{1}{2} u.$

120. $\displaystyle\int \cosh^2 u \, du = \frac{1}{4} \sinh 2u + \frac{1}{2} u.$

**Wallis' Formulas**

121. $\displaystyle\int_0^{\pi/2} \sin^m u \, du = \int_0^{\pi/2} \cos^m u \, du = \frac{(m-1)(m-3)\ldots(2) \text{ or } (1)}{m(m-2)\ldots(3) \text{ or } (2)} M,$

where $M = \pi/2$ if $m$ is even and $M = 1$ if $m$ is odd.

122. $\displaystyle\int_0^{\pi/2} \sin^m u \cos^n u \, du$

$$= \frac{[(m-1)(m-3)\ldots(2) \text{ or } (1)][(n-1)(n-3)\ldots(2) \text{ or } (1)]}{(m+n)(m+n-2)\ldots(2) \text{ or } (1)} N,$$

where $N = \pi/2$ if both $m$ and $n$ are even; otherwise, $N = 1$.

# APPENDIX D  Numerical Tables

## Table 1. Powers, Roots, Reciprocals

### 1-50

| $N$ | $N^2$ | $\sqrt{N}$ | $\sqrt{10N}$ | $N^3$ | $\sqrt[3]{N}$ | $\sqrt[3]{10N}$ | $\sqrt[3]{100N}$ | $1000/N$ |
|---|---|---|---|---|---|---|---|---|
| 1 | 1 | 1.00 000 | 3.16 228 | 1 | 1.00 000 | 2.15 443 | 4.64 159 | 1000.00 |
| 2 | 4 | 1.41 421 | 4.47 214 | 8 | 1.25 992 | 2.71 442 | 5.84 804 | 500.00 0 |
| 3 | 9 | 1.73 205 | 5.47 723 | 27 | 1.44 225 | 3.10 723 | 6.69 433 | 333.33 3 |
| 4 | 16 | 2.00 000 | 6.32 456 | 64 | 1.58 740 | 3.41 995 | 7.36 806 | 250.00 0 |
| 5 | 25 | 2.23 607 | 7.07 107 | 125 | 1.70 998 | 3.68 403 | 7.93 701 | 200.00 0 |
| 6 | 36 | 2.44 949 | 7.74 597 | 216 | 1.81 712 | 3.91 487 | 8.43 433 | 166.66 7 |
| 7 | 49 | 2.64 575 | 8.36 660 | 343 | 1.91 293 | 4.12 129 | 8.87 904 | 142.85 7 |
| 8 | 64 | 2.82 843 | 8.94 427 | 512 | 2.00 000 | 4.30 887 | 9.28 318 | 125.00 0 |
| 9 | 81 | 3.00 000 | 9.48 683 | 729 | 2.08 008 | 4.48 140 | 9.65 489 | 111.11 1 |
| 10 | 100 | 3.16 228 | 10.00 00 | 1 000 | 2.15 443 | 4.64 159 | 10.00 00 | 100.00 0 |
| 11 | 121 | 3.31 662 | 10.48 81 | 1 331 | 2.22 398 | 4.79 142 | 10.32 28 | 90.90 91 |
| 12 | 144 | 3.46 410 | 10.95 45 | 1 728 | 2.28 943 | 4.93 242 | 10.62 66 | 83.33 33 |
| 13 | 169 | 3.60 555 | 11.40 18 | 2 197 | 2.35 133 | 5.06 580 | 10.91 39 | 76.92 31 |
| 14 | 196 | 3.74 166 | 11.83 22 | 2 744 | 2.41 014 | 5.19 249 | 11.18 69 | 71.42 86 |
| 15 | 225 | 3.87 298 | 12.24 74 | 3 375 | 2.46 621 | 5.31 329 | 11.44 71 | 66.66 67 |
| 16 | 256 | 4.00 000 | 12.64 91 | 4 096 | 2.51 984 | 5.42 884 | 11.69 61 | 62.50 00 |
| 17 | 289 | 4.12 311 | 13.03 84 | 4 913 | 2.57 128 | 5.53 966 | 11.93 48 | 58.82 35 |
| 18 | 324 | 4.24 264 | 13.41 64 | 5 832 | 2.62 074 | 5.64 622 | 12.16 44 | 55.55 56 |
| 19 | 361 | 4.35 890 | 13.78 40 | 6 859 | 2.66 840 | 5.74 890 | 12.38 56 | 52.63 16 |
| 20 | 400 | 4.47 214 | 14.14 21 | 8 000 | 2.71 442 | 5.84 804 | 12.59 92 | 50.00 00 |
| 21 | 441 | 4.58 258 | 14.49 14 | 9 261 | 2.75 892 | 5.94 392 | 12.80 58 | 47.61 90 |
| 22 | 484 | 4.69 042 | 14.83 24 | 10 648 | 2.80 204 | 6.03 681 | 13.00 59 | 45.45 45 |
| 23 | 529 | 4.79 583 | 15.16 58 | 12 167 | 2.84 387 | 6.12 693 | 13.20 01 | 43.47 83 |
| 24 | 576 | 4.89 898 | 15.49 19 | 13 824 | 2.88 450 | 6.21 446 | 13.38 87 | 41.66 67 |
| 25 | 625 | 5.00 000 | 15.81 14 | 15 625 | 2.92 402 | 6.29 961 | 13.57 21 | 40.00 00 |
| 26 | 676 | 5.09 902 | 16.12 45 | 17 576 | 2.96 250 | 6.38 250 | 13.75 07 | 38.46 15 |
| 27 | 729 | 5.19 615 | 16.43 17 | 19 683 | 3.00 000 | 6.46 330 | 13.92 48 | 37.03 70 |
| 28 | 784 | 5.29 150 | 16.73 32 | 21 952 | 3.03 659 | 6.54 213 | 14.09 46 | 35.71 43 |
| 29 | 841 | 5.38 516 | 17.02 94 | 24 389 | 3.07 232 | 6.61 911 | 14.26 04 | 34.48 28 |
| 30 | 900 | 5.47 723 | 17.32 05 | 27 000 | 3.10 723 | 6.69 433 | 14.42 25 | 33.33 33 |
| 31 | 961 | 5.56 776 | 17.60 68 | 29.791 | 3.14 138 | 6.76 790 | 14.58 10 | 32.25 81 |
| 32 | 1 024 | 5.65 685 | 17.88 85 | 32 768 | 3.17 480 | 6.83 990 | 14.73 61 | 31.25 00 |
| 33 | 1 089 | 5.74 456 | 18.16 59 | 35 937 | 3.20 753 | 6.91 042 | 14.88 81 | 30.30 30 |
| 34 | 1 156 | 5.83 095 | 18.43 91 | 39 304 | 3.23 961 | 6.97 953 | 15.03 69 | 29.41 18 |
| 35 | 1 225 | 5.91 608 | 18.70 83 | 42 875 | 3.27 107 | 7.04 730 | 15.18 29 | 28.57 14 |
| 36 | 1 296 | 6.00 000 | 18.97 37 | 46 656 | 3.30 193 | 7.11 379 | 15.32 62 | 27.77 78 |
| 37 | 1 369 | 6.08 276 | 19.23 54 | 50 653 | 3.33 222 | 7.17 905 | 15.46 68 | 27.02 70 |
| 38 | 1 444 | 6.16 441 | 19.49 36 | 54 872 | 3.36 198 | 7.24 316 | 15.60 49 | 26.31 58 |
| 39 | 1 521 | 6.24 500 | 19.74 84 | 59 319 | 3.39 121 | 7.30 614 | 15.74 06 | 25.64 10 |
| 40 | 1 600 | 6.32 456 | 20.00 00 | 64 000 | 3.41 995 | 7.36 806 | 15.87 40 | 25.00 00 |
| 41 | 1 681 | 6.40 312 | 20.24 85 | 68 921 | 3.44 822 | 7.42 896 | 16.00 52 | 24.39 02 |
| 42 | 1 764 | 6.48 074 | 20.49 39 | 74 088 | 3.47 603 | 7.48 887 | 16.13 43 | 23.80 95 |
| 43 | 1 849 | 6.55 744 | 20.73 64 | 79 507 | 3.50 340 | 7.54 784 | 16.26 13 | 23.25 58 |
| 44 | 1 936 | 6.63 325 | 20.97 62 | 85 184 | 3.53 035 | 7.60 590 | 16.38 64 | 22.72 73 |
| 45 | 2 025 | 6.70 820 | 21.21 32 | 91 125 | 3.55 689 | 7.66 309 | 16.50 96 | 22.22 22 |
| 46 | 2 116 | 6.78 233 | 21.44 76 | 97 336 | 3.58 305 | 7.71 944 | 16.63 10 | 21.73 91 |
| 47 | 2 209 | 6.85 565 | 21.67 95 | 103 823 | 3.60 883 | 7.77 498 | 16.75 07 | 21.27 66 |
| 48 | 2 304 | 6.92 820 | 21.90 89 | 110 592 | 3.63 424 | 7.82 974 | 16.86 87 | 20.83 33 |
| 49 | 2 401 | 7.00 000 | 22.13 59 | 117 649 | 3.65 931 | 7.88 374 | 16.98 50 | 20.40 82 |
| 50 | 2 500 | 7.07 107 | 22.36 07 | 125 000 | 3.68 403 | 7.93 701 | 17.09 98 | 20.00 00 |
| $N$ | $N^2$ | $\sqrt{N}$ | $\sqrt{10N}$ | $N^3$ | $\sqrt[3]{N}$ | $\sqrt[3]{10N}$ | $\sqrt[3]{100N}$ | $1000/N$ |

# Table 1. Powers, Roots, Reciprocals

## 50-100

| $N$ | $N^2$ | $\sqrt{N}$ | $\sqrt{10N}$ | $N^3$ | $\sqrt[3]{N}$ | $\sqrt[3]{10N}$ | $\sqrt[3]{100N}$ | $1000/N$ |
|---|---|---|---|---|---|---|---|---|
| **50** | 2 500 | 7.07 107 | 22.36 07 | 125 000 | 3.68 403 | 7.93 701 | 17.09 98 | 20.00 00 |
| 51 | 2 601 | 7.14 143 | 22.58 32 | 132 651 | 3.70 843 | 7.98 957 | 17.21 30 | 19.60 78 |
| 52 | 2 704 | 7.21 110 | 22.80 35 | 140 608 | 3.73 251 | 8.04 145 | 17.32 48 | 19.23 08 |
| 53 | 2 809 | 7.28 011 | 23.02 17 | 148 877 | 3.75 629 | 8.09 267 | 17.43 51 | 18.86 79 |
| 54 | 2 916 | 7.34 847 | 23.23 79 | 157 464 | 3.77 976 | 8.14 325 | 17.54 41 | 18.51 85 |
| 55 | 3 025 | 7.41 620 | 23.45 21 | 166 375 | 3.80 295 | 8.19 321 | 17.65 17 | 18.18 18 |
| **56** | 3 136 | 7.48 331 | 23.66 43 | 175 616 | 3.82 586 | 8.24 257 | 17.75 81 | 17.85 71 |
| 57 | 3 249 | 7.54 983 | 23.87 47 | 185 193 | 3.84 850 | 8.29 134 | 17.86 32 | 17.54 39 |
| 58 | 3 364 | 7.61 577 | 24.08 32 | 195 112 | 3.87 088 | 8.33 955 | 17.96 70 | 17.24 14 |
| 59 | 3 481 | 7.68 115 | 24.28 99 | 205 379 | 3.89 300 | 8.38 721 | 18.06 97 | 16.94 92 |
| 60 | 3 600 | 7.74 597 | 24.49 49 | 216 000 | 3.91 487 | 8.43 433 | 18.17 12 | 16.66 67 |
| **61** | 3 721 | 7.81 025 | 24.69 82 | 226 981 | 3.93 650 | 8.48 093 | 18.27 16 | 16.39 34 |
| 62 | 3 844 | 7.87 401 | 24.89 98 | 238 328 | 3.95 789 | 8.52 702 | 18.37 09 | 16.12 90 |
| 63 | 3 969 | 7.93 725 | 25.09 98 | 250 047 | 3.97 906 | 8.57 262 | 18.46 91 | 15.87 30 |
| 64 | 4 096 | 8.00 000 | 25.29 82 | 262 144 | 4.00 000 | 8.61 774 | 18.56 64 | 15.62 50 |
| 65 | 4 225 | 8.06 226 | 25.49 51 | 274 625 | 4.02 073 | 8.66 239 | 18.66 26 | 15.38 46 |
| **66** | 4 356 | 8.12 404 | 25.69 05 | 287 496 | 4.01 124 | 8.70 659 | 18.75 78 | 15.15 15 |
| 67 | 4 489 | 8.18 535 | 25.88 44 | 300 763 | 4.06 155 | 8.75 034 | 18.85 20 | 14.92 54 |
| 68 | 4 624 | 8.24 621 | 26.07 68 | 314 432 | 4.08 166 | 8.79 366 | 18.94 54 | 14.70 59 |
| 69 | 4 761 | 8.30 662 | 26.26 79 | 328 509 | 4.10 157 | 8.83 656 | 19.03 78 | 14.49 28 |
| 70 | 4 900 | 8.36 660 | 26.45 75 | 343 000 | 4.12 129 | 8.87 904 | 19.12 93 | 14.28 57 |
| **71** | 5 041 | 8.42 615 | 26.64 58 | 357 911 | 4.14 082 | 8.92 112 | 19.22 00 | 14.08 45 |
| 72 | 5 184 | 8.48 528 | 26.83 28 | 373 248 | 4.16 017 | 8.96 281 | 19.30 98 | 13.88 89 |
| 73 | 5 329 | 8.54 400 | 27.01 85 | 389 017 | 4.17 934 | 9.00 411 | 19.39 88 | 13.69 86 |
| 74 | 5 476 | 8.60 233 | 27.20 29 | 405 224 | 4.19 834 | 9.04 504 | 19.48 70 | 13.51 35 |
| 75 | 5 625 | 8.66 025 | 27.38 61 | 421 875 | 4.21 716 | 9.08 560 | 19.57 43 | 13.33 33 |
| **76** | 5 776 | 8.71 780 | 27.56 81 | 438 976 | 4.23 582 | 9.12 581 | 19.66 10 | 13.15 79 |
| 77 | 5 929 | 8.77 496 | 27.74 89 | 456 533 | 4.25 432 | 9.16 566 | 19.74 68 | 12.98 70 |
| 78 | 6 084 | 8.83 176 | 27.92 85 | 474 552 | 4.27 266 | 9.20 516 | 19.83 19 | 12.82 05 |
| 79 | 6 241 | 8.88 819 | 28.10 69 | 493 039 | 4.29 084 | 9.24 434 | 19.91 63 | 12.65 82 |
| 80 | 6 400 | 8.94 427 | 28.28 43 | 512 000 | 4.30 887 | 9.28 318 | 20.00 00 | 12.50 00 |
| **81** | 6 561 | 9.00 000 | 28.46 05 | 531 441 | 4.32 675 | 9.32 170 | 20.08 30 | 12.34 57 |
| 82 | 6 724 | 9.05 539 | 28.63 56 | 551 368 | 4.34 448 | 9.35 990 | 20.16 53 | 12.19 51 |
| 83 | 6 889 | 9.11 043 | 28.80 97 | 571 787 | 4.36 207 | 9.39 780 | 20.24 69 | 12.04 82 |
| 84 | 7 056 | 9.16 515 | 28.98 28 | 592 704 | 4.37 952 | 9.43 539 | 20.32 79 | 11.90 48 |
| 85 | 7 225 | 9.21 954 | 29.15 48 | 614 125 | 4.39 683 | 9.47 268 | 20.40 83 | 11.76 47 |
| **86** | 7 396 | 9.27 362 | 29.32 58 | 636 056 | 4.41 400 | 9.50 969 | 20.48 80 | 11.62 79 |
| 87 | 7 569 | 9.32 738 | 29.49 58 | 658 503 | 4.43 105 | 9.54 640 | 20.56 71 | 11.49 43 |
| 88 | 7 744 | 9.38 083 | 29.66 48 | 681 472 | 4.44 796 | 9.58 284 | 20.64 56 | 11.36 36 |
| 89 | 7 921 | 9.43 398 | 29.83 29 | 704 969 | 4.46 475 | 9.61 900 | 20.72 35 | 11.23 60 |
| 90 | 8 100 | 9.48 683 | 30.00 00 | 729 000 | 4.48 140 | 9.65 489 | 20.80 08 | 11.11 11 |
| **91** | 8 281 | 9.53 939 | 30.16 62 | 753 571 | 4.49 794 | 9.69 052 | 20.87 76 | 10.98 90 |
| 92 | 8 464 | 9.59 166 | 30.33 15 | 778 688 | 4.51 436 | 9.72 589 | 20.95 38 | 10.86 96 |
| 93 | 8 649 | 9.64 365 | 30.49 59 | 804 357 | 4.53 065 | 9.76 100 | 21.02 94 | 10.75 27 |
| 94 | 8 836 | 9.69 536 | 30.65 94 | 830 584 | 4.54 684 | 9.79 586 | 21.10 45 | 10.63 83 |
| 95 | 9 025 | 9.74 679 | 30.82 21 | 857 375 | 4.56 290 | 9.83 048 | 21.17 91 | 10.52 63 |
| **96** | 9 216 | 9.79 796 | 30.98 39 | 884 736 | 4.57 886 | 9.86 485 | 21.25 32 | 10.41 67 |
| 97 | 9 409 | 9.84 886 | 31.14 48 | 912 673 | 4.59 470 | 9.89 898 | 21.32 67 | 10.30 93 |
| 98 | 9 604 | 9.89 949 | 31.30 50 | 941 192 | 4.61 044 | 9.93 288 | 21.39 97 | 10.20 41 |
| 99 | 9 801 | 9.94 987 | 31.46 43 | 970 299 | 4.62 607 | 9.96 655 | 21.47 23 | 10.10 10 |
| 100 | 10 000 | 10.00 000 | 31.62 28 | 1 000 000 | 4.64 159 | 10.00 000 | 21.54 43 | 10.00 00 |
| $N$ | $N^2$ | $\sqrt{N}$ | $\sqrt{10N}$ | $N^3$ | $\sqrt[3]{N}$ | $\sqrt[3]{10N}$ | $\sqrt[3]{100N}$ | $1000/N$ |

## Table 2. Trigonometric Functions for Angles in Degrees

| Deg. | Sin | Tan | Cot | Cos | Deg. |
|---|---|---|---|---|---|
| 0 | .00000 | .00000 | — | 1.00000 | 90 |
| 1 | .01745 | .01746 | 57.290 | .99985 | 89 |
| 2 | .03490 | .03492 | 28.636 | .99939 | 88 |
| 3 | .05234 | .05241 | 19.081 | .99863 | 87 |
| 4 | .06976 | .06993 | 14.301 | .99756 | 86 |
| 5 | .08716 | .08749 | 11.430 | .99619 | 85 |
| 6 | .10453 | .10510 | 9.5144 | .99452 | 84 |
| 7 | .12187 | .12278 | 8.1443 | .99255 | 83 |
| 8 | .13917 | .14054 | 7.1154 | .99027 | 82 |
| 9 | .15643 | .15838 | 6.3138 | .98769 | 81 |
| 10 | .17365 | .17633 | 5.6713 | .98481 | 80 |
| 11 | .19081 | .19438 | 5.1446 | .98163 | 79 |
| 12 | .20791 | .21256 | 4.7046 | .97815 | 78 |
| 13 | .22495 | .23087 | 4.3315 | .97437 | 77 |
| 14 | .24192 | .24933 | 4.0108 | .97030 | 76 |
| 15 | .25882 | .26795 | 3.7321 | .96593 | 75 |
| 16 | .27564 | .28675 | 3.4874 | .96126 | 74 |
| 17 | .29237 | .30573 | 3.2709 | .95630 | 73 |
| 18 | .30902 | .32492 | 3.0777 | .95106 | 72 |
| 19 | .32557 | .34433 | 2.9042 | .94552 | 71 |
| 20 | .34202 | .36397 | 2.7475 | .93969 | 70 |
| 21 | .35837 | .38386 | 2.6051 | .93358 | 69 |
| 22 | .37461 | .40403 | 2.4751 | .92718 | 68 |
| 23 | .39073 | .42447 | 2.3559 | .92050 | 67 |
| 24 | .40674 | .44523 | 2.2460 | .91355 | 66 |
| 25 | .42262 | .46631 | 2.1445 | .90631 | 65 |
| 26 | .43837 | .48773 | 2.0503 | .89879 | 64 |
| 27 | .45399 | .50953 | 1.9626 | .89101 | 63 |
| 28 | .46947 | .53171 | 1.8807 | .88295 | 62 |
| 29 | .48481 | .55431 | 1.8040 | .87462 | 61 |
| 30 | .50000 | .57735 | 1.7321 | .86603 | 60 |
| 31 | .51504 | .60086 | 1.6643 | .85717 | 59 |
| 32 | .52992 | .62487 | 1.6003 | .84805 | 58 |
| 33 | .54464 | .64941 | 1.5399 | .83867 | 57 |
| 34 | .55919 | .67451 | 1.4826 | .82904 | 56 |
| 35 | .57358 | .70021 | 1.4281 | .81915 | 55 |
| 36 | .58779 | .72654 | 1.3764 | .80902 | 54 |
| 37 | .60182 | .75355 | 1.3270 | .79864 | 53 |
| 38 | .61566 | .78129 | 1.2799 | .78801 | 52 |
| 39 | .62932 | .80978 | 1.2349 | .77715 | 51 |
| 40 | .64279 | .83910 | 1.1918 | .76604 | 50 |
| 41 | .65606 | .86929 | 1.1504 | .75471 | 49 |
| 42 | .66913 | .90040 | 1.1106 | .74314 | 48 |
| 43 | .68200 | .93252 | 1.0724 | .73135 | 47 |
| 44 | .69466 | .96569 | 1.0355 | .71934 | 46 |
| 45 | .70711 | 1.00000 | 1.0000 | .70711 | 45 |
| Deg. | Sin | Tan | Cot | Cos | Deg. |

## Table 3a
### Radians to Degrees

| Radians | Degrees |
|---|---|
| 1 | 57.295 |
| 2 | 114.592 |
| 3 | 171.887 |
| 4 | 229.183 |
| 5 | 286.479 |
| 6 | 343.775 |
| 7 | 401.070 |
| 8 | 458.366 |
| 9 | 515.662 |

## Table 3b
### Degrees to Radians

| Degrees | Radians |
|---|---|
| 10 | 0.17453 |
| 20 | 0.34907 |
| 30 | 0.52360 |
| 40 | 0.69813 |
| 50 | 0.87266 |
| 60 | 1.04720 |
| 70 | 1.22173 |
| 80 | 1.39626 |
| 90 | 1.57080 |

# Table 4. Trigonometric Functions for Angles in Radians 0-1.00

| Rad. | Sin | Tan | Cot | Cos | Rad. | Sin | Tan | Cot | Cos |
|------|-----|-----|-----|-----|------|-----|-----|-----|-----|
| 0.00 | .00000 | .00000 | — | 1.00000 | 0.50 | .47943 | .54630 | 1.8305 | .87758 |
| .01 | .01000 | .01000 | 99.997 | 0.99995 | .51 | .48818 | .55936 | 1.7878 | .87274 |
| .02 | .02000 | .02000 | 49.993 | .99980 | .52 | .49688 | .57256 | 1.7465 | .86782 |
| .03 | .03000 | .03001 | 33.323 | .99955 | .53 | .50553 | .58592 | 1.7067 | .86281 |
| .04 | .03999 | .04002 | 24.987 | .99920 | .54 | .51414 | .59943 | 1.6683 | .85771 |
| | | | | | | | | | |
| .05 | .04998 | .05004 | 19.983 | .99875 | .55 | .52269 | .61311 | 1.6310 | .85252 |
| .06 | .05996 | .06007 | 16.647 | .99820 | .56 | .53119 | .62695 | 1.5950 | .84726 |
| .07 | .06994 | .07011 | 14.262 | .99755 | .57 | .53963 | .64097 | 1.5601 | .84190 |
| .08 | .07991 | .08017 | 12.473 | .99680 | .58 | .54802 | .65517 | 1.5263 | .83646 |
| .09 | .08988 | .09024 | 11.081 | .99595 | .59 | .55636 | .66956 | 1.4935 | .83094 |
| | | | | | | | | | |
| 0.10 | .09983 | .10033 | 9.9666 | .99500 | 0.60 | .56464 | .68414 | 1.4617 | .82534 |
| .11 | .10978 | .11045 | 9.0542 | .99396 | .61 | .57287 | .69892 | 1.4308 | .81965 |
| .12 | .11971 | .12058 | 8.2933 | .99281 | .62 | .58104 | .71391 | 1.4007 | .81388 |
| .13 | .12963 | .13074 | 7.6489 | .99156 | .63 | .58914 | .72911 | 1.3715 | .80803 |
| .14 | .13954 | .14092 | 7.0961 | .99022 | .64 | .59720 | .74454 | 1.3431 | .80210 |
| | | | | | | | | | |
| .15 | .14944 | .15114 | 6.6166 | .98877 | .65 | .60519 | .76020 | 1.3154 | .79608 |
| .16 | .15932 | .16138 | 6.1966 | .98723 | .66 | .61312 | .77610 | 1.2885 | .78999 |
| .17 | .16918 | .17166 | 5.8256 | .98558 | .67 | .62099 | .79225 | 1.2622 | .78382 |
| .18 | .17903 | .18197 | 5.4954 | .98384 | .68 | .62879 | .80866 | 1.2366 | .77757 |
| .19 | .18886 | .19232 | 5.1997 | .98200 | .69 | .63654 | .82534 | 1.2116 | .77125 |
| | | | | | | | | | |
| 0.20 | .19867 | .20271 | 4.9332 | .98007 | 0.70 | .64422 | .84229 | 1.1872 | .76484 |
| .21 | .20846 | .21314 | 4.6917 | .97803 | .71 | .65183 | .85953 | 1.1634 | .75836 |
| .22 | .21823 | .22362 | 4.4719 | .97590 | .72 | .65938 | .87707 | 1.1402 | .75181 |
| .23 | .22798 | .23414 | 4.2709 | .97367 | .73 | .66687 | .89492 | 1.1174 | .74517 |
| .24 | .23770 | .24472 | 4.0864 | .97134 | .74 | .67429 | .91309 | 1.0952 | .73847 |
| | | | | | | | | | |
| .25 | .24740 | .25534 | 3.9163 | .96891 | .75 | .68164 | .93160 | 1.0734 | .73169 |
| .26 | .25708 | .26602 | 3.7591 | .96639 | .76 | .68892 | .95045 | 1.0521 | .72484 |
| .27 | .26673 | .27676 | 3.6133 | .96377 | .77 | .69614 | .96967 | 1.0313 | .71791 |
| .28 | .27636 | .28755 | 3.4776 | .96106 | .78 | .70328 | .98926 | 1.0109 | .71091 |
| .29 | .28595 | .29841 | 3.3511 | .95824 | .79 | .71035 | 1.0092 | .99084 | .70385 |
| | | | | | | | | | |
| 0.30 | .29552 | .30934 | 3.2327 | .95534 | 0.80 | .71736 | 1.0296 | .97121 | .69671 |
| .31 | .30506 | .32033 | 3.1218 | .95233 | .81 | .72429 | 1.0505 | .95197 | .68950 |
| .32 | .31457 | .33139 | 3.0176 | .94924 | .82 | .73115 | 1.0717 | .93309 | .68222 |
| .33 | .32404 | .34252 | 2.9195 | .94604 | .83 | .73793 | 1.0934 | .91455 | .67488 |
| .34 | .33349 | .35374 | 2.8270 | .94275 | .84 | .74464 | 1.1156 | .89635 | .66746 |
| | | | | | | | | | |
| .35 | .34290 | .36503 | 2.7395 | .93937 | .85 | .75128 | 1.1383 | .87848 | .65998 |
| .36 | .35227 | .37640 | 2.6567 | .93590 | .86 | .75784 | 1.1616 | .86091 | .65244 |
| .37 | .36162 | .38786 | 2.5782 | .93233 | .87 | .76433 | 1.1853 | .84365 | .64483 |
| .38 | .37092 | .39941 | 2.5037 | .92866 | .88 | .77074 | 1.2097 | .82668 | .63715 |
| .39 | .38019 | .41105 | 2.4328 | .92491 | .89 | .77707 | 1.2346 | .80998 | .62941 |
| | | | | | | | | | |
| 0.40 | .38942 | .42279 | 2.3652 | .92106 | 0.90 | .78333 | 1.2602 | .79355 | .62161 |
| .41 | .39861 | .43463 | 2.3008 | .91712 | .91 | .78950 | 1.2864 | .77738 | .61375 |
| .42 | .40776 | .44657 | 2.2393 | .91309 | .92 | .79560 | 1.3133 | .76146 | .60582 |
| .43 | .41687 | .45862 | 2.1804 | .90897 | .93 | .80162 | 1.3409 | .74578 | .59783 |
| .44 | .42594 | .47078 | 2.1241 | .90475 | .94 | .80756 | 1.3692 | .73034 | .58979 |
| | | | | | | | | | |
| .45 | .43497 | .48306 | 2.0702 | .90045 | .95 | .81342 | 1.3984 | .71511 | .58168 |
| .46 | .44395 | .49545 | 2.0184 | .89605 | .96 | .81919 | 1.4284 | .70010 | .57352 |
| .47 | .45289 | .50797 | 1.9686 | .89157 | .97 | .82489 | 1.4592 | .68531 | .56530 |
| .48 | .46178 | .52061 | 1.9208 | .88699 | .98 | .83050 | 1.4910 | .67071 | .55702 |
| .49 | .47063 | .53339 | 1.8748 | .88233 | .99 | .83603 | 1.5237 | .65631 | .54869 |
| 0.50 | .47943 | .54630 | 1.8305 | .87758 | 1.00 | .84147 | 1.5574 | .64209 | .54030 |
| | | | | | | | | | |
| Rad. | Sin | Tan | Cot | Cos | Rad. | Sin | Tan | Cot | Cos |

## Table 4. Trigonometric Functions for Angles in Radians
### 1.00-1.60

| Rad. | Sin | Tan | Cot | Cos | Rad. | Sin | Tan | Cot | Cos |
|------|-----|-----|-----|-----|------|-----|-----|-----|-----|
| **1.00** | .84147 | 1.5574 | .64209 | .54030 | **1.30** | .96356 | 3.6021 | .27762 | .26750 |
| 1.01 | .84683 | 1.5922 | .62806 | .53186 | 1.31 | .96618 | 3.7471 | .26687 | .25785 |
| 1.02 | .85211 | 1.6281 | .61420 | .52337 | 1.32 | .96872 | 3.9033 | .25619 | .24818 |
| 1.03 | .85730 | 1.6652 | .60051 | .51482 | 1.33 | .97115 | 4.0723 | .24556 | .23848 |
| 1.04 | .86240 | 1.7036 | .58699 | .50622 | 1.34 | .97348 | 4.2556 | .23498 | .22875 |
| | | | | | | | | | |
| 1.05 | .86742 | 1.7433 | .57362 | .49757 | 1.35 | .97572 | 4.4552 | .22446 | .21901 |
| 1.06 | .87236 | 1.7844 | .56040 | .48887 | 1.36 | .97786 | 4.6734 | .21398 | .20924 |
| 1.07 | .87720 | 1.8270 | .54734 | .48012 | 1.37 | .97991 | 4.9131 | .20354 | .19945 |
| 1.08 | .88196 | 1.8712 | .53441 | .47133 | 1.38 | .98185 | 5.1774 | .19315 | .18964 |
| 1.09 | .88663 | 1.9171 | .52162 | .46249 | 1.39 | .98370 | 5.4707 | .18279 | .17981 |
| | | | | | | | | | |
| **1.10** | .89121 | 1.9648 | .50897 | .45360 | **1.40** | .98545 | 5.7979 | .17248 | .16997 |
| 1.11 | .89570 | 2.0143 | .49644 | .44466 | 1 41 | .98710 | 6.1654 | .16220 | .16010 |
| 1.12 | .90010 | 2.0660 | .48404 | .43568 | 1.42 | .98865 | 6.5811 | .15195 | .15023 |
| 1.13 | .90441 | 2.1198 | .47175 | .42666 | 1.43 | .99010 | 7.0555 | .14173 | .14033 |
| 1.14 | .90863 | 2.1759 | .45959 | .41759 | 1.44 | .99146 | 7.6018 | .13155 | .13042 |
| | | | | | | | | | |
| 1.15 | .91276 | 2.2345 | .44753 | .40849 | 1.45 | .99271 | 8.2381 | .12139 | .12050 |
| 1.16 | .91680 | 2.2958 | .43558 | .39934 | 1.46 | .99387 | 8.9886 | .11125 | .11057 |
| 1.17 | .92075 | 2.3600 | .42373 | .39015 | 1.47 | .99492 | 9.8874 | .10114 | .10063 |
| 1.18 | .92461 | 2.4273 | .41199 | .38092 | 1.48 | .99588 | 10.983 | .09105 | .09067 |
| 1.19 | .92837 | 2.4979 | .40034 | .37166 | 1.49 | .99674 | 12.350 | .08097 | .08071 |
| | | | | | | | | | |
| **1.20** | .93204 | 2.5722 | .38878 | .36236 | **1.50** | .99749 | 14.101 | .07091 | .07074 |
| 1.21 | .93562 | 2.6503 | .37731 | .35302 | 1.51 | .99815 | 16.428 | .06087 | .06076 |
| 1.22 | .93910 | 2.7328 | .36593 | .34365 | 1.52 | .99871 | 19.670 | .05084 | .05077 |
| 1.23 | .94249 | 2.8198 | .35463 | .33424 | 1.53 | .99917 | 24.498 | .04082 | .04079 |
| 1.24 | .94578 | 2.9119 | .34341 | .32480 | 1.54 | .99953 | 32.461 | .03081 | .03079 |
| | | | | | | | | | |
| 1.25 | .94898 | 3.0096 | .33227 | .31532 | 1.55 | .99978 | 48.078 | .02080 | .02079 |
| 1.26 | .95209 | 3.1133 | .32121 | .30582 | 1.56 | .99994 | 92.621 | .01080 | .01080 |
| 1.27 | .95510 | 3.2236 | .31021 | .29628 | 1.57 | 1.00000 | 1255.8 | .00080 | .00080 |
| 1.28 | .95802 | 3.3413 | .29928 | .28672 | 1.58 | .99996 | −108.65 | −.00920 | −.00920 |
| 1.29 | .96084 | 3.4672 | .28842 | .27712 | 1.59 | .99982 | −52.067 | −.01921 | −.01920 |
| **1.30** | .96356 | 3.6021 | .27762 | .26750 | **1.60** | .99957 | −34.233 | −.02921 | −.02920 |
| | | | | | | | | | |
| Rad. | Sin | Tan | Cot | Cos | Rad. | Sin | Tan | Cot | Cos |

## Table 5. Four-place Natural Logarithms

To find ln $N$ when $N$ is beyond the range of this table, write $N$ in the form $P \times 10^m$, where $P$ lies within the range of the table, and $m$ is a positive or negative integer. Then use

$$\ln N = \ln (P \times 10^m) = \ln P + m \ln 10.$$

| | | | |
|---|---|---|---|
| ln 10 = | 2.3026 | 6 ln 10 = | 13.8155 |
| 2 ln 10 = | 4.6052 | 7 ln 10 = | 16.1181 |
| 3 ln 10 = | 6.9076 | 8 ln 10 = | 18.4207 |
| 4 ln 10 = | 9.2103 | 9 ln 10 = | 20.7233 |
| 5 ln 10 = | 11.5129 | 10 ln 10 = | 23.0259 |

## Table 5. Four-place Natural Logarithms
## 1.00-5.59

| N | .00 | .01 | .02 | .03 | .04 | .05 | .06 | .07 | .08 | .09 |
|---|-----|-----|-----|-----|-----|-----|-----|-----|-----|-----|
| **1.0** | 0.0000 | 0.0100 | 0.0198 | 0.0296 | 0.0392 | 0.0488 | 0.0583 | 0.0677 | 0.0770 | 0.0862 |
| 1.1 | 0.0953 | 0.1044 | 0.1133 | 0.1222 | 0.1310 | 0.1398 | 0.1484 | 0.1570 | 0.1655 | 0.1740 |
| 1.2 | 0.1823 | 0.1906 | 0.1989 | 0.2070 | 0.2151 | 0.2231 | 0.2311 | 0.2390 | 0.2469 | 0.2546 |
| 1.3 | 0.2624 | 0.2700 | 0.2776 | 0.2852 | 0.2927 | 0.3001 | 0.3075 | 0.3148 | 0.3221 | 0.3293 |
| 1.4 | 0.3365 | 0.3436 | 0.3507 | 0.3577 | 0.3646 | 0.3716 | 0.3784 | 0.3853 | 0.3920 | 0.3988 |
| **1.5** | 0.4055 | 0.4121 | 0.4187 | 0.4253 | 0.4318 | 0.4383 | 0.4447 | 0.4511 | 0.4574 | 0.4637 |
| 1.6 | 0.4700 | 0.4762 | 0.4824 | 0.4886 | 0.4947 | 0.5008 | 0.5068 | 0.5128 | 0.5188 | 0.5247 |
| 1.7 | 0.5306 | 0.5365 | 0.5423 | 0.5481 | 0.5539 | 0.5596 | 0.5653 | 0.5710 | 0.5766 | 0.5822 |
| 1.8 | 0.5878 | 0.5933 | 0.5988 | 0.6043 | 0.6098 | 0.6152 | 0.6206 | 0.6259 | 0.6313 | 0.6366 |
| 1.9 | 0.6419 | 0.6471 | 0.6523 | 0.6575 | 0.6627 | 0.6678 | 0.6729 | 0.6780 | 0.6831 | 0.6881 |
| **2.0** | 0.6931 | 0.6981 | 0.7031 | 0.7080 | 0.7129 | 0.7178 | 0.7227 | 0.7275 | 0.7324 | 0.7372 |
| 2.1 | 0.7419 | 0.7467 | 0.7514 | 0.7561 | 0.7608 | 0.7655 | 0.7701 | 0.7747 | 0.7793 | 0.7839 |
| 2.2 | 0.7885 | 0.7930 | 0.7975 | 0.8020 | 0.8065 | 0.8109 | 0.8154 | 0.8198 | 0.8242 | 0.8286 |
| 2.3 | 0.8329 | 0.8372 | 0.8416 | 0.8459 | 0.8502 | 0.8544 | 0.8587 | 0.8629 | 0.8671 | 0.8713 |
| 2.4 | 0.8755 | 0.8796 | 0.8838 | 0.8879 | 0.8920 | 0.8961 | 0.9002 | 0.9042 | 0.9083 | 0.9123 |
| **2.5** | 0.9163 | 0.9203 | 0.9243 | 0.9282 | 0.9322 | 0.9361 | 0.9400 | 0.9439 | 0.9478 | 0.9517 |
| 2.6 | 0.9555 | 0.9594 | 0.9632 | 0.9670 | 0.9708 | 0.9746 | 0.9783 | 0.9821 | 0.9858 | 0.9895 |
| 2.7 | 0.9933 | 0.9969 | 1.0006 | 1.0043 | 1.0080 | 1.0116 | 1.0152 | 1.0188 | 1.0225 | 1.0260 |
| 2.8 | 1.0296 | 1.0332 | 1.0367 | 1.0403 | 1.0438 | 1.0473 | 1.0508 | 1.0543 | 1.0578 | 1.0613 |
| 2.9 | 1.0647 | 1.0682 | 1.0716 | 1.0750 | 1.0784 | 1.0818 | 1.0852 | 1.0886 | 1.0919 | 1.0953 |
| **3.0** | 1.0986 | 1.1019 | 1.1053 | 1.1086 | 1.1119 | 1.1151 | 1.1184 | 1.1217 | 1.1249 | 1.1282 |
| 3.1 | 1.1314 | 1.1346 | 1.1378 | 1.1410 | 1.1442 | 1.1474 | 1.1506 | 1.1537 | 1.1569 | 1.1600 |
| 3.2 | 1.1632 | 1.1663 | 1.1694 | 1.1725 | 1.1756 | 1.1787 | 1.1817 | 1.1848 | 1.1878 | 1.1909 |
| 3.3 | 1.1939 | 1.1969 | 1.2000 | 1.2030 | 1.2060 | 1.2090 | 1.2119 | 1.2149 | 1.2179 | 1.2208 |
| 3.4 | 1.2238 | 1.2267 | 1.2296 | 1.2326 | 1.2355 | 1.2384 | 1.2413 | 1.2442 | 1.2470 | 1.2499 |
| **3.5** | 1.2528 | 1.2556 | 1.2585 | 1.2613 | 1.2641 | 1.2669 | 1.2698 | 1.2726 | 1.2754 | 1.2782 |
| 3.6 | 1.2809 | 1.2837 | 1.2865 | 1.2892 | 1.2920 | 1.2947 | 1.2975 | 1.3002 | 1.3029 | 1.3056 |
| 3.7 | 1.3083 | 1.3110 | 1.3137 | 1.3164 | 1.3191 | 1.3218 | 1.3244 | 1.3271 | 1.3297 | 1.3324 |
| 3.8 | 1.3350 | 1.3376 | 1.3403 | 1.3429 | 1.3455 | 1.3481 | 1.3507 | 1.3533 | 1.3558 | 1.3584 |
| 3.9 | 1.3610 | 1.3635 | 1.3661 | 1.3686 | 1.3712 | 1.3737 | 1.3762 | 1.3788 | 1.3813 | 1.3838 |
| **4.0** | 1.3863 | 1.3888 | 1.3913 | 1.3938 | 1.3962 | 1.3987 | 1.4012 | 1.4036 | 1.4061 | 1.4085 |
| 4.1 | 1.4110 | 1.4134 | 1.4159 | 1.4183 | 1.4207 | 1.4231 | 1.4255 | 1.4279 | 1.4303 | 1.4327 |
| 4.2 | 1.4351 | 1.4375 | 1.4398 | 1.4422 | 1.4446 | 1.4469 | 1.4493 | 1.4516 | 1.4540 | 1.4563 |
| 4.3 | 1.4586 | 1.4609 | 1.4633 | 1.4656 | 1.4679 | 1.4702 | 1.4725 | 1.4748 | 1.4770 | 1.4793 |
| 4.4 | 1.4816 | 1.4839 | 1.4861 | 1.4884 | 1.4907 | 1.4929 | 1.4951 | 1.4974 | 1.4996 | 1.5019 |
| **4.5** | 1.5041 | 1.5063 | 1.5085 | 1.5107 | 1.5129 | 1.5151 | 1.5173 | 1.5195 | 1.5217 | 1.5239 |
| 4.6 | 1.5261 | 1.5282 | 1.5304 | 1.5326 | 1.5347 | 1.5369 | 1.5390 | 1.5412 | 1.5433 | 1.5454 |
| 4.7 | 1.5476 | 1.5497 | 1.5518 | 1.5539 | 1.5560 | 1.5581 | 1.5602 | 1.5623 | 1.5644 | 1.5665 |
| 4.8 | 1.5686 | 1.5707 | 1.5728 | 1.5748 | 1.5769 | 1.5790 | 1.5810 | 1.5831 | 1.5851 | 1.5872 |
| 4.9 | 1.5892 | 1.5913 | 1.5933 | 1.5953 | 1.5974 | 1.5994 | 1.6014 | 1.6034 | 1.6054 | 1.6074 |
| **5.0** | 1.6094 | 1.6114 | 1.6134 | 1.6154 | 1.6174 | 1.6194 | 1.6214 | 1.6233 | 1.6253 | 1.6273 |
| 5.1 | 1.6292 | 1.6312 | 1.6332 | 1.6351 | 1.6371 | 1.6390 | 1.6409 | 1.6429 | 1.6448 | 1.6467 |
| 5.2 | 1.6487 | 1.6506 | 1.6525 | 1.6544 | 1.6563 | 1.6582 | 1.6601 | 1.6620 | 1.6639 | 1.6658 |
| 5.3 | 1.6677 | 1.6696 | 1.6715 | 1.6734 | 1.6752 | 1.6771 | 1.6790 | 1.6808 | 1.6827 | 1.6845 |
| 5.4 | 1.6864 | 1.6882 | 1.6901 | 1.6919 | 1.6938 | 1.6956 | 1.6974 | 1.6993 | 1.7011 | 1.7029 |
| **5.5** | 1.7047 | 1.7066 | 1.7084 | 1.7102 | 1.7120 | 1.7138 | 1.7156 | 1.7174 | 1.7192 | 1.7210 |
| N | .00 | .01 | .02 | .03 | .04 | .05 | .06 | .07 | .08 | .09 |

# Table 5. Four-place Natural Logarithms
## 5.50-10.09

| N | .00 | .01 | .02 | .03 | .04 | .05 | .06 | .07 | .08 | .09 |
|---|------|------|------|------|------|------|------|------|------|------|
| 5.5 | 1.7047 | 1.7066 | 1.7084 | 1.7102 | 1.7120 | 1.7138 | 1.7156 | 1.7174 | 1.7192 | 1.7210 |
| 5.6 | 1.7228 | 1.7246 | 1.7263 | 1.7281 | 1.7299 | 1.7317 | 1.7334 | 1.7352 | 1.7370 | 1.7387 |
| 5.7 | 1.7405 | 1.7422 | 1.7440 | 1.7457 | 1.7475 | 1.7492 | 1.7509 | 1.7527 | 1.7544 | 1.7561 |
| 5.8 | 1.7579 | 1.7596 | 1.7613 | 1.7630 | 1.7647 | 1.7664 | 1.7681 | 1.7699 | 1.7716 | 1.7733 |
| 5.9 | 1.7750 | 1.7766 | 1.7783 | 1.7800 | 1.7817 | 1.7834 | 1.7851 | 1.7867 | 1.7884 | 1.7901 |
| 6.0 | 1.7918 | 1.7934 | 1.7951 | 1.7967 | 1.7984 | 1.8001 | 1.8017 | 1.8034 | 1.8050 | 1.8066 |
| 6.1 | 1.8083 | 1.8099 | 1.8116 | 1.8132 | 1.8148 | 1.8165 | 1.8181 | 1.8197 | 1.8213 | 1.8229 |
| 6.2 | 1.8245 | 1.8262 | 1.8278 | 1.8294 | 1.8310 | 1.8326 | 1.8342 | 1.8358 | 1.8374 | 1.8390 |
| 6.3 | 1.8405 | 1.8421 | 1.8437 | 1.8453 | 1.8469 | 1.8485 | 1.8500 | 1.8516 | 1.8532 | 1.8547 |
| 6.4 | 1.8563 | 1.8579 | 1.8594 | 1.8610 | 1.8625 | 1.8641 | 1.8656 | 1.8672 | 1.8687 | 1.8703 |
| 6.5 | 1.8718 | 1.8733 | 1.8749 | 1.8764 | 1.8779 | 1.8795 | 1.8810 | 1.8825 | 1.8840 | 1.8856 |
| 6.6 | 1.8871 | 1.8886 | 1.8901 | 1.8916 | 1.8931 | 1.8946 | 1.8961 | 1.8976 | 1.8991 | 1.9006 |
| 6.7 | 1.9021 | 1.9036 | 1.9051 | 1.9066 | 1.9081 | 1.9095 | 1.9110 | 1.9125 | 1.9140 | 1.9155 |
| 6.8 | 1.9169 | 1.9184 | 1.9199 | 1.9213 | 1.9228 | 1.9242 | 1.9257 | 1.9272 | 1.9286 | 1.9301 |
| 6.9 | 1.9315 | 1.9330 | 1.9344 | 1.9359 | 1.9373 | 1.9387 | 1.9402 | 1.9416 | 1.9430 | 1.9445 |
| 7.0 | 1.9459 | 1.9473 | 1.9488 | 1.9502 | 1.9516 | 1.9530 | 1.9544 | 1.9559 | 1.9573 | 1.9587 |
| 7.1 | 1.9601 | 1.9615 | 1.9629 | 1.9643 | 1.9657 | 1.9671 | 1.9685 | 1.9699 | 1.9713 | 1.9727 |
| 7.2 | 1.9741 | 1.9755 | 1.9769 | 1.9782 | 1.9796 | 1.9810 | 1.9824 | 1.9838 | 1.9851 | 1.9865 |
| 7.3 | 1.9879 | 1.9892 | 1.9906 | 1.9920 | 1.9933 | 1.9947 | 1.9961 | 1.9974 | 1.9988 | 2.0001 |
| 7.4 | 2.0015 | 2.0028 | 2.0042 | 2.0055 | 2.0069 | 2.0082 | 2.0096 | 2.0109 | 2.0122 | 2.0136 |
| 7.5 | 2.0149 | 2.0162 | 2.0176 | 2.0189 | 2.0202 | 2.0215 | 2.0229 | 2.0242 | 2.0255 | 2.0268 |
| 7.6 | 2.0281 | 2.0295 | 2.0308 | 2.0321 | 2.0334 | 2.0347 | 2.0360 | 2.0373 | 2.0386 | 2.0399 |
| 7.7 | 2.0412 | 2.0425 | 2.0438 | 2.0451 | 2.0464 | 2.0477 | 2.0490 | 2.0503 | 2.0516 | 2.0528 |
| 7.8 | 2.0541 | 2.0554 | 2.0567 | 2.0580 | 2.0592 | 2.0605 | 2.0618 | 2.0631 | 2.0643 | 2.0656 |
| 7.9 | 2.0669 | 2.0681 | 2.0694 | 2.0707 | 2.0719 | 2.0732 | 2.0744 | 2.0757 | 2.0769 | 2.0782 |
| 8.0 | 2.0794 | 2.0807 | 2.0819 | 2.0832 | 2.0844 | 2.0857 | 2.0869 | 2.0882 | 2.0894 | 2.0906 |
| 8.1 | 2.0919 | 2.0931 | 2.0943 | 2.0956 | 2.0968 | 2.0980 | 2.0992 | 2.1005 | 2.1017 | 2.1029 |
| 8.2 | 2.1041 | 2.1054 | 2.1066 | 2.1078 | 2.1090 | 2.1102 | 2.1114 | 2.1126 | 2.1138 | 2.1150 |
| 8.3 | 2.1163 | 2.1175 | 2.1187 | 2.1199 | 2.1211 | 2.1223 | 2.1235 | 2.1247 | 2.1258 | 2.1270 |
| 8.4 | 2.1282 | 2.1294 | 2.1306 | 2.1318 | 2.1330 | 2.1342 | 2.1353 | 2.1365 | 2.1377 | 2.1389 |
| 8.5 | 2.1401 | 2.1412 | 2.1424 | 2.1436 | 2.1448 | 2.1459 | 2.1471 | 2.1483 | 2.1494 | 2.1506 |
| 8.6 | 2.1518 | 2.1529 | 2.1541 | 2.1552 | 2.1564 | 2.1576 | 2.1587 | 2.1599 | 2.1610 | 2.1622 |
| 8.7 | 2.1633 | 2.1645 | 2.1656 | 2.1668 | 2.1679 | 2.1691 | 2.1702 | 2.1713 | 2.1725 | 2.1736 |
| 8.8 | 2.1748 | 2.1759 | 2.1770 | 2.1782 | 2.1793 | 2.1804 | 2.1815 | 2.1827 | 2.1838 | 2.1849 |
| 8.9 | 2.1861 | 2.1872 | 2.1883 | 2.1894 | 2.1905 | 2.1917 | 2.1928 | 2.1939 | 2.1950 | 2.1961 |
| 9.0 | 2.1972 | 2.1983 | 2.1994 | 2.2006 | 2.2017 | 2.2028 | 2.2039 | 2.2050 | 2.2061 | 2.2072 |
| 9.1 | 2.2083 | 2.2094 | 2.2105 | 2.2116 | 2.2127 | 2.2138 | 2.2148 | 2.2159 | 2.2170 | 2.2181 |
| 9.2 | 2.2192 | 2.2203 | 2.2214 | 2.2225 | 2.2235 | 2.2246 | 2.2257 | 2.2268 | 2.2279 | 2.2289 |
| 9.3 | 2.2300 | 2.2311 | 2.2322 | 2.2332 | 2.2343 | 2.2354 | 2.2364 | 2.2375 | 2.2386 | 2.2396 |
| 9.4 | 2.2407 | 2.2418 | 2.2428 | 2.2439 | 2.2450 | 2.2460 | 2.2471 | 2.2481 | 2.2492 | 2.2502 |
| 9.5 | 2.2513 | 2.2523 | 2.2534 | 2.2544 | 2.2555 | 2.2565 | 2.2576 | 2.2586 | 2.2597 | 2.2607 |
| 9.6 | 2.2618 | 2.2628 | 2.2638 | 2.2649 | 2.2659 | 2.2670 | 2.2680 | 2.2690 | 2.2701 | 2.2711 |
| 9.7 | 2.2721 | 2.2732 | 2.2742 | 2.2752 | 2.2762 | 2.2773 | 2.2783 | 2.2793 | 2.2803 | 2.2814 |
| 9.8 | 2.2824 | 2.2834 | 2.2844 | 2.2854 | 2.2865 | 2.2875 | 2.2885 | 2.2895 | 2.2905 | 2.2915 |
| 9.9 | 2.2925 | 2.2935 | 2.2946 | 2.2956 | 2.2966 | 2.2976 | 2.2986 | 2.2996 | 2.3006 | 2.3016 |
| 10.0 | 2.3026 | 2.3036 | 2.3046 | 2.3056 | 2.3066 | 2.3076 | 2.3086 | 2.3096 | 2.3106 | 2.3115 |
| N | .00 | .01 | .02 | .03 | .04 | .05 | .06 | .07 | .08 | .09 |

# Table 6. Exponential and Hyperbolic Functions
## 0.00-0.50

| x | $e^x$ | $e^{-x}$ | Sinh x | Cosh x | Tanh x | x |
|---|---|---|---|---|---|---|
| **0.00** | 1.0000 | 1.00000 | .00000 | 1.0000 | .00000 | **0.00** |
| 0.01 | 1.0101 | 0.99005 | .01000 | 1.0001 | .01000 | 0.01 |
| 0.02 | 1.0202 | .98020 | .02000 | 1.0002 | .02000 | 0.02 |
| 0.03 | 1.0305 | .97045 | .03000 | 1.0005 | .02999 | 0.03 |
| 0.04 | 1.0408 | .96079 | .04001 | 1.0008 | .03998 | 0.04 |
| **0.05** | 1.0513 | .95123 | .05002 | 1.0013 | .04996 | **0.05** |
| 0.06 | 1.0618 | .94176 | .06004 | 1.0018 | .05993 | 0.06 |
| 0.07 | 1.0725 | .93239 | .07006 | 1.0025 | .06989 | 0.07 |
| 0.08 | 1.0833 | .92312 | .08009 | 1.0032 | .07983 | 0.08 |
| 0.09 | 1.0942 | .91393 | .09012 | 1.0041 | .08976 | 0.09 |
| **0.10** | 1.1052 | .90484 | .10017 | 1.0050 | .09967 | **0.10** |
| 0.11 | 1.1163 | .89583 | .11022 | 1.0061 | .10956 | 0.11 |
| 0.12 | 1.1275 | .88692 | .12029 | 1.0072 | .11943 | 0.12 |
| 0.13 | 1.1388 | .87810 | .13037 | 1.0085 | .12927 | 0.13 |
| 0.14 | 1.1503 | .86936 | .14046 | 1.0098 | .13909 | 0.14 |
| **0.15** | 1.1618 | .86071 | .15056 | 1.0113 | .14889 | **0.15** |
| 0.16 | 1.1735 | .85214 | .16068 | 1.0128 | .15865 | 0.16 |
| 0.17 | 1.1853 | .84366 | .17082 | 1.0145 | .16838 | 0.17 |
| 0.18 | 1.1972 | .83527 | .18097 | 1.0162 | .17808 | 0.18 |
| 0.19 | 1.2092 | .82696 | .19115 | 1.0181 | .18775 | 0.19 |
| **0.20** | 1.2214 | .81873 | .20134 | 1.0201 | .19738 | **0.20** |
| 0.21 | 1.2337 | .81058 | .21155 | 1.0221 | .20697 | 0.21 |
| 0.22 | 1.2461 | .80252 | .22178 | 1.0243 | .21652 | 0.22 |
| 0.23 | 1.2586 | .79453 | .23203 | 1.0266 | .22603 | 0.23 |
| 0.24 | 1.2712 | .78663 | .24231 | 1.0289 | .23550 | 0.24 |
| **0.25** | 1.2840 | .77880 | .25261 | 1.0314 | .24492 | **0.25** |
| 0.26 | 1.2969 | .77105 | .26294 | 1.0340 | .25430 | 0.26 |
| 0.27 | 1.3100 | .76338 | .27329 | 1.0367 | .26362 | 0.27 |
| 0.28 | 1.3231 | .75578 | .28367 | 1.0395 | .27291 | 0.28 |
| 0.29 | 1.3364 | .74826 | .29408 | 1.0423 | .28213 | 0.29 |
| **0.30** | 1.3499 | .74082 | .30452 | 1.0453 | .29131 | **0.30** |
| 0.31 | 1.3634 | .73345 | .31499 | 1.0484 | .30044 | 0.31 |
| 0.32 | 1.3771 | .72615 | .32549 | 1.0516 | .30951 | 0.32 |
| 0.33 | 1.3910 | .71892 | .33602 | 1.0549 | .31852 | 0.33 |
| 0.34 | 1.4049 | .71177 | .34659 | 1.0584 | .32748 | 0.34 |
| **0.35** | 1.4191 | .70469 | .35719 | 1.0619 | .33638 | **0.35** |
| 0.36 | 1.4333 | .69768 | .36783 | 1.0655 | .34521 | 0.36 |
| 0.37 | 1.4477 | .69073 | .37850 | 1.0692 | .35399 | 0.37 |
| 0.38 | 1.4623 | .68386 | .38921 | 1.0731 | .36271 | 0.38 |
| 0.39 | 1.4770 | .67706 | .39996 | 1.0770 | .37136 | 0.39 |
| **0.40** | 1.4918 | .67032 | .41075 | 1.0811 | .37995 | **0.40** |
| 0.41 | 1.5068 | .66365 | .42158 | 1.0852 | .38847 | 0.41 |
| 0.42 | 1.5220 | .65705 | .43246 | 1.0895 | .39693 | 0.42 |
| 0.43 | 1.5373 | .65051 | .44337 | 1.0939 | .40532 | 0.43 |
| 0.44 | 1.5527 | .64404 | .45434 | 1.0984 | .41364 | 0.44 |
| **0.45** | 1.5683 | .63763 | .46534 | 1.1030 | .42190 | **0.45** |
| 0.46 | 1.5841 | .63128 | .47640 | 1.1077 | .43008 | 0.46 |
| 0.47 | 1.6000 | .62500 | .48750 | 1.1125 | .43820 | 0.47 |
| 0.48 | 1.6161 | .61878 | .49865 | 1.1174 | .44624 | 0.48 |
| 0.49 | 1.6323 | .61263 | .50984 | 1.1225 | .45422 | 0.49 |
| **0.50** | 1.6487 | .60653 | .52110 | 1.1276 | .46212 | **0.50** |
| x | $e^x$ | $e^{-x}$ | Sinh x | Cosh x | Tanh x | x |

# Table 6. Exponential and Hyperbolic Functions
## 0.50-1.00

| x | $e^x$ | $e^{-x}$ | Sinh x | Cosh x | Tanh x | x |
|---|---|---|---|---|---|---|
| **0.50** | 1.6487 | .60653 | .52110 | 1.1276 | .46212 | **0.50** |
| 0.51 | 1.6653 | .60050 | .53240 | 1.1329 | .46995 | 0.51 |
| 0.52 | 1.6820 | .59452 | .54375 | 1.1383 | .47770 | 0.52 |
| 0.53 | 1.6989 | .58860 | .55516 | 1.1438 | .48538 | 0.53 |
| 0.54 | 1.7160 | .58275 | .56663 | 1.1494 | .49299 | 0.54 |
| **0.55** | 1.7333 | .57695 | .57815 | 1.1551 | .50052 | **0.55** |
| 0.56 | 1.7507 | .57121 | .58973 | 1.1609 | .50798 | 0.56 |
| 0.57 | 1.7683 | .56553 | .60137 | 1.1669 | .51536 | 0.57 |
| 0.58 | 1.7860 | .55990 | .61307 | 1.1730 | .52267 | 0.58 |
| 0.59 | 1.8040 | .55433 | .62483 | 1.1792 | .52990 | 0.59 |
| **0.60** | 1.8221 | .54881 | .63665 | 1.1855 | .53705 | **0.60** |
| 0.61 | 1.8404 | .54335 | .64854 | 1.1919 | .54413 | 0.61 |
| 0.62 | 1.8589 | .53794 | .66049 | 1.1984 | .55113 | 0.62 |
| 0.63 | 1.8776 | .53259 | .67251 | 1.2051 | .55805 | 0.63 |
| 0.64 | 1.8965 | .52729 | .68459 | 1.2119 | .56490 | 0.64 |
| **0.65** | 1.9155 | .52205 | .69675 | 1.2188 | .57167 | **0.65** |
| 0.66 | 1.9348 | .51685 | .70897 | 1.2258 | .57836 | 0.66 |
| 0.67 | 1.9542 | .51171 | .72126 | 1.2330 | .58498 | 0.67 |
| 0.68 | 1.9739 | .50662 | .73363 | 1.2402 | .59152 | 0.68 |
| 0.69 | 1.9937 | .50158 | .74607 | 1.2476 | .59798 | 0.69 |
| **0.70** | 2.0138 | .49659 | .75858 | 1.2552 | .60437 | **0.70** |
| 0.71 | 2.0340 | .49164 | .77117 | 1.2628 | .61068 | 0.71 |
| 0.72 | 2.0544 | .48675 | .78384 | 1.2706 | .61691 | 0.72 |
| 0.73 | 2.0751 | .48191 | .79659 | 1.2785 | .62307 | 0.73 |
| 0.74 | 2.0959 | .47711 | .80941 | 1.2865 | .62915 | 0.74 |
| **0.75** | 2.1170 | .47237 | .82232 | 1.2947 | .63515 | **0.75** |
| 0.76 | 2.1383 | .46767 | .83530 | 1.3030 | .64108 | 0.76 |
| 0.77 | 2.1598 | .46301 | .84838 | 1.3114 | .64693 | 0.77 |
| 0.78 | 2.1815 | .45841 | .86153 | 1.3199 | .65271 | 0.78 |
| 0.79 | 2.2034 | .45384 | .87478 | 1.3286 | .65841 | 0.79 |
| **0.80** | 2.2255 | .44933 | .88811 | 1.3374 | .66404 | **0.80** |
| 0.81 | 2.2479 | .44486 | .90152 | 1.3464 | .66959 | 0.81 |
| 0.82 | 2.2705 | .44043 | .91503 | 1.3555 | .67507 | 0.82 |
| 0.83 | 2.2933 | .43605 | .92863 | 1.3647 | .68048 | 0.83 |
| 0.84 | 2.3164 | .43171 | .94233 | 1.3740 | .68581 | 0.84 |
| **0.85** | 2.3396 | .42741 | .95612 | 1.3835 | .69107 | **0.85** |
| 0.86 | 2.3632 | .42316 | .97000 | 1.3932 | .69626 | 0.86 |
| 0.87 | 2.3869 | .41895 | .98398 | 1.4029 | .70137 | 0.87 |
| 0.88 | 2.4109 | .41478 | .99806 | 1.4128 | .70642 | 0.88 |
| 0.89 | 2.4351 | .41066 | 1.0122 | 1.4229 | .71139 | 0.89 |
| **0.90** | 2.4596 | .40657 | 1.0265 | 1.4331 | .71630 | **0.90** |
| 0.91 | 2.4843 | .40252 | 1.0409 | 1.4434 | .72113 | 0.91 |
| 0.92 | 2.5093 | .39852 | 1.0554 | 1.4539 | .72590 | 0.92 |
| 0.93 | 2.5345 | .39455 | 1.0700 | 1.4645 | .73059 | 0.93 |
| 0.94 | 2.5600 | .39063 | 1.0847 | 1.4753 | .73522 | 0.94 |
| **0.95** | 2.5857 | .38674 | 1.0995 | 1.4862 | .73978 | **0.95** |
| 0.96 | 2.6117 | .38289 | 1.1144 | 1.4973 | .74428 | 0.96 |
| 0.97 | 2.6379 | .37908 | 1.1294 | 1.5085 | .74870 | 0.97 |
| 0.98 | 2.6645 | .37531 | 1.1446 | 1.5199 | .75307 | 0.98 |
| 0.99 | 2.6912 | .37158 | 1.1598 | 1.5314 | .75736 | 0.99 |
| **1.00** | 2.7183 | .36788 | 1.1752 | 1.5431 | .76159 | **1.00** |
| x | $e^x$ | $e^{-x}$ | Sinh x | Cosh x | Tanh x | x |

# ANSWERS, HINTS, AND SOLUTIONS
## TO ODD-NUMBERED PROBLEMS

(Some answers have intentionally been omitted.)

### Exercises 1.2, Pages 6–7

**1. (a)** Yes. It is a consequence of the definitions that $4! = 4(3!)$, $3! = 3(2!)$, $2! = 2(1!)$, and $1! = 1$. Hence, $4! = 4 \cdot 3 \cdot 2 \cdot 1$.

**(b)** No. The restriction $n = 2, 3, 4, \ldots$ leaves $0!$ undefined.

**(c)** The only correct statement is $\dfrac{10!}{8!} \neq \dfrac{10}{8}$. A consequence of the definition is that $\dfrac{10!}{8!} = 10 \cdot 9$, but it is not correct to use the symbol $.=.$ here.

**3. (a)** The implication is not valid. The two lines determine a plane that is perpendicular to the given line. Every line that lies in the plane and passes through the foot of the perpendicular is perpendicular to the given line.

**(b)** The implication is valid. This is a basic theorem in plane geometry.

**(c)** The implication is not valid. The diagonals of a parallelogram bisect each other whether the parallelogram is a rhombus or not.

**(e)** The implication is valid. This can be seen by writing $2 = 1$ and $1 = 2$ and multiplying these two equations together to get $2 = 2$.

**5. (a)** Converse: $ab = 12 \Rightarrow a = 3$ and $b = 4$. This is not valid since $a = 3$, $b = 4$ is not the only pair of numbers whose product is 12.

**(c)** Converse: The corresponding angles of two triangles are equal $\Rightarrow$ the triangles are congruent. This is not a valid implication since the triangles may be similar but different in size.

**(e)** Converse: $x^2 = 9 \Rightarrow x = 3$. This is not a valid implication since $x$ may be $-3$.

**(g)** Converse: One angle of a triangle is equal to an angle of another triangle $\Rightarrow$ the remaining two angles of the first triangle are equal respectively to the remaining two angles of the second triangle. This is obviously not valid.

### Exercises 1.4, Pages 10–11

**1. (a)** *Converse:* Two triangles have corresponding angles equal $\Rightarrow$ the triangles are congruent. False.
*Contrapositive:* Two triangles do not have corresponding angles equal $\Rightarrow$ the triangles are not congruent. True.

**(c)** *Converse:* $x^2 = 4 \Rightarrow x = 2$. False.
*Contrapositive:* $x^2 \neq 4 \Rightarrow x \neq 2$. True.

**3.** Suppose there are $n - 1$ lines, and $A_{n-1}$ regions. The $n$th line cuts each of $n$ regions into two new regions and thus adds $n$ new regions. Therefore,

$$A_n = A_{n-1} + n$$
$$\Rightarrow A_2 = A_1 + 2 = 2 + 2 = 4$$
$$A_3 = A_2 + 3 = 7$$
$$\cdots\cdots\cdots\cdots\cdots\cdots\cdots\cdots\cdots\cdots\cdots\cdots$$
$$A_n = 2 + 2 + 3 + 4 + 5 + \cdots + n$$
$$= 1 + (1 + 2 + 3 + 4 + \cdots + n) = 1 + \frac{n(n+1)}{2}.$$

**5.** Yes. Suppose $m$ is a divisor of $n$. Then, $n/m$ is also a divisor of $n$. These divisors occur in pairs unless $n$ is a perfect square, say $n = k^2$. Then $k = n/k$ and the total number of distinct divisors is odd.

**7.** Assume $(a/b)^2 = 3$, $a$ and $b$ have no common factor. Then $a^2 = 3b^2 \Rightarrow a = 3c$ since only multiples of 3 have squares that are multiples of 3, and

$$9c^2 = 3b^2 \Rightarrow 3c^2 = b^2 \Rightarrow b = 3d$$

so that $a$ and $b$ have 3 as a common factor. This is a contradiction.

**9.** Since $m$ cannot be divisible by any of the first $n$ primes, it either has a prime factor greater than $p_n$ or is itself a prime greater than $p_n$. Hence $p_n$ cannot be the greatest prime.

## Exercises 1.5, page 16

**1.** (a) $\{2, 4, 6, 8, 10\}$ ; (c) $\{31, 37\}$.
**3.** (a) $\mathfrak{A} \not\subset \mathfrak{B}$; $\mathfrak{B} \not\subset \mathfrak{A}$; no; no; (c) $\mathfrak{A} \subset \mathfrak{B}$; $\mathfrak{B} \subset \mathfrak{A}$; no; no.  **5.** (a) No.
**7.** Since the empty set is a subset of every set, $\varnothing \subset \varnothing'$ and $\varnothing' \subset \varnothing$. Therefore, $\varnothing = \varnothing'$.

## Exercises 1.6, Pages 19–20

**1.** (a) $\{b, c\}$ ; (c) $\{c, d\}$ ; (e) $\{c, d, e, f, g, h\}$ ; (g) $\varnothing$; (i) $\{c, d\}$ ; (k) $\{b, c, h\}$.
**3.** (d) $\mathfrak{A} \cap \mathfrak{A}' = \varnothing$; (f) $\mathfrak{A} \cap \mathfrak{A} = \mathfrak{A}$; (i) $(\mathfrak{A}')' = \mathfrak{A}$; (k) $(\mathfrak{A} - \mathfrak{B}) \cup \mathfrak{B} = \mathfrak{A} \cup \mathfrak{B}$;
(m) $\mathfrak{A} \cap (\mathfrak{A} - \mathfrak{B}) = \mathfrak{A} - \mathfrak{B}$; (n) $(\mathfrak{A} - \mathfrak{B})' = \mathfrak{A}' \cup \mathfrak{B}$.
**5.** (a) $(x \in \mathfrak{A} \cup \mathfrak{B}) \Rightarrow (x \in \mathfrak{A} \text{ and/or } x \in \mathfrak{B}) \Rightarrow (x \in \mathfrak{C} \text{ and/or } x \in \mathfrak{D}) \Rightarrow x \in \mathfrak{C} \cup \mathfrak{D}$.
 Therefore $\qquad \mathfrak{A} \cup \mathfrak{B} \subset \mathfrak{C} \cup \mathfrak{D}$.
 (b) $(x \in \mathfrak{A} \cap \mathfrak{B}) \Rightarrow (x \in \mathfrak{A} \text{ and } x \in \mathfrak{B}) \Rightarrow (x \in \mathfrak{C} \text{ and } x \in \mathfrak{D}) \Rightarrow x \in \mathfrak{C} \cap \mathfrak{D}$.
 Therefore $\qquad \mathfrak{A} \cap \mathfrak{B} \subset \mathfrak{C} \cap \mathfrak{D}$.

## Exercises 1.7, Pages 25–26

**1.** Yes. The set is closed with respect to addition. Addition is associative. The additive identity, zero, is an element of the set. The additive inverse of each element is an element of the set.

**3.** Yes for both questions. *Hint:* $\dfrac{1}{a + b\sqrt{2}} = \dfrac{a - b\sqrt{2}}{a^2 - 2b^2}$, and the denominator cannot be zero since $a, b \in \mathfrak{F}$.

**5.** No. Try multiplying two numbers of this form.
**7.** $\frac{2}{7}$.  **9.** $\frac{98}{99}$.  **11.** $\frac{13}{99}$.  **13.** $0.6\overline{0}$.

**15.** $\frac{22}{7} = 3.\overline{142854}$, $\pi = 3.1415926\ldots$.

**17.** $0.\overline{1}$.      **19.** $0.\overline{20} = \frac{20}{99}$, $0.\overline{03} = \frac{3}{99}$, $0.\overline{23} = \frac{23}{99}$.

**21.** $S \subset \mathfrak{F}$. l.u.b. $= \frac{3}{2} \in \mathfrak{F}$.      **23.** $S \subset \mathfrak{F}$. l.u.b. $= \sqrt{5} \notin \mathfrak{F}$.

**25.** No. For example, $\sqrt{2} + (3 - \sqrt{2}) = 3$ and $(1 + \sqrt{2})(1 - \sqrt{2}) = -1$.

### Exercises 1.8, Pages 30–31

**7.** $-1 + 9i$.   **9.** $11 + 2i$.   **11.** $x^2 + y^2$.   **13.** $2 - 2i$.   **15.** $-\frac{1}{25} + \frac{32}{25}i$.

**17.** $-\frac{7}{25} + \frac{24}{25}i$.   **19.** $2i$.   **21.** $\frac{42}{29} - \frac{40}{29}i$.

### Exercises 1.9, Pages 38–39

**1.** (a) $r(x) = 0$, $s(x) = 2x^2 - x + 3$; (b) $r(x) = x + 1$, $s(x) = \frac{3}{2}x + 1$.

**3.** $-1$; $-9$.   **5.** $152$; $37$.   **7.** $0$; $320$.   **9.** $-326$; $4$.   **11.** $2$ is a zero.   **13.** $2$ is not a zero.   **15.** $A = 2$, $B = 1$, $C = -2$.   **17.** $A = 2$, $B = -24$, $C = -60$, $D = 83$.

**19.** $-1$, $-2$.   **21.** $-2$, $1$.   **23.** $-2i$, $2$, $-1$.   **25.** $2 - i$, $-2$, $1$.   **27.** $-2$, $-2$.

**29.** $2 - \sqrt{3}$, $-2$, $-1$.   **31.** *Hint:* To show that $d$ is a divisor of $a_0$, substitute $c/d$ in the equation and multiply both sides by $d^{n-1}$. All the terms, except possibly the first, are integers. Can the left side be zero if the first term is not an integer? Use a similar argument to show that $c$ is a divisor of $a_n$.

### Exercises 1.10, Pages 43–44

**5.** *Hint:* Add corresponding members of the inequalities

$$(a - b)^2 \geqq 0, \quad (b - c)^2 \geqq 0, \quad (c - a)^2 \geqq 0.$$

**7.** $\sqrt{15} - \sqrt{5} > 3 - \sqrt{2}$.      **9.** $\sqrt{19} - \sqrt{14} < \sqrt{29} - \sqrt{22}$.

**11.** $a > b > 0 \Rightarrow a^2 > b^2$ (Theorem 1.10e). Assume $a^k > b^k$. Then, by Theorem 1.10e,

$$a \cdot a^k > b \cdot b^k \Rightarrow a^{k+1} > b^{k+1}.$$

This completes the proof by mathematical induction.

**13.** $a < b \Rightarrow b = a + p$, $p > 0 \Rightarrow -a = -b + p \Rightarrow -a > -b$.

**15.** False. Try it for $a = 1$, $b = 2$, $c = 3$, $d = 4$.

**17.** Let $a^{1/p} = x$, $b^{1/p} = y$. Then $a = x^p$, $b = y^p$,

$$a > b \Rightarrow x^p > y^p.$$

Suppose $x \leqq y$. Then $x^p \leqq y^p \Rightarrow a \leqq b$, which is a contradiction. Hence, $x > y$, as was to be shown.

**19.** $1 < a \Rightarrow a < a^2 \Rightarrow a^2 < a^3 \Rightarrow \cdots \Rightarrow a^{p-1} < a^p \Rightarrow a < a^p$.

$1 < a < a^p \Rightarrow 1 < a^{1/p} < a$.

**21.** $y = ax^2 + bx + c = a\left(x + \dfrac{b}{2a}\right)^2 + c - \dfrac{b^2}{4a}$. Thus $y > 0$ for all $x \in \mathfrak{R} \Leftrightarrow a > 0$

and $c - \dfrac{b^2}{4a} > 0$, or $a > 0$ and $b^2 - 4ac < 0$.

### Exercises 2.1, Pages 48–49

**1.** (a) $4$, $-4$.      (c) $3$, $+3$.      (f) $\sqrt{3} + \sqrt{6}$, $-\sqrt{6} - \sqrt{3}$.

**5.** (a) $\{x : x < -2\} \cup \{x : x > 5\}$;      (c) $\{x : x \leqq 2\} \cup \{x : x \geqq 4\}$.

**Exercises 2.2, Pages 53–54**

**1. (a)** The points are on a straight line.    **(b)** The points are not on a straight line.
**3.** The quadrilateral is a parallelogram.
**5.** The triangle is a right triangle because the sides satisfy the Pythagorean Theorem.
**7.** $(4, 5)$, $(4, -1)$, $(-2, 7)$.        **11. (a)** $(\frac{1}{5}, -\frac{2}{5})$. **(d)** $(-7, \frac{19}{2})$.
**9.** $(-1, -2)$.                                **13.** $(4, 7)$, $(8, 1)$, $(2, -3)$.

**Exercises 2.3, Pages 58–59**

**1.** *Domain:* $\{1, 2, 3, 4\}$, *range:* $\{1, 2, 3\}$.
**3.** *Domain:* $\{1, 2, 3, 4, 5, 6, 7, 8, 9, 10\}$, *range:* $\{1, 4, 9, 16, 25, 36, 49, 64, 81, 100\}$.
**5.** *Domain:* $\{0, 1, 4, 9, 16, 25, 36, 49, 64, 81, 100\}$,
    *range:* $\{0, \pm1, \pm2, \pm3, \pm4, \pm5, \pm6, \pm7, \pm8, \pm9, \pm10\}$.
**7.** *Domain:* $\mathcal{R}$, *range:* $\mathcal{R}$.
**9.** *Domain:* $\{x: 0 \leq x \leq 2\}$, *range:* $\{y: 0 \leq y \leq 5\}$.
**11.** *Domain:* $\{x: 0 \leq x \leq 2\}$, *range:* $\{y: 0 \leq y \leq 4\}$.
**13.** *Domain:* $\{x: 0 < x \leq 3\}$, *range:* $\{y: y > \frac{1}{2}\}$.
**15.** *Domain:* $\{-\frac{4}{5}, \frac{4}{5}\}$, *range:* $\{\frac{3}{5}\}$.
**17. (a)** $\{(2, 3), (4, 3), (2, 5), (6, 3)\}$. **(b)** $2^3 = 8$.         **19.** *Domain:* $\mathcal{R}$, *range:* $\mathcal{R}$.
**21.** *Domain:* $\{x: -2 \leq x \leq 2\}$, *range:* $\{y: -2 \leq y \leq 0\}$.
**23.** *Domain:* $\mathcal{R} - \{0\}$, *range:* $\mathcal{R} - \{0\}$.     **25.** *Domain:* $\mathcal{R} - \{2\}$, *range:* $\mathcal{R} - \{4\}$.
**27.** Not a function. There are two values of $y$ for each $x > 0$.
**29.** *Domain:* $\mathcal{R}$, *range:* $\{y: y \leq 1\}$.
**31.** Not a function. There are two values of $y$ for each value of $x \in \{x: -3 < x < 2\}$.
**33.** $-1$; undefined; $\dfrac{h}{1 - 4h}$; $\dfrac{x}{1 - 4x}$.     **35.** $2x + 2h + 3$; $\dfrac{2}{x} + 3$.
**37.** $-3$; $-3$; $\frac{27}{20}$.

**Exercises 2.4, Page 64**

**1.** *Domain:* $\{-3, -2, -1, 0, 1, 2, 3\}$, *range:* $\{0, 1, 2, 3\}$. Not a function. Symmetry
    with respect to the $y$-axis.
**3.** *Domain:* $\mathcal{R}$, *range:* $\mathcal{R}$. A function. Symmetry with respect to the origin.
**5.** *Domain:* $\{-4\}$, *range:* $\mathcal{R}$. Not a function. Symmetry with respect to the $x$-axis.
**7.** *Domain:* $\{x: x \leq 0\}$, *range:* $\mathcal{R}$. Not a function. Symmetry with respect to the
    $x$-axis.
**9.** *Domain:* $\mathcal{R}$, *range:* $\{y: y \leq 4\}$. A function. Symmetry with respect to the $y$-axis.
**11.** *Domain:* $\mathcal{R}$, *range:* $\{y: y \geq 0\}$. A function. Symmetry with respect to the $y$-axis.
**13.** *Domain:* $\mathcal{R}$, *range:* $\{y: y \geq 0\}$. A function. No symmetry.
**15.** *Domain:* $\{x: -4 \leq x \leq 4\}$, *range:* $\{y: -4 \leq y \leq 4\}$. Not a function. Sym-
    metry with respect to both axes and the origin.
**17.** Satisfied by no real $(x, y)$.
**19.** *Domain:* $\mathcal{R}$, *range:* $\{y: |y| \geq \sqrt{2}\}$. Not a function. Symmetry with respect to
    both axes and the origin.
**21.** *Domain:* $\mathcal{R}$, *range:* $\mathcal{R}$. Not a function. Symmetry with respect to the line $y = -x$.
**23.** *Domain:* $\{0\}$, *range:* $\{1\}$. A function.
**25.** *Domain:* $\mathcal{R}$, *range:* $\mathcal{R}$. Not a function. Symmetry with respect to the line $y = x$.

**Exercises 2.5, Pages 68–69**

1. *Domain:* $\mathcal{R}$, *range:* $\mathcal{I}$. No symmetry with respect to the axes or the origin.
3. *Domain:* $\{x: |x| \geqq 2\}$, *range:* $\{y: y \geqq 0\}$. Symmetry with respect to the $y$-axis.
5. *Domain:* $\mathcal{R}$, *range:* $\{y: y \geqq 0\}$. No symmetry with respect to the axes or the origin.
7. *Domain:* $\mathcal{R}$, *range:* $\{y: -1 < y \leqq 0\}$. No symmetry. Periodic with period 1.
9. *Domain:* $\mathcal{R}$, *range:* $\{-1, 0\}$. No symmetry with respect to the axes or the origin.
11. *Domain:* $\mathcal{R}$, *range:*
$$\{y: 0 \leqq y < 1\} \cup \{y: -2 \leqq y < -1\} \cup \{y: -4 \leqq y < -3\} \cup \cdots$$
$$\cup \{y: -2n \leqq y < -2n + 1\} \cup \cdots, \qquad n = 1, 2, 3, \ldots.$$
No symmetry.
13. *Domain:* $\mathcal{R}$, *range:* $\{-1, 0, 1\}$. Symmetry with respect to the origin.
15. *Domain:* $\mathcal{R}$, *range:* $\{y: 0 \leqq y < 1\}$. Symmetry with respect to the $y$-axis.
17. *Domain:* $\mathcal{R}$, *range:* $\{y: 0 \leqq y \leqq 1\}$. No symmetry with respect to the axes or the origin.
19. *Domain:* $\mathcal{R}$, *range:* $\{0, 1\}$. No symmetry with respect to the axes or the origin.
21. $L = 1000[U(x) + 2U(x - c) - 3U(x - 2c)]$.

**Exercises 2.6, Pages 72–74**

1. (a) $f^{-1} = \{(10, 1), (20, 2), (30, 3)\}$.
   (c) The inverse relation is $\{(1, 2), (3, 4), (5, 6), (1, 8), (2, 10)\}$. Since there are two distinct pairs, $(1, 2)$ and $(1, 8)$, with the same first number, the inverse relation is not a function.
   (f) $G^{-1} = \{(x, \sqrt{-x}), x \leqq 0\}$.      (h) $F^{-1} = \{(u, v): v = 1 - \frac{1}{2}u\}$.
3. $f = \{(x, y): y = f(x)\} \Rightarrow f^{-1} = \{(y, x): y = f(x)\}$
$$\Rightarrow (f^{-1})^{-1} = \{(x, y): y = f(x)\} = f.$$
5. (a) Let $f(y) = y - (1/y)$, $y \neq 0$, and $g(x) = \sqrt{x}$, $x > 0$. Then $h(x) = f[g(x)]$, $x > 0$.
   (b) Let $f(y) = \sqrt{y}$, $y \geqq 0$, and $g(x) = x/(x - 1)$, $x \leqq 0$ or $x > 1$. Then
$$h(x) = f[g(x)], \qquad x \leqq 0 \text{ or } x > 1.$$
7. (a) $f(x) = x - 2$; (b) $g(x) = 1 + \frac{2}{x}$; (c) $F(x) = (x + 1)^6$; (d) $G(x) = \dfrac{1 - x}{1 + x}$.

9. $g[g(x)] = x^4 + 2x^2 + 2$.      11. $G[H(x)] = \sqrt{\dfrac{4x - 1}{x}}, 0 < x \leqq \dfrac{1}{4}$.

**Exercises 3.1, Pages 78–79**

1. The figure is a trapezoid and includes two right angles.
7. *DE:* $[-5, 12]$, *DF:* $[33, 56]$.
9. *Altitudes:* $[5, 1], [2, -2], [7, -1]$. *Medians:* $[1, 3], [0, 1], [1, -1]$.
11. $-\frac{20}{3}$.      13. $(-3, 0)$ and $(6, 3)$.

**Exercises 3.2, Pages 83–84**

1. (a) $2x + 3y = 5$. (c) $x - y = 1$. (e) $3y = 4x - 12$.      3. $(\frac{7}{8}, 0)$.
5. $(y_2 - y_1)x - (x_2 - x_1)y = x_1y_2 - x_2y_1$.      7. $(\frac{35}{13}, \frac{33}{13})$.

**9.** $2y = 3x + 2$. **11.** $x - x_0 = k(y - y_0)$. **13.** $x = 4t + 2$, $y = -t + 3$.

**15.** No. If the line did pass through $(14, 2)$, there would be a value of $t$ such that $14 = 5 - 3t$ and $2 = -3 + 2t$. But the first of these gives $t = -3$ and the second $t = \frac{5}{2}$.

**17.** $(3, -3)$. 　　　　　　　　　　　　　　**19.** $(-2, -4)$.

**21.** Direction numbers of $ax + by = c_1$ are $[b, -a]$, and of $bx - ay = c_2$ are $[a, b]$. Since $(a)(b) + (b)(-a) = 0$, the lines are perpendicular.

## Exercises 3.3, Pages 87–88

**1. (a)** $m = \frac{2}{3}$, $b = \frac{7}{3}$. **(c)** $m = -30$, $b = 60$. **(f)** $m = -\frac{3}{2}$, $b = 12$.

**3. (a)** $m = -\frac{7}{5}$, $a = \frac{11}{7}$, $b = \frac{11}{5}$. **(c)** $m = 1$, $a = -1$, $b = 1$.

**5.** No. The equation of the line is $y = -4x + 2$, which is not satisfied by $(100, -392)$.

**7.** $\frac{4}{5}\sqrt{5}$. *Hint:* Draw a figure and use the similar right triangles.

**9.** $(-\frac{25}{11}, \frac{7}{11})$. 　　**11.** $(1, \frac{4}{3})$. 　　**13.** Yes. 　　**15.** Yes. $3x + 2y = 22$.

## Exercises 3.4, Pages 91–92

**1.** $\{3, 4\}$. 　**3.** $\{-2, -1, 0\}$. 　**5.** $\{-1, 2, 3\}$. 　**7.** $\{7\}$. 　**9.** $\varnothing$. 　**11.** $\{3\}$. 　**13.** $\varnothing$.

**15.** $\{\frac{1}{4}, \frac{11}{2}\}$. 　**17.** $\{-1 + i, -1 - i\}$. 　**19.** $\left\{\dfrac{3 + \sqrt{41}}{8}, \dfrac{3 - \sqrt{41}}{8}\right\}$.

**21.** $\{-p + \sqrt{p^2 - q}, -p - \sqrt{p^2 - q}\}$. 　**23.** $\{-\sqrt{3}\}$; $-\sqrt{3}$ is a double root.

**25.** $\left\{\dfrac{-1 + \sqrt{321}}{400}, \dfrac{-1 - \sqrt{321}}{400}\right\}$. 　**27.** $-\dfrac{b}{a}$. 　**31.** $x = -\frac{1}{2}, -4$.

**33.** $\{-1 + i, -1 - i, -1 + \sqrt{2}, -1 - \sqrt{2}\}$. 　**35.** $x = -2, 1$. 　**37.** $x = 16$.

**39.** *Hint:* Solve for $x$. 　**41.** $\pm 8\sqrt{2}$. 　**43.** $3y = x^2 + 6x + 15$.

**45.** $\frac{1}{2}(1 + i\sqrt{3})$ or $\frac{1}{2}(1 - i\sqrt{3})$.

## Exercises 3.5, Pages 97–98

**1.** $\{x : x > \frac{5}{3}\}$. 　**3.** $\{x : x < -\frac{9}{2}\}$. 　**5.** $\varnothing$. 　**7.** $\{x : x > 0, x \neq 2\}$.

**9.** $\{x : x < -1\} \cup \{x : x > 3\}$. 　**11.** $\{w : -\frac{1}{2} \leq w \leq 2\}$.

**13.** $\{x : x < 2\} \cup \{x : x > \frac{5}{2}\}$. 　**15.** $\{x : -3 < x < -2\}$.

**17.** $\{x : -1 < x < 0\} \cup \{x : x > 2\}$. 　**19.** $\{x : -8 \leq x \leq -\frac{4}{3} \text{ and } x \neq -3\}$.

**21.** $\varnothing$. 　**23.** $|x - 2| < 3$.

**25.** Let $x_0 \in \mathcal{S}[f(x) > g(x)]$. Then $f(x_0) > g(x_0)$ and $f(x_0) + p(x_0) > g(x_0) + p(x_0)$. Therefore, $x_0 \in \mathcal{S}[f(x) + p(x) > g(x) + p(x)]$. Reverse the argument to complete the proof.

**27.** The sum of the grades on the remaining two tests must be greater than or equal to 190.

**29.** Since $A > W, \dfrac{5}{4} < \dfrac{A}{A - W} < \dfrac{3}{2} \Rightarrow \dfrac{5}{4}A - \dfrac{5}{4}W < A < \dfrac{3}{2}A - \dfrac{3}{2}W$.

Also, $\dfrac{5}{4}A - \dfrac{5}{4}W < A \Rightarrow \dfrac{1}{4}A < \dfrac{5}{4}W \Rightarrow \dfrac{1}{5}A < W$,

and $A < \dfrac{3}{2}A - \dfrac{3}{2}W \Rightarrow \dfrac{3}{2}W < \dfrac{1}{2}A \Rightarrow W < \dfrac{1}{3}A$. Therefore,

$$\frac{1}{5}A < W < \frac{1}{3}A.$$

**31.** $3 < x < 3.5$. 　**33.** $\{x : x < -1\} \cup \{x : x > 3\}$. 　**35.** $0 < R_1 \leq 2$ or $8 \leq R_1 < 10$.

**Exercises 3.6, Pages 102–103**

**1.** Parabola; vertex at origin; axis, $x = 0$; opens downward.
**3.** Circle; center at origin; radius $\frac{3}{2}$.       **5.** Two straight lines: $y = \pm\frac{1}{2}x$.
**7.** Parabola; vertex at $(1, 2)$; axis, $x = 1$; opens upward.
**9.** Parabola; vertex at $(-3, 2)$; axis, $y = 2$; opens to the left.
**11.** Ellipse; intercepts $(0, 3)$, $(0, -3)$, $(2, 0)$, $(-2, 0)$.
**13.** Hyperbola in second and fourth quadrants; asymptotes, $x = 0$, $y = 0$.
**15.** No graph since equation is satisfied by no real values of $(x, y)$.
**17.** $x^2 + y^2 = 17$.   **19.** Two: $y = 4x^2 + 8x$, $16x = y^2 + 8y$.   **21.** $h = 18\frac{3}{4}$ feet.
**23.** The line is tangent to the parabola. Tangents to curves are discussed in Chapter 5.

**Exercises 3.7, Pages 107–108**

**1.** $y + 1 = m(x - 3)$.   **3.** $3x + 2y = c$.   **5.** $y = mx + m$.
**7.** All have the same $y$ intercept, 3.   **9.** All pass through the point $(6, -6)$.
**11.** Since the equation is linear, it is that of a straight line. Also
$$aL_1(x_1, y_1) + bL_2(x_1, y_1) = a \cdot 0 + b \cdot 0 = 0.$$
Hence, every line passes through $(x_1, y_1)$.
**13.** They all have a common axis of length 4 units along the $x$-axis.
**15. (a)** The vertices are all at the origin. All have the $y$-axis for axis.
**(c)** The vertices are all on the $x$-axis. The parabolas all open up and have exactly the same shape.
**(e)** The line $y = -1$ is the common axis for the entire family.

**Exercises 4.1, Pages 114–115**

**1. (b)** All points in $\{x: 0 < x < 1\}$. **(d)** None.
**3. (b)** For each $k > 0$, there is an $h > 0$ such that $x \in \mathfrak{N}^*(2, h) \Rightarrow y \in \mathfrak{N}(4, k)$.
**(e)** For each $M_1 > 0$, there is an $h_1 > 0$ such that $x \in \mathfrak{N}^*(1^-, h_1) \Rightarrow y < -M_1$
and for each $M_2 > 0$, there is an $h_2 > 0$ such that $x \in \mathfrak{N}^*(1^+, h_2) \Rightarrow y > M_2$
**5.** $A = \frac{5}{4}$, $B = -2$.     **7.** $A = 12$, $B = 5$.     **9.** $A = 2$, $B = -2$.

**Exercises 4.2, Pages 119–120**

**1.** *Intercepts:* None. *Asymptotes:* $x$-axis, $y$-axis. *Symmetry:* Origin (and the lines $y = x$, $y = -x$.)
**3.** *Intercepts:* $x = 0 \Rightarrow y = -3$. *Asymptotes:* $x = 1$, $y = 0$. *Symmetry:* None with respect to the axes or the origin.
**5.** *Intercepts:* $x = 0 \Leftrightarrow y = 0$. *Asymptotes:* $y = 0$. *Symmetry:* Origin.
**7.** *Intercepts:* $x = 0 \Leftrightarrow y = 0$. *Asymptotes:* $x = 1$, $x = 3$, $y = -1$. *Symmetry:* None
**9.** *Intercepts:* $x = 0 \Rightarrow y = \frac{1}{2}$. *Asymptotes:* $x = -2$, $x = 2$, $y = 0$. *Symmetry:* $y$-axis
**11.** *Intercepts:* $x = 0 \Leftrightarrow y = 0$. *Asymptotes:* $x = -1$, $x = 1$, $y = 0$. *Symmetry:* Origin
**13.** *Intercepts:* $x = 0 \Leftrightarrow y = 0$. *Asymptotes:* $x = 3$, $y = 0$. *Symmetry:* None.
**15.** *Intercepts:* $x = 0 \Rightarrow y = -1$; $y = 0 \Rightarrow x = \pm 3$. *Asymptotes:* $y = 1$. *Symmetry* $y$-axis.
**17.** *Intercepts:* $x = 0 \Rightarrow y = -\frac{4}{9}$; $y = 0 \Rightarrow x = \pm 2$. *Asymptotes:* $y = -1$, $x = 3$ $x = -3$. *Symmetry:* $y$-axis.

**19.** *Intercepts:* $x = 0 \Rightarrow y = \frac{1}{2}$. *Asymptotes:* $x = -2$, $y = 0$. *Symmetry:* None. Note that $y$ is undefined at $x = 2$.

**21.** *Intercepts:* $x = 0 \Leftrightarrow y = 0$. *Asymptotes:* $y = 1$, $x = -1$. *Symmetry:* None.

**23.** *Intercepts:* $x = 0 \Rightarrow y = \pm\frac{2}{3}$. *Asymptotes:* $y = 0$. *Symmetry:* $x$-axis, $y$-axis, origin.

**25.** *Intercepts:* None. *Asymptotes:* $x = 0$, $y = \frac{1}{3}x$. *Symmetry:* Origin. Note that for $x$ very large $1/(2x)$ is negligible and $y = \frac{1}{3}x$, approximately. This leads to the oblique asymptote.

**27.** $h = (2/r)\sqrt{4 - 2r^2}$, $0 < r \le \sqrt{2}$. *Intercepts:* $h = 0 \Rightarrow r = \sqrt{2}$. *Asymptotes:* $r = 0$ (upper portion). *Symmetry:* None.

### Exercises 4.3, Pages 125–126

**1. (a)** $h \le \frac{1}{50}$ will suffice. **(b)** $h \le \frac{1}{500}$ will suffice. **(c)** $h \le$ the smaller of $\frac{1}{5}\epsilon$ and 1 will suffice.

**3. (a)** $h \le 0.6$ will suffice. **(b)** $h \le 0.06$ will suffice. **(c)** $h \le$ the smaller of $6\epsilon$ and 1 will suffice.

**5.** Suppose such an $h$ exists. Then
$$x \in \mathfrak{N}^*(0^-, h) \Rightarrow f(x) \in \mathfrak{N}(1, \tfrac{1}{10}),$$
or
$$-h < x < 0 \Rightarrow |x^3 - 1| < \tfrac{1}{10}.$$
Let $x = -a$, where $-h < -a < 0$. Then
$$|-a^3 - 1| < \tfrac{1}{10} \quad \text{or} \quad a^3 + 1 < \tfrac{1}{10},$$
which is impossible for $a > 0$.

**7. (a)** $h \le 0.01$. **(b)** $h \le 10^{-6}$. **(c)** $h \le \epsilon^2$.

**9. (a)** No. If there were such an $h$ for each $\epsilon$, then
$$x \in \mathfrak{N}^*(0^-, h) \Rightarrow y \in \mathfrak{N}(\tfrac{1}{2}, \epsilon),$$
or
$$-h < x < 0 \Rightarrow \tfrac{1}{2} - \epsilon < y < \tfrac{1}{2} + \epsilon.$$
But $y = |x| = -x$, so $\tfrac{1}{2} - \epsilon < -x < \tfrac{1}{2} + \epsilon$. Suppose $\epsilon = \tfrac{1}{10}$, then
$$0.4 < -x < 0.6, \quad \text{or} \quad -0.6 < x < -0.4.$$
This means that values such that $-0.4 < x < 0$ are excluded, which contradicts $x \in \mathfrak{N}^*(0^-, h)$. The graph shows that $y \to 0$ (not $\tfrac{1}{2}$) as $x \to 0^-$.

**(b)** Yes. Take $h \le$ the smaller of $\epsilon$ and 1.

### Exercises 4.4, Page 131

**1.** $|x^2 - x + 1 - 3| = |x^2 - x - 2| = |x - 2||x + 1|$.
$$|x - 2| < h \Rightarrow 2 - h < x < 2 + h.$$
If $h < 1$, then $1 < x < 3 \Rightarrow 2 < x + 1 < 4$. Thus, $|x - 2||x + 1| < 4|x - 2|$, and
$$4|x - 2| < \epsilon \Rightarrow |x - 2| < \tfrac{1}{4}\epsilon.$$
Therefore, for $h = \min(\tfrac{1}{4}\epsilon, 1)$,
$$x \in \mathfrak{N}^*(2, h) \Rightarrow (x^2 - x + 1) \in \mathfrak{N}(3, \epsilon),$$
so that $\lim_{x \to 2} (x^2 - x + 1) = 3$.

**3.** $|x^3 - 2x^2 + x - 2| = |x - 2|(x^2 + 1)$.
$$|x - 2| < h \Rightarrow 2 - h < x < 2 + h.$$

If $h < 1$, then $1 < x < 3 \Rightarrow 2 < x^2 + 1 < 10$. Thus, $|x - 2||x^2 + 1| < 10|x - 2|$, and

$$10|x - 2| < \epsilon \Rightarrow |x - 2| < \tfrac{1}{10}\epsilon.$$

Therefore, for $h = \min(\tfrac{1}{10}\epsilon, 1)$,

$$x \in \mathfrak{N}^*(2, h) \Rightarrow (x^3 - 2x^2 + x) \in \mathfrak{N}(2, \epsilon),$$

so that $\lim_{x \to 2}(x^3 - 2x^2 + x) = 2$.

**5.** Take $h = \epsilon$.     **7.** *Hint:* For $x \neq 3$, $\dfrac{x^2 - 9}{x - 3} = x + 3$.

**9.** $\dfrac{x - 2}{x^2 + 2x - 8} = \dfrac{1}{x + 4}$ for $x \neq 2$.

$$\left| \frac{1}{x + 4} - \frac{1}{6} \right| = \frac{|x - 2|}{6|x + 4|}.$$

$$|x - 2| < h \Rightarrow 2 - h < x < 2 + h.$$

If $h < 1$, then $1 < x < 3 \Rightarrow 5 < x + 4 < 7$. Thus, $\dfrac{|x - 2|}{6|x + 4|} < \dfrac{|x - 2|}{30}$, and

$$\frac{|x - 2|}{30} < \epsilon \Rightarrow |x - 2| < 30\epsilon.$$

Therefore, for $h = \min(30\epsilon, 1)$,

$$x \in \mathfrak{N}^*(2, h) \Rightarrow \frac{x - 2}{x^2 + 2x - 8} \in \mathfrak{N}(\tfrac{1}{6}, \epsilon),$$

so that $\lim_{x \to 2} \dfrac{x - 2}{x^2 + 2x - 8} = \tfrac{1}{6}$.

**11.** $\lim_{x \to 0^-} \dfrac{x}{|x|} = -1$, $\lim_{x \to 0^+} \dfrac{x}{|x|} = 1$. Since these are not equal, $\lim_{x \to 0} \dfrac{x}{|x|}$ does not exist.

**13.** $\lim_{x \to 0} \dfrac{|x|}{x^2} = \lim_{x \to 0} \dfrac{1}{|x|}$, which does not exist since $\dfrac{1}{|x|} \to \infty$ as $x \to 0$.

**15.** $\left| \sin \dfrac{1}{x} \right| \leq 1 \Rightarrow \left| x \sin \dfrac{1}{x} \right| \leq |x|$. Since $|x| \to 0$ as $x \to 0$, $\lim_{x \to 0} x \sin \dfrac{1}{x} = 0$.

**17.** No. For $0 < x - 2 < h$, we have $\sqrt{x - 2} < \sqrt{h}$ and $\dfrac{1}{\sqrt{x - 2}} > \dfrac{1}{\sqrt{h}} \to \infty$ as $h \to 0$.

### Exercises 4.5, Pages 137–138

**1.** $-6$.     **3.** $-4$.     **5.** The absolute value of the fraction $\to \infty$ as $x \to \infty$.
**7.** $\tfrac{3}{2}$.     **9.** The limit from the left is $-3$. What is it from the right?     **11.** $0$.
**13.** $0$.     **15.** *Hint:* Multiply by $\dfrac{\sqrt{x^2 + 1} + x}{\sqrt{x^2 + 1} + x}$.     **17.** $-1$.

**19.** $\lim_{x \to a} f(x) = A \Rightarrow$ corresponding to each $\epsilon_1$, there is an $h > 0$ such that

$$|f(x) - A| < \epsilon_1 \text{ for } |x - a| < h.$$

Also, $|cf(x) - cA| = |c||f(x) - A| < |c|\epsilon_1$ for $|x - a| < h$, and $c \neq 0$. Therefore, the choice $\epsilon_1 = \epsilon/|c|$ yields $|cf(x) - cA| < \epsilon$ for $|x - a| < h$.

For $c = 0$, the theorem is trivial.

**21.** For each $\epsilon > 0$, there is an $M$ such that

$$x > M \Rightarrow f(x) \in \mathfrak{N}(A, \epsilon).$$

**23.** $\lim_{x \to a} f_1(x) = A \Rightarrow$ corresponding to each $\epsilon > 0$, there is an $h_1$ such that

(1) $\qquad A - \epsilon < f_1(x) < A + \epsilon$ for $|x - a| < h_1$.

$\lim_{x \to a} f_2(x) = A \Rightarrow$ corresponding to each $\epsilon > 0$, there is an $h_2$ such that

(2) $\qquad A - \epsilon < f_2(x) < A + \epsilon$ for $|x - a| < h_2$.

Both (1) and (2) are true for $h = \min (h_1, h_2)$. Therefore,

$$A - \epsilon < f_1(x) < g(x) < f_2(x) < A + \epsilon,$$

or

$$|g(x) - A| < \epsilon \quad \text{for } |x - a| < h.$$

Hence, $\lim_{x \to a} g(x) = A$.

**Exercises 4.6, Pages 143–144**

**1.** Continuous everywhere except at $x = \pm 1$. The discontinuities are infinite ones.

**3.** Continuous everywhere.

**5.** Continuous except for a finite discontinuity at $x = 2$.

**7.** An infinite discontinuity at $x = -3$. A removable discontinuity at $x = 2$. The latter can be removed by defining $f(2) = \frac{1}{5}$. The function is otherwise continuous everywhere.

**9.** Continuous for $x < 1$. A removable discontinuity at $x = 1$. Can be made (one-sided) continuous there by defining $f(1) = 0$.

**1.** Infinite discontinuity at $t = -a$. Removable discontinuity at $t = a$. Can be made continuous at $t = a$ by defining $f(a) = 0$. Otherwise function is continuous everywhere.

**3.** Continuous for $t > 0$ except for a removable discontinuity at $t = 2$. The latter can be removed by defining $g(2) = 0$.

**5.** Continuous everywhere on $-2 \leq x < 2$, except at $x = 0$, where there is a finite discontinuity.

**7.** Let $1/t = n + x$, $0 \leq x < 1$, $n \in \mathfrak{N}$. Then $\left[\left[\dfrac{1}{t}\right]\right] = n$, $t = \dfrac{1}{n + x}$, and

$$g(t) = \left[\left[\dfrac{n}{n + x}\right]\right] = \begin{cases} 0 & \text{for } 0 < x < 1, \\ 1 & \text{for } x = 0. \end{cases}$$

Thus, there is a removable discontinuity at each integral value of $x$. These discontinuities can be removed by defining $g(n) = 0$ in place of $g(n) = 1$.

**9.** Since $\lim_{x \to a} P(x) = P(a)$ and $\lim_{x \to a} Q(x) = Q(a) \neq 0$,

$$\lim_{x \to a} \frac{P(x)}{Q(x)} = \frac{P(a)}{Q(a)}.$$

**1.** For $a = 0$, take $h = \epsilon^3$, since $|x| < \epsilon^3 \Rightarrow |x^{1/3}| < \epsilon$. For $a \neq 0$, proceed as follows:

$$|x^{1/3} - a^{1/3}| = \frac{|x - a|}{|x^{2/3} + a^{1/3}x^{1/3} + a^{2/3}|}.$$

If $|x - a| < h$, then $a - h < x < a + h$. For $a > 0$, let $h \leq \frac{7}{8}a$ so that $\frac{1}{8}a < x < \frac{15}{8}a$. Thus $x^{2/3} + a^{1/3}x^{1/3} + a^{2/3} > (\frac{1}{8}a)^{2/3} + a^{1/3}(\frac{1}{8}a)^{1/3} + (\frac{1}{8}a)^{2/3} = a^{2/3}$, and so $|x^{1/3} - a^{1/3}| < a^{-2/3}|x - a| < a^{-2/3}h$.

Consequently, if $h = \min (\frac{7}{8}a, \epsilon a^{2/3})$, then

$$x \in \mathfrak{N}(a, h) \Rightarrow y \in \mathfrak{N}(a^{1/3}, \epsilon).$$

Thus $y = x^{1/3}$ defines a continuous function for $a \geq 0$. By symmetry, the function is also continuous for $a < 0$.

**3.** $f$ is continuous only if $g(b) = \lim_{x \to b^+} h(x)$.

**Exercises 4.7, Pages 151–153**

1. Continuous for all $x$.      3. Continuous for all $x$.

5. Continuous except at $x = 0$, where the function has a removable discontinuity.

7. Yes. Since $f$ is continuous on the closed interval, Theorem 4.5c does apply.

9. $M = 97$.      11. $M = 1$.      13. $M = 4$.

15. (a) l.u.b. $= 1$, not attained.

       g.l.b. $= 0$, $f(1) = 0 = f(2) = f(3) = f(0)$.

   (b) l.u.b. $= 1$, $f\left(\dfrac{1}{n}\right) = 1$, $n = 1, 2, 3, \ldots$.

       g.l.b. $= 0$, $f(x) = 0$ for all $x > 1$.

17. No. A function may be discontinuous on an interval but still be bounded. Consider any function with only finite discontinuities.

19. Since, for each $c$ in the interval, $\lim_{x \to c} f(x) = f(c)$ and $\lim_{x \to c} g(x) = g(c)$, then
$$\lim_{x \to c} [f(x)g(x)] = [\lim_{x \to c} f(x)][\lim_{x \to c} g(x)] = f(c)g(c).$$
Therefore, the product function is continuous at each point where both factors are continuous.

21. Simply replace $>$ with $<$ in the statement of Theorem 4.5c.

    *Proof:* $f$ is continuous at $c \Rightarrow$ for each $\epsilon > 0$, there is a $\mathfrak{N}(c, h)$ such that
$$x \in \mathfrak{N}(c, h) \Rightarrow f(c) - \epsilon < f(x) < f(c) + \epsilon.$$
Choose $\epsilon = -\tfrac{1}{2}f(c)$. Then $\tfrac{3}{2}f(c) < f(x) < \tfrac{1}{2}f(c)$ for $x \in \mathfrak{N}(c, h)$. Since $f(c) < 0$, this proves the theorem.

23. No, because $f$ is not continuous on the interval.

25. (a) False. For example, let $f(x) .= . 1/x$, $0 < x \leq 1$, $f(0) .= . 0$. Then $f$ is defined on the closed interval $0 \leq x \leq 1$, but is not bounded there.

   (b) False. For example, let $f(x) .= . x$, $0 \leq x < 1$, $f(x) .= . x - 1$, $1 \leq x \leq \tfrac{3}{2}$. Then the l.u.b. is 1, but $f(x) = 1$ for no $x$ in the domain.

27. Take $f(x) = x^2$, $-1 \leq x \leq 1$.

29. $f$ is not strictly increasing (decreasing) on its entire domain. The theorem does apply for $x \leq \tfrac{1}{2}$ or for $x \geq \tfrac{1}{2}$.

**Exercises 5.1, Pages 159–160**

1. *Tangent:* $4x - y = 7$, *normal:* $x + 4y = -11$.

3. *Tangent:* $5x + y = 4$, *normal:* $x - 5y = 6$.

5. *Tangent:* $x - 4y = -8$, *normal:* $4x + y = 36$.

7. *Tangent:* $x + y = 0$, *normal:* $x - y = -2$.

9. *Tangent:* $x + 4y = 12$, *normal:* $4x - y = 14$.

11. $4x - y = 4$.      13. $(1, 2)$ and $(-1, -4)$.

**Exercises 5.2, Page 162**

1. 9 feet/second.      3. $-24$ feet/second.      5. $-9$ feet/second.

7. $\tfrac{1}{4}$ foot/second.      9. $v = v_0 - gt_1$.      11. $18\tfrac{3}{4}$ feet.

13. Motion in positive direction for $0 < t < 2$ and for $t > 4$. Motion in negative direction for $2 < t < 4$.

15. $t = 0$, $v_1 = -4$ feet/second, $v_2 = 3$ feet/second.

    $t = \tfrac{7}{2}$, $v_1 = 3$ feet/second, $v_2 = -4$ feet/second.

### Exercises 5.3, Page 165

**1.** 10 (inches)$^2$/inch.  **3.** $64\pi$ (inches)$^3$/inch.
**5.** $3\pi$ (inches)$^3$/inch.  **7.** $-0.4096\pi$ (inches)$^3$/minute.
**9.** $t = 0$, $a = -6$ feet/(second)$^2$; $t = 2$, $a = 6$ feet/(second)$^2$.
**11.** $(-\frac{1}{2}, -\frac{3}{4})$, $(-\frac{3}{2}, -\frac{3}{4})$.  **13.** $\pi r^2$ (linear units)$^3$/linear unit.

### Exercises 5.4, Pages 169–170

**1.** $10x - 21x^2$.  **3.** $4x + 3$.  **5.** $3y^2 + 4y$.  **7.** $3(t - 1)^2$.  **9.** $-1/x^3$.
**11.** $-1/(2\sqrt{3}x^{3/2})$.  **13.** $-\dfrac{1}{t^2} + \dfrac{6}{t^3} - \dfrac{1}{t^4}$.  **15.** $-\frac{3}{2}u^{-5/2}$.  **17.** (a) 2. (b) 2.
**19.** (a) $\frac{1}{8}$. (b) $-\frac{3}{32}$.
**21.** $t = 0$, $s = 0$ feet, $v = 16$ feet/second, $a = -32$ feet/(second)$^2$.
   $t = \frac{1}{2}$, $s = 4$ feet, $v = 0$ feet/second, $a = -32$ feet/(second)$^2$.
**23.** $t = 1$, $s = 2$ feet, $v = 1$ foot/second, $a = -\frac{1}{2}$ foot/(second)$^2$.
   $t = 4$, $s = 4$ feet, $v = \frac{1}{2}$ foot/second, $a = -\frac{1}{16}$ foot/(second)$^2$.
**25.** $\pm 6\sqrt{3}$.  **27.** $y = -4$ and $y = 4x$.
**29.** $\frac{1}{4}\sqrt{S/\pi}$.  **31.** 1.00425 calories/degree.

### Exercises 5.5, Pages 172–173

**1.** $\frac{1}{2}x^4 - x^3 - x^2 + 7x + C$.  **3.** $-\dfrac{1}{4x^2} - \dfrac{3}{x} + 4x + C$.
**5.** $\frac{2}{3}\sqrt{2}s^{3/2} + \sqrt{2}s^{1/2} + C$.  **7.** $9x + 4x^3 + \frac{4}{5}x^5 + C$.
**9.** $\frac{1}{3}x^3 + \frac{3}{2}x^2 + 4x - (1/x) + C$.  **11.** $\frac{3}{7}t^{2/3} - \frac{24}{11}t^{11/3} + C$.
**13.** $\dfrac{(2s^3 - 1)^4}{24} + C$.  **15.** $\frac{2}{3}x^{3/2} - \frac{12}{7}x^{7/2} + \frac{24}{11}x^{11/2} - \frac{16}{15}x^{15/2} + C$.
**17.** $y = 2x^3 + 2x^2 + 3x + 4$.  **19.** $y = \frac{1}{4}x^4 - 2x^2 + x + 9$.
**21.** $3y = 2x\sqrt{2x} + 4$.  **23.** $s = \frac{1}{6}t^4 + \frac{1}{2}t^3 + 2t^2 + 10t$.
**25.** 164 feet, $-16\sqrt{41}$ feet/second.  **27.** $12y = x^3 + 16$.

### Exercises 6.1, Pages 176–177

**1.** $\mathfrak{D}_f = \mathfrak{R}$; $\mathfrak{D}_{f'} = \mathfrak{R}$.  **3.** $\mathfrak{D}_f = \{x: x \geqq 0\}$; $\mathfrak{D}_{f'} = \{x: x > 0\}$.
**5.** $\mathfrak{D}_f = \mathfrak{R} - \{0\}$; $\mathfrak{D}_f = \mathfrak{R} - \{0\}$.  **7.** $f'_+(1) \neq f'_-(1)$.
**9.** $f'_+(0) \neq f'_-(0)$.  **11.** $f'_+(-3) \neq f'_-(-3)$.  **13.** $f'_+(0) \neq f'_-(0)$.
**15.** (a) $f_1$ is differentiable on $0 < x < 1$ except at $x = \frac{1}{2}$.
   (b) $f_n$ is continuous on $0 \leqq x \leqq 1$ and is differentiable on this interval except at
   $x = k \cdot 2^{-n}$, where $k = 1, 2, 3, \ldots, 2^n - 1$.
   (c) The limit function $F$ is given by $F(x) = 0$, $0 \leqq x \leqq 1$. It is continuous and
   differentiable on its entire domain.

### Exercises 6.2, Page 181

**1.** $2x$.  **3.** $4x^3 + 18x^2 + 22x + 6$.  **5.** $-2(x - 1)^{-2}$.  **7.** $\dfrac{1}{(x + 1)^2}$.

**9.** $\dfrac{2 + \sqrt{x}}{2(1 + \sqrt{x})^2}$. **11.** $t = 2$. **13.** $t = 1$. **15.** $25y + 2x = 7$. **17.** $y = -x$.

**19.** *Hint:* Apply the Product Rule for Differentiation $n$ times, first writing the product as $(f_1)(f_2 f_3 \cdots f_n)$ and then proceeding in the obvious fashion.

**21.** $D_x(uv^{-1}) = (D_x u)\, v^{-1} + u\, D_x(v^{-1}) = v^{-1}\, D_x u - uv^{-2}\, D_x v$
$\qquad = v^{-2}(v\, D_x u - u\, D_x v)$.

### Exercises 6.3, Pages 185–186

**1.** $\dfrac{1}{2\sqrt{x + 2}}$. **3.** $\dfrac{1}{2(2 - t)^{3/2}}$. **5.** $\dfrac{2}{(2s - 1)^{1/2}(2s + 1)^{3/2}}$. **7.** $\dfrac{-6u^2}{(u^3 + 8)^{1/2}(4 + u^3)^{3/2}}$.

**9.** $\dfrac{1}{t^2}$, $t \ne 0, 1$. **11.** $\dfrac{2x(x^2 - 9)}{\sqrt{(x^2 - 9)^2}}$. **13.** $\dfrac{2x^2 - 1}{\sqrt{x^2 - 1}}$. **15.** $\dfrac{z^3 + 2z}{(1 + z^2)^{3/2}}$.

**17.** $1 - \dfrac{a^{1/2}}{x^{1/2}}$. **19.** $(0, 1)$.

**21.** $y = \sqrt{|x|} = \begin{cases} \sqrt{x}, & x \ge 0, \\ \sqrt{-x}, & x < 0. \end{cases}$

$y' = \dfrac{1}{2\sqrt{x}}$, $x > 0$ and $y' = -\dfrac{1}{2\sqrt{-x}}$ for $x < 0$.

Thus, $|y'| \to \infty$ as $x \to 0$ and there is a vertical tangent at $(0, 0)$.

**23.** Let $y = u^n$, where $u = f(x)$ and apply the chain rule to get
$$D_x y = (D_u y)(D_x u) = nu^{n-1}\, D_x u.$$

**25.** Suppose $f'(x_0) = 0$. Then, if $y = [f(x)]^n$, $y' = n[f(x)]^{n-1} f'(x)$. Therefore, $y' = 0$ for $x = x_0$, and the curve $y = [f(x)]^n$ has a horizontal tangent at $x = x_0$.

   The converse is not necessarily true since, for $n \ge 2$, it is possible that $y' = 0$ and $f'(x) \ne 0$ at a point where $f(x) = 0$. An example is furnished by $y = (x^2 - 1)^2$.

**27.** $v = 0$ for $t = 0$ only. There are no times when $v = 1$ foot/second.

**29.** By Theorem 6.3a, if $f$ and $g$ are differentiable on $a < x < b$ and if $f(x)$ is a value such that $a < f(x) < b$, then $g(f)$ is differentiable there. If $f(x)$ is not a value in this interval, then nothing can be guaranteed. Hence, in general, the answer is no. For example, let the interval be $0 < x < 2$ and take $g(x) .=. 1/x, f(x) .=. (x - 1)^2$. Is $g(f)$ differentiable at $x = 1$?

### Exercises 6.4, Pages 187–188

**1.** $\dfrac{4}{(x - 1)^3}$. **3.** $-\dfrac{x + 4}{4(x + 1)^{5/2}}$. **5.** $10(1 + 3t)^{-8/3}$.

**7.** $y' = \tfrac{1}{2}x^{-1/2}$, $y^{(n)} = (1/2_n)(-1)^{n-1}(1)(3)\cdots(2n - 3)x^{-(2n-1)/2}$, $n = 2, 3, 4, \ldots$.

**9.** $t = 1$, $s = 0$ feet, $v = 3$ feet/second.

**11.** $t = 2$, $s = -68$ feet, $v = -52$ feet/second.

**13.** $t = 2$, $s = 2$ feet, $v = -\tfrac{1}{2}$ foot/second.

**15.** At $(0, 0)$, $y' = 1$; at $(2, -222)$ and at $(-2, 222)$, $y' = -239$. **17.** 72

**19.** $f'(x) = \begin{cases} 2x, & x \ge 0, \\ -2x, & x < 0. \end{cases}$ $\qquad f''(x) = \begin{cases} 2, & x > 0, \\ -2, & x < 0. \end{cases}$

**21.** **(b)**, **(c)**, **(e)** are true; **(a)** and **(d)** are false.

**Exercises 6.5, Pages 192–193**

**1.** The equation defines no real function.
**3.** The equation defines no real function.
**5.** $-\dfrac{4x}{y}$.  **7.** $\dfrac{5-x}{y+2}$.  **9.** $\dfrac{x^2}{t^2-1}$.  **11.** $\frac{1}{10}$.  **13.** Undefined.  **15.** $-\frac{1}{4}$.  **17.** $-\dfrac{1}{y^3}$.
**19.** 0.  **21.** $\frac{1}{3}a^{2/3}x^{-4/3}y^{-1/3}$.  **23.** 0.  **25.** $\frac{1}{4}$ and $-\frac{1}{4}$.

**Exercises 6.6, Pages 198–199**

**7.** $(-7, -2), (-7, 2)$.  **9.** $(0, \sqrt{2})$.  **11.** $(0, 2\sqrt{2})$.  **13.** $y = 3x$.  **15.** $4x - 3y = 1$.
**17.** $\dfrac{9u}{4}$, $u \neq 0$; $\dfrac{9}{16u}$.  **19.** $\dfrac{2b}{a} t^{1/2} + \dfrac{4c}{a} t^{3/2}$; $\dfrac{2b}{a^2} + \dfrac{12c}{a^2} t$.
**21.** Hypotheses are satisfied on any interval in $\mathcal{R} - \{0\}$.
**23.** Hypotheses are satisfied on any interval in $\mathcal{R} - \{-1, 1\}$.

**Exercises 6.7, Pages 204–205**

**1.** $\Delta y = 3.25, dy = 3$.  **3.** $\Delta y = 0.00998, dy = 0.01$.  **5.** $-\dfrac{x}{y}$.  **7.** $-\dfrac{x^2 + y}{x + y^2}$.
**9.** $\dfrac{4t}{1 + t^2}$.  **11.** 0.3988.  **13.** 3.0067.  **15.** 0.0101.
**17.** $V = V_0(1 + \alpha t)^3, dV = 3\alpha V_0(1 + \alpha t)^2 \, dt$.  **19.** $8\frac{1}{3}\%$.  **21.** $8\frac{1}{3}\%$.
**23.** 2.099 centimeters.  **25.** $d(u + v) = du + dv$.

**Exercises 7.1, Pages 210–211**

**1.** Increasing for $x > 0$; decreasing for $x < 0$.
**3.** Decreasing on $\mathcal{R} - \{1\}$.      **5.** Increasing on $\mathcal{R}$.
**7.** Increasing for $x < -1$ and for $x > \frac{1}{3}$; decreasing for $-1 < x < \frac{1}{3}$.
**9.** Increasing for $x > -2$; decreasing for $x < -2$.
**11.** $f(0) = 0$ is the least value of $f$, and $f'$ does not exist at $x = 0$.
**13.** At $x = \pm a$, $y = 0$. This is the least value of $y$, and $y'$ does not exist at $x = 0$.
**15.** The greatest value is $\frac{1}{5}$; the least is 0.

**Exercises 7.2, Page 217**

**1.** Concave up for $-1 < x < 0$, $x > 1$. Concave down for $x < -1$, $0 < x < 1$. *Inflection points:* $(-1, 7), (0, 0), (1, -7)$.
**3.** Concave up for $0 < x < 2$. Concave down for $x < 0$, $x > 2$. *Inflection points.* $(0, 0), (2, 16)$.
**5.** Concave up for $x < 0$. Concave down for $x > 0$. No inflection points.
**7.** Concave up for $-a\sqrt{3} < x < 0$, $x > a\sqrt{3}$. Concave down for $x < -a\sqrt{3}$, $0 < x < a\sqrt{3}$. *Inflection points:* $(-a\sqrt{3}, -\frac{1}{4}a\sqrt{3}), (0, 0), (a\sqrt{3}, \frac{1}{4}a\sqrt{3})$.
**9.** *Hint:* The inflection point occurs for $x = -\frac{1}{3}(b/a)$.

**11.** $22y = -x^4 + 2x^3 + 12x^2 + 13x + 22.$

**13.** Falling curve with a horizontal inflectional tangent at $[a, f(a)]$. Concave up to the left and down to the right of $x = a$.

**15.** Rising curve, concave down.

**17.** Falling curve with inflection point $[a, f(a)]$. Concave up to the right and down to the left of $x = a$.

**19.** Impossible. The conditions are inconsistent since $f'$ is discontinuous for $x = a$, so that $f''$ cannot exist there.


### Exercises 7.3, Pages 224–225

**1.** $f(-3) = -2$, min; $f(-1) = 2$, max; $f(3) = -14$, min.

**3.** $F(0) = 1$, max.      **5.** No extremes.      **7.** $f(0) = 0$, min.

**9.** $(-2, 4 + \sqrt[3]{4})$, max point; $(0, 4)$, min point; $(3, 4 + \sqrt[3]{9})$, max point.

**11.** $(1, 0)$, min point.      **13.** No max or min points.

**15.** $(1, 1)$, min point; $(\frac{13}{9}, \frac{31}{27})$, max point.      **17.** $(-1, 2)$, min point.

**19.** $(4, \frac{3}{4})$, min point.      **21.** $c = 0$, $b > 0$, $3a + 2b = 0$.

**23.** $\left[ \dfrac{m}{m + n}, \dfrac{m^m n^n}{(m + n)^{m+n}} \right]$ is always a max point.

For $m$ even, $(0, 0)$ is a min point.

For $n$ odd, $(1, 0)$ is a min point.

No other extremes occur.

**25.** $x_c$ is the only critical point $\Rightarrow$ no extreme on the interval $a < x < x_c$ or $x_c < x < b$. Hence, $f$ has only end point extremes for $a \leq x \leq x_c$ and $x_c \leq x \leq b$. Since $f(x_c) > f(a)$ and $f(x_c) > f(b)$, then $f(x_c)$ is the greatest value of $f$ on the interval $a \leq x \leq b$.

**27.** **(a)** A rising curve with a vertical inflectional tangent or else a sharp corner at $x = a$, concave up to the left and down to the right of $x = a$.


### Exercises 7.4, Page 229

**1.** 1.      **3.** $1 + \sqrt{3}$.      **5.** $\frac{1}{6}(\sqrt{39} - 3)$.      **7.** $1/\sqrt{2}$.

**11.** No, since $f'$ does not exist at $x = 0$, which is in the given interval.


### Exercises 7.5, Pages 236–237

**1.** *Intercepts:* $x = 0 \Leftrightarrow y = 0$; $y = 0 \Rightarrow x = \pm 2\sqrt{2}$.

*Symmetry:* $y$-axis.

$y$ increasing for $-2 < x < 0$, $x > 2$, decreasing for $x < -2$, $0 < x < 2$.

Max point $(0, 0)$. Min points $(\pm 2, -16)$.

Concave up, $x < -\frac{2}{3}\sqrt{3}$, $x > \frac{2}{3}\sqrt{3}$; concave down, $-\frac{2}{3}\sqrt{3} < x < \frac{2}{3}\sqrt{3}$.

Inflection points $(\pm \frac{2}{3}\sqrt{3}, -\frac{80}{9})$.

**3.** *Intercepts:* $y = 0 \Rightarrow x = \pm 3$. *Symmetry:* $y$-axis. *Extent:* $|x| \geq 3$, $y \geq 0$.

$y$ increasing for $x > 3$, decreasing for $x < -3$.

Min points $(\pm 3, 0)$. Vertical tangents at these points.

Concave down, $x < -3$ and $x > 3$.

**5.** *Intercepts:* $x = 0 \Leftrightarrow y = 0$. *Symmetry: y*-axis.
$y$ decreasing for $x < 0$, increasing for $x > 0$.
Min point $(0, 0)$. Derivative does not exist there.
Concave up, $x < 0$ and $x > 0$.

**7.** *Intercepts:* $x = 0 \Rightarrow y = -1$; $y = 0 \Rightarrow x = 1$.
*Asymptotes:* $x = -1$, $y = 1$. $y$ increasing on $x < -1$ and $x > -1$.
Concave up, $x < -1$; concave down, $x > -1$.

**9.** *Intercepts:* $y = 0 \Rightarrow x = \pm 2$. Note that $(0, 0)$ is an isolated point.
*Symmetry:* Origin. *Extent:* $x = 0$, $|x| \geq 2$.
$y$ increasing for $x < -2$ and for $x > 2$.
Max point $(-2, 0)$; min point $(2, 0)$. Vertical tangents at these points.
Concave up, $-\sqrt{6} < x < -2$, $x > \sqrt{6}$; concave down, $x < -\sqrt{6}$, $2 < x < \sqrt{6}$.
Inflection points $(-\sqrt{6}, -2\sqrt{3})$, $(\sqrt{6}, 2\sqrt{3})$.

**11.** *Intercepts:* $x = 0 \Leftrightarrow y = 0$. *Symmetry: y*-axis. *Asymptotes: x*-axis.
$y$ increasing for $x < -1$, $0 < x < 1$, decreasing for $-1 < x < 0$, $x > 1$.
Max points $(\pm 1, \frac{1}{2})$; min point $(0, 0)$. Note that the derivative has a finite discontinuity at $x = 0$.
Concave up, $x < -\sqrt{3}$, $x > \sqrt{3}$; concave down, $-\sqrt{3} < x < 0$, $0 < x < \sqrt{3}$.
Inflection points $(\pm\sqrt{3}, \frac{1}{4}\sqrt{3})$.

**13.** *Intercepts:* $y = 0 \Rightarrow x = -5, 3$; $x = 0 \Rightarrow y = 20.80$.
$y$ increasing for $x < -\frac{1}{5}$, $x > 3$, decreasing for $-\frac{1}{5} < x < 3$.
Min point $(3, 0)$; max point $(-\frac{1}{5}, 20.85)$. Vertical tangent at $(3, 0)$.
Concave up, $x > 4.6$; concave down, $x < 3$, $3 < x < 4.6$.
Inflection point $(4.6, 26.81)$.

**15.** *Intercepts:* $y = 0 \Rightarrow x = 0, 5$. *Asymptotes:* $y = -1$, $x = -2$.
$y$ decreasing for $x < -2$, $x > \frac{10}{9}$, increasing for $-2 < x < \frac{10}{9}$.
Max point $(\frac{10}{9}, \frac{25}{56})$.
Concave up, $x > \frac{8}{3}$; concave down, $x < -2$, $-2 < x < \frac{8}{3}$.
Inflection point $(\frac{8}{3}, \frac{2}{7})$.

**17.** *Intercepts:* $x = 0 \Rightarrow y = 2a$. *Symmetry: y*-axis. *Asymptotes:* $y = 0$.
$y$ increasing for $x < 0$; decreasing for $x > 0$. Max point $(0, 2a)$.
Concave up, $|x| > \frac{2}{3}\sqrt{3}a$; concave down, $|x| < \frac{2}{3}\sqrt{3}a$.
Inflection points $(\pm\frac{2}{3}\sqrt{3}a, \frac{3}{2}a)$.

**19.** *Intercepts:* $y = 0 \Rightarrow x = -a, 0$. *Asymptotes:* $x = a$. *Symmetry: x*-axis.
*Extent:* $-a \leq x < a$.
For $y_1 = x\sqrt{\dfrac{a + x}{a - x}}$,
$y_1$ increasing for $\frac{1}{2}a(1 - \sqrt{5}) < x < a$, decreasing for $-a < x < \frac{1}{2}a(1 - \sqrt{5})$.
Min point $(-0.62a, -0.49a)$.
Concave up, $-a < x < a$. Vertical tangent at $(-a, 0)$.
For $y_2 = -x\sqrt{\dfrac{a + x}{a - x}}$, use the symmetry.

**21.** Parabola, vertex at $(-2, 1)$, axis $x = -2$. Opens upward.

**23.** The curve is symmetric to the *x*-axis, so consider only $t \geq 0$.
*Intercepts:* $y = 0 \Rightarrow x = 0, -6$.
$y$ increasing for $x > -4$, decreasing for $-6 < x < -4$.

Min point $(-4, -8)$.

Concave up, $x > -6$. Vertical tangent at $(-6, 0)$.

Use symmetry for $t \leq 0$.

**25.** **(a)** $f(x) + g(x) = 0$ or $g(x) = -f(x)$.

    **(b)** If $y_1 = f(x)$ has a max point at $x_1$ then there is a $\mathfrak{N}(x_1, h)$ such that $x \in \mathfrak{N}(x_1, h) \Rightarrow f(x_1) > f(x) \Rightarrow -f(x_1) < -f(x) \Rightarrow g(x_1) < g(x) \Rightarrow g$ has a min value at $x_1$.

    **(c)** *Hint:* Consider the difference $f(x) - t(x)$, where $t$ is the linear function defined in the proof of Theorem 7.2b.

### Exercises 7.6, Pages 242–244

**1.** 6, 6.   **3.** $x = \frac{1}{2}A\sqrt{2} = y$.   **7.** 3 inches.   **9.** Height $= \frac{1}{2}$ length of base.   **11.** $\frac{1}{3}h$.
**13.** Rectangle twice as wide as high.   **15.** Height = radius at base.   **17.** $R = r$.
**19.** Depth $= \sqrt{2}$ times the width.   **21.** $1\frac{1}{2}\%$.   **23.** $AB = 37\frac{1}{2}$ feet.

### Exercises 7.7, Pages 246–247

**1.** $\dfrac{4\pi}{r}$ (inches)$^2$/second.   **3.** 6.4 mph; no.   **5.** 1.8 feet/second.

**7.** $\frac{5}{18}$ foot/minute; $\frac{1}{6}$ foot/minute.   **9.** $\frac{64}{73}\sqrt{73}$ inches/minute.   **11.** 12.5 mph.
**13.** $32\sqrt{5}$ mph. No, since $D_t^2 s$ is not zero.

### Exercises 8.1, Pages 252–253

**1.** **(a)** $\displaystyle\sum_{k=1}^{n} 2^k$.             **(b)** $\displaystyle\sum_{k=0}^{n}\left[7 + \frac{k(k+1)}{2}\right]$.

**3.** **(a)** $a_1 + a_2 + a_3 + a_4$.

    **(c)** $\dfrac{1}{n-1} + \dfrac{1}{n-2} + \dfrac{1}{n-3} + \dfrac{1}{n-4} + \dfrac{1}{n-5}$.

    **(e)** $0 + 1 + 0 + 1$.

**9.** $2^n$; 0.

**11.** **(a)** $64a^6 - 576a^5b^2 + 2160a^4b^4 - 4320a^3b^6 + 4860a^2b^8 - 2916ab^{10} + 729b^{12}$.

    **(b)** $\dfrac{a^7}{128} - \dfrac{7a^4}{32} + \dfrac{21a}{8} - \dfrac{35}{2a^2} + \dfrac{70}{a^5} - \dfrac{168}{a^8} + \dfrac{224}{a^{11}} - \dfrac{128}{a^{14}}$.

**13.** **(a)** $14{,}784a^7$.

    **(c)** $\dfrac{12{,}155x^9y^{16}}{128}$.

**15.** $\dfrac{1001}{248{,}832}$.

**19.** $(n+1)! - 1$.

### Exercises 8.2, Pages 258–259

**1.** $\frac{1}{4}, \frac{2}{5}, \frac{3}{6}, \frac{4}{7}, \frac{5}{8}, \ldots$ Cluster point 1; limit 1.
**3.** $-\frac{1}{2}, \frac{1}{4}, -\frac{1}{8}, \frac{1}{16}, -\frac{1}{32}, \ldots$ Cluster point 0; limit 0.
**5.** $-\frac{3}{2}, \frac{3}{4}, -\frac{9}{8}, \frac{15}{16}, -\frac{33}{32}, \ldots$ Cluster points $-1$, 1; limit does not exist.
**7.** $a, a^2, a^3, a^4, a^5, \ldots$
    If $|a| < 1$, then 0 is a cluster point and the limit is 0.

If $|a| > 1$, there are no cluster points and the limit does not exist.

If $a = 1$, then 1 is a cluster point and the limit is 1.

If $a = -1$, then 1 and $-1$ are cluster points and the limit does not exist.

**9.** $-\frac{3}{5}, -\frac{15}{17}, -\frac{63}{65}, -\frac{255}{257}, -\frac{1023}{1025}, \ldots$ Cluster point $-1$; limit $-1$.

**11.** $-8, -\frac{13}{2}, -\frac{56}{9}, -\frac{49}{8}, -\frac{152}{25}, \ldots$ Cluster point $-6$; limit $-6$.

**13.** Nine terms $\notin \mathfrak{N}(0, 0.001)$.

**15.** $s_n = \dfrac{2n + 1}{2n + 3} < 1$, so that the sequence is bounded above.

$\dfrac{2n + 3}{2n + 5} > \dfrac{2n + 1}{2n + 3}$ since $4n^2 + 12n + 9 > 4n^2 + 12n + 5$.

Therefore, the sequence is increasing. By Theorem 8.2b, the sequence converges.

**17.** $s_n = 1 - \dfrac{1}{2^n} < 1$ so that the sequence is bounded above.

$1 - \dfrac{1}{2^n} < 1 - \dfrac{1}{2^{n+1}} \Rightarrow$ the sequence is increasing. By Theorem 8.2b, the sequence converges.

### Exercises 8.3, Pages 263–264

**1.** 10 (linear units)$^2$.      **3.** $15\frac{1}{3}$ (linear units)$^2$.

**5.** $A_n = \displaystyle\sum_{k=0}^{n-1} \frac{1}{n}\left(\frac{k}{n}\right)^2 = \frac{1}{n^3}\sum_{k=1}^{n-1} k^2 = \frac{(n-1)(n)(2n-1)}{6n^3}.$

$\displaystyle\lim_{n\to\infty} A_n = \lim_{n\to\infty}\left[\left(1 - \frac{1}{n}\right)\left(\frac{1}{3} - \frac{1}{6n}\right)\right] = \frac{1}{3}.$

**7.** $A = \displaystyle\lim_{n\to\infty} \sum_{k=1}^{n} \frac{r}{n}\sqrt{r^2 - \frac{k^2 r^2}{n^2}} = \frac{\pi r^2}{4} \Rightarrow \lim_{n\to\infty}\sum_{k=1}^{n} \frac{1}{n}\sqrt{1 - \frac{k^2}{n^2}} = \frac{\pi}{4}.$

### Exercises 8.4, Page 269

**1.** $V_n = nhr^2 \sin\dfrac{\pi}{n} = \pi r^2 h\, \dfrac{\sin \pi/n}{\pi/n}.$

$\displaystyle\lim_{n\to\infty} \pi r^2 h\, \frac{\sin \pi/n}{\pi/n} = \pi r^2 h.$

**3.** $V_n = \dfrac{\pi r^2 h}{n^3}\displaystyle\sum_{k=1}^{n} k^2 = \dfrac{\pi r^2 h}{6n^3}(n)(n+1)(2n+1).$

$\displaystyle\lim_{n\to\infty} V_n = \frac{1}{3}\pi r^2 h.$

**5.** $\frac{1}{2}wb^3\sqrt{2}$ pounds.      **7.** $\frac{1}{6}wbh(3H + b)$ pounds.

**9.** Example 8.4b: $F_n = \displaystyle\sum_{k=1}^{n} \frac{pba}{n}\left(H + b - \frac{kb}{n}\right).$

Let $\Delta x_k = \dfrac{b}{n}$, $f(x) = pa(H + b - x)$, $x_k = \dfrac{kb}{n}$. Then, $F_n = \displaystyle\sum_{k=1}^{n} f(x_k)\,\Delta x_k.$

### Exercises 8.5, Pages 273–274

**1.** *c.*      **5.** 8.      **9.** $\displaystyle\int_1^2 dx/x.$

**3.** $2m.$      **7.** $\frac{1}{2}.$

**Exercises 8.7, Page 280**

1. This follows the same line of argument as the first part of the theorem. Replace the words "greatest lower bound" by "least upper bound," and proceed as in the first half of the proof.

3. Repeat the proof of the first part of the theorem but with upper sums rather than lower sums.

5. A succession of refinements starting with $s_p$ always produces a *nondecreasing* sequence with limit equal to $\lim_{n \to \infty} s_n$. Hence

$$s_p \leq \lim_{n \to \infty} s_n.$$

**Exercises 8.8, Page 284**

1. $\displaystyle\int_b^a f(x)\, dx = \lim_{\delta \to 0} \sum_{k=1}^n f(x_k^*)\, \Delta \bar{x}_k = \lim_{\delta \to 0} \sum_{k=1}^n -f(x_k^*)\, \Delta x_{n-k}$

$\displaystyle \qquad = -\lim_{\delta \to 0} \sum_{\alpha=1}^n f(x_\alpha^*)\, \Delta x_\alpha = -\int_a^b f(x)\, dx.$

3. $\displaystyle\int_2^7 x^2\, dx = \frac{335}{3}, \int_2^5 x^2\, dx = \frac{117}{3}, \int_5^7 x^2\, dx = \frac{218}{3}.$

$$\frac{117}{3} + \frac{218}{3} = \frac{335}{3}.$$

5. $\displaystyle\int_2^7 x^2\, dx = \frac{335}{3}, \int_2^9 x^2\, dx = \frac{721}{3}, \int_9^7 x^2\, dx = -\frac{386}{3}.$

$$\frac{721}{3} + \left(-\frac{386}{3}\right) = \frac{335}{3}.$$

7. $\displaystyle\int_a^b [f(x) + g(x)]\, dx = \lim_{\delta \to 0} \sum_{k=1}^n [f(x_k^*) + g(x_k^*)]\, \Delta x_k$

$\displaystyle \qquad = \lim_{\delta \to 0} \left[ \sum_{k=1}^n f(x_k^*)\, \Delta x_k + \sum_{k=1}^n g(x_k^*)\, \Delta x_k \right]$

$\displaystyle \qquad = \lim_{\delta \to 0} \sum_{k=1}^n f(x_k^*)\, \Delta x_k + \lim_{\delta \to 0} \sum_{k=1}^n g(x_k^*)\, \Delta x_k$

$\displaystyle \qquad = \int_a^b f(x)\, dx + \int_a^b g(x)\, dx,$

since both $f$ and $g$ are integrable.

9. For the same partitions for both integrals,

$$\int_a^b f(x)\, dx = \lim_{\delta \to 0} \sum_{k=1}^n f(x_k^*)\, \Delta x_k \leq \lim_{\delta \to 0} \sum_{k=1}^n g(x_k^*)\, \Delta x_k = \int_a^b g(x)\, dx.$$

**Exercises 8.9, Pages 290–291**

1. $-\frac{4}{3}$. 3. $\frac{1}{3}(9 - 4\sqrt{2})$. 5. $\frac{251}{15}$. 7. 2. 9. $\frac{1.6}{105}a^3$. 11. $\frac{1}{8}$. 13. 10. 15. $\frac{2}{3}\sqrt{2}$.

17. $\frac{1}{3}(2t + 1)^{3/2} - 9$ for $t \geq 0$ and $-\frac{1}{3}(1 - 2t)^{3/2} - \frac{25}{3}$ for $t < 0$.

19. $2(x^{1/2} + 2x^{1/4} - 3)$. 21. $\frac{3}{2}t^2$ for $t \geq 0$, $-\frac{1}{2}t^2$ for $t < 0$. 23. $\sqrt{1 + x^4}$.

25. $\dfrac{s - a}{s + a}$. 27. $\dfrac{2}{1 - x^2}$.

**Exercises 8.10, Pages 294–295**

**1.** 36 (l.u.)$^2$.  **3.** $\frac{8}{3}$ (l.u.)$^2$.  **5.** $\frac{17}{20}$ (l.u.)$^2$.  **7.** 1 (l.u.)$^2$.
**9.** $\frac{8}{3}$ (l.u.)$^2$.  **11.** 8 (l.u.)$^2$.  **13.** 16 (l.u.)$^2$.  **15.** $\frac{51}{2}$ (l.u.)$^2$.
**17.** $A = \int_0^1 [(1 + \sqrt{x}) - (1 - \sqrt{x})]\, dx + \int_1^4 [(1 + \sqrt{x}) - (x - 1)]\, dx = \frac{9}{2}$ (l.u.)$^2$.


**Exercises 8.11, Pages 298–299**

**1.** $V = \frac{1}{12}a^3\sqrt{2}$.  **3.** $\frac{16}{3}$ (l.u.)$^3$.  **5.** $V = \frac{4}{3}\pi b^3$.  **7.** $V = \frac{4}{3}\pi ab^2$.
**9.** (a) $\frac{2}{5}\pi a^3$ (l.u.)$^3$. (c) $\frac{2}{3}\pi a^3$ (l.u.)$^3$.  **11.** $V = \frac{1}{12}na^2h \cot(\pi/n)$.  **13.** $\frac{128}{15}\pi$ (l.u.)$^3$.
**15.** (a) $\frac{32}{105}\pi$ (l.u.)$^3$.


**Exercises 8.12, Pages 307–309**

**1.** $\frac{2}{3}a$.  **3.** $\frac{4}{3}\sqrt{2}$.  **5.** $\frac{1}{2}r^2$.  **7.** $(\frac{55}{16}, \frac{17}{8})$.  **9.** $(0, \frac{4}{3}(a/\pi))$.  **11.** $(\frac{1}{2}, \frac{2}{5})$.  **13.** $(\frac{3}{7}, \frac{12}{25})$.
**15.** $(\frac{1}{2}, \frac{8}{5})$.  **17.** $(1, \frac{6}{5})$.  **19.** $(\frac{8}{5}, -\frac{88}{35})$.  **23.** $\frac{408}{5}\pi$ (l.u.)$^3$.  **25.** $\pi$ (inches)$^3$.


**Exercises 8.13, Pages 312–314**

**1.** $9\frac{3}{8}$ foot-pounds.  **3.** $22\frac{2}{9}\%$.  **5.** $27648\pi w$ foot-pounds.
**7.** $640{,}000\pi w/3$ foot-pounds.  **9.** $12{,}480w$ foot-pounds.
**11.** $2w \int_{-4}^{4} (4 - y)\sqrt{16 - y^2}\, dy$.  **13.** $\frac{5}{6}bh^2w$ pounds.  **15.** $256w/5$ pounds.
**17.** $\frac{1}{10}(k/a)(5\sqrt{2} - 2\sqrt{5})$.  **19.** $384 \times 10^7$ foot-pounds.  **21.** 736 foot-pounds.
**23.** $8\frac{1}{2}$ inches.  **25.** $\dfrac{km^2}{(x_3 - x_1)(x_3 - x_2)}$.


**Exercises 8.14, Pages 318–319**

**1.** 0.  **3.** $\frac{64}{3}$.  **5.** $\frac{2}{3}n$.  **7.** $\frac{1}{2}n(n + 1)$.
**9.** $T - 2k$ for $2k \le T \le 2k + 1 \le n$,
$2k + 2 - T$ for $2k + 1 \le T \le 2k + 2 \le n$,
$k = 0, 1, 2, \ldots$.


**Exercises 9.1, Page 327**

**1.** $\dfrac{\log_{10} 3}{\log_{10} 2} = 1.59$.  **3.** $\dfrac{\log_{10} 2}{\log_{10} 3 - \log_{10} 2} = 1.71$.  **5.** $\frac{1}{9}$.  **7.** $\frac{1}{5}$.
**9.** $x = \log_a M, y = \log_a N \Rightarrow a^x = M, a^y = N$
$\Rightarrow \dfrac{M}{N} = a^{x-y} \Rightarrow \log_a \dfrac{M}{N} = x - y = \log_a M - \log_a N$.
**11.** $x = \log_a N \Rightarrow a^x = N$. Then, by substitution, $a^{\log_a N} = N$.
**13.** $-\log_5 y$.  **15.** $\frac{1}{3}(y \log_2 3 - 1)$.  **21.** 0.69897.  **23.** $-0.69897$.  **25.** 2.17609.
**27.** 0.82660.  **29.** 0.59272.

## Exercises 9.2, Pages 334–335

**1.** $\dfrac{1 - 3 \ln x}{x^4}$. **3.** $\dfrac{18 \ln x}{x}$. **5.** $\dfrac{x(2 \ln x - 1)}{3(\ln x)^2}$. **7.** $-\dfrac{y}{x}$. **9.** $\dfrac{4 - x^2}{x(4 + x^2)}$.

**11.** $-\dfrac{\ln t}{2 + \ln t}$. **13.** $\dfrac{1}{\sqrt{x^2 + 1}}$. **15.** $\dfrac{4x}{x^4 - 1}$.

**17.** $x + 2x \ln 3x; \; 3 + 2 \ln 3x$. **19.** $2s^2; \; 4s^2$.

**21.** *Intercepts:* $y = 0 \Rightarrow x = 1$. *Extent:* $x > 0$.
$y$ decreasing for $0 < x < e^{-1}$, increasing for $x > e^{-1}$.
Min point $(e^{-1}, -e^{-1})$. Concave up for $x > 0$.

**23.** *Intercepts:* $y = 0 \Rightarrow x = 9$. *Extent:* $x > 0$.
*Asymptotes:* Lower portion of $y$-axis.
$y$ increasing for $x > 0$. Concave down for $x > 0$.

**25.** *Intercepts:* $y = 0 \Rightarrow x = 1$. *Extent:* $x > 0$. *Asymptotes:* $x = 0$, $y = 0$.
$y$ increasing for $0 < x < e$, decreasing for $x > e$.
Max point $(e, 3e^{-1})$.
Concave up for $x > e^{3/2}$, down for $0 < x < e^{3/2}$.
Inflection point $(e^{3/2}, \frac{9}{2}e^{-3/2})$.

**27.** $\ln y = kt \Rightarrow y = e^{kt} \Rightarrow D_t y = k e^{kt} = ky$.

**29.** Let $f(x) = \ln x$. Then $f'(x) = 1/x$, so that the Mean Value Theorem gives
$$\ln (x + h) = \ln x + \frac{h}{x + \theta h}, \qquad 0 < \theta < 1.$$
For $x = 1$ and $h = 0.01$, this becomes
$$\ln 1.01 = \ln 1 + \frac{0.01}{1 + 0.01\theta}$$
or
$$\ln 1.01 = \frac{1}{100 + \theta}.$$
Thus, $0 < \theta < 1 \Rightarrow 1/101 < \ln 1.01 < 1/100$.

**31.** $D_x R = \dfrac{k}{(x - a)^2}\left(1 - \dfrac{a}{x} - \ln \dfrac{x}{a}\right)$, and $\dfrac{k}{(x - a)^2} > 0$.

Let $y = 1 - \dfrac{a}{x} - \ln \dfrac{x}{a}$. Then $y' = \dfrac{a}{x^2} - \dfrac{1}{x} = \dfrac{a - x}{x^2}$. By inspection, $y = 0$ for $x = a$ and $y' < 0$ for $x > a$. Thus $y$ is decreasing for $x > a$ and therefore $y < 0$ for $x > a$. Hence, $D_x R < 0$ for $x > a$, and $R$ is decreasing.

## Exercises 9.3, Pages 337–338

**1.** $3x^2 \exp (x^3)$. **3.** $3^{2y}(1 + 2y \ln 3)$. **5.** $\dfrac{5^{\sqrt{4 + u^2}} u \ln 5}{\sqrt{4 + u^2}}$. **7.** $\dfrac{y(x - 1 - xye^{xy})}{x(1 + xye^{xy})}$.

**9.** $e^u(u + 1)$. **11.** $x^x(\ln x + 1)$. **13.** $0$. **15.** $\dfrac{e^w}{w}(1 + w \ln w)$. **17.** $-\dfrac{6e^{3x}}{e^{6x} - 1}$.

**19.** $\dfrac{e^x - e^{-x}}{e^x + e^{-x}} \log_{10} e$. **21.** $y'' = 2x(2x^4 - 7x^2 + 3) \exp (-x^2)$.

**23.** $y'' = (4x^2 - 4x + 3) \exp (x^2 - x)$.

**25.** *Intercepts:* $y = 0 \Rightarrow x = 1$. *Symmetry: y*-axis. *Asymptotes:* $y = 0$.
$y$ increasing for $x < 0$, decreasing for $x > 0$.
Max point $(0, 1)$.
Concave up for $|x| > 1/\sqrt{2}$, down for $|x| < 1/\sqrt{2}$.
Inflection points $(\pm 1/\sqrt{2}, e^{-1/2})$.

**27.** *Intercepts:* $y = 0 \Leftrightarrow x = 0$. *Symmetry:* Origin.
$y$ increasing for all $x$.
Concave down for $x < 0$, up for $x > 0$. Inflection point $(0, 0)$.

**29.** *Intercepts:* $x = 0 \Leftrightarrow y = 0$. *Asymptotes:* $y = -1$.
$y$ increasing for all $x$. Concave up for all $x$.

**31.** *Intercepts:* $x = 0 \Rightarrow y = 1$. *Symmetry: y*-axis.
$y$ increasing for $x > 0$, decreasing for $x < 0$.
Min point $(0, 1)$. Concave up for $x < 0$ and for $x > 0$.

**33.** 2.7998.   **35.** 61.34.

**37.** Let $f(x) = e^x$. Then $f'(x) = e^x$, and
$$e^{x+h} = e^x + he^{x+\theta h}, \quad 0 < \theta < 1.$$
For $x = 1$ and $h = 0.02$,
$$e^{1.02} = e + 0.02e^{1+0.02\theta}.$$
$$0 < \theta < 1 \Rightarrow e^{1.02} > e + 0.02e = 1.02e$$
and
$$e^{1.02} < e + 0.02e^{1.02}, \text{ or } 0.98e^{1.02} < e.$$
Hence,
$$1.02e < e^{1.02} < \frac{e}{0.98}.$$
That is,
$$2.7726 < e^{1.02} < 2.7737.$$

**39.** $x + y = \frac{1}{2}(1 + \ln 2)$.

**Exercises 9.4, Pages 341–342**

**1.** $\frac{1}{3} \ln |1 + x^3| + C$.
**3.** $-\sqrt{1 - x^2} + C$.
**5.** $-\frac{1}{2} \exp(-x^2) + C$.
**7.** $\ln(e^x + e^{-x}) + C$.
**9.** $\frac{1}{2}t^2 + \ln |t^2 - 1| + C$.
**11.** $-e^{1/x} + C$.
**13.** $3^{3x-1} \log_3 e + C$.

**15.** $-\ln(1 + e^{-t}) + C$.
**17.** $\frac{1}{3}e^{2+3x} + C$.
**19.** $-\dfrac{1}{2(1 + y^2)} + C$.
**21.** $\frac{3}{2} \ln \frac{5}{17}$.
**23.** $2(\sqrt{2} - 1)$.
**25.** $1 - \ln 2$.
**27.** $\frac{1}{2}(e - e^9)$.

**29.** $\frac{1}{2} \ln \frac{3}{7}$.
**31.** $\frac{1}{2} \ln 5$ (l.u.)$^2$.
**33.** $\ln 3$ (l.u.)$^2$.
**35.** 46.4 minutes (approx.).
**37.** 1700 years (approx.).
**39.** $(1/\ln 2, 1/\ln 2)$.

**Exercises 9.5, Pages 343–344**

**1.** $\dfrac{2y}{x} \ln x$.

**3.** $\dfrac{y}{x} e^{-x}(1 - x \ln x)$.

**5.** $x \left[ \dfrac{5}{y} - \dfrac{2y}{3(1 - y^2)} - \dfrac{3}{2(1 + 3y)} \right]$.

**7.** $u \left[ \ln \ln 2v + \dfrac{1}{\ln 2v} \right]$.

**9.** $\dfrac{1}{4} y \left[ \dfrac{2x}{x^2 + 4} - \dfrac{x}{1 + x^2} - \dfrac{3x^2}{x^3 + 2} \right]$.

**11.** $(w/u^2)(1 - \ln u)$.

**13.** $u^v(D_x v) \ln u + vu^{v-1} D_x u$.

**Exercises 10.1, Page 348**

**1.** The limit does not exist.　　**3.** 1.　　　　　　　**5.** 0.

**9.** Continuous except for infinite discontinuities at $v = n\pi$, $n \in \mathcal{I}$.

**11.** Continuous except for infinite discontinuities at $x = n\pi$, $n \in \mathcal{I}$.

**13.** Continuous except for infinite discontinuities at $s = (2n - 1)\pi/2$, $n \in \mathcal{I}$.

**Exercises 10.2, Page 351**

**3.** $D_x \cos x = \lim\limits_{h \to 0} \dfrac{\cos(x + h) - \cos x}{h}$

$\qquad = \lim\limits_{h \to 0} \dfrac{\cos x \cos h - \sin x \sin h - \cos x}{h}$

$\qquad = \lim\limits_{h \to 0} \left( -\sin x \dfrac{\sin h}{h} - \cos x \dfrac{1 - \cos h}{h} \right)$

$\qquad = \lim\limits_{h \to 0} \left( -\sin x \dfrac{\sin h}{h} - \cos x \dfrac{\sin h/2}{h/2} \sin \dfrac{h}{2} \right)$

$\qquad = -\sin x.$

**5.** $-5 \sin 5x.$　**7.** $2t \cos t^2.$　**9.** $-2 \csc 2\theta.$　**11.** $-e^w \csc e^w \cot e^w.$　**13.** $e^{\sin x} \cos x.$

**15.** $12 \sin^3 3x \cos 3x.$　**17.** $8 \tan 4x \sec^2 4x.$　**19.** $-9 \sec^2 3w.$　**21.** $8 \cos(2 - 4z).$

**23.** $-\frac{1}{2}[(n + m)^2 \sin(n + m)t + (n - m)^2 \sin(n - m)t].$

**25.** $\dfrac{t \cos t^2}{\sqrt{\sin t^2}}.$　**27.** $-\dfrac{\sec y}{1 + x \sec y \tan y}.$　**29.** $\dfrac{\cos x \cos^2 y - \sin^2 x \sin y}{\cos^3 y}.$

**31.** $-\dfrac{\sin t}{2 \cos 2t}.$　**33.** $\cot \frac{1}{2}u.$　**35.** $-\cot t.$　**37.** $-\cos x.$

**39.** $D_x \cos x = -\sin x = \cos(x + \frac{1}{2}\pi).$

　　Assume $D_x^k \cos x = \cos(x + \frac{1}{2}k\pi)$. Then

$$D_x^{k+1} \cos x = D_x \cos(x + \tfrac{1}{2}k\pi) = -\sin(x + \tfrac{1}{2}k\pi)$$
$$= \cos(x + \tfrac{1}{2}k\pi + \tfrac{1}{2}\pi) = \cos[x + \tfrac{1}{2}(k + 1)\pi].$$

　　This completes the proof by Mathematical Induction.

**Exercises 10.3, Pages 355–357**

**1.** Concave up, $\pi < x < 3\pi$; concave down, $0 < x < \pi$ and $3\pi < x < 4\pi$.
Max points $(0, 2)$, $(4\pi, 2)$; min point $(2\pi, -2)$.
Inflection points $(\pi, 0)$, $(3\pi, 0)$.

**3.** Concave up, $0 < x < \frac{1}{2}\pi$; concave down, $\frac{1}{2}\pi < x < \pi$.
Min points $(\frac{1}{4}\pi, -4)$, $(\pi, 0)$; max points $(0, 0)$, $(\frac{3}{4}\pi, 4)$.
Inflection point $(\frac{1}{2}\pi, 0)$.

**5.** Concave up, $\pi < x < \frac{3}{2}\pi$; concave down, $0 < x < \pi$ and $\frac{3}{2}\pi < x < 2\pi$.
Max point $(\frac{1}{2}\pi, 1)$. Inflection point $(\frac{3}{2}\pi, 0)$.

**7.** Concave up, $-\pi < x < -\frac{1}{2}\pi$ and $\frac{1}{2}\pi < x < \pi$; concave down, $-\frac{1}{2}\pi < x < 0$ and $0 < x < \frac{1}{2}\pi$.
Max points $(\pm\pi, 0)$, $(\pm\frac{1}{4}\pi, 5)$; min points $(\pm\frac{3}{4}\pi, -5)$.
Inflection points $(\pm\frac{1}{2}\pi, 0)$.

**9.** Concave up, $\frac{1}{4}(4n - 1)\pi < x < \frac{1}{4}(4n + 1)\pi$, $n \in \mathcal{I}$;
concave down, $\frac{1}{4}(4n + 1)\pi < x < \frac{1}{4}(4n + 3)\pi$, $n \in \mathcal{I}$.

Max points $(\frac{1}{2}(2n-1)\pi, 3)$; min points $(n\pi, 1)$, $n \in \mathcal{I}$.
Inflection points $(\frac{1}{4}(2n-1)\pi, 2)$, $n \in \mathcal{I}$.

**11.** No max or min points. Inflection points $(n\pi, 2n\pi)$, $n \in \mathcal{I}$.

**13.** Max points $(\frac{1}{4}\pi, \sqrt{2})$, $(2\pi, 1)$; min points $(0, 1)$, $(\frac{5}{4}\pi, -\sqrt{2})$.
Inflection points $(\frac{3}{4}\pi, 0)$, $(\frac{7}{4}\pi, 0)$.

**15.** Max points $(n\pi + \frac{1}{3}\pi, n\pi + \frac{1}{3}\pi - 2 + \frac{1}{2}\sqrt{3})$, $n \in \mathcal{I}$;
min points $(n\pi - \frac{1}{3}\pi, n\pi - \frac{1}{3}\pi - 2 - \frac{1}{2}\sqrt{3})$, $n \in \mathcal{I}$.
Inflection points $(\frac{1}{2}n\pi, \frac{1}{2}n\pi - 2)$, $n \in \mathcal{I}$.

**17.** Max points $(2n\pi - \pi, \frac{3}{2})$, $(2n\pi, -\frac{1}{2})$, $n \in \mathcal{I}$; min points $(2n\pi \pm \frac{1}{3}\pi, -\frac{3}{2})$, $n \in \mathcal{I}$.

**19.** *Hint:* Use the formula for $\sin A - \sin B$.
Max points $(2n\pi, -1)$, $(2n\pi \pm \frac{3}{5}\pi, 4.05)$, $n \in \mathcal{I}$;
min points $(2n\pi + \pi, -5)$, $(2n\pi \pm \frac{1}{5}\pi, -1.55)$, $n \in \mathcal{I}$.

**21.** The curve $y = \sin x$ goes through one cycle in $2\pi$ units and the curve $y = \sin\sqrt{2}x$ goes through $\sqrt{2}$ cycles in $2\pi$ units. Since $\sqrt{2}$ is irrational, the two component curves have no common period. Hence, the given curve is not periodic.

**23.** $3r$.

**25.** Largest volume, $r = h = 2$ inches; smallest volume, $h = 3$ inches, $r = 1\frac{1}{2}$ inches.

**27.** $\text{Tan}^{-1}(\frac{1}{6}\sqrt{3})$.

**29.** $\frac{1}{12}\pi a\sqrt{3}$ l.u./second; $\frac{1}{12}\pi a$ l.u./second; $-\frac{1}{12}\pi a$ l.u./second.

**31.** Approx. 0.53 millimeters/minute.

## Exercises 10.4, Pages 360–361

**1.** $\frac{3}{2}\sin\frac{2}{3}x + C$.  **3.** $\frac{1}{2}\ln|\sin 2x| + C$.  **5.** $\frac{1}{3}\sec 3r + C$.  **7.** $\frac{1}{3}\cos(2 - 3t) + C$.

**9.** $-\frac{1}{2}\cot 2w + C$.  **11.** $\frac{1}{3}\ln|\sec 3x + \tan 3x| + C$.  **13.** $e^{\sin y} + C$.

**15.** $-\frac{1}{4}\csc 4y + C$.  **17.** $-\frac{1}{2}\cos(1 + x^2) + C$.  **19.** $-\frac{1}{3}\ln(1 + \cos 3\theta) + C$.

**21.** $\dfrac{\pi^3 + 24}{24}$.  **23.** $\dfrac{1}{2\pi}$.  **25.** $2\sqrt{2} - 2$.  **27.** 4.  **29.** $-\frac{1}{2}$.

**31.** 
$$\int \csc x \, dx = \int \frac{\csc^2 x - \csc x \cot x}{\csc x - \cot x} dx$$
$$= \ln|\csc x - \cot x| + C = \ln\left|\frac{1 - \cos x}{\sin x}\right| + C$$
$$= \ln|\tan\frac{1}{2}x| + C.$$

**33.** 4 (l.u.)$^2$.  **35.** $\dfrac{2a}{b}$ (l.u.)$^2$.  **37.** $\pi$ (l.u.)$^3$.  **39.** $\dfrac{\pi}{3}(1 - \ln 2)$ (l.u.)$^3$.

**41.** $\dfrac{A}{k}(1 - \cos k\xi)$.

## Exercises 10.5, Pages 365–366

**1.** $n\pi + (-1)^{n-1}\frac{1}{3}\pi$, $n \in \mathcal{I}$.  **3.** $2n\pi \pm \frac{1}{4}\pi$, $n \in \mathcal{I}$.  **5.** $-\frac{1}{4}\pi$.  **7.** $\frac{5}{6}\pi$.

**9.** 0.  **11.** $\frac{3}{4}\pi$.  **13.** $\{(x, y): x = \cot y\}$.  **15.** $\{(x, y): x = \csc y\}$.

**17.** Yes. Let $y = \text{Sin}^{-1}(-x)$; then
$(-\frac{1}{2}\pi \leq y \leq \frac{1}{2}\pi$ and $\sin y = -x) \Rightarrow \sin(-y) = x \Rightarrow y = -\text{Sin}^{-1} x$.

**19.** $x = \frac{1}{2}\tan 2y$.  **21.** $x = -1 + \cos\frac{1}{2}(y + 1)$.

**23.** *Hint:* The graph is that of $x = \frac{1}{3}\sin 2y$.

**25.** *Hint:* The graph is that of $x = 1 + \tan \frac{1}{3}y$ for $-\frac{3}{2}\pi < y < \frac{3}{2}\pi$.

**27.** $\dfrac{x}{\sqrt{1 - x^2}}$. **29.** $\dfrac{1}{\sqrt{x^2 - 3}}$. **31.** $\dfrac{840}{841}$. **33.** $\frac{3}{4}$.

**35.** $\frac{2}{9}(1 + \sqrt{10})$; $\frac{1}{9}(4\sqrt{2} - \sqrt{5})$; $\frac{2}{3}(\sqrt{2} + \sqrt{5})$.

**37.** $\frac{1}{10}(3\sqrt{3} - 4)$; $\frac{1}{10}(4\sqrt{3} + 3)$; $\frac{1}{39}(48 - 25\sqrt{3})$.

**39.** $\frac{253}{325}$; $\frac{204}{325}$; $\frac{253}{204}$. **41.** $\frac{1}{4}$. **43.** $-2$. **45.** 1. **47.** $\dfrac{h + k}{1 - hk}$.

## Exercises 10.6, Pages 368–370

**3.** Let $y = \text{Cos}^{-1} u$, where $0 < y < \pi$. Then $u = \cos y$ and

$$D_x u = -\sin y \, D_x y \Rightarrow D_x y = \frac{-D_x u}{\sin y} = -\frac{D_x u}{\sqrt{1 - u^2}},$$

since $\sin y > 0$. Note that Theorem 6.6b applies.

**5.** $\dfrac{2}{4 + s^2}$. **7.** $\dfrac{1}{\sqrt{2u - 4u^2}}$. **9.** $2e^{2x} \text{Tan}^{-1} e^{2x} + \dfrac{2e^{4x}}{1 + e^{4x}}$.

**11.** $3 \text{Sin}^{-1} 2x + \dfrac{6x}{\sqrt{1 - 4x^2}}$. **13.** $\dfrac{2}{(4 + s^2) \text{Tan}^{-1}(s/2)}$. **15.** $\dfrac{(1 + 4v^2) \text{Tan}^{-1} 2v - 2v}{(1 + 4v^2)(\text{Tan}^{-1} 2v)^2}$.

**17.** $2 \text{Tan}^{-1}(s/2) + C$. **19.** $-\frac{1}{4}\sqrt{1 - 4x^2} + C$. **21.** $\frac{1}{2} \text{Tan}^{-1} 2e^v + C$.

**23.** $t - \ln(1 + t) + C$. **25.** $\text{Tan}^{-1}(\sin u) + C$. **27.** $\frac{1}{6}\pi$. **29.** $\text{Tan}^{-1} e - \frac{1}{4}\pi$.

**31.** $\frac{1}{8}\pi$ (l.u.)$^2$.

**33.** *Intercepts:* $y = 0 \Rightarrow x = 0$, $x = 2$. *Extent:* $0 \leq x \leq 2$, $0 \leq y \leq \frac{1}{2}\pi$.
$y$ increasing for $0 < x < 1$; decreasing for $1 < x < 2$.
Max point $(1, \frac{1}{2}\pi)$; min points $(0, 0)$, $(2, 0)$.
Concave down, $0 < x < 1$, $1 < x < 2$.

**35.** $\text{Tan}^{-1}\left(\dfrac{1 + x}{1 - x}\right) = \text{Tan}^{-1} x + \dfrac{\pi}{4}$.

**37.** $x = \pm\dfrac{1}{\sqrt{2}} \exp\left(\dfrac{\pi}{4} - 1\right) = y$. **39.** $\frac{1}{6}\pi$ (l.u.)$^2$. **41.** $30\sqrt{5}$ feet.

**43.** $\text{Tan}^{-1}(x + h) = \text{Tan}^{-1} x + \dfrac{h}{1 + (x + \theta h)^2}$, $0 < \theta < 1$

$\Rightarrow \text{Tan}^{-1} 1.02 = \text{Tan}^{-1} 1 + \dfrac{0.02}{1 + (1 + 0.02h)^2}$

$\Rightarrow \dfrac{\pi}{4} + \dfrac{0.02}{1 + (1.02)^2} < \text{Tan}^{-1} 1.02 < \dfrac{\pi}{4} + \dfrac{0.02}{1 + 1^2}$

$\Rightarrow 0.7952 < \text{Tan}^{-1} 1.02 < 0.7954$.

**45.** 0.0308 radian/second. **47.** $-\frac{24}{73}$ radian/minute. **49.** $\frac{4}{101}$ radian/minute.

## Exercises 10.7, Pages 376–377

**27.** $\frac{1}{6} \sinh^2 3x + C$. **29.** $\frac{1}{2} \ln \cosh 2x + C$. **31.** $\ln \cosh x - \frac{1}{2} \tanh^2 x + C$.

**33.** $\frac{1}{2} \text{Cosh}^{-1} \frac{2}{3}x + C$. **35.** $\frac{1}{2} \tanh^{-1} \frac{1}{2}x + C$. **37.** $-\dfrac{1}{12} \tanh^{-1} \dfrac{4}{3x} + C$.

**39.** $-\frac{1}{18} \ln|4 - 9x^2| + C$. **41.** $\frac{1}{4}\pi a^3(2 + \sinh 2)$ (l.u.)$^3$.

**43.** The curve is the hyperbola $\frac{1}{6}x^2 - \frac{1}{16}y^2 = 1$.

**Exercises 10.8, Page 381**

**1.** $k$. **3.** The fraction $\to \infty$ as $x \to 0$. **5.** 0. **7.** The fraction $\to \infty$ as $t \to \infty$.
**9.** 0. **11.** $-\frac{1}{2}$. **13.** 0. **15.** $\ln(a/b)$. **17.** 1. **19.** $\frac{1}{16}$. **21.** $\frac{1}{4}$.

**Exercises 10.9, Page 383**

**1.** The expression $\to \infty$ as $x \to \infty$. **3.** 1. **5.** 0. **7.** 0. **9.** $-\frac{1}{3}$. **11.** $-\frac{1}{2}$.
**13.** $e^{-1}$. **15.** 1. **17.** 1. **19.** $e^{2a}$.

**Exercises 10.10, Pages 389–390**

| | | | |
|---|---|---|---|
| **1.** 0.703. | **5.** 0.443. | **9.** 0.682. | **13.** 2.053. |
| **3.** 2.104. | **7.** 1.306. | **11.** 2.551. | **15.** $335°2.4'$. |

**Exercises 11.1, Pages 395–396**

**1.** (a) $(6, 1)$. (d) $\sqrt{74}$. (e) $(16, -1)$. **3.** 0.
**5.** (b) $-2i + 4j$. (d) $\sqrt{221}$. (f) $\sqrt{13} + \sqrt{17}$. (h) $3\sqrt{13} - 2\sqrt{17}$.
**11.** $\dfrac{5}{\sqrt{41}} i + \dfrac{4}{\sqrt{41}} j$.
**13.** $|a + c| \leq |a| + |c|$. Let $c = b - a$. Then
$$|b| \leq |a| + |b - a| \Rightarrow |b| - |a| \leq |b - a|.$$
Similarly, $|a| - |b| \leq |a - b|$. Therefore, $|a - b| \geq ||a| - |b||$.
**15.** $\sqrt{505}$. **17.** No. Any three noncoplanar vectors may be used.

**Exercises 11.2, Pages 399–400**

**1.** $\sqrt{113}$ in the direction $[8, 7]$.
**3.** $\sqrt{70 + 48\sqrt{2}}$ in the direction $[3\sqrt{2} + 4, -1]$.
**5.** 96.9 pounds, approximately in the direction $[19, -12]$.
**7.** $\sqrt{641}$ knots in the direction $[4, 25]$.
**9.** $5\sqrt{169 + 60\sqrt{2}}$ pounds in the direction $[5 + 12\sqrt{2}, 5]$.
**11.** $[\sqrt{17}, 1]$. **13.** $1500\sqrt{2}$ pounds, $300\sqrt{5}$ pounds.

**Exercises 11.3, Pages 404–405**

**1.** $z_1 = x_1 + iy_1$, $z_2 = x_2 + iy_2 \Rightarrow \bar{z}_1 = x_1 - iy_1$, $\bar{z}_2 = x_2 - iy_2$.
$$\overline{z_1 + z_2} = \overline{x_1 + iy_1 + x_2 + iy_2} = \overline{x_1 + x_2 + i(y_1 + y_2)}$$
$$= x_1 + x_2 - i(y_1 + y_2) = (x_1 - iy_1) + (x_2 - iy_2)$$
$$= \bar{z}_1 + \bar{z}_2.$$
**3.** This is essentially equivalent to the geometric theorem that the sum of the lengths of two sides of a triangle is greater than the length of the third side.
**5.** Let $z_1 = z_2 z_3 w$. By Number 4, $|z_1| = |z_2||z_3||w|$. Hence, $|w| = \left| \dfrac{z_1}{z_2 z_3} \right| = \dfrac{|z_1|}{|z_2||z_3|}$.
**7.** $3 + i3\sqrt{3}$. **9.** $\dfrac{1}{128} + i\dfrac{\sqrt{3}}{128}$. **11.** $-\dfrac{1}{2} - i\dfrac{\sqrt{3}}{2}$. **13.** $\dfrac{1}{32} - i\dfrac{\sqrt{3}}{32}$. **15.** $-\dfrac{1}{2} + i\dfrac{\sqrt{3}}{2}$.

### Exercises 11.4, Pages 412–413

**1. (a)** The graph is the ray $y = x$, $x \geq 0$. **(c)** The graph is the circle $x^2 + y^2 = y$.
**3. (a)** $-2 \sin 2s + i2 \cos 2s$. **(c)** $(-1 + i) \sin 2u$.
**5. (a)** $4e^{i7\pi/6}$. **(c)** $10 \exp(i \cos^{-1} \frac{3}{5})$.
**11. (a)** $i \sinh 1$. **(c)** $-\frac{1}{2}\sqrt{2} \cosh 1 + i\frac{1}{2}\sqrt{2} \sinh 1$. **(e)** $\frac{1}{2}\sqrt{2} + i\frac{1}{2}\sqrt{2}$.
　**(g)** $\ln 2 + i\frac{1}{2}\pi$. **(i)** $\ln 3 + i\pi$.

### Exercises 11.5, Page 416

**1.** $2$, $-1 + i\sqrt{3}$, $-1 - i\sqrt{3}$. **3.** $i$, $-\frac{1}{2}\sqrt{3} - \frac{1}{2}i$, $\frac{1}{2}\sqrt{3} - \frac{1}{2}i$.
**5.** $\sqrt{2} + i\sqrt{2}$, $-\sqrt{2} + i\sqrt{2}$, $-\sqrt{2} - i\sqrt{2}$, $\sqrt{2} - i\sqrt{2}$.
**7.** $\sqrt{3} + i$, $-\sqrt{3} + i$, $-2i$. **9.** $-\frac{1}{2}\sqrt{6} + \frac{1}{2}\sqrt{2}i$, $\frac{1}{2}\sqrt{6} - \frac{1}{2}\sqrt{2}i$.
**11.** $\sqrt[3]{5} \exp(i\frac{1}{3}\alpha)$, $\sqrt[3]{5} \exp(i\frac{1}{3}\alpha + i\frac{2}{3}\pi)$, $\sqrt[3]{5} \exp(i\frac{1}{3}\alpha + i\frac{4}{3}\pi)$, where $\alpha = \cos^{-1}(-\frac{3}{5})$.
**13.** $2\sqrt[4]{2} \exp(i\frac{5}{8}\pi)$, $2\sqrt[4]{2} \exp(i\frac{13}{8}\pi)$. **15.** $\exp(i\frac{1}{4}n\pi)$, $n = 0, 1, 2, 3, 4, 5, 6, 7$.
**17.** $\frac{1}{2} + \frac{1}{2}\sqrt{3}i$, $-\frac{1}{2} + \frac{1}{2}\sqrt{3}i$, $-\frac{1}{2} - \frac{1}{2}\sqrt{3}i$, $\frac{1}{2} - \frac{1}{2}\sqrt{3}i$. **19.** $2 \exp(i\frac{1}{2}2n\pi)$, $n = 1, 2, 3, 4$.
**21.** $-64$. **25.** *Hint:* $\omega^4 + \omega^3 + \omega^2 + \omega + 1 = 0$.

### Exercises 12.1, Pages 419–420

**1.** $x^4 + \frac{8}{3}x^3 + 7x + C$. **3.** $\frac{1}{3}\sin^3 t + C$. **5.** $\frac{1}{3}(w^2 + 1)^{3/2} + C$.
**7.** $x - \ln|x + 1| + C$. **9.** $\frac{1}{3}e^{3u} + C$. **11.** $\sec v + C$. **13.** $2 \ln|\sec \sqrt{x}| + C$.
**15.** $\sqrt{w^2 + 4} + C$. **17.** $\frac{1}{2} \ln|t^2 - 9| + C$. **19.** $(2^{x^2-1}/\ln 2) + C$.
**21.** $\sqrt{u^2 - 4} + C$. **23.** $\frac{1}{10}\tan^{-1}(\frac{2}{5}x) + C$. **25.** $\sin^{-1}(\frac{1}{2}y) + C$.
**27.** $-\frac{1}{3} \ln|\csc u^3 + \cot u^3| + C$. **29.** $w^2 + \frac{4}{3}\sqrt{2}w^{3/2} + w + C$. **31.** $\frac{1}{8}\sin^4 2x + C$.
**33.** $(2^w/\ln 2) + C$. **35.** $9 - 6\sqrt{2}$. **37.** $1$. **39.** $\frac{3}{2}(e^4 - 1)$. **41.** $0$. **43.** $\frac{1}{4}\pi$.

### Exercises 12.2, Pages 422–424

**1.** $\frac{1}{9}\cos^3 3x - \frac{1}{3}\cos 3x + C$. **3.** $\tan \theta + C$. **5.** $\frac{1}{4}\sec^2 2r + C$.
**7.** $\frac{1}{21}\sec^7 3y - \frac{2}{15}\sec^5 3y + \frac{1}{9}\sec^3 3y + C$. **9.** $\frac{1}{4}\sec^2 2s + \frac{1}{2}\ln|\cos 2s| + C$.
**11.** $\frac{1}{3}\sin^3 y - \frac{1}{5}\sin^5 y + C$. **13.** $\frac{1}{10}\sin^5 2w - \frac{1}{3}\sin^3 2w + \frac{1}{2}\sin 2w + C$.
**15.** $-\frac{1}{2}\csc^2 x + C$. **17.** $\frac{1}{8}x - \frac{1}{64}\sin 8x + C$. **19.** $\frac{2}{3}\sin^3 x + C$.
**21.** $\frac{1}{3}\ln(1 + \sin 3y) + C$. **23.** $-\frac{1}{8}\csc^4 2r + \frac{1}{2}\csc^2 2r + \frac{1}{2}\ln|\sin 2r| + C$.
**25.** $\sqrt{2}\sin x + C$ for $2n\pi - \frac{1}{2}\pi \leq x \leq 2n\pi + \frac{1}{2}\pi$,
　$-\sqrt{2}\sin x + C$ for $(2n + 1)\pi - \frac{1}{2}\pi < x < (2n + 1)\pi + \frac{1}{2}\pi$.
**27.** $\frac{1}{2}\ln|\csc 2\theta - \cot 2\theta| + \frac{1}{2}\ln|\sin 2\theta| + C$. **29.** $2 \cot \frac{1}{2}w - 2 \csc \frac{1}{2}w + w + C$.
**31.** $-\frac{1}{10}\cot^5 2u + \frac{1}{6}\cot^3 2u - \frac{1}{2}\cot 2u - u + C$. **33.** $\frac{1}{2}(1 - \ln 2)$. **35.** $\frac{3}{16}\pi$.
**37.** $\sqrt{3} - 1$. **39.** $\frac{2}{3}$. **41.** $\frac{28}{15}$. **43.** $\frac{1}{5}\ln\left|\dfrac{2(5 + 4 \sin t - 3 \cos t)}{4 \cos t + 3 \sin t}\right|$.
**45.** $\dfrac{\sin x}{3(3 \cos x - 4 \sin x)}$. **47.** $-\frac{2}{5}$. **49.** $\frac{1}{48}(3\sqrt{3} + 8)$. **53.** $\frac{1}{4}(4 - \pi)$ (l.u.)$^2$.
**55.** $\frac{1}{8}(\pi - 2)$ (l.u.)$^2$. **57.** $\pi(1 - \frac{1}{4}\pi)$ (l.u.)$^3$. **59.** $30RI_0^2$ joules.

## Exercises 12.3, Pages 429–430

**1.** $\frac{2}{3}(x - 8)\sqrt{x + 4} + C$.  **3.** $-\frac{1}{5}(s^2 + 6)(9 - s^2)^{3/2} + C$.

**5.** $\text{Sin}^{-1}\left[\frac{1}{3}(x - 1)\right] + C$.  **7.** $\sqrt{u^2 - 4u + 8} + 2\sinh^{-1}\left[\frac{1}{2}(u - 2)\right] + C$.

**9.** $\frac{1}{2}\ln(w^2 - 4w + 13) + C$.  **11.** $\frac{1}{3}\sqrt{x^2 - 9} - \text{Tan}^{-1}(\frac{1}{3}\sqrt{x^2 - 9}) + C$.

**13.** $\dfrac{1}{\sqrt{2}}\text{Tan}^{-1}\left(\dfrac{t + 1}{\sqrt{2}}\right) + C$.  **15.** $(y^2 + 8)(y^2 + 4)^{-1/2} + C$.

**17.** $\frac{5}{8}x^{9/5} + \frac{15}{4}x^{4/5} + C$.  **19.** $\frac{2}{15}(3s^2 - 4s + 8)\sqrt{s + 1} + C$.

**21.** $\frac{3}{4}(y - 3)\sqrt[3]{y + 1} + C$.  **23.** 14.1.  **25.** $\frac{1}{12}\pi$.  **27.** $\frac{5832}{35}$.  **29.** $\frac{1}{3}(9\sqrt{3} - 10\sqrt{2})$.

**31.** $\frac{5}{3}$.  **33.** $\frac{1}{2}(2\sqrt{2} - \sqrt{5})$.  **35.** 4 (l.u.)². **37.** $(15 - \ln 16)$ (l.u.)².

**39.** $\frac{1}{5}\pi(717 - 20\ln 4)$ (l.u.)².

## Exercises 12.4, Pages 434–435

**3.** $\frac{9}{2}\text{Sin}^{-1}(\frac{1}{3}x) - \frac{1}{2}x\sqrt{9 - x^2} + C$.  **5.** $\frac{1}{2}\text{Sin}^{-1}t + \frac{1}{2}t\sqrt{1 - t^2} + C$.

**7.** $-\dfrac{\sqrt{4 - s^2}}{4s} + C$.  **9.** $\frac{1}{3}(y^2 - 8)\sqrt{y^2 + 4} + C$.  **11.** $\dfrac{x}{4\sqrt{4 + x^2}} + C$.

**13.** $\dfrac{1}{2}\ln\left|\dfrac{\sqrt{x^2 + 4} - 2}{x}\right| + C$.  **15.** $-\frac{1}{3}(18 + x^2)(9 - x^2)^{1/2} + C$.

**17.** $2\text{Sin}^{-1}(\frac{1}{2}\sqrt{y}) + C$.  **19.** $\frac{1}{6}(2\pi - 3\sqrt{3})$.  **21.** $\frac{1}{30}(5\sqrt{3} - 2\sqrt{15})$.

**23.** $\frac{1}{2}\text{Sec}^{-1}3 - \frac{1}{6}\pi$.  **25.** $\dfrac{2\pi + 3\sqrt{3}}{192}$.  **27.** $6\pi$ (l.u.)².  **29.** $\frac{1}{5}\pi$ (l.u.)².

**31.** $[\ln(2 + \sqrt{3}) - \frac{1}{2}\sqrt{3}]$ (l.u.)².  **33.** $\frac{1}{8}\pi$ (l.u.)².  **35.** $\frac{3}{8}\pi a^2$ (l.u.)².

## Exercises 12.5, Pages 437–438

**1.** $\frac{1}{3}w\sin 3w + \frac{1}{9}\cos 3w + C$.  **3.** $(2 - x^2)\cos x + 2x\sin x + C$.

**5.** $w\text{Tan}^{-1}w - \frac{1}{2}\ln(1 + w^2) + C$.  **7.** $\frac{3}{8}(2x^2 - 1)\cos 2x + \frac{1}{4}(2x^3 - 3x)\sin 2x + C$.

**9.** $\frac{1}{4}y^2(2\ln y - 1) + C$.  **11.** $\frac{1}{4}(2y^2 - 1)\text{Sin}^{-1}y + \frac{1}{4}y\sqrt{1 - y^2} + C$.

**13.** $-x\cot x + \ln\sin x + C$.  **15.** $\frac{1}{13}e^{2x}(3\sin 3x + 2\cos 3x) + C$.

**17.** $\frac{1}{4}(x^4 - 1)\text{Tan}^{-1}x - \frac{1}{12}(x^3 - 3x) + C$.  **19.** $\theta\tan\theta + \ln\cos\theta + C$.

**21.** $\frac{2}{25}y^{5/2}(5\ln 3y - 2) + C$.  **23.** $\frac{1}{2}\sec t\tan t + \frac{1}{2}\ln|\sec t + \tan t| + C$.

**25.** 1.  **27.** $\frac{1}{4}\pi - \frac{1}{2}\ln 2$.  **29.** $\frac{1}{2}(2 + e^{\pi/4})$.  **31.** $\frac{506}{15}$.  **33.** $(1 - 2e^{-1})$ (l.u.)².

**35.** $(\frac{1}{12}\sqrt{3}\pi - \frac{1}{4})$ (l.u.)².  **37.** $\left(\dfrac{25\ln 5 - 12}{10\ln 5 - 8}, \dfrac{5\ln^2 5 - 10\ln 5 + 8}{10\ln 5 - 8}\right)$.  **39.** 1.

**41.** The symbol $\int f(x)\,dx$ stands for *any* inverse derivative of $f(x)$. If $F$ is any function such that $F'(x) = f(x)$, then $\int f(x)\,dx = F(x) + C$, where the value of $C$ depends on additional given conditions. Thus the seemingly contradictory result must be interpreted to mean $F(x) + C_1 = c + F(x) + C_2$, so that $C_1 = c + C_2$.

## Exercises 12.6, Pages 443–444

**1.** $\frac{2}{3}$.  **3.** $\frac{3}{16}\pi$.  **5.** $\frac{2}{15}$.  **7.** $\frac{2}{35}$.  **9.** $\frac{1}{2}\pi$.  **11.** $\frac{2}{3}$.  **13.** $\frac{8}{3}$.  **15.** $\frac{1}{8}\pi$.  **17.** $\frac{4}{15}$.

**19.** $\frac{5}{128}\pi$.  **21.** $\frac{8}{35}$.  **23.** $\frac{5}{16}\pi$.  **25.** $\frac{1}{2}\pi$.  **27.** $4\pi$.  **29.** $\frac{1}{2}\pi$.  **31.** $\frac{3}{32}\pi a^2$.

**33.** $\frac{4}{9}$ (l.u.)². **35.** $\frac{3}{16}\pi^2$ (l.u.)³. **37.** $\frac{1}{16}\pi$ (l.u.)².

**39.** $\dfrac{4(2m)(2m-2)\cdots(2)(2n-1)(2n-3)\cdots(1)}{(2m+2n+1)(2m+2n-1)\cdots(1)}$ (l.u.)².

### Exercises 12.7, Pages 449–450

**1.** $\frac{1}{4}\ln\left|\dfrac{x-2}{x+2}\right| + C.$

**3.** $2\ln|w-2| + 3\ln|w+2| + C.$

**5.** $\ln\dfrac{|x^3(x-1)|}{(x+1)^2} + C.$

**7.** $\ln w^2 - \dfrac{3}{w+2} + C.$

**9.** $t + \ln\dfrac{(t-2)^4}{|t-1|} + C.$

**11.** $\ln|x| - \dfrac{3}{x+1} + C.$

**13.** $3\ln|w| - \frac{2}{3}\ln|3w-1| + \frac{1}{3}\ln|3w+1| + C.$

**15.** $2\ln|t| + 3\ln|t+1| + \dfrac{1}{t+1} + C.$

**17.** $4\ln|w-1| + \frac{1}{3}\ln|w+1| + \frac{5}{3}\ln|w-2| + C.$ **19.** $\ln\frac{9}{8}.$ **21.** $\frac{3}{28} + \ln 16.$
**23.** $\ln\frac{20}{9}.$ **25.** $\frac{1}{2} + \ln\frac{36}{25}.$ **27.** $\ln\frac{9}{2}$ (l.u.)². **29.** $(\frac{29}{112} + \frac{1}{6}\ln\frac{7}{4})$ (l.u.)².

**31.** $\dfrac{6\ln 3 - 2\ln 2 + 2}{\ln 9 - \ln 2}.$ **33.** $2\pi(6\ln 3 - 2\ln 2 + 2)$ (l.u.)³.

### Exercises 12.8, Pages 454–455

**1.** $\ln[|y+1|(y^2+1)] + C.$

**3.** $9\ln|t+3| - \frac{5}{2}\ln(t^2+4t+8) - 2\,\text{Tan}^{-1}[\frac{1}{2}(t+2)] + C.$

**5.** $2\ln|w| + \frac{3}{2}\,\text{Tan}^{-1}(\frac{1}{2}w) + C.$

**7.** $\ln|x-2| + \ln(x^2+2x+10) + \frac{7}{3}\,\text{Tan}^{-1}[\frac{1}{3}(x+1)] + C.$

**9.** $\dfrac{1}{3\sqrt{2}}\,\text{Tan}^{-1}\left(\dfrac{s}{\sqrt{2}}\right) + \dfrac{1}{3}\ln\left|\dfrac{s-1}{s+1}\right| + C.$

**11.** $-\ln|x| + 3\,\text{Tan}^{-1}(x-1) + C.$

**13.** $\ln|w-1| + \ln(w^2+3w+8) + C.$

**15.** $\ln|w+1| + 2w + \frac{3}{2}\,\text{Tan}^{-1}(\frac{1}{2}w) + C.$

**17.** $3\ln|x| + 2\ln(x^2+4x+5) - 9\,\text{Tan}^{-1}(x+2) + C.$

**19.** $3\ln|x+1| + \dfrac{5}{2(x^2+1)} + C.$

**21.** $\frac{1}{4}\,\text{Tan}^{-1}(\frac{1}{2}x^2) + C.$

**23.** $\frac{5}{2}\ln 2 - \frac{1}{12}\pi.$

**25.** $\ln\frac{9}{2} - \frac{1}{3}\pi.$

**27.** $2\ln\frac{6}{5} + \frac{1}{2}\ln 2 - \frac{3}{4}\pi.$

**29.** $2\ln 2 + \frac{3}{2}\ln 3 + \pi - 4\,\text{Tan}^{-1} 3.$

**31.** $1 + \frac{1}{36}(12-\pi)\sqrt{3}.$

**33.** $\frac{1}{96}(12 - 4\sqrt{3} - \pi)$ (l.u.)².

**35.** $(\frac{1}{3}\pi\sqrt{3} + \ln\frac{2}{3}\sqrt{3})$ (l.u.)².

### Exercises 12.9, Pages 462–463

**1.** Divergent. **3.** $\frac{1}{2}.$ **5.** Divergent. **7.** $-4.$ **9.** $-1.$ **11.** Divergent. **13.** $0.$

**17.** *Hint:* Write $\displaystyle\int_0^\infty x^k e^{-x}\,dx = \lim_{t\to\infty}\int_0^t x^k e^{-x}\,dx,$ and use integration by parts.

**19.** $2km/a$ force units. **21.** Converges. **23.** Converges. **25.** Diverges.

### Exercises 12.10, Pages 467–468

**1. (a)** $T = 0.1088$, $|E| \leq 0.0128$. **(b)** $S = 0.1024$, $E = 0$.
**3. (a)** $T = 0.9871$, $|E| \leq 0.0202$. **(b)** $S = 1.0001$, $|E| \leq 0.00021$.
**5. (a)** $T = 0.6549$. **(b)** $S = 0.6577$.
**7. (a)** $T = 0.0220$. **(b)** $S = 0.0213$.
**9. (a)** $T = 1.6240$. **(b)** $S = 1.5629$.
**11. (a)** $T = 1.5716$. **(b)** $S = 1.5690$.
**13.** *Hint:* If $r_m$ is the radius of the midsection, then Simpson's Rule gives
$$V = \tfrac{1}{6}\pi h(r_1^2 + 4r_m^2 + r_2^2).$$
Show that $4r_m^2 = 2r_1^2 + 2r_2^2 + h^2$.
**15.** 0.1544. **17.** *Hint:* See the error formula.

### Exercises 12.11, Pages 469–470

**9.** *Hint:* Use partial fractions.
**11.** *Hint:* Use a trigonometric substitution and integration by parts.
**13.** $-\dfrac{\sqrt{x^2+1}}{2x^2} - \dfrac{1}{2}\ln\left|\dfrac{1+\sqrt{x^2+1}}{x}\right| + C$.
**15.** $\tfrac{1}{8}y^2 + \tfrac{1}{32}\ln|4y^2 - 1| + C$.    **19.** $\tfrac{1}{2}y\sin 2y - \tfrac{1}{4}(2y^2 - 1)\cos 2y + C$.
**17.** $\tfrac{1}{5}(w^2 - 4)^{5/2} + \tfrac{4}{3}(w^2 - 4)^{3/2} + C$.    **21.** $x\ln^2|2x| - 2x\ln|2x| + 2x + C$.
**23.** $-\tfrac{1}{16}y(9 - 4y^2)^{3/2} + \tfrac{9}{32}y(9 - 4y^2)^{1/2} + \tfrac{81}{64}\text{Sin}^{-1}\left(\tfrac{2}{3}y\right) + C$.
**25.** $-\dfrac{(4 - y^2)^{3/2}}{y} - \dfrac{3}{2}y(4 - y^2)^{1/2} - 6\,\text{Sin}^{-1}\left(\dfrac{1}{2}y\right) + C$.
**27.** $\tfrac{1}{13}e^{2x}(2\sin 3x - 3\cos 3x) + C$.
**29.** $\dfrac{2}{5}\sqrt{2 + 3x} + \dfrac{1}{5}\sqrt{2}\ln\left|\dfrac{\sqrt{2+3x}-\sqrt{2}}{\sqrt{2+3x}+\sqrt{2}}\right| + C$.
**31.** $\tfrac{1}{2}\cos t - \tfrac{1}{10}\cos 5t + C$.    **39.** $4\pi$.
**33.** $\tfrac{1}{8}(4 - \pi)$.    **41.** $\tfrac{1}{4}\pi - \tfrac{1}{2}\ln 2$.
**35.** $\tfrac{2}{9}(8\sqrt{14} + \sqrt{5})$.    **43.** $\tfrac{1}{32}(8 + 3\pi)$.
**37.** $\tfrac{7}{8}\sqrt{2} + \tfrac{3}{8}\ln(1 + \sqrt{2})$.    **45.** $\tfrac{1}{24}(\pi - 12 + 6\sqrt{3})$.

### Exercises 12.12, Pages 471–472

**1.** $(\tfrac{1}{2}\pi, \tfrac{3}{8})$.  **3.** $(\pi, \tfrac{5}{6}a)$.  **5.** $\tfrac{3}{2}\ln 3 - 1$.  **7.** $\tfrac{1}{4}\pi a$.  **9.** $\tfrac{32}{105}\pi a^3$ (l.u.)$^3$.
**11.** $\bar{x} = \dfrac{(3 + 2\sinh 2 - \cosh 2)a}{4 + 2\sinh 2}$.  **13.** $\dfrac{143\pi}{72\ln 2}$ (feet)$^3$.  **15.** $\tfrac{16}{3}w$ pounds.
**17.** $\tfrac{1}{4}mA^2\omega^2$.  **19.** $I_e = \tfrac{1}{2}\sqrt{2}I_0$.  **21.** $\dfrac{2km}{a}$ force units.
**23.** $2\pi k\mu\left(1 - \dfrac{s}{\sqrt{s^2 + b^2}}\right)$ force units.

### Exercises 13.1, Pages 478–479

**1.** $(x - 1)(x - 5) = 0$.    **3.** $y(x - 8) = 0$, $(x, y) \neq (0, 0)$ or $(4, 0)$.

**5.** $y = x$.

**7.** $\begin{cases} x = 3, y < 3, \\ x = 2y - 3, y \geq 3. \end{cases}$

**9.** $x^2 + (y - 2)^2 = 25$.

**11.** $y^2 - 4x - 6y - 3 = 0$.

**13.** $3x^2 + 3y^2 - 30x - 20y + 95 = 0$.

**15.** $2x + 8y = 35$.

**17.** $|x + 2| = x^2 + y^2$, equivalent to $x^2 + y^2 = x + 2$, since there are no real points satisfying $x^2 + y^2 = -x - 2$.

**19.** $x^2 - 4x + 6y - 11 = 0$.

**21.** The distance, $d_p$, of a point on $y^2 = 12(x - 1)$ from $(4, 0)$ satisfies
$$d_p^2 = (x - 4)^2 + y^2 = x^2 + 4x + 4,$$
so that $d_p = x + 2, x > -2$. The distance from the line is $d_l = |x - 2| = x - 2$, $x > 2$. Hence $d_p = d_l + 4$. If $x < 2$, $d_l = 2 - x$, and then $d_p \neq d_l + 4$, as is required.

**23.** $x^3 + xy^2 - 3ax^2 + ay^2 = 0, y = 0$.

**25.** $x^2 + y^2 - 4x - 8y = 30$ or $x^2 + y^2 - 2x + 6y = 40$.

**27.** $8x^2 + 9y = 18$.

**29.** $4x^2 + 4y^2 = a^2$.

### Exercises 13.2, Page 483

**1.** $(-3, 2)$. **3.** $(-10, -1)$.

**5.** (a) $(0, 6)$, (b) $(-8, 6)$, (c) $(-10, 5)$, (d) $(x_0 - 4, y_0 + 3)$.

**7.** $\mathbf{a} = (-4, -5), \mathbf{b} = (-7, -1)$. **9.** $\mathbf{a} = (-15, -2), \mathbf{b} = (-12, -9)$.

**11.** $x = u, y = v + \frac{7}{5}; x = u - \frac{7}{9}, y = v; 9u = 5v$.

**13.** $x = u, y = v + b; x = u + a, y = v; u/a + v/b = 0$.

**15.** $O_n$ is $(2, -\frac{9}{2}); u^2 + v^2 = \frac{97}{4}$.

**17.** $O_n$ is $(1, -\frac{1}{2}); 2uv = -1$. **19.** $O_n$ is $(-1, -2); u^2v = 2$.

**21.** $x = u + 5, y = v + 1, u^2 = 2v$. **23.** $x = u - 13, y = v + 8, v^2 = 5u$.

### Exercises 13.3, Pages 489–490

**1.** $(5, \pi - \text{Tan}^{-1} \frac{4}{3}); (13, \pi + \text{Tan}^{-1} \frac{12}{5}); (2\sqrt{2}, -\frac{1}{4}\pi)$.

**3.** $(\sqrt{2}, \frac{7}{4}\pi); (\sqrt{2}, \frac{3}{4}\pi); (\sqrt{2}, \frac{5}{4}\pi)$.

**5.** $(0, -1); (0, -1); (0, -1)$. **7.** $(\frac{3}{2}, -\frac{3}{2}\sqrt{3}); (-\frac{3}{2}, \frac{3}{2}\sqrt{3}); (-\frac{3}{2}, \frac{3}{2}\sqrt{3})$.

**9.** $r = 4 \csc \theta \cot \theta$. **11.** $r^2 = 2 \csc 2\theta - \sec^2 \theta$.

**13.** $x^2 + y^2 = 2y$. **15.** $(x^2 + y^2)^2 = x^3 - 3xy^2$.

**17.** The coordinate curves are families of straight lines:
$$x + y = 2u, \quad x - y = 2v.$$

**19.** $x^2 + y^2 = 4$.

**21.** Requirement (a) in Definition 13.3a is not satisfied, since
$$s((1, 2), (-2, 1)) = 0, \quad \text{but} \quad A \neq B.$$

### Exercises 13.4, Pages 496–497

**1.** $y = -2$, a straight line parallel to and two units below the $x$-axis.

**3.** $x^2 + y^2 = 25$, circle of radius five units, with center at the pole.

**5.** $x^2 + y^2 = 4x$, circle of radius two units, with center at $(2, 0)$.

**7.** $x^2 + y^2 = x + y$, circle with center at $(\frac{1}{2}, \frac{1}{2})$, radius $\frac{1}{2}\sqrt{2}$.

**9.** $x - y = 2$, straight line of slope 1 and $y$-intercept $-2$.

**11.** $(x - \sqrt{2})^2 + (y - \sqrt{2})^2 = 12$, circle with center at $(\sqrt{2}, \sqrt{2})$, radius $2\sqrt{3}$.

**13.** (1) $(2, 0)$, $(3, \frac{1}{2}\pi)$, $(2, \pi)$, $(1, \frac{3}{2}\pi)$.

(2) $y$-axis.

(3) No tangents to the curve at the origin.

(4) As $\theta$ increases from 0 to $\frac{1}{2}\pi$, $r$ increases from 2 to 3; as $\theta$ increases from $\frac{1}{2}\pi$ to $\frac{3}{2}\pi$, $r$ decreases from 3 to 1; as $\theta$ increases from $\frac{3}{2}\pi$ to $2\pi$, $r$ increases from 1 to 2.

(5) Horizontal tangents at $\theta = \frac{1}{2}\pi$, $r = 3$; $\theta = \frac{3}{2}\pi$, $r = 1$. Vertical tangents at

$$\theta = \text{Sin}^{-1} \frac{-1 + \sqrt{3}}{2}, r = \frac{3}{2} + \frac{1}{2}\sqrt{2};$$

$$\theta = \pi - \text{Sin}^{-1} \frac{-1 + \sqrt{3}}{2}, r = \frac{3}{2} + \frac{1}{2}\sqrt{2}.$$

**15.** (1) $(-3, 0)$, $(3, \frac{1}{2}\pi)$, $(9, \pi)$, $(3, \frac{3}{2}\pi)$.

(2) $x$-axis.

(3) $\theta = \frac{1}{3}\pi$, $\theta = -\frac{1}{3}\pi$ are tangent lines to the curve at the origin.

(4) As $\theta$ increases from 0 to $\pi$, $r$ increases from $-3$ to 9; as $\theta$ increases from $\pi$ to $2\pi$, $r$ decreases from 9 to $-3$.

(5) Vertical tangents at $\theta = 0$, $r = -3$; $\theta = \pi$, $r = 9$; $\theta = \text{Cos}^{-1} \frac{1}{4}$, $r = \frac{3}{2}$; $\theta = -\text{Cos}^{-1} \frac{1}{4}$, $r = \frac{3}{2}$. Horizontal tangents at

$$\theta = \pm\text{Cos}^{-1} \frac{1 + \sqrt{33}}{8}, r = \frac{9 - 3\sqrt{33}}{4};$$

$$\theta = \pm\text{Cos}^{-1} \frac{1 - \sqrt{33}}{8}, r = \frac{9 + 3\sqrt{33}}{4}.$$

**17.** (1) $(5, 0)$, $(3, \frac{1}{2}\pi)$, $(1, \pi)$, $(3, \frac{3}{2}\pi)$.

(2) $x$-axis.

(3) The curve does not pass through the origin.

(4) As $\theta$ increases from 0 to $\pi$, $r$ decreases from 5 to 1; as $\theta$ increases from $\pi$ to $2\pi$, $r$ increases from 1 to 5.

(5) Vertical tangents at $\theta = 0$, $r = 5$; $\theta = \pi$, $r = 1$; $\theta = \pi \pm \text{Cos}^{-1} \frac{3}{4}$, $r = \frac{3}{2}$. Horizontal tangents at

$$\theta = \pm\text{Cos}^{-1} \left( \frac{-3 + \sqrt{41}}{8} \right), r = \frac{21 + \sqrt{41}}{8}.$$

**19.** (1) Intersects axes at origin only.

(2) $x$-axis, $y$-axis, origin.

(3) Tangent lines to the curve at the origin are $\theta = \frac{1}{4}n\pi$, $n = 0, 1, 2, 3$.

(4) As $\theta$ increases from 0 to $\frac{1}{8}\pi$, $r$ increases from 0 to 1; as $\theta$ increases from $\frac{1}{8}\pi$ to $\frac{1}{4}\pi$, $r$ decreases from 1 to 0. This part of the curve is a loop symmetric to $\theta = \frac{1}{8}\pi$. As $\theta$ increases from $\frac{1}{4}\pi$ to $\frac{3}{8}\pi$, $r$ decreases from 0 to $-1$; as $\theta$ increases from $\frac{3}{8}\pi$ to $\frac{1}{2}\pi$, $r$ increases from $-1$ to 0. This part of the curve is of the same shape as the preceding loop, but is in the third quadrant, tangent to the line $y = x$ and the $y$-axis. The rest of the curve can be obtained from symmetry. There are eight loops in all.

**21.** (1) $(0, 5)$, $(-5, \frac{1}{2}\pi)$, $(5, \pi)$, $(-5, \frac{3}{2}\pi)$.

(2) $x$-axis, $y$-axis, origin.

(3) Tangent lines to the curve at the origin are $\theta = (2n - 1)\pi/4$.

(4) As $\theta$ increases from 0 to $\frac{1}{4}\pi$, $r$ decreases from 5 to 0; as $\theta$ increases from $\frac{1}{4}\pi$ to $\frac{1}{2}\pi$, $r$ decreases from 0 to $-5$. The rest of the curve may be obtained from symmetry.

**23.** (1) $(0, 0)$, $(4, \frac{1}{2}\pi)$, $(8, \pi)$, $(4, \frac{3}{2}\pi)$.

   (2) $x$-axis.

   (3) Tangent lines to the curve at the origin are $\theta = 0$.

   (4) As $\theta$ increases from 0 to $\pi$, $r$ increases from 0 to 8; as $\theta$ increases from $\pi$ to $2\pi$, $r$ decreases from 8 to 0.

   (5) Vertical tangents at $\theta = \pi$, $r = 8$; $\theta = \frac{1}{3}\pi$, $r = 2$; $\theta = -\frac{1}{3}\pi$, $r = 2$. Horizontal tangents at $\theta = 0$, $r = 0$; $\theta = \frac{2}{3}\pi$, $r = 6$; $\theta = \frac{4}{3}\pi$, $r = 6$.

**25.** (1) $(0, 0)$, $(1, \frac{1}{2}\pi)$, $(0, \pi)$, $(1, \frac{3}{2}\pi)$.

   (2) $x$-axis, $y$-axis, origin.

   (3) Tangent lines to curve at origin are $\theta = n\pi$, $n \in \mathfrak{N} \cup \{0\}$.

   (4) As $\theta$ increases from 0 to $\frac{1}{2}\pi$, $r$ increases from 0 to 1; as $\theta$ increases from $\frac{1}{2}\pi$ to $\pi$, $r$ decreases from 1 to 0. The remainder of the curve may be obtained from symmetry.

   (5) Horizontal tangents at $\theta = \frac{1}{2}\pi$, $r = 1$; $\theta = \frac{3}{2}\pi$, $r = 1$; $\theta = 0$, $r = 0$. Vertical tangents at

$$\theta = \pm \text{Cos}^{-1} (\tfrac{1}{3}\sqrt{3}), \; r = \tfrac{2}{3};$$
$$\theta = \pi \pm \text{Cos}^{-1} (\tfrac{1}{3}\sqrt{3}), \; r = \tfrac{2}{3}.$$

**27.** The curve is of the same general shape as the curve in Number 21 (a four-leaved rose curve), but rotated through an angle of $\frac{1}{6}\pi$, with maximum $r$ values of 3 rather than 5.

**29.** A curve in the shape of a figure eight tilted at $\frac{1}{4}\pi$ toward the right.

**31.** A spiral curve starting at the origin, with $r$ increasing as $\theta$ increases.

**33.** The curve is asymptotic to the negative $x$-axis. The line $\theta = \frac{1}{4}\pi$ is tangent to the curve at the origin. As $\theta$ increases from 0, $r$ increases, so that the curve is spiral-like for positive values of $\theta$. The curve crosses itself at $\theta = \frac{1}{2}(-n\pi + \sqrt{n^2\pi^2 + 4})$, $n \in \mathfrak{N}$.

**35.** $r = \cos 3\theta$. (A three-leaved rose curve.)

   (1) $(2, 0)$, $(0, \frac{1}{2}\pi)$.

   (2) $x$-axis.

   (3) Tangent lines to the curve at the origin are $\theta = \frac{1}{6}(2n - 1)\pi$, $n \in \mathcal{I}$.

   (4) As $\theta$ increases from 0 to $\frac{1}{6}\pi$, $r$ decreases from 2 to 0; as $\theta$ increases from $\frac{1}{6}\pi$ to $\frac{1}{3}\pi$, $r$ decreases from 0 to $-2$; as $\theta$ increases from $\frac{1}{3}\pi$ to $\frac{1}{2}\pi$, $r$ increases from $-2$ to 0. The rest of the curve may be obtained by symmetry. The entire curve is traced once as $\theta$ increases from 0 to $\pi$.

**37.** Center $\left(\dfrac{k^2a}{k^2 - 1}, 0\right)$, radius $\dfrac{ka}{|k^2 - 1|}$.　**39.** $\text{Tan } \theta = m$, $\theta = \alpha$.

**41.** $\theta = 0$, $r = 0$; $\theta = \pi$, $r = 0$; $\theta = \pm \text{Cos}^{-1} (1/\sqrt{3})$ or $\theta = \pi \pm \text{Cos}^{-1} (1/\sqrt{3})$, $r = \frac{2}{3}a\sqrt{2}$.

**43.** $(4, \frac{1}{3}\pi)$, $(4, -\frac{1}{3}\pi)$.　**45.** $(1, 0)$; the origin.　**47.** $(\frac{1}{2}, \pm\frac{2}{3}\pi)$.

### Exercises 13.5, Pages 500–501

**1.** $e = \frac{1}{2}$, $p = 4$, ellipse, major axis along the line $\theta = \frac{1}{2}\pi$.

**3.** $e = 1$, $p = 2$, parabola, opens to the right.

**5.** $e = 2$, $p = 2$, hyperbola, symmetric about polar axis.

**7.** $e = \frac{1}{3}$, $p = 9$, ellipse, major axis along the line $\theta = \frac{1}{2}\pi$.

**9.** $e = 2$, $p = \frac{5}{2}$, hyperbola, symmetric about polar axis.

**11.** $e = \frac{1}{2}$, $p = 2$, ellipse, major axis along line $\theta = \frac{1}{2}\pi$.

**13.** $e = b/a$, $p = 1/b$.

**15.** *Hint:* Substitute $\pi - \theta$ for $\theta$ to show symmetry with respect to the axis $\frac{1}{2}\pi$.

**17.** The slope of the parabola at $(r, \theta)$ is $\tan(\theta/2)$, so that $\psi = \theta/2$.

**19.** $e = \dfrac{5}{171}$.

### Exercises 13.7, Pages 504–505

**1.** Vertex, $(0, 0)$; focus, $(0, -\frac{3}{2})$; directrix, $y = \frac{3}{2}$.

**3.** Vertex, $(0, 0)$; focus, $(0, \frac{1}{16})$; directrix, $y = -\frac{1}{16}$.

**5.** Vertex, $(3, 0)$; focus, $(4, 0)$; directrix, $x = 2$.

**7.** Vertex, $(-2, -3)$; focus, $(-\frac{5}{2}, -3)$; directrix, $x = -\frac{3}{2}$.

**9.** $x^2 - 6x + 4y + 5 = 0$. **11.** $x + 2y + 3 = 0$.

**13.** $4x + y = 7$. **15.** $A = \frac{8}{3}$ (l.u.)$^2$.

**17.** $y^2 = 16(x - 1)$. The curve is a parabola, vertex at $(1, 0)$; axis is the $x$-axis; opens to the right.

**19.** The curves have the same tangent line at $(1, 2)$.

### Exercises 13.8, Pages 508–509

**1.** $e = \frac{1}{4}\sqrt{15}$; the foci are at $(\sqrt{15}, 0)$, $(-\sqrt{15}, 0)$; the directrices are $x = \pm\frac{16}{15}\sqrt{15}$.

**3.** $e = \frac{1}{2}\sqrt{3}$; foci, $(3 + \sqrt{3}, 0)$, $(3 - \sqrt{3}, 0)$; directrices, $x = 3 \pm \frac{4}{3}\sqrt{3}$.

**5.** $e = \frac{1}{3}\sqrt{5}$; foci, $(-1, 1 \pm \frac{1}{2}\sqrt{5})$; directrices, $y = 1 \pm \frac{9}{10}\sqrt{5}$.

**7.** $e = \frac{1}{2}\sqrt{3}$; foci, $(-1 \pm \sqrt{3}, -5)$; directrices, $x = \pm\frac{4}{3}\sqrt{3} - 1$.

**9.** $x - 2\sqrt{3}\, y = 4$. **11.** $\dfrac{(x + 2)^2}{5} + \dfrac{(y - 4)^2}{9} = 1$. **13.** $y = \frac{15}{2}\sqrt{3}$ feet.

**15.** If $\frac{1}{2}\sqrt{2} < e < 1$, there are four points at each of which the focal radii are perpendicular.

### Exercises 13.9, Pages 514–515

**1.** $e = \frac{1}{2}\sqrt{5}$; foci, $(0, \pm 2\sqrt{5})$; vertices, $(0, \pm 4)$; directrices, $y = \pm\frac{8}{5}\sqrt{5}$; asymptotes, $y = \pm 2x$.

**3.** $e = \sqrt{5}$; foci, $(0, \pm 3\sqrt{5})$; vertices, $(0, \pm 3)$; directrices, $y = \pm\frac{3}{5}\sqrt{5}$; asymptotes, $x \pm 3y = 0$.

**5.** $e = \frac{1}{3}\sqrt{10}$; foci, $(-2 \pm \sqrt{10}, 0)$; vertices, $(1, 0)$, $(-5, 0)$; directrices, $x = -2 \pm \frac{9}{10}\sqrt{10}$; asymptotes, $x \pm 3y + 2 = 0$.

**7.** $e = \frac{1}{3}\sqrt{13}$; foci, $(1, -2 \pm \sqrt{13})$; vertices, $(1, 1)$, $(1, -5)$; directrices, $y = -2 \pm \frac{9}{13}\sqrt{13}$; asymptotes, $3x - 2y - 7 = 0$, $3x + 2y + 1 = 0$.

**9.** $(y - 3)^2 - \frac{1}{3}(x - 1)^2 = 1$. **11.** Chord length is $2b^2/a$.

**13.** Points of intersection are $(\pm 12, \pm 10)$.

### Exercises 14.1, Pages 520–522

**1.** $0$. **3.** $\mathbf{r} = t(3, -2)$. **5.** $\mathbf{r} = t(a, -b) + (0, b)$. **7.** $x = \frac{1}{3}$.

**9. (a)** $r = t(0, 1) - (3, 0)$. **(b)** $r = t(1, 0) + (0, 4)$. **11.** $r = (-\frac{1}{2}, -2)$.
**15.** $r = (x_1, y_1) + t(B, -A)$.


### Exercises 14.2, Pages 525–526

**1. (a)** $\sqrt{30}$. **(c)** $\sqrt{83}$.
**3.** Since $(PR)^2 = (PQ)^2 + (QR)^2$, the triangle is a right triangle.
**5.** $(-\frac{11}{5}, -\frac{1}{5}, \frac{23}{5})$. **9.** $\left( \dfrac{x_1 + x_2}{2}, \dfrac{y_1 + y_2}{2}, \dfrac{z_1 + z_2}{2} \right)$.
**11. (a)** $(-2, 5, 3)$. **(c)** $(2, 5, -3)$. **(e)** $(-2, -5, 3)$.
**13.** Two: $[0, 1, 1]$ and $[0, 1, -1]$.


### Exercises 14.3, Pages 530–531

**1.** The direction angles are each $\text{Cos}^{-1}(1/\sqrt{3})$.
**3.** $\frac{1}{3}\pi$, $\frac{2}{3}\pi$.  **5.** $\frac{1}{3}\pi \leq \beta \leq \frac{2}{3}\pi$.
**7. (a)** $\alpha = 140°29.4'$, $\beta = 98°52.6'$, $\gamma = 128°6.8'$.
  **(c)** $\alpha = 83°5.1'$, $\beta = 103°55.9'$, $\gamma = 164°23.1'$.
**9.** If $a$ and $b$ are parallel; that is, if $a = kb$. **11.** $r = t(5, 3, -2) + (-2, -1, 4)$.
**13.** $\dfrac{x + 2}{5} = \dfrac{y + 1}{3} = \dfrac{z - 4}{-2}$. **15.** $r = (\frac{25}{8}, \frac{31}{8}, \frac{7}{8})$.


### Exercises 14.4, Pages 537–539

**1.** $c \cdot c = (a - b) \cdot (a - b) \Rightarrow c^2 = a^2 + b^2 - 2ab \cos \theta$.
**3.** $r - a$ is always perpendicular to $r$.
**5. (a)** $\overrightarrow{AB} \cdot \overrightarrow{BC} = 0 \Rightarrow \overrightarrow{AB}$ is perpendicular to $\overrightarrow{BC}$.
**7.** The points are not on a straight line because $\overrightarrow{AB}$ does not have the same direction as $\overrightarrow{BC}$.
**9.** $r - a$ is always perpendicular to $r - b$. Therefore, $(r - a) \cdot (r - b) = 0$ describes a circle of diameter $|a - b|$ passing through the points $(a_1, a_2)$, $(b_1, b_2)$.
**11.** $r = (-2, 3, -4) + t(-3, 2, 1)$.
**13. (a)** $(\frac{20}{49}, \frac{30}{49}, \frac{60}{49})$. **(b)** $(\frac{16}{29}, \frac{12}{29}, \frac{8}{29})$. **(c)** $-5i + 7j + 10k$. **(d)** $(0, -8, 0)$.
  **(e)** $(-\frac{20}{3}, -\frac{20}{3}, -\frac{20}{3})$.
**15.** $a \cdot (b + c) = (a_1, a_2, a_3) \cdot (b_1 + c_1, b_2 + c_2, b_3 + c_3)$  by definition of addition,
$\qquad\qquad = a_1(b_1 + c_1) + a_2(b_2 + c_2) + a_3(b_3 + c_3)$  by definition of the dot product,
$\qquad\qquad = (a_1 b_1 + a_2 b_2 + a_3 b_3) + (a_1 c_1 + a_2 c_2 + a_3 c_3)$  by distributive and associative properties of real numbers,
$\qquad\qquad = a \cdot b + a \cdot c$  by definition of the dot product.
**17.** $a$ perpendicular to $b \Rightarrow a \cdot b = 0$, and $a$ perpendicular to $c \Rightarrow a \cdot c = 0$. Therefore, $a \cdot (mb + nc) = 0$, $m,n$ not both 0. That is, $a$ is perpendicular to all nonzero vectors in the plane of $b$ and $c$, so that $a$ is normal to the plane of $b$ and $c$.

**19.** $\mathbf{r} = (3, 2, -1) + t(2, 1, -2)$.

**21.** (a) $F = \dfrac{\alpha}{(x^2 + 25)^{3/2}}(x, -5)$.     (b) $\dfrac{\alpha x}{(x^2 + 25)^{3/2}}$.     (c) $\dfrac{\alpha}{25}(5 - \sqrt{5})$.

### Exercises 14.5, Pages 546–547

**1.** (a) $(2, -5, -4)$.           (c) $(-2, 3, 2)$.
  (b) $(0, 6, 0)$.                (d) $(-11, -5, -7)$.

**3.** Area $= \sqrt{389}$ (l.u.)$^2$.      **5.** Area $= \frac{1}{2}\sqrt{734}$ (l.u.)$^2$.

**7.** $\left(-\dfrac{5}{\sqrt{83}}, -\dfrac{3}{\sqrt{83}}, -\dfrac{7}{\sqrt{83}}\right)$.

**9.** Prove by counter example; consider $\mathbf{i} \times (\mathbf{i} \times \mathbf{j})$.

**11.** No. $\mathbf{b} = \mathbf{c}$ or $\mathbf{a} = 0$ or $\mathbf{a}$ is parallel to $\mathbf{b} - \mathbf{c}$.

**13.** (a) Area $= 15\sqrt{2}$ (l.u.)$^2$.      (b) Area $= \sqrt{89}$ (l.u.)$^2$.

### Exercises 14.6, Pages 553–554

**1.** $-3$; $(37, 31, 25)$.    **3.** $\mathbf{a} \cdot \mathbf{b} \times \mathbf{c} = 1$, $\mathbf{a} \times (\mathbf{b} \times \mathbf{c}) = 0$.

**5.** Volume $= 24$ (l.u.)$^3$.

**7.** The points do not lie on a plane through the origin.

**9.** The points are not coplanar.    **11.** The points are coplanar.

**13.** The points are coplanar.

**15.** The set is an orthogonal set:
$$\mathbf{f}_1 = \tfrac{1}{3}(2, 2, 1), \ \mathbf{f}_2 = \tfrac{1}{3}(-2, 1, 2), \ \mathbf{f}_3 = \tfrac{1}{3}(1, -2, 2),$$
$$\mathbf{u} = 2\mathbf{f}_1 - 3\mathbf{f}_2 - \mathbf{f}_3.$$

**17.** $(\mathbf{a} \times \mathbf{b}) \times \mathbf{c} = (\mathbf{c} \cdot \mathbf{a})\mathbf{b} - (\mathbf{c} \cdot \mathbf{b})\mathbf{a}$.

### Exercises 14.7, Pages 560–561

**1.** $x + y \pm \sqrt{2}\, z = 4$.    **3.** $B = 6$, $C = 2$.    **5.** $3x - 4y + z = -17$.

**7.** $\sqrt{2}\, x + y \pm z = 12$.    **9.** $6/\sqrt{29}$ units.    **11.** $3x - 14y - 19z = -67$.

**13.** $6x + 16y - 23z = -46$.    **15.** $x - 2y + z = 1$.

**17.** The normal form of the equation of a plane is $x \cos \alpha + y \cos \beta + z \cos \gamma = p$. If the plane is perpendicular to the $xy$-plane then $\beta = \frac{1}{2}\pi - \alpha$ and $\gamma = \frac{1}{2}\pi$, and the equation becomes $x \cos \alpha + y \sin \alpha = p$.

### Exercises 14.8, Pages 566–567

**1.** (a) $\mathbf{r} = (\frac{3}{4}, -\frac{3}{4}, 1) + t(3, 1, -4)$.
  (b) $x - 3y = 3$, $4x + 3z = 6$, $4y + z = -2$.

**3.** (a) $\mathbf{r} = (\frac{65}{8}, 7, 0) + t(3, 2, -2)$.
  (b) $y + z = 7$, $8x + 12z = 65$, $8x - 12y = -19$.

**5.** (a) $\mathbf{r} = (1, 1, 5) + t(1, 2, -1)$.
  (b) $2x - y = 1$, $x + z = 6$, $2z + y = 11$.

**7.** (a) $\mathbf{r} = (-1, 3, 6) + t(0, -1, 3)$.
  (b) $x = -1$, $3y + z = 15$.

**9. (a)** $\mathbf{r} = (x_1, y_1, z_1) + t(x_2 - x_1, y_2 - y_1, z_2 - z_1)$.

**(b)** $(y_2 - y_1)x - (x_2 - x_1)y = x_1y_2 - x_2y_1$,

$(z_2 - z_1)y - (y_2 - y_1)z = y_1z_2 - y_2z_1$,

$(z_2 - z_1)x - (x_2 - x_1)z = x_1z_2 - x_2z_1$.

**11.** $31x + 13y - 11z = 0$.    **13.** $\theta = \mathrm{Cos}^{-1} \dfrac{13\sqrt{43}}{86} = 7°35.3'$.

**15.** $\dfrac{x - 5}{3} = \dfrac{y + 3}{-1} = \dfrac{z - 4}{2}$.    **17.** $\mathbf{r} = (1, -2, 0) + t(2, 1, 1)$.

**21.** The equations are of the form

$$ax + by = d, \ z = z_0,$$

or

$$x = at + x_0, \ y = bt + y_0, \ z = z_0.$$

The intersection is always a straight line.

### Exercises 15.1, Pages 572–573

**1. (a)** $\begin{bmatrix} 2 & -1 & 3 \\ 1 & 0 & 1 \end{bmatrix}$.

**(c)** $\begin{bmatrix} 3 & -1 & 2 & 4 \\ 1 & -2 & -1 & 1 \\ 2 & 1 & -3 & 7 \end{bmatrix}$.

**(b)** $\begin{bmatrix} -1 & 2 & -1 & 0 \\ 2 & -1 & 2 & 0 \\ 3 & 1 & -4 & 0 \end{bmatrix}$.

**(d)** $\begin{bmatrix} 1 & 1 & -1 & 2 & 1 \\ 1 & 2 & 1 & 0 & 3 \\ 0 & 0 & 1 & 1 & 2 \end{bmatrix}$.

**3. (a)** $a_{24} = 7$, $a_{54} = -4$, $a_{43} = 5$, $a_{26} = -3$.

**(b)** $a_{21} = a_{32} = a_{42} = 2$, $a_{13} = a_{23} = a_{41} = 3$, $a_{43} = 5$.

**5.** $x = \frac{24}{7}$, $y = \frac{2}{7}$.   **7.** $x = -2$, $y = 3$, $z = -5$.

### Exercises 15.2, Page 577

**1.** Let    $A = [a_{ij}]$, $B = [b_{ij}]$. Then

$A + B = [a_{ij} + b_{ij}]$   by definition of addition,

      $= [b_{ij} + a_{ij}]$   by the commutative law of addition for real numbers,

      $= [b_{ij}] + [a_{ij}]$   by definition of addition,

      $= B + A$.

**3.** $(k + m)A = (k + m)[a_{ij}] = [(k + m)a_{ij}]$   by definition of scalar multiplication,

      $= [ka_{ij} + ma_{ij}]$   by the distributive law for real numbers,

      $= [ka_{ij}] + [ma_{ij}]$   by definition of addition,

      $= k[a_{ij}] + m[a_{ij}]$   by definition of scalar multiplication,

      $= kA + mA$.

**5.** Let    $A = [a_{ij}]$, $C = [c_{ij}]$. Then

$A + C = [a_{ij} + c_{ij}]$   by definition of addition,

$(A + C)^{\mathsf{T}} = [b_{ij} + d_{ij}]$,   where $b_{ij} = a_{ji}$, $d_{ij} = c_{ji}$,   by definition of transpose,

      $= [b_{ij}] + [d_{ij}]$   by definition of addition,

      $= [a_{ij}]^{\mathsf{T}} + [c_{ij}]^{\mathsf{T}}$   by definition of transpose,

      $= A^{\mathsf{T}} + C^{\mathsf{T}}$.

**7.**  $kA = k[a_{ij}] = [ka_{ij}]$  by definition of scalar multiplication,
$(kA)^\mathsf{T} = [ka_{ij}]^\mathsf{T} = [kb_{ij}]$,  where $b_{ij} = a_{ji}$,  by definition of transpose,
$\qquad = k[b_{ij}]$  by definition of scalar multiplication,
$\qquad = kA^\mathsf{T}$  by definition of transpose.

**9.**
(a) $\begin{bmatrix} -4 & 9 & -6 \\ 1 & 0 & 1 \\ -12 & -1 & -8 \end{bmatrix}$.

(c) $\begin{bmatrix} 0 & -1 & -8 \\ 7 & 0 & 1 \\ -2 & 3 & -4 \end{bmatrix}$.

(b) $\begin{bmatrix} -5 & 11 & 0 \\ -1 & 4 & 6 \\ -9 & 1 & -7 \end{bmatrix}$.

(d) $\begin{bmatrix} 3 & -2 & -1 \\ 2 & 0 & 2 \\ 2 & 3 & 1 \end{bmatrix}$.

(e) Same as (d).

**11.** $k = m = n = 0$ only.

**13.** $A + C = B + C \Rightarrow (A + C) + (-C) = (B + C) + (-C)$, by the substitution axiom, $\Rightarrow A + (C + (-C)) = B + (C + (-C))$, by the associative law, $\Rightarrow A + 0 = B + 0 \Rightarrow A = B$. Moreover, $A = B$ and $A + C = A + C \Rightarrow A + C = B + C$, by the substitution axiom.

**Exercises 15.3, Pages 585–586**

**1.** (a) $\begin{bmatrix} 11 & 5 \\ 6 & 4 \end{bmatrix}$.  (b) $\begin{bmatrix} 14 & 0 \\ -9 & 1 \end{bmatrix}$.  (c) $\begin{bmatrix} -13 & -4 \\ 1 & -4 \\ 4 & 5 \end{bmatrix}$.  (d) $\begin{bmatrix} -11 & -10 & -6 \\ -1 & 2 & 6 \\ 5 & 2 & -3 \end{bmatrix}$.

(e) $\begin{bmatrix} 10 & 6 \\ 4 & -7 \end{bmatrix}$.  (f) $\begin{bmatrix} 26 & 32 & 33 \\ 18 & 20 & 18 \end{bmatrix}$.

**3.** $\begin{bmatrix} 4 & 6 & 2 \\ 6 & 14 & 2 \\ 2 & 2 & 2 \end{bmatrix}$.  **5.** $\begin{bmatrix} -1 - i & 12 + 16i \\ 2 + 6i & -9 + 15i \end{bmatrix}$.  **7.** $A^4 = O_{44}$.

**9.** $(AA^\mathsf{T})^\mathsf{T} = (A^\mathsf{T})^\mathsf{T}A^\mathsf{T} = AA^\mathsf{T}$. Hence $AA^\mathsf{T}$ is symmetric.

**11.** $(A - B)(A + B) = A^2 - BA + AB - B^2$. In general, $AB \neq BA$; therefore the two expressions are not equal.

**13.** Yes, it can be shown by induction on $n$ with $m$ fixed.

**15.** No. $AJ = A$ only for $A$ and possibly for certain other matrices, but since $XJ \neq X$ for *all* $X$, $J$ is not a multiplicative identity for all $2 \times 3$ matrices.

**Exercises 15.4, Pages 591–592**

**1.** (a) $\begin{bmatrix} 1 & 1 \\ 0 & 0 \end{bmatrix}$.  (b) $\begin{bmatrix} 1 & 0 & 0 \\ 0 & 1 & 0 \\ 0 & 0 & 1 \end{bmatrix}$.  (c) $\begin{bmatrix} 1 & 0 & 0 \\ 0 & 1 & 0 \\ 0 & 0 & 1 \\ 0 & 0 & 0 \\ 0 & 0 & 0 \end{bmatrix}$.

(d) $\begin{bmatrix} 1 & 0 & 0 \\ 0 & 1 & 0 \\ 0 & 0 & 1 \\ 0 & 0 & 0 \end{bmatrix}$.  (e) $\begin{bmatrix} 1 & -1 & 2 & 0 \\ 0 & 0 & 0 & 1 \\ 0 & 0 & 0 & 0 \\ 0 & 0 & 0 & 0 \end{bmatrix}$.  (f) $\begin{bmatrix} 1 & 0 & 0 & abc \\ 0 & 1 & 0 & -(ab + bc + ca) \\ 0 & 0 & 1 & a + b + c \end{bmatrix}$.

**3.** $\frac{1}{8}\begin{bmatrix} 2 & 2 & -2 \\ 3 & -1 & 5 \\ -1 & 3 & 1 \end{bmatrix}$.  **5.** $A \sim_r D$.

**Exercises 15.5, Pages 595–596**

**1. (a)** Right inverse $\begin{bmatrix} -1 \\ 1 \end{bmatrix}$.

**(c)** Right inverse $\begin{bmatrix} 1 & 0 \\ 0 & 0 \\ 0 & 1 \end{bmatrix}$.

**(b)** Left inverse $[1, 2]$.

**3.** No inverse.

**5.** $A^{-1} = \frac{1}{7}\begin{bmatrix} 3 & 2 & 1 \\ -1 & 4 & 2 \\ 1 & 3 & 5 \end{bmatrix}$.

**7.** $A^{-1} = \begin{bmatrix} 11 & 2 & -8 & -2 \\ \frac{3}{2} & \frac{1}{2} & -1 & 0 \\ \frac{5}{2} & \frac{1}{2} & -2 & 0 \\ -\frac{13}{2} & -\frac{3}{2} & 5 & 1 \end{bmatrix}$.

**9.** If $A \sim_r B$, then there is a sequence of elementary matrices $E_1, \ldots, E_k$ such that $E_1 \cdots E_k A = B$. Let $S = E_1 \cdots E_k$. Then $S$ is nonsingular because each $E_i$ is nonsingular, and $S^{-1} = E_k^{-1} \cdots E_1^{-1}$.

**11.** *Hint:* (i) If $A \sim_r I$, then there are elementary matrices $E_1, E_2, \ldots, E_k$ such that
$$E_k \cdots E_2 E_1 A = I.$$
(ii) If $A$ is nonsingular, then there is a matrix $B$ such that $BA = I$. The required result then follows from the proof of Theorem 15.5c.

**Exercises 15.6, Pages 605–606**

**1.** Rank $= 3$.     **3.** Rank $= 3$.     **5.** Rank $= 2$.
**7.** Rank $= 3$.     **9.** $x = 2$, $y = -1$, $z = 1$; three planes with one common point.
**11.** $u = 3$, $v = 2$, $w = 1$; three planes with one common point.
**13.** $r = 0$, $s = 0$, $t = 0$; three planes with one common point.
**15.** $w = -2$, $x = 2$, $y = 3$, $z = -1$.     **17.** No solution.

**Exercises 15.7, Pages 611–612**

**1. (a)** Even,    **(b)** Even,    **(c)** Even,    **(d)** Odd,    **(e)** Odd,    **(f)** Odd.
**2. (a)** $-$,    **(b)** $+$,    **(c)** $+$,    **(d)** $+$,    **(e)** $-$,    **(f)** $-$.
**3.** 0.
**5.** $A^T = -A$. Therefore, $\det(A^T) = -\det A \Rightarrow \det A = -\det A \Rightarrow \det A = 0$.
**7.** The hint suggests a solution.

**Exercises 15.8, Pages 619–620**

**1.** 276.     **3.** $(2 + a + b)(a - b)^2(a + b - 2)$.     **5.** $-196$.
**7.** $x = 3$, $y = -1$, $z = -1$.     **9.** $u = 2$, $v = 1$, $w = -2$, $x = 3$.

**Exercises 15.9, Pages 624–625**

**1.** 8.     **3.** 0.     **9.** $k = -\frac{15}{8}$; $u = 176t$, $v = 187t$, $s = 44t$.
    $k = 3$; $u = 11t$, $v = -20t$, $s = -7t$.
**11.** $k = 5$; $x = -\frac{1}{4}$, $y = \frac{3}{4}$.
**13.** Yes. $AA^{-1} = I \Rightarrow \det(AA^{-1}) = 1 \Rightarrow \det A^{-1} = (\det A)^{-1}$.

**15.** Yes. $AA^{-1} = I \Rightarrow (AA^{-1})^{\mathsf{T}} = (A^{-1})^{\mathsf{T}} A^{\mathsf{T}} = I$
$$\Rightarrow (A^{-1})^{\mathsf{T}} A = I \Rightarrow (A^{-1})^{\mathsf{T}} = A^{-1}.$$
Hence, $A^{-1}$ is symmetric.

## Exercises 16.1, Pages 632–633

**1. (a)** $(2, -2) = 2\sqrt{2}\, \mathbf{e}_1 + 0\mathbf{e}_2.$      **(c)** $(2, -2) = -2(3, 4) + 2(4, 3).$

**3.** No. Suppose $\mathbf{r} = u\mathbf{e}_1 + v\mathbf{e}_2$. Then $\mathbf{r} \cdot \mathbf{e}_1 = u\mathbf{e}_1 \cdot \mathbf{e}_1 + v\mathbf{e}_1 \cdot \mathbf{e}_2$, and if $\mathbf{e}_1 \cdot \mathbf{e}_2 \neq 0$, then
$u \neq (\mathbf{r} \cdot \mathbf{e}_1)/(\mathbf{e}_1 \cdot \mathbf{e}_1).$

**4. (b)** $(1, 1) = (0, 2) + (1, -1) = -\frac{2}{5}(2, -1) + \frac{3}{5}(3, 1).$

**5.** $\mathbf{f}_1 = (\frac{9}{10}, \frac{13}{10}), \mathbf{f}_2 = (\frac{13}{10}, -\frac{9}{10}).$

**7. (a)** $(3, 1, 2) = 2\mathbf{e}_1 - \mathbf{e}_2 + 2\mathbf{e}_3.$

     **(b)** Same as in part (a).

     **(c)** $(3, 1, 2) = \frac{19}{5}\mathbf{e}_1 + \frac{17}{5}\mathbf{e}_2 - \frac{8}{5}\mathbf{e}_3.$

## Exercises 16.2, Pages 640–641

**1.** A rotation through $\frac{1}{3}\pi$.    **3.** A rotation through $-\frac{1}{4}\pi$.

**5.** A rotation through $\pi + \operatorname{Tan}^{-1}\frac{1}{2}$.    **7.** $25v^2 = 4.$    **9.** $9u^2 - 4v^2 = 4.$

## Exercises 16.3, Pages 649–650

**1.** $T = \dfrac{1}{\sqrt{2}}\begin{bmatrix} 1 & -1 \\ 1 & 1 \end{bmatrix}, \; 3v^2 - u^2 = 9.$      **3.** $T = \dfrac{1}{\sqrt{5}}\begin{bmatrix} 2 & -1 \\ 1 & 2 \end{bmatrix}, \; u^2 + 4v^2 = 16.$

**5.** $T = \dfrac{1}{\sqrt{10}}\begin{bmatrix} 3 & -1 \\ 1 & 3 \end{bmatrix}, \; 2u^2 - v^2 = 8.$      **7.** $T = \frac{1}{5}\begin{bmatrix} 3 & -4 \\ 4 & 3 \end{bmatrix}, \; v^2 = 2u.$

**9.** $T = \frac{1}{2}\begin{bmatrix} \sqrt{3} & -1 \\ 1 & \sqrt{3} \end{bmatrix}, \; 4u^2 = -24v + 24.$

     Translate coordinates by $u = u_1, v = v_1 + 1$ to obtain $u_1^2 = -6v_1.$

**11.** $T = \dfrac{1}{\sqrt{5}}\begin{bmatrix} 1 & -2 \\ 2 & 1 \end{bmatrix}; \; u = u_1 - 3, v = v_1 - \frac{3}{2}; \dfrac{u_1^2}{6} - \dfrac{v_1^2}{9} = 1.$

**13.** First, show that $(\overline{AB}) = \overline{A}\,\overline{B}$. Then $(\overline{AB})^{\mathsf{T}} = (\overline{A}\,\overline{B})^{\mathsf{T}} = (\overline{B})^{\mathsf{T}}(\overline{A})^{\mathsf{T}} \Rightarrow (AB)^* = B^*A^*.$

**15.** If $A = [a_{ij} + ib_{ij}]$, then $A^* = [a_{ji} - ib_{ji}]$, and $(A^*)^* = [a_{ij} + ib_{ij}] = A.$

**17.** The eigenvalues are $a$ and $c$. The normalized eigenvectors are
$$\begin{bmatrix} 1 \\ 0 \end{bmatrix} \quad \text{and} \quad \begin{bmatrix} 0 \\ 1 \end{bmatrix}.$$
If the two eigenvalues are equal, the equation $X^{\mathsf{T}}SX = r^2$ is that of a circle.

## Exercises 16.4, Pages 656–658

**1.** Eigenvalues: $\lambda_1 = 2, \lambda_2 = 3, \lambda_3 = -3;$

     Eigenvectors: $T_1 = \begin{bmatrix} 1 \\ 0 \\ 0 \end{bmatrix}, T_2 = \dfrac{1}{\sqrt{2}}\begin{bmatrix} 0 \\ 1 \\ -1 \end{bmatrix}, T_3 = \dfrac{1}{\sqrt{2}}\begin{bmatrix} 0 \\ 1 \\ 1 \end{bmatrix};$

Transformation: $T = [T_1 T_2 T_3] = \begin{bmatrix} 1 & 0 & 0 \\ 0 & \dfrac{1}{\sqrt{2}} & \dfrac{1}{\sqrt{2}} \\ 0 & -\dfrac{1}{\sqrt{2}} & \dfrac{1}{\sqrt{2}} \end{bmatrix}$.

**3.** Eigenvalues: $\lambda_1 = 1$, $\lambda_2 = 4$, $\lambda_3 = -2$;

Eigenvectors: $T_1 = \frac{1}{3}\begin{bmatrix} -2 \\ 2 \\ 1 \end{bmatrix}$, $T_2 = \frac{1}{3}\begin{bmatrix} 1 \\ 2 \\ -2 \end{bmatrix}$, $T_3 = \frac{1}{3}\begin{bmatrix} 2 \\ 1 \\ 2 \end{bmatrix}$;

Transformation: $T = [T_2 T_1 T_3] = \frac{1}{3}\begin{bmatrix} 1 & -2 & 2 \\ 2 & 2 & 1 \\ -2 & 1 & 2 \end{bmatrix}$.

**5.** Eigenvalues: $\lambda_1 = 4$, $\lambda_2 = \lambda_3 = 1$;

Eigenvectors: $T_1 = \dfrac{1}{\sqrt{3}}\begin{bmatrix} 1 \\ -1 \\ 1 \end{bmatrix}$, $T_2 = \dfrac{1}{\sqrt{6}}\begin{bmatrix} 2 \\ 1 \\ -1 \end{bmatrix}$, $T_3 = \dfrac{1}{\sqrt{2}}\begin{bmatrix} 0 \\ 1 \\ 1 \end{bmatrix}$;

Transformation: $T = [T_1 T_2 T_3] = \begin{bmatrix} \dfrac{1}{\sqrt{3}} & \dfrac{2}{\sqrt{6}} & 0 \\ -\dfrac{1}{\sqrt{3}} & \dfrac{1}{\sqrt{6}} & \dfrac{1}{\sqrt{2}} \\ \dfrac{1}{\sqrt{3}} & -\dfrac{1}{\sqrt{6}} & \dfrac{1}{\sqrt{2}} \end{bmatrix}$.

**7.** Suppose we want to find the points $(x, y, z)$ that are invariant. Then $x$, $y$, $z$ must satisfy the equation

$$\begin{bmatrix} x \\ y \\ z \end{bmatrix} = \begin{bmatrix} a_1 & b_1 & c_1 \\ a_2 & b_2 & c_2 \\ a_3 & b_3 & c_3 \end{bmatrix}\begin{bmatrix} x \\ y \\ z \end{bmatrix},$$

and

$$(a_1 - 1)x + b_1 y + c_1 z = 0,$$
$$a_2 x + (b_2 - 1)y + c_2 z = 0,$$
$$a_3 x + b_3 y + (c_3 - 1)z = 0.$$

Since $A$ is orthonormal, $\det A = 1$, and

$$\det \begin{bmatrix} a_1 - 1 & b_1 & c_1 \\ a_2 & b_2 - 1 & c_2 \\ a_3 & b_3 & c_3 - 1 \end{bmatrix} = 0.$$

This last equation may be established as follows:

$$AA^\mathsf{T} = I \Rightarrow \det (A - I) = 0,$$

since

$$\det (A - I) = \det A \det (I - A^\mathsf{T}) = (-1)^3 \det (A^\mathsf{T} - I) = -\det [(A - I)^\mathsf{T}]$$
$$= -\det (A - I) \Rightarrow \det (A - I) = 0.$$

Hence, the three equations are linearly dependent, so that two of $x$, $y$, $z$ can be found in terms of the third to give the equations of a line as the set of invariant points. For the given matrix, the axis of rotation is the line $x = z$, $y = 0$.

**9.** The eigenvalues of $A$ are 1, 1. To find eigenvectors we solve

$$\begin{bmatrix} 0 & 2 \\ 0 & 0 \end{bmatrix}\begin{bmatrix} x \\ y \end{bmatrix} = \begin{bmatrix} 0 \\ 0 \end{bmatrix}.$$

Hence, $x$ can be any number other than zero, and $y = 0$. Since there is only one unit vector of this form, $\begin{bmatrix} 1 \\ 0 \end{bmatrix}$, a transformation using only eigenvectors cannot be found. Suppose

$$T = \begin{bmatrix} x & u \\ y & v \end{bmatrix}$$

and

$$\begin{bmatrix} 1 & 2 \\ 0 & 1 \end{bmatrix} \begin{bmatrix} x & u \\ y & v \end{bmatrix} = \begin{bmatrix} x & u \\ y & v \end{bmatrix} \begin{bmatrix} \alpha & 0 \\ 0 & \beta \end{bmatrix}.$$

Then $x + 2y = x\alpha$, $y = \alpha y \Rightarrow \alpha = 1 \Rightarrow y = 0$. Similarly, $u + 2v = \beta u$, $v = \beta v \Rightarrow \beta = 1 \Rightarrow v = 0$. Hence, the bottom row of $T$ is 0, and $T^{-1}$ does not exist.

11. $AA^{-1} = I$. $\det (A - \lambda I) = 0$, $\lambda$ is an eigenvalue of $A$,

$$\Rightarrow \det [A(I - \lambda A^{-1})] = 0 \text{ or } \det \left[ A \left( \frac{1}{\lambda} I - A^{-1} \right) \right] = 0.$$

$$\Rightarrow \det \left[ A^{-1} - \frac{1}{\lambda} I \right] = 0 \Rightarrow \text{ an eigenvalue of } A^{-1} \text{ is } \frac{1}{\lambda}.$$

13. Direction of $x$ stress is $[\frac{2}{3}, -\frac{2}{3}, \frac{1}{3}]$; magnitude is 6.
    Direction of $y$ stress is $[\frac{2}{3}, \frac{1}{3}, -\frac{2}{3}]$; magnitude is 3.
    Direction of $z$ stress is $[\frac{1}{3}, \frac{2}{3}, \frac{2}{3}]$; magnitude is 3.
    Eigenvalues: $\lambda_1 = 6$, $\lambda_2 = -3$, $\lambda_3 = -3$.

    Eigenvectors: $T_1 = \frac{1}{3} \begin{bmatrix} 2 \\ -2 \\ 1 \end{bmatrix}$, $T_2 = \frac{1}{3} \begin{bmatrix} 2 \\ 1 \\ -2 \end{bmatrix}$, $T_3 = \frac{1}{3} \begin{bmatrix} 1 \\ 2 \\ 2 \end{bmatrix}$.

## Exercises 17.1, Page 662

1. Center, $(-2, -3, 0)$; radius, 4.   3. Center, $(-1, 2, 4)$; radius, $\frac{1}{2}\sqrt{2}$.
5. Center, $(a_1, a_2, a_3)$; radius, $|\mathbf{a}|$.   7. $x + 2y + 2z = 12$.
9. The equation of the set, $(x + \frac{2}{3})^2 + (y + \frac{2}{3})^2 + z^2 = \frac{32}{9}$, is that of a sphere with center at $(-\frac{2}{3}, -\frac{2}{3}, 0)$ and of radius $\frac{4}{3}\sqrt{2}$.
11. Show that the sum of the radii equals the distance between their centers.
13. Traces in planes parallel to the $xy$-plane are hyperbolas, $xy = c$.
    Traces in planes parallel to the $xz$-plane are exponential curves, $x = ke^z$.
    Traces in planes parallel to the $yz$-plane are exponential curves, $y = ke^z$.
15. Traces in planes parallel to the $xy$-plane are hyperbolas, $xy = k$.
    Traces in planes parallel to the $xz$-plane are straight lines, $z = cx$.
    Traces in planes parallel to the $yz$-plane are straight lines, $z = cy$.
17. Traces in planes parallel to the $xz$-plane are parabolas, $x = 2z^2$.
    Traces in planes parallel to the $xy$-plane are lines, $x = 2c$.

    Traces in planes parallel to the $yz$-plane are pairs of lines, $z = \pm\sqrt{c/2}$, $c \geq 0$.
19. Traces in planes parallel to the $xy$-plane are circles, $x^2 + y^2 = k$.
    Traces in planes parallel to the $xz$-plane are exponential curves,
    $$z = \exp [-(x^2 + a^2)].$$
    Traces in planes parallel to the $yz$-plane are exponential curves,
    $$z = \exp [-(a^2 + y^2)].$$

**Exercises 17.2, Page 666**

**13.** $y = x^2 + z^2$.  **15.** $x^2 + y^2 + z^2 = 16$.
**17.** $9x^2 + 4y^2 + 9z^2 = 36$.
**19.** The transformed equation is $v^2 - w^2 = 9$, a hyperbolic cylinder.
**21.** The transformed equation is $u^2 + v^2 = w^2$, a right circular cone.

**Exercises 17.3, Pages 671–672**

**1.** Hyperboloid of one sheet; axis is $z$-axis.
**3.** Hyperboloid of two sheets; axis is $y$-axis.
**5.** Sphere.  **7.** Hyperbolic paraboloid.  **9.** Elliptic cone; axis is $x$-axis.
**11.** Right circular cylinder; axis is $x$-axis.  **13.** Elliptic paraboloid; axis is $z$-axis.
**15.** Elliptic paraboloid; axis is $y$-axis.  **17.** Hyperbolic cylinder.  **19.** Sphere.
**21.** (a) A plane through the origin.
  (b) A sphere through the origin with center at $\frac{1}{2}\mathbf{a}$.
  (c) A right circular cylinder of radius 1, axis in the direction of $\mathbf{a}$.
  (d) A portion of a cone, axis in the direction of $\mathbf{a}$.
**23.** Upon eliminating $t$, we get
$$\frac{x^2}{a^2} + \frac{y^2}{b^2} - \frac{z^2}{c^2} = 1,$$
which is the equation of a hyperboloid of one sheet.
**25.** $\dfrac{dy}{dx} = \dfrac{mgx\omega^2}{mg} \Rightarrow y = \frac{1}{2}x^2\omega^2 + C$.

**Exercises 17.4, Page 675**

**13.** $x = e^{-t}$, $y = t$, $z = e^t$.
**15.** The curve may be considered as the intersection of the right circular cylinder $x^2 + y^2 = a^2$ and the cylindrical surface $x = a \sin (\omega z/b)$.

**Exercises 17.5, Pages 677–678**

**1.** $u^2 + 4v^2 + 2w^2 = 16$; an ellipsoid.
**3.** $v^2 + w^2 - u^2 = \frac{1}{4}$; a hyperboloid of one sheet.

**5.** $T = \begin{bmatrix} \dfrac{3}{\sqrt{11}} & \dfrac{2}{\sqrt{22}} & 0 \\[2mm] -\dfrac{1}{\sqrt{11}} & \dfrac{3}{\sqrt{22}} & \dfrac{1}{\sqrt{2}} \\[2mm] \dfrac{1}{\sqrt{11}} & -\dfrac{3}{\sqrt{22}} & \dfrac{1}{\sqrt{2}} \end{bmatrix}$; $u^2 = 4$; two parallel planes.

**7.** $T = \begin{bmatrix} \dfrac{1}{\sqrt{2}} & \dfrac{1}{3\sqrt{2}} & \dfrac{2}{3} \\[2mm] -\dfrac{1}{\sqrt{2}} & \dfrac{1}{3\sqrt{2}} & \dfrac{2}{3} \\[2mm] 0 & -\dfrac{4}{3\sqrt{2}} & \dfrac{1}{3} \end{bmatrix}$; $u^2 + v^2 = 4$; a right circular cylinder.

**9.** $T = \begin{bmatrix} 1 & 0 & 0 \\ 0 & \dfrac{1}{\sqrt{2}} & \dfrac{1}{\sqrt{2}} \\ 0 & -\dfrac{1}{\sqrt{2}} & \dfrac{1}{\sqrt{2}} \end{bmatrix}$; $u^2 - 2w^2 = 0$; two intersecting planes passing through the $v$-axis.

**11.** $T = \begin{bmatrix} \dfrac{1}{\sqrt{2}} & \dfrac{1}{\sqrt{3}} & \dfrac{1}{\sqrt{6}} \\ -\dfrac{1}{\sqrt{2}} & \dfrac{1}{\sqrt{3}} & \dfrac{1}{\sqrt{6}} \\ 0 & -\dfrac{1}{\sqrt{3}} & \dfrac{2}{\sqrt{6}} \end{bmatrix}$; $u = \xi,\ v = \eta + \sqrt{3},\ w = \zeta$;

$\xi^2 + \eta^2 - 2\zeta^2 = 8$; a hyperboloid of one sheet.

**13.** $T = \begin{bmatrix} \dfrac{1}{2} & \dfrac{1}{\sqrt{2}} & \dfrac{1}{2} \\ \dfrac{\sqrt{2}}{2} & 0 & -\dfrac{\sqrt{2}}{2} \\ -\dfrac{1}{2} & \dfrac{1}{\sqrt{2}} & -\dfrac{1}{2} \end{bmatrix}$; $u = \xi,\ v = \eta,\ w = \zeta + 2$;

$\xi^2 - \zeta^2 = 4$; a hyperbolic cylinder.

## Exercises 18.1, Pages 685–686

**1.** $\mathbf{r}$ is continuous for all values of $t \in \mathcal{R}$.  **3.** Continuous for all $t$ except $t = \pm 2$.
**5.** Continuous for all values of $s$.  **7.** Continuous for all values of $t$.
**9.** Continuous for all values of $t$.  **11.** $4\mathbf{i} + \tfrac{1}{4}\mathbf{j}$.
**13.** $|\mathbf{u} \cdot \mathbf{v} - \mathbf{U} \cdot \mathbf{V}| = |\mathbf{u} \cdot \mathbf{v} - \mathbf{u} \cdot \mathbf{V} + \mathbf{u} \cdot \mathbf{V} - \mathbf{U} \cdot \mathbf{V}| \leq |\mathbf{u} \cdot (\mathbf{v} - \mathbf{V})| + |(\mathbf{u} - \mathbf{U}) \cdot \mathbf{V}|$
$\qquad\qquad \leq |\mathbf{u}||\mathbf{v} - \mathbf{V}||\cos \theta_1| + |\mathbf{V}||\mathbf{u} - \mathbf{U}||\cos \theta_2| \leq |\mathbf{u}||\mathbf{v} - \mathbf{V}| + |\mathbf{V}||\mathbf{u} - \mathbf{U}|$.

But, $\lim\limits_{t \to a} \mathbf{u}(t) = \mathbf{U} \Rightarrow$ there is a $\delta_1$ such that $t \in \mathcal{N}^*(a, \delta_1) \Rightarrow \mathbf{u}(t) \in \mathcal{N}\left(\mathbf{U}, \dfrac{\epsilon}{k_1}\right)$, and

$\lim\limits_{t \to a} \mathbf{v}(t) = \mathbf{V} \Rightarrow$ there is a $\delta_2$ such that $t \in \mathcal{N}^*(a, \delta_2) \Rightarrow \mathbf{v}(t) \in \mathcal{N}\left(\mathbf{V}, \dfrac{\epsilon}{k_2}\right)$. Let
$k_1 = 2|\mathbf{V}|$ and $k_2 = 2|\mathbf{u}|$ when $|\mathbf{V}| \neq 0$ or $|\mathbf{u}| \neq 0$, and let $\delta = \min(\delta_1, \delta_2)$. Then
$t \in \mathcal{N}^*(a, \delta) \Rightarrow \mathbf{u} \cdot \mathbf{v} \in \mathcal{N}(\mathbf{U} \cdot \mathbf{V}, \epsilon)$.

**15.** $\mathbf{r} = \dfrac{2}{\sin \theta - 2 \cos \theta}\, \mathbf{e}_r$.  **17.** $\mathbf{r} = 2a \cos(\theta - \alpha)\mathbf{e}_r$.

**19.** $r = \dfrac{1}{1 - \frac{1}{2} \cos \theta}$, an ellipse.  **21.** $r = 1 - 3 \sin \theta$, a limaçon.

## Exercises 18.2, Pages 692–693

**1. (a)** $D_t\mathbf{r} = -a \sin t\, \mathbf{i} + a \cos t\, \mathbf{j}$.  **(b)** $D_t\mathbf{r} = -2t \sin t^2\, \mathbf{i} + 2t \cos t^2\, \mathbf{j}$.
$\qquad \mathbf{T} = -\sin t\, \mathbf{i} + \cos t\, \mathbf{j}$.  $\qquad\qquad \mathbf{T} = \sin t^2\, \mathbf{i} + \cos t^2\, \mathbf{j}$.
$\qquad \mathbf{N} = -\cos t\, \mathbf{i} - \sin t\, \mathbf{j}$.  $\qquad\qquad \mathbf{N} = -\cos t^2\, \mathbf{i} - \sin t^2\, \mathbf{j}$.
**(c)** $D_t\mathbf{r} = (3t^2 - 3)\mathbf{i} + 6t\mathbf{j}$.
$\qquad \mathbf{T} = \left(\dfrac{t^2 - 1}{t^2 + 1}\right)\mathbf{i} + \dfrac{2t}{t^2 + 1}\mathbf{j}$.
$\qquad \mathbf{N} = \dfrac{1}{1 + t^2}\,[2t\, \mathbf{i} + (1 - t^2)\mathbf{j}]$.

**(d)** $D_t\mathbf{r} = -a\omega\sin\omega t\,\mathbf{i} + a\omega\cos\omega t\,\mathbf{j} + b\omega\mathbf{k}.$

$$\mathbf{T} = \frac{1}{\sqrt{a^2 + b^2}}[-a\sin\omega t\,\mathbf{i} + a\cos\omega t\,\mathbf{j} + b\mathbf{k}].$$

$$\mathbf{N} = -\cos\omega t\,\mathbf{i} - \sin\omega t\,\mathbf{j}.$$

**(e)** $D_t\mathbf{r} = 3a(1 - t^2)\mathbf{i} + 6at\,\mathbf{j} + 3a(1 + t^2)\mathbf{k}.$

$$\mathbf{T} = \frac{1}{\sqrt{2}}\left[\frac{1 - t^2}{1 + t^2}\mathbf{i} + \frac{2t}{1 + t^2}\mathbf{j} + \mathbf{k}\right].$$

$$\mathbf{N} = -\frac{2t}{1 + t^2}\mathbf{i} + \frac{1 - t^2}{1 + t^2}\mathbf{j}.$$

**(f)** $D_t\mathbf{r} = [-\tan w\,\mathbf{i} + \cot w\,\mathbf{j} + \sqrt{2}\mathbf{k}]D_t w.$

$$\mathbf{T} = -\sin^2 w\,\mathbf{i} + \cos^2 w\,\mathbf{j} + \sqrt{2}\cos w\sin w\,\mathbf{k}.$$

$$\mathbf{N} = \frac{1}{\sqrt{2}}[-\sin 2w\,\mathbf{i} + \sin 2w\,\mathbf{j} + \sqrt{2}\cos 2w\,\mathbf{k}].$$

**3.** Either $\mathbf{r} = \mathbf{c}$, a constant, or $D_t\mathbf{r}$ is parallel to $\mathbf{r}$.

**5.** $|\mathbf{v}|^2 = \mathbf{v}\cdot\mathbf{v} \Rightarrow 2|\mathbf{v}|D_t|\mathbf{v}| = 2\mathbf{v}\cdot D_t\mathbf{v} \Rightarrow \mathbf{v}\cdot D_t\mathbf{v} = vD_tv.$

**7.** $D_t(\mathbf{r}\times\mathbf{p}) = (D_t\mathbf{r})\times\mathbf{p} + \mathbf{r}\times D_t\mathbf{p} = (\boldsymbol{\omega}\times\mathbf{r})\times\mathbf{p} + \mathbf{r}\times(\boldsymbol{\omega}\times\mathbf{p})$
$$= -(\mathbf{p}\cdot\mathbf{r})\boldsymbol{\omega} + (\mathbf{p}\cdot\boldsymbol{\omega})\mathbf{r} + (\mathbf{r}\cdot\mathbf{p})\boldsymbol{\omega} - (\mathbf{r}\cdot\boldsymbol{\omega})\mathbf{p} = \boldsymbol{\omega}\times(\mathbf{r}\times\mathbf{p}).$$

**9. (a)** $\mathbf{p}(s) = (1, 0, 2) + s(1, 4, 4).$

**(b)** $\mathbf{p}(s) = \left(\dfrac{a\sqrt{3}}{2}, \dfrac{a}{2}, \dfrac{b}{6}\right) + s\left(-\dfrac{a}{2}, \dfrac{a\sqrt{3}}{2}, \dfrac{b}{\pi}\right).$

**(c)** $\mathbf{p}(s) = (2a, 3a, 4a) + s(0, a, a).$

**(d)** $\mathbf{r}(s) = (-1, 0, -2) + s(0, -1, 2).$

**11.** $D_\theta\mathbf{r} = a\mathbf{e}_\theta.$   **13.** $D_\theta\mathbf{r} = \frac{1}{2}\sqrt{3}\,\mathbf{e}_r + \frac{1}{2}\mathbf{e}_\theta.$   **15.** $D_\theta\mathbf{r} = 2\sqrt{5}\,\mathbf{e}_r + \sqrt{5}\,\mathbf{e}_\theta.$

### Exercises 18.3, Pages 698–699

**1.** $4\sqrt{2}$ l.u.   **3.** $\sqrt{2}(e - 1)$ l.u.   **5.** $\frac{2}{27}(11\sqrt{22} - 4)$ l.u.

**7.** $2\sinh 2$ l.u.   **9.** $\frac{8}{27}(10^{3/2} - 1)$ l.u.   **11.** $5a\pi^2/8$ l.u.

**13.** $[1 + \frac{1}{2}\sqrt{2}\ln(1 + \sqrt{2})]$ l.u.   **15.** $5\pi$ l.u.   **17.** $8a$ l.u.

**19.** $s = \displaystyle\int_0^{2\pi}\sqrt{(a^2 + b^2) + 2ab\cos\theta}\,d\theta.$   **21.** $x = a\cos\dfrac{s}{a}, y = a\sin\dfrac{s}{a}.$

**23.** $s = e^t - e^{-t}.$   **25.** They are equal.

### Exercises 18.4, Pages 703–704

**1.** $\mathbf{v} = 6\mathbf{i} + \mathbf{j}; \mathbf{a} = 2\mathbf{i}; D_t s = \sqrt{37}.$

**3.** $\mathbf{v} = -2\mathbf{i} + \dfrac{\sqrt{2}}{2}\mathbf{j}; \mathbf{a} = -\dfrac{\sqrt{2}}{2}\mathbf{j}; D_t s = \dfrac{3\sqrt{2}}{2}.$

**5.** $\mathbf{v} = -\dfrac{\sqrt{2}}{2}\omega\mathbf{i} + \dfrac{\sqrt{2}}{2}\omega\mathbf{j} + \omega\mathbf{k}, \mathbf{a} = -\dfrac{\omega^2\sqrt{2}}{2}\mathbf{i} - \dfrac{\omega^2\sqrt{2}}{2}\mathbf{j}, D_t s = \omega\sqrt{2}.$

**7.** $\mathbf{v} = \pi\mathbf{i} - \sqrt{3}\pi\mathbf{j} + \pi\mathbf{k}, \mathbf{a} = -\pi^2\sqrt{3}\mathbf{i} - \pi^2\mathbf{j} - \pi^2\sqrt{3}\mathbf{k}, D_t s = \pi\sqrt{5}.$

**9.** $\mathbf{v} = -\frac{1}{2}\pi a\sqrt{3}\mathbf{i} + \frac{1}{2}\pi a\mathbf{j} + 2\pi a\sqrt{3}\mathbf{k}, \mathbf{a} = -\frac{1}{2}\pi^2 a\mathbf{i} - \frac{1}{2}\pi^2 a\sqrt{3}\mathbf{j} + 8\pi^2 a\mathbf{k},$
$D_t s = \pi a\sqrt{13}.$

**11.** $\mathbf{v} = -\mathbf{i} + \mathbf{j} + \sqrt{2}\mathbf{k}$, $\mathbf{a} = -2\mathbf{i} - 2\mathbf{j}$, $D_t s = 2$.

**13.** $\mathbf{v} = \dfrac{2}{\sqrt{65}}(8\mathbf{i} + \mathbf{j})$, $\mathbf{a} = \dfrac{32}{4225}(\mathbf{i} - 8\mathbf{j})$, $D_t \theta = -\dfrac{8}{17\sqrt{65}}$ radian/second.

**15.** $\mathbf{v} = 2\mathbf{i} + \frac{1}{4}\mathbf{j}$, $\mathbf{a} = -\frac{1}{16}\mathbf{j}$, $D_t\theta = -\frac{1}{17}$ radian/second.

**17.** $D_t \alpha = -\frac{2}{7}\pi$ radian/unit time.

### Exercises 18.5, Page 709

**1.** 2 l.u.   **3.** $\frac{9}{2}$ l.u.   **5.** $125\sqrt{2}/48$ l.u.   **7.** $\frac{3}{2}a$ l.u.   **9.** $\frac{7}{4}\sqrt{7}$ l.u.

**13.** $K = a/(a^2 + b^2)$.   **15.** $a_T = 2$, $a_N = 2$.   **17.** $a_T = 2a$, $a_N = \pi a$.

**21.** $R = \frac{5}{2}$.   **23.** $R = 2\sqrt{2}a$.

### Exercises 18.6, Pages 712–713

**1.** *Hint:* Draw a figure.

**3.** $\varphi = \frac{1}{2}\pi$ at $r = 0$; $\varphi = \frac{1}{6}\pi$ at $r = \frac{3}{2}a$, $\theta = \pm\frac{1}{3}\pi$.   **5.** $\mathbf{a} = (2\mathbf{e}_r + 4\mathbf{e}_\theta)\omega_0^2$.

**7.** $\mathbf{a} = [-\frac{5}{2}\sqrt{3}\mathbf{e}_r + 2\mathbf{e}_\theta]\omega_0^2$.   **9.** $\mathbf{a} = -a2^{3/4}(2\mathbf{e}_r + \mathbf{e}_\theta)\omega_0^2$.

**11.** $\mathbf{v} = b\omega\mathbf{k} + \boldsymbol{\omega}_1 \times \mathbf{r}$, $\boldsymbol{\omega}_1 = -a\omega\mathbf{k}$ is the angular velocity.

**13.** $\mathbf{a} = (-2a \sin t^2 - 4t^2a \cos t^2)\mathbf{i} + (2a \cos t^2 - 4t^2a \sin t^2)\mathbf{j}$.

### Exercises 19.1, Page 716

**1.** Domain: $\{(x, y): 1 + xy > 0\}$.   **3.** Domain: $\{(x, y): x^2 + y^2 \leq 4\}$.

**5.** Domain: $\{(x, y): x^2 + y^2 \geq 1\}$.   **7.** Domain: $\{(x, y): x^2 + y^2 \neq 1\}$.

### Exercises 19.2, Page 720

**1.** $\mathcal{S}^e = \{(x, y): x < 0 \text{ or } x > 2\} \cup \{(x, y): y < 0 \text{ or } y > 1\}$.
   $\mathcal{S}^i = \{(x, y): 0 < x < 2 \text{ and } 0 < y < 1\}$.
   $\mathcal{S}^b = \{(x, y): 0 \leq x \leq 2 \text{ and } y = 0 \text{ or } y = 1\} \cup \{(x, y): 0 \leq y \leq 1 \text{ and } x = 0$
      or $x = 2\}$.

**3.** $\mathcal{S}^e = \{(x, y): x^2 + y^2 > 1\} \cap \{(x, y): x^2 + y^2 < 4\}$.
   $\mathcal{S}^i = \mathcal{S}$.
   $\mathcal{S}^b = \{(x, y): x^2 + y^2 = 1 \text{ or } x^2 + y^2 = 4\}$.

**5.** $\mathcal{S}^i = \mathcal{S}$.
   $\mathcal{S}^e = \{(x, y): x + 2y > 4\} \cup \{(x, y): x + 2y < 2\}$.
   $\mathcal{S}^b = \{(x, y): x + 2y = 4\} \cup \{(x, y): x + 2y = 2\}$.

**7.** $\mathcal{S}^i = \mathcal{S}$.
   $\mathcal{S}^e = \{(x, y): x + 2y = 4\} \cup \{(x, y): x < y\}$.
   $\mathcal{S}^b = \{(x, y): x + 2y = 4, x \geq \frac{4}{3}\} \cup \{(x, y): x = y, x < \frac{4}{3}\}$.

**9.** $\mathcal{S}^i = \varnothing$.
   $\mathcal{S}^b = \mathcal{S} \cup \{(x, y): 0 \leq x \leq 2, y = 1\} \cup \{(0, y): y = 1 - 1/n\}$
      $\cup \{(2, y): y = 1 - 1/n\}$.
   $\mathcal{S}^e = (\mathcal{S}^b)'$.

**Exercises 19.3, Pages 725–726**

**1.** The limit does not exist. Let $y = mx$, and then let $x \to 0$.
**3.** The limit does not exist. Let $y = mx$, and then let $x \to 0$.
**5.** Since $\dfrac{x^2 y^2}{x^2 + y^2} \leq r^2 \sin^2 \theta \cos^2 \theta = \frac{1}{4} r^2 \sin^2 2\theta \leq \frac{1}{4} r^2$, we require that $\frac{1}{4} r^2 < \epsilon$, which
implies that $r^2 \leq \delta^2 = 4\epsilon$, or $\delta = 2\sqrt{\epsilon}$.
**7.** Yes. Let $f(0, 0) .= . 0$.
**9. (a)** Domain: $\{(x, y): y^2 - 4x^2 \geq 4\} \cup \{(0, y)\}$,
   Region of continuity: $\{(x, y): y^2 - 4x^2 > 4\}$.
   **(b)** Domain: $\{(x, y): x^2 + y^2 \geq 1\} \cup \{(x, 0)\}$,
   Region of continuity: $\{(x, y): x^2 + y^2 > 1\}$.

**Exercises 19.4, Pages 729–730**

**1.** $u_x = y - \dfrac{1}{x}, u_y = x - \dfrac{1}{y}$. **3.** $z_x = \dfrac{4xy^2}{x^4 - y^4}, z_y = -\dfrac{4x^2 y}{x^4 - y^4}$.
**5.** $u_x = y \cos xy, u_y = x \cos xy$. **7.** $z_u = \dfrac{v}{u^2 + v^2}, z_v = -\dfrac{u}{u^2 + v^2}$.
**9.** $z_x = -u \sin ux \sin uy, z_u = -x \sin ux \sin uy + y \cos ux \cos uy$.
**11.** $2z$. **13.** $0$. **15.** $x = 3, \dfrac{y - 10}{2} = \dfrac{z - 1}{1}$.
**17.** $x = 1, \dfrac{y - 1}{1} = \dfrac{z - e}{e}$. **19.** $y_1 = \sqrt{7}$.

**Exercises 19.5, Page 732**

**1.** $f_{xx} = -\dfrac{2y}{x^3}, f_{xy} = f_{yx} = \dfrac{1}{x^2} - \dfrac{1}{y^2}, f_{yy} = \dfrac{2x}{y^3}$.
**3.** $z_{xx} = y^2 e^{xy}, z_{xy} = z_{yx} = (1 + xy)e^{xy}, z_{yy} = x^2 e^{xy}$.
**5.** $u_{xx} = -y^2 z^2 \sin xyz$,
   $u_{xy} = u_{yx} = z \cos xyz - xyz^2 \sin xyz$,
   $u_{yy} = -x^2 z^2 \sin xyz$,
   $u_{xz} = u_{zx} = y \cos xyz - xy^2 z \sin xyz$,
   $u_{zz} = -x^2 y^2 \sin xyz$,
   $u_{yz} = u_{zy} = x \cos xyz - x^2 yz \sin xyz$.
**7.** $u_{xx} = \dfrac{2xy}{(x^2 + y^2)^2}, u_{xy} = \dfrac{y^2 - x^2}{(x^2 + y^2)^2} = u_{yx}, u_{yy} = -\dfrac{2xy}{(x^2 + y^2)^2}$.
**15.** $f_x(0, 0) = \lim\limits_{h \to 0} \dfrac{f(h, 0) - f(0, 0)}{h} = \lim\limits_{h \to 0} \dfrac{0}{h} = 0$.
   **(a)** Yes.
   **(b)** $f_x(x, y) = \dfrac{2y^3 - 2x^2 y}{(x^2 + y^2)^2}$ and $\lim\limits_{(x,y) \to (0,0)} f_x(x, y)$ does not exist. Therefore, $f_x(x, y)$
   is not continuous.
   **(c)** No, because $f_x(0, y) \to \infty$ as $y \to 0$.
**17.** $f_{xy}(0, 0) = -1, f_{yx}(0, 0) = 1$.

**Exercises 19.6, Pages 736–737**

**1.** $dz = (3x^2 + 2xy) dx + (x^2 - 3y^2) dy$. **3.** $du = \dfrac{x\,dx + y\,dy + z\,dz}{x^2 + y^2 + z^2}$.

**5.** $du = e^{xyz}(yz\,dx + xz\,dy + xy\,dz)$. **7.** $\Delta z = 0.0097980101$, $dz = 0.01$.

**9.** $\Delta z = 0.3719$, $dz = 0.37$. **11.** $\Delta z = 0.03015$, $dz = 0.03$. **13.** 7.14.

**15.** $dV = \frac{8}{3}\pi$ cubic inches. **17.** Error $\leqq 4\%$. **19.** $e\%$.

**Exercises 20.1, Page 743**

**1.** $u_r = (3x^2 - 3y)(2r) + (-3x + 3y^2)s^2$.

**3.** $D_t u = ye^t \left(\dfrac{t-1}{t^2}\right) - (x+z)e^{-t}\left(\dfrac{t+1}{t^2}\right) + 2ty$.

**5.** $z_u = \left(\dfrac{2x}{x^2+y^2} + \dfrac{x}{\sqrt{x^2+y^2}}\right)e^u \cos v + \left(\dfrac{2y}{x^2+y^2} + \dfrac{y}{\sqrt{x^2+y^2}}\right)e^u \sin v$.

**7.** $u_r = (y+z)srs^{-1} + (x+z)s + (y+x)$.

**9.** $u_r = yz^2e^s + xz^2e^{-s} + 2xyzs^{-1}$; $u_s = yz^2re^s - xz^2re^{-s} - 2xyzrs^{-2}$.

**11.** $u_x^2 + u_y^2$.

**13.** *Hint:* Let $u = y/x$ so that $z = x\,F(u)$. Then $z_x = F(u) + x\,D_u F(u)\,u_x$, or $z_x = F(u) + x\,D_u F(u)(-y/x^2)$. Find $z_y$ in a similar way.

**Exercises 20.2, Pages 748–749**

**1.** $D_x y = -\dfrac{e^x \sin y - e^y \sin x}{e^x \cos y + e^y \cos x}$. **3.** $D_x y = \dfrac{x+y}{x-y}$.

**5.** $z_x = -\dfrac{y+z-9yz}{y+x-9xy}$, $z_y = -\dfrac{x+z-9xz}{y+x-9xy}$.

**7.** $z_x = -\dfrac{z}{x+y\sin yz}$, $z_y = -\dfrac{z\sin yz}{x+y\sin yz}$.

**9.** $D_x y = -\dfrac{y^2(z-x)}{x^2(z-y)}$. **11.** $D_x y = -\dfrac{x}{y}$. **13.** $u_x = \dfrac{3x^2+4v}{2(u+v)}$, $v_x = \dfrac{4u-3x^2}{2(u+v)}$.

**15.** $x_u = -\dfrac{xy(uy+1)}{2u^2y^2+uy-uvx}$, $y_v = \dfrac{uy-uxy-v}{2u^2y^2+uy-uvx}$.

**17.** $(\frac{8}{3}\sqrt[3]{3}, \frac{8}{3}\sqrt[3]{9})$. **23.** $z_{xx} = -\dfrac{F_z^2 F_{xx} - 2F_{xz}F_x F_z + F_x^2 F_{zz}}{F_z^3}$.

**Exercises 20.3, Page 754**

**1.** $2\mathbf{i} + 2\mathbf{j} - \mathbf{k}$. **3.** $\theta = \text{Cos}^{-1}\left(-\dfrac{5\sqrt{34}}{102}\right)$. **5.** $[1, 1, 6]$.

**7.** Tangent plane: $6x - 6y - z = 0$;

Normal line: $\dfrac{x-2}{6} = \dfrac{y-2}{-6} = \dfrac{z}{-1}$.

**9.** Tangent plane: $6x - 8y - z = 5$;

Normal line: $\dfrac{x-3}{6} = \dfrac{y-1}{-8} = \dfrac{z-5}{-1}$.

**11.** Tangent plane: $x + 8y - 5z = 25$;

Normal line: $\dfrac{x - 2}{1} = \dfrac{y - 1}{8} = \dfrac{z + 3}{-5}$.

**13.** Since $\mathbf{n}_1 \cdot \mathbf{n}_2 = 0$ at the points of intersection for which $x^2 + y^2 = 1$, the surfaces are orthogonal there.

**15.** Yes. For $z = \sqrt{f(x, y)}$, the direction numbers of a normal are $\left[ \dfrac{f_x}{2\sqrt{f}}, \dfrac{f_y}{2\sqrt{f}}, -1 \right]$,

and those for $z^2 = f(x, y)$ are $[f_x, f_y, -2z]$. Since $z = \sqrt{f}$, the direction numbers are proportional.

### Exercises 20.4, Pages 759–760

**1.** At $(2, 1)$, $D_s z = 3\sqrt{2}$; at $(6, 3)$, $D_s z = 9\sqrt{2}$.

**3.** $\frac{1}{4}(1 + \sqrt{3})$.      **5.** $-\frac{19}{7}$.      **7.** 0.      **9.** $[1, 2]$.

**11.** The direction of the curve at $(1, 3, 2)$ is $[2, 3, 1]$, and the direction of the normal at $(1, 3, 2)$ is $[4, 6, 2]$.

**13.** $\theta = \text{Cos}^{-1} \dfrac{\sqrt{7}}{14}$.

### Exercises 20.5, Page 766

**1.** $u$-curves: straight lines with slope $\frac{1}{2}$;
$v$-curves: straight lines with slope $\frac{2}{3}$; $J = 1$.
Inverse transformation: $v = 2y - x$, $u = 2x - 3y$.

**3.** $u$-curves: straight lines through the origin with slope $\tanh v$;
$v$-curves: hyperbolas, $x^2 - y^2 = u^2$; $J = u$.
The transformation is not one-to-one for the points $(u = 0, v)$.

Inverse transformation: $u = \pm\sqrt{x^2 - y^2}$, $v = \tanh^{-1}\left(\dfrac{y}{x}\right)$.

**5.** The transformation is a rigid rotation through the angle $\theta$; $J = 1$.

**7.** In $uv$-coordinates, the equation of the curve is $u^2 + v^2 = 1$, which is a circle in the $uv$-plane.

**9.** $x = u^2 - v^2$, $y = 2uv$. $J = 0 \Rightarrow u = 0$, $v = 0 \Rightarrow x = 0$, $y = 0$. The transformation is one-to-one at this point.

### Exercises 20.6, Pages 771–772

**1.** $r = z$.      **3.** $r^2 \cos 2\theta = z^2$.      **5.** $r^2 = \dfrac{z^2}{\cos 2\theta - \sin 2\theta}$.

**7.** $\rho = a$.      **9.** $\rho = \csc \varphi \cot \varphi$.      **11.** $\rho = a \cos^3 \varphi$.

**13.** **(a)** Not orthogonal,    **(b)** orthogonal,    **(c)** not orthogonal.

**15.** Yes, where $r = 0$.

### Exercises 21.1, Pages 775–776

**1.** $u = \dfrac{xy^3}{6} - \dfrac{y^4}{12} + y\varphi(x) + \psi(x)$.    **3.** $u = \dfrac{y^2 x^2}{2} + \dfrac{x^2}{2} + x\varphi(y) + \psi(y)$.

**5.** $u = \frac{1}{2} \sin x \sin 2y + \frac{1}{2}e^{2x} + e^y - \frac{1}{2}$.

**7.** $u = \frac{1}{6}e^{2x} \sin 3y - \frac{1}{2}\cos 2y - \frac{1}{6}\sin 3y + \frac{1}{2}$. **9.** 1. **11.** $-\frac{1}{4}$. **13.** $\frac{1}{8}\pi$.
**15.** $\frac{1}{2}(e-1)^2$. **17.** $1 - \frac{1}{2}\pi + \frac{1}{8}\pi^2$. **19.** 1. **21.** $\frac{4}{9}$. **23.** $\frac{1}{2}(2-\pi)$. **25.** $\frac{4}{9} - \frac{1}{12}\pi$.

## Exercises 21.2, Pages 781–782

**1.** $\int_{\Re} xy \, dm$, where $\Re$ is the region in the $xy$-plane over which the mass $m$ is distributed.

**3.** The volume of a right circular cylinder of unit radius and height 4.

**5.** The volume of the solid in the first octant above the triangle enclosed by the coordinate axes and the line $x + y = 2$, and below the plane $x + y + z = 2$.

**7.** The volume of the solid that lies below the paraboloid of revolution $x^2 + y^2 = z$, and above the region $\Re$ enclosed by the ellipse $x^2 + 4y^2 = 4$ in the $xy$-plane.

**9.** The volume of the solid that lies below the cone $x^2 + y^2 = z^2$ and above the region $\Re$ enclosed by the circle $x^2 + y^2 = 9$ in the $xy$-plane.

**11.** The volume of the solid that lies below the plane $z = 2$ and above the region $\Re$ in the $xy$-plane bounded by the parabolic arc $y = \sqrt{x}$ and the lines $x = 0$, $y = 1$.

## Exercises 21.3, Pages 788–789

**1.** $\frac{1}{6}$ (l.u.)$^2$. **3.** $\frac{3}{4}\sqrt{3}$ (l.u.)$^2$. **5.** $4\pi$ (l.u.)$^2$. **7.** $10\pi$ (l.u.)$^2$. **9.** $\frac{16}{3}$ (l.u.)$^2$.

**11.** $(\frac{2}{3}\pi + \sqrt{3})$ (l.u.)$^2$. **13.** $(e^3 - 3\ln 3 - e + 2)$ (l.u.)$^2$. **15.** $(\frac{3}{5}, \frac{12}{35})$. **17.** $(\frac{4}{5}, \frac{4}{5})$.

**19.** $(\frac{5}{12}, \frac{10}{21})$. **21.** $\bar{x} = \bar{y} = \dfrac{2048}{315\pi}$. **23.** $\frac{1}{28}$ (l.u.)$^4$. **25.** $\frac{5}{12}$ (l.u.)$^4$. **27.** $168\pi$ (l.u.)$^4$.

**29.** $\frac{1}{2}$ (l.u.)$^3$. **31.** 9 (l.u.)$^3$. **33.** $\dfrac{37k}{840}$. **35.** $\dfrac{243\pi k}{2}$. **37.** $\dfrac{2^{23}k}{13 \cdot 11 \cdot 7 \cdot 5 \cdot 3}$. **39.** $\dfrac{2ka^5}{15}$.

## Exercises 21.4, Pages 793–794

**1.** $(8 - \pi)$ (l.u.)$^2$. **3.** $\dfrac{27\pi + 48}{4}$ (l.u.)$^2$. **5.** $8\pi$ (l.u.)$^2$. **7.** $(\frac{1}{2}\pi - \frac{1}{2})$ (l.u.)$^2$.

**9.** $\bar{x} = \dfrac{12\sqrt{3}}{4\pi - 3\sqrt{3}}$, $\bar{y} = 0$. **11.** $\bar{x} = \frac{5}{2}$, $\bar{y} = 0$. **13.** $(\frac{37}{38}, 0)$.

**15.** $I_x = 20\pi$ (l.u.)$^4$, $I_y = 4\pi$ (l.u.)$^4$. **17.** $\dfrac{40\pi k}{3}$. **19.** $\dfrac{32\pi}{3}[8 - 3\sqrt{3}]$ (l.u.)$^3$.

**21.** $\dfrac{1 - \cos 1}{2}$. **23.** $\dfrac{e - 1}{2}$. **25.** $2\ln(\sqrt{2} + 1)$. **27.** $\dfrac{a^3\pi}{6}$.

## Exercises 21.5, Pages 799–800

**1.** $\sqrt{2}$ (l.u.)$^2$. **3.** $4a^2$ (l.u.)$^2$. **5.** $\frac{1}{6}\sqrt{3}\pi$ (l.u.)$^2$. **7.** $2a^2[\frac{1}{6}\pi + \sqrt{3} - 2]$ (l.u.)$^2$.

**9.** $\dfrac{12\pi a^2}{5}$ (l.u.)$^2$. **11.** $90\pi$ (l.u.)$^2$. **13.** $2\pi[1 + \sinh 1 - \cosh 1]$ (l.u.)$^2$.

**15.** $\dfrac{32\pi a^2}{5}$ (l.u.)$^2$.

## Exercises 21.6, Page 805

**1.** $\left(\dfrac{a}{2}, \dfrac{a}{2}, \dfrac{a}{2}\right)$.

**3.** $S = \dfrac{13\pi}{12}$, $\bar{z} = \dfrac{149}{130}$, $\bar{x} = \bar{y} = \dfrac{306\sqrt{2} - 3\ln(3 + 2\sqrt{2})}{208\pi}$.

**7.** $\pi c$.

**9.** $4\pi a^3$.

## Exercises 21.7, Pages 811–812

**1.** $6$ (l.u.)$^3$.  **3.** $\frac{8}{5}\sqrt{2}$ (l.u.)$^3$.  **5.** $\frac{16}{15}$ (l.u.)$^3$.  **7.** $\frac{81}{2}$ (l.u.)$^3$.  **9.** $8\pi$ (l.u.)$^3$.

**11.** $(\frac{5}{12}\sqrt{2}, \frac{10}{7}, \frac{5}{9})$.  **13.** $272\sqrt{2}/63$ (l.u.)$^5$.  **15.** $k/5$.  **17.** $\bar{x} = \frac{16}{15}, \bar{y} = \frac{4}{5}, \bar{z} = \frac{2}{5}$.

**19.** $(\frac{95}{238}, \frac{100}{119}, \frac{185}{357})$.  **21.** $\dfrac{23k}{126}$.

## Exercises 21.8, Pages 819–821

**1.** $(0, 0, 3)$.  **3.** $36\pi$ (l.u.)$^3$.  **5.** $8\pi$ (l.u.)$^3$.  **7.** $(0, 2, \frac{20}{3})$.  **9.** $\dfrac{2a^2}{5} M$.

**11.** $36\pi$ (l.u.)$^3$.  **13.** $(0, 0, \frac{2}{5})$.  **15.** $(\frac{9}{8}, \frac{9}{8}, \frac{9}{8})$.  **17.** $(\frac{6}{5}, 0, 9\sqrt{3}\pi/128)$.

**19.** $\left(\dfrac{3\pi a \sin\beta}{16\beta}, 0, 0\right)$.  **21.** $\dfrac{\pi a^3}{12b}(8b - 3a)$ (l.u.)$^3$.  **23.** $\dfrac{\pi b^3 h}{6}$.

**25.** $\dfrac{\pi a^5}{20}$.  **27.** $\dfrac{11\sqrt{2}}{48} \ln(1 + \sqrt{2}) - \frac{1}{24}$.

## Exercises 21.9, Pages 826–827

**1.** $\displaystyle\oint_S \mathbf{N}\cdot\mathbf{u}\,dS = \int_\mathcal{V} \nabla\cdot\mathbf{u}\,d\tau = 3\int_\mathcal{V} d\tau = 3V$.

**5.** $\mathbf{N} = \cos\alpha\,\mathbf{i} + \cos\beta\,\mathbf{j} + \cos\gamma\,\mathbf{k}$.

$\mathbf{N}\cdot\nabla g = g_x\cos\alpha + g_y\cos\beta + g_z\cos\gamma = D_s g$.

**7.** $\displaystyle\int_\mathcal{V} \nabla^2 g\,d\tau = \int_\mathcal{V} \nabla\cdot\nabla g\,d\tau = \oint_S \mathbf{N}\cdot\nabla g\,dS = \oint_S D_s g\,dS$.

## Exercises 22.1, Pages 834–835

**1.** $a_n = \dfrac{1}{2} + \dfrac{1}{2^{n+1}}$, or $|\frac{1}{2} - a_n| = \dfrac{1}{2^{n+1}}$. Since $|\frac{1}{2} - a_n| < \epsilon$ if $\dfrac{1}{2^{n+1}} < \epsilon$, it follows that

$$n > -\dfrac{\ln \epsilon}{\ln 2} - 1 \Longrightarrow |\tfrac{1}{2} - a_n| < \epsilon,$$

and the sequence converges to $\frac{1}{2}$.

**3.** The sequence converges to 0.

**5.** The sequence is divergent, since it has two cluster points, 0 and 1.

**7.** The sequence converges to 0.

**9.** The sequence converges to 0.

**11.** Convergent to $e^a$.

**13.** $a_n = 1 \cdot \dfrac{2}{3} \cdot \dfrac{4}{5} \cdots \dfrac{2n - 2}{2n - 1} \cdot \dfrac{2n}{n^2} < \dfrac{2}{n}$, and $0 < a_n < \dfrac{2}{n}$.

As $n \to \infty$, $2/n \to 0 \Longrightarrow a_n \to 0$.

**15.** Write $\left(1 + \dfrac{a}{n}\right)^n = \left[\left(1 + \dfrac{a}{n}\right)^{n/a}\right]^a$.

**17.** $(x_{n+1} - x_n) = \dfrac{1}{2n + 2} - \dfrac{1}{n} < 0 \Rightarrow x_{n+1} < x_n$.

Since $x_n > 0$ for every $n$, the sequence is decreasing and bounded, and therefore it is convergent.

**19.** $\lim\limits_{n \to \infty} a_n = 0 \Rightarrow a_n < k\epsilon$ for all $n > N$. Then

$$x_n = \frac{1}{n}\left(\sum_{\alpha=1}^{N} a_\alpha + \sum_{\alpha=N+1}^{n} a_\alpha\right) \leq \frac{1}{n} N \max a_\beta + \frac{1}{n}(n - N)k\epsilon,$$

where $\beta \leq N$, or

$$x_n < k\epsilon + \frac{1}{n}(N \max a_\beta - Nk\epsilon).$$

Let $k = \frac{1}{2}$. For $n$ sufficiently large, $A/n < \epsilon/2$, where $A = N \max a_\beta - Nk\epsilon$, and $x_n < \epsilon$. Since $\epsilon$ is arbitrary, $x_n \to 0$ as $n \to \infty$.

## Exercises 22.2, Page 840

**1.** Divergent, since $u_n \to 2$ as $n \to \infty$. **3.** Divergent. **5.** Divergent. **7.** Divergent.

**9.** $s_n - s_1 = \displaystyle\int_1^n e^{-x^2}\, dx < \int_1^n e^{-x}\, dx = 1 - e^{-n} \to 1$ as $n \to \infty$. Hence, $\{s_n\}$ is bounded and increasing, and therefore has a limit. Thus, the series converges.

**11.** $s_n = \displaystyle\int_1^{n+1} \left|\dfrac{\sin \dfrac{\pi x}{2}}{x^2}\right| dx < \int_1^{n+1} \dfrac{dx}{x^2} = 1 - \dfrac{1}{n+1} \to 1$ as $n \to \infty$. Therefore, $\{s_n\}$ is increasing and bounded, and the series converges.

**13. (a)** The series converges to 1.
　　**(b)** The series converges to $\frac{1}{2}$.

## Exercises 22.3, Pages 843–844

**1.** Divergent. **3.** Divergent. **5.** Convergent. **7.** Convergent.
**9.** Convergent. **11.** Divergent. **13.** Convergent. **15.** Convergent.

**17.** If $\dfrac{a_n}{b_n} \to 0$ as $n \to \infty$, then $a_n < \epsilon b_n$ for all $n > N$, where $N$ is some sufficiently large positive integer. Since $\displaystyle\sum_{n=1}^{\infty} b_n$ converges, $\displaystyle\sum_{n=1}^{\infty} a_n$ converges by the comparison test.

## Exercises 22.4, Pages 847–848

**1.** Divergent. **3.** Divergent. **5.** Convergent. **7.** Divergent.
**9.** Divergent. **11.** Divergent. **13.** Divergent.

**15.** $R_m < \displaystyle\int_m^{\infty} f(x)\, dx$. We want $\displaystyle\int_m^{\infty} \dfrac{1}{x^2}\, dx < 0.001$ or $\dfrac{1}{m} < 0.001$. Hence, $m > 1000$, and 1000 terms must be used.

**19. (a)** No. Consider $\displaystyle\sum_{n=1}^{\infty} \dfrac{1}{n^2}$. **(b)** No. Consider $\displaystyle\sum_{n=1}^{\infty} \dfrac{1}{n^2}$.

**Exercises 22.5, Pages 851–852**

1. Divergent.   3. Convergent.   5. Convergent.   7. Convergent.   9. Divergent.
11. Convergent.   13. Convergent.   15. Convergent.   17. Divergent.
21. Consider the fact that $\dfrac{u_{n+1}}{u_n} \to \infty \Rightarrow \dfrac{u_{n+1}}{u_n} > M$, $M$ is arbitrarily large for all $n > N$,
which $\Rightarrow u_{n+1} > u_N M^n$, and use the comparison test.

**Exercises 22.6, Pages 858–859**

1. Conditionally convergent.   3. Absolutely convergent.   5. Divergent.
7. Conditionally convergent.   9. Divergent.   11. Conditionally convergent.
13. Divergent.   15. Divergent.   17. Absolutely convergent.
19. Conditionally convergent.   21. Divergent.
23. Since

$$a_n^2 > \frac{a_n^2}{1 + a_n^2},$$

and since $\sum\limits_{n=1}^{\infty} a_n$ converges absolutely $\Rightarrow \sum\limits_{n=1}^{\infty} a_n^2$ converges, then, by the comparison
test,

$$\sum_{n=1}^{\infty} a_n^2/(1 + a_n^2)$$

converges.
25. Since

$$S_{2^n} = \sum_{k=1}^{2n} \frac{1}{k} - \sum_{k=1}^{n} \frac{1}{2^k},$$

and the first sum $\to \infty$ while the second sum $\to 2$, $\lim\limits_{n \to \infty} S_{2^n}$ does not exist.

**Exercises 22.7, Pages 862–863**

1. $0.00833 < \sum\limits_{n=5}^{\infty} \dfrac{1}{n!} < 0.0100$.   3. $0.0001547 < R_5 < 0.0001954$.
5. $0.01024 < R_5 < 0.01192$.   7. 3 terms.   9. 2 terms.   11. 0.1235.
13. 0.3333.   15. 0.6321.

**Exercises 23.1, Pages 866–867**

1. Converges for all $x \in \mathcal{R} - \{0\}$.
3. $\dfrac{u_{n+1}}{u_n} < e^{-x} < 1 \Rightarrow$ the series converges for all $x > 0$. If $x < 0$, then

$$\frac{u_{n+1}}{u_n} \to e^{-x} > 1,$$

and the series diverges. For $x = 0$, the series converges.
5. The series converges if $|x| \leq 1$.
7. The series converges for $x \geq -\frac{1}{2}$.
9. Since $\left| \dfrac{x}{1 + x^2} \right| < 1$ for all $x$, the series converges for all $x$ by the comparison test.

**11.** For any given value of $x$, and for $n$ sufficiently large, $u_{n+1} < u_n$, and $u_n \to 0$ as $n \to \infty$. Hence the series converges by Leibniz's Test.

**13.** Compare with the series $\sum\limits_{k=1}^{\infty} kx^k$. The ratio test cannot be used because

$$\lim_{m \to \infty} \frac{\varphi(m+1)}{\varphi(m)}$$

does not exist.

### Exercises 23.2, Pages 871–872

**1.** The series converges if $|x| \leq 1$. **3.** The series converges if $|x| < 1$.
**5.** The series converges for all $x$. **7.** The series converges only if $x = 0$.
**9.** The series converges for $-2 < x \leq 2$. **11.** The series converges only if $x = -1$.
**13.** The series converges if $-1 \leq x < 1$. **15.** The series converges for $3 \leq x \leq 7$.
**17.** The series converges for $|x| > 1$. **19.** The series converges for $-3 \leq x \leq -1$.

**21.** The series converges for $|x| < 1$, by comparison with $\sum\limits_{n=1}^{\infty} nx^n$.

### Exercises 23.3, Pages 877–878

**1.** $\sum\limits_{n=1}^{\infty} (-1)^{n-1} \dfrac{(2x)^{2n-1}}{(2n-1)!}$; all $x$. **3.** $\sum\limits_{n=0}^{\infty} \dfrac{x^n}{n!}$; all $x$. **5.** $\dfrac{1}{2} \sum\limits_{n=1}^{\infty} (-1)^{n-1} \left(\dfrac{x}{2}\right)^{n-1}$; $|x| < 2$.

**7.** $\sum\limits_{n=0}^{\infty} \cos\left(\tfrac{1}{4}\pi + \tfrac{1}{2}n\pi\right) \dfrac{(x - \tfrac{1}{4}\pi)^n}{n!}$; all $x$. **9.** $e^2 \sum\limits_{n=0}^{\infty} \dfrac{(x-2)^n}{n!}$; all $x$.

**11.** $1 + \dfrac{1}{2}(x-1) - \dfrac{1}{4} \dfrac{(x-1)^2}{2!} + \dfrac{3}{8} \dfrac{(x-1)^3}{3!} - \dfrac{15}{16} \dfrac{(x-1)^4}{4!} + \cdots$.

**15.** $-0.14 < x < 0.091$. **17.** $|x| < 0.310$. **19.** $0.87462$. **21.** $0.87462$.

**23.** $R_n = \left| \displaystyle\int_0^t (-1)^{n-1} \dfrac{x^{2n}}{x^2+1} \, dx \right| < \displaystyle\int_0^t x^{2n} \, dx = \dfrac{t^{2n+1}}{2n+1}$, $-1 \leq t \leq 1$.

**25.** $|x| < 0.17$.

### Exercises 23.4, Pages 886–887

**1.** All $x$. **3.** All $x$. **5.** $|x| < |a|$. **7.** All $x$.

### Exercises 23.5, Pages 893–894

**1.** $\tfrac{1}{2}$. **3.** 1. **5.** $-1$. **7.** $\sin x = \sum\limits_{n=1}^{\infty} (-1)^{n-1} \dfrac{x^{2n-1}}{(2n-1)!}$.

**9.** $(1 - x^2)^{-2} = \sum\limits_{n=1}^{\infty} nx^{2n-2}$; $|x| < 1$. **11.** $\operatorname{sech}^2 x = 1 - x^2 + \tfrac{2}{3}x^4 - \tfrac{17}{45}x^6 + \cdots$.

**13.** $\sin x = \sum\limits_{n=0}^{\infty} (-1)^n \dfrac{x^{2n+1}}{(2n+1)!}$; all $x$.

**15.** $\operatorname{Sin}^{-1} x = \sum\limits_{n=0}^{\infty} (-1)^n \binom{-\tfrac{1}{2}}{n} \dfrac{x^{2n+1}}{2n+1}$; $|x| < 1$.

**17.** $\ln \left| \dfrac{a+x}{a-x} \right| = 2 \sum\limits_{n=0}^{\infty} \dfrac{1}{n+1} \left(\dfrac{x}{a}\right)^{n+1}$; $\left|\dfrac{x}{a}\right| < 1$.

**19.** $0.0203$. **21.** $0.4969$. **23.** $0.1001$. **25.** $\tfrac{1}{2}(\sin 1 - \cos 1)$.

**Exercises 23.6, Pages 896–897**

**1.** $x^2 - xy^2 = -3 - 2(x - 1) + 4(y + 2) + (x - 1)^2 + 4(x - 1)(y + 2)$
$-(y + 2)^2 - (x - 1)(y + 2)^2.$

**3.** $\ln(x + y) = \ln 3 + \dfrac{1}{3}(x - 1) + \dfrac{1}{3}(y - 2) - \dfrac{1}{18}(x - 1)^2 - \dfrac{1}{9}(x - 1)(y - 1)$
$- \dfrac{1}{18}(y - 1)^2 + \cdots.$

**5.** $e^y \ln(2 + x) = \ln 2 + \dfrac{x}{2} + y \ln 2 - \dfrac{1}{8}x^2 + \dfrac{1}{2}xy + \dfrac{\ln 2}{2}y^2 + \cdots.$

**7.** $e^x \cos y = 1 + x + \frac{1}{2}(x^2 - y^2) + \cdots.$

**9.** $\sqrt{1 + x + y} = 1 + \frac{1}{2}x + \frac{1}{2}y - \frac{1}{8}x^2 - \frac{1}{4}xy - \frac{1}{8}y^2 + \cdots.$

**Exercises 23.7, Pages 899–900**

**1.** Minimum of $-4$ at $(1, 0)$.   **3.** Maximum of 4 at $(1, 1)$.   **5.** Minimum of $-\frac{84}{9}$ at $(-\frac{2}{3}, \frac{10}{3})$.   **7.** Maximum of $\frac{19}{3}$ at $(-\frac{7}{3}, -\frac{8}{3})$.   **9.** Maximum of 27 at $(3, 3)$.

**11.** $(-\frac{5}{7}, -\frac{13}{14}, -\frac{5}{14})$.   **13.** $\left(\dfrac{1}{n}\sum\limits_{k=1}^{n} x_k, \dfrac{1}{n}\sum\limits_{k=1}^{n} y_k\right).$

**Exercises 24.2, Pages 909–910**

**1.** $xy'' = y'.$          **3.** $y'' + y = 0.$          **5.** $y'' - y = 0.$
**7.** $(y - x)y'' + (1 + y')[1 + (y')^2] = 0.$
**9.** $(x - a)^2 y'' - 2(x - a)y' + 2(y - b) = 0.$
**11. (a)** $x^2 y'' - n(n - 1)y = 0.$ **(b)** $x^2 yy''' + 2xyy'' - x^2 y'y'' = 0.$
**13.** $x^4 + y^4 = C.$   **15.** $s = Ce^t.$   **17.** $2x^3 + 3y^{-2} = C.$   **19.** $r(2 - \theta) = C.$
**21.** $Cy^3 = 2 + e^{3x}.$   **23.** $\operatorname{Sin}^{-1} x = \frac{1}{2}\operatorname{Tan}^{-1}(y/2) + C.$
**25.** $2\operatorname{Tan}^{-1} y = \ln(\sec x + \tan x) + C.$   **27.** $(\rho^2 - 1)\cos\theta = C\rho.$   **29.** $u^3 v^2 = 8.$
**31.** $\exp(y^2) = 2e^{-1} + e - 2e^{-x}.$   **33.** $2x - e^{-2y} = 6.$   **35.** $v = e^{-10} - 1.$

**Exercises 24.3, Pages 913–914**

**1.** $s \approx \frac{187}{32}$ feet, $v \approx 3$ feet per second.   **3.** $(y + 1)^2 = (x + 1)^2 + 7.$
**5.** $t = 13.86$ yr.   **7.** $x = \exp(-1.54 \times 10^{-10}t).$
**9.** $v = 120(1 - e^{-t/10})/(1 + e^{-t/10}).$ As $t \to \infty$, $v \to 120$ feet per second.
**11.** $z = 100[(1.2)^{t/10} - 1]/[5(1.2)^{t/10} - 4].$   **13.** $90.1°C.$
**15.** $x = Mx_0/[x_0 + (M - x_0)e^{-Mkt}].$

**Exercises 24.4, Pages 917–918**

**1.** $y = x \ln Cx.$   **3.** $\operatorname{Tan}^{-1}(y/x) = x + C.$   **5.** $x^2 - 2xy - y^2 = C.$
**7.** $y^3 \ln y^3 = x^3 + Cy^3.$   **9.** $y^2 - 2x^2 \sin(y/x) = C.$
**11.** $3y^2 + 2xy + 2x^2 - 4x + 8y = C.$   **13.** $6x - 3y = 5 \ln(3x - 3y - 2) + C.$
**15.** $x + y + 5 \ln(6 - x - 2y) = 3.$   **17.** $(x - y + 1)^3 + (x + y) = 3.$

## Exercises 24.5, Page 922

**1.** $x^3 - 3x^2y + 6y^2 = C.$
**3.** $x^2 + y^2 + 2\,\mathrm{Tan}^{-1}(x/y) = C.$
**5.** $\sin x \sec y = C.$
**7.** $x^3y^2 = 3x^2y^4 + C.$
**9.** $x^3y^4 - 3x = Cy.$
**11.** $x^2y^2 + 1 = Cxy^2.$
**13.** $e^{x-y} = xy + C.$
**15.** $(x + y)e^y = C.$
**17.** $x^2 \sin y + 3xy = 2 + \pi.$
**19.** $4x^2 + y^5 = 24y.$

## Exercises 24.6, Pages 927–928

**1.** $4y + 2x + 1 = Ce^{2x}.$
**3.** $ay = b + Ce^{-ax}.$
**5.** $y + 2\cos^2 x = C \cos x.$
**7.** $y \sin^2 x + \cos x = C.$
**9.** $x^{1/2} = Ce^{y/2} - y - 2.$

**11.** $\exp(x^2/2) \sin y = \displaystyle\int_0^x t^2 \exp(t^2/2)\,dt + C.$

**13.** $2y = e^{-3x} + 5e^{-5x}.$

**15.** $y(\sec x + \tan x) = \tfrac{1}{2}x^2 + \sin x - x \cos x + 2.$

**17. (a)** 375 lb. **(b)** 0.6094 lb/gal.

**19.** $i = I_0e^{-Rt/L}.$   **21.** $4y = -2x^2 - 2x - 1 + 9e^{2x}.$

## Exercises 25.1, Pages 932–933

**1.** No, $xD$ is an operator; $Dx = 1.$   **3.** Yes.
**5.** No. $(D - 2)(D - x) = D^2 - (x + 2)D + (2x - 1);$
$\qquad (D - x)(D - 2) = D^2 - (x + 2)D - 2x.$
**7.** $e^{-3x},\ e^{-2x}.$   **9.** $e^x,\ e^{(1+i)x},\ e^{(1-i)x}.$   **11.** $e^{-2x}.$
**13.** $e^{\sqrt{2}x},\ e^{-\sqrt{2}x},\ e^{i\sqrt{2}x},\ e^{-i\sqrt{2}x}.$   **15.** $e^{2ix},\ e^{-2ix}.$

## Exercises 25.2, Page 937

**1.** Independent.   **3.** Dependent.   **5.** Dependent.
**9.** Suppose $c_1u_1 + c_2u_2 + c_3u_3 = 0.$ Differentiate this equation twice and form the determinant of the coefficients of $c_1, c_2, c_3.$

## Exercises 25.3, Pages 941–942

**1.** $y = c_1 + c_2e^{-5x} + c_3e^{3x}.$   **3.** $y = c_1e^{-x} + c_2e^{-4x}.$
**5.** $y = c_1e^{-2x} + c_2e^{(1+\sqrt{2})x} + c_3e^{(1-\sqrt{2})x}.$   **7.** $y = (c_1 + c_2x + c_3x^2)e^{2x}.$
**9.** $y = c_1 + c_2x + c_3x^2 + c_4e^{3x} + c_5e^{-3x}.$
**11.** $y = (c_1 + c_2x)e^{-x} + c_3e^{(1+\sqrt{3})x} + c_4e^{(1-\sqrt{3})x}.$   **13.** $y = [1 + (e^3 - 1)x]e^{-3x}.$
**15.** $y = A \cos x.$   **17.** $y = (c_1 + c_2x) \cos 3x + (c_3 + c_4x) \sin 3x.$
**19.** $y = A(k^2 - b^2)^{-1/2}e^{-bx} \sin[x(k^2 - b^2)^{1/2}].$   **21.** $2(1 - e^{-4}).$

## Exercises 25.4, Page 946

**1.** $D^3.$   **3.** $D^2 + 9.$   **5.** $(D^2 - 2D + 2)^2.$   **7.** $D^4(D^2 - 2D + 5).$
**9.** $D^3(D - 1)(D^2 + 1).$   **11.** $y = c_1e^{3x} + c_2e^{-x} - \tfrac{1}{4}e^x.$

**13.** $y = c_1 e^{2x} + c_2 e^{-x} - 3x + \frac{3}{2} - 2xe^{-x}$.

**15.** $y = c_1 e^x + c_2 e^{-x} + c_3 \cos x + c_4 \sin x - x^2 - \frac{1}{4}x \sin x$.

**17.** $y = c_1 \cos \sqrt{5}x + c_2 \sin \sqrt{5}x + \frac{6}{5} + 6 \cos 2x$.

**19.** $y = c_1 e^{12x} + c_2 e^{-7x} - 2e^{-3x} + 3e^{-2x}$.

**21.** $y = e^{-x}(c_1 \cos \sqrt{3}x + c_2 \sin \sqrt{3}x) - \frac{4}{13} \cos x + \frac{6}{13} \sin x + \frac{1}{4} \sin 2x$.

**23.** $y = c_1 e^x + (c_2 + c_3 x)e^{-x} + \frac{1}{5}(\cos x + 2 \sin x) + \frac{1}{8}x^2 - \frac{1}{4}$.

**25.** $y = \sinh x + (x^2 - x)e^x$. **27.** $21e^{-2}$.

## Exercises 25.5, Page 949

**1.** $y = c_1 \cos x + c_2 \sin x + x \sin x + (\cos x) \ln \cos x$.

**3.** $y = c_1 \cos x + c_2 \sin x - \frac{1}{2} + \frac{1}{6} \sec^2 x + \frac{1}{2}(\sin x) \ln (\sec x + \tan x)$.

**5.** $y = c_1 \cos x + c_2 \sin x - (\sin x) \ln (\csc x + \cot x)$.

**7.** $y = c_1 \cos x + c_2 \sin x + \frac{1}{4}x \cos x + \frac{1}{4}x^2 \sin x$.

**9.** $y = (c_1 \sin x + c_2 \cos x)e^x - e^x(\cos x) \ln (\sec x + \tan x) + \frac{3}{2}x + \frac{3}{2}$.

**11.** $y = c_1 \sin 2x + c_2 \cos 2x + (\sin 2x) \ln \tan x$.

**13.** $y = c_1 e^x + c_2 e^{-x} + \frac{1}{2}e^x \ln x - \frac{1}{2}e^{-x} \int_1^x \frac{e^{2t}}{t} \, dt$.

**15.** $y = c_1 x + c_2 e^x + x^2 + x + 1$.

## Exercises 25.6, Pages 954–955

**1.** $x = e^{-0.8t}(3 \cos 7.96t + 0.302 \sin 7.96t)$; period $= 0.79$ second.

**3.** $0.20$ second.

**5.** $x = \frac{1}{12} \cos 11.17t$; period $= 0.56$ second.

**7.** Period $= 0.506$ second; $R \approx 1.50$.

**9.** $x = (c_1 + c_2 t)e^{-\alpha t} + \dfrac{a}{(\omega^2 + \alpha^2)^2} [(\alpha^2 - \omega^2) \cos \omega t + 2\alpha\omega \sin \omega t]$.

**11.** $x = (c_1 + c_2 t)e^{-8t}$.

## Exercises 25.7, Pages 958–959

**1.** $i = \dfrac{E}{R}(1 - e^{-Rt/L})$. **3.** $i = \left(\dfrac{E}{R} - \dfrac{q_0}{RC}\right)e^{-t/(RC)}$; $i_0 = \dfrac{E}{R} - \dfrac{q_0}{RC}$.

**5.** $i = \dfrac{E}{2bL} [e^{-(a-b)t} - e^{-(a+b)t}]$. **7.** $i = \dfrac{E}{bL} e^{-at} \sin bt$. **9.** $i = -900e^{-5t} \sin 5t$.

## Exercises 25.8, Pages 968–969

**1.** $x_1 = 2c_1 e^t + c_2 e^{-t}$,
$x_2 = c_1 e^t + c_2 e^{-t}$.

**3.** $x_1 = e^{2t}(2c_1 + 2c_2 t + c_2)$,
$x_2 = e^{2t}(c_1 + c_2 t)$.

**5.** $x_1 = e^{3t}[A \cos (2t + \pi) + B \sin (2t + \pi)]$,
$x_2 = \sqrt{2}e^{3t}[A \cos (2t + \frac{1}{4}\pi) + B \sin (2t + \frac{1}{4}\pi)]$.

**7.** $x_1 = -c_1 e^t + 3c_2 e^{5t} - c_3 e^{-2t}$,
$x_2 = -2c_1 e^t + 2c_2 e^{5t} + 4c_3 e^{-2t}$,
$x_3 = 5c_1 e^t + c_2 e^{5t} + 2c_3 e^{-2t}$.

**9.** $x_1 = e^t(c_1 + c_2 t) + c_3 e^{2t}$,
$x_2 = e^t(c_1 + c_2 + c_2 t) + 2c_3 e^{2t}$,
$x_3 = e^t(c_1 + 2c_2 + c_2 t) + c_3 e^{2t}$.

**11.** $x = e^t(c_2 \cos t + c_3 \sin t)$,

$y = c_1 + \sqrt{2} e^t [c_2 \cos (t + \frac{3}{4}\pi) + c_3 \sin (t + \frac{3}{4}\pi)]$.

**13.** $x = c_1 e^t + c_2 e^{-3t} + \frac{1}{3}t - \frac{4}{9}$,

$y = 3c_1 e^t - c_2 e^{-3t} - \frac{1}{3}t - \frac{5}{9}$.

**15.** $x = -c_1 e^{-t} - c_2 e^{2t} + c_3$,

$y = c_1 e^{-t} + c_2 e^{2t} + 2t$.

**17.** $x_1 = ae^{-k_1 t}$,

$$x_2 = \frac{k_1 a}{k_2 - k_1} (e^{-k_1 t} - e^{-k_2 t}),$$

$$x_3 = k_1 k_2 a \left[ \frac{e^{-k_1 t}}{(k_2 - k_1)(k_3 - k_1)} + \frac{e^{-k_2 t}}{(k_1 - k_2)(k_3 - k_2)} + \frac{e^{-k_3 t}}{(k_1 - k_3)(k_2 - k_3)} \right].$$

Note: This result assumes that the $k$'s are all different.

### Exercises 25.9, Pages 975–976

**1.** $x = \frac{50}{3} e^{-t/100} + \frac{100}{3} e^{-4t/100}$,

$y = \frac{100}{3} e^{-t/100} - \frac{100}{3} e^{-4t/100}$.

**3.** $x = \frac{3}{35} x_0 - \frac{2}{7} x_0 e^{-7t/16} + \frac{6}{5} x_0 e^{-15t/16}$,

$y = \frac{16}{35} x_0 + \frac{8}{7} x_0 e^{-7t/16} - \frac{8}{5} x_0 e^{-15t/16}$,

$z = \frac{16}{35} x_0 - \frac{6}{7} x_0 e^{-7t/16} + \frac{2}{5} x_0 e^{-15t/16}$.

**5.** $\dfrac{dx}{dt} = -\dfrac{r_1}{m_1} x + u$,

$\dfrac{dy}{dt} = -\dfrac{r_2}{m_2} y + v$,

$\dfrac{du}{dt} = -\dfrac{k_1}{m_1} x + \dfrac{k_2}{m_1} (y - x)$,

$\dfrac{dv}{dt} = -\dfrac{k_2}{m_2} (y - x)$.

**7.** $i_1 = \frac{1}{3} e^{-50t} + \frac{2}{3} e^{-200t}$,

$i_2 = \frac{2}{3} e^{-50t} - \frac{2}{3} e^{-200t}$.

**9.** $i_2 = \frac{1}{4} \sqrt{3} \sin 50\sqrt{3} t$.

# Index

# APPENDIX A    List of symbols

## GREEK ALPHABET

| | | | | | | | | | |
|---|---|---|---|---|---|---|---|---|---|
| Alpha | A | $\alpha$ | Iota | I | $\iota$ | Rho | P | $\rho$ |
| Beta | B | $\beta$ | Kappa | K | $\kappa$ | Sigma | $\Sigma$ | $\sigma$ |
| Gamma | $\Gamma$ | $\gamma$ | Lambda | $\Lambda$ | $\lambda$ | Tau | T | $\tau$ |
| Delta | $\Delta$ | $\delta$ | Mu | M | $\mu$ | Upsilon | $\Upsilon$ | $\upsilon$ |
| Epsilon | E | $\epsilon$ | Nu | N | $\nu$ | Phi | $\Phi$ | $\varphi$ |
| Zeta | Z | $\zeta$ | XI | $\Xi$ | $\xi$ | Chi | X | $\chi$ |
| Eta | H | $\eta$ | Omicron | O | $o$ | Psi | $\Psi$ | $\psi$ |
| Theta | $\Theta$ | $\theta$ | Pi | $\Pi$ | $\pi$ | Omega | $\Omega$ | $\omega$ |

## SPECIAL SYMBOLS